NATURAL HAZARDS

EARTH'S PROCESSES AS HAZARDS, DISASTERS, AND CATASTROPHES

CANADIAN EDITION

EDWARD A. KELLER
University of California, Santa Barbara

ROBERT H. BLODGETT
Austin Community College

JOHN J. CLAGUE
Simon Fraser University

Toronto

Library and Archives Canada Cataloguing in Publication

Keller, Edward A., 1942–
Natural hazards: earth's processes as hazards, disasters, and catastrophes/Edward A. Keller, Robert H. Blodgett, John J. Clague.—Canadian ed.

Includes index.
ISBN-13: 978-0-13-223202-9
ISBN-10: 0-13-223202-2

1. Natural disasters—Textbooks. I. Blodgett, Robert H., 1951– . II. Clague, J. J. (John Joseph), 1946– . III. Title.

GB5014.K44 2008 551 C2006-905901-2

ISBN-13: 978-0-13-223202-9
ISBN-10: 0-13-223202-2

Editor-in-Chief: Gary Bennett
Executive Marketing Manager: Marlene Olsavsky
Acquisitions Editor: Michelle Sartor
Developmental Editor: Paul Donnelly
Production Editor: Marisa D'Andrea
Copy Editor: Dawn Hunter
Proofreader: Karen Alliston
Production Coordinator: Patricia Ciardullo
Indexer: Nancy Mucklow
Photo and Permissions Researcher: Sandy Cooke
Compositor: Hermia Chung
Art Director: Julia Hall
Interior Design: Monica Kompter
Cover Design: Miguel Acevedo
Cover Image: Getty Images/Stone/Paul Taylor

For permission to reproduce copyrighted material, the publisher gratefully acknowledges the copyright holders listed throughout the text, which are considered an extension of this copyright page. Credits for photos on pp. vii–xviii: p. vii Pablo Bartholomew/Getty Images, Inc.–Liaison; p. viii Pallava Bagla/Corbis/Sygma; p. ix Roger Werth, Long View Daily News/Woodfin Camp and Associates; p. x AP Wide World Photos; p. xi Mark Rawsthorne; p. xii Photo by Professor V. E. Romanovsky, University of Alaska Fairbanks; p. xiii Eric Hylden/Grand Forks Herald; p. xiv NOAA Photo Library, NOAA Central Library, OAR/ERL/National Severe Storms Laboratory; p. xv Peter Cade/Getty Images, Inc.–Stone Allstock; p. xvi (top) A. T. Willett/Alamy Images; p. xvi (bottom) John J. Clague; p. xvii © Aaron Horowitz/CORBIS.

3 4 5 11 10 09 08

Printed and bound in the United States.

ABOUT THE AUTHORS

Edward A. Keller

Ed Keller is a teacher, researcher, and writer. Born and raised in California (Bachelor's degrees in Geology and Mathematics from California State University at Fresno, Master's degree in Geology from the University of California at Davis), it was while pursuing his Ph.D. in Geology from Purdue University in 1973 that Ed wrote the first edition of *Environmental Geology*, the text that became the foundation of the environmental geology curriculum. Ed joined the faculty of the University of California at Santa Barbara in 1976 and has been there since, serving multiple times as the chair of both the Environmental Studies and Hydrologic Science programs. In that time he has been an author on more than 100 articles, including seminal works on fluvial processes and tectonic geomorphology. Ed's academic honours include the Quatercentenary Fellowship from Cambridge University, England (2000); two Outstanding Alumnus Awards from Purdue University (1994, 1996); a Distinguished Alumnus Award from California State University at Fresno (1998); the Outstanding Outreach Award from the Southern California Earthquake Center (1999); and the Don J. Easterbrook Distinguished Scientist Award from the Quaternary Geology and Geomorphology Division of the Geological Society of America (2004).

Ed is also a passable fisherman.

Robert H. Blodgett

Bob Blodgett is Professor of Geology at Austin Community College in Austin, Texas, where he teaches environmental, physical, and historical geology, as well as environmental science, and manages the college's Edwards Aquifer Monitoring Well. Bob has more than 20 years of teaching experience including positions on the faculties of Ohio State University and Dickinson College.

He is a Licensed Professional Geoscientist and worked for six years in the State of Texas Public Drinking Water Program leading a team of scientists evaluating the vulnerability of drinking water to contamination, and for two years at the Texas Bureau of Economic Geology conducting environmental assessments of abandoned mined lands. His research on terrestrial sedimentary processes resulted in published papers on braided streams, ancient soils, and fossil burrows.

Bob has practical experience planning for and responding to natural hazards. While in the Air Force, he served as the disaster preparedness officer for the remote Indian Mountain Air Force Station in Alaska, and for the underground Cheyenne Mountain command post of the North American Aerospace Defense Command in Colorado Springs.

He traces his interest in natural hazards back to Alma Petrini, his second-grade teacher in Detroit, whose lesson on volcanoes and earthquakes came alive with stories and pictures of her trips to Parícutin and Pompeii, and to lava samples that Gordon Macdonald, then Director of the Hawaiian Volcano Observatory, sent him for his class project. These experiences led to a lifelong interest in geology, including three degrees: a B.S. from the University of Wisconsin at Madison, an M.S. from the University of Nebraska at Lincoln, and a Ph.D. from the University of Texas at Austin.

John J. Clague

John Clague is Professor of Earth Sciences at Simon Fraser University (SFU) in Burnaby, British Columbia, and an emeritus scientist with the Geological Survey of Canada. John was employed as a research scientist with the Geological Survey of Canada for 24 years, specializing in natural hazards, climate change, and ice age geology of western Canada.

In 1998, he accepted a faculty position in the Department of Earth Sciences at SFU, where he is currently based. John became a Canada Research Chair in natural hazards research in 2003 and is currently Director of the Centre for Natural Hazard Research. John is the author of 300 scientific papers on subjects as diverse as earthquakes, geochemistry, and archaeology. He has written popular books on Canadian Earth science issues and on earthquakes and tsunamis in the Pacific Northwest. He is a Fellow of the Royal Society of Canada, former President of the Geological Association of Canada, current President of the International Union for Quaternary Research, and recipient of numerous awards and honours.

John is a strong proponent of the philosophy captured so eloquently by Margaret Mead: "Never doubt that a small group of committed people can change the world. Indeed, it is the only thing that has."

BRIEF CONTENTS

CONTENTS

2 Earthquakes 28

6 Subsidence 158

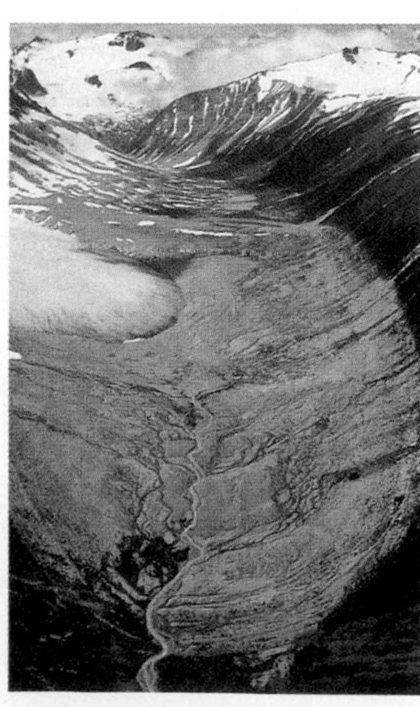

Natural Hazards: Earth's Processes as Hazards, Disasters, and Catastrophes is a university-level, non-technical survey of Earth's surface processes that have direct, often sudden, and violent impacts on humanity. The book integrates principles of geology, geography, meteorology, climatology, oceanography, ecology, and solar system astronomy. It has been designed for a course for non-science majors and will help instructors guide student readers who have little, if any, background in science through both the geologic underpinnings and the societal repercussions of hazardous Earth processes. It is also suitable for topical introductory courses in physical geology, physical geography, and Earth science.

In the past decade, the world experienced a devastating tsunami in the Indian Ocean; deadly earthquakes in India, Turkey, and northern Pakistan; catastrophic flooding in Venezuela, Bangladesh, and central Europe; and the strongest El Niño on record. In the Americas, deadly hurricanes struck New Orleans and central America; record-setting wildfires torched Arizona, Colorado, and California; Oklahoma experienced its worst tornadoes ever; a record-matching series of four hurricanes made landfall in Florida and the Carolinas within a six-week period; an ice storm paralyzed southern Quebec, southern Ontario, and New England; southern Manitoba and North Dakota experienced their second-largest flood of record; and climate warmed over much of the planet, with the greatest temperature increases at high latitudes in northern Canada, Alaska, and Siberia. These events are the result of enormous forces that are at work both inside and on the surface of our planet. In this book, the authors explain destructive Earth forces in an understandable way, illustrate how they affect us, and discuss how we can better prepare for, and adjust to, inevitable natural disasters and catastrophes.

An important point, central to both this text and course, is that Earth processes are not in and of themselves "hazards," even though we describe them as such. Earthquakes, tsunami, volcanic eruptions, landslides, tornadoes, hurricanes, and wildfires are natural processes and have occurred for hundreds of millions of years, indifferent to the presence of humanity. They are hazards only when they impact people. Ironically, human behaviour can turn hazardous events into disasters or, worse, catastrophes. The text strives to present these phenomena as natural geologic processes that have human impacts.

A course in natural hazards offers many benefits besides satisfying students' natural curiosity about such events. An informed citizenry is our best guarantee of a prosperous future. Armed with insights into the complex relations between people and the geologic environment, we will ask better questions and make better choices. At the local level, we will be better prepared to make informed decisions about where to live and how best to invest our time and resources. At the national and global levels, we will be better able to hold our leaders accountable for their choices and responses to disasters.

Distinguishing Features

With these objectives in mind, the authors have incorporated into *Natural Hazards* several features designed to support the student and instructor.

A Balanced Approach

Many readers will focus on natural hazards that threaten their community, province, or country. However, economic globalization, near-universal information access, and the deleterious effects of humans on our planet require a broader, balanced approach to the study of hazards and risk. A major earthquake in Tokyo would affect trade in the ports of Vancouver and Seattle, the economy of Silicon Valley in California, and the price of computers in Toronto and Halifax. The authors have tried to provide balanced coverage of natural hazards, with examples from Canada, the United States, as well as other countries. Topics covered in this edition include earthquakes and tsunami on the British Columbia coast; the 1929 Grand Banks earthquake and tsunami; disastrous floods on the Fraser River in 1948 and the Red River in 1997; a discussion of how Canada deals with disastrous floods; catastrophic landslides at Frank, Alberta, in 1903 and near Hope, British Columbia, in 1965; the 1998 ice storm in Ontario and Quebec; the 1983 Edmonton tornado; Hurricanes Katrina, Hazel, and Juan; the 2003 Kelowna fire; and an expanded treatment of climate change and its impacts in Canada. This edition also features a chapter on snow avalanches.

The book treats each topic as both a natural phenomenon and a human hazard. For example, the discussion of tsunami not only includes a description of their characteristics, causes, global distribution, frequency, and effects, but also a discussion of engineering and nonstructural approaches that can be taken to reduce tsunami risk.

Five Fundamental Concepts

Five key concepts provide a conceptual framework of understanding that guide the reader and that can be used to make informed choices when confronted with danger from geologic processes:

1. **Hazards can be predicted through scientific analysis.** Most hazardous events and processes can be monitored and mapped, and their future activity forecasted based on the frequency of past events, patterns in their occurrence, and precursor events.

2. **Risk analysis is an important element of understanding the effects of hazardous processes.**
   Hazardous processes are amenable to risk analysis because the probability and consequences of an event can be determined or estimated.

3. **Linkages exist among different natural hazards and between hazards and the physical environment.**
   Hazardous processes are linked in many ways. For example, earthquakes can produce landslides and tsunami, and hurricanes cause flooding and coastal erosion.

4. **Damage from natural disasters is increasing.**
   Hazardous events that previously produced disasters are now producing catastrophes. Populations and economic wealth at risk from hazardous processes are rapidly growing; consequently, events that were local disasters in the past may now become regional, even global catastrophes. In addition, the magnitude and frequency of some hazardous events may be influenced by human activity.

5. **Damage and loss of life from natural disasters can be minimized.**
   Minimizing the adverse effects of hazardous natural processes requires an integrated approach that includes scientific understanding, land-use planning and regulation, engineering, education, and proactive disaster preparedness.

These five concepts are introduced in the first chapter and are revisited throughout the text. They provide a framework for understanding that can extend beyond this course into everyday life.

Survivor Stories and Professional Profiles

Most chapters contain the personal story of someone who has had a brush with disaster, as well as the profile of a scientist or other professional who has studied the hazard. Although most of us will never experience a volcanic eruption, tsunami, or hurricane, we are naturally curious about what we would see, hear, and feel if we did. For example, a scientific description of a volcanic eruption does not convey the amazement and terror that Canadian volcanologist Catherine Hickson experienced on the morning of May 18, 1980, when Mount St. Helens exploded (see the Professional Profile on page 94). To fully understand natural hazards, we need both scientific knowledge and human experience. As you read the survivor stories, ask yourself what you would do in a similar situation, especially once you more fully understand the hazard. Who knows? This knowledge may some day save your life, as it did for Tilly Smith and her family on the beach in Phuket, Thailand, on December 26, 2004 (see Case Study 9.2).

People study and work with natural hazards for many reasons—curiosity, monetary reward, excitement, or the desire to help others prepare for events that might threaten their lives and property. As you read each professional profile, think about the person's motivation, the type of work he or she does, and how that work contributes to increasing human knowledge or reducing risk. For example, Clair Israelson, Executive Director of the Canadian Avalanche Association, has studied snow avalanches in western Canada for nearly four decades (see the Professional Profile on page 154). For him, this study is both a vocation and an avocation. He has had a life-long interest in avalanches and is striving to reduce avalanche injuries and deaths by promoting scientific research, educational programs, and heightened awareness of the hazard. Most of the professional profiles are based on interviews conducted exclusively for *Natural Hazards*.

Learning Devices

- Each chapter begins with a set of learning objectives that clearly state what the reader should have achieved after completing the chapter.
- Selected features, called Case Studies, are added where appropriate to help the reader understand natural hazards through real-world examples.
- A chapter summary reinforces the major points of the chapter to help the student focus on important concepts.
- References and selected Web resources provide additional sources of information and give credit to the scholars who did the research reported in the chapter.
- Key terms are presented at the end of each chapter to help the reader identify important concepts and terminology. A glossary of more than 450 terms is included at the end of the book.
- Review questions help the reader focus on important subject matter.
- Critical thinking questions stimulate discussion and analysis of some of the important issues in each chapter.
- The appendices provide additional information useful for understanding some of the more applied aspects of geology that relate to natural hazards. This information may be helpful in supplementing laboratory and field exercises for students.

Instructional Resources

Pearson Education Canada has assembled a first-rate resource package for *Natural Hazards*.

- **Prentice Hall's Environmental Geology Videos DVD:** The DVD contains more than 35 video segments focusing on first-person experiences of Earth processes. These focused segments average 30 seconds to three minutes in length. Examples include
  - Surveillance camera video of an earthquake
  - Volcanic destruction

- Urban flooding
- Dust storms
- Landslide devastation
- Hurricane storm surge
- Tornadoes
- Giant sinkholes

The DVD will play in computer and traditional DVD players. The video included on the DVD is of the highest quality to allow for full-screen viewing on a computer or for projection in large lecture classrooms.

- **Hazard City: Assignments in Applied Geology CD-ROM, 3e:** Included with every text, Hazard City provides the instructor with meaningful, easy-to-assign, and easy-to-grade assignments. Based on the idealized town of Hazard City, the assignments put users in the role of a practising geologist—gathering and analyzing real data, evaluating risk, and making assessments and recommendations. The third edition of this widely used CD contains updated and revised versions of most assignments, including new assignments on map reading and hurricane and tsunami topics. For a detailed description of Hazard City, please see pages xxiii and xxiv.
- **The Prentice Hall Geoscience Animations Library:** The Prentice Hall Geoscience Animations Library resulted from a survey in which we asked instructors to identify the concepts most difficult to teach using traditional, static resources. Then we animated them. Created through a unique collaboration among five of Prentice Hall's leading geoscience authors, these animations represent a significant leap forward in lecture presentation. Available on the IRCD, each animation is mapped to the corresponding chapter in *Natural Hazards*. They are provided as Flash files and, for convenience, pre-loaded into PowerPoint slides. The list of animations includes

Atmosphere Energy Balance
Atmosphere Stability
Beach Drift and Longshore Currents
Coastal Stabilization Structures
Cold Fronts and Warm Fronts
Collapse of Mount St. Helens
Convection and Tectonics
Correlating Processes and Plate Boundaries
Cyclones and Anticyclones
Density and Magma Movement
Earthquake Waves
Earth's Water and the Hydrologic Cycle
Earth–Sun Relations
Effects of Groins and Jetties
Elastic Rebound
El Niño and La Niña
Faults
Flooding and the Formation of Natural Levees
Formation of Crater Lake
Forming a Divergent Boundary
Forming Volcanoes
Glacial Processes
Global Atmospheric Circulation Model
Global Warming
Global Wind Patterns
Hot Spot Volcano Tracts
How Calderas Form
How Wind Moves Sediment
Hurricane Wind Patterns
Hydrologic Cycle
Liquefaction
Mass Movements
Meandering Stream Processes
Mid-latitude Cyclones
Motion at Plate Boundaries
Motion at Transform Boundaries
Nebular Hypothesis of Solar System Formation
Ocean Circulation
Ozone Depletion
Properties of Waves
Radioactive Decay
Relative Geologic Dating
Sea-Floor Spreading
Sea-Floor Spreading and Rock Magnetism
Seasonal Pressure and Precipitation Patterns
Seismic Wave Motion
Seismographs
Stream Processes and Floodplain Development
Tectonic Settings and Volcanic Activity
Terrane Formation
Tornado Wind Patterns
Transform Faults
Tsunami
Unconformities
Uplift and Mass Movement
Wave Motion/Wave Refraction

- **Instructor's Resource CD-ROM, including PowerPoint® Presentations and Animations:** Included on the IRCD are two PowerPoint presentations for each chapter:

1. Art only—every figure and many of the photos in the text, pre-loaded in order onto PowerPoint slides.
2. Animations—high-quality animations of key geologic processes. Also included are all illustrations and a selection of photos for the text in JPEG format.

- **Instructor's Manual:** The Instructor's Manual provides chapter outlines and objectives, classroom discussion topics, and answers to the end-of-chapter questions in the text.
- **Test Generator:** The TestGen provides more than 500 questions in multiple-choice, true/false, short-answer, and essay format, as well as testing recall, understanding, and application of the chief data and concepts presented in the text.

Acknowledgments

Many individuals, companies, and agencies provided information and images that we included in the book. In particular, we are indebted to the Geological Survey of Canada (Natural Resources Canada), Environment Canada, the U.S. Geological Survey, and the National Oceanic and Atmospheric Administration for their excellent natural hazard programs and publications. We would also like to extend thanks to Tricouni Press for providing many of the figures and photos.

We appreciate and thank authors of papers cited in this book for their contributions. Without their work, this book could not have been written. We also thank the following scholars who dedicated their to time reviewing chapters of the book:

Ihsan Al-Aasm, *University of Windsor*
Ross Chapman, *University of Victoria*
Stan Dosso, *University of Victoria*
Michael Gipp, *University of Toronto at Scarborough*
John Gosse, *Dalhousie University*
Jeremy Hall, *Memorial University of Newfoundland*
Sara E. Harris, *University of British Columbia*
Jean Hutchinson, *Queen's University*
Francis Jones, *University of British Columbia*
Barbara Murck, *University of Toronto*
Richard Petrone, *Wilfrid Laurier University*
Steven Sadura, *University of Guelph*
Claire Samson, *Carleton University*
Cheryl Schreader, *Capilano College*
Sue Vajoczki, *McMaster University*

We would also like to acknowledge our editors at Pearson Education Canada for their help and guidance in the preparation of the Canadian edition. Our appreciation is extended to Michelle Sartor, Acquisitions Editor; Paul Donnelly, Developmental Editor; and Marisa D'Andrea, Production Editor. Thanks are also due to Dawn Hunter, who copyedited the manuscript, and Steve Hicock, who technically reviewed the material. John is particularly grateful to Alexis Clague, who spent numerous hours proofreading the final draft of the manuscript.

Edward A. Keller
Santa Barbara, California

Robert H. Blodgett
Austin, Texas

John J. Clague
Burnaby, British Columbia

Hazard City: Assignments in Applied Geology CD-ROM

Included with every text, *Hazard City* provides you with **meaningful, easy-to-assign, and easy-to-grade assignments.** Based on the idealized town of Hazard City, the assignments put students in the role of a practising geologist—gathering and analyzing real data, evaluating risk, and making assessments and recommendations. The third edition of this widely used CD contains two new modules, Map Reading and Tsunami/Storm Surge.

Easy to Assign

Ground Water Contamination: Students use field and laboratory data to prepare a contour map of the water table, determine the direction of ground water flow, and map a contaminated area.

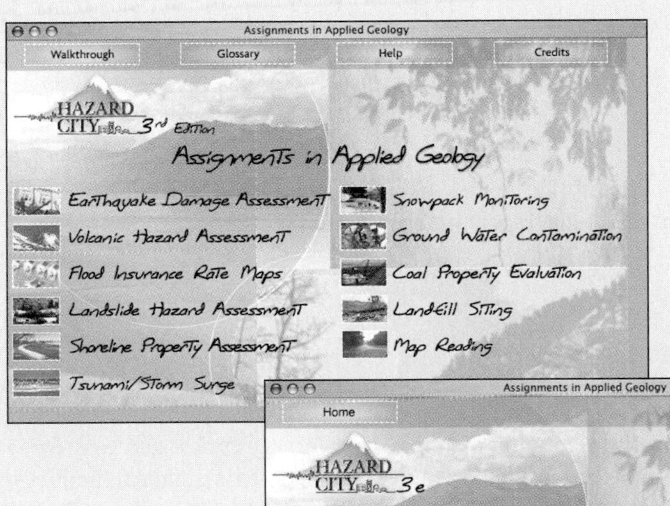

Volcanic Hazard Assessment: Researching volcanic hazards, collecting field information, and decision making are all used to determine the potential impact of a volcanic eruption on different parts of Hazard City.

Landslide Hazard Assessment: Students research the factors that determine landslide hazard at five construction sites and make recommendations for development.

Earthquake Damage Assessment: Students research the effects of earthquakes on buildings, explore Hazard City, and determine the number of people needing emergency housing given an earthquake of specific intensity.

Flood Insurance Rate Maps: Flood insurance premiums are estimated using a flood insurance rate map, insurance tables, and site characteristics.

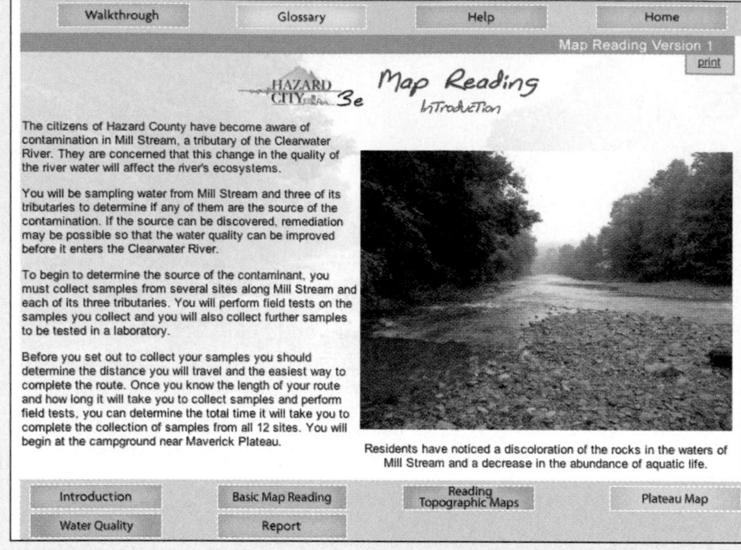

Snowpack Monitoring: Students utilize climatic data to estimate variables that are key to flood control and water supply management.

Coal Property Evaluation: The potential value of a mineral property is estimated by learning about mining and property evaluation and applying that knowledge in a resource calculation.

Landfill Siting: Students use maps and geological data to determine if any of five proposed sites meet the requirements of the State Administrative Code for landfill siting.

Shoreline Property Assessment: Students visit four related waterfront building sites—some developed and some not—and analyze the risk each faces due to shoreline erosion processes.

Tsunami/Storm Surge: Students research the causes and effects of tsunami and storm surge and then prepare a risk assessment report for a small oceanside village near Hazard City.

Map Reading: In order to identify the source of water contamination in a local stream, students learn how to read topographic maps and use their knowledge to plan their field work.

Easy to Grade

The students' work in each project requires them to research, explore, learn on their own, and think. However, the questions are multiple choice, making them quick and easy for instructors to grade. The solutions are available only via the instructor's manual, helping preserve their integrity for assignment in later semesters. The students can submit their answers via worksheets contained on the CD-ROM, which they can print out, complete, and submit. The worksheets are designed to be graded in seconds.

Supplemental assignments can be found on the *www.hazcity.com* website. These assignments are more open-ended and in-depth (e.g., creating an earthquake hazard map) and can be used to expand on the topics being studied.

Class Tested

All activities included on this CD have been refined through testing in both the traditional classroom and the online classroom.

CHAPTER 1

▶ Kusol Wetchakul offers prayers for the soul of his sister on the beach near Khao Lak, Thailand. She was swept out to sea by the tsunami of December 26, 2004, as she sold goods to tourists on a popular tourist beach north of Phuket. *(David Longstreath, AP Photo)*

Learning Objectives

Natural processes, such as volcanic eruptions, earthquakes, landslides, tsunami, floods, and hurricanes, threaten human life and property throughout the world. As the world's population continues to grow, disasters and catastrophes will become more common. Your goals in reading this chapter should be to

- Learn about hazardous natural processes
- Recognize that many disasters and catastrophes are the result of naturally occurring, high-energy events
- Understand the differences among hazards, risks, disasters, and catastrophes
- Recognize that natural hazards and risk are best understood in the context of time
- Understand the link between the geologic cycle and natural hazards
- Understand the scientific method, processes for predicting and warning about natural hazards, and techniques for risk analysis
- Understand that many natural hazards are linked to one another and to the physical environment
- Recognize that population growth, concentration of infrastructure and wealth in hazardous areas, and poor land-use decisions are increasing our vulnerability to natural disasters
- Understand that hazardous natural processes can also provide benefits
- Understand that the frequency and severity of some destructive natural events may be affected by climate change

Introduction to Natural Hazards

The 2004 South Asia Tsunami: Lessons Learned

One of the fundamental realities in the study of natural hazards is that people and governments are poorly prepared for rare natural disasters; they commonly behave as if these disasters will never happen. This unfortunate reality is well illustrated by three recent catastrophes: the tsunami in the Indian Ocean in December 2004, Hurricane Katrina on the U.S. Gulf Coast in August 2005, and the earthquake in northern Pakistan in October 2005. Each of these events provides hard lessons that can help us reduce the toll of future disasters. Here, we illustrate these lessons by using the Indian Ocean tsunami as an example.

The tsunami in the Indian Ocean on December 26, 2004, was one of the worst natural catastrophes in human history, claiming more than 200,000 lives in 11 countries and leaving millions homeless.[1,2] In the past 100 years, only a flood in China in 1938, an earthquake in the same country in 1976, and a cyclone in Bangladesh in 1970 have claimed more lives.

Most large tsunami are triggered at subduction zones. A *subduction zone* is a long, relatively narrow strip of Earth's *lithosphere* where one of the large *tectonic plates* that constitute Earth's thin outer shell subducts or moves beneath another. The zone of collision between the two plates is a huge fault that extends for hundreds of kilometres along the ocean floor, parallel to the edge of a continent or an island, such as Sumatra. Giant earthquakes, the strongest on Earth, occur at these sites, releasing energy that has slowly built up along the fault over centuries.

The Indonesian earthquake that triggered the tsunami was a subduction-zone event. It was the second-largest quake of the past 100 years, with a magnitude of 9.3. Aftershocks as large as magnitude 7.2 occurred for months after the main quake, and a magnitude 8.7 quake ruptured another section of the fault on March 26, 2005. The December earthquake occurred along the fault that separates the India and Burma plates, west and northwest of the island of Sumatra (Figure 1.1). There, the India plate moves eastward beneath the Eurasia plate, along the Sunda Trench west of Thailand and Indonesia.

About 1200 km of the fault separating the Australia and Eurasia plates ruptured. Measurements and computer models indicate that the seafloor moved as much as 15 m along the fault. Parts of the Andaman and Nicobar islands were elevated by the movement, whereas land

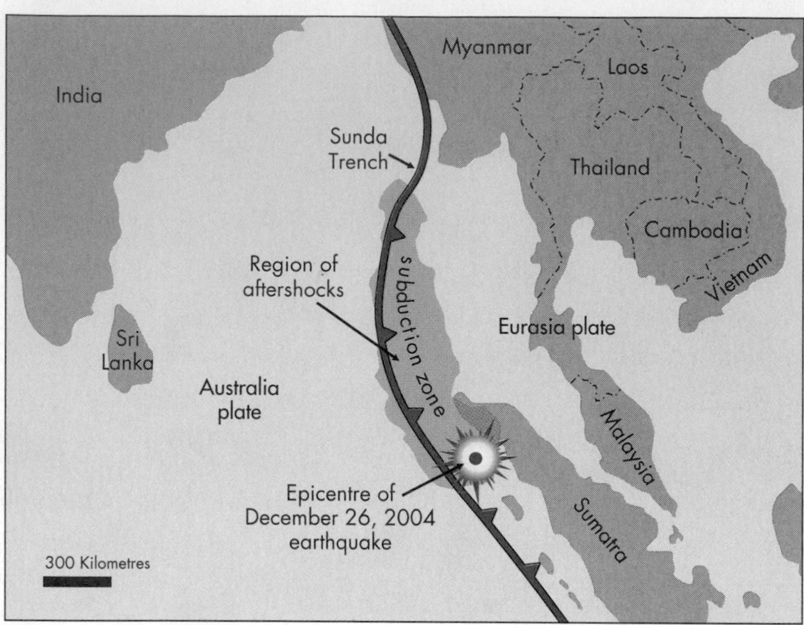

◄ **FIGURE 1.1 GREAT INDONESIAN EARTHQUAKE OF 2004** The source area of the December 2004 earthquake off the coast of Sumatra, showing the location of the initial fault rupture and aftershock epicentres. *(From Clague, J., C. Yorath, R. Franklin, and B. Turner. 2006. At risk: Earthquakes and tsunamis on the west coast. Vancouver, BC: Tricouni Press)*

along the western coast of Sumatra subsided up to 2 m, moving parts of the coastline below sea level.

The seafloor behaved like a piston, displacing the column of water above it and setting in motion energy waves that moved upward and outward at speeds of up to 700 km/h (Figure 1.2). Most of the wave energy was directed west and east, perpendicular to the fault line. At the ocean surface, waves were widely separated and had small heights, unnoticeable to a person in a boat. When the tsunami approached the shore, however, its energy became confined by the shoaling water, causing the waves to draw together and grow in height. Finally, the waves surged ashore. Within minutes, the first tsunami waves swept across the coastal plain of northwest Sumatra, reaching elevations up to 30 m above sea level, completely destroying scores of coastal towns, including much of the provincial capital city of Banda Aceh. The eastward-moving waves slowed as they crossed the shallow continental shelf west of Thailand and thus did not reach the tourist resorts of that country until about 10:00 A.M., two hours after the earthquake (Figure 1.3). Shortly thereafter, waves up to 4 m high swept inland on

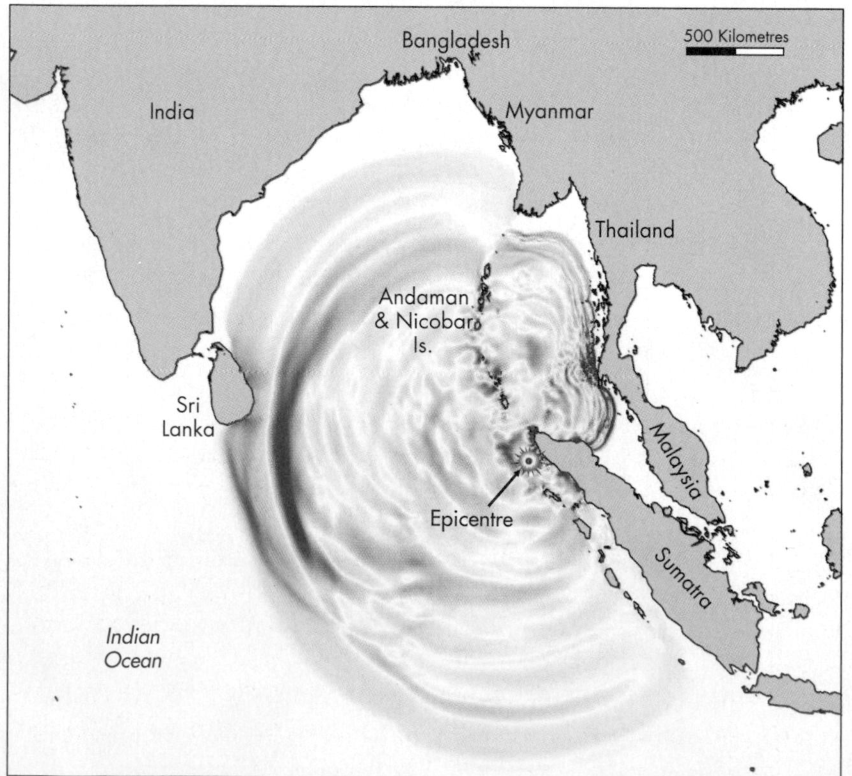

◄ **FIGURE 1.2 THE TSUNAMI MOVES ACROSS THE INDIAN OCEAN** A computer simulation of the tsunami triggered by the giant earthquake of December 26, 2004. The image shows the tsunami approaching Sri Lanka about two hours after the earthquake. Wave crests and troughs are shown, respectively, in red and blue. The colour intensity is a measure of the height of the wave or depression of the trough. *(Kenji Satake)*

◄ **FIGURE 1.3 THE KILLER TSUNAMI STRIKES THAILAND** The tsunami rushes into Khao Lak, Thailand, two hours after the giant earthquake of December 26, 2004. *(Copyright © 2005 John M. Thompson)*

the east coast of Sri Lanka and then southern India, causing widespread damage and claiming tens of thousands of lives. Waves as high as 4 m struck the Horn of Africa eight hours after the quake. The tsunami eventually entered the Pacific Ocean and was even recorded at tidal stations on the coasts of North America.

A warning system, even a rudimentary one, might have saved many thousands of lives. The tsunami struck Sri Lanka and India more than two hours after the earthquake, yet the people of these countries didn't know it was coming. Warning systems, however, are useful only when the source of the tsunami is far from populated shores. A warning system would have helped people in Thailand, Sri Lanka, and India but not residents of Banda Aceh, where the tsunami hit with full force less than 30 minutes after the earthquake. Warning systems require a communications infrastructure that permits information to rapidly reach emergency officials in areas at risk. Those officials, in turn, should have plans to rapidly evacuate people from low-lying coastal areas.

Although it had horrific consequences, the strength of the Indian Ocean tsunami was not unprecedented. Tsunami in the Pacific Ocean triggered by earthquakes in Chile in 1960 and Alaska in 1964 produced waves just as large as those in the Indian Ocean, albeit nowhere near as lethal. The situation in the Pacific, however, is different from that in South Asia. First, since 1964, a tsunami warning system has been in place in the North Pacific, centred at Honolulu, Hawaii, and Palmer, Alaska. Second, large areas bordering the Indian Ocean are broad, low-lying coastal plains less than 10 m above sea level and thus within the run-up zone of large tsunami. Much of the coastlines of the Pacific Ocean, especially in North America, are higher and steeper than are those in the Indian Ocean, which limits the landward extent of tsunami damage. Third, most structures in which people live and work along the coasts of the Indian Ocean are flimsy and no match for a tsunami. Debris entrained by the tsunami is just as lethal as the surging water itself. Although homes and other buildings in tsunami-inundation zones on the Pacific Coast would also be damaged and destroyed, better construction practices and materials ensure that this problem is not as severe.

Even without a warning system, however, the death toll in South Asia could have been much lower if people had responded to two tsunami-warning signs. First, the strong ground shaking close to the *epicentre*, for example in Banda Aceh, warned of the approaching tsunami, providing residents in those areas time to move inland or to higher ground. Second, at many distant locations, where people would not have felt shaking, the first wave was preceded by a rapid withdrawal of the sea to low levels that coastal residents would never have seen, a sure sign that a giant wave would soon strike the shore.

The catastrophe in the Indian Ocean carries a strong message for people living along other coasts vulnerable to tsunami, including much of the west coast of North America. It was a rare event, something that no one in the region had experienced before or could imagine, even though some scientists had warned of the possibility and smaller tsunami had occurred in the Indian Ocean in the eighteenth and nineteenth centuries. Given their lack of experience, people and governments were complacent and could not conceive of such an event happening; they were thus completely unprepared. Scientists have shown that an earthquake and tsunami nearly identical to that in the Indian Ocean will strike the British Columbia, Washington, and Oregon coasts sometime in the future, although they cannot say when. We are arguably better prepared than people and governments in South Asia before December 26, 2004, but how will we cope when it's our turn?

What are the lessons of the South Asia tsunami? The existing Pacific tsunami warning system must be improved and new systems installed in other parts of the world where large tsunami are possible. New technologies, including satellite-based sensors, offer opportunities to track tsunami in real time. Perhaps more important, however, is communication. We must review and upgrade communication infrastructures and chain-of-command protocols in tsunami-prone areas to ensure that emergency officials in coastal communities receive timely information. And people living near the sea must become aware of what to do in the event of a tsunami. A public education program should teach people about tsunami and provide instructions on how to get information during an alert, where to go, and what to take. Educational initiatives should be entrenched into school curricula. Tsunami evacuation routes should be publicized and marked by signs, as has been done in Japan, the United States, and New Zealand. Tsunami information can be printed in newspapers and telephone books, along with phone numbers of local emergency service offices.

1.1 Why Studying Natural Hazards Is Important

Since 1995, the world has experienced the devastating tsunami in the Indian Ocean; catastrophic flooding in Venezuela, Bangladesh, and central Europe; the strongest El Niño on record; and deadly earthquakes in India, Iran, Turkey, and, most recently, Pakistan. In the same period, Central America experienced a deadly Category 5 hurricane; New Orleans was devastated by Hurricane Katrina; Arizona and California experienced record-setting wildfires; Oklahoma had the worst tornadoes in its history; an ice storm crippled Ontario, Quebec, and New England; record-setting hail hit Nebraska; and Earth experienced many of the warmest years of the past 100 years and probably of the past 1000 years. These events are the result of enormous forces that are at work both inside and on the surface of our planet. In this book, we explain these forces and their impacts on people and property. We also discuss how we can better prepare for natural disasters, thus minimizing their impacts when they do happen.

Processes: Internal and External

In our discussion of natural hazards, we will use the word *process* to mean the ways in which events, such as volcanic eruptions, earthquakes, landslides, and floods, affect Earth's surface. Some of these processes—for example, volcanic eruptions and earthquakes—are the result of internal forces explained by the theory of plate tectonics, one of the basic unifying theories of science. In fact, most earthquakes and active volcanoes occur at boundaries between tectonic plates, large blocks of the Earth's crust.

Other hazardous natural processes result from external forces operating at or very near Earth's surface. For example, energy from the Sun warms Earth's atmosphere and surface, producing winds and evaporating water. Wind and ocean circulation and water evaporation determine Earth's climate and drive the hydrologic cycle. These forces, in turn, are directly related to hazardous processes, such as violent storms, floods, and coastal erosion.

Mass wasting is driven by both internal and external forces. Landslides result from gravity acting on hillslopes that have been formed by tectonic processes and erosion. Gravity is the force that attracts one body to another—in this case the attraction of surface materials toward the centre of Earth. Because of gravitational attraction, rocks and soils on mountainsides and the water that falls as precipitation all move downslope.

Thus, the processes we consider to be hazards are natural and derive from the internal heating of Earth and external energy from the Sun. The amount of energy released by natural processes differs greatly. For example, the average tornado expends about 1000 times as much energy as a lightning bolt does, whereas the volcanic eruption of Mount St. Helens in May 1980 released approximately 1 million times as much energy as a lightning bolt. The amount of solar energy Earth receives each day is about a trillion times as much as a lightning bolt. However, it is important to keep in mind that a lightning bolt focuses its energy at a point (for example, a tree), whereas solar energy is spread around the entire globe.

Events such as earthquakes, tsunami, volcanic eruptions, floods, and fires are natural processes that have been occurring on Earth's surface for billions of years. They become hazardous only when they threaten human beings. We use the terms *hazard*, *risk*, *disaster*, and *catastrophe* to describe our interaction with these natural processes.

Of course, not all hazards are "natural." Many hazards are caused by people, such as pandemics, warfare, and technological disasters like regional power failures. Over the past century, the distinction between natural and human-induced hazards has become increasingly vague, and technological disasters are increasing as the world's population grows and state economies become increasingly connected and interdependent. Social and technological hazards are important and interesting in their own right, but they are beyond the scope of this book. Our focus is on hazardous solid Earth and atmospheric processes.

Hazard, Risk, Disaster, and Catastrophe

In the context of this book, a **hazard** is any natural process that threatens human life or property. The process itself is not a hazard; rather, it becomes a hazard only when threatening human interests. **Risk** may be expressed as the probable severity that a destructive event will occur multiplied by the event's likely impact on people and property. Risk thus integrates hazard and social vulnerability. The terms **disaster**, or natural disaster, and **catastrophe** refer to events that cause serious injury, loss of life, and property damage over a limited

◀ **FIGURE 1.4 KILLER CYCLONE** The aftermath of the 1991 cyclone that devastated Bangladesh and killed approximately 145,000 people. *(Pablo Bartholomew/Getty Images, Inc.-Liaison)*

time and within a specific geographic area. Although the distinction between *disaster* and *catastrophe* is rather arbitrary, the latter is more massive and affects a larger number of people and more infrastructure than the former. Disasters may be regional or even national in scope, whereas catastrophes commonly have consequences far beyond the area that is directly affected and require huge expenditures of time and money for recovery. Examples of catastrophes are the South Asia tsunami of December 2004 and Hurricane Katrina in August 2005.

Natural hazards affect the lives of millions of people around the world. All areas of Canada and the United States are at risk from more than one hazardous process.[3,4] Parts of western North America are prone to earthquakes and landslides and experience rare volcanic eruptions; the Pacific Coast is vulnerable to tsunami; the Atlantic and Gulf of Mexico Coasts are threatened by hurricanes; forested areas of the continent are prone to wildfires; the mid-continent from Texas to Ontario is subject to tornadoes and blizzards; and droughts and floods can occur almost anywhere. No area is considered hazard free.

During the past few decades, earthquakes, floods, and hurricanes have killed several million people; the average annual loss of life has been about 150,000, with more than 300,000 deaths in 2005 alone. Financial loss from natural disasters now exceeds $50 billion per year and can reach over $200 billion, as happened in 2005; that figure represents direct property damage and does not include such losses as loss of employment, mental anguish, and reduced productivity. Two catastrophes, a cyclone accompanied by flooding in Bangladesh in 1970 and an earthquake in China in 1976, each claimed more than 300,000 lives. The Indian Ocean tsunami in 2004 resulted in at least 200,000 deaths, and another cyclone that struck Bangladesh in 1991 claimed 145,000 lives (Figure 1.4). An earthquake in Kobe, Japan, in 1995 claimed more than 5000 lives, destroyed many thousands of buildings, and caused more than $100 billion in property damage (Figure 1.5).

◀ **FIGURE 1.5 DEVASTATING EARTHQUAKE** An earthquake struck Kobe, Japan, in January 1995, killing more than 5000 people and causing more than $100 billion damage. *(Roger Hutchinson, NOAA, National Geophysical Data Center; from Clague, J., C. Yorath, R. Franklin, and B. Turner. 2006. At risk: Earthquakes and tsunamis on the west coast. Vancouver, BC: Tricouni Press, p. 112)*

The United Nations designated the 1990s as the International Decade for Natural Hazards Reduction. The objectives of the UN program were to minimize loss of life and property damage from natural disasters, but the objectives were not met; rather, losses from disasters increased dramatically in the 1990s. Achieving the UN objectives will require education and large expenditures to mitigate specific hazards and contain diseases that accompany disasters and catastrophes. The term **mitigation** is used by scientists, planners, and policy-makers when describing efforts to prepare for disasters and to minimize their harmful effects. After floods, for example, water supplies may be contaminated by bacteria, causing disease to spread. To mitigate the effects of this contamination, a relief agency or government may deploy portable water treatment plants, disinfect water wells, and distribute bottled water.

Death and Damage Caused by Natural Hazards

When we compare the effects of different natural hazards in North America, we find that those that cause the greatest loss of life are not the same as those that cause the most property damage. Tornadoes and windstorms cause the largest number of deaths each year, although lightning, floods, and hurricanes also take a heavy toll (Table 1.1). Loss of life from earthquakes in North America is surprisingly low, largely because of the high standards of building construction. But a single large earthquake can cause tremendous property damage. For example, the Northridge earthquake in Los Angeles in 1994 caused US$20 billion to US$30 billion in property damage, but killed only 60 people. The next great earthquake in a densely populated part of California could cause more than US$100 billion damage.[5]

The property damage caused by each type of hazard is considerable. Natural disasters cost Canada billions of dollars annually. Because the population levels are increasing in high-risk areas of Canada, such as earthquake- and landslide-prone areas in southern British Columbia and southern Quebec, we can expect this number to increase significantly. Floods, landslides, expansive soils that shrink and swell, and frost each cause in excess of US$1.5 billion in damage each year in the United States alone.

It is important to note that the relations between loss of life and property damage discussed above apply only to the fully developed world, mainly North America, Europe, Australia, and New Zealand. Natural disasters in most developing countries claim far more lives than comparable events in North America. For example, the tsunami in the Indian Ocean in December 2004 killed more than 200,000 people, and the large earthquake the following year in northern Pakistan claimed 80,000 lives. In comparison, the tsunami in the North Pacific in 1964, though equal in size to the one in the Indian Ocean, killed 119 people, and no earthquake in North America since the 1906 San Francisco earthquake has claimed more than 100 lives. A notable characteristic of North American disasters is their very large toll on the economy. Category 4 and 5 hurricanes typically cause billions of dollars in damage in southern U.S. states; the direct damage from Hurricane Katrina, the worst storm in U.S. history, was more than US$80 billion, and indirect damage, including lost economic activity and employment, was several times that amount.[6]

Natural hazards differ greatly in their potential to create a catastrophe (Table 1.1). Floods, hurricanes, earthquakes, volcanic eruptions, and large wildfires are most likely to create catastrophes. Landslides, snow avalanches, and tornadoes generally affect a small area and thus are rarely cat-

TABLE 1.1 Effects of Selected Hazards in Canada and the United States

Hazard	Deaths per Year	Catastrophe Potential
Flood	100	High
Earthquake	> 50	High
Landslide	30	Low
Snow avalanche	20	Low
Volcano	< 1	High
Coastal erosion	0	Low
Expansive soils	0	Very low
Hurricane	60	High
Tornado and windstorm	220	Medium
Lightning	125	Very low
Drought	0	Medium
Heat	> 600	Medium
Freezing and frozen rain	> 800	Medium

Estimates based on recent or predicted loss over a 150-year period. Actual losses differ considerably from year to year and could be much greater in a given year.

Source: Modified from White, G. F., and J. E. Haas. 1975. Assessment of research on natural hazards. Cambridge, MA: MIT Press.

astrophic. Coastal erosion, lightning, and expansive soils do not create catastrophes but can still cause much damage.[7]

Risks associated with natural hazards change with time because of changes in land-use patterns. Hazardous land, such as steep hillsides and floodplains, may be developed as cities grow. Such expansion is a serious problem in many large, rapidly growing cities in developing nations. Urbanization alters drainage, increases the steepness of some hillslopes, and removes vegetation. Agriculture, forestry, and mining also remove natural vegetation and can increase erosion and sedimentation. Overall, damage from most hazardous natural processes in Canada is increasing, but the number of deaths from many hazards is decreasing because of better planning, forecasting, warning, and engineering. Canada is a world leader in research on natural hazards and disaster risk reduction.

1.2 Role of Time in Understanding Hazards

Natural disasters are recurrent events; therefore, study of their history provides needed information for risk reduction. Whether we are studying floods, landslides, volcanic eruptions, or earthquakes, knowledge of historic events and the recent geologic history of an area is vital to understanding the hazard and assessing its risk. For example, to evaluate the risk of flooding along a particular river, we must identify floods that have occurred in the historic and recent prehistoric past. We can obtain useful information by studying aerial photographs and maps as far back as the record allows. We can extend the historic record by searching for evidence of past floods in stream deposits. Commonly, these deposits contain organic material, such as wood or shells, that can be dated by the *carbon-14 method* to provide a chronology of ancient flood events. This chronology can then be combined with the historic record of high flows to provide an overall perspective of the frequency and size of floods. Similarly, if we are studying landslides in a particular area, we must investigate both historic and prehistoric events to properly forecast the likelihood of future landslides. Geologists have the tools and training to "read the landscape" for evidence of past events and, by linking prehistoric and historic records, they extend our perspective of recurrent natural events far back in time.

In summary, before we can truly appreciate a hazardous process, we must study in detail its past history and the geologic features that it has produced or affected. The latter may be landforms, such as channels or beaches; structures, such as faults or folded rock; or materials, such as lava flows, meteorites, or tsunami deposits. Hazard forecasts and warnings are more accurate if we combine information about the past behaviour of the process with an understanding of present conditions.

To fully understand natural hazards, some background knowledge of the processes that function on Earth is necessary. In the next few sections, we discuss these basic processes within the context of cycles. We then introduce five concepts that are fundamental to understanding natural processes as hazards.

1.3 Geologic Cycle

Geology, topography, and climate govern the type, location, and intensity of natural processes. For example, earthquakes and volcanoes do not occur at random across Earth's surface; rather, most of them mark the boundaries of lithospheric plates. The location of landslides, too, is governed by geologic conditions. Slopes composed of a weak rock, such as shale, are more likely to fail than those made of a strong rock, such as granite. Hurricanes and cyclones form only over warm oceans and have different impacts depending on the topography, and therefore geology, of the areas they strike.

Throughout much of the 4.6 billion years of Earth history, the materials on or near the surface of the planet have been created and modified by numerous physical, chemical, and biological processes. These processes produce the mineral resources, fuels, land, water, and atmosphere we require for our survival. Collectively, they are referred to as the **geologic cycle**, which comprises

- the tectonic cycle
- the rock cycle
- the hydrologic cycle
- biogeochemical cycles

The Tectonic Cycle

The term *tectonic* refers to the large-scale geologic processes that deform Earth's crust and produce such features as ocean basins, continents, and mountains. Tectonic processes are driven by forces deep within Earth. To describe these processes, we must use information about the composition and layering of Earth's interior and about the large blocks that form the outer shell of Earth, called *tectonic plates*. The **tectonic cycle** involves the creation, movement, and destruction of tectonic plates, and one cycle can last more than 200 million years.

Earth's Lithosphere and Crust Earth comprises several internal layers that differ in composition and physical properties (Figure 1.6). The outermost or surface layer, called the *lithosphere,* is stronger and more rigid than deeper material. Below the lithosphere lies the *asthenosphere,* a hot layer of relatively low-strength rock that extends to an average depth of about 250 km. Through detailed study of ocean basins and continents, geophysicists have established that the average thickness of the lithosphere is about 100 km; it ranges from a few kilometres thick beneath the crests of mid-ocean ridges to 400 km thick beneath continents.

The upper part of the lithosphere is the *crust*. Crustal rocks are less dense than the rocks below. There are two types of crust: oceanic and continental. Oceanic crust is denser than continental crust (Figure 1.6). It is also thinner—the ocean floor has an average crustal thickness of about 7 km, whereas

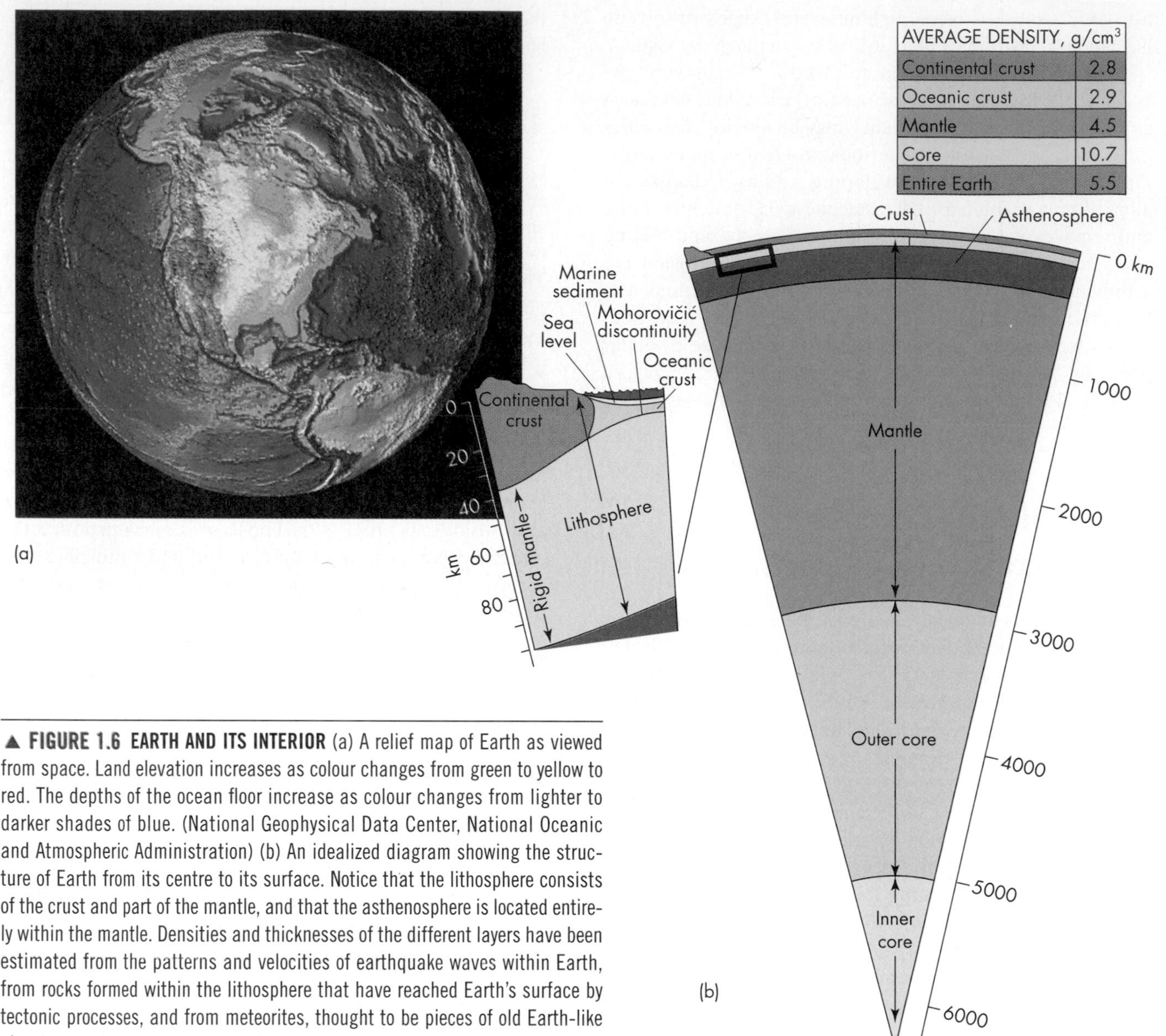

▲ **FIGURE 1.6 EARTH AND ITS INTERIOR** (a) A relief map of Earth as viewed from space. Land elevation increases as colour changes from green to yellow to red. The depths of the ocean floor increase as colour changes from lighter to darker shades of blue. (National Geophysical Data Center, National Oceanic and Atmospheric Administration) (b) An idealized diagram showing the structure of Earth from its centre to its surface. Notice that the lithosphere consists of the crust and part of the mantle, and that the asthenosphere is located entirely within the mantle. Densities and thicknesses of the different layers have been estimated from the patterns and velocities of earthquake waves within Earth, from rocks formed within the lithosphere that have reached Earth's surface by tectonic processes, and from meteorites, thought to be pieces of old Earth-like planets. *(From Levin, H. L. 1986. Contemporary physical geology, 2nd ed. Philadelphia: Saunders)*

continental crust is about 30 km thick on average and up to 70 km thick beneath mountainous regions.

Types of Plate Boundaries Unlike the asthenosphere, which is thought to be more or less continuous, the lithosphere is broken into large fragments called lithospheric or tectonic plates that move relative to one another (Figure 1.7).[8] Processes associated with the origin, movement, and destruction of these plates are collectively termed *plate tectonics*. Tectonic plates are formed and destroyed at their margins or boundaries. Plate boundaries may be *divergent*, *convergent*, or *transform* (Figure 1.8).[9] These boundaries are not narrow cracks, but rather broad zones of intense deformation tens to hundreds of kilometres wide that extend through the crust. It is at these boundaries that most earthquakes and active volcanoes occur.

Divergent boundaries occur where two plates move away from each other and new lithosphere is produced. Places where this separation occurs are large, underwater mountain ridges known as *mid-ocean ridges* (Figure 1.8). By a process known as *seafloor spreading*, lithosphere breaks or *rifts* apart along a series of cracks more or less parallel to the ridge crest. Many of the cracks in the underwater rift zone are injected with molten rock, or *magma*, from below. New lithosphere forms as the magma solidifies and is slowly rafted, in a conveyor-belt fashion, away from the ridge crest. The tectonic plates on each side of the ridge move apart at a rate of tens of millimetres to a few hundred millimetres each year (Figure 1.7).

Convergent boundaries occur where two plates collide head on (Figure 1.8). Commonly, a higher density oceanic plate is drawn down beneath a lower density continental plate. This process is called *subduction*, and convergent boundaries of this type are called *subduction zones* (Figure 1.9). The oceanic plate heats as it moves beneath the continental plate. At depths of 100 km to 120 km, it reaches temperatures in excess of 700°C and releases H_2O, CO_2, and other gases that rise into the lower part of the continental crust. The super-

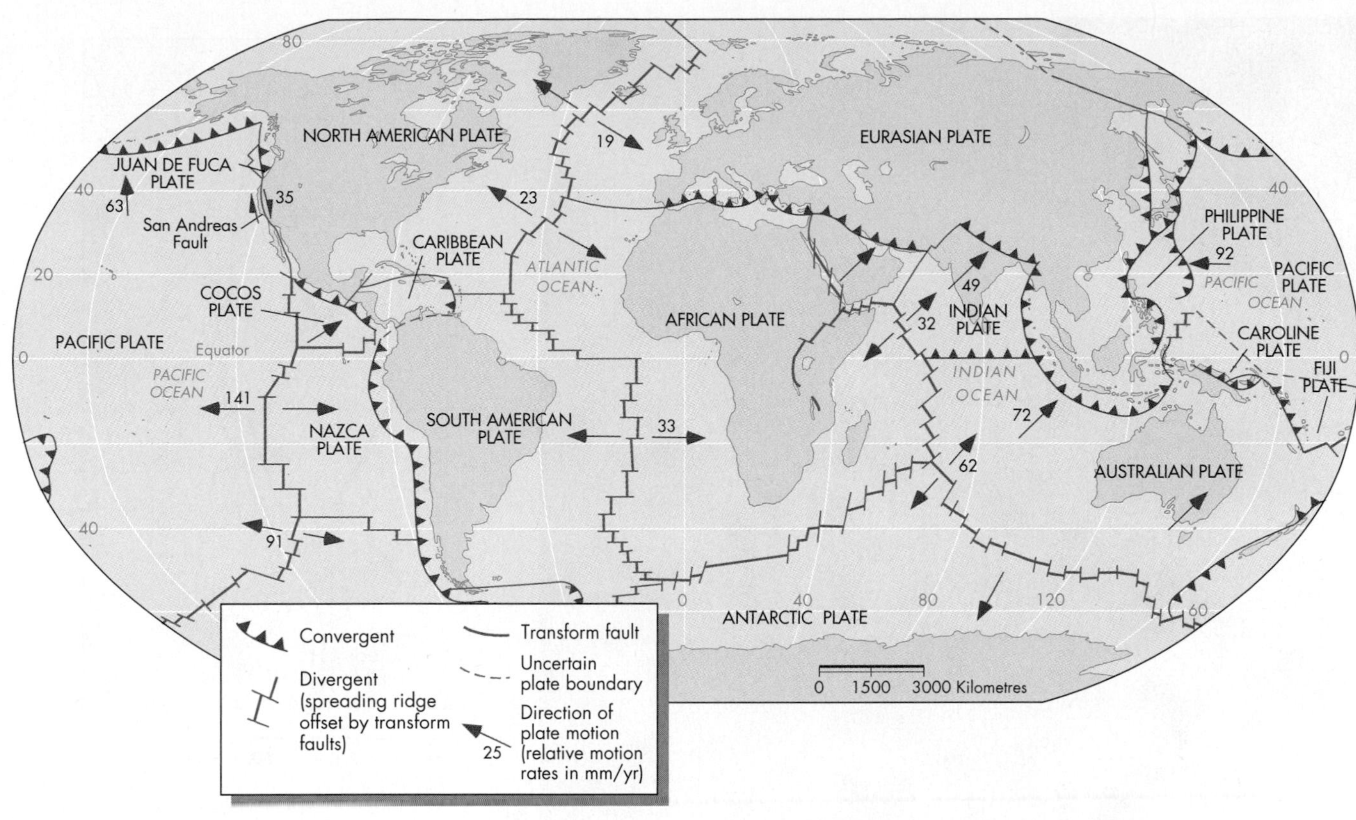

▲ **FIGURE 1.7 EARTH'S TECTONIC PLATES** A map showing the major tectonic plates, plate boundaries, and directions of plate movement. *(Modified from Christopherson, R. W. 1994. Geosystems, 2nd ed. New York: Macmillan; Press, F., R. Siever, J. Grotzinger, and T. H. Jordan. 2003. Understanding Earth, 4th ed. New York: W.H. Freeman)*

heated gases cause lower crustal rocks to melt, and the magma moves slowly up through the crust along fractures. Some of the magma reaches the surface, where it erupts and builds volcanoes. A chain of active volcanoes that have formed from repeated eruptions marks the inboard margin of the *Cascadia subduction zone,* which extends along the west coast of North America from northern California to central Vancouver Island (Figure 1.9). Well-known volcanoes in this chain include Mount Baker, Mount Rainier, Mount St. Helens, Mount Hood, and Mount Lassen. Other important chains of active volcanoes produced by subduction include the Andes of South America, the Aleutian volcanoes in southwestern Alaska, and the volcanoes of Indonesia, Japan, and the Caribbean.

Subduction adds material to continents. Crustal fragments rafted on the mantle (for example, islands that are too light to move under a continent) are accreted to the continent. Thick sediments and sedimentary rocks covering the subducting plate are also added to the continent.

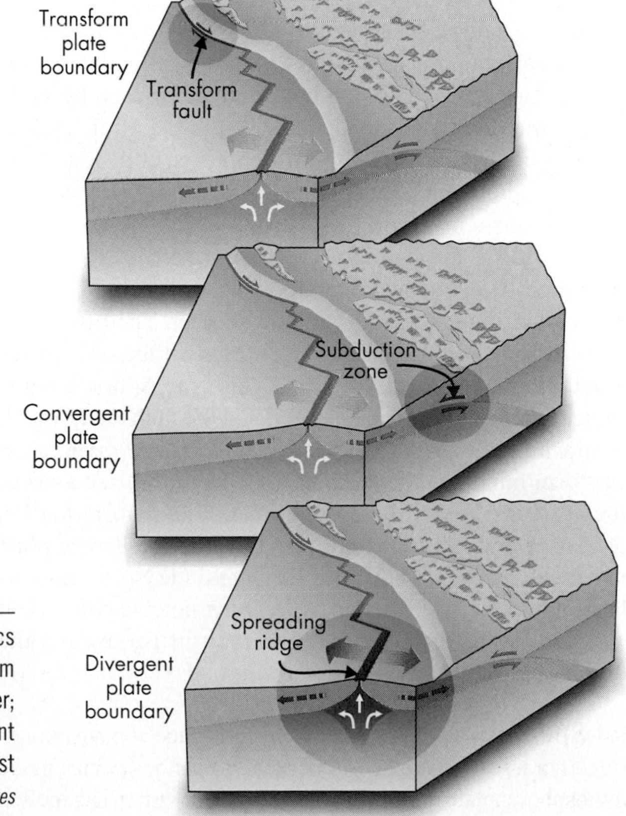

▶ **FIGURE 1.8 PLATE TECTONICS** Schematic diagram showing plate tectonics processes. Boundaries between tectonic plates are of three types: transform plate boundaries, along which adjacent plates move horizontally past one another; convergent plate boundaries, where one plate moves under another; and divergent plate boundaries, where two plates spread apart at a ridge and new oceanic crust is created. *(From Clague, J., C. Yorath, R. Franklin, and B. Turner. 2006. At risk: Earthquakes and tsunamis on the west coast. Vancouver, BC: Tricouni Press)*

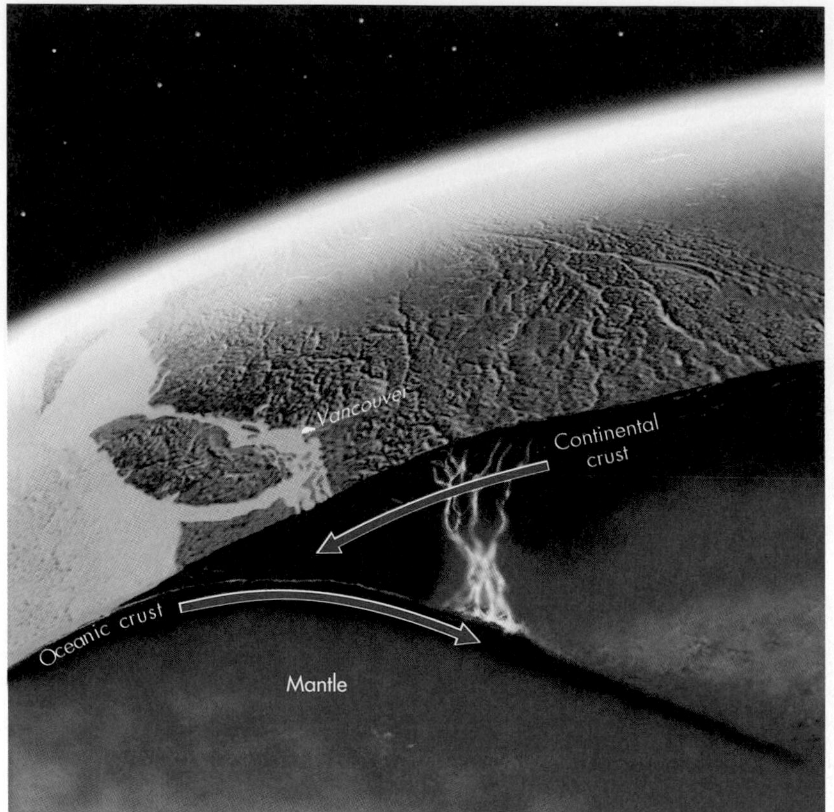

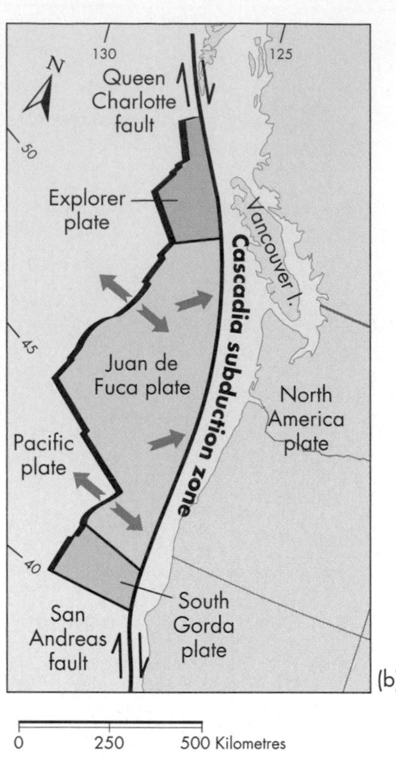

▲ **FIGURE 1.9 SUBDUCTION ZONE OFF CANADA'S WEST COAST** An artist's rendition (a) and map (b) of subduction of the oceanic Juan de Fuca plate beneath the continental North America plate off the southwest coast of British Columbia. *(From Clague, J., C. Yorath, R. Franklin, and B. Turner. 2006. At risk: Earthquakes and tsunamis on the west coast. Vancouver, BC: Tricouni Press)*

If the two colliding plates are both continental, they have roughly the same density and it is more difficult for one to sink beneath the other. In such a situation, the plates meet along a continental collision boundary delineated by high, faulted, and crumpled mountains, such as the Himalayas in central Asia. Over the past 13 million years, collision of the Indian subcontinent with Asia to the north has elevated the Tibetan Plateau by 5 km.

Mapping of the seafloor has demonstrated that mid-ocean ridges are not continuous features, but rather consist of a series of spreading ridges offset from one another. The offsets are the third type of plate boundary, where two tectonic plates slide horizontally past each other. This type of boundary is referred to as a *transform boundary*, and the fault along which the movement occurs is known as a *transform fault*. Most transform faults are located beneath oceans, but some occur on continents. A well-known continental transform fault is the San Andreas fault in California, where the Pacific plate on the west side is sliding horizontally past the North America plate on the east side (Figure 1.10). Other notable continental transform faults are the Anatolian fault in Turkey and the Alpine fault in New Zealand.

Hot Spots Not all tectonic activity takes place at plate boundaries. In a number of places on Earth, volcanoes occur inside a lithospheric plate at locations known as *hot spots*. The molten rock reaching the surface at hot spots is associated with convection deep within the mantle, the layer between the core and crust that makes up most of the interior of Earth.[10,11] An example of a continental hot spot is the Yellowstone National Park thermal area. Hot spots also occur beneath the Atlantic, Pacific, and Indian Oceans.

If a hot spot is anchored in the slowly convecting mantle, it will remain relatively fixed as a lithospheric plate moves over it. This motion will produce a line of volcanoes like those that form the Hawaiian–Emperor chain in the Pacific Ocean (Figure 1.11). Along this chain, volcanic rocks increase in age toward the northwest. The Emperor *seamounts*, which delineate the oldest part of chain, are former islands that subsided after volcanoes moved off the hot spot and became inactive.

The Tectonic Cycle and Natural Hazards The importance of the tectonic cycle to natural hazards cannot be overstated. All of Earth's inhabitants are affected by plate tectonics. As plates slowly move, so do the continents and ocean basins. Most earthquakes and volcanoes that threaten people are near or at plate boundaries; most tsunami are generated by subduction-zone earthquakes; and landslides are concentrated in mountains produced by plate collisions.

The Rock Cycle

Rocks are aggregates of one or more *minerals*. A mineral is a naturally occurring, crystalline substance with a specific

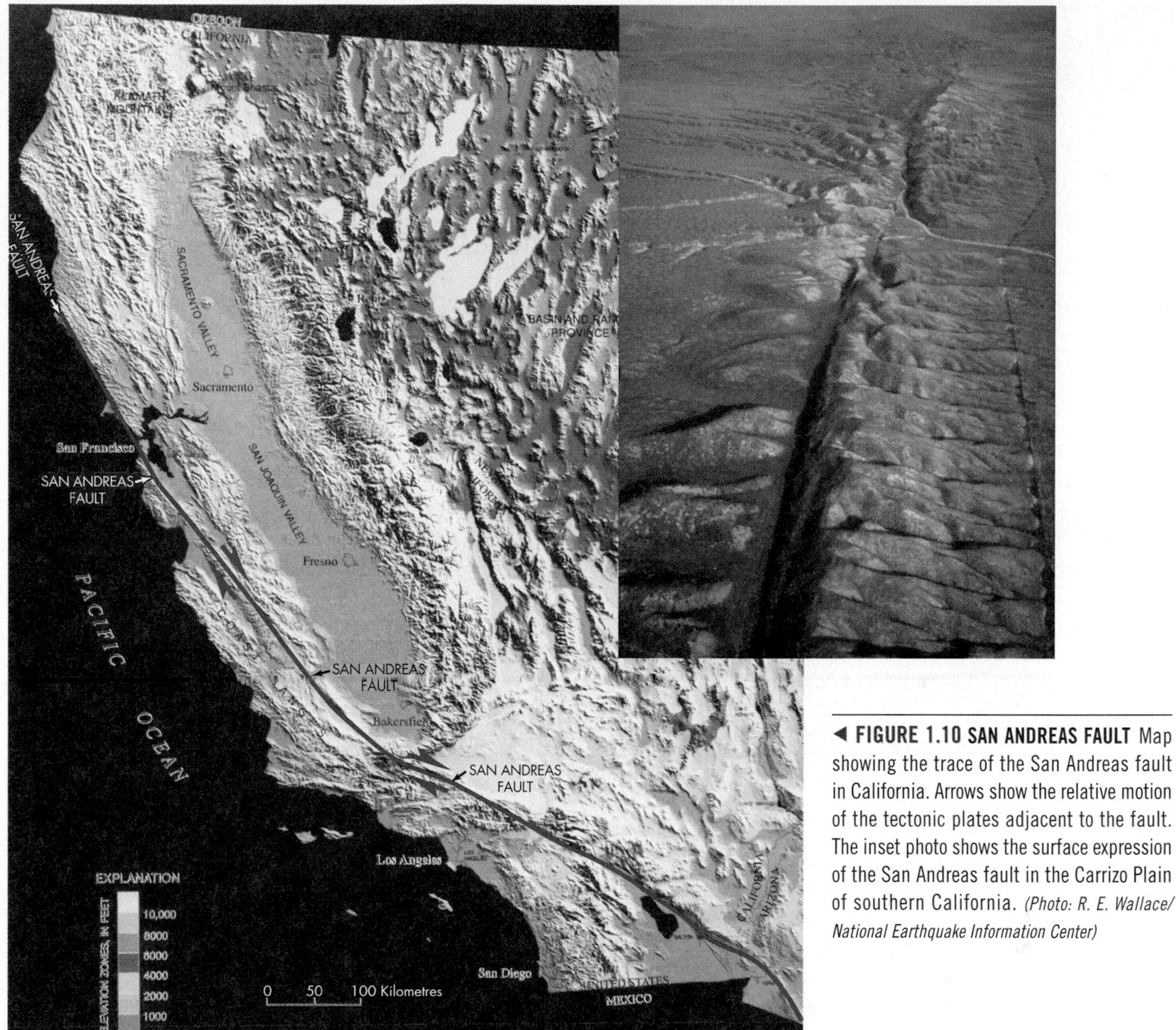

◄ **FIGURE 1.10 SAN ANDREAS FAULT** Map showing the trace of the San Andreas fault in California. Arrows show the relative motion of the tectonic plates adjacent to the fault. The inset photo shows the surface expression of the San Andreas fault in the Carrizo Plain of southern California. *(Photo: R. E. Wallace/ National Earthquake Information Center)*

elemental composition and a narrow range of physical properties (see Appendix A). The term **rock cycle** refers to worldwide recycling of three major groups of rocks, driven by Earth's internal heat and by energy from the Sun. The rock cycle is linked to the other cycles, because it depends on the tectonic cycle for heat and energy, the biogeochemical cycle for materials, and the hydrologic cycle for water. Water plays a central role in weathering, erosion, transportation, deposition, and lithification of sediment.

Although rocks differ greatly in their composition and properties, they can be classified into three general types, or families, according to how they formed (Figure 1.12; see Appendix B). *Crystallization* of molten rock produces *igneous rocks* beneath and on Earth's surface. Rocks at or near the surface break down chemically and physically by *weathering* to form particles known as *sediment*. These particles range in size from clay to very large boulders and blocks. Sediment formed by weathering is transported by wind, water, ice, and gravity to depositional sites, such as lakes and oceans. When wind or flowing water slackens, ice melts, or material moving under the influence of gravity reaches a flat surface, the sediment is *deposited*. During burial, the sediment is converted to *sedimentary rock* by a process called *lithification*. Lithification takes place by compaction and cementation of sediment during burial. With deep burial, sedimentary rocks may be *metamorphosed* by heat, pressure, and chemically active fluids into *metamorphic rock*. Metamorphic rocks may be buried to depths where pressure and temperature conditions cause them to melt, beginning the entire rock cycle again. Like any of Earth's cycles, there are many exceptions to the idealized sequence outlined above. For example, metamorphic rock may be changed into a new metamorphic rock without undergoing weathering or erosion (Figure 1.12), or sedimentary and metamorphic rocks may be uplifted and weathered before they can continue on to the next stage in the cycle. Finally, some sediments have a biological or chemical origin and types of metamorphism that do not involve deep burial.

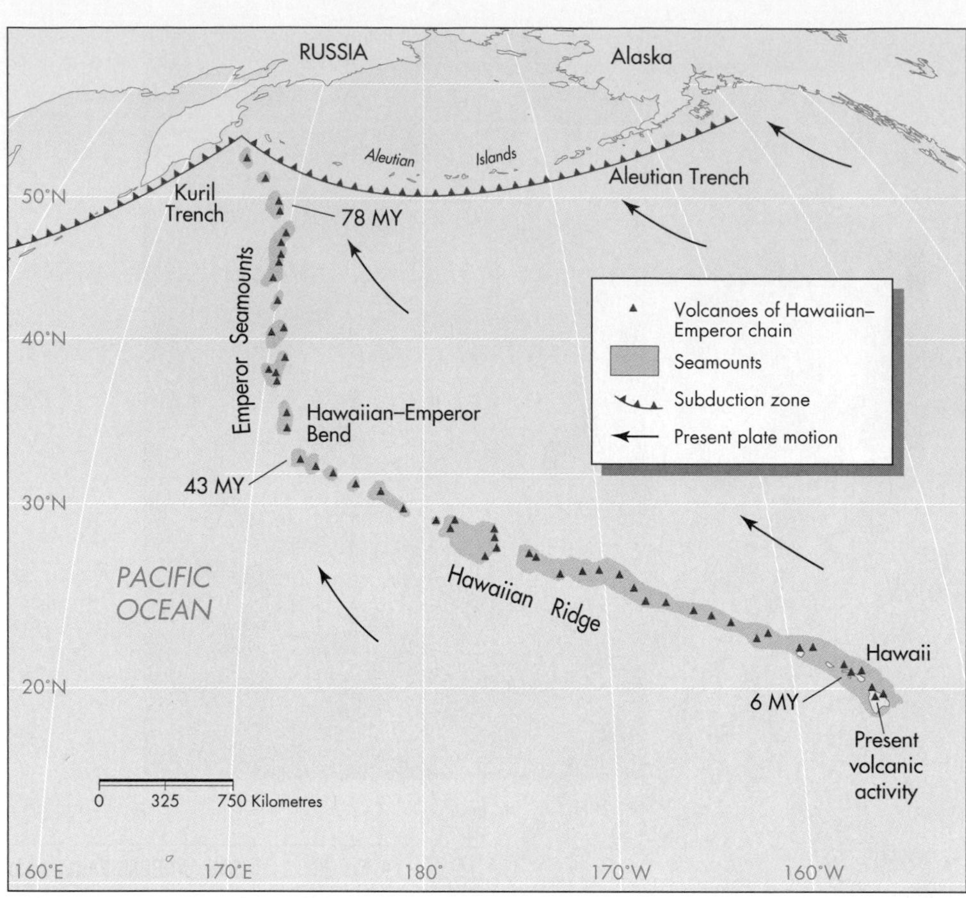

◄ **FIGURE 1.11 HAWAII HOT SPOT** Map showing the Hawaiian–Emperor chain of volcanic islands and seamounts. Volcanic activity is presently restricted to the Big Island of Hawaii at the southeast end of the chain. *(Modified from Clague, D. A., G. B. Dalrymple, and R. Moberly. 1975. Petrography and K-Ar ages of dredged volcanic rocks from the western Hawaiian Ridge and southern Emperor Seamount chain. Geological Society of America Bulletin 86:991–998)*

The Hydrologic Cycle

The cycling of water from the oceans to the atmosphere, to continents and islands, and back again to the oceans is called the **hydrologic cycle** (Figure 1.13). This cycle is driven by solar energy and operates by way of evaporation, precipitation, surface runoff, and subsurface flow. Along the way, water is stored in different compartments, including oceans, atmosphere, rivers and streams, groundwater, lakes, and glaciers (Table 1.2). The **residence time**, or estimated average amount of time that a drop of water spends in any one compartment, ranges from days in the atmosphere to hundreds of thousands of years in ice sheets.

As you can see by studying Table 1.2, only a tiny amount of the total water on Earth is active at the surface at any time. Although the combined percentage of water in the atmosphere, rivers, lakes, and shallow subsurface sediments and rocks is only about 0.3 percent of the total, this water is tremendously important for life on Earth and for the rock and biogeochemical cycles. Surface and near-surface water helps move chemical elements in solution, sculpts the landscape, weathers rocks, and transports and deposits sediments. It is also the source of the freshwater that makes life on land possible.

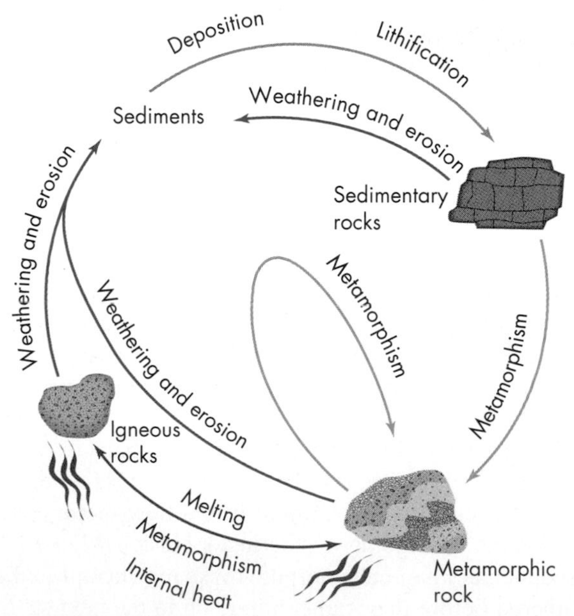

▲ **FIGURE 1.12 THE ROCK CYCLE** An idealized cycle showing the three families of rocks and important processes that form them.

Biogeochemical Cycles

A **biogeochemical cycle** is the transfer or cycling of an element or elements through the atmosphere, lithosphere, hydrosphere, and biosphere. It follows from this definition that biogeochemical cycles are intimately related to the tectonic, rock, and hydrologic cycles. The tectonic cycle provides water and gases from volcanic activity, as well as heat and energy, all of which are required to transfer dissolved solids in gases, aerosols, and solutions. The rock and hydro-

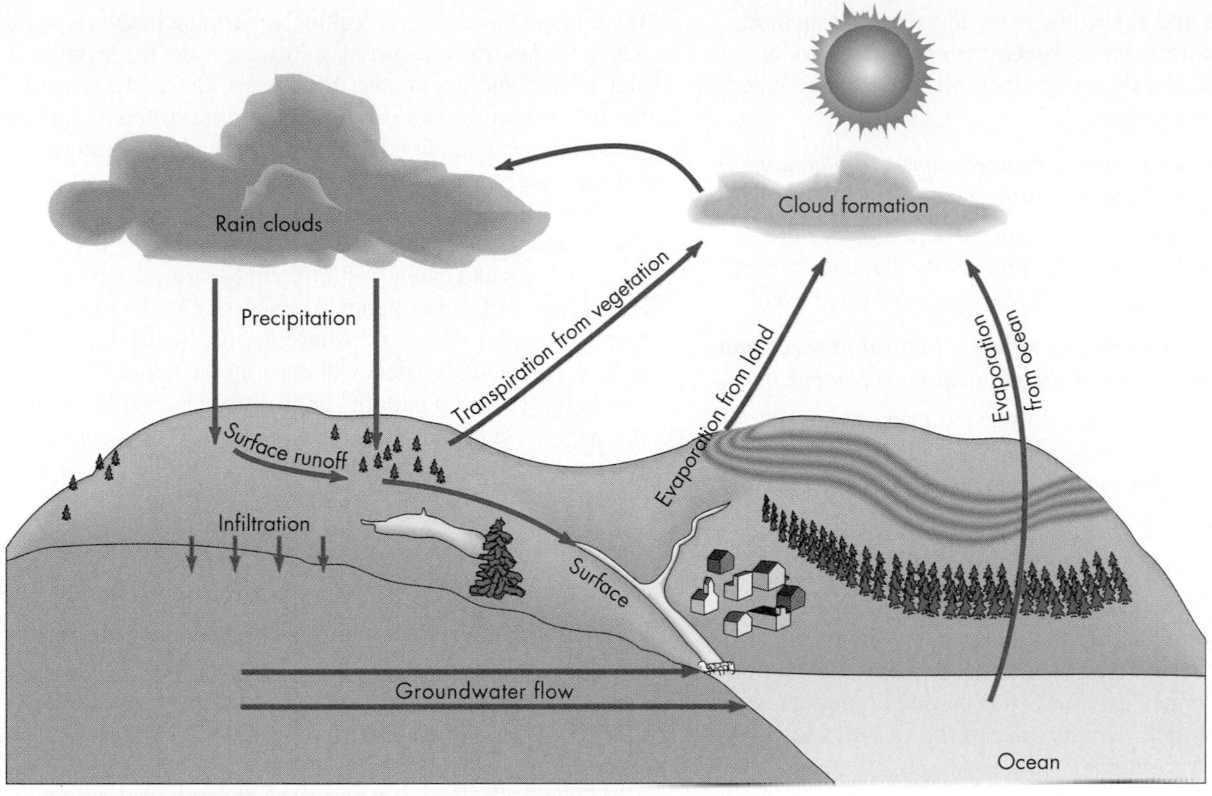

▲ **FIGURE 1.13 HYDROLOGIC CYCLE** Idealized diagram showing important processes and transfers that define the hydrologic cycle. *(Modified from Council on Environmental Quality and Department of State. 1980. The Global 2000 Report to the President. Vol. 2)*

logic cycles transfer and store chemical elements in water, soil, and rock.

Elements and chemical compounds are transferred via a series of storage compartments or reservoirs, which include air, soil, groundwater, and vegetation. For example, carbon is exhaled by animals, enters the atmosphere, and is then taken up by plants by *photosynthesis*. When a biogeochemical cycle is well understood, the rate of transfer, or *flux,* among all of the compartments is known. However, determining these rates globally is a daunting task. The amounts of such important elements as carbon, nitrogen, and phosphorus in each compartment, and their rates of transfer between compartments, are known only approximately.

1.4 Fundamental Concepts for Understanding Natural Processes as Hazards

The five concepts described below are basic to understanding natural hazards. They provide a conceptual framework for the detailed discussions of specific hazards in subsequent chapters of this book.

1. ***Hazards can be predicted through scientific analysis.*** Natural hazards, such as earthquakes, volcanic eruptions, landslides, and floods, are natural processes that can be

TABLE 1.2 The World's Water Supply

Location	Surface Area (km^2)	Water Volume (km^3)	Percentage of Total Water	Estimated Average Residence Time
Oceans	361,000,000	1,230,000,000	97.2	Thousands of years
Atmosphere	510,000,000	12,700	0.001	9 days
Rivers and streams	—	1200	0.0001	2 weeks
Groundwater; shallow	130,000,000	4,000,000	0.31	Hundreds to many thousands of years to depth of 0.8 km
Lakes (freshwater)	855,000	123,000	0.009	Tens of years
Ice caps and glaciers	28,200,000	28,600,000	2.15	Hundreds of years to hundreds of thousands of years

Source: Data are from U.S. Geological Survey.

identified and studied by using the scientific method. Most disasters can be forecast from past history of similar events, patterns in their occurrence, and types of precursor events.

2. ***Risk analysis is an important element of understanding the effects of hazardous processes.***

   Hazardous processes are amenable to *risk analysis*, which considers both the probability that a damaging event will occur and the consequences of that event.

3. ***Linkages exist between different natural hazards and between hazards and the physical environment.***

   Hazardous processes are linked in many ways. For example, earthquakes can produce landslides and tsunami, and hurricanes often cause flooding and coastal erosion.

4. ***Damage from natural disasters is increasing.***

   The human and economic costs of natural disasters are increasing because of the growth in population, property development in hazardous areas, and poor land-use practices. Events that caused limited disasters in the twentieth century are causing catastrophes in the twenty-first century.

5. ***Damage and loss of life from natural disasters can be minimized.***

   Minimizing the adverse effects of hazardous events requires an integrated approach that includes scientific understanding, land-use planning and regulation, engineering, and proactive disaster preparedness.

Hazards can be predicted through scientific analysis.

Science and Natural Hazards

Science is founded on investigations and experiments, the results of which are subject to verification. The **scientific method** involves a series of steps, the first of which is to formulate a question. With respect to a hazardous event, a geologist might ask: Why did a particular landslide occur? To answer this question, the geologist will spend time examining the failed slope. She may notice that a great deal of water is flowing from the toe of the landslide. If she also knows that a water pipe is buried in the slope, she may refine the question to: Did the water in the slope cause the landslide? This question is the basis for a hypothesis that may be stated as follows: The landslide occurred because a buried water pipe broke, causing a large amount of water to enter the slope and reduce the strength of the slope materials.

A **hypothesis** is a possible answer to a question and is an idea that can be tested. In our example, we can test the hypothesis that a broken water line caused a landslide by excavating the slope to determine the source of the water. In science we test hypotheses in an attempt to disprove them. If we found there was no leaking water pipe in the slope on which the landslide occurred, we would reject the hypothesis and develop and test another hypothesis. Use of the scientific method has improved our understanding of many natural processes, including flooding, volcanic eruptions, earthquakes, tsunami, hurricanes, and coastal erosion.

Scientists identify where hazardous processes are active, their magnitude, and how frequently they occur. They also map the types and extents of different hazards. Coupled with knowledge of the frequency of past events, they use such maps to predict when and where floods, landslides, earthquakes, and other disasters will occur in the future. They also search for types and patterns of precursor events. For example, *foreshocks* precede a large earthquake, and a change in gas emissions may signal an imminent volcanic eruption.

Hazardous Processes Are Natural

Throughout history, people have had to adjust to events that make their lives difficult, such as earthquakes, tsunami, floods, volcanic eruptions, and severe storms. These events have occurred against a backdrop of major climate change. Humans are apparently a product of the ice ages of the *Pleistocene Epoch*, which started about 2.6 million years ago (Table 1.3). The Pleistocene Epoch was a time of large fluctuations of climate—from cold, harsh glacial conditions as recently as 12,000 years ago to the relatively benign interglacial conditions we enjoy today. Adjusting to harsh and changing climatic conditions has been necessary for our survival from the very beginning.

Hazardous Earth processes are natural and thus are not the direct result of human activity. Nothing that people do, for example, changes the behaviour of volcanoes. However, land-use changes, such as urbanization and deforestation, may increase the frequency, or amplify the effects, of some processes, notably flooding and landslides. To reduce damage and loss of life, hazardous processes must be identified and information made available to planners and decision makers. However, because these processes are natural, we face fundamental philosophical issues when making choices about how to minimize their adverse effects. We realize, for example, that flooding is a natural part of river dynamics and must ask ourselves if it is wiser to attempt to control floods or, alternatively, to make sure that people and property are out of harm's way when they occur.

Although we can, to a degree, control some hazards, many are completely beyond our control. For example, we have some success in preventing damage from forest fires by using controlled burns and advanced firefighting techniques, but we will never be able to prevent earthquakes. In fact, we may actually worsen the effects of some natural processes simply by labelling them as hazardous. Rivers will always flood, but because we choose to live and work on floodplains, we have labelled floods as hazards, which has led to efforts to control them. Unfortunately, as we will discuss later, some flood-control measures intensify the effects of flooding, thereby increasing the risk of the event that we are trying to prevent (Chapter 7). The best approach to hazard reduction

TABLE 1.3 Geologic Time with Some Important Events

Era	Period	Epoch	Million Years before Present	Events: Life	Events: Earth	Million Years before Present	True Scale (Million Years before Present)
Cenozoic	Quaternary	Holocene	0.01	• Extinction event • Modern humans	Ice Age; Rise of St. Elias Mountains		Cenozoic
		Pleistocene	1.8	• Early humans		1.8	
	Tertiary	Pliocene	5.3		Formation of Andes Mountains		
		Miocene	23	• Grasses	Collision of India with Asia forming Himalayan Mountains and Tibetan Plateau		
		Oligocene	34	• Whales			
		Eocene	56	• Extinction event			
		Paleocene	65	• Mammals expand	Rocky Mountains form	65	Mesozoic
Mesozoic	Cretaceous		146	• Dinosaur extinction,[1] extinction event • Flowering plants	Alberta and Saskatchewan are covered by the sea		
	Jurassic		200	• Birds	• Supercontinent Pangaea begins to break up		
	Triassic		251	• Mammals • Dinosaurs		251	Paleozoic
Paleozoic	Permian		299	• Extinction event • Reptiles	• Ice Age		
	Carboniferous		359	• Coal swamps	Appalachian Mountains form		
	Devonian		416	• Extinction event • Trees			
	Silurian		444	• Land plants • Extinction event			
	Ordovician		488	• Fish			
	Cambrian		542	• Explosion of organisms with shells		542	Precambrian
Precambrian time			2500	• Multicelled organisms • Free oxygen in atmosphere and ozone layer in stratosphere	• Ice Age • Ice Age		
			3500	• Primitive life (first fossils)			
			4000		• Oldest rocks		
			4600		• Age of Earth	4600	4600

[1] Some scientists believe that not all dinosaurs became extinct but that some evolved into birds.

is to identify hazardous processes and delineate the geographic areas where they occur. Every effort should be made to avoid putting people and property in harm's way, especially for those hazards that we cannot control, such as earthquakes.

Prediction and Warning

Learning how to predict disasters so that we can minimize loss of life and property is an important endeavour. In some cases, we have enough information to accurately forecast disasters. When, however, information is insufficient to make accurate forecasts, the best we can do is identify areas where disasters can be expected in the future based on past history. If we know both the probability and the possible consequences of an event at a particular location, we can quantify the risk of the event, even if we cannot accurately predict when it will occur.

Damage inflicted by a natural disaster can be reduced if the event can be forecast and a warning issued. Attempting to do this involves the following elements:

- Identifying the location of a hazard
- Determining the probability that an event of a given magnitude will occur
- Identifying any precursor events, forecasting the event, and issuing a warning

Location We can identify areas at risk from different hazardous processes (Appendix C). Major zones of earthquakes and volcanic eruptions have been identified by mapping (1) where earthquakes have occurred historically, (2) areas of young volcanic rocks, and (3) locations of active and recently active volcanoes. On a local scale, we can study the eruptive history of a volcano to identify areas that are likely to be affected in future eruptions. Volcanic hazard maps have been prepared for most Cascade volcanoes in the Pacific Northwest and for volcanoes in Japan, Italy, Colombia, and elsewhere. Detailed mapping of soils, rocks, groundwater conditions, surface drainage, and evidence for ground instability can pinpoint slopes that are likely to fail. We can also predict where flooding is likely to occur by mapping the extent of recent floods.

Probability of Occurrence Determining the probability of a particular event at a specific site is an essential part of hazard analysis (Appendix D). We have sufficiently long flow records for many rivers to develop probability models that can reasonably predict the number of floods of a given size that will occur within a particular period. Likewise, the probability of droughts can be determined from the history of past rainfall in the region, and the probability of earthquakes of specific magnitudes can be estimated from historic earthquake records. However, these probabilities are subject to the same elements of chance as throwing a particular number on a die or drawing an inside straight in poker. For example, although a flood may occur, on average, only once every 10 years, it is possible to have two or more or no floods of this magnitude in that time, just as it is possible to throw a six twice in a row with a die. Probabilities of rare events within a specific region, for example, volcanic eruptions, tsunami, and meteorite impacts, are much more difficult to estimate and are subject to large uncertainties.

Precursor Events Many disasters are preceded by *precursor events*. For example, the surface of the ground may creep for weeks, months, or years before a catastrophic landslide, and the rate of creep may increase just before final failure. Volcanoes sometimes swell or bulge before an eruption, accompanied by an increase in earthquake activity in the area. Foreshocks or unusual uplift of the land may precede an earthquake.

Identification of precursor events helps scientists predict when and where a disaster will happen. Documentation of landslide creep or swelling of a volcano may lead authorities to issue a warning and evacuate people from a hazardous area.

Forecasting With some natural processes, it is possible to **forecast** accurately when a possible damaging event will occur. For example, spring flooding of the Fraser or Mississippi River, in response to snowmelt and warm wet weather, is fairly predictable. In fact, government agencies generally can accurately forecast when large rivers will reach a particular flood stage. We can also forecast when and where hurricanes will strike land by tracking them at sea. Arrival times of tsunami can be precisely predicted if a warning system detects the waves.

Warning Once a hazardous event has been predicted or a forecast made, the public must be warned. The flow of information leading to a public **warning** of a possible disaster, such as a large earthquake or flood, should move along a predefined path (Figure 1.14). The public does not always welcome such warnings, however, especially when the predicted event does not occur. In 1982, geologists issued an advisory that a volcanic eruption was likely near Mammoth Lakes, California. The advisory caused loss of tourist business and apprehension on the part of residents. The eruption did not occur and the advisory was eventually lifted. In July 1986, a series of earthquakes occurred over a four-day period near Bishop, California, in the eastern Sierra Nevada Mountains, beginning with a magnitude 3 event and culminating in a damaging magnitude 6.1 earthquake. Scientists concluded that there was a high probability that a larger earthquake would occur in the area in the near future and issued a warning. Local business owners, who feared the loss of summer tourism, felt that the warning was irresponsible; in fact, the predicted quake never occurred.

Incidents of this kind have led some people to conclude that scientific predictions are worthless and that advisory warnings should not be issued. Part of the problem is poor communication among scientists, the news media, and the public. Newspaper, television, and radio reports may fail to explain the evidence or the probabilistic nature of disaster forecasting and prediction, leading the public to expect black-

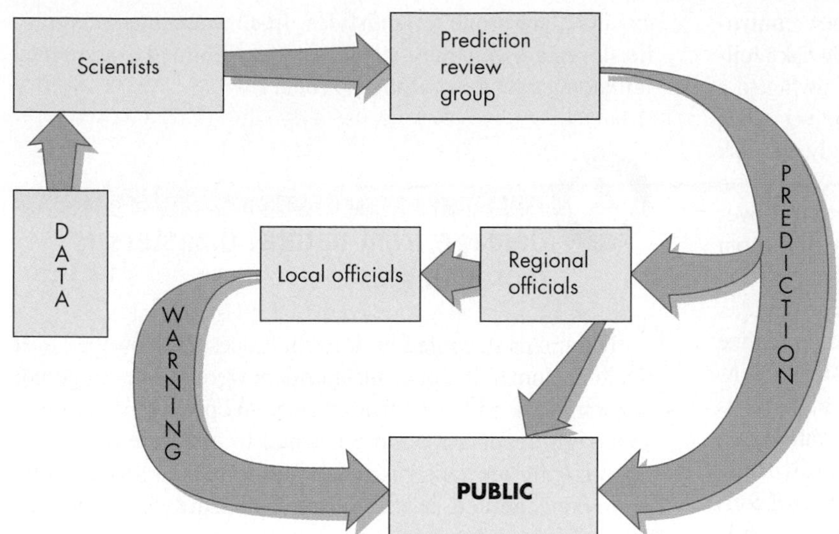

◀ **FIGURE 1.14 HAZARD PREDICTION OR WARNING** Possible path for issuing a prediction or warning of a natural disaster.

and-white statements about what will happen. Although scientists are not yet able to predict volcanic eruptions and earthquakes accurately, they have a responsibility to publicize their informed judgments. An informed public is better able to act responsibly than is an uninformed public, even if the subject makes people uncomfortable. Ships' captains, who depend on weather advisories and warnings of changing conditions, do not suggest they would be better off not knowing about an impending storm, even though the storm might not materialize or might take an unexpected course. Just as weather warnings have proved very useful for planning, official warnings of earthquakes, volcanic eruptions, landslides, and floods are also useful to people when they decide where to live, work, or travel. The Indian Ocean tsunami has spurred efforts to establish warning systems in all oceans where there is a risk of tsunami.

Let's consider again the prediction of a volcanic eruption in the Mammoth Lakes area. The location and depth of earthquakes suggested to scientists that molten rock was moving toward the surface. In light of the possibility that the volcano could erupt, and the possible loss of life if it did, it would have been irresponsible for scientists not to have issued the advisory. Although the predicted eruption did not occur, the advisory led to the development of evacuation routes and a consideration of disaster preparedness. This planning may eventually prove useful, because the most recent eruption in the Mammoth Lakes area occurred only 600 years ago and it is likely that one will occur in the future. As a result of the forecast, the community is better informed than it was before and thus is better prepared to deal with an eruption when it does occur.

Forecasts and warnings are useful only if they provide people adequate time to respond in an appropriate manner. A minimum of several hours of warning is required in most instances, and much more time is needed if evacuation of urban areas is required. Warnings of many hours to days are possible for hurricanes, many volcanic eruptions, large floods, and some tsunami, but earthquakes and landslides commonly occur without any warning at all.

Risk analysis is an important element of understanding the effects of hazardous processes.

Hazardous processes are amenable to *risk analysis*, which considers both the probability that a damaging event will occur and the consequences of that event. For example, if we were to estimate that, in any given year, Vancouver has a 1 percent chance of a moderate earthquake, and if we know the consequences of that earthquake in terms of loss of life and damage, we can then calculate the risk to society.

Before people can discuss and adjust to hazards, they must understand the risk that they face in various circumstances. The field of risk assessment is rapidly growing, and its application to natural hazard science is expanding.

The *risk* of a particular event is defined as the product of the probability of that event and the consequences should it occur.[12] Consequences include injury, death, property damage, and secondary effects, such as lost economic activity. Consequences can be expressed in a variety of ways. If, for example, we are considering the risk of earthquake damage to a nuclear reactor, we would evaluate the consequences in terms of radiation released, which then can be related to injury to people and other living things. In any such risk assessment, it is important to calculate risks for various possible scenarios, for example earthquakes of different magnitudes. A large earthquake has a lower probability than a small one, but its consequences will be greater.

Determining *acceptable risk* is more complicated, because individuals, social groups, and countries have different attitudes about what level of risk is acceptable to them. Acceptable risk also depends on the situation. Driving an automobile is fairly risky, but most of us accept that risk as part of living in a modern world. In contrast, for many people, the acceptable level of risk represented by a nuclear power plant is very low because they consider any possibility of radiation poisoning unacceptable. Nuclear power plants are controversial because many people perceive them as high-risk facilities. Even though the probability of an accident owing to a geologic hazard, such as an earthquake, might be very low, the consequences could be devastating; accordingly, the risk is relatively high.

At the individual level, people have some control over the level of risk they are willing to accept. For the most part, you can choose where you live. If you choose to live in Vancouver, you may experience a damaging earthquake. If you move to the North Carolina coast, you should realize you are putting yourself in the path of potentially deadly hurricanes. So why do people live in hazardous areas? Perhaps the allure of mountains and the ocean drew you to Vancouver, or you were offered an excellent job in North Carolina. Whatever the case, individuals must weigh the pros and cons of living in a particular area and decide whether or not it is worth the risk. This assessment should consider such factors as the frequency of damaging events, the potential damage the events could cause, and the extent of the geographic area at risk. The assessment should compare these factors to the potential benefits of living in the high-risk area. In this way, we determine acceptable risk, which differs from person to person.

A frequent problem of risk analysis is that the data required to determine the probability or consequences of an event are either inadequate or lacking. It can be difficult to assign probabilities to geologic events, such as earthquakes and volcanic eruptions, because the known record of past events is too short or incomplete.[12] Similarly, it may not be possible to accurately determine the consequences of an event from sparse data. For example, if we are concerned about the consequences of releasing radiation into the environment, we need information about the local biology, geology, hydrology, and meteorology, all of which may be complex and difficult to analyze. We also need information about the infrastructure at risk and the numbers and distribution of people living and working in the area of concern. Despite these limitations, risk analysis is a step in the right direction. As we learn more about the probability and consequences of a hazardous event, we can make a more reliable risk assessment for appropriate decision making.

Linkages exist among different natural hazards and between hazards and the physical environment.

Many hazardous natural processes are directly or indirectly linked. For example, intense precipitation and surges accompanying hurricanes cause flooding, coastal erosion, and landslides. Volcanic eruptions on land cause volcanic debris flows (*lahars*) and floods, and some volcanic eruptions on islands can trigger tsunami.

Natural hazards also have linkages with Earth materials. Slopes developed on shale or loose glacial sediments, for example, are prone to landslides. In contrast, massive granite slopes are generally stable, although jointed granite may fail along fractures within the rock.

Damage from natural disasters is increasing.

Early humans struggled with Earth processes. However, over much of human history, our numbers were neither large nor concentrated, so losses from hazardous processes were not very significant. As people learned to cultivate crops and domesticate animals, populations increased and became more concentrated, in many cases in hazardous areas. This concentration of people and resources increased losses from periodic earthquakes, floods, and other natural disasters. Population growth and urbanization have accelerated in recent centuries, and today billions of people live in areas vulnerable to damage by hazardous Earth processes. Because more and more people are living in hazardous areas, the need for planning to minimize losses from natural disasters is increasing.

An emerging issue related to natural hazards is the link between disasters and technological dependence. The ice storm in southern Quebec and Ontario in 1998 was a disaster mainly because electric power was lost when transmission lines failed. The ice storm would not have been a large disaster 100 years earlier when people did not use electricity to keep themselves warm in winter. Related to the issue of overdependence on complex and fallible technological systems is the interrelation of different technological systems. Turning again to the Quebec–Ontario ice storm, the loss of hydroelectric power required the use of generators to produce electricity. However, there were not enough generators to filter water at the same rate as is normally done, and the population came close to suffering a shortage of drinking water.

Inequities in health, education, and wealth between developed and developing countries aggravate these problems. Population growth in developing countries is far outstripping that in North America, Europe, Japan, and other wealthy countries. Most people in developing countries lack resources to protect themselves from hazardous events. Thus, when a disaster happens in a densely populated area in a developing country, the consequences are likely to be catastrophic. The same event in a fully developed country would probably injure and kill far fewer people, although the economic cost could be huge.

Examples of Disasters in Densely Populated Areas

Mexico City is the centre of the world's most populous urban area. Approximately 23 million people are concentrated in an area of about 2300 km^2. The average family in this area has five members, and about one-third of the families live in a single room. Mexico City is built on an ancient lake bed, and the thick silts and clays that underlie the city render it especially vulnerable to damage from earthquakes. In addition, parts of the city have been sinking several centimetres per year from the pumping of groundwater. The subsidence has not been uniform; thus, some buildings are tilted and even more vulnerable to earthquake damage.[13] In September 1985, a magnitude 8.0 earthquake off the Pacific Coast of Mexico killed about 10,000 people in Mexico City.[14]

The two Izmit, Turkey, earthquakes in 1999 are another example of a disaster in a densely populated area.[15] These quakes killed more than 17,000 people because they happened in a heavily populated area where many buildings are poorly constructed and unable to withstand strong seismic shaking.

A third example is the devastation of New Orleans, Louisiana, and Biloxi, Mississippi, wrought by Hurricane Katrina in August 2005. This hurricane was a Category 5 cyclone, and its eye passed very close to both these cities. The huge direct economic losses (US$81 billion), injuries, and loss of life (about 1800 people) were the consequences of the concentration of people in harm's way.

Population Growth

The world's population has more than tripled in the last 70 years. Between 1830 and 1930, the population doubled from 1 billion to 2 billion people. By 1970 it had nearly doubled again, and by 2000 Earth's population reached about 6 billion people (see Case Study 1.1). This rapid increase in population has been *exponential*—the population grows each year, not by the addition of a constant number of people, but rather by the addition of a constant percentage of the current population (Figure 1.15). The exponential growth in population can be expressed by the following equation:

$$N_t = N_0 e^{rt}$$

where N_t is the population at time t, N_0 is the starting population, r is the growth rate, and e is the base of the natural logarithm (2.71828).

This equation does not directly take into account changes in life expectancy, but it clearly shows that future population numbers are dependent on the *rate* of growth in population. At the current annual rate of growth, the population will increase from its current level of 6.6 billion to about 9.2 billion by 2050. In contrast, if the annual rate of increase were only half its present level, the population level in 2050 would be about the same as today.

Population growth is hazardous to our survival and cannot continue. With it comes more exposure to hazardous natural processes; increased pollution; reduced availability of food, clean drinking water, and other vital resources; and a greater need for waste disposal. The question is: Can our planet support the number of people who currently live on it, much less the estimated 9 billion people predicted by the middle of this century?

There is no easy answer to the problem of population growth, but universal education and a more equitable global distribution of wealth and resources are of paramount importance. As a country's standard of living and level of literacy improve, the rate of population growth in that country will decrease. Given the variety of cultures, values, and norms in the world today, our greatest hope for controlling population is through improving the well-being of people in developing countries.[16]

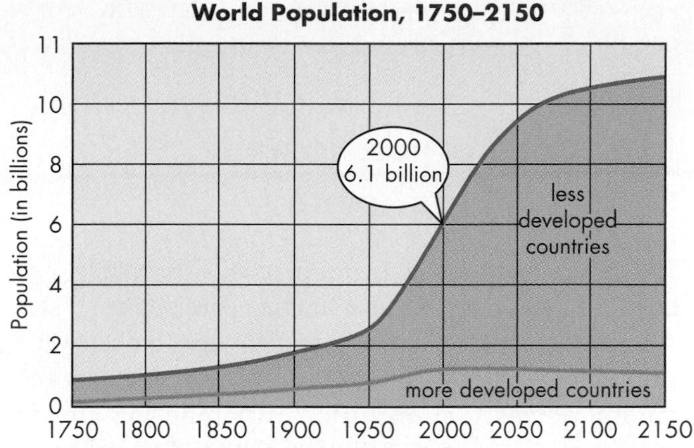

▲ **FIGURE 1.15 POPULATION GROWTH** The rapid increase in population has been *exponential*. *(United Nations, World Population Prospects, the 1998 Revision (New York: UN, 1998); and estimates by the Population Reference Bureau)*

Magnitude and Frequency of Hazardous Events

The *impact* of a series of hazardous events is partly a function of their **magnitude**, or amount of energy released, and partly a function of their **frequency**. Impact is also influenced by many other factors, including climate, geology, vegetation, population, and land use. In general, the magnitude of an event is inversely related to its frequency. Small earthquakes, for example, are more common than large ones (see Case Study 1.2). A large, uncommon event, such as a massive forest fire, will do far more damage than a small one. However, large forest fires are much less frequent than small ones and therefore may have less impact. Forest fires of intermediate size may do more damage, collectively, than either more frequent, small fires or rare, large ones.

Land use can directly affect the magnitude and frequency of events. People have long tried to reduce the threat of floods, for example, by building levees along rivers. However, levees constrict the width of rivers, and the reduced width lessens the amount of water that can be transported during flood conditions. In effect, our efforts to reduce floods may actually be causing larger, more frequent floods.

Two of the worst natural disasters in recent years were Hurricane Mitch and a flood on the Yangtze River in China, both in 1998. Hurricane Mitch devastated parts of Central America and caused approximately 11,000 deaths; the Yangtze River flood claimed nearly 4000 lives. Land-use changes made the damage from these events particularly severe. For example, Honduras lost nearly one-half its forests in the past century, and wildfires before Hurricane Mitch burned an

1.1 CASE STUDY

Human Population through History

The increase in the number of people on our planet can be related to various stages of human development (Table 1.4). When we were hunter-gatherers, our numbers were small and growth rates were low. With agriculture and animal domestication, rates of population growth increased by several hundred times. Growth rates increased again by about 10 times during the early industrial period (A.D. 1600 to 1800). Since the Industrial Revolution, with modern sanitation and medicine, growth rates have increased another 10 times. The human population reached 6 billion in 2000, and by 2013 it will be 7 billion, that is, 1 billion new people in only 13 years! By comparison, the total human population reached 1 billion in about A.D. 1800, more than 40,000 years after our species first appeared on Earth.

Population Growth and the Future

Because the human population is increasing exponentially, many people are concerned that it will be impossible to supply resources and a high-quality environment for the billions of new people born later this century. The problem will become acute over the next decade or two, given the rapid industrialization and economic growth that is happening in India, China, and other countries with large populations. Increasing population at local, regional, and global levels increases the impact of all hazardous processes.

There is no obvious answer to this problem. Shortages of fossil fuels, clean water, and other resources will severely limit our ability to cope with the growing population. Some studies suggest that the present population is already above a comfortable **carrying capacity** for the planet. Carrying capacity is the maximum number of people Earth can support at a sustainable level, that is, without causing environmental degradation that reduces the ability of the planet to support the existing population.[16]

Most of the increase in population will be in developing nations. India will have the largest population of all countries by 2050, about 18 percent of the world total; China will have about 15 percent of the world total. By 2050, these two countries will have more than 30 percent of the total world population![17]

The news about human population growth is not all bad—for the first time in the past 50 years the rate of increase in human population is decreasing. Growth may have peaked at 85 million people per year in the late 1980s; by 1995 the increase was 80 million new people per year. This reduction in the rate of growth is a milestone and is encouraging.[18] Although population growth is difficult to project because of uncertainties in agriculture, technology, sanitation, medicine, disease, culture, and education, the human population is forecast to be between 7.3 billion and 10.7 billion in 2050. However, until the *rate* of growth reaches zero, the number of people on Earth will continue to grow. If the rate of growth is reduced to 0.7 percent per year, that is, one-half the current rate of 1.4 percent, the population will still double in 100 years.

TABLE 1.4 How We Became 6 Billion+

40,000–9000 B.C.: HUNTERS AND GATHERERS
Population density about 1 person per 100 km^2 of habitable area*; total population probably less than a few million; average annual growth rate less than 0.0001% (doubling time about 700,000 years)
9000 B.C.–A.D. 1600: PREINDUSTRIAL AGRICULTURAL
Population density about 1 person per 1 km^2 of habitable area; total population several hundred million; average annual growth rate about 0.03% (doubling time about 2300 years)
A.D. 1600–1800: EARLY INDUSTRIAL
Population density about 7 persons per 1 km^2 of habitable area; total population by 1800 about 1 billion; annual growth rate about 0.1% (doubling time about 700 years)
A.D. 1800–2000: MODERN
Population density about 40 persons per 1 km^2 of habitable area; total population in 2000 about 6.1 billion; annual growth rate in 2000 about 1.4% (doubling time about 50 years)

*Habitable area is assumed to be about 150,000,000 km^2.

Source: Modified from Botkin, D. B., and E. A. Keller. 2000. Environmental science, 3rd ed. New York: John Wiley and Sons.

1.2 CASE STUDY

The Magnitude-Frequency Concept

The *magnitude-frequency concept* asserts that an inverse exponential relationship exists between the magnitude of an event and its frequency (Figure 1.A). Large floods or earthquakes, for example, are infrequent, whereas small floods or earthquakes are common. The magnitude-frequency relation for many natural phenomena can be approximated by an exponential equation of the type:

$$M = Fe^{-x}$$

where M is the magnitude of the event, F is the frequency, e is the base of the natural logarithm, and x is a constant.

The magnitude-frequency concept also includes the idea that Earth's surface is shaped mainly by events of moderate magnitude and frequency, rather than by events of low magnitude and high frequency or by events of extremely high magnitude but very low frequency. For example, most of the sediment carried by rivers in Canada is transported in spring by flows of moderate magnitude and frequency. However, there are many exceptions. In arid regions, for example, much of the sediment in normally dry channels may be transported by rare high-magnitude flows produced by intense but infrequent rainstorms.

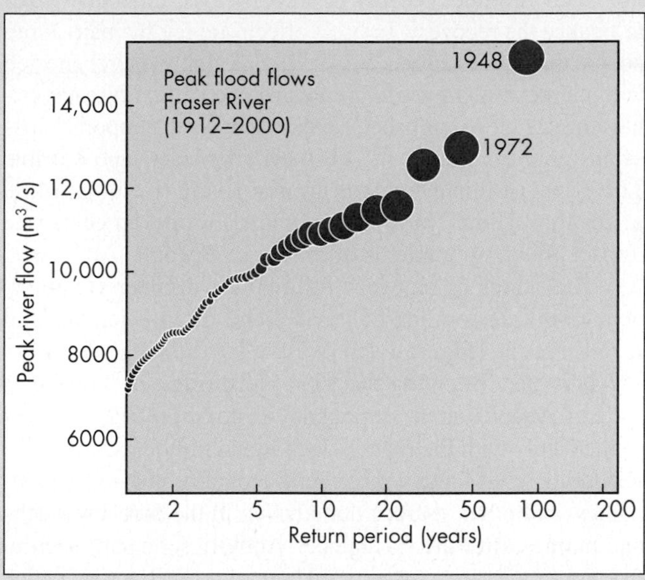

▲ **FIGURE 1.A MAGNITUDE-FREQUENCY RELATION** The size and frequency of many physical processes are inversely related. The concept is illustrated here with this plot of average return periods for Fraser River floods of different sizes. Note that the horizontal scale (return period) is logarithmic, not linear. *(Brian Menounos; from Clague, J., and B. Turner. 2006. Vancouver, city on the edge: Living with a geological landscape. Vancouver, BC: Tricouni Press)*

area of 11,000 km^2. As a result of deforestation and the fire, hillside soils washed away and with them went farms, homes, roads, and bridges. The story is much the same in the case of China. About 85 percent of the forest in the Yangtze River basin has been removed through timber harvesting and conversion of land to agriculture. As a result of these land-use changes, flooding on the Yangtze River is probably much more common and severe than it was previously.[19] To remediate this problem, China has banned timber harvesting in the upper Yangtze River basin, limited use of the Yangtze floodplain, and allocated several billion dollars for reforestation.

These and other catastrophes are a warning of things to come. Human activities are likely increasing the severity of some natural disasters. If we want to minimize damage from natural disasters, we need to rehabilitate the land and strive for a more harmonious relationship with the processes that shape Earth's surface. An ancillary benefit of this approach is that future generations will have access to the resources that our planet offers.[19] Population growth in developing countries and reckless squandering of resources in the developed world, however, will make it difficult for humanity to achieve this goal.

Damage and loss of life from natural disasters can be minimized.

We deal with natural hazards primarily in *reactive* ways—following a disaster, we engage in search and rescue, firefighting, and the provision of emergency food, water, and shelter. These activities reduce loss of life and property and must, of course, be continued. However, a higher level of hazard reduction requires a *proactive* approach, in which we anticipate and prepare for disasters. Land-use planning that limits construction in hazardous areas, hazard-resistant construction, and hazard modification or control (such as flood control channels) are some of the proactive measures that can be taken before disastrous events to reduce our vulnerability to them.[5]

Reactive Response: Recovery from Disasters

The effects of a disaster on a population may be either direct or indirect. *Direct effects* include deaths, injuries, displacement of people, and damage to property and other infrastructure. *Indirect effects* are post-disaster impacts, including crop failure, starvation, emotional distress, loss of employment, reduction in tax revenues because of property loss, and higher taxes to finance the recovery. Indirect effects are felt by many more people than direct effects are.[20,21] In our highly interconnected and interdependent world, a catastrophic natural disaster can have nearly global impacts. An example is the temporary loss of oil-refining capacity in Louisiana after Hurricane Katrina. The effect of this event was an immediate rise in gasoline prices throughout North America and Europe, an economic impact affecting hundreds of millions of people.

The stages of recovery following a disaster are emergency work, restoration of services and communication, and reconstruction (Figure 1.16). We can see the stages in recovery activities following the 1994 Northridge earthquake in the Los Angeles area. Emergency restoration began almost immediately with the repair of roads and utilities. Continuing restoration used funds from federal programs, insurance companies, and other sources that arrived in the first few weeks and months after the earthquake. Activity soon shifted from the restoration phase to the first phase of reconstruction, which lasted until about 2000. The effects of the earthquake on highway overpasses and bridges, buildings, and other structures were carefully evaluated and new structures have been built to a higher seismic standard. Large earthquakes are certain to occur again in the Los Angeles area; therefore, efforts to reduce the damage they cause must continue.

Now that Los Angeles is past the final phase of the reconstruction period, the lessons from two past disasters should be remembered: the Anchorage, Alaska, earthquake in 1964 and the flash flood that devastated Rapid City, South Dakota, in 1972. Restoration following the Anchorage earthquake began almost immediately with a tremendous influx of money from U.S. federal disaster programs, insurance companies, and other sources. Reconstruction was rapid and proceeded without much thought, as everyone competed for the available funds. Apartments and other buildings were hurriedly constructed in areas that had suffered ground rupture. Building sites were prepared by simply filling in cracks and regrading the surface. By ignoring the potential benefits of careful land-use planning, Anchorage has made itself vulnerable to the same type of earthquake damage as it experienced in 1964. In contrast, in Rapid City the restoration did not peak until approximately 10 weeks after the flood, and the community took time to carefully think through alternatives. As a result, Rapid City today uses the floodplain as a greenbelt, an entirely different use than before the 1972 flood. The change has reduced the flood risk substantially.[7,20,21]

The pace of recovery depends on several factors, the most important of which are the magnitude of the disaster and social and economic context. Recovery is more rapid following smaller disasters, such as the Northridge earthquake, than after catastrophes, such as Hurricane Katrina and the 2004 Indian Ocean tsunami. Recovery also proceeds more rapidly in wealthy countries, such as Canada, the United States, and Japan, than in countries that have few resources to deal with natural disasters, like Pakistan (2005 earthquake) and Indonesia (2004 tsunami). The global community has a responsibility to provide both immediate and long-term assistance to countries that do not have the ability to deal with catastrophes themselves.

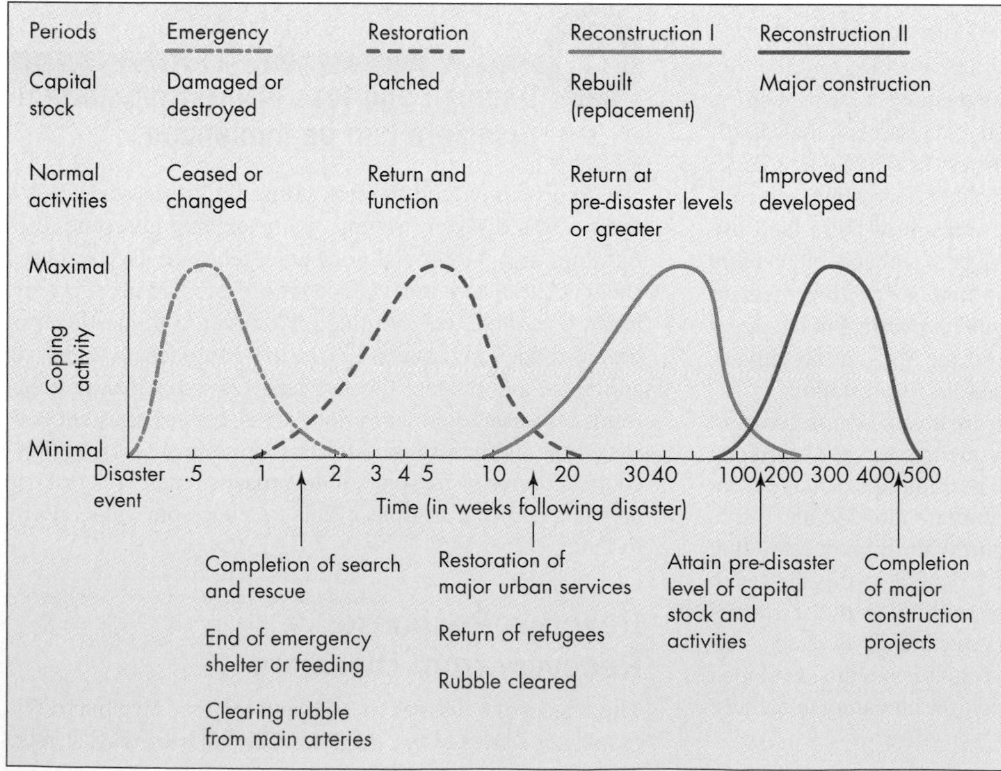

◀ **FIGURE 1.16 RECOVERY FROM DISASTER** Generalized model of recovery following a disaster. The first two weeks after a disaster are the period of emergency, during which normal activities cease or are changed. In the restoration phase, which typically lasts several months, normal activities return, although perhaps not at pre-disaster levels. Finally, during reconstruction, the capital stock is replaced, major new construction is completed, and normal activities return. *(From Kates, R. W., and D. Pijawka. 1977. From rubble to monument: The pace of reconstruction. In Disaster and reconstruction, eds. J. E. Haas, R. W. Kates, and M. J. Bowden, pp. 1–23. Cambridge, MA: MIT Press)*

Proactive Response: Avoiding and Adjusting to Hazards

The decisions we make, individually and collectively, in preparing for natural disasters depend in part on our perception of risk. Much research has been done in recent years to try to understand how people perceive different natural hazards. This understanding is important because the success of risk-reduction programs depends on the attitudes of the people who are likely to be affected. Although there may be adequate awareness of hazard and risk at the government level, this awareness may not filter down to the general population. Such a lack of awareness is particularly true for events that occur infrequently; people are more aware of hazards that occur every few years, for example brush or forest fires. Standard procedures, as well as local ordinances, may already be in place to control damage from these events. For example, some expensive new homes in Pemberton, British Columbia, have been constructed on pads of artificial fill elevated above the adjacent floodplain to provide protection from frequent floods that occur there. Similarly, some landowners in tsunami-prone areas on the island of Hawaii have elevated their homes on piles anchored in the ground. Although this is costly, tsunami have been sufficiently frequent in the past 100 years that the owners view the extra cost as a good investment.

One of the most environmentally sound and cost-effective adjustments to hazards involves **land-use planning**. People can avoid building on floodplains, in areas where there are active landslides, or in places where tsunami or coastal erosion are likely to occur. In many Canadian and U.S. cities, floodplains have been delineated and zoned for a particular land use. Legal requirements for soil engineering and engineering geology studies at building sites may greatly reduce potential damage from landslides. Damage from tsunami and coastal erosion can be minimized by requiring adequate setback of buildings from the shoreline or sea cliff. It may be possible to control physical processes in some instances, but land-use planning is often preferable to a technological fix that may or may not work.

Insurance is another option for dealing with natural hazards. Flood and earthquake insurance is available in many areas. However, huge insured losses stemming from recent hurricanes, earthquakes, and other disasters are forcing insurance companies to increase their premiums or deductibles in many hazard-prone areas or simply to discontinue some types of insurance.

Evacuation is a reaction to the hurricane hazard in states along the Gulf of Mexico and the eastern seaboard of the United States. Sufficient time is generally available for people to evacuate coastal areas, provided they heed warnings. However, if people do not react quickly or if the population in the affected area is large, evacuation routes may become clogged, as happened in Texas in September 2005 during Hurricane Rita.

Disaster preparedness is an option that individuals, families, cities, states, and entire nations can use to reduce risk. Of particular importance are public education and emergency preparedness training.

Attempts at *artificial control* of landslides, floods, lava flows, and other hazardous processes have met with mixed success. Seawalls built to control coastal erosion may protect property to some extent, but they tend to narrow or even eliminate the beach. Retaining walls and other structures may protect slopes from landslides if well designed. They are necessary where potentially unstable slopes are excavated or where buildings border steep slopes. Common methods of flood control are channelization and construction of dams and levees. Unfortunately, flood-control projects tend to provide residents with a false sense of security; no method can completely protect floodplain residents from extreme floods.

An option that is all too often chosen is to simply accept the risk and bear the loss in the event of a disaster. Many people are optimistic about their chances of making it through any disaster and therefore will take little action on their own. They also believe that governments will step in with relief following a disaster, which is commonly the case. The do-nothing response is particularly true for those hazards, such as volcanic eruptions and earthquakes, that are rare in a given area.

1.5 Many Hazards Provide a Natural Service Function

It is ironic that the same natural events that injure people and destroy property also provide important benefits, which we will refer to as *natural service functions*. The following examples illustrate this point. Floods add new sediment to floodplains, creating the fertile soils that support agriculture (Figure 1.17). They cause erosion but also deliver sediment

▲ **FIGURE 1.17 A BENEFIT OF FLOODS** Some of the most productive agricultural soils in Canada are those of the Fraser River delta. Before the river was dyked, periodic floods deposited nutrient-rich silt and clay on the floodplain. *(Waite Air Photos Inc.)*

to beaches and flush pollutants from coastal estuaries. Some volcanic eruptions create new land, as in the case of the Hawaiian Islands, which are completely volcanic in origin. Nutrient-rich volcanic ash enriches soils, making them more productive for crops and wild plants. Earthquakes contribute to mountain building and thus are responsible for many of the scenic landscapes of the world. Faults on which earthquakes occur may serve as paths for groundwater, creating springs that are important sources of water.

1.6 Climate Change and Natural Hazards

Global and regional climatic change may alter the incidence of some hazardous natural processes, notably storms, coastal erosion landslides, drought, and fires. How might climatic change affect the magnitude and frequency of these events? With global warming, sea levels will rise as warmer ocean waters expand and glaciers melt. Rising seas will induce or accelerate coastal erosion in some areas. Climate change may shift food production areas or force a change in the types of crops grown in specific areas. Deserts and semi-arid areas may expand, and warmer northern latitudes could become more productive. Permafrost is likely to degrade, causing problems for people who live in high northern latitudes. Some of these changes could force shifts in populations, which might bring about social and political upheaval.

Global warming will feed more energy from warmer ocean water into the atmosphere, which may increase the severity and frequency of thunderstorms, tornadoes, and hurricanes. This trend may already be underway—2005 set a new record for direct economic losses from weather-related disasters, which cost at least $200 billion worldwide. This figure represents more than a 100 percent increase over the previous record of $100 billion set in 1998.

Our ability to adjust to climate change will be determined, in large part, by the rate at which the change happens. If climate changes slowly, we should be able to adjust our agricultural practices and settlement patterns without major economic and social disruption. If, however, the change occurs rapidly, we may not have the capacity to easily adapt.

Summary

Natural hazards are responsible for significant damage and a substantial number of deaths worldwide each year. Natural processes that cause disasters are of two types: (1) internal and resulting from Earth's heat, such as volcanic eruptions and earthquakes, and (2) external and driven by Sun's energy, such as hurricanes and floods.

Central to an understanding of natural hazards is awareness that disasters result from natural processes that have been operating for billions of years. These natural processes become hazards only when they threaten human life or property.

Natural disasters are repetitive events, and study of their history provides information required for risk reduction. A better understanding of hazardous events and the risks they pose can be obtained by integrating information on historic and prehistoric events, geomorphology, and land-use change.

Geologic conditions and materials govern the type, location, and intensity of some natural processes. Earth operates by means of a number of self-regulating cycles, including the tectonic cycle, rock cycle, hydrologic cycle, and various biogeochemical cycles. The tectonic cycle describes large-scale geologic processes that deform Earth's crust, producing landforms, such as ocean basins, continents, and mountains. The rock cycle is a worldwide material recycling process driven by Earth's internal heat, which melts and metamorphoses crustal rocks. Weathering and erosion of surface rocks produce sediments and, ultimately, sedimentary rocks, which are added to the crust, offsetting materials lost through subduction. The hydrologic cycle is driven by solar energy and operates by way of evaporation, precipitation, surface runoff, and subsurface flow. Biogeochemical cycles involve transfers of chemical elements through a series of storage compartments or reservoirs, such as air or vegetation.

Five fundamental concepts establish a philosophical framework for studying natural hazards:

1. Hazards can be predicted through scientific evaluation.
2. Risk analysis is an important element of understanding the effects of hazardous processes.
3. Linkages exist between different natural hazards and between hazards and the physical environment.
4. Damage from natural disasters is increasing.
5. Damage and loss of life from natural disasters can be minimized.

Key Terms

biogeochemical cycle (p. 14)
carrying capacity (p. 22)
catastrophe (p. 6)
disaster (p. 6)
forecast (p. 18)
frequency (p. 21)
geologic cycle (p. 9)
hazard (p. 6)
hydrologic cycle (p. 14)
hypothesis (p. 16)
land-use planning (p. 25)
magnitude (p. 21)
mitigation (p. 8)
residence time (p. 14)
risk (p. 6)
rock cycle (p. 13)
scientific method (p. 16)
tectonic cycle (p. 9)
warning (p. 18)

Review Questions

1. What forces drive Earth's internal and external processes?
2. What is the distinction between a natural hazard and a disaster, and between a disaster and a catastrophe?
3. What is the difference between a hazard and a risk?
4. Which hazardous processes are likely to create catastrophes?
5. Explain why the effects of natural hazards vary over time.
6. Why is history important in understanding natural hazards?
7. What kinds of information must be assembled to conduct a risk assessment?
8. What are the five fundamental concepts for understanding natural processes as hazards?
9. Explain the scientific method as it is applied to natural hazards.
10. Explain why calling something a "natural" hazard may act as a philosophical barrier to dealing with it.
11. What are the elements involved in making a hazard forecast and warning?
12. Explain why two 10-year floods might occur in the same year in the same place.
13. What is a precursor event? Give some examples.
14. Explain the magnitude-frequency concept.
15. How do risk and acceptable risk differ?
16. Explain how population growth increases risk.
17. What is the difference between direct and indirect effects of disasters?
18. What are the stages of disaster recovery? How do they differ?
19. Describe four common adjustments to natural hazards.
20. What are natural service functions of natural hazards?

Critical Thinking Questions

1. How would you use the scientific method to test the hypothesis that sand on the beach comes from nearby mountains?
2. It has been argued that we must curb human population growth because otherwise we won't be able to feed everyone. Even if we could feed 10 billion to 15 billion people, would we still want a smaller population? Why or why not?
3. Because the processes we call natural hazards have been occurring on Earth for billions of years, how can we lessen loss of life and property damage from natural disasters?

Selected Web Resources

Natural Resources Canada
http://ess.nrcan.gc.ca/2002_2006/nher/index_e.php
Homepage of NRCan's Natural Hazards and Emergency Response program

Canadian Centre for Emergency Preparedness
www.ccep.ca Nonprofit organization for emergency preparedness and disaster management

Public Safety and Emergency Preparedness Canada
www.psepc-sppcc.gc.ca From the Canadian federal agency responsible for natural hazard preparedness and mitigation

Canadian Natural Hazards Assessment Project
www.crhnet.ca/docs/Hazards_Assessment_Summary_eng.pdf Assessment of natural hazards and disasters in Canada from Natural Resources Canada

FEMA
www.fema.gov Homepage of the U.S. Federal Emergency Management Agency (FEMA)

United States Geological Survey
http://geology.usgs.gov/realtime.shtml Real-time hazard information from the U.S. Geological Survey

NASA Earth Observatory
http://earthobservatory.nasa.gov/NaturalHazards
Information on recent natural hazard events from the National Aeronautics and Space Administration (NASA)

Earthweek
www.earthweek.com Weekly summary of natural disasters by an information service

International Strategy for Disaster Reduction
www.unisdr.org United Nations program to build disaster-resilient communities

CDC: Centers for Disease Control and Prevention
www.bt.cdc.gov/disasters/illness.asp Information about health aspects of natural hazards from the U.S. Department of Health and Human Services

NOAA Natural Hazards Data
www.ngdc.noaa.gov/seg/hazard Natural hazards information from the National Oceanic and Atmospheric Administration National Geophysical Data Center

Natural disaster summaries
www.absconsulting.com/catastropheReports.html
Summaries of numerous natural disasters from ABS Consulting, an international insurance company

CHAPTER 2

▶ THE COLLAPSE OF POORLY CONSTRUCTED BUILDINGS
Even reinforced-concrete frame buildings collapsed during the magnitude 7.7 earthquake in Gujarat state, India. Thirty-three deaths were reported after half of this 14-storey apartment building collapsed in Ahmedabad. *(CORBIS)*

Learning Objectives

Earthquakes cannot yet be predicted and commonly occur without warning. People have no time to evacuate or to take precautions to limit property damage. Your goals in reading this chapter should be to

- Know what an earthquake is
- Understand how *seismologists*, scientists who study earthquakes, measure them
- Be familiar with earthquake processes, such as faulting, tectonic creep, and the formation and movement of seismic waves
- Know which regions are most at risk from earthquakes and why
- Know and understand the effects of earthquakes, such as shaking, ground rupture, tsunami, and liquefaction
- Identify how earthquakes are linked to other natural hazards, such as landslides, fire, and tsunami
- Know the important natural service functions of earthquakes
- Know how people interact with and affect the earthquake hazards
- Understand how people can minimize earthquake risk and take measures to protect themselves

Earthquakes

The Toll of Earthquakes

Earthquakes are one of the greatest natural hazards: During the twentieth century alone, more than 2 million people died in earthquakes and from the fires, tsunami, and landslides the earthquakes triggered (Table 2.1). The twenty-first century promises to be even more devastating: In October 2005, about 80,000 people died in an earthquake in northern Pakistan; in December 2004, more than 200,000 people in 11 countries lost their lives to the tsunami resulting from the earthquake off the west coast of Sumatra in Indonesia; and in December 2003, the ancient city of Bam in Iran was destroyed by an earthquake, killing more than 30,000 people.

The worst disaster in modern times occurred in China in July 1976, when an entire city was destroyed and more than 240,000 people killed in less than six minutes. In 1556, an earthquake in north-central China killed an estimated 800,000 people and stands as one of the worst natural disasters in recorded history. Some famous cities of antiquity, such as Corinth; the Bronze Age cities of Troy, Mycenae, and Knossus; and Alexandria, were partially to totally destroyed by earthquakes. The great city of Harappa in the Indus Valley was destroyed sometime after 2000 B.C., ending its dominance in the region. And the ancient cities of Megiddo and Jericho, lying along one of Earth's great fault systems that extends from the Red Sea along the Dead Sea rift valley, were destroyed by earthquakes.

The consequences of an earthquake depend on magnitude, depth, distance from populated areas, the nature of the local Earth materials, and engineering and construction practices. Differences in these factors explain why, in early 2001, large earthquakes killed thousands of people in El Salvador and tens of thousands of people in India, yet killed no one in Washington State.

The first devastating earthquake of 2001 occurred in Central America in eastern El Salvador.[1] This magnitude 7.7 earthquake was centred about 110 km south-southeast of San Salvador, the capital city. It was felt as far as 1370 km to the northwest in Mexico City and more than 1160 km to the southeast in parts of northern Colombia. The quake's effects were greatest in the countryside, where in some areas more than 95 percent of homes were flattened. Earthquake-triggered landslides were responsible for many deaths, especially in the community of Santa Tecla, where a hillside collapsed and buried 500 homes (Figure 2.1).

TABLE 2.1 Earthquakes Causing More Than 10,000 Deaths, 1900–2005

Date	Location	Deaths	Magnitude
April 4, 1905	Kangra, India	19,000	8.6
August 17, 1906	Valparaiso, Chile	20,000	8.2
October 21, 1907	Central Asia	12,000	8.1
December 28, 1908	Messina, Italy	70,000 to 100,000	7.2
January 13, 1915	Avezzano, Italy	30,000	7.5
January 21, 1917	Bali, Indonesia	15,000	—
February 13, 1918	Kwangtung, China	10,000	7.3
December 16, 1920	Gansu, China	200,000	8.6
September 1, 1923	Kanto, Japan	143,000	7.9
May 22, 1927	Tsinghai, China	200,000	7.9
December 25, 1932	Gansu, China	70,000	7.6
August 25, 1933	China	10,000	7.4
January 15, 1934	Bihar, India	10,700	8.1
May 30, 1935	Quetta, Pakistan	30,000 to 60,000	7.5
January 25, 1939	Chillan, Chile	28,000	8.3
December 26, 1939	Erzincan, Turkey	30,000	7.8
October 5, 1948	Turkmenistan, Ashgabat	110,000	7.3
February 29, 1960	Agadir, Morocco	10,000 to 15,000	5.7
September 1, 1962	Qazvin, Iran	12,000	7.3
August 31, 1968	Iran	12,000 to 20,000	7.3
January 4, 1970	Yunnan Province, China	10,000	7.5
May 31, 1970	Peru	66,000	7.9
May 10, 1974	China	20,000	6.8
February 4, 1975	China	10,000	7.0
February 4, 1976	Guatemala	23,000	7.5
July 27, 1976	Tangshan, China	250,000 to 650,000	7.5
September 16, 1978	Iran	15,000	7.8
September 19, 1985	Michoacan, Mexico	9,500 to 30,000	8.0
December 7, 1988	Spitak, Armenia	25,000	6.8
June 20, 1990	Western Iran	40,000 to 50,000	7.7
August 17, 1999	Turkey	17,000	7.6
January 26, 2001	India	20,000	7.7
December 26, 2003	Southeastern Iran	26,000	6.6
December 26, 2004	South Asia	200,000 to 300,000	9.3
October 5, 2005	Pakistan	80,000	7.6

Source: From the U.S. Geological Survey. 2006. Earthquakes with 1000 or more deaths since 1900. **http://earthquake.usgs.gov/regional/world/world_deaths.php**. *Accessed November 6, 2006.*

The earthquake was followed by more than 3000 *aftershocks*, some of which were larger than magnitude 5. In all, at least 5000 people lost their lives, and another 250,000 were left homeless. Exactly one month later, a magnitude 6.1 quake struck the same area, killing or injuring more than 3500 people and destroying 55,000 homes.

Two weeks after the first El Salvador earthquake, northwest India was rocked by the most powerful earthquake to strike the country in 50 years. The magnitude 7.7 earthquake was centred near Bhuj, a desert town of 150,000 people in western Gujarat state, near the border with Pakistan.[2] It occurred on a national holiday, when many people were home from work or school

▲ **FIGURE 2.1 LANDSLIDE IN EL SALVADOR** The brown area in the centre of this image is the path of the landslide that buried more than 500 homes in the Las Colinas neighbourhood of Santa Tecla, a suburb of San Salvador, in January 2001. The landslide, which killed more than 500 people, was triggered by an earthquake. *(U.S. Geological Survey)*

▲ **FIGURE 2.2 COLLAPSED SCHOOL BUILDING** This four-storey school building in Ahmedabad, India, collapsed during the magnitude 7.7 earthquake in 2001. Each floor "pancaked" onto the floor below. *(Pallava Bagla/Corbis/Sygma)*

(Figure 2.2). Buildings shook for nearly two minutes during the earthquake, and many towns in rural areas were almost completely levelled. More than 250 aftershocks occurred in the first few days after the quake. At least 20,000 people were killed, and damage was greater than $1 billion.

The magnitude 6.8 earthquake in Washington State in 2001 was significantly stronger than the second one in El Salvador. Centred near Olympia, about 55 km southwest of Seattle, it caused US$1.5 billion in damage but killed no one.[3]

What can explain the large differences in the number of casualties and damage from these four earthquakes? First, they occurred at different depths within Earth. The two in El Salvador and the one in India took place at shallow depths in the *crust*, whereas the Washington earthquake was relatively deep. In deep earthquakes some of the energy dissipates by the time the *seismic waves* reach the surface, resulting in less damage.

Second, building and zoning regulations were important in determining the damage these earthquakes caused. In Washington, most of the damaged buildings were constructed more than 25 years ago, before building codes included strict earthquake guidelines aimed at minimizing damage from ground shaking. Unfortunately, most developing nations do not have rigorous building codes and, if they do, the codes are commonly ignored or circumvented. Following the India earthquake, criminal complaints were lodged against several construction companies that, experts say, used poor materials and ignored building codes. The pattern of damage from the earthquake supports these complaints—many older homes were shaken but not damaged, whereas newer homes were reduced to rubble. Eighty percent of the earthquake-damaged buildings in Ahmedabad, India, violated construction codes, and many of the responsible parties went into hiding shortly after the earthquake.

Finally, in El Salvador, as in many cities, it was not just *how* structures were built that affected the number of casualties but also *where* they were built. Most lives were lost in Las Colinas through earthquake-triggered landslides, mainly from one large failure (Figure 2.1). The Las Colinas disaster resulted from poor land-use practices. Balsamo Ridge, the hill above the community, consists of volcanic ash and other material that are susceptible to landslides. Local authorities and environmentalists also claim that deforestation and greed contributed to the disaster. Residents of Las Colinas had pleaded with the government to block the construction of mansions on the hillside above them. They argued that removing vegetation from the slope would leave them vulnerable to landslides. Their pleas were ignored, the mansions went up, and, during the earthquake, the slope came down.

Although we can't control the geologic environment or depth of an earthquake, we can do much to reduce the damage and loss of life from earthquakes. The deaths in India and El Salvador are especially tragic because much of the devastation could have been prevented if buildings had been properly constructed and the protection of people had been more important than greater profits. A lesson provided by the Washington earthquake is that we can save lives by designing and building structures to withstand earthquake shaking.

2.1 Introduction to Earthquakes

Earthquakes result from the rupture of rocks along a **fault**, a fracture in Earth's crust. Rocks on opposite sides of a fault move suddenly, and energy is released in the form of **seismic waves**. The waves radiate outward in all directions from the **focus**, where the initial rupture occurs, like ripples on a pond after a pebble hits the water. It is the passage of these waves through the ground that we perceive as an earthquake, although the term *earthquake* also refers to the fault rupture that gives rise to the waves.

Worldwide, people feel an estimated 1 million earthquakes a year. However, few of these earthquakes are noticed more than a few kilometres from their source, and even fewer cause damage (Table 2.2).

Let's begin our discussion of earthquakes by examining how they are measured and compared. Earthquakes are compared by the amount of energy released, their **magnitude**, and by the effects of ground motion on people and structures, their **intensity**.

Earthquake Magnitude

The **epicentre** of the earthquake is the point on the surface of Earth directly above the fault rupture (Figure 2.3). The *focus*, or *hypocentre*, is the location of the initial rupture along the fault, directly below the epicentre.

The size, or magnitude, of the quake is expressed as a decimal number (e.g., 6.8). In 1931, the Japanese seismologist Kiyoo Wadati devised the first quantitative magnitude scale; in 1935 it was further developed by Charles F. Richter at the California Institute of Technology. The scale, somewhat to Richter's embarrassment, became known in the popular press as the **Richter scale**. It quantified the magnitude of local (California) earthquakes as the logarithm to the base 10 of the maximum signal wave amplitude recorded on a then-standard seismogram at a distance of 100 km from the epicentre.

Although some news reports still refer to the Richter scale, it is no longer in common use by seismologists, scientists who study earthquakes. Several earthquake magnitude scales

TABLE 2.2 Selected Major Earthquakes in North America

Year	Locality	Damage ($millions)	Number of Deaths
1811–1812	New Madrid, Missouri	Unknown	Unknown
1886	Charleston, South Carolina	23	60
1906	San Francisco, California	524	700
1925	Santa Barbara, California	8	13
1929	Sea floor off Newfoundland	Unknown	28
1933	Long Beach, California	40	115
1940	Imperial Valley, California	6	9
1946	Vancouver Island, British Columbia	Several million	2
1949	Queen Charlotte Islands	Sparsely populated area	0
1952	Kern County, California	60	14
1959	Hebgen Lake, Montana (damage to timber and roads)	11	28
1964	Prince William Sound, Alaska (includes tsunami damage near Anchorage and on the Pacific Coast of Canada and the United States)	500	131
1965	Puget Sound, Washington	13	7
1971	Sylmar (San Fernando), California	553	65
1983	Coalinga, California	31	0
1983	Central Idaho	15	2
1987	Whittier, California	358	8
1989	Loma Prieta (San Francisco), California	6000	63
1992	Landers, California	271	1
1994	Northridge, California	40,000	61
2001	Nisqually, Washington	2000	0
2002	South-Central Alaska	Sparsely populated area	0

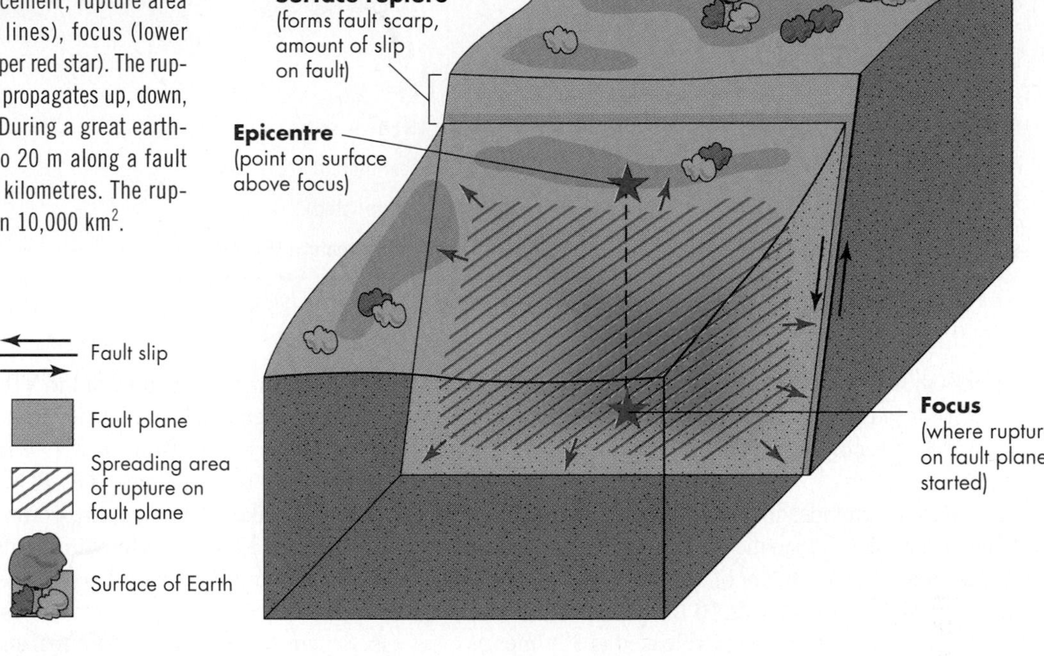

▶ **FIGURE 2.3 BASIC EARTHQUAKE FEATURES** This block diagram shows a fault plane (light tan surface), amount of displacement, rupture area (closely spaced diagonal lines), focus (lower red star), and epicentre (upper red star). The rupture starts at the focus and propagates up, down, and laterally (red arrows). During a great earthquake, slip may be 10 m to 20 m along a fault length of several hundred kilometres. The rupture area may be more than 10,000 km^2.

have been developed since Richter's time. Today, the most commonly used measure of earthquake size is **moment magnitude**, M_w. It is determined from an estimate of the area that ruptured along a fault plane during the quake, the amount of movement or slippage along the fault, and the rigidity of the rocks near the focus. An increase from one whole number to the next represents a 10-fold increase in the amount of shaking and about a 30-fold increase in the amount of energy released (Figure 2.4).

Except for very large earthquakes, the magnitude on the Richter scale is approximately equal to the moment magnitude. Because of this relation, we will refer to the size of an earthquake simply as its magnitude, represented by the symbol **M**, without specifying Richter or moment magnitude.

Earthquakes are given descriptive adjectives to further characterize their magnitude (Table 2.3). Most damaging earthquakes are *major* (**M** 7–7.9) or *strong* (**M** 6–6.9). Major earthquakes can cause widespread and serious damage. Strong earthquakes can also cause considerable damage depending on their location and the nature of the local geologic materials. Fortunately, powerful *great* (**M** 8) and *giant* (**M** 9) earthquakes are uncommon; the worldwide average is one **M** 8 quake per year and about three **M** 9 quakes per century (Table 2.3). In contrast, more than 1 million *very minor earthquakes* (**M** less than 3) occur each day. Most of these quakes are too small or too distant to be felt by people.

The amount of ground motion, or shaking, that occurs during an earthquake is related to the magnitude of the quake.

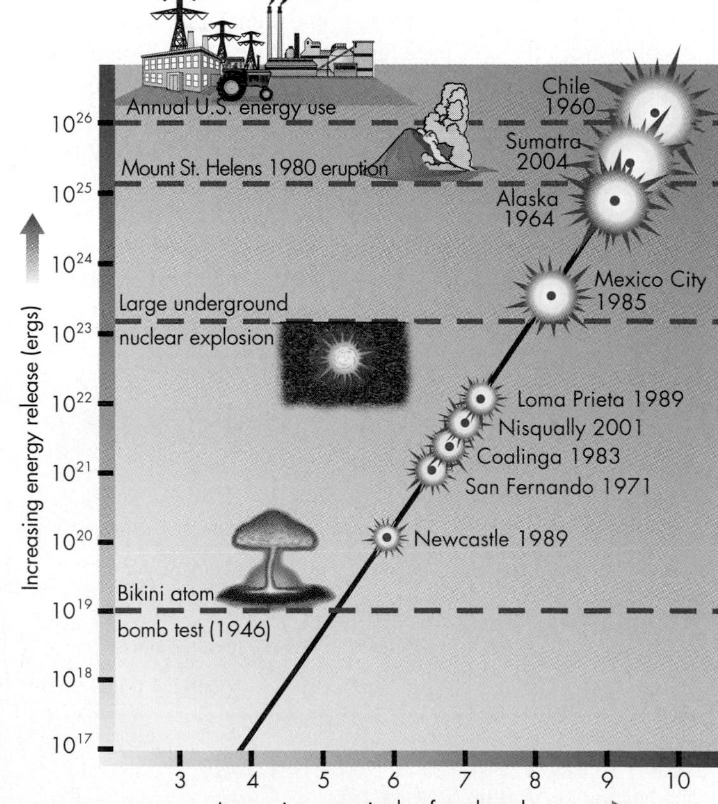

▶ **FIGURE 2.4 EARTHQUAKE ENERGY** The relation between earthquake magnitude and released energy allows comparisons with other energy sources. The energy released by the 1960 earthquake in Chile, the most powerful historic seismic event, was greater than the entire annual consumption of commercial energy in the United States. *(Modified from the U.S. Geological Survey)*

TABLE 2.3 Magnitude and Frequency of Earthquakes Worldwide

Descriptor	Magnitude	Average Annual Number of Events
Great	8 and higher	1
Major	7–7.9	17
Strong	6–6.9	134
Moderate	5–5.9	1319
Light	4–4.9	13,000 (estimated)
Minor	3–3.9	130,000 (estimated)
Very minor	2–2.9	1,300,000 (estimated) (approximately 150 per hour)

Source: From the U.S. Geological Survey. 2000. Earthquakes, facts and lists. http://neic.usgs.gov. *Accessed January 18, 2005.*

We will discuss this relationship in general terms here and in more detail later. Ground motion, in either a vertical or a horizontal direction, is recorded by an instrument known as a **seismograph**.

As earthquake magnitudes increase, the amount of ground motion changes more slowly than the amount of energy released (Table 2.4). For example, the amount of displacement, or ground motion, from an **M** 7 earthquake is 10 times that of an **M** 6 earthquake, but the amount of energy released is 32 times as much. If we compare an **M** 5 with an **M** 7 earthquake, the differences are much greater. The energy released is 32 × 32 or about 1000 times greater. About 33,000 (32 × 32 × 32) shocks of **M** 5 are required to release as much energy as a single earthquake of **M** 8!

Earthquake Intensity

Another measure of earthquake size is intensity. The intensity of an earthquake at any location depends on magnitude, distance from the epicentre, and the nature of the ground at the site. The **Modified Mercalli Intensity Scale** measures the degree to which an earthquake affects people, property, and the ground. The 12 categories on this scale are assigned Roman numerals (Table 2.5). Each category contains a description of how people perceive the shaking from a quake and the extent of damage to buildings and other structures. For example, the 1971 Sylmar earthquake in the San Fernando Valley, California, had a single magnitude (6.6), but its Mercalli Intensity ranged from I to VII (Figure 2.5). Similarly, the 1949 Queen Charlotte Island earthquake, Canada's largest quake, had a magnitude of 8.1, with Modified Mercalli Intensities up to IX (Figure 2.6).

Earthquake intensities are commonly shown on maps. Conventional Modified Mercalli Intensity maps, like those in Figures 2.5 and 2.6, take days or even weeks to complete. They are based on newspaper articles, reports from damage assessment teams, and questionnaires sent to residents near the epicentre. The procedure, however, is changing. Intensity maps for earthquakes in some regions of Canada and the United States are now created by using the Internet. People access web pages of the Geological Survey of Canada and U.S. Geological Survey (USGS) to electronically submit forms detailing their experience in an earthquake. Earthquake intensity maps can be generated in a few minutes in the United States and in less than 24 hours in Canada, and efforts are under-

TABLE 2.4 Relationships among Magnitude, Displacement, and Energy of Earthquakes

Magnitude Change	Ground Displacement Change[1]	Energy Change
1	10 times	About 32 times
0.5	3.2 times	About 5.5 times
0.3	2 times	About 3 times
0.1	1.3 times	About 1.4 times

[1]Displacement, vertical or horizontal, that is recorded on a standard seismograph.

Source: U.S. Geological Survey. 2000. Earthquakes, facts and lists. http://neic.usgs.gov. *Accessed January 18, 2005.*

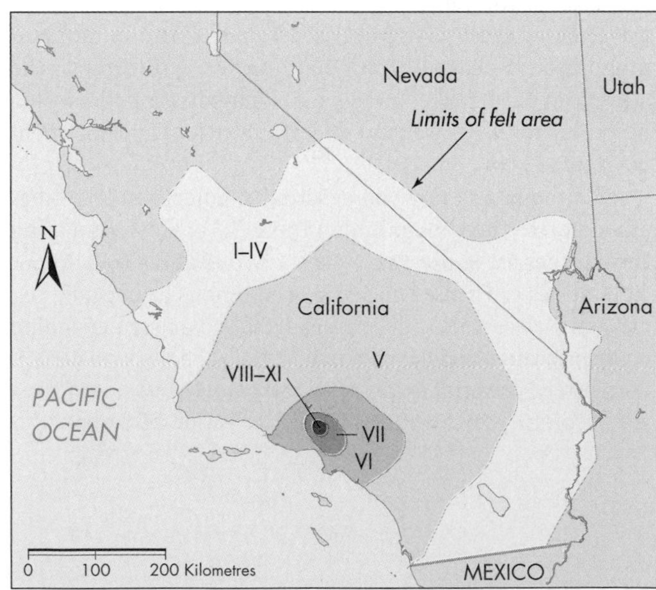

▲ **FIGURE 2.5 INTENSITY OF SHAKING** A Modified Mercalli Intensity map of the 1971 Sylmar, California, earthquake (**M** 6.6). The red and bright orange areas experienced damaging shaking. See Table 2.5 for an explanation of the Roman numerals. *(U.S. Geological Survey. 1974. Earthquake Information Bulletin 6[5])*

TABLE 2.5 Modified Mercalli Intensity Scale (abridged)

Intensity	Effects
I	Felt by very few people.
II	Felt by only a few people at rest, especially on upper floors of buildings. Delicate suspended objects may swing.
III	Felt noticeably indoors, especially on upper floors of buildings, but many people do not recognize the shaking as an earthquake. Stationary cars may rock slightly. Vibration feels like the passing of a truck.
IV	During the day, felt indoors by many, outdoors by few. At night, some people awakened. Dishes, windows, doors disturbed; walls make cracking sound. Stationary cars rock noticeably. Sensation is that of a heavy truck striking a building.
V	Felt by nearly everyone; many people awakened. Some dishes and windows broken; a few instances of cracked plaster; unstable objects overturned. Disturbances of trees, poles, and other tall objects are sometimes noticed. Pendulum clocks may stop.
VI	Felt by all; many people frightened and run outdoors. Some heavy furniture moved; a few instances of fallen plaster or damaged chimneys. Damage is slight.
VII	Almost everybody runs outdoors. Damage is negligible in buildings of good design and construction; slight to moderate in well-built ordinary structures; considerable in poorly built or badly designed structures; some chimneys broken. Noticed by people driving cars.
VIII	Damage slight in specially designed structures; considerable in ordinary substantial buildings, with partial collapse; great in poorly built structures. Panel walls thrown out of frames; chimneys, factory stacks, columns, monuments, and walls collapse; heavy furniture overturned. Sand and mud ejected in small amounts; changes in well water. Disturbs people driving cars.
IX	Damage considerable even in specially designed structures; great in substantial buildings, with partial collapse. Well-designed frame structures thrown out of plumb; some buildings are shifted off foundations. Ground cracks conspicuous. Underground pipes are broken.
X	Some well-built wooden structures are destroyed; most masonry and frame structures with foundations destroyed; ground badly cracked. Train rails bent. Many landslides from riverbanks and steep slopes. Some sand and mud liquefies. Water is splashed over banks.
XI	Few, if any, masonry structures remain standing; bridges are destroyed. Large fissures open in ground. Landslides are common.
XII	Damage is total. Waves are seen on the ground surface. Lines of sight distorted. Objects are thrown into the air.

Source: Modified from Wood and Neuman, 1931; U.S. Geological Survey. 1974. Earthquake Information Bulletin 6(5):28.

way to integrate the two systems. The online *community internet intensity maps* produced by the U.S. Geological Survey are updated every few minutes.

One of the major challenges during a damaging earthquake is to quickly determine where the damage is most severe. This information is now available in parts of California, the Pacific Northwest, and Utah, where there are dense networks of seismograph stations. The stations transmit direct measurements of ground motion during the earthquake. This information, known as *instrumental intensity,* is used to immediately produce what is called a "*ShakeMap*," which shows both perceived shaking and potential damage (Figure 2.7). ShakeMaps are valuable to emergency response teams who must locate and rescue people in collapsed buildings and identify sites where natural gas lines and other utilities might be damaged. The cost of seismographs is small compared with damage from earthquake shaking and the value of lives saved by prompt rescue.

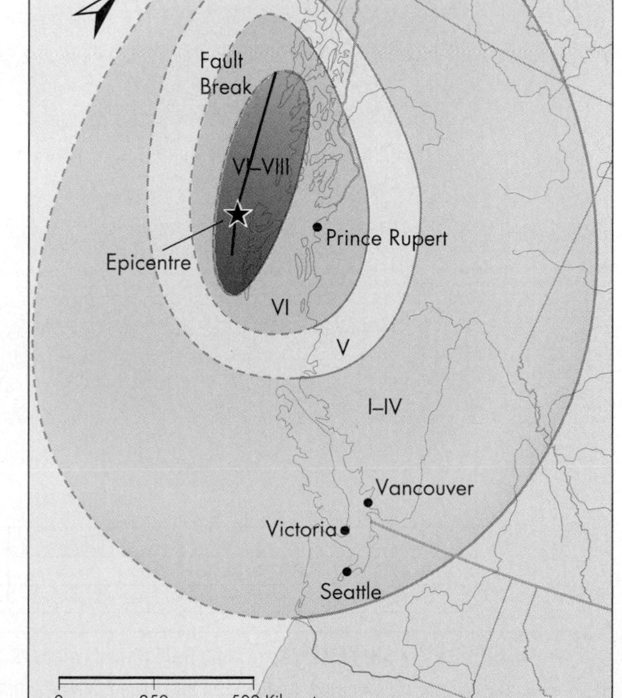

▶ **FIGURE 2.6 CANADA'S LARGEST EARTHQUAKE** A Modified Mercalli Intensity map of the 1949 Queen Charlotte Island earthquake (**M** 8.1). *(Reproduced with the permission of the Minister of Public Works and Government Services Canada, 2007, and courtesy of Natural Resources Canada, Geological Survey of Canada)*

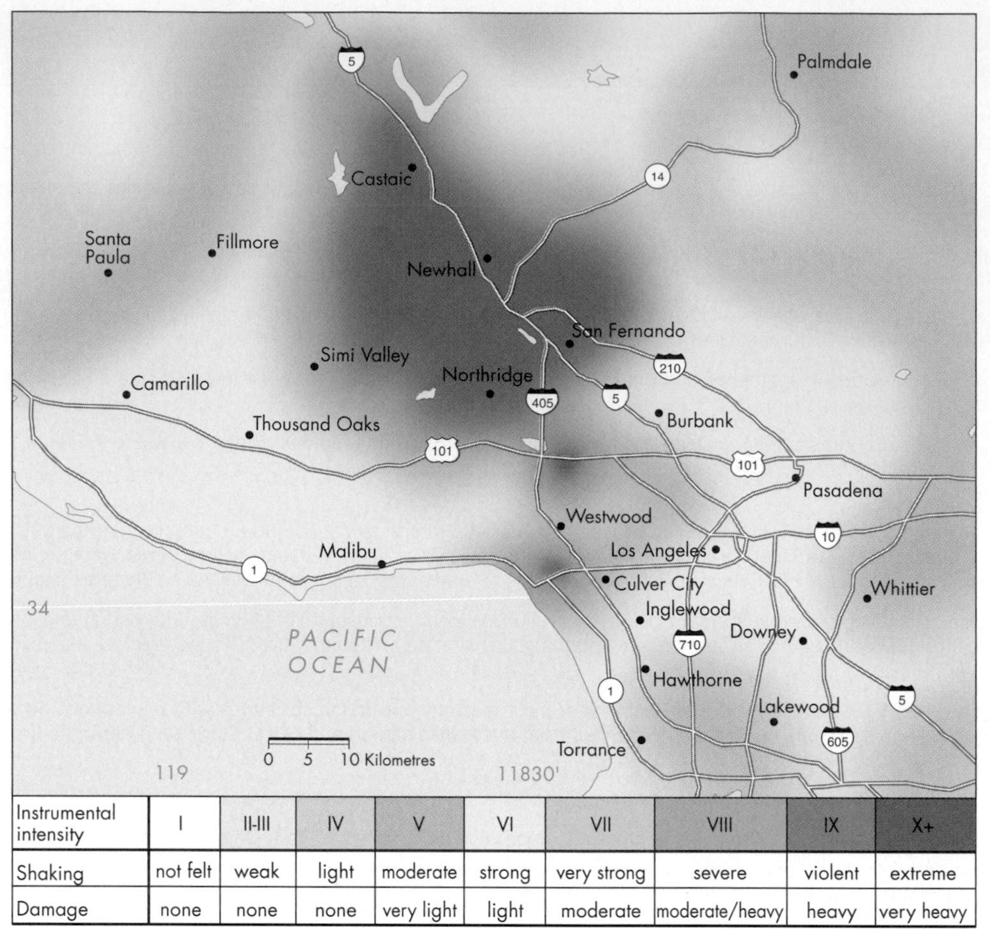

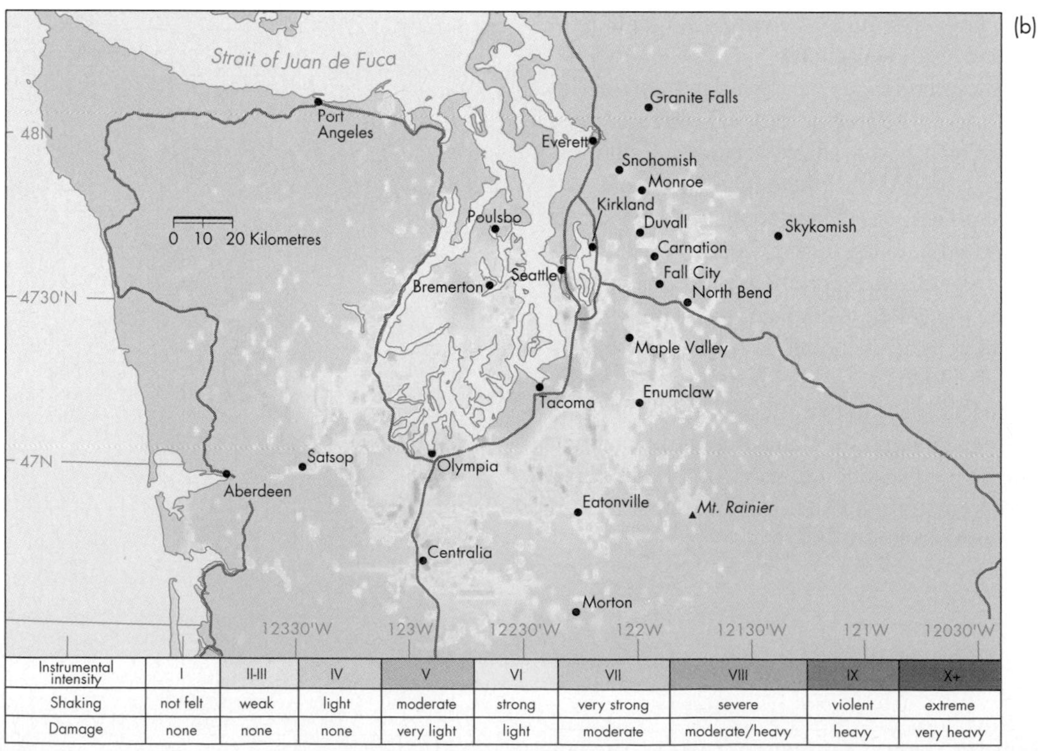

▲ **FIGURE 2.7 SHAKEMAPS** Instrumental intensity maps of (a) the 1994 Northridge, California, earthquake (**M** 6.7) *(U.S. Geological Survey; courtesy of David Wald)*, and (b) the 2001 Nisqually, Washington, earthquake (**M** 6.8). *(Pacific Northwest Seismograph Network, University of Washington)*

2.2 Earthquake Processes

Earth is a dynamic evolving planet, driven by plate tectonic processes. Slow movements of lithospheric plates have formed ocean basins, continents, and mountain ranges. Plate movements are also responsible for earthquakes and volcanic eruptions, both of which are most common at and near plate boundaries (Figures 2.8 and 2.9). For example, in Canada, most earthquakes and all active volcanoes are in the western part of the country, near the boundaries of three tectonic plates (Figure 2.10).

Process of Faulting

The process of fault rupture, or *faulting,* can be compared to sliding two rough boards past each other. Friction along the boundary between the boards may temporarily slow their motion, but rough edges break off and motion occurs at various places along the plane. Similarly, lithospheric plates moving past each other are slowed by friction along their boundaries. This braking action exerts forces on rocks near the plate boundary. As a result, the rocks undergo strain or deformation. When stress on rocks exceeds their breaking point, referred to as their *strength,* the rocks suddenly move along a fault. The rupture starts at the focus and propagates up, down, and laterally along the fault plane during the earthquake. The rupture produces waves of vibrational energy, called seismic waves, that can shake the ground. Faults are therefore *seismic sources,* and identifying them is the first step in evaluating the risk of an earthquake, or the seismic risk, in a given area.

Fault Types There are two basic types of geologic faults, and they are distinguished by the direction of displacement of rocks or sediment bordering them. In the case of **strike-slip faults**, displacements are mainly horizontal, whereas in the case of **dip-slip faults** displacements are mainly vertical. Examples of well-known strike-slip faults include the San Andreas fault in California (Figure 2.11), the Alpine Fault in New Zealand, and the Fairweather fault in Alaska. A dip-slip fault is classified as a **reverse fault** or a **normal fault** depending on which way the bounding Earth materials move. The faults marked by the deep-sea trenches off Japan, the Aleutian Islands, the west coast of South America, and elsewhere are low-angle reverse faults called **thrust faults**.

Geologists use centuries-old mining terminology to distinguish reverse and normal faults. Many early underground mines were dug at an incline to mine mineralized fault zones, and miners called the block below their feet the *footwall* and the block above their heads the *hanging-wall.* In the case

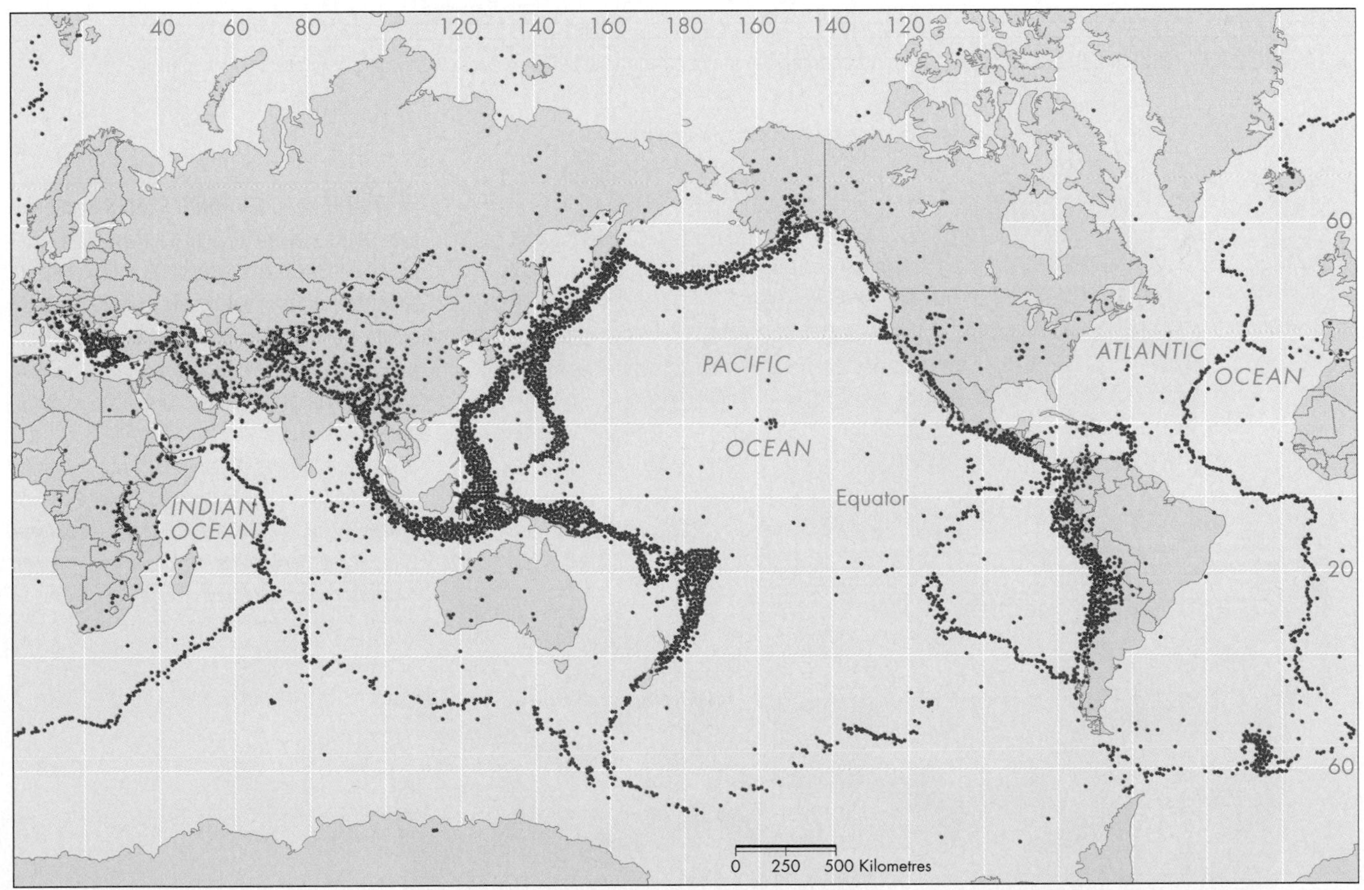

▲ **FIGURE 2.8 GLOBAL EARTHQUAKE DISTRIBUTION** A map of global seismicity (1963–1988, **M** 5+), showing epicentres of plate boundary (heavy concentration of dots) and intraplate (isolated dots) earthquakes. *(U.S. Geological Survey National Earthquake Information Center)*

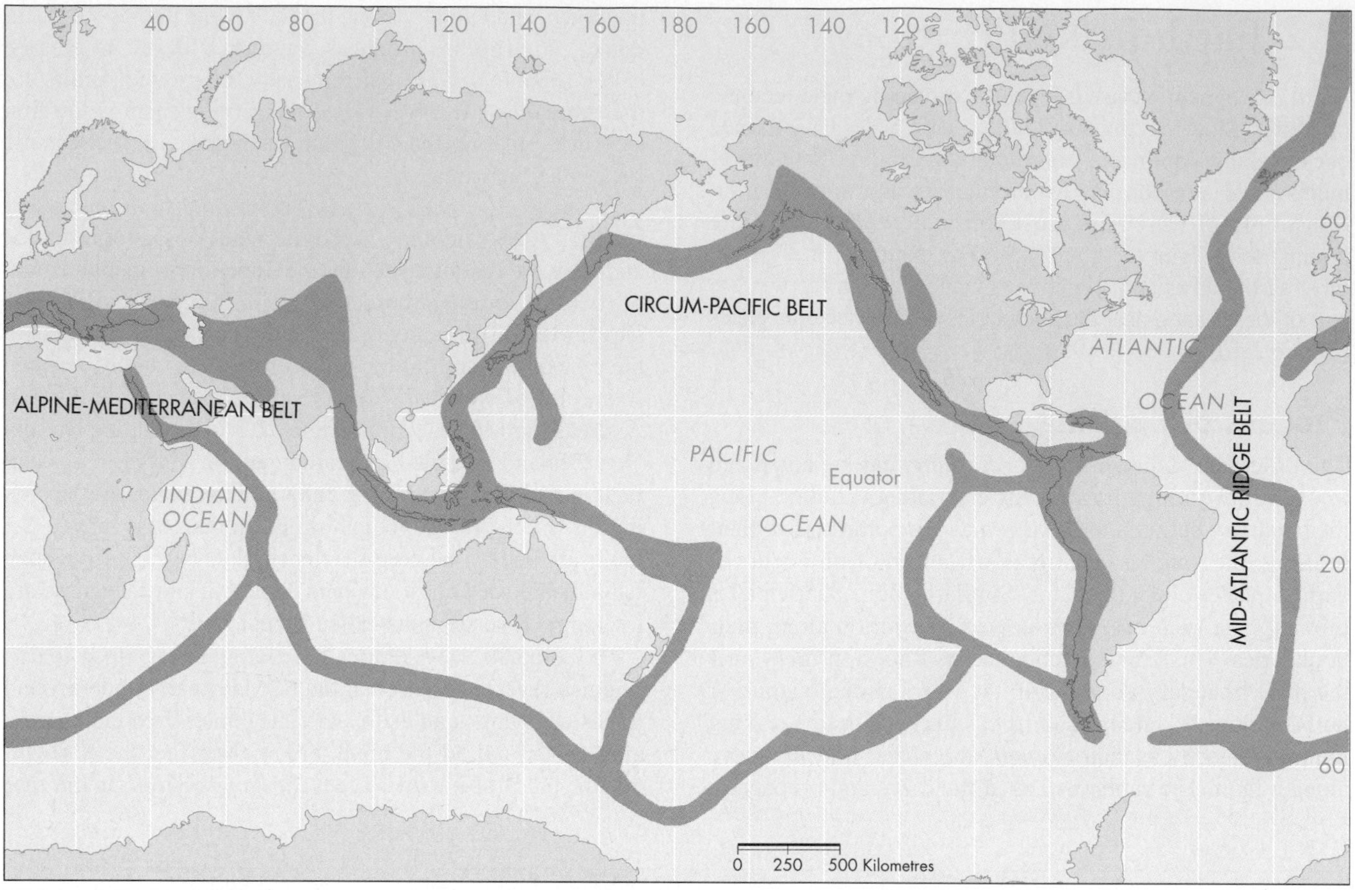

▲ **FIGURE 2.9 EARTHQUAKE BELTS** A map of the world showing the major earthquake belts. *(National Oceanic and Atmospheric Administration)*

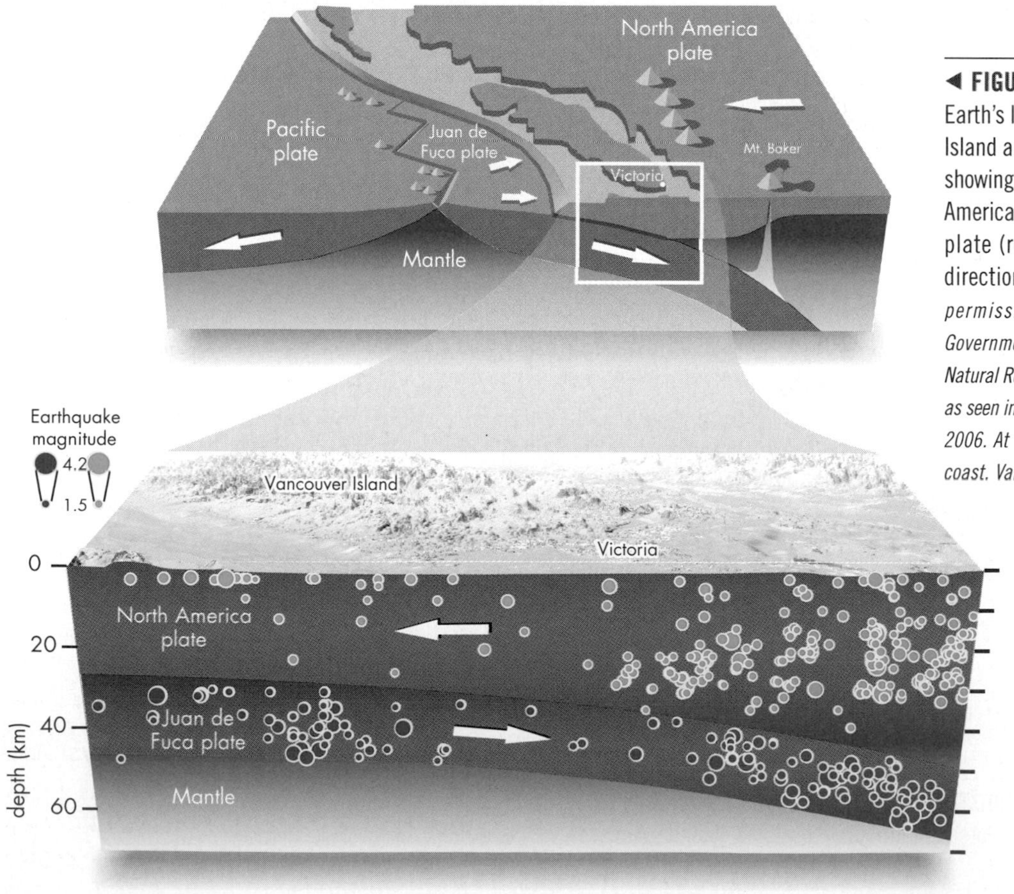

◀ **FIGURE 2.10 TECTONIC PLATES** Section of Earth's lithosphere through southern Vancouver Island and the northern tip of Olympic Peninsula showing sources of earthquakes within the North America plate (blue dots) and the Juan de Fuca plate (red dots). White arrows show relative directions of plate motion. *(Reproduced with the permission of the Minister of Public Works and Government Services Canada, 2007, and courtesy of Natural Resources Canada, Geological Survey of Canada; as seen in Clague, J., C. Yorath, R. Franklin, and B. Turner. 2006. At risk: Earthquakes and tsunamis on the west coast. Vancouver, BC: Tricouni Press)*

of a *reverse fault*, the hanging-wall has moved up relative to the footwall along a plane inclined at an angle steeper than 45 degrees (Figure 2.12). *Thrust faults* are similar to reverse faults, except that the angle of the fault plane is 45 degrees or less. If the hanging-wall has moved downward relative to the footwall, the fault is called a *normal fault.*

Until recently, geologists thought that most active faults extended to and ruptured the ground surface. However, we now know that some faults are buried, or *blind,* and do not reach the surface (Figure 2.13). This discovery has made it more difficult to evaluate earthquake risk in some areas.

Fault Activity

Most geologists consider a particular fault to be *active* if it has moved during the past 10,000 years (the *Holocene Epoch*) and *potentially active* if it shows evidence of movement during the past 2 million years (the *Pleistocene Epoch*) (Table 2.6).

Faults that have not moved during the past 2 million years are generally classified as *inactive*. However, it may be difficult to determine when a fault was last active, especially if it has no historical earthquakes. In many cases, geologists must determine the *paleoseismicity* of the fault, that is, the prehistoric record of earthquakes. They do so by identifying faulted rock or sediment and determining the age of the most recent displacement.

▲ **FIGURE 2.11 SAN ANDREAS FAULT** Northwest view along the San Andreas fault in southern California. The fault separates the North America and Pacific plates and is the source of many large earthquakes in California. *(Clague, J., C. Yorath, R. Franklin, and B. Turner. 2006. At risk: Earthquakes and tsunamis on the west coast. Vancouver, BC: Tricouni Press)*

Tectonic Creep

Some active faults exhibit **tectonic creep**, or *fault creep*, which is gradual movement along a fault without accompanying felt earthquakes. This process can slowly damage roads, sidewalks, building foundations, and other structures (Figure 2.14). Tectonic creep has damaged culverts under the University of California at Berkeley football stadium. Movement of 2.2 cm was measured beneath the stadium in only 11 years, and periodic repairs were necessary as the cracks developed.[4] More rapid creep has been recorded on the Calaveras fault near Hollister, California. A winery on that fault is slowly being pulled apart at about 1 cm per year.[5] A related phenomenon is the creep taking place along a portion of plate-boundary fault at the Cascadia **subduction zone** off southwestern British Columbia and Washington State. The creep is responsible for periodic **slow earthquakes** that are not felt and have only recently been detected.[6,7] Fault creep does not preclude damaging earthquakes. In many cases, creep is a small portion of the total slip on a fault; periodic sudden displacements producing earthquakes can also be expected.

Seismic Waves

Some of the seismic waves generated by fault rupture travel within the body of Earth and others travel along the surface. The types of **body waves** are P waves and S waves.

P waves, also called *compressional* or *primary* waves, are the faster of the two types of body waves (Figure 2.15a). They can travel through a solid, a liquid, or a gas. P waves travel much faster through solids than through liquids. The average velocity of P waves in Earth's crust is 6 km/s, in contrast to 1.5 km/s in water. Interestingly, when P waves reach Earth's surface, they may produce sound that can be heard by people and some animals.[8] However, the sound that most people hear during an earthquake is the noise of objects vibrating, not the P wave itself.

S waves, also called *shear* or *secondary* waves, travel through only solid materials (Figure 2.15b). They have an average velocity through Earth's crust of 3 km/s, half the velocity of P waves. S waves produce a back-and-forth motion at right angles to the direction the waves are moving. This movement is similar to the whipping motion of a long jump rope held by two people on a playground. When liquids are subjected to sideways shear, they are unable to spring back, explaining why S waves can't move through liquids.[8]

Complex **surface waves** form when P and S waves reach Earth's surface and move along it (Figure 2.15c). They travel more slowly than either P or S waves and cause much of the damage near the epicentre. Surface waves produce a complex

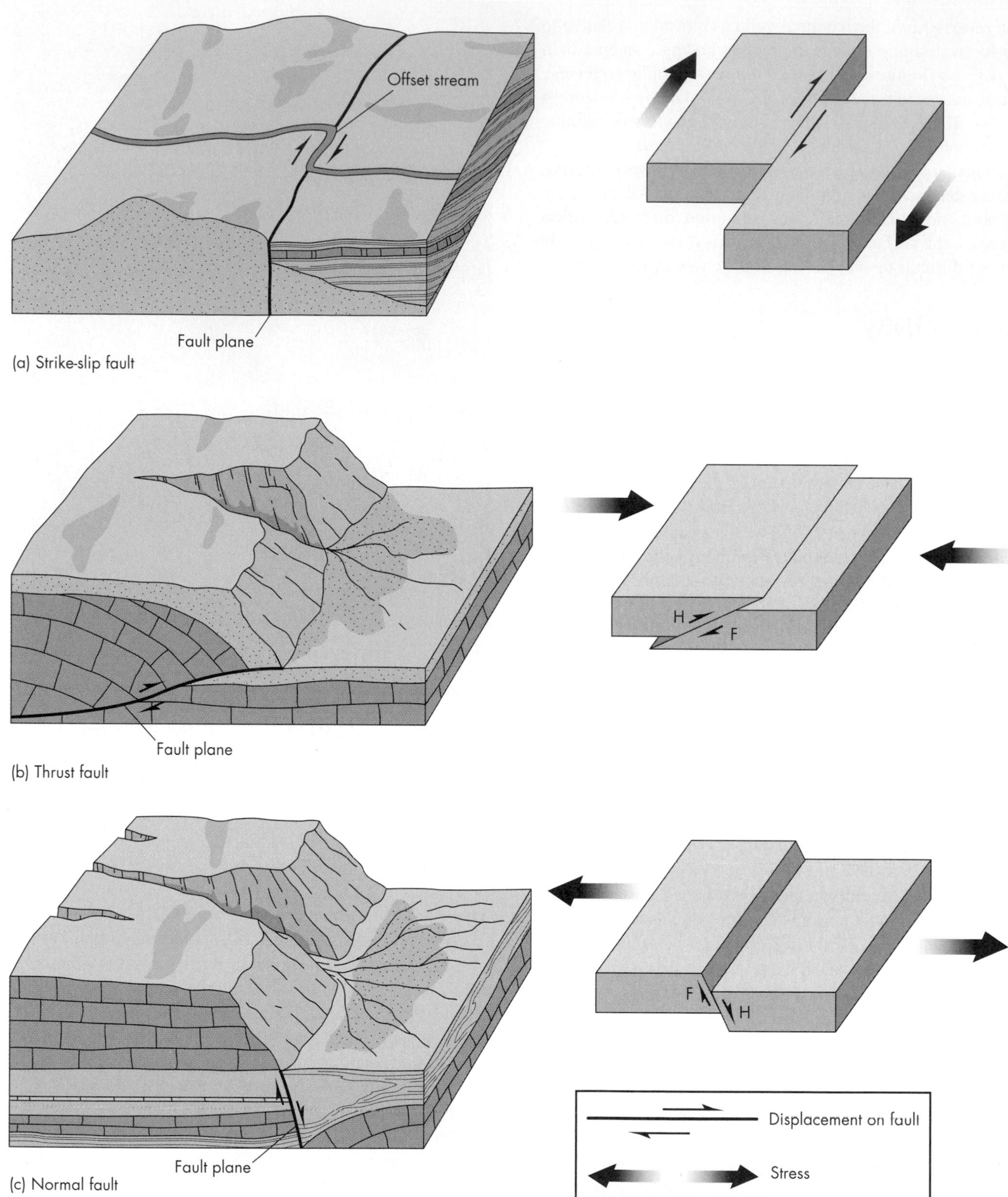

▲ **FIGURE 2.12 TYPES OF GEOLOGIC FAULTS** The three common types of faults and their effects on the landscape. (a) Strike-slip fault with horizontal displacement along the fault plane. (b) Thrust fault in which the hanging-wall (H) has moved up and over the footwall (F). (c) Normal fault in which the hanging-wall (H) has dropped down. The coloured diagrams on the left show the landscape after movement along the fault (thick black line). The grey diagrams on the right show directions of stress (thick arrows) that produce the displacements (thin half arrows).

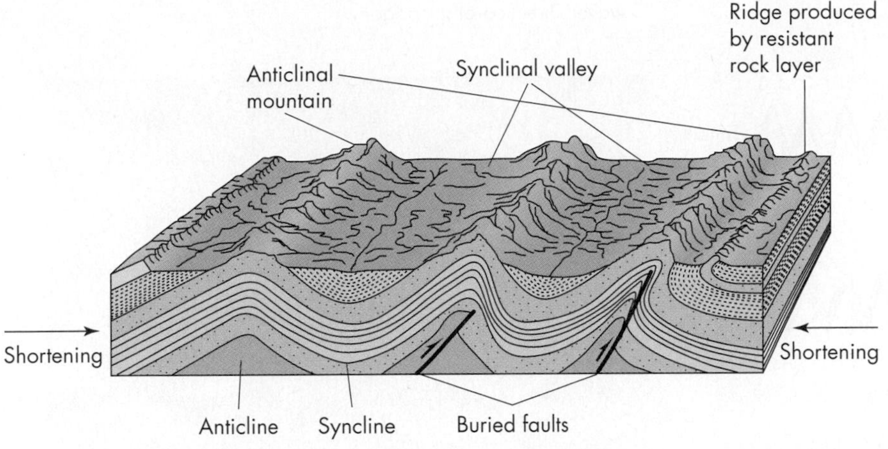

◄ **FIGURE 2.13 BURIED FAULTS** "Blind," or buried, faults do not reach the surface but can contribute to the formation of mountains. In this illustration, buried reverse faults lie beneath two anticlines (upward-directed folds of rock). *(Modified after Lutgens, F., and E. Tarbuck. 1992. Essentials of geology, 4th ed. New York: Macmillan)*

TABLE 2.6 Fault Terminology Based on Most Recent Activity

GEOLOGIC AGE				Start of Time Interval (in Years before Present)	Fault Status
Era	Period	Epoch			
Cenozoic	Quaternary	Holocene	Historic	200	Active
			Prehistoric	10,000	
		Pleistocene		1,650,000*	Potentially Active
	Tertiary			65,000,000	Inactive
	Pre-Cenozoic time			4,600,000,000 (Age of the Earth)	

*Time span used for regulatory purposes. The actual time span of the Pleistocene Epoch is 1.8 million to 10,000 years ago (see Chapter 1).

Source: After California State Mining and Geology Board Classification, 1973.

horizontal and vertical movement or rolling motion and, consequently, may damage walls and foundations of buildings, bridges, and roads. People near the epicentre of a strong earthquake have reported seeing these waves rippling across the land surface. One type of surface wave, called a *Love wave,* causes horizontal shaking that is especially damaging to foundations. Another type of surface wave is the slower-moving *Rayleigh wave*, which travels with an elliptical motion, like rolling ocean waves; surface materials move vertically as the wave moves forward.

◄ **FIGURE 2.14 TECTONIC CREEP** Slow, continual movement along the San Andreas fault has split this concrete drainage ditch at the Almaden Vineyards south of Hollister, California. A person's shoe and blue pant leg in the upper left corner of the image provides scale. *(James A. Sugar/NGS Image Collection)*

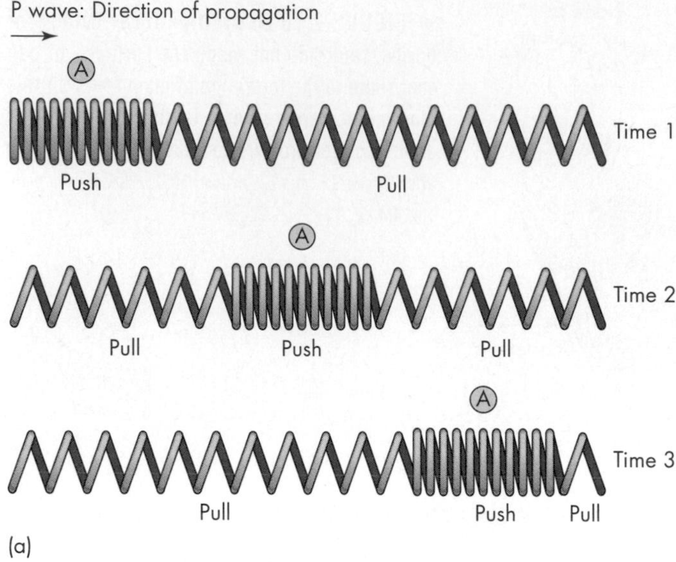

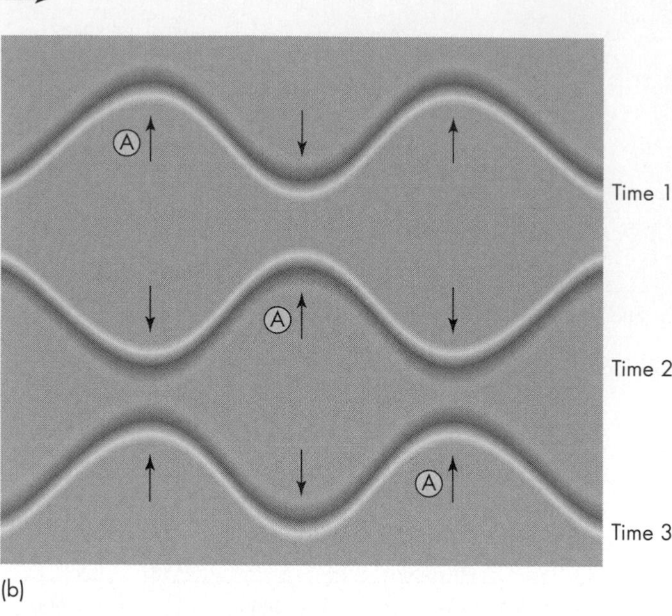

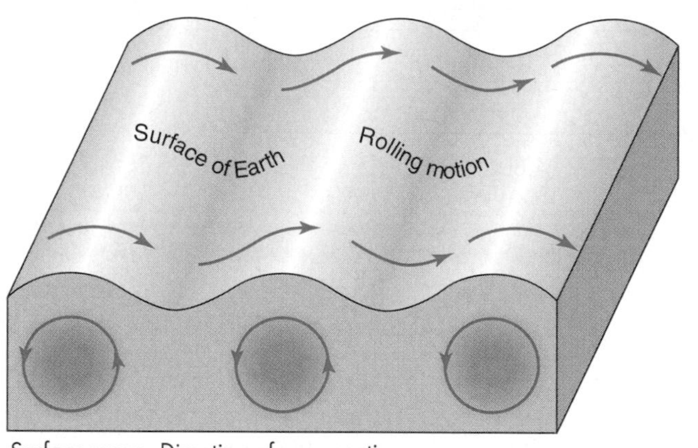

◄ **FIGURE 2.15 SEISMIC WAVES** An idealized diagram showing the behaviour of the three major types of earthquake waves. (a) A P wave is a compressional wave. The coil compresses to form wave A, which passes from left to right from time 1 at the top of the illustration to time 3 on the bottom. (b) An S wave is a shear wave. Atoms vibrate at right angles to the direction the wave is travelling. In this example, vibrations move the white rope up and down as wave A moves from left to right from time 1 at the top of the illustration to time 3 on the bottom. (c) A surface wave produces a rolling motion on Earth's surface as it passes through from left to right.

2.3 Earthquake Shaking

Three important factors determine the shaking people experience during an earthquake: (1) earthquake's magnitude, (2) a person's distance from the focus, and (3) local soil and rock conditions. In general, strong shaking may be expected from earthquakes of moderate magnitude (**M** 5–5.9) and larger. The strong motion produced by earthquakes makes the Earth "rock and roll" and causes much of the damage to buildings and other structures.

Distance to the Focus

To determine the distance to the source of an earthquake, the epicentre is located using the P and S waves detected by seismographs (Figures 2.16a and 2.16b). The analog or digital record of these waves is called a *seismogram*. Seismic waves appear on a seismogram as an oscillating line that resembles an electrocardiograph of a person's heartbeat (Figure 2.16c). Because P waves travel faster than S waves, they appear first on a seismogram. Seismologists use the difference between the arrival times of the first P and S waves to determine the distance of the epicentre from the seismograph. For example, in Figure 2.16c the S waves arrived 50 seconds after the P waves. Knowing the velocities of P and S waves, the seismologist determines that this 50-second delay would occur if the epicentre is about 420 km away. Seismographs around the globe will record different arrival times for P and S waves from the same earthquake. Stations farthest from the epicentre will record the greatest difference between P and S wave arrival times (Figure 2.16d).

The epicentre of an earthquake can be located by using P and S arrival times at three or more seismographs at different locations (Figure 2.17). The distance to the epicentre is calculated for each seismograph, and a circle with a radius equal to that distance is drawn around the seismic station. Circles drawn around three or more stations will intersect at

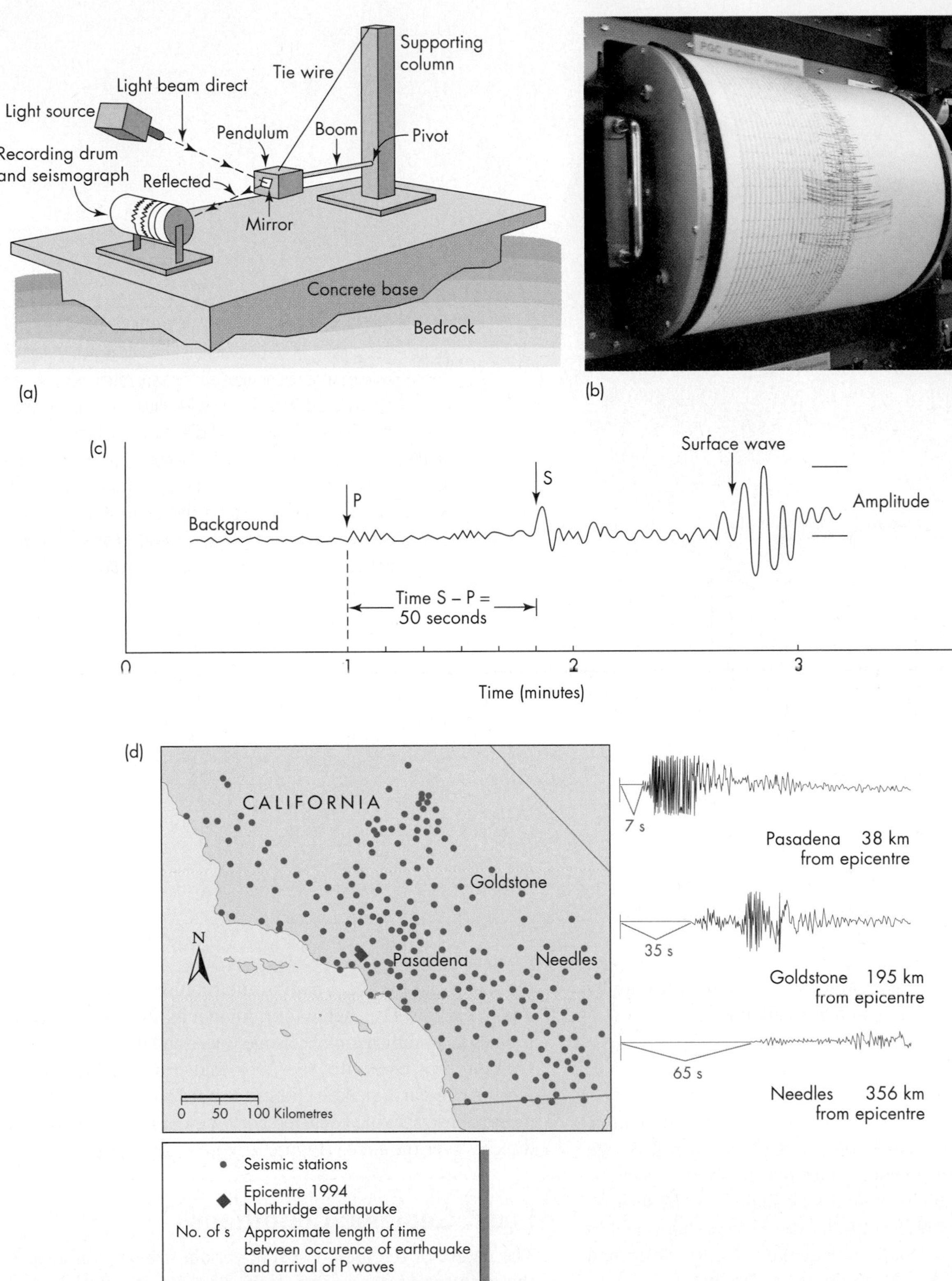

▲ **FIGURE 2.16 SEISMOGRAPHS AND SEISMOGRAMS** (a) A sketch showing how a seismograph works. (b) The recording drum of a seismograph at the Pacific Geoscience Centre near Victoria, British Columbia, showing the seismogram of the Washington State earthquake of February 28, 2001 (**M** 6.8). *(Ian McKain/AP Wide World Photos)* (c) A seismogram of an earthquake, showing successive arrivals of P, S, and surface waves. The difference of 50 seconds in first arrivals of S and P waves tells us that the epicentre is about 420 km from the seismograph. (d) Three seismograms of the 1994 Los Angeles (Northridge) earthquake, recorded at different distances from the epicentre. The seismic waves take longer to reach the seismograph and their amplitudes decrease with increasing distance from the epicentre. The greater the amplitude of the waves on the seismogram, the stronger the ground shaking. *(Modified from Southern California Earthquake Center)*

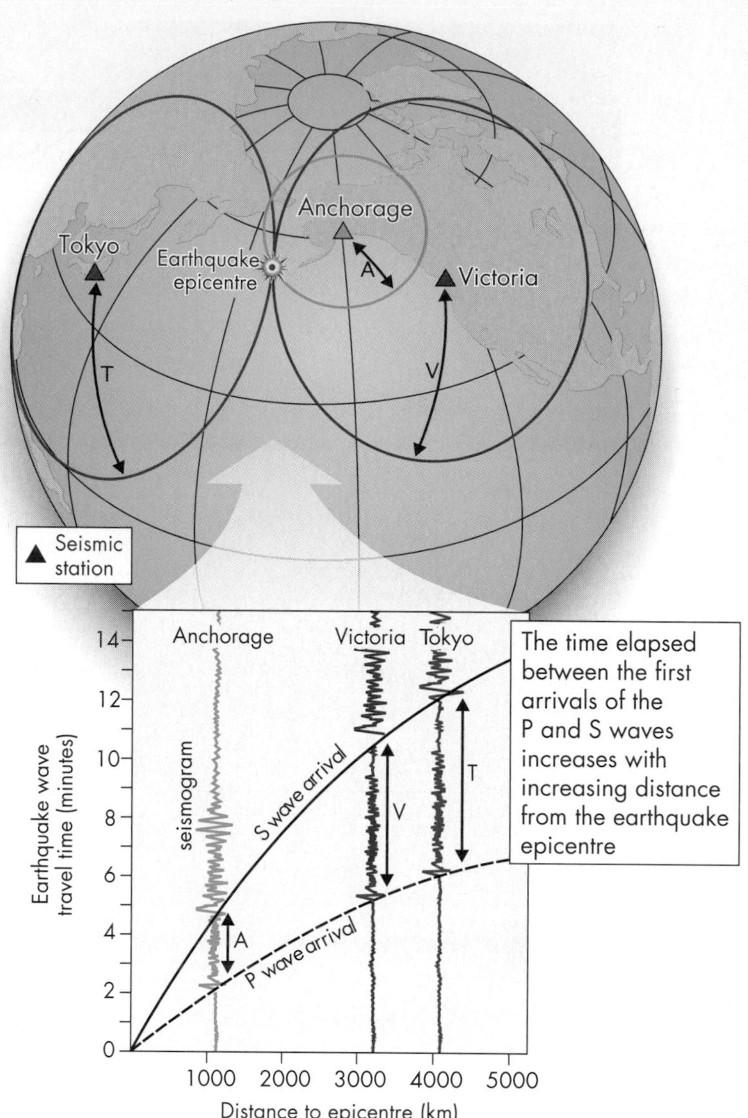

◄ **FIGURE 2.17 LOCATING AN EARTHQUAKE** The epicentre of an earthquake can be determined from the arrival times of P and S waves at three or more widely separated sites. P and S waves travel at different velocities, thus the time between their first arrivals at a site provides a measure of the distance of the recording seismographs to the epicentre. A circle with a radius equal to the epicentral distance is drawn around each seismograph station. The intersection of the three circles is the epicentre. *(Dolgott and Anatole. Essentials of physical geology, First edition. Copyright © 1998 by Houghton Mifflin Company. Used by permission).*

a point—the epicentre. The process of locating a feature by using distances from three points is called *triangulation.*

Depth of Focus

The depth of an earthquake also influences the amount of shaking. Seismic waves lose some of their energy before they reach the surface. In general, the deeper the source, or focus, of the earthquake, the less intense the shaking at the surface. This loss of energy, referred to as *attenuation,* happened in the 2001 Washington State earthquake (**M** 6.8), which had a focal depth of 52 km. In comparison, the attenuation was less, and the shaking stronger, during the 1994 Northridge quake (**M** 6.7), with a focal depth of only 19 km (Figure 2.18).

Direction of the Epicentre

A third factor that influences the amount of shaking is the direction that the rupture moves along the fault during the earthquake. A rupture may proceed in many directions from the focus, but the main path of the rupture can focus earthquake energy. This behaviour, known as **directivity**, contributes to amplification of seismic waves and thus to increased shaking. For example, the fault that produced the 1994 Northridge earthquake ruptured toward the northwest; the most intense shaking occurred northwest of the epicentre, not directly over the focus (Figure 2.18).

Local Geologic Conditions

The nature of the local Earth materials strongly influences the amount of ground motion. The dense granitic and metamorphic rocks of the Canadian Shield transmit earthquake energy very efficiently, thus even moderate earthquakes can cause damage over large areas (Figure 2.19). In contrast, seismic energy, and thus ground shaking, attenuate rapidly away from the epicentres of most earthquakes in the extremely heterogeneous, folded, and faulted crust of western North America. Seismic waves also move much slower through unconsolidated sediment than they do through bedrock. They slow even further if the unconsolidated

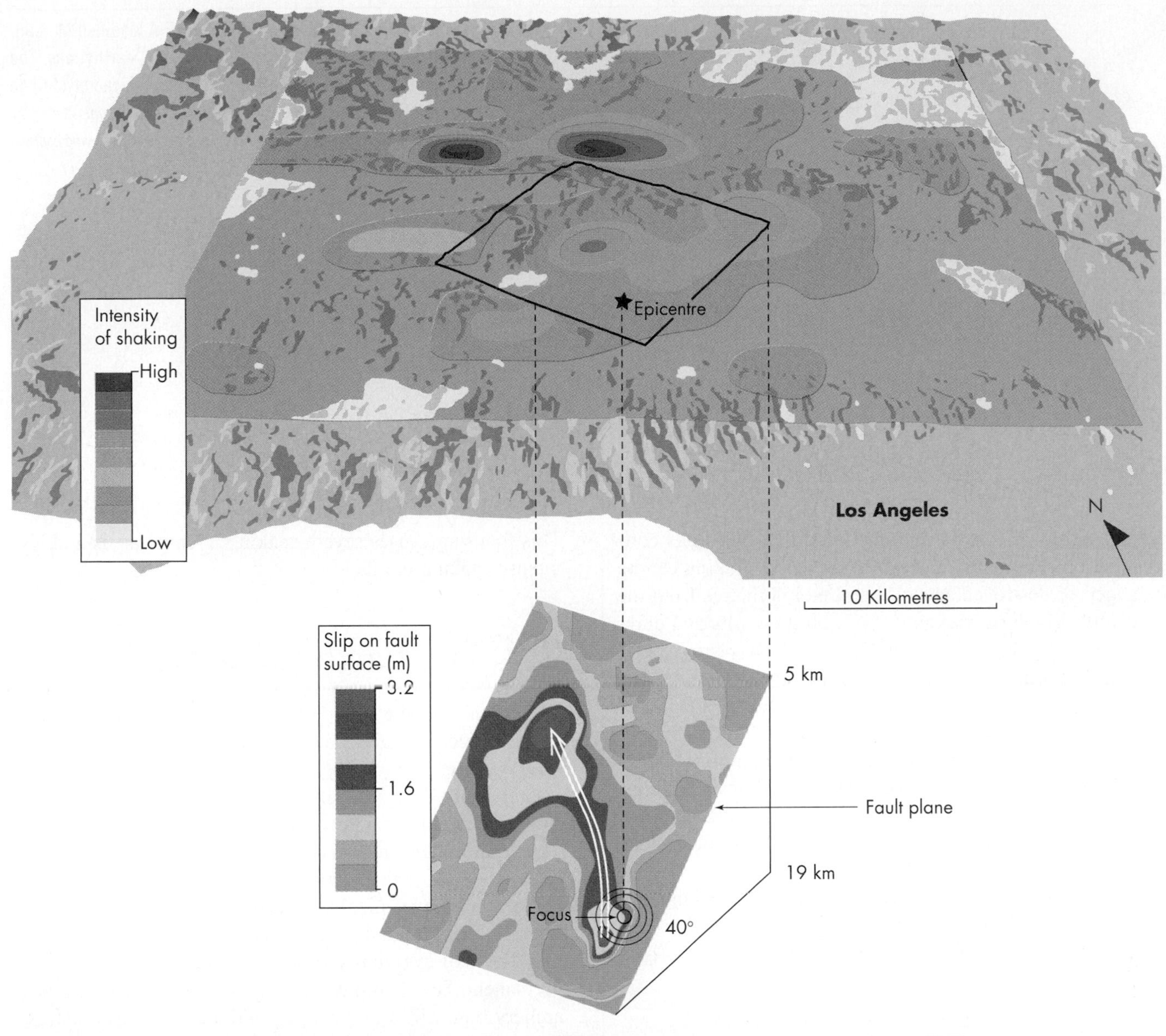

▲ **FIGURE 2.18 DIRECTIVITY OF FAULT RUPTURE** View to the north of the Los Angeles basin, showing the epicentre and intensity pattern of the 1994 Northridge earthquake. The red area 10 km northwest of the epicentre experienced the most intense shaking. The lower part of the figure shows the focus and a section of the fault plane that ruptured during the quake. Colours on the fault plane indicate the amount of slip during the earthquake. Slip was greatest in the reddish-purple zone northwest of the focus. The rupture started at the focus and progressed northwest in the direction of the white arrow. *(U.S. Geological Survey. 1996. USGS response to an urban earthquake, Northridge '94. U.S. Geological Survey Open File Report 96–263)*

material has a high water content. For example, seismic waves typically slow as they move from bedrock to stream, or *alluvial*, sands and gravels, and then slow again as they move through marine silts and clays (Figure 2.20). As P and S waves slow, some of their forward-directed energy is transferred to surface waves. This effect, known as **material amplification**, increases the amount of ground motion experienced in an earthquake.

For example, ground shaking during the 1989 Loma Prieta, California, earthquake (**M** 7.1) was particularly strong along the shores of San Francisco Bay (Figure 2.21). Amplified ground motions collapsed the upper deck of the Nimitz Freeway in Oakland, killing 41 people, and caused extensive damage in the Marina district of San Francisco (Figures 2.22 and 2.23). The portion of the freeway that collapsed was built on soft San Francisco Bay muds, and the Marina district was created after the 1906 San Francisco earthquake by filling in part of the bay with debris from damaged buildings and with mud pumped from the bottom of bay.[9] The loose nature of the fill and its high water content amplified the ground shaking to levels higher than were experienced closer to the epicentre, 100 km away.

The 1985 Mexico earthquake (**M** 8.0), which killed nearly 10,000 people in Mexico City, is another tragic example of

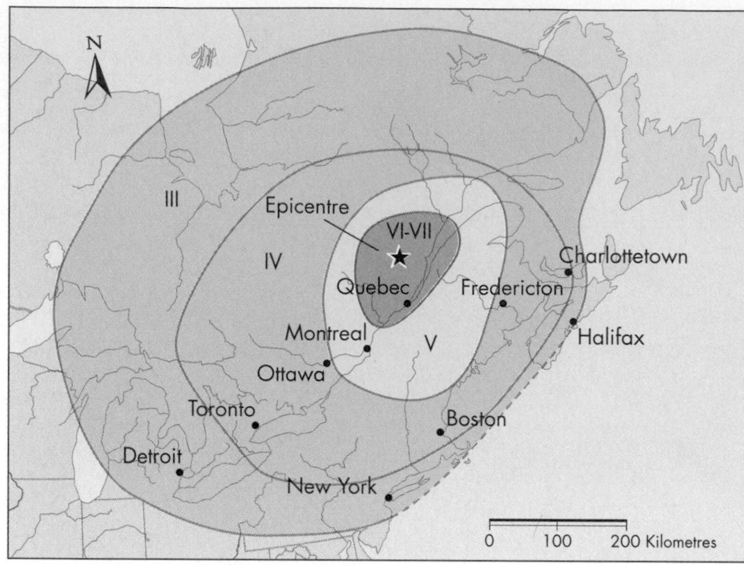

◄ **FIGURE 2.19 CHICOUTIMI EARTHQUAKE** A Modified Mercalli Intensity map of the 1988 Chicoutimi (Quebec) earthquake. The earthquake transmitted energy efficiently through the crystalline rocks of the Canadian Shield. *(Reproduced with the permission of the Minister of Public Works and Government Services Canada, 2007, and courtesy of Natural Resources Canada, Geological Survey of Canada)*

amplification. It further demonstrated that buildings constructed on sediments that amplify seismic shaking can be damaged or destroyed several hundred kilometres from the epicentre. Much of Mexico City is built on silts and clays of ancient Lake Texcoco (Figure 2.24a). When seismic waves moved through the thick, fine-grained lake sediments, the amplitude of the long-period waves increased by a factor of four or five. The natural vibration period of buildings 10 to 20 storeys high was the same as that of the amplified long-period seismic waves, and more than 500 of these buildings literally tore themselves apart.[10] In many cases, the amplified shaking collapsed upper floors onto lower ones, like a stack of pancakes[11] (Figure 2.24b).

Local geologic structures can also amplify shaking. For example, *synclines* and fault-bounded sedimentary basins can focus seismic waves like a magnifying lens focuses sunlight. This focusing causes severe shaking in some areas and less intense shaking in others.

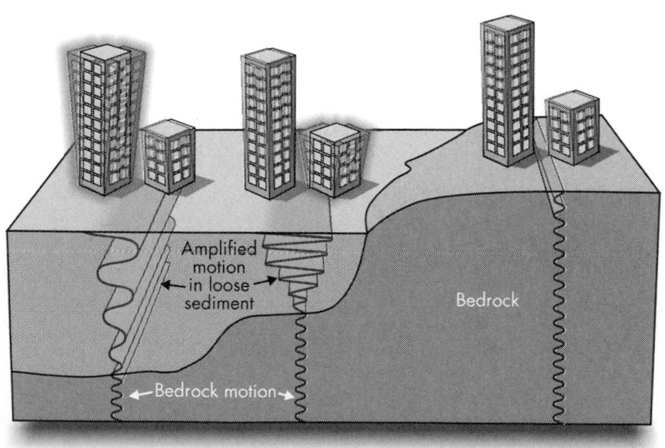

▲ **FIGURE 2.20 AMPLIFICATION OF GROUND SHAKING** The generalized relation between near-surface geologic materials and ground motion amplification during an earthquake. Amplification is highest in water-saturated sediment. *(Clague, J., C. Yorath, R. Franklin, and B. Turner. 2006. At risk: Earthquakes and tsunamis on the west coast. Vancouver, BC: Tricouni Press)*

2.4 The Earthquake Cycle

Observations of the 1906 San Francisco earthquake (**M** 7.8) led to the recognition of what has since been called the **earthquake cycle**. The idea behind the earthquake cycle is that elastic strain drops abruptly after an earthquake and then slowly accumulates before the next event.

Strain is deformation resulting from stress. *Elastic strain* can be thought of as temporary deformation. When the stress is released, the elastically deformed material returns to its original shape. If the stress continues to increase, the deformed material will eventually rupture, making the deformation permanent. For example, a stretched rubber band or a bent archery bow will break with a continued increase in stress. When the rubber band or bow breaks, the broken ends snap back, releasing the pent-up energy. A similar effect, referred to as *elastic rebound,* occurs after an earthquake (Figures 2.25 and 2.26).

Seismologists speculate that a typical earthquake cycle has three or four stages.[12] The first is a long period of inactivity along a fault segment. In the second stage, accumulated elastic strain produces small earthquakes. A third stage, characterized by *foreshocks*, may occur hours or days before a large earthquake. Foreshocks are small- to moderate-size earthquakes that precede the main quake. However, some large earthquakes occur without foreshocks, thus this third stage is absent. The fourth stage is the *mainshock,* the major earthquake, and its aftershocks.[12] An *aftershock* is a smaller earthquake that occurs a few minutes to a year or more after the mainshock and has an epicentre in the same general area as the mainshock. The earthquake cycle is hypothetical and periods between major earthquakes are variable, but the four stages described above have been recognized along many active faults.

▶ **FIGURE 2.21 LOMA PRIETA EARTHQUAKE** A simplified geologic map of the San Francisco Bay area, showing the locations of the San Andreas fault zone and the epicentre of the 1989 Loma Prieta earthquake. Fault zones are shown as solid and dashed red lines; arrows indicate displacement directions. The most severe shaking occurred along the San Francisco Bay shoreline and where the bay had been filled in to create new land (bay fill shown in dark orange). Shaking caused the collapse of the Nimitz Freeway in Oakland and damage to buildings in the Marina district of San Francisco (northwest part of map). *(Modified after T. Hall from U.S. Geological Survey)*

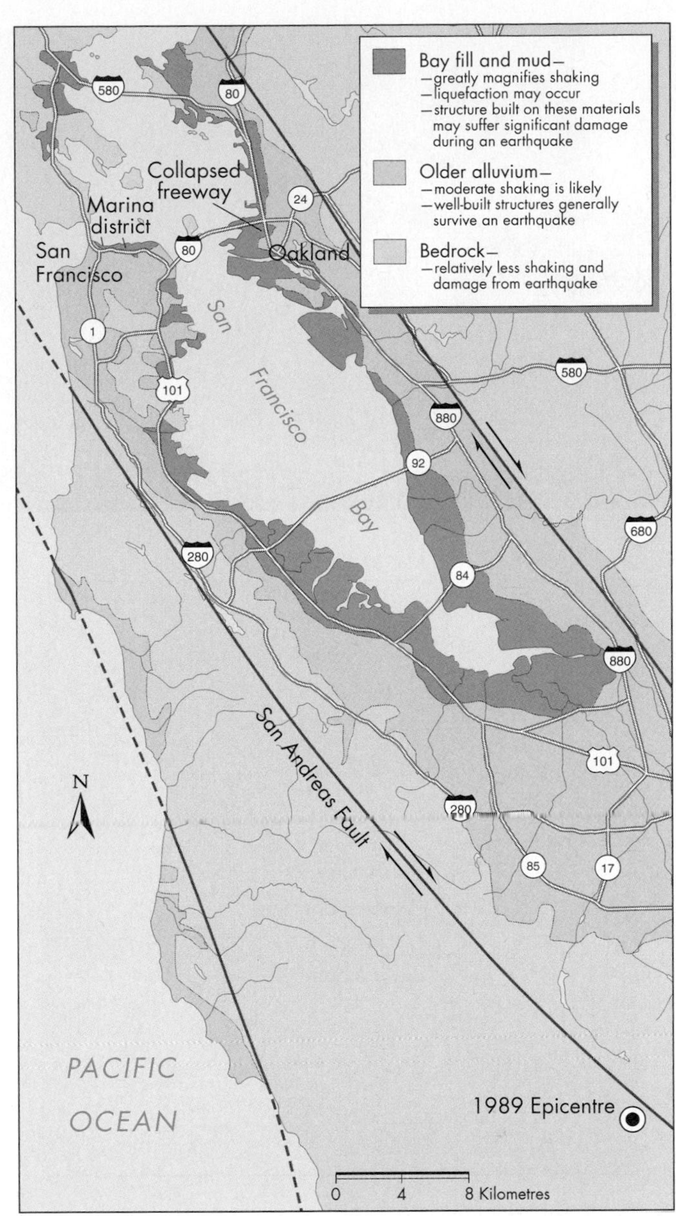

▼ **FIGURE 2.22 COLLAPSE OF A FREEWAY** (a) A generalized geologic map of part of the east shore of San Francisco Bay, showing areas of bay fill and mud (dark orange) and alluvium (light orange). The section of the Nimitz Freeway (I-880) that collapsed is located above the word "Oakland" in the northwest corner of the map. *(Modified from Hough, S. E., et al., 1990. Nature 344:853–855. Copyright © Macmillan Magazines Ltd., 1990. Used by permission of the author)* (b) The collapsed upper deck of the Nimitz Freeway. The road level for the lower deck was approximately at the level of the break in the concrete column. *(Dennis Laduzinski)*

(a)

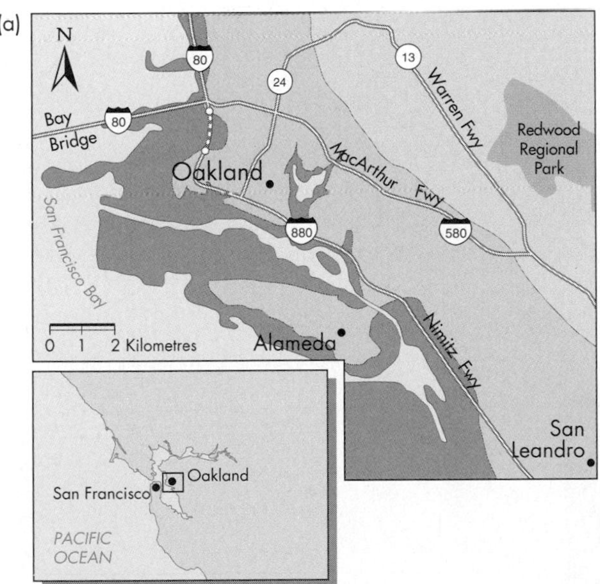

Collapse of two-tier section of Nimitz Freeway

Bay fill and mud
Greatly magnifies shaking—liquefaction may occur. Structures built on these materials may suffer significant damage during an earthquake.

Older alluvium
Moderate shaking is likely. Well-built structures generally survive an earthquake.

(b)

◄ **FIGURE 2.23 EARTHQUAKE DAMAGE** Damage to a building in the Marina district of San Francisco caused by the 1989 Loma Prieta earthquake. The poorly supported first floor of the building shifted from intense, amplified ground shaking. *(John K. Nakata/U.S. Geological Survey, Denver)*

(a)

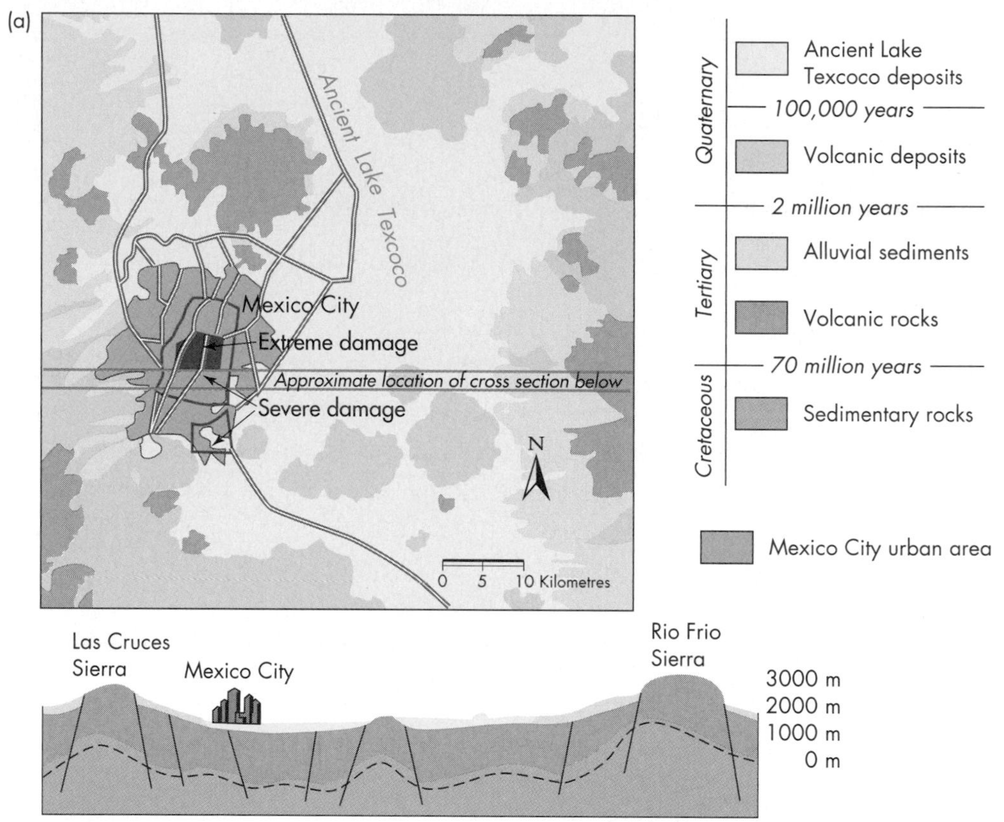

(b)

◄ **FIGURE 2.24 EARTHQUAKE DAMAGE IN MEXICO CITY** (a) A generalized geologic map and cross-section of Mexico City, showing the distribution of ancient lake deposits (yellow) where damage during the 1985 earthquake was greatest. Damage was extreme in the solid red area and severe in the zone delineated by the red line. (b) One of many buildings that collapsed during the 1985 earthquake. *(Map and photo courtesy of T. C. Hanks and Darrell Herd/U.S. Geological Survey, Denver)*

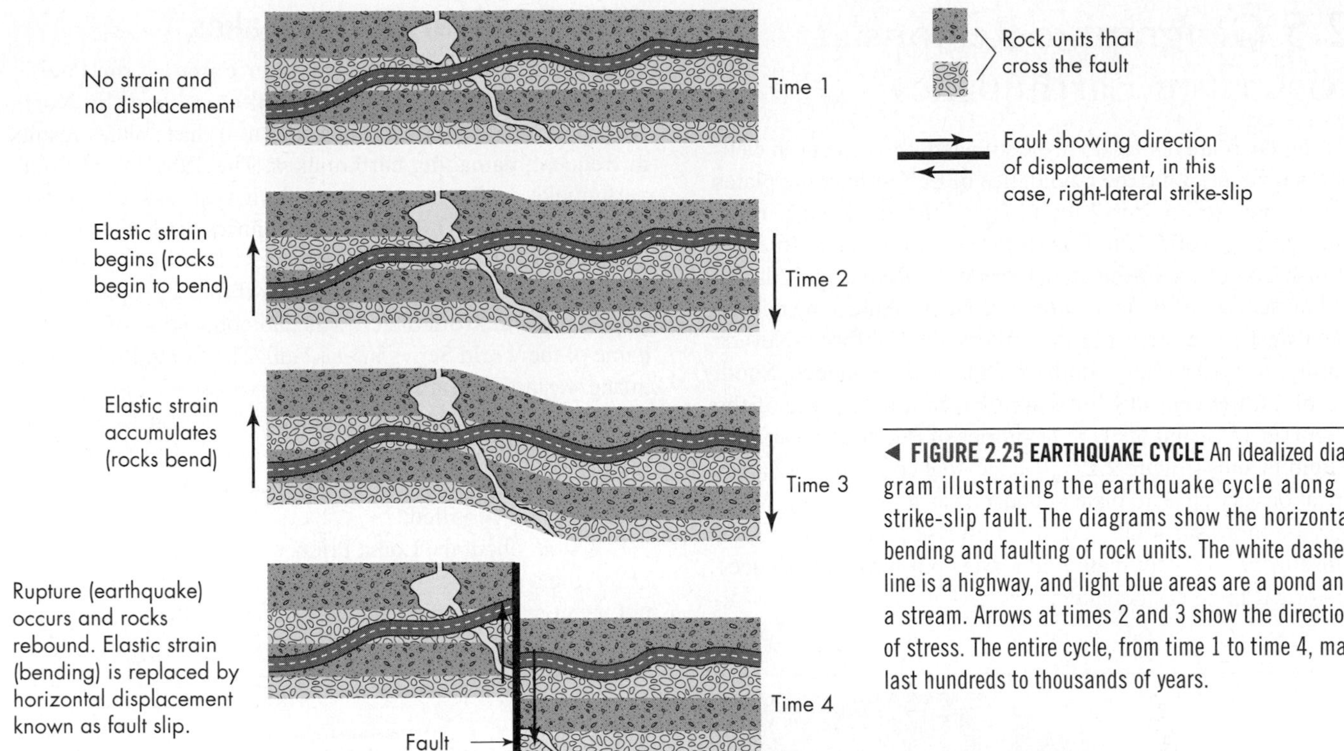

◀ **FIGURE 2.25 EARTHQUAKE CYCLE** An idealized diagram illustrating the earthquake cycle along a strike-slip fault. The diagrams show the horizontal bending and faulting of rock units. The white dashed line is a highway, and light blue areas are a pond and a stream. Arrows at times 2 and 3 show the direction of stress. The entire cycle, from time 1 to time 4, may last hundreds to thousands of years.

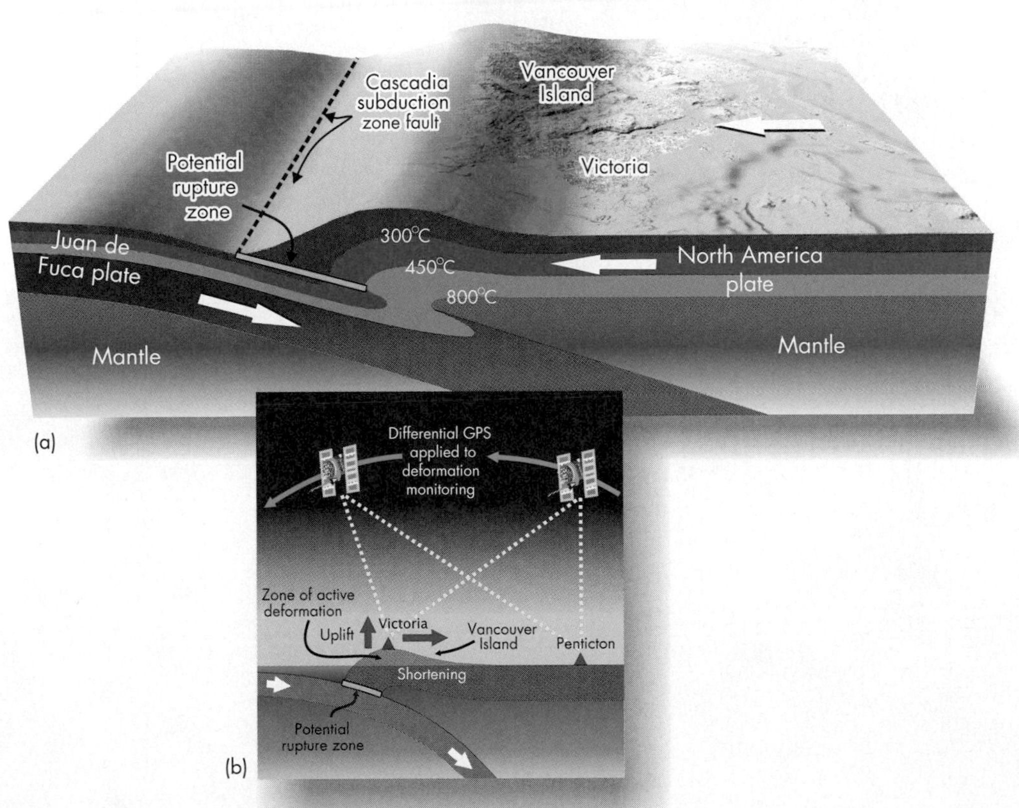

▲ **FIGURE 2.26 ACCUMULATION OF ELASTIC STRAIN ALONG A SUBDUCTION ZONE** The Juan de Fuca plate is presently locked to the continental North America plate off the west coast of North America. (a) The locked part of the fault zone ranges in temperature from about 150°C to 350°C. This zone is where the next great Cascadia earthquake will be initiated. (b) Vancouver Island is being flexed upward because of compression and elastic shortening of the North America plate above the locked interface. This deformation has been detected from satellite measurements of small changes in the relative position of points on Earth's surface. Sometime within the next several hundred years, the plates will suddenly unlock, triggering a great earthquake. *(Reproduced with the permission of the Minister of Public Works and Government Services Canada, 2007, and courtesy of Natural Resources Canada, Geological Survey of Canada; as seen in Clague, J., C. Yorath, R. Franklin, and B. Turner. 2006. At risk: Earthquakes and tsunamis on the west coast. Vancouver, BC: Tricouni Press)*

2.5 Geographic Regions at Risk from Earthquakes

Earthquakes are not randomly distributed. Most occur in well-defined zones along the boundaries of Earth's tectonic plates (refer back to Figures 2.8 and 2.9). Earthquakes are most common in North America in the Pacific coastal areas of British Columbia, Washington, Oregon, California, and Alaska. Other seismically active areas in North America include southwest and eastern Yukon Territory, the California-Nevada border, northern Utah, southern Ontario and Quebec, South Carolina, the central Mississippi River valley, some of the Arctic Islands, and the U.S. territories of Puerto Rico and the Virgin Islands (Figure 2.27). The fact that some of these areas are at or very close to plate boundaries is not surprising. What may be more surprising are the high-risk zones that are not close to present-day plate boundaries but have experienced historical large earthquakes.

Plate Boundary Earthquakes

California straddles two lithospheric plates: the Pacific plate west of the San Andreas fault zone and the North America plate to the east. The motion of these plates results in frequent, damaging earthquakes. The 1989 Loma Prieta earthquake on the San Andreas fault system south of San Francisco caused 63 deaths, 3757 injuries, and an estimated US$5.6 billion in property damage.[13] Deaths and injuries would have been significantly greater if many people had not stayed home to avoid the crowds and congestion of the third game of the World Series in Oakland. The Loma Prieta earthquake was not a great earthquake, the so-called "big one" that Californians fear. If a great earthquake (**M** 8 and higher) were to occur today in a densely populated part of California, damage would exceed US$100 billion and several thousand people would be killed.[14]

A story about the Loma Prieta earthquake illustrates how observing a sequence of events related to an earthquake does not mean understanding the causes behind them:

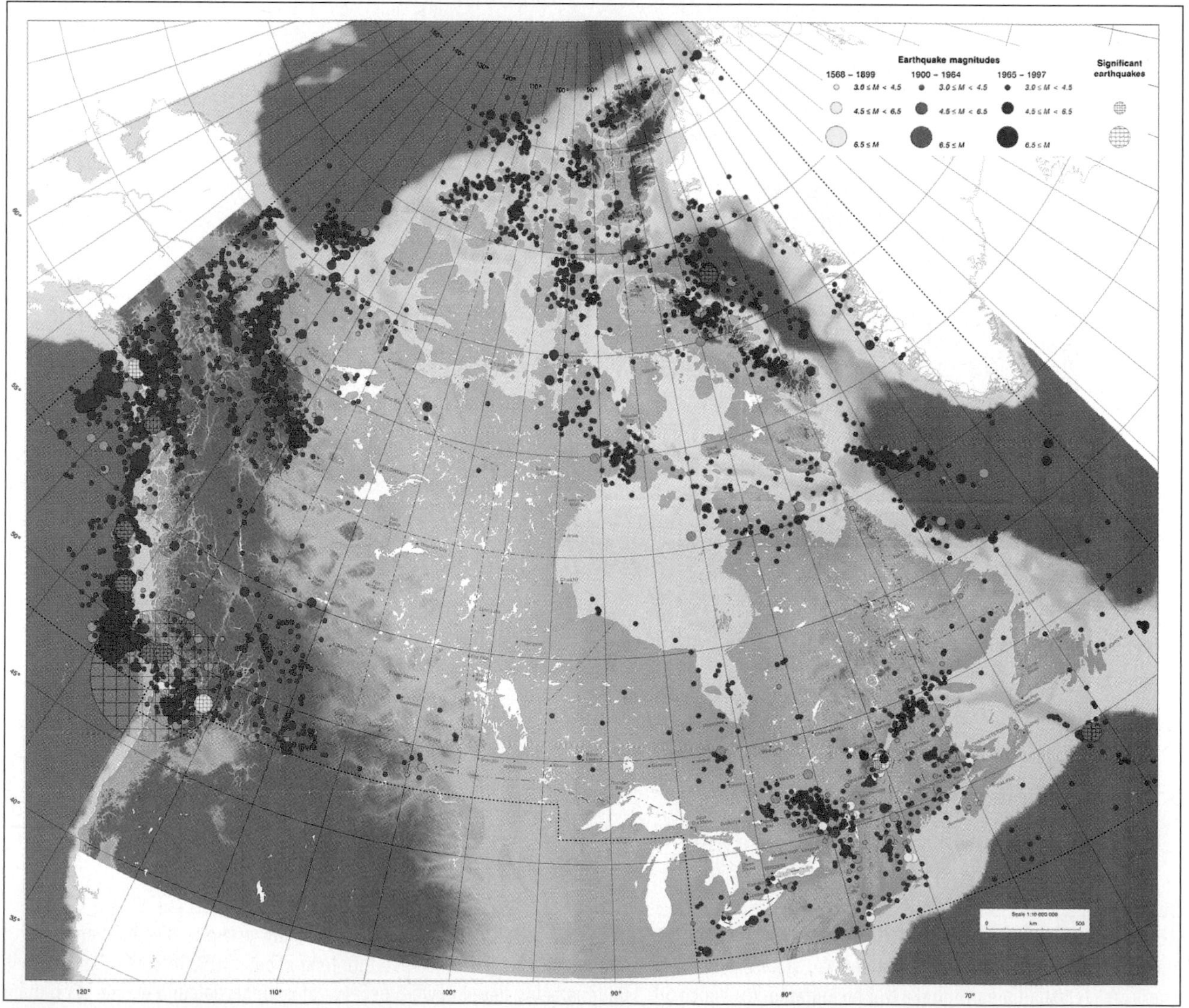

▲ **FIGURE 2.27 EARTHQUAKES IN CANADA** A map showing epicentres of historic earthquakes in Canada (**M** ≥ 2.5). *(Reproduced with the permission of the Minister of Public Works and Government Services Canada, 2007, and courtesy of Natural Resources Canada, Geological Survey of Canada)*

Shortly before the quake struck, a two-year-old boy was playing in his yard and discovered how to turn on the lawn sprinklers. His mother was not amused and sent him to his room for disobeying her instructions. Shortly after she had returned to the yard, the ground began to violently shake. She heard her child yell and ran back into the house to find him terrified. He then remained very quiet until his father came home from work. On seeing his father, the child's first words were an emotional "Daddy, don't turn on the sprinklers!"[15]

Another type of **interplate earthquake**, termed a **subduction earthquake**, occurs along the thrust fault separating the North America and Juan de Fuca plates (Figure 2.28). Subduction earthquakes occur when strain energy that has accumulated in rocks adjacent to the plate-boundary fault because of the convergence of the two plates is suddenly released (Figure 2.26). The last subduction earthquake in the Pacific Northwest occurred in January 1700, nearly 100 years before the first Europeans visited the area.[16] Geological evidence from tidal marshes in northern California, Oregon, Washington, and British Columbia, together with written records of tsunami damage in Japan, indicate that the quake had a magnitude larger than 9.0 (Figure 2.29).[17,18] The **M** 9.3 quake off Sumatra in 2004 and the **M** 9.2 earthquake in southern Alaska in 1964 are recent examples of giant subduction events. They are, respectively, the second- and third-largest seismic events ever recorded, with the largest being an **M** 9.5 subduction earthquake off Chile in 1960.

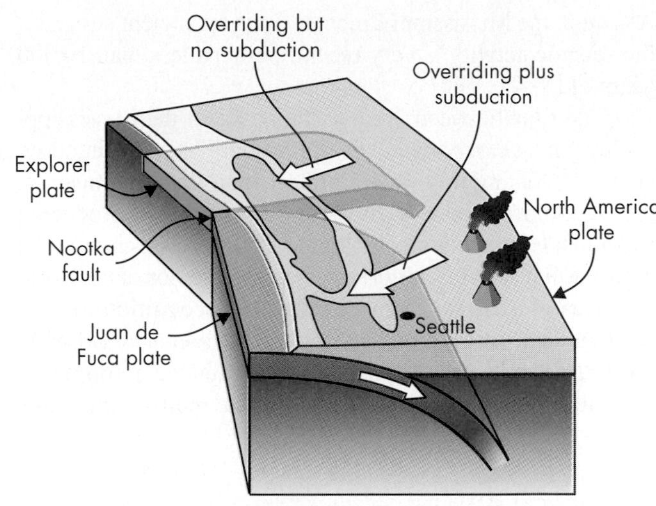

▲ **FIGURE 2.28 CASCADIA SUBDUCTION ZONE** The geometry of plates at the north end of the Cascadia subduction zone. The oceanic Juan de Fuca plate is subducting beneath the North America plate. The Nootka fault forms the boundary between the Juan de Fuca plate and the smaller Explorer plate to the north. *(Clague, J., C. Yorath, R. Franklin, and B. Turner. 2006. At risk: Earthquakes and tsunamis on the west coast. Vancouver, BC: Tricouni Press)*

Intraplate Earthquakes

Intraplate, or "within plate," **earthquakes** can be large and extremely damaging. Because large intraplate quakes are infrequent, people are generally unprepared for them and buildings may not be able to withstand their strong shaking. At least two **M** 8 intraplate earthquakes occurred in the winter of 1811–1812 in the central Mississippi Valley. The earthquakes destroyed the town of New Madrid, Missouri, and were felt in nearly every city of eastern North America from New Orleans to Quebec City, an area of more than 2.5 million km.[2,19] The shaking rang church bells in Boston, more than 1600 km away! Forests were flattened; fractures opened in the ground, forcing people to cut down trees to cross them; and some land sank several metres, causing local flooding. Journals and newspapers reported that local uplift of the land reversed the flow of the Mississippi River for a short time.[20]

The earthquakes occurred within the New Madrid seismic zone, which is the active part of an ancient down-warped area of thin lithosphere known as the "Mississippi Embayment" (Figure 2.30). The lithosphere thinned in this area about 600 million years ago, when a divergent plate boundary developed in what is now the southeastern United States.[19]

◀ **FIGURE 2.29 EARTHQUAKE STRATIGRAPHY** Exposure of sediments in the bank of the Niawiakum River in southwest Washington. Evidence of five large earthquakes can be seen in this tidal channel at Willapa Bay, Washington. Fossil tidal marsh soils (dark horizons, indicated by arrows) represent old marsh surfaces, each of which subsided 1 m to 2 m during an earthquake. After the earthquakes, the marsh surfaces were buried by tidal mud (light-coloured layers). The dates on the left side of the photograph are approximate ages of the earthquakes. The uppermost buried soil records the last subduction earthquake in January 1700. During the next subduction earthquake, the modern marsh (top surface) will subside and become covered with sea water. Over time, tidal mud will bury the marsh, providing the substrate for a new marsh. The underlying sediments will record this story. Divisions on shovel handle (circled) are 10 cm. *(Brian Atwater, U.S. Geological Survey; as it appears in Clague, J., C. Yorath, R. Franklin, and B. Turner. 2006. At risk: Earthquakes and tsunamis on the west coast. Vancouver, BC: Tricouni Press)*

Although the Mississippi Embayment is an ancient structure, the seismic activity is very recent, perhaps less than 10,000 years old.

The time between large earthquakes in the Mississippi Valley, or *recurrence interval,* is probably several hundred years.[20,21] Taking into account likely material amplification, the New Madrid seismic zone appears capable of producing earthquake intensities comparable to those associated with great earthquakes in California. Thus, the interior of the North America plate is far from "stable." In recognition of this, the U.S. Federal Emergency Management Agency (FEMA) and vulnerable states and municipalities have adopted a new building code designed to mitigate major earthquake hazards.

Moderate to large intraplate earthquakes occur frequently in southern Ontario and Quebec.[22] Most of these quakes are associated with the ancient rifted edge of the North American continent, which lies along the St. Lawrence River valley from Montreal to Sept Iles, Quebec; related rift structures also occur along the Ottawa and Saguenay river valleys. Strain accumulates on these structures because of ocean-floor spreading on the Mid-Atlantic Ridge at the east margin of the North America plate. The seismicity involves thrust earthquakes at depths of 5 km to 30 km and occurs in three clusters: western Quebec, which experienced moderate earthquakes in 1732 (**M** 5.8), 1935 (**M** 6.2), and 1944 (**M** 5.8); Charlevoix, northeast of Quebec City (1663, 1791, 1860, 1870, and 1925; **M** 6.0–7.0); and the lower St. Lawrence

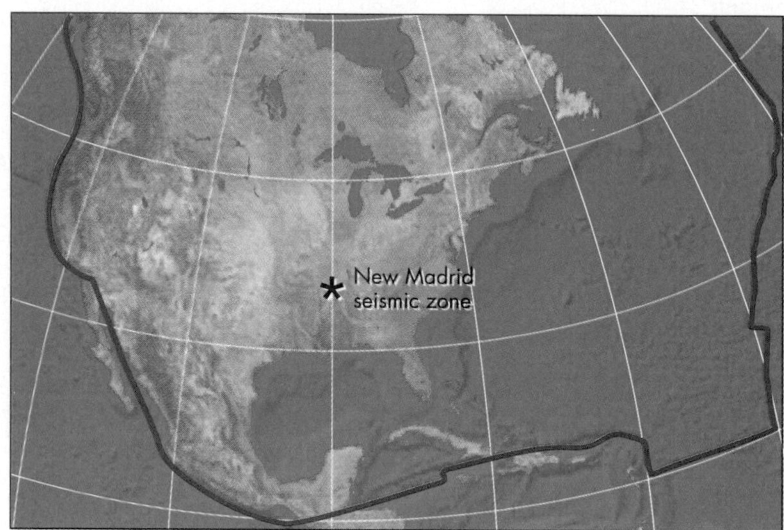

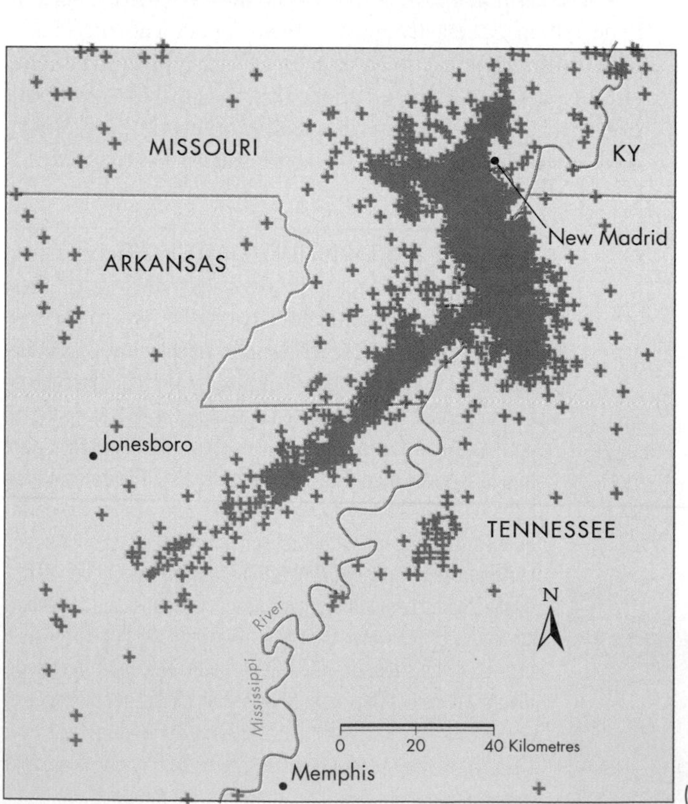

◄ **FIGURE 2.30 NEW MADRID SEISMIC ZONE** (a) This earthquake zone is thousands of kilometres from the nearest plate boundary (red lines). (b) The locations of recorded earthquakes since 1974 (crosses); New Madrid is in the northeast corner of the map. The New Madrid seismic zone is the most earthquake-prone region in the United States east of the Rocky Mountains. *(U.S. Geological Survey)*

region near Baie-Comeau, Quebec, a diffuse cluster of mostly small earthquakes.[22] The most recent widely felt earthquake in central Canada occurred in the Saguenay region of Quebec in 1988 (**M** 5.9).

Intraplate earthquakes in Ontario and Quebec are generally more damaging and felt over a much larger area than similar magnitude earthquakes in British Columbia or Yukon Territory. The crystalline rocks of the Canadian Shield and the sedimentary rocks that overlie them more efficiently transmit earthquake waves than does the thick, heavily faulted crust that underlies western Canada.

A large, damaging intraplate earthquake (**M** 7.3) occurred on the night of August 31, 1886, near Charleston, South Carolina. It killed about 60 people and damaged or destroyed most buildings in Charleston. More than 102 buildings were completely destroyed and nearly 14,000 chimneys fell, many because of poor construction following a great fire in 1838.[19] The earthquake was felt from Canada to Cuba and as far west as Arkansas.[19] Effects of the earthquake were reported at distances greater than 1000 km from the epicentre.

2.6 Effects of Earthquakes and Linkages with Other Natural Hazards

Shaking is not the only cause of death and damage in earthquakes. Many of the other effects of earthquakes are also damaging and provide excellent examples of how natural hazards are linked. Primary effects of earthquakes include ground shaking and surface rupture. Secondary effects include liquefaction, land-level change, landslides, fire, tsunami, and disease. We discuss each of these effects below, with the exception of tsunami, which are covered in Chapter 9.

Shaking and Ground Rupture

Large earthquakes produce strong ground shaking and, in some instances, surface rupture (see the Survivor Story). Most ground cracks that appear during earthquakes are caused by

SURVIVOR STORY

Earthquake off the Queen Charlotte Islands

Harv Smerychynski has seen more than a few earthquakes in the 50 years he has lived in British Columbia, including about a half-dozen ones that he remembers vividly.

"They occur very frequently here in Masset," Smerychynski says. Masset, at the northern tip of the Queen Charlotte Islands, is located in an area of frequent earthquakes east of the Queen Charlotte fault, which separates the Pacific and North America plates (Figure 2.A).

For the old timers on the Queen Charlotte Islands, earthquakes are a fact of life. "Although the buildings are shaking and the telephone poles are swaying, the earthquakes are not particularly dangerous," Smerychynski points out.

He recalls a recent earthquake that struck while he was at work and that lasted about 30 seconds. The sound was that of a large, heavy vehicle speeding past. "All of a sudden, you hear a rumble like a heavy truck going by." The floor began to shake from side to side, "similar to what you feel on a railway car." He describes how the telephone poles were waving back and forth, causing the lines to go alternately slack and tight, "moving up and down quite dramatically."

"The rumbling eventually stopped," he says. "Afterward, there's an air of expectancy that it will start up again."

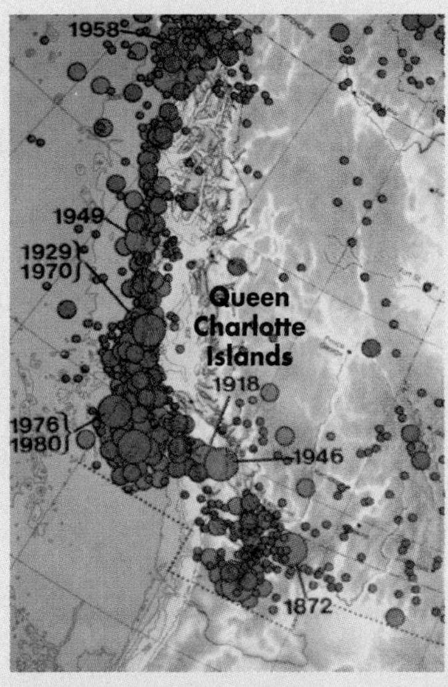

▲ **FIGURE 2.A WEST COAST EARTHQUAKES** A map showing epicentres of significant earthquakes off the west coast of Canada. The belt of earthquakes that extends north from the latitude of Vancouver Island past the Queen Charlotte Islands is associated with the Queen Charlotte fault, which separates the Pacific and North America plates. *(Reproduced with the permission of the Minister of Public Works and Government Services Canada, 2007, and courtesy of Natural Resources Canada, Geological Survey of Canada)*

Many large earthquakes are accompanied by a sustained rumbling. "Some rumbles are quite faint, like a heavy truck coming by," Smerychynski says. "Of course, at two in the morning in Masset, there are no trucks driving by."

—***Chris Wilson***

liquefaction and mass movement (discussed below), but the ground can rupture along the fault that generated the quake. The rupture commonly produces a low cliff, called a *fault scarp,* that extends for hundreds of metres to kilometres along the fault (Figure 2.31). Contrary to many Hollywood movies, the Earth rarely cracks open and then closes during an earthquake.

The 1906 San Francisco earthquake produced up to 6.5 m of horizontal displacement along the San Andreas fault north of San Francisco. The maximum intensity of the quake was XI on the Modified Mercalli Intensity Scale.[8] At this intensity, ground motion can uproot and snap large trees, throw people to the ground, and collapse large buildings, bridges, dams, tunnels, pipelines, and other rigid structures.[23]

The great Alaska earthquake in 1964 damaged roads, railroads, airports, and buildings throughout southern Alaska. The 1989 Loma Prieta and 1994 Northridge earthquakes were much smaller than the Alaska earthquake, with more localized strong shaking, but they were far more costly. In inflation-adjusted dollars, the Loma Prieta quake was 5 times as costly and the Northridge quake 20 times as costly as the Alaska quake. The Northridge earthquake was one of the worst disasters in U.S. history, with losses estimated at US$30 billion.[24] It caused so much damage because there was so much to be damaged. The quake occurred in a densely populated area with trillions of dollars of property at risk.

Large earthquakes in Canada have caused little damage by California standards. The **M** 8.1 Queen Charlotte Islands earthquake in 1949 was about the same size as the 1906 San Francisco earthquake, but it caused little damage and no loss of life because no more than a few thousand people lived in the area of strong ground shaking at the time of the quake. Similarly, the epicentre of the 1946 Vancouver Island earthquake (**M** 7.3) was far enough away from towns and other infrastructure that the damage was limited. Today, the same area supports a much larger population and far more economic wealth than in 1946, thus if the same event were to occur today, damage would likely be in the tens of millions of dollars, perhaps more.

The intensity of seismic shaking is commonly expressed as a ratio of *ground acceleration* to the acceleration from gravity (g). For example, a large earthquake might produce ground accelerations of 0.6 g, which is 60 percent of the acceleration from gravity (980 cm/s^2).

Strong ground shaking can be especially damaging to a building if the horizontal component of motion is strong or if the frequency of the shaking matches the natural vibrational frequency of the building, a phenomenon called *resonance*. In general, high-frequency, short-period seismic waves damage low buildings and low-frequency, long-period waves damage tall buildings.

Liquefaction

Intense seismic shaking can cause water-saturated loose sediment to change from a solid to a liquid. This effect, called **liquefaction**, takes place at shallow depths when pore water pressures become so elevated that the water suspends sediment particles, allowing the deposit to flow (Figure 2.32). Once the pressures decrease, the liquefied sediment compacts and regains its solid form. Liquefaction is generally accompanied by lateral shifts of a layer of solid sediment on one or more layers of fluidized sediment. Watery sand and silt may also flow upward along fractures in overlying solid materials and erupt onto the surface as *sand blows*, also called *sand volcanoes*. Liquefaction causes the land surface to settle irregularly, with potential damage to foundations of buildings, water and sewer lines, and other buried utilities.

Liquefaction of poorly compacted sediment has caused multistorey apartment buildings to tip over, highway bridges to collapse, and dams to fail (Figure 2.33).[25] It is also implicated in some slope failures and ground subsidence.

Land-Level Changes

Some earthquakes raise or lower the land over large areas. These changes can cause substantial damage along shorelines and streams, and they can raise or lower the groundwater table.

◀ **FIGURE 2.31 FAULT SCARP** This small scarp was produced by ground rupture during the 1992 Landers earthquake (**M** 7.3) in California. The rupture could be traced over a distance of 70 km in the Mojave Desert. *(Edward A. Keller)*

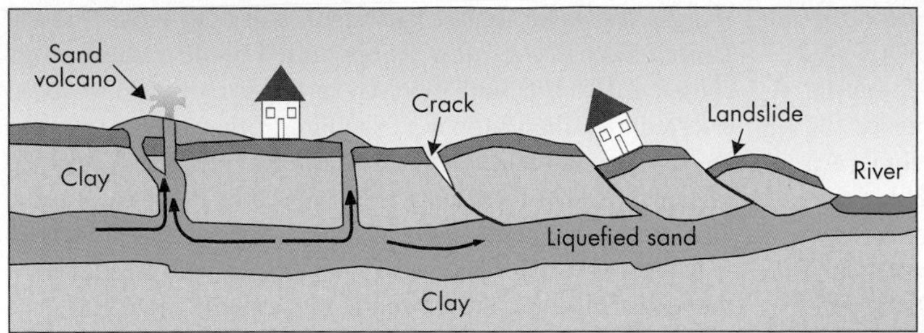

◀ **FIGURE 2.32 LIQUEFACTION** The liquefaction of water-saturated silt or sand during an earthquake may cause the ground to fracture and subside, damaging or destroying buildings and other human works. *(Clague, J. and B. Turner. 2003. Vancouver, city on the edge: Living with a dynamic geological landscape. Vancouver, BC: Tricouni Press)*

The most recent great earthquake at the Cascadia subduction zone in A.D. 1700 caused the Pacific coasts of Vancouver Island, Washington, and Oregon to subside up to 2 m, inundating coastal marshes and forests with sea water.[17,26] The 1964 Alaska earthquake had similar effects, causing measurable surface deformation over an area of 300,000 km^2, which is nearly half the size of Alberta.[27] Uplift of up to 10 m exposed and killed intertidal organisms, lifted docks out of the water, and shifted the shoreline away from fish canneries. In other areas, the land subsided up to 2.4 m, partially flooding several coastal communities. Both the uplift and subsidence changed the groundwater table. Finally, a large earthquake near Seattle, Washington, about 1000 years ago uplifted the land surface up to 7 m (Figure 2.34).[28]

▲ **FIGURE 2.33 LIQUEFACTION DAMAGE** Damage to apartment buildings in Niigata, Japan, caused by liquefaction during a strong earthquake on June 16, 1964. About one-third of the city subsided as much as 2 m because of liquefaction. *(National Oceanic and Atmospheric Administration, National Geophysical Data Center)*

Landslides

Two of the most closely linked natural hazards are earthquakes and landslides. Large earthquakes can trigger hundreds, even

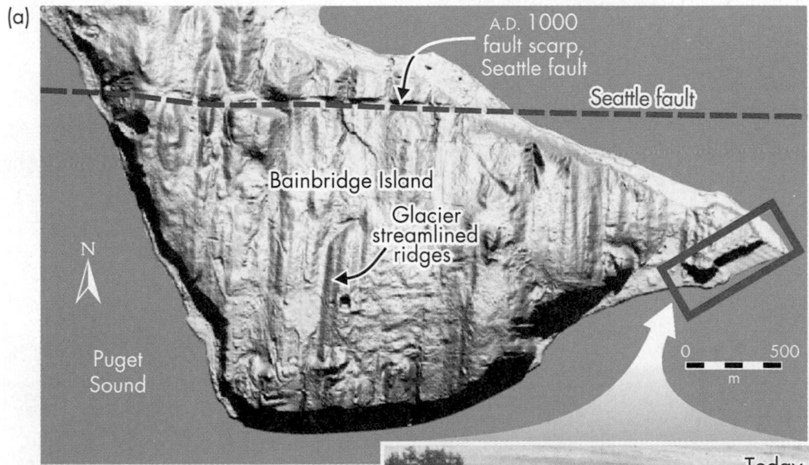

▶ **FIGURE 2.34 SEATTLE FAULT** (a) A LIDAR (Light Detection and Ranging) image of part of Bainbridge Island in Puget Sound. The image accurately depicts the ground surface with vegetation removed. The dashed red line shows the trace of the Seattle fault. (b) Slip along the fault about 1000 years ago raised a wave-cut terrace 7 m above sea level. *(Clague, J., C. Yorath, R. Franklin, and B. Turner. 2006. At risk: Earthquakes and tsunamis on the west coast. Vancouver, BC: Tricouni Press)*

thousands of landslides in mountainous areas. Some earthquake-triggered landslides can cause great loss of life. As mentioned at the beginning of this chapter, a landslide caused by the El Salvador earthquake in January 2001 buried the community of Las Colinas, killing hundreds of people. An earthquake in Peru in 1970 triggered a huge landslide that buried the cities of Yungay and Ranrahirca (Figure 2.35).[29] About 20,000 of the 70,000 people who died in the earthquake were killed by this landslide. Both the 1964 Alaska earthquake and the 1989 Loma Prieta earthquake triggered landslides that damaged buildings, roads, and other structures.

Fires

Fire is another major hazard linked to earthquakes. Ground shaking and surface rupture can sever electrical power and gas lines, starting fires. These fires may be difficult to suppress because firefighting equipment may be damaged; streets, roads, and bridges blocked; and water mains broken. Appliances, such as gas water heaters, may topple when shaken, producing gas leaks that ignite. Earthquakes in both Japan and the United States have been accompanied by devastating fires (Figure 2.36). The San Francisco earthquake of 1906 has been referred to as the "San Francisco Fire," because 80 percent of the damage was caused by a firestorm that ravaged the city for several days after the quake. The 1989 Loma Prieta earthquake also caused large fires in the Marina district of San Francisco.

Most fires after an earthquake are not wildfires because they start in urban areas where gas and electrical lines are located. However, in a warm, dry area, such as southern California, it is possible for an urban fire to spread to wild lands, causing a wildfire.

Disease

Some large earthquakes cause outbreaks of disease. A loss of sanitation and housing, contaminated water supplies, and disruption of public health services contribute to the spread of disease. Earthquakes rupture sewer and water lines, causing water to become polluted by disease-causing organisms.

◄ **FIGURE 2.35 HUASCARÁN LANDSLIDE** Oblique aerial photograph of Nevados Huascarán and the valley of the Rio Santa in Peru shortly after the catastrophic landslide of May 31, 1970. A large earthquake destabilized the north wall of Huascarán, inducing a landslide that destroyed the towns of Yungay and Ranrahrica, killing about 20,000 people. The source of the landslide is the dark area left of the words "Avalanche source." The landslide path is the light-toned area extending from the base of Huascarán through Yungay and Ranrahrica, a distance of more than 18 km. *(Dr. George Plafker/U.S. Geological Survey)*

◄ **FIGURE 2.36 EARTHQUAKE AND FIRE** Fires associated with the 1995 Kobe, Japan, earthquake caused extensive damage to part of the city. *(Corbis/Bettman)*

Desert soils in the southwestern United States and northwestern Mexico contain spores of a fungus that causes a respiratory illness known as *valley fever*. After the 1994 Northridge earthquake in California, landslides triggered by earthquake raised large volumes of dust containing these fungal spores. Winds carried the dust and spores to urban areas, where there was an outbreak of valley fever. More than 200 cases of the disease were diagnosed within eight weeks after the earthquake, 16 times the normal number of cases. Fifty of these people were hospitalized and three died.[30]

2.7 Natural Service Functions of Earthquakes

Earthquakes are so destructive that it's hard to imagine they have any benefits. However, earthquakes, like many natural hazards, do provide natural service functions. They contribute to the development of groundwater and energy resources, the formation of valuable mineral resources, and the development of landforms.

Groundwater and Energy Resources

Geologic faults produced by earthquakes influence the flow of water, oil, and gas. Fault zones provide paths for the downward flow of surface water. They also channel groundwater to surface discharge points, called *springs*.

In other settings, faults create natural subsurface barriers that slow or redirect the flow of water, oil, or natural gas. Faulting commonly pulverizes rock to form an impervious clay barrier. It also can place impervious rock against rock containing water, oil, or natural gas. Such subsurface barriers are responsible for oases in arid areas of southern California and for many underground accumulations of oil and gas in Alberta, Texas, Oklahoma, and elsewhere.

Mineral Resources

Faulting can contribute to the accumulation of economically valuable minerals. Some valuable minerals are preferentially deposited along faults in what are called *veins*. Veins associated with major fault zones may contain enough gold, silver, or platinum to be mined.

Landform Development

Earthquakes occurring episodically over hundreds of thousands to millions of years can form scenic landscapes. The uplift of rocks along faults can produce hills, mountain ranges, and coastal and stream terraces. Weak rocks along fault zones may be eroded by streams to form valleys.

2.8 Human Interaction with Earthquakes

Earthquakes cannot be prevented or controlled, but several human activities are known to trigger earthquakes or increase their frequency. The damage is regrettable, but these quakes provide important lessons that help us better understand seismic hazards and risk.

Earthquakes Caused by Human Activity

People can cause earthquakes by[31]

- building a dam and flooding a valley
- injecting liquid waste deep into the ground
- detonating underground nuclear explosions

Reservoirs Flooding a valley behind a dam may induce earthquakes. The water loads the underlying crust and can create or extend fractures. These effects may produce new faults or reactivate existing faults. Several hundred small earthquakes occurred in the decade following completion of Hoover Dam and filling of Lake Mead in Arizona and Nevada. One of these quakes had a magnitude of 5 and two were about **M** 4.[31] Reservoir filling in India and China has triggered earthquakes up to **M** 6.0. Two of the quakes killed hundreds of people and severely damaged the dams impounding the reservoirs.[32]

Deep Waste Disposal In the early 1960s, an unplanned experiment by the U.S. Army provided the first direct evidence that injecting fluids into the Earth can cause earthquakes. Several hundred earthquakes occurred in the Denver, Colorado, area between April 1962 and November 1965. One of the quakes, an **M** 4.3 event, was large enough to knock bottles off shelves in stores. A geologist traced the source of the earthquakes to the Rocky Mountain Arsenal, a chemical warfare plant at the northeast side of Denver. Liquid waste from the plant was being injected under pressure down a deep disposal well to a depth of 3600 m in the crust. The injected liquid increased fluid pressures and caused slippage of numerous fractures in the host rocks. The geologist demonstrated a high correlation between the rate of waste injection and the times and locations of the earthquakes. When the waste disposal stopped, so did the earthquakes[33] (Figure 2.37). Deep injection of fluids in wells has also triggered earthquakes in Ohio[34] and Texas.[35]

Recognizing that injection of fluids into the crust could trigger earthquakes was an important development because it drew attention to the relation between fluid pressure and earthquakes. Subsequent studies of subduction zones and active fold belts showed that high fluid pressures are present in many areas where earthquakes occur. One hypothesis to explain this association is that fluid pressure rises until rocks break, triggering an earthquake and discharging fluid upward. After the event, fluid pressure begins to build up again, beginning a new cycle.

Nuclear Explosions Underground testing of nuclear weapons in Nevada has triggered numerous earthquakes up to **M** 6.3.[31] Analysis of aftershock sequences suggests that the explosions may have released some natural strain within Earth. This idea has led some scientists to suggest that nuclear explosions can be used to prevent large earthquakes by releasing strain before it reaches a critical threshold.

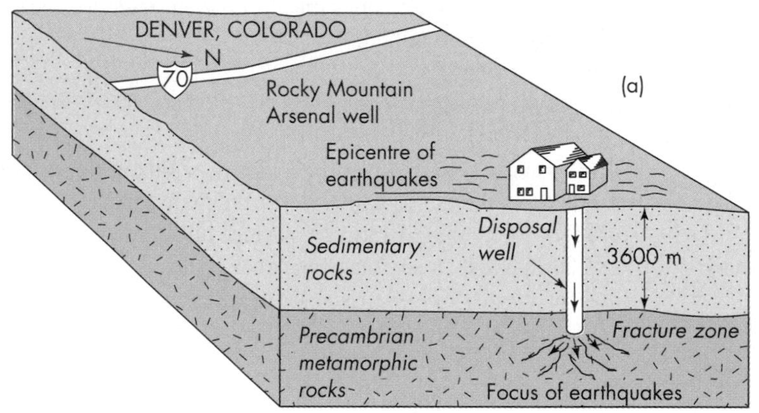

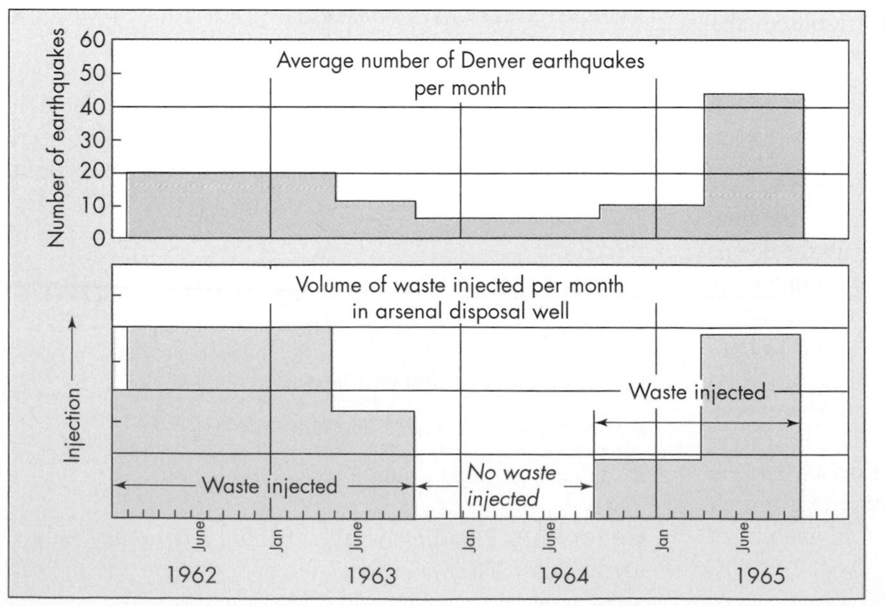

◀ **FIGURE 2.37 HUMAN-CAUSED EARTHQUAKES** (a) A generalized block diagram showing the deep disposal well at Rocky Mountain Arsenal in Colorado. (b) A graph showing the relation between earthquake frequency and the amount of injected liquid waste. *(After Evans, D. M. 1966. Geotimes 10. Reprinted by permission)*

2.9 Minimizing the Earthquake Hazard

An important reason why earthquakes cause so much damage and loss of life is that they generally strike without warning. Much research is being done to anticipate earthquakes, but the best we can do, at present, is forecast the likelihood that an earthquake will happen in a particular area or on a particular segment of a fault. A *forecast* states that an earthquake of a specified magnitude has a certain probability of occurring in an area within a specified number of years. Earthquake forecasts assist planners and officials responsible for seismic safety and people who are choosing where to live. Long-term forecasts, however, do not help residents of a seismically active area prepare for a specific earthquake. A *prediction* specifying the exact time and place of an earthquake would be much more useful, but we are unable to make such predictions at present.

Earthquake Hazard Reduction Programs

The Geological Survey of Canada and the U.S. Geological Survey, in conjunction with university and other scientists, are developing programs to reduce earthquake hazards in Canada and the United States. The programs have four major goals:[36]

1. Develop an understanding of earthquake sources by obtaining information on the physical properties and mechanical behaviour of faults and developing quantitative models of the earthquake process.
2. Determine earthquake potential by conducting detailed studies of seismically active areas. Scientists identify active faults, document past earthquakes from geologic evidence, and determine average slip rates of active faults. This information is used to make probabilistic forecasts of earthquakes.
3. Predict effects of earthquakes on buildings and other structures from estimates of shaking intensity and amounts of surface rupture. This information is needed to evaluate losses from earthquakes of different magnitudes.
4. Communicate research results to educate individuals, communities, and governments in order to reduce loss of life and property from earthquakes.

Estimation of Seismic Risk

Hazard maps are used to portray earthquake risk. The simplest maps show locations of epicentres of historic earthquakes of different magnitudes. Other, more complex maps display probabilities of earthquakes of different sizes or the amount of shaking likely to occur. For example, the seismic ground acceleration map of Canada (Figure 2.38) shows zones of different ground accelerations, expressed at a 10 percent probability of exceedance in 50 years. It is based largely on the instrumented records of earthquakes in Canada (Figure 2.27). The map is used to establish engineering standards for public buildings in earthquake-prone areas, notably the south coast of British Columbia and the St. Lawrence Valley in southern Ontario and Quebec.

Another common type of hazard map depicts areas where certain secondary earthquake effects, notably liquefaction, landslides, and tsunami, are most likely to occur. Maps of this type have been prepared for many populated areas in the western United States (Figure 2.39).

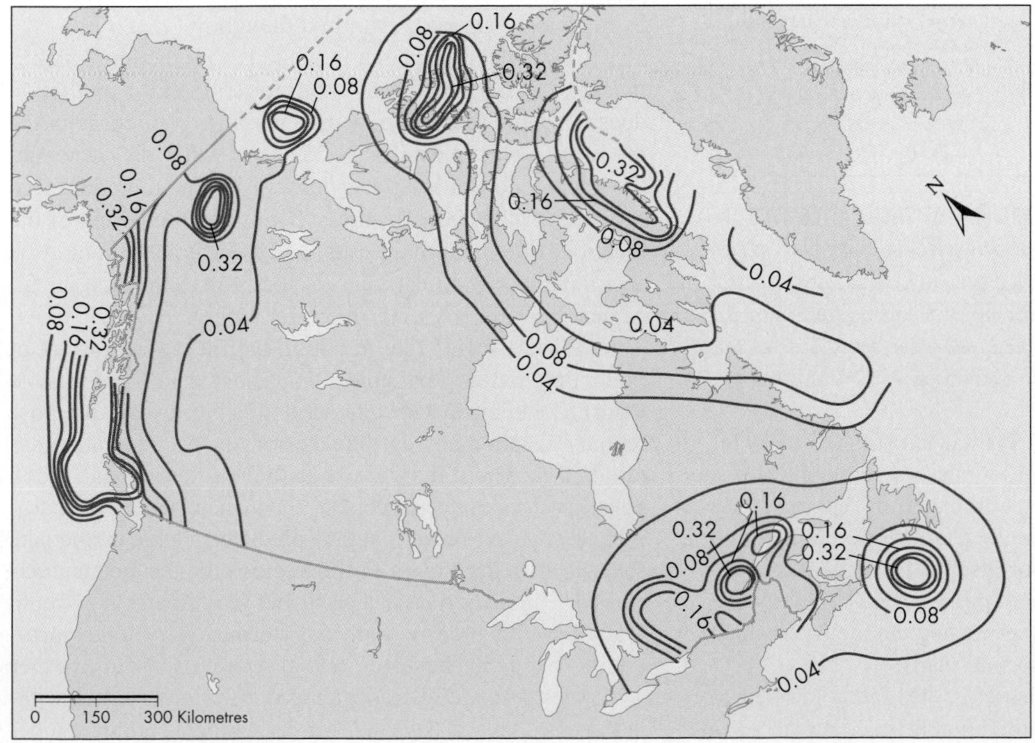

◀ **FIGURE 2.38 SEISMIC ZONE MAP** The peak horizontal ground accelerations that have a 10 percent chance of occurring in the next 50 years in Canada. Ground acceleration is a measure of the intensity of earthquake shaking and is used by engineers to design safe buildings and other structures. *(Basham, P. W., D.H. Weichert, F. M. Anglin, and M. J. Berry. 1985. New probabilistic strong ground motion maps of Canada. Bulletin of the Seismological Society of America, v. 75, pp. 563–595. © Seismological Society of America)*

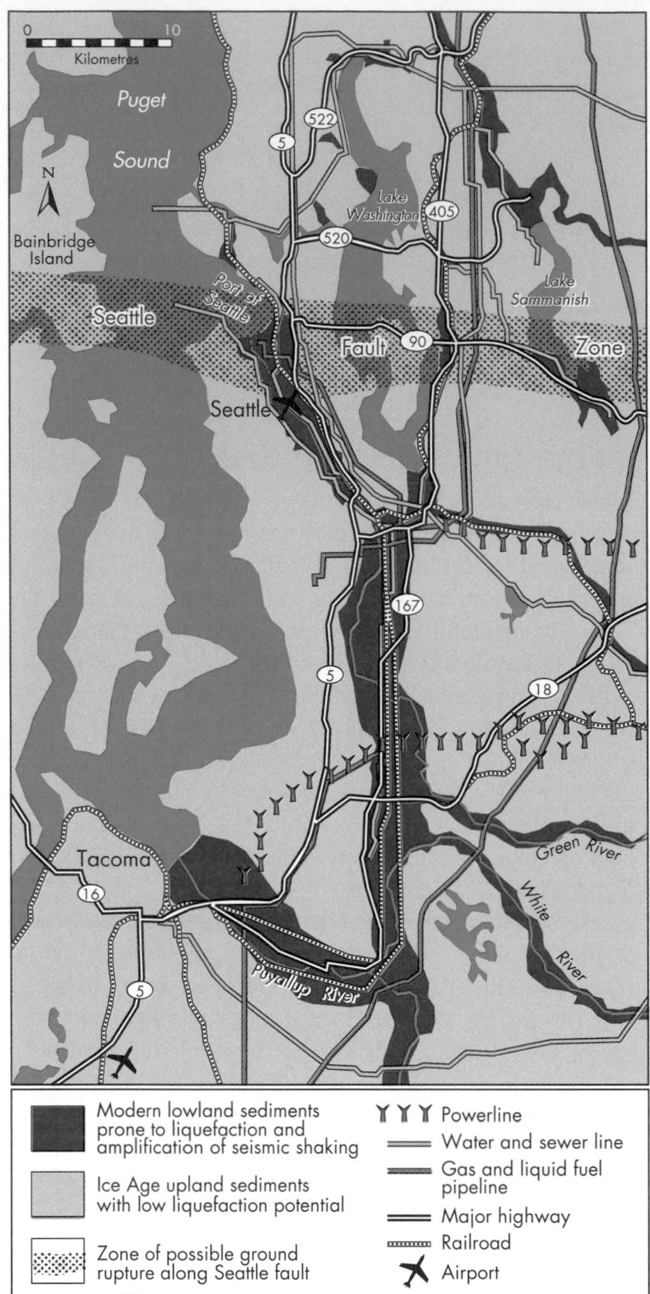

▲ **FIGURE 2.39 EARTHQUAKE HAZARD MAP OF THE SEATTLE AREA** The map shows areas that are susceptible to liquefaction and ground motion amplification, and the zone of possible ground rupture and displacement associated with the Seattle fault. Major infrastructure is also shown. *(U.S. Geological Survey; as seen in Clague, J., C. Yorath, R. Franklin, and B. Turner. 2006. At risk: Earthquakes and tsunamis on the west coast. Vancouver, BC: Tricouni Press)*

Following the damaging Sylmar earthquake in 1971, the State of California passed legislation requiring that a geological site investigation be completed in "special study zones," encompassing the rupture zones of potentially and recently active faults.[37] The purpose of the legislation is to determine whether an active fault passes through a proposed building site. The special study zones and the faults on which they are based are shown on special maps.

The State of California also classifies faults in order to evaluate seismic risk. The classification is based on the maximum magnitude the fault can produce and on the fault's long-term *slip rate*. The slip rate is the average displacement rate on the fault measured over thousands of years and numerous earthquakes. Classifying faults provides more information than simply determining whether a fault has been active in the past 10,000 years, but the long-term slip rates of most major faults in North America are unknown or very poorly known.[38]

Long-term slip rates can be estimated by **paleoseismologists**—geologists who examine the recent geologic record of faulting to determine times and sizes of prehistoric earthquakes. Paleoseismologists excavate trenches across faults at key locations, identify offsets of sediment layers, and date the offsets by the radiocarbon method (Figure 2.40). The complete history of movement on a fault cannot be determined from evidence in a single trench; rather data must be collected and synthesized from many trenches. Geologists in Canada, the United States, Japan, and New Zealand have been world leaders in paleoseismological research.

Short-Term Prediction

Two approaches have been used to anticipate future earthquakes. One is called *prediction* and the other, *forecasting*. A prediction specifies that an earthquake of a given magnitude will occur in a defined region within a restricted period of time (hours, days, weeks). Predictions are based on **precursors**, measurable changes, such as the frequency and strength of foreshocks, water levels in wells, and magnetic, electrical, and acoustic properties of the crust. Predicting earthquakes was once thought to be as easy as "one-two-three."[39] First, deploy instruments to detect precursors; second, detect and recognize the precursors that tell you when and how big an earthquake will be; and third, after reviewing the data, publicly predict the earthquake. Unfortunately earthquake prediction is much more complex than first thought.[39]

A significant dilemma in making a prediction is that it must be reliable; there is no room for error. If the prediction does not come to fruition, people will lose confidence in the predictor, a classic example of the "cry wolf" phenomenon. We are probably at least decades away from predictions that approach 100 percent accuracy. Thus, any prediction of the location, time, and magnitude of an earthquake should be accompanied by an estimate of the probability that it will happen.

"Seismo-seers" like to claim that they were correct in predicting that an earthquake would occur in California or British Columbia in a specific week of a given year. But those regions sustain many earthquakes of low to moderate magnitude throughout the year, thus the prediction has a good statistical chance of being correct, although not useful. Similarly, some seers like to brag that they predicted a large earthquake somewhere in the circum-Pacific region or in the mountainous areas of Europe or Asia in a particular year. Again, they would likely have been correct anyway because very large earthquakes occur in these regions at a rate of about one per year. A testable, useful prediction is one that gives a *time*, within a span of several days, a *location*, within a certain number

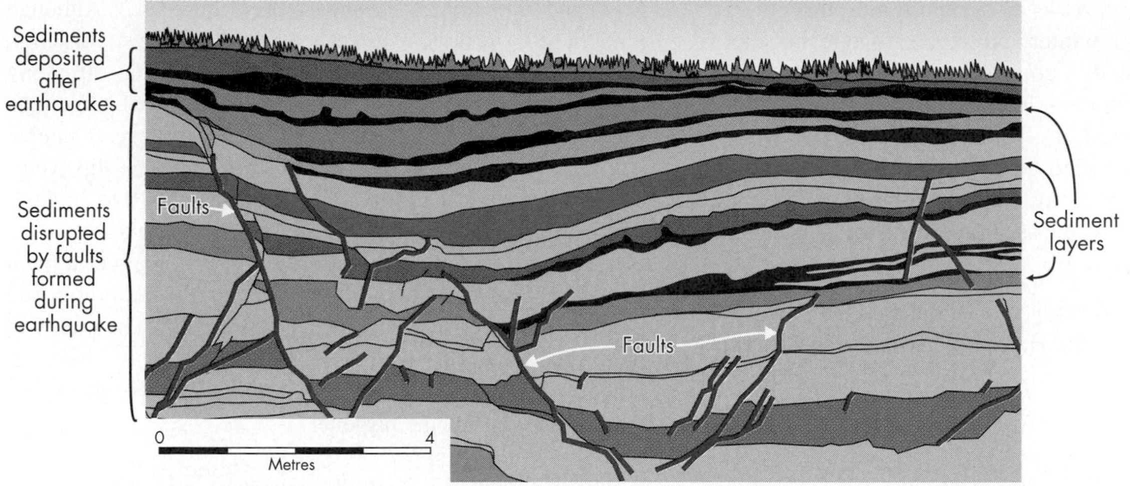

▲ **FIGURE 2.40 DISPLACEMENT OF SEDIMENTS BY FAULT** A drawing of sediment layers exposed in the wall of a trench excavated to document prehistoric earthquakes. The lowest, oldest layers of sediment in the trench are broken and displaced by numerous faults (red lines), recording sudden movements during at least one earthquake. In contrast, the upper sediment layers are not displaced by the faults and, therefore, must be younger than the earthquake that broke the underlying layers. The approximate time of the earthquake can be determined from the ages of the two sets of strata. *(Clague, J., C. Yorath, R. Franklin, and B. Turner. 2006. At risk: Earthquakes and tsunamis on the west coast. Vancouver, BC: Tricouni Press)*

of square kilometres, a *magnitude*, and a believable *scientific rationale*. For several years, the U.S. Geological Survey operated a recording telephone service for people wanting to make earthquake predictions. None of the recorded predictions met these criteria. Predictions based on the arrangement of planets in the solar system, the appearance of comets and meteor showers, peculiar weather, strange behaviours of animals (Figure 2.41), unexplained changes in the functioning of mechanical or electrical devices (such as clocks and TV sets), or the sudden appearance of corns on Aunt Masie's left foot should not be taken seriously.

Japanese seismologists made the first attempts at earthquake prediction by using the frequency of very small *microearthquakes* (magnitude less than 2), precise repeated geodetic surveys to detect tilting of the land surface, and repeat measurements of the local magnetic field of Earth. They found that earthquakes in the areas they studied were nearly always accompanied by swarms of microearthquakes several months before the major shocks. Furthermore, they found that tilting of the ground correlated strongly with earthquake activity.[31]

In 1975, Chinese scientists predicted a major earthquake (**M** 7.0) that saved thousands of lives. The prediction was based primarily on a series of progressively larger foreshocks that began four days before the mainshock. It appears to have been a lucky coincidence, because Chinese scientists previously had issued many unsuccessful predictions and they subsequently failed to predict major quakes. Nonetheless, the result was beneficial.[38] The earthquake destroyed or damaged about 90 percent of buildings in the city of Haicheng. Most of the 1 million people living in the city were saved because they had been evacuated the day before the quake struck.

Unfortunately, most large earthquakes are not preceded by foreshocks. In 1976, one of the deadliest earthquakes in

▲ **FIGURE 2.41** Peculiar behaviour of animals should not be viewed as earthquake predictors.

recorded history struck near the mining town of Tangshan, China, killing more than 240,000 people. There were no foreshocks.

People have proposed phenomena ranging from lunar tides to unusual animal behaviour as earthquake precursors. Odd animal behaviour includes unusual barking of dogs, chickens that refuse to lay eggs, horses or cows that run in circles, rats perched on power lines, and snakes that emerge from the ground in the winter and freeze. To date, no scientific studies have shown a convincing correlation between unusual animal behaviour or lunar tides and earthquakes.

Earthquake prediction is still elusive. Even if reliable precursors can be identified, reliable short-range prediction of earthquakes is years away. Such predictions, if they are possible, will most likely be based on precursory phenomena, such as the following:

- The pattern and frequency of earthquakes, such as foreshocks that preceded the Haicheng earthquake, discussed above
- Land-level change
- Seismic gaps along faults
- Physical and chemical changes in Earth's crust

Land-Level Change Changes in land elevation, referred to as *uplift* and *subsidence,* may precede earthquakes and provide help to forecast them. For example, several centimetres of uplift occurred in the decade before the 1964 Niigata earthquake (**M** 7.5) in Japan.[40] Similar amounts of uplift occurred over the five years before the 1983 Sea of Japan earthquake (**M** 7.7).[40,41]

Uplifts of 1 m to 2 m also preceded large earthquakes in Japan in 1793, 1802, 1872, and 1927. These uplifts were recognized by rapid withdrawals of the sea along the coast. On the morning of the 1802 earthquake, the sea withdrew about 300 m because of an uplift of about 1 m. The earthquake struck four hours later, destroying many houses and uplifting the land another metre.[41]

Canadian geophysicists recently identified a possible precursory sign of great interplate earthquakes at the Cascadia subduction zone in the Pacific Northwest. By using data from continuously monitored Global Positioning System (GPS) stations, they recognized episodes of slip along the megathrust fault at depths of 20 km to 40 km, well landward of and below the locked portion of the fault.[7] Simultaneously, they identified non-earthquake tremors at about the same depth and same time as the slip events (Figure 2.42). Although it might seem as if these slip events would relieve strain across the fault, the opposite is true: strain increases up-dip along the locked part of the fault during each episode of slip on the deeper, unlocked part. In effect, the silent-slip events ratchet up the strain on the locked portion of the fault. The slip events occur at intervals of 13 to 15 months, last from 10 to 20 days, and migrate laterally along the length of the subduction zone. A future silent-slip event will probably trigger a giant megathrust earthquake, and its associated tremors indicate times of increased probability of such an event. The trick will be to recognize the specific slip event that tips the balance. If that were possible, the tremors might give people a few days to prepare for the big one.

Seismic Gaps A potentially important indicator of future earthquakes along faults is what is termed a *seismic gap*. Portions of long faults that mark plate boundaries, such as the San Andreas fault in California, the Anatolian fault in Turkey, and the Queen Charlotte fault off the west coast of the Queen Charlotte Islands (Figure 2.43), have had no earthquakes for long periods, even though other parts of the faults have recently been active. It is reasonable to assume that all parts of these faults are active and will ultimately slip. Therefore, zones that have been seismically quiet in the recent past may be more likely to experience an earthquake than those that have produced quakes recently. Some seismic gaps, notably those along the Anatolian fault, have produced devastating earthquakes in the past few decades, but many have not. Moreover, some parts of seismically active faults have produced several large earthquakes within short intervals.

Since 1965, the seismic-gap concept has been used successfully in forecasts of at least 10 large, plate boundary earthquakes. One of these quakes took place in Alaska, three in Mexico, one in South America, and three in Japan. Seismic gaps along the San Andreas fault in California include one near Fort Tejon that last ruptured in 1857 and one along the Coachella Valley, a segment that has not produced a great earthquake for several hundred years. Both gaps are likely to produce a large earthquake in the next few decades.[12,42]

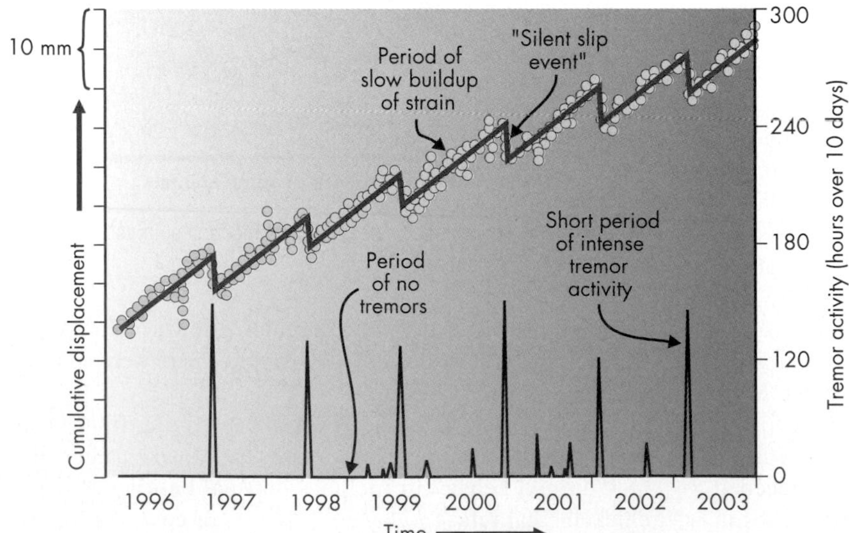

◀ **FIGURE 2.42 SILENT SLIP** Slow slip events along the deep portion of the Cascadia subduction zone and non-earthquake tremor activity recorded in the Victoria area. The blue circles represent day-to-day changes in the position of a GPS site at Victoria with respect to a GPS site near the inland city of Penticton, British Columbia, which is assumed to be stationary and fixed to the North America plate. The red line segments show the progressive movements between slip events, marked by reversals every 13 to 16 months. Since 1996 Victoria has moved 50 mm closer to Penticton. The bottom graph shows the total number of hours of tremor activity per 10-day period for southern Vancouver Island. Slip events have an average duration of 10 days. *(Clague, J., C. Yorath, R. Franklin, and B. Turner. 2006. At risk: Earthquakes and tsunamis on the west coast. Vancouver, BC: Tricouni Press)*

Physical and Chemical Phenomena Local changes in gravity and the magnetic and electrical properties of near-surface crustal materials have preceded large earthquakes. For example, changes in *electrical resistivity* have been reported before earthquakes in the United States, Eastern Europe, and China.[40] Changes have also been observed in groundwater levels, temperature, and chemistry.[43] For example, significant increases in the radon content of well water were reported in the month or so before the 1995 Kobe earthquake.[43] Many of these physical and chemical changes may occur when rocks expand and fracture in the hours or days preceding an earthquake.

Status of Earthquake Prediction and Forecasting

Optimistic scientists believe that we will someday be able to make not only reliable long- and intermediate-range forecasts but also short-range predictions (seconds to weeks) of the locations and magnitudes of damaging earthquakes. Although progress on earthquake prediction has not matched expectations, intermediate- to long-range forecasting, including hazard evaluation and probabilistic analysis of areas along active faults, has progressed faster than expected (see the Professional Profile).[44] For example, the 1983 Borah Peak earthquake (**M** 7) on the Lost River fault in central Idaho has been lauded as a success story in intermediate-range earthquake forecasting. Previous investigations demonstrated that the fault was active and that a large earthquake was likely to happen in the future.[45] The earthquake killed two people and caused approximately US$15 million in damage. Movement during the earthquake created a scarp up to several metres high along the 36 km length of the rupture zone. Field studies after the earthquake found that the new fault scarp coincided with the previously mapped fault trace, validating the usefulness of careful mapping of scarps produced by prehistoric earthquakes. Where the ground has broken before, it may break again!

The U.S. Geological Survey established a plan for issuing earthquake warnings and predictions nearly 30 years ago (Figure 2.44). The plan requires that warnings be independently reviewed by scientists before being transmitted to government officials and the public.

Government officials and news media that publicize and thus give credence to earthquake predictions that have not been scientifically reviewed do a disservice to the public. In 1990, a pseudoscientific prediction of an earthquake in New Madrid, Missouri, was acted on by some government and business leaders and was publicized by local, state, and national media, even after the prediction was dismissed by the National Earthquake Prediction Evaluation Council.[46] Schools and businesses closed, public events were cancelled, people evacuated their homes, and more than 30 television and radio vans converged on the predicted epicentre.[47] The earthquake didn't happen. Widely publicizing earthquake predictions that have not been independently vetted by seismologists is the geologic equivalent of yelling "fire" in a crowded movie theatre.

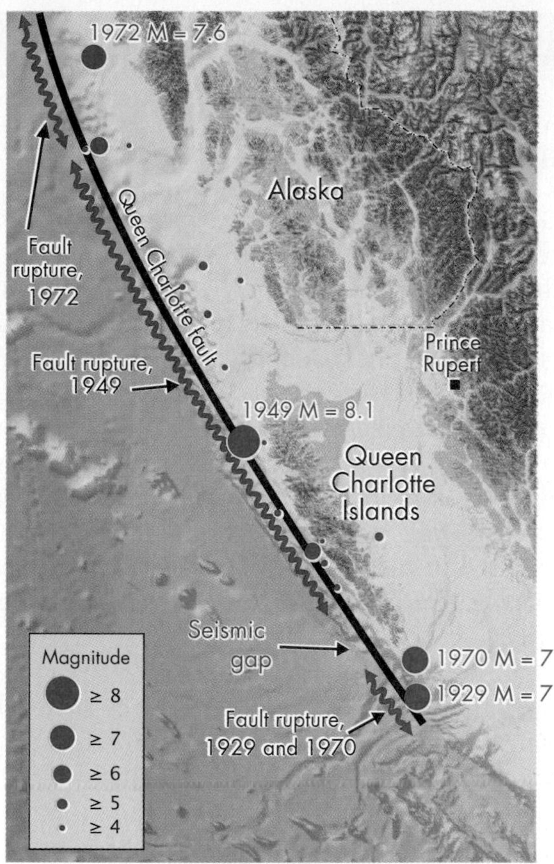

▲ **FIGURE 2.43 SEISMIC GAP** A map showing seismic gap along the Queen Charlotte fault. The red dots show epicentres of historical earthquakes; the red wriggly lines demarcate the rupture extents of large earthquakes in 1929, 1949, 1970, and 1972. *(Clague, J., C. Yorath, R. Franklin, and B. Turner. 2006. At risk: Earthquakes and tsunamis on the west coast. Vancouver, BC: Tricouni Press)*

The difficulty of predicting, even forecasting, earthquakes is shown by the experience of the U.S. Geological Survey at Parkfield, California. The town of Parkfield, located on the San Andreas fault, sustained large (about **M** 6) earthquakes at about 20-year intervals between 1857 and 1966, gaining the dubious title of California's earthquake capital. On the basis of this history, the USGS in 1984 forecast that a large earthquake would strike the Parkfield area sometime between 1987 and 1993. In 1985, it initiated a long-term earthquake monitoring project, termed the Parkfield Experiment, to better understand what happens on the San Andreas fault before, during, and after an earthquake. The experiment involved more than 100 researchers from the U.S. Geological Survey, universities, and government laboratories. The scientists installed a dense network of instruments to capture the anticipated earthquake and reveal the quake process in unprecedented detail.[48] And then they waited and they waited. The time of the forecast proved to be incorrect, although finally, on September 28, 2004, a magnitude 6 quake struck close to the town. During the time of the experiment, much larger, unanticipated earthquakes occurred on the San Andreas fault at Loma Prieta (1989) and Landers (1992). These quakes may have temporarily reduced the stress on the Parkfield portion of the fault.

PROFESSIONAL PROFILE

Gail Atkinson, Seismologist

Dr. G. M. Atkinson (Figure 2.B), Canada Research Chair in geophysics and professor in the Department of Earth Sciences at the University of Western Ontario, is an internationally recognized engineering seismologist. She is known for her work in engineering ground motion studies, earthquake source and attenuation processes, and seismic hazard analysis. Her numerous papers have been widely used in engineering applications and have changed the state of the art in earthquake engineering practice. "There are many well-inhabited areas that are at considerable risk of earthquakes," Atkinson says. "We need to continue to learn how to assess earthquake hazard."

Atkinson has been involved in seismic hazard analyses and ground motion studies for major engineering projects, including nuclear power plants, dams, tailings dams, offshore structures, liquid natural gas facilities, pipelines, waste-disposal facilities, and buildings in Canada, the United States, and overseas. For more than a dozen years, she has been an active member of the Canadian National Council of Earthquake Engineering (CANCEE), the body responsible for developing seismic design regulations for the National Building Code of Canada. Atkinson is the director of the Ottawa-Carleton Earthquake Engineering Research Centre, and her work is highly regarded in the United States, where she served as president of the Seismological Society of America from 2001 to 2003, and as chair of its government relations committee. She participates actively in the U.S. National Earthquake Hazards Reduction Program (NEHRP), having been awarded close to US$1 million in NEHRP research grants over the past seven years.

Atkinson is also president of the POLARIS Consortium, a $10 million multi-institutional project involving 90 portable geophysical observatories that collect and analyze data on Earth's structure, resources, and earthquake hazards. POLARIS stands for Portable Observatories for Lithosphere Analysis and Research Investigating Seismicity. For the past four years, Atkinson and a group of colleagues have been studying earthquakes in Canada and around the world to determine how to deal with these disasters. The team has set up three seismographic arrays in Ontario, British Columbia, and the Northwest Territories. Each array has 30 seismographs. Every seismograph is linked to a satellite, which sends data directly to Atkinson and other members of the team via the internet. This system allows the team to see earthquakes across Canada and the world in real time on their computers.

▲ **FIGURE 2.B GAIL ATKINSON, SEISMOLOGIST** Dr. Gail Atkinson, director of the Ottawa-Carleton Earthquake Engineering Research Centre, is one of Canada's leading engineering seismologists. She and her students study how earthquake shaking might affect critical infrastructure such as nuclear power plants, dams, and pipelines. *(Gail Atkinson)*

Atkinson hopes these seismographs will enable her team to know what actually happens during an earthquake. She says that the key to understanding earthquakes is to understand their waves.

"There is no way to predict where or when an earthquake will happen, but the ability to know the difference between P and S waves will change our warning systems," Atkinson says.

Although both P and S waves leave the earthquake source at the same time, the P waves move faster. As the waves move farther from the source, the P and S waves get farther apart from each other.

"Though the time between the P and S waves may only be a matter of seconds, our hope is that with the ability to determine which is a P wave and which is an S wave, a better warning system can be put in place," Atkinson says. This warning system could include automatic shutoffs for gas lines and nuclear power plants that would help decrease damage. The warnings could give people just enough time to get to a safer location.

—John J. Clague

Earthquake Warning Systems

Technically, it is possible to develop a warning system that could provide an alert to the Los Angeles area about one minute before the arrival of damaging earthquake waves from an event several hundred kilometres away. Similarly, Seattle, Vancouver, and Portland could receive half a minute of warning of a great earthquake at the Cascadia subduction zone off the west coast of North America. Such a system would be based on the principle that radio waves travel much faster than seismic waves. The Japanese have a functioning system that provides earthquake warnings for their high-speed "bullet" trains; derailment of one of these trains by an earthquake could kill hundreds of people.

A proposed system for California involves a sophisticated network of seismometers and transmitters along the San Andreas fault. This system would first sense motion associated with a large earthquake and then send a warning to Los Angeles, which would then relay the warning to critical facilities, schools, and the general population (Figure 2.45).

The warning times these systems could provide range from as short as 15 seconds to as long as 1 minute depending on the location of the earthquake epicentre. This interval could be enough time for many people to shut off gas valves, shut down machinery and computers, and take cover.[49] Remember that an earthquake warning system is not a prediction tool, because it only warns that an earthquake has already occurred.

Some people believe that the damage to scientific credibility caused by false alarms would be far greater than the benefits of a brief warning of an approaching earthquake. In the case of the Japanese high-speed rail system, about 5 percent of the warnings are false alarms. Others have expressed concern for liability issues resulting from warning system failures, and damage and suffering stemming from actions taken based on false early warnings.

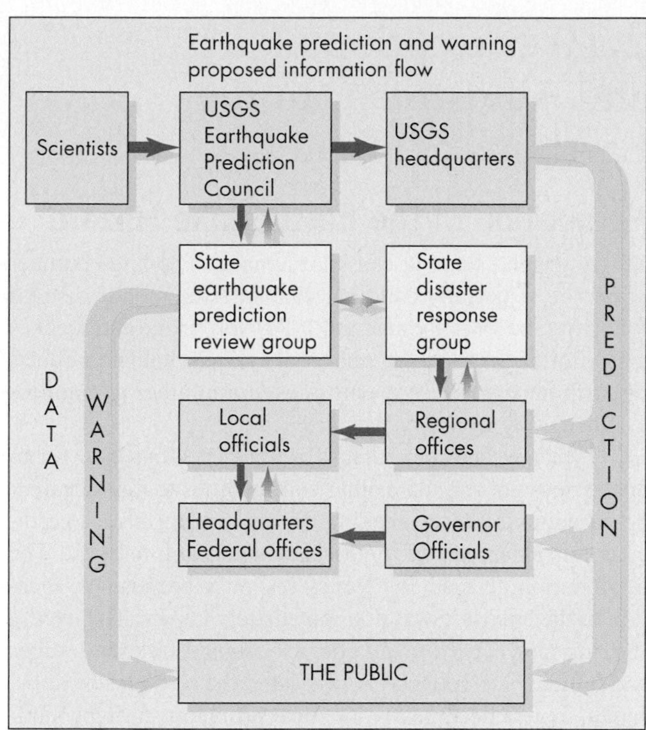

▲ **FIGURE 2.44 U.S. GEOLOGICAL SURVEY PLAN FOR ISSUING EARTHQUAKE WARNINGS AND PREDICTIONS** A National Earthquake Prediction Council, consisting of seismologists from government, universities, and the private sector, evaluates warnings and predictions before they are passed on to government officials and the public. *(From McKelvey, V. E. 1976. Earthquake prediction—opportunity to avert disaster. U.S. Geological Survey Circular 729)*

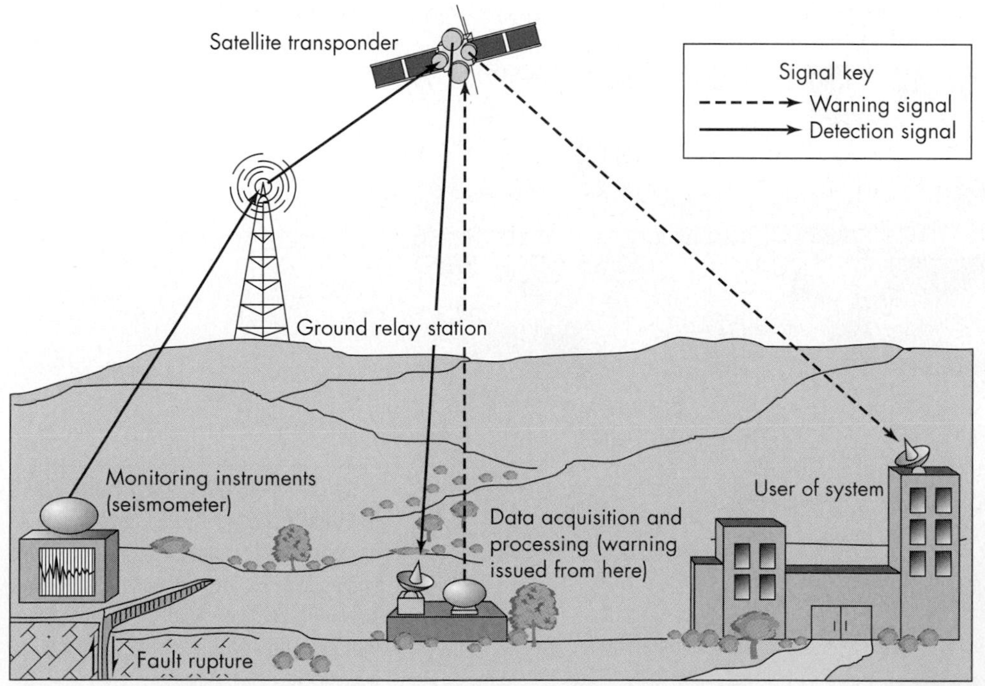

◄ **FIGURE 2.45 EARTHQUAKE WARNING** An idealized diagram showing an earthquake warning system that uses radio waves, which travel faster than seismic waves. Once an earthquake is detected, a warning signal is sent ahead of the seismic waves. The warning time depends on the distance of the earthquake source from the affected city. It could be long enough to close gas lines, shut down critical facilities, and advise people to take cover. *(After Holden, R., R. Lee, and M. Reichle. 1989. California Division of Mines and Geology Bulletin 101)*

2.10 Perception of and Adjustment to the Earthquake Hazard

Perception of the Earthquake Hazard

Severe ground shaking can be traumatic. The large number of people, especially children, who suffered mental distress following the 1971 Sylmar and 1994 Northridge earthquakes in California attests to the emotional and psychological effects of earthquakes. These events caused a number of families to move away from Los Angeles.

Typically, one community's experience with a large earthquake does not stimulate other communities to improve their preparedness. Intense shaking during the Northridge earthquake disabled part of the local seismograph network. The malfunction delayed emergency response because the location of the epicentre was not immediately known. The intense shaking also caused many poorly designed freeway bridges and buildings to collapse. A year later, the residents of Kobe, Japan, experienced nearly identical problems during a similar earthquake. Communication problems and damage to critical infrastructure prevented the Japanese government from quickly and effectively responding to the disaster. Japan is one of the most earthquake-prepared countries in the world, yet significant relief did not reach Kobe until about 10 hours after the earthquake!

Two large (**M** 7.6 and **M** 7.2) earthquakes in Turkey in 1999 provide another example of the problems earthquakes pose to modern society. The first earthquake, on August 17, levelled thousands of concrete buildings. About 250,000 people were left homeless and approximately 17,000 people died. Many modern buildings collapsed during the intense shaking of the earthquake, whereas older buildings were left standing (Figure 2.46). As in the case of the 2001 Bhuj earthquake in India, poor construction practices probably contributed to the collapse of the newer buildings. Allegations were made that some of the Turkish contractors bulldozed collapsed buildings soon after the earthquake to remove evidence of shoddy construction. If those allegations are true, the contractors tied up equipment that could have been used to rescue people trapped in other collapsed buildings.

The lessons learned from California, Japan, and Turkey are bitter ones. Our vulnerability to catastrophic loss from large earthquakes is large and growing. Older, unreinforced concrete and masonry buildings not designed to withstand strong ground motion may collapse during a large earthquake. As a rule, reinforced concrete buildings constructed to meet modern seismic provisions of building codes should experience little damage compared with older buildings.

Community Adjustments to the Earthquake Hazard

It is impossible to prevent human habitation in earthquake-prone areas, thus countries, provinces, territories, states, municipalities, and individuals must take steps to minimize seismic risk. The steps include careful location of critical facilities, structural protection, education, and ready availability of insurance and emergency relief. Individuals must also take steps to protect themselves.

Location of Critical Facilities Important public and community buildings and other structures, commonly referred to as *critical facilities,* must be located as safely as possible. Critical facilities include hospitals, schools, power plants, communication systems, and police and fire stations. Selecting safe locations requires site-specific investigation of earthquake hazards, such as the potential for liquefaction and landslides. Planning commonly involves *microzonation,* which is the identification of areas subject to different earthquake hazards.

◀ **FIGURE 2.46 COLLAPSE OF BUILDINGS IN TURKEY** Damage to the town of Golcuk in western Turkey from an **M** 7.6 earthquake in August 1999. The old mosque at the left side of the photo is standing, whereas many modern buildings collapsed. *(Enric Marti/AP/Wide World Photos)*

Microzonation is necessary because the ground response to seismic shaking within even a small area can differ greatly. In urban areas, where individual properties may be worth millions of dollars, detailed maps of ground response to seismic shaking help engineers and architects design buildings and other structures that can better withstand earthquakes. Microzonation requires a significant investment of time and money, but it provides important information on how specific sites will respond if a strong earthquake does occur. Although we will never be able to completely eliminate death and injury from earthquakes, we can reduce the number of casualties by safely locating and building critical facilities.

Structural Protection The statement "earthquakes don't kill people, buildings kill people" succinctly captures the importance of building design and construction in reducing damage and injury from earthquakes. Buildings, bridges, pipelines, and other structures must be constructed to withstand at least moderate shaking in seismically active regions. Appropriate construction practices require that governments adopt and enforce building codes with seismic provisions similar to those in the National Building Code of Canada and the International Building Code. When applying these provisions, architects and engineers try to balance earthquake risk reduction against the additional costs of earthquake-resistant design (Figure 2.47).[38]

Education As with all other natural hazards, education is an important component of earthquake preparedness at the community level. An educational program might include distribution of pamphlets and videos to the public; instruction on earthquakes in primary and secondary schools; workshops and training sessions for engineers, architects, geologists, and community planners; and the provision of information on the internet. In areas of high risk, education also takes place through earthquake and tsunami drills in schools and through earthquake disaster exercises for government officials and emergency responders.

Availability of Insurance and Emergency Relief Insurance and emergency relief are vital to help a community, province, territory, state, or country recover from an earthquake disaster. Losses from a major earthquake can be huge—tens of billions of dollars. After the 1906 San Francisco earthquake, only 6 of the 65 companies that insured property in the city were able to pay their liabilities in full.[10] Potential insured losses from a large earthquake in a densely urbanized area, such as Vancouver, Seattle, San Francisco, Los Angeles, or San Diego, are enormous and probably beyond the capability of the insurance industry to handle. Insurance claims paid after the 1994 Northridge earthquake were US$15.3 billion, but this amount is dwarfed by the more than $200 billion in losses from the 1995 Kobe quake.[10] In the early 1990s, a large international reinsurance company completed a study of damage likely to be caused by an **M** 6.5 earthquake with a source 10 km beneath Vancouver. The bottom line of the report is that losses could total tens of billions of dollars.[50] Yet an **M** 6.5 earthquake is by no means the largest that could occur in Vancouver. An earthquake of this magnitude, for example, happened beneath Seattle in 1965.

The State of California has partially addressed the problem of catastrophic earthquake losses by making state-subsidized earthquake insurance available through the nonprofit California Earthquake Authority. Even with state subsidies, barely 25 percent of California residents have earthquake insurance, in part because of the high deductible.[10] Unlike flood insurance and crop insurance, the U.S. government has no federally subsidized program of earthquake insurance. Likewise, Canada does not offer any form of earthquake insurance, in spite of the high seismic risk in some parts of the country. However, it would likely step in with relief funds in the event of a catastrophic earthquake.

◄ **FIGURE 2.47 CRITICAL INFRASTRUCTURE** The Lions Gate Bridge in Vancouver is one of the many bridges in the Pacific Northwest that have been upgraded at considerable cost to better withstand earthquake shaking. *(John J. Clague)*

Personal Adjustments before, during, and after an Earthquake

Individual actions before, during, and after a major earthquake can reduce death, injury, and property damage. Close to 180 million people in 6 provinces, 3 territories, and 39 American states live in seismically active areas. In damage alone, billions of dollars could be saved if our buildings and their contents were better secured to withstand shaking from earthquakes. Earthquake preparedness is the responsibility of individuals, communities, and governments. An informed and prepared populace will result in greatly reduced injury and death when a large quake occurs.

Before the Shaking Starts Most earthquake casualties result from partial building collapse and falling objects, such as chimneys and light fixtures.[51] Consequently, it is important to know the safe spots in each room of a house or apartment. Safe spots include inside walls, supported archways, and the undersides of sturdy tables and desks. Danger spots include windows, fireplaces, and areas adjacent to heavy hanging objects and tall unsecured furniture. Do not rush outside during an earthquake, as debris from the outside of the building and power lines may fall to the ground.

Families should discuss and prepare an emergency plan.[52] Start by discussing what to do at home, at school, or at work if an earthquake strikes. Prepare a list of what needs to be done ahead of time. Divide the tasks so that everyone involved participates as much as possible. Write down and try out your plan, and make sure everyone in the family has a copy. People who live alone should develop a plan for themselves with links to neighbours and friends. Select an appropriate out-of-the-area contact who should be notified about the family's status after the earthquake. This contact, ideally a family member or close family friend, can pass on news to other family members if individuals are separated. Learn first aid and CPR, and keep a list of emergency telephone numbers. Ask for the emergency plan at your children's school. Know the safe places to be, and where not to be, in your home during an earthquake.

You can take simple, inexpensive measures to prepare your home for a quake:[52,53]

- Learn how to shut off your gas, water, and electricity. Clearly label the off position for the gas, water, and electricity.
- Make sure your house is bolted to its foundation.
- Repair loose roof shingles.
- Make sure chimneys are strong and well braced.
- Keep breakable and heavy objects on bottom shelves of cabinets.
- Secure heavy furniture that could topple, such as bookcases, cabinets, and wall units.
- Strap water heaters to walls.
- Secure appliances that could move enough to rupture gas or electricity lines.
- Do not place heavy pictures and other items over beds.
- Locate beds and chairs away from chimneys and windows.
- Put secure latches on cabinet doors to prevent dishes and glassware from spilling out.
- Put anti-skid pads under televisions, VCRs, computers, and small appliances or secure them with hook-and-loop-type fasteners or other such products.
- Keep flammable and other hazardous liquids, such as paints, in the garage or in a shed away from the house.
- Check chimneys, roofs, walls, and foundations for structural damage.
- Put up plywood in the attic on joists around each chimney to prevent masonry from coming through the ceiling.
- Maintain a supply of emergency food, water, and other supplies, including a flashlight, candles, waterproof matches, fire extinguisher, duct tape, pen, note pad, wrench, pocket knife, manual can opener, whistle, battery-powered radio, extra batteries, essential medication, personal toiletry items, money, first-aid kit, temporary shelter (a plastic tarpaulin or small tent), and clothing, in a secure, easily accessible area. Your food and water should be sufficient to last for three to five days. Choose foods that require no refrigeration, cooking, or preparation and are compact and lightweight.
- Store an emergency kit in your car, tool shed, or garage in case you have to evacuate your home and can't go back in.

During the Shaking The best advice during an earthquake is "Don't panic." Remember what you learned in this chapter. P waves will arrive first causing initial vibrations, followed by heavy shaking from the S and surface waves. If at least 20 seconds elapse between the arrivals of the P and S waves, the earthquake is from a distant source. The noise of the ground vibrating will be deep and loud and may begin suddenly like a loud clap of thunder if you are close to the epicentre.[51] Books, dishes, glass, furniture, and other objects may come crashing down. Car alarms will go off and there may be explosive flashes from electrical transformers and falling power lines. The length of shaking depends on the magnitude of the earthquake. For example, strong shaking during the 1994 Northridge quake (**M** 6.7) lasted around 15 seconds, whereas strong shaking during the 1964 Alaska quake (**M** 9.2) lasted 3 minutes.

If you are indoors, stay there. Move away from windows, glass partitions, mirrors, fireplaces, bookcases, tall furniture, and light fixtures. Get under a desk or table, or place yourself in an archway or inside corner of a room. Once there, protect your head and face. Avoid doorways, as doors may slam shut and cause injury. Do not use an elevator or run from the building. If you are in an elevator, get out as soon as you can. If you are outdoors, move to an open area away from buildings, windows, trees, and power lines. If driving, pull over to the side of the road away from power lines, bridges, overpasses, and buildings. Stay in your vehicle until the shaking stops. If you are in a crowded public place, try to take cover where you won't get trampled. Do not run for exits; sidewalks next to tall buildings are particularly dangerous because of falling glass and other materials. Keep away from windows, skylights, and display shelves laden with heavy objects.

When the Shaking Stops Try to remain calm, even though you may feel dizzy and sick.[51] Take several deep breaths, look around, and then leave the building, carefully watching for fallen and falling objects. Check yourself and others nearby for injuries. Administer first aid, but do not move seriously injured individuals unless their lives are in immediate danger. Place a HELP sign in your window if you need assistance. Put on sturdy shoes and protective clothing to prevent injury from debris and hunt for hazards:

- Look for fires, gas and water leaks, arcing electrical wires, and broken sewage lines. If you suspect damage, turn off the utility at the source. However, do not turn off the gas if there is no damage.
- If you smell gas, extinguish all fires, do not use matches, and do not operate electrical switches. Open the windows, shut off the gas valve, leave the building, and, if possible, report the leak to authorities.
- Check your home for damage, including the roof, chimney, and foundation.

The next step is to check and secure your food and water supplies. If tap water is available, fill a bathtub or other containers. Emergency water may also be obtained from water heaters, melted ice cubes, and toilet tanks. Purify water by boiling it for several minutes. If you have lost your power, strain the water through paper towels or several layers of clean cloth. Wear proper hand and eye protection to clean up any spilled hazardous materials. Do not use barbecues, camp stoves, or unvented heaters indoors. Do not flush toilets if the sewage line is damaged. Do not use the telephone unless there is a severe injury or fire; chances are that phones will not work anyway. Emergency phone numbers are found on the inside cover of most telephone books. Do not use your vehicle unless there is an emergency, as it is important to keep the streets clear for emergency vehicles. Do not leave your car if downed power lines are across it. Avoid waterfront areas in case of a tsunami. If you have pets, try to find and comfort them. Confine them at home if you have to evacuate. Turn on your portable radio or television for instructions and news reports. Rely on emergency authorities for guidance. Be prepared for aftershocks.

The most hazardous period for aftershocks is in the minutes, hours, and the first day following the mainshock. Both the number and the intensity of aftershocks will decrease in the days and weeks following the mainshock.

The good news is that in most developed countries large earthquakes are very survivable. In areas of greatest hazard, including Japan and California, public buildings are constructed to withstand earthquake shaking, and wood-frame houses seldom collapse.

For more information on earthquake preparedness, you can contact the

- Geological Survey of Canada
- U.S. Federal Emergency Management Agency (FEMA)
- United States Geological Survey

Summary

Seismologists use a variety of magnitude (**M**) scales to measure the amount of energy released during an earthquake. In the case of the commonly used moment magnitude scale, an increase from one whole number to the next larger one represents a 10-fold increase in the amount of shaking and about a 30-fold increase in the amount of energy released. The Geological Survey of Canada and the U.S. Geological Survey National Earthquake Information Center calculate a preliminary magnitude for a large earthquake and later revise the value after further analysis.

Scientists determine the intensity of an earthquake from its effects on people and structures. Earthquake intensity depends on the severity and duration of shaking, distance to the focus, and the local geological environment. The Modified Mercalli Intensity Scale has 12 intensity categories that are based on people's experience and property damage. Instrumental intensity is determined by using a dense network of seismographs. Information on intensity helps emergency responders focus relief efforts on areas that have experienced the most intense shaking. Other measurements, such as ground acceleration, are needed to design structures that can withstand shaking during future earthquakes.

Earthquakes occur when rocks or sediments are displaced rapidly along faults. Displacements are mainly horizontal along strike-slip faults and mainly vertical along dip-slip faults. Thrust faults are low-angle, dip-slip faults along which material above the fault plane (hanging-wall) is displaced up and over material below it (footwall). Fault rupture may extend to the surface, creating a scarp, or it may terminate at depth as a blind fault.

A fault is considered active if it has moved at some time in the past 10,000 years and potentially active if it has moved in the past 2 million years. Some faults exhibit tectonic creep, which is slow continuous movement that is not accompanied by felt earthquakes. Strain accumulates in rocks along a fault as the sides pull in different directions between earthquakes. Eventually, the accumulated strain exceeds the strength of the rocks and they rupture. Waves of energy, called seismic waves, radiate outward in all directions from the rupture.

Seismic waves compress (P waves) or shear (S waves) rock and sediment; some travel across the ground as surface waves. P waves travel the fastest, but S and surface waves cause most shaking damage. The severity of ground shaking is affected by the type and thickness of the materials through which seismic waves travel, the direction of fault rupture, and focal depth.

Buildings most likely to be damaged by earthquakes are (1) those that are constructed on artificially filled land or water-saturated, granular sediments that amplify shaking or liquefy, (2) those that are not designed to withstand significant horizontal acceleration of the ground, and (3) those that have natural vibrational frequencies that match the frequencies of the seismic waves.

Seismologists recognize an earthquake cycle comprising three or four phases. The cycle begins with a period of seismic inactivity, during which elastic strain builds up in the rocks bordering a fault. The second phase is marked by small or moderate earthquakes, which happen when the accumulated strain locally exceeds the strength of the rocks. The third phase, which occurs in only some earthquake cycles, is characterized by foreshocks. The final stage is brief: the fault ruptures, producing elastic rebound and seismic waves.

Interplate earthquakes occur on faults at plate boundaries, such as the San Andreas fault and the Cascadia subduction zone. Intraplate earthquakes occur locally within the North America plate, for example in eastern Yukon Territory, western and mid-continent United States, southern Ontario and Quebec, parts of eastern and Arctic Canada, and South Carolina. The largest intraplate earthquakes in North America occurred in the central Mississippi Valley in 1811 and 1812.

Large earthquakes produce violent ground motion that may damage or destroy buildings, bridges, dams, tunnels, pipelines, and other rigid structures. Secondary effects of earthquakes include liquefaction, regional subsidence and uplift of the land, landslides, fires, tsunami, and disease. Large earthquakes release accumulated strain on faults and temporarily reduce the probability of another large quake in the same area. Some faults channel groundwater flow to springs, trap gas and oil, and expose or contribute to the formation of valuable mineral deposits.

People have increased earthquake activity by flooding valleys behind dams, by raising fluid pressures along faults through disposal of liquid waste in deep wells, and by detonating underground nuclear explosions.

Regional earthquake hazards and risk can be determined through detailed geologic mapping of fault zones, excavation of trenches across faults to determine earthquake history and frequency, and analysis of sediments sensitive to shaking. Earthquake risk can be reduced by updating and enforcing the seismic provisions of building codes and by retrofitting existing vulnerable structures.

Earthquake prediction is a long-term goal of seismologists, but is decades from being achieved. Scientists have successfully made long- and intermediate-term forecasts of earthquakes by using probabilistic methods, but they have been unable to make consistent, accurate, short-term predictions. A problem in predicting earthquakes is that they are variable in time and space, with clusters of events separated by longer periods with low activity.

Warning systems and earthquake prevention are not reliable alternatives to earthquake preparedness. Communities in seismically active areas must develop emergency plans that allow them to effectively respond to a catastrophic earthquake. Effective emergency plans include earthquake education, disaster-response protocols, and availability of earthquake insurance. Individuals who live in or visit seismically active areas must learn how to react if a large earthquake occurs.

Key Terms

body wave (p. 39)
dip-slip fault (p. 37)
directivity (p. 44)
earthquake (p. 32)
earthquake cycle (p. 46)
epicentre (p. 32)
fault (p. 32)
focus (p. 32)
intensity (p. 32)
interplate earthquake (p. 51)
intraplate earthquake (p. 51)
liquefaction (p. 54)
magnitude (p. 32)
material amplification (p. 45)
Modified Mercalli Intensity Scale (p. 34)
moment magnitude (p. 33)
normal fault (p. 37)
P wave (p. 39)
paleoseismologists (p. 60)
precursors (p. 60)
reverse fault (p. 37)
Richter scale (p. 32)
S wave (p. 39)
seismic wave (p. 32)
seismograph (p. 34)
slow earthquake (p. 39)
strike-slip fault (p. 37)
subduction earthquake (p. 51)
subduction zone (p. 39)
surface wave (p. 39)
tectonic creep (p. 39)
thrust fault (p. 37)

Review Questions

1. What is the difference between the epicentre and focus of an earthquake?
2. What is moment magnitude? How is it related to the amount of shaking and energy released by an earthquake?
3. What is instrumental intensity? What is its relation to a ShakeMap?
4. Explain how faulting occurs.
5. How are active and potentially active faults defined?
6. What is the difference in the rates of travel of P, S, and surface waves? How is this difference important in locating earthquakes?
7. How do seismologists locate earthquakes?
8. How does the depth of an earthquake affect ground shaking and damage?
9. What types of geologic materials amplify seismic waves?
10. Explain the earthquake cycle.
11. What are foreshocks and aftershocks?
12. Where are earthquakes most likely to occur in the world? In North America?
13. List the major primary and secondary effects of earthquakes.
14. How do plate boundary and intraplate earthquakes differ?
15. Why aren't the largest earthquakes always the most damaging?
16. Where does liquefaction occur and what are its effects?
17. Why do outbreaks of disease follow some major earthquakes and other natural disasters?

18. How can earthquakes be beneficial?
19. Name three ways people have caused earthquakes.
20. What kinds of information are useful in assessing seismic risk?
21. What kinds of phenomena may be earthquake precursors?
22. What is the difference between an earthquake prediction and a forecast?
23. How can a community prepare for an earthquake?
24. What is seismic retrofitting?

Critical Thinking Questions

1. You live in an area where a large earthquake might happen. The community is debating the merits of developing an earthquake warning system. Some people worry that false alarms will be common. Others argue that the cost of the system is far greater than the benefits it provides. What are your views on these points? Do you think the public should pay for an earthquake warning system, assuming such a system is feasible? What are potential implications of not developing a warning system if a large earthquake results in damage that could otherwise have been partially avoided?
2. You are considering buying a house in Victoria, British Columbia. You know that large earthquakes can occur in the area. What questions would you ask before purchasing the home? For example, consider the effects of earthquakes, the type of rock or sediment underlying the property, and the age of the house. What might you do to protect yourself both financially and physically if you decide to buy the house?
3. You are working in a developing country where most buildings are unreinforced and built of bricks. The last damaging earthquake in the area happened 200 years ago and killed thousands of people. How would you describe the earthquake risk to your family members who live there with you? What steps could you take to reduce the risk?

Selected Web Resources

Earthquakes Canada
http://earthquakescanada.nrcan.gc.ca/index_e.php
Information on earthquakes in Canada from Natural Resources Canada

U.S. Geological Survey Earthquake Hazards Program
http://earthquake.usgs.gov Homepage of the U.S. Geological Survey Earthquake Hazards Program

U.S. Geological Survey: Earthquakes
http://pubs.usgs.gov/gip/earthq1 A general interest publication from the USGS

U.S. Geological Survey: Earthquake List
http://earthquake.usgs.gov/eqcenter/recenteqsww/Quakes/quakes_all.php A nearly real-time list of earthquakes

University of Washington
www.geophys.washington.edu/SEIS University of Washington, Geophysics Program, earthquake information for the Pacific Northwest

Global Earthquake Response Center
www.earthquake.org News, information, and preparedness supplies, and a comprehensive guide to online resources about earthquakes

Earthquakes
www.iris.edu/quakes/quakes.htm Information on earthquakes from the Incorporated Research Institutions for Seismology (IRIS)

HAZARD CITY: ASSIGNMENTS IN APPLIED GEOLOGY

Earthquake Damage Assessment

The Issue

In 1897 the Twin Fork Fault produced an earthquake with a Modified Mercalli Intensity of IX in Hazard City. A recent major earthquake in British Columbia has caused the citizens of Hazard City to worry about the impact of an earthquake similar to that of 1897 on their town.

Your Task

You have been hired by Hazard City's engineering department to assess the situation. To complete your study, you must clearly understand what IX on the Modified Mercalli Intensity Scale means in terms of damage to buildings and probable injuries to citizens. Tour Hazard City to learn where residential neighbourhoods and commercial properties are located, what types of buildings are found in each area, and the number of residents in each neighbourhood. Consult reference materials to learn how the residential and commercial buildings in Hazard City will respond if shaken at the equivalent of Mercalli Intensity IX. You must choose the methods you will use in your investigation.

Average Completion Time

1 hour

CHAPTER 3

▶ **PYROCLASTIC FLOW**
Eruption of Mount Unzen, Japan, June 1991. The grey cloud moving rapidly downslope toward the town is an incandescent pyroclastic flow of hot gases, volcanic ash, and large rocks. The firefighter is running for his life.
(AP/Wide World Photos)

Learning Objectives

There are about 1500 active volcanoes on Earth, almost 400 of which have erupted in the last century. Volcanoes occur on all seven continents as well as in the ocean. While you are reading this paragraph, at least 20 volcanoes are erupting on our planet. Your goals in reading this chapter should be to

- Know the different types of volcanoes
- Understand the relation between volcanoes and plate tectonics
- Know where volcanoes occur on Earth
- Understand the effects of volcanoes
- Know how volcanoes are linked to other natural hazards
- Recognize the benefits of volcanic eruptions
- Know the premonitory signs of volcanic eruptions
- Know what adjustments people can make to avoid death and damage from volcanoes

Volcanoes

Mount Unzen, 1991

Japan has 19 active volcanoes, one of the most destructive of which is Mount Unzen in the southwestern corner of the country. More than 200 years ago, Mount Unzen erupted and killed an estimated 15,000 people. The volcano then lay dormant until June 3, 1991, when another violent eruption forced the evacuation of thousands of people. By the end of 1993, Mount Unzen had produced about 0.2 km^3 of lava and more than 8000 superheated flows of hot gas, ash, and large rock fragments, more than any other volcano in recent time.[1,2] The 1991 eruption also produced damaging flows of volcanic debris and water, which geologists refer to as **lahars**. A specially designed channel was constructed to contain the lahars, but the flows overran the channel, burying many homes in mud (Figure 3.1).

The Mount Unzen story emphasizes three of this book's fundamental principles: the 1991 eruption had historical precursors; two different hazardous processes—pyroclastic flows and lahars—occurred in tandem; and evacuation of people reduced the loss of life.

3.1 Introduction to Volcanoes

Volcanic activity, or volcanism, is directly related to plate tectonics, and most active volcanoes are located near plate boundaries[3] (see "Volcano Origins" later in this chapter). Mid-ocean ridges and subduction zones are sites where molten rock, or **magma**, reaches the surface. Approximately two-thirds of all active volcanoes on land are located along the *Ring of Fire*, which surrounds the Pacific Ocean (Figure 3.2). The volcanoes lie above the subduction zones bordering the Pacific, Nazca, Cocos, Philippine, and Juan de Fuca plates.

The size, shape, and behaviour of volcanoes are closely related to their plate tectonic setting and to their magma chemistry and gas content. Magmas that form volcanoes contain mainly eight elements: oxygen (O), silicon (Si), aluminum (Al), iron (Fe), magnesium (Mg), calcium (Ca), sodium (Na), and potassium (K). The two most abundant elements are Si and O; when combined, they are referred to as silica (SiO_2). The names that geologists apply to volcanic rocks depend on the amount of silica present in the rock. *Basalt*, the most common volcanic rock on Earth, contains between 45 percent and 52 percent SiO_2 by weight. *Andesite* contains more silica than *basalt* does (52 percent to 63 percent) and is not as common. *Dacite* (63 percent to 68 percent silica) and *rhyolite* (more than 68 percent silica) are even less common.

(a)

(b)

▲ **FIGURE 3.1 MOUNT UNZEN LAHARS** Volcanic debris flows, or lahars, from Mount Unzen, the volcano at the top centre of (a) caused much damage in Shimabara, Japan, in 1991. The lahars overflowed the channels (b) that were constructed to contain them, engulfing many houses and other buildings. *(Michael S. Yamashita)*

Magma also contains small but significant amounts of dissolved gases, mostly water vapour and carbon dioxide. Most active volcanic areas have a variety of interesting surface features connected to their underground "plumbing system"—fractures and chambers through which magma, volcanic gases, and hot waters flow.

Volcano Types

Volcanoes have different shapes and eruptive styles that are related to the chemistry and *viscosity*, or fluidity, of their magmas (Table 3.1). Such fluids as cold honey and peanut butter have a high viscosity (low fluidity), whereas water and

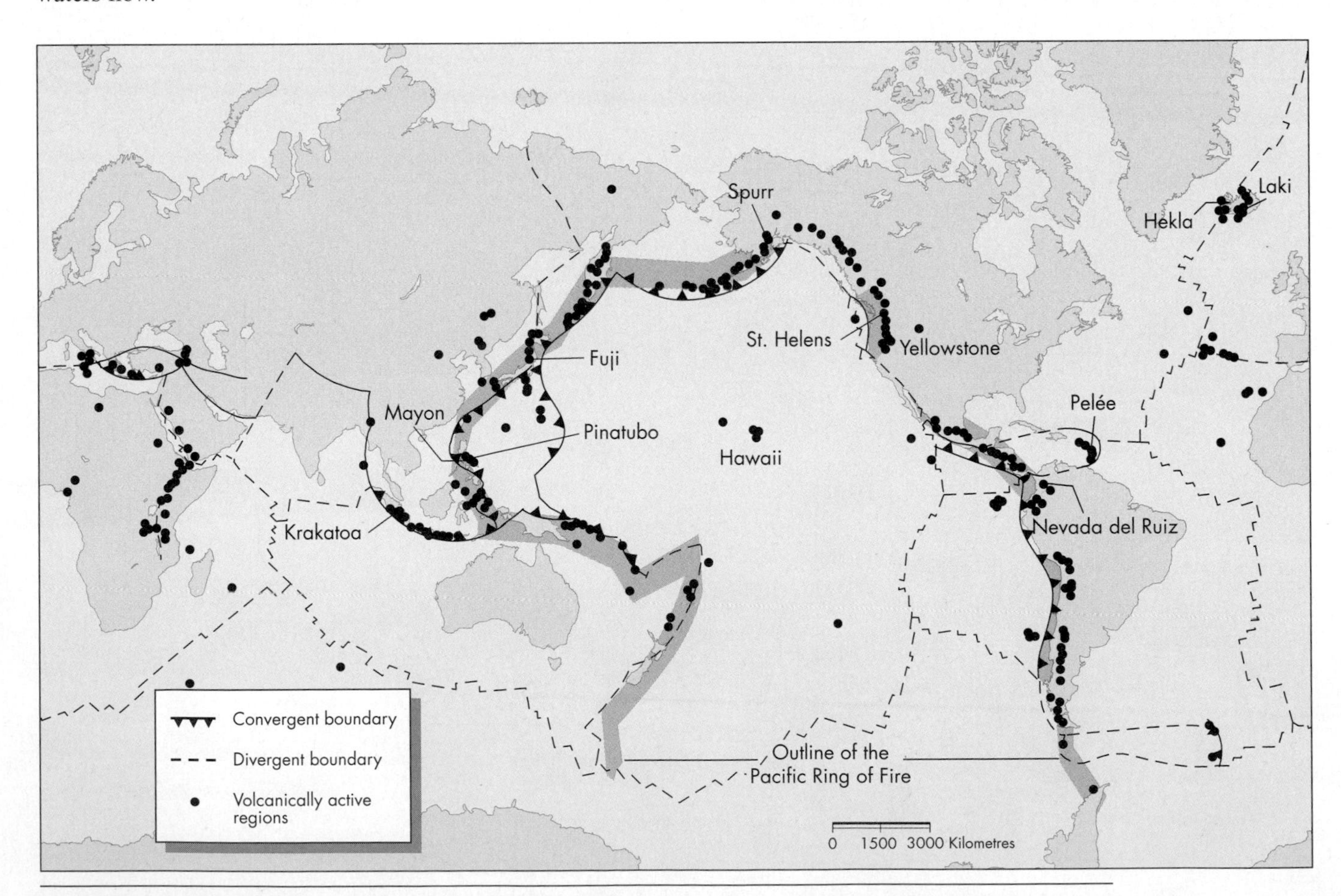

▲ **FIGURE 3.2 THE RING OF FIRE** The red band in this drawing is the *Ring of Fire*, a belt of active volcanoes and frequent earthquakes bordering the Pacific plate. The Ring of Fire includes most of the world's onshore volcanoes. *(Modified from Costa, J. E., and V. R. Baker. 1981. Surficial geology. Fairfax, VA: Tech Books)*

TABLE 3.1 Types of Volcanoes

Volcano Type	Shape	Silica Content of Magma	Viscosity	Rock Type	Eruption Type	Example
Shield volcano	Gentle arch or dome with gentle slopes	Low	Low	Basalt	Lava flows, some explosive activity	Mauna Loa, Hawaii, Figure 3.3
Composite volcano or stratovolcano	Cone-shaped with steep sides	Intermediate	Intermediate	Andesite	Combination of lava flows and explosive activity	Volcan Osorno, Chile, Figure 3.5
Volcanic dome	Dome shaped	High	High	Rhyolite	Highly explosive	Mono Craters, California, Figure 3.8
Cinder cone	Steep cone, commonly with summit crater	Low	Low	Basalt	Explosive activity	Mount Edziza, British Columbia, Figure 3.9

TABLE 3.2 Silica Contents, Temperatures, and Viscosities of Magmas

Silica Content (%)	Temperature of Magma (°C)	Viscosity
65–75	800	High
55–65	900	Intermediate
45–55	1000–1200	Low

Source: From Tarbuck, E. J., and F. K. Lutgens. 2002. Earth: An introduction to physical geology, 7th ed. Upper Saddle River, NJ: Prentice Hall.

warm honey have a low viscosity. Magma viscosity is determined mainly by silica content and temperature (Table 3.2). Magmas with high silica contents are cooler, more viscous, and have more dissolved gases than magmas with relatively low silica contents. As dacite, rhyolite, or other high-viscosity magmas move toward Earth's surface and experience lower pressures at shallow depths, dissolved gases come out of solution, much as carbon dioxide bubbles out of solution when cans or bottles of carbonated soft drinks are opened. Rapid degassing of high-viscosity magmas triggers explosive eruptions, such as those of Mount St. Helens, Washington, in 1980 and Mount Pinatubo in the Philippines in 1991. In contrast, basalt and andesite magmas have low viscosities and relatively low gas contents. When these magmas reach the surface, they tend to flow rather than explode.

Shield Volcanoes The largest volcanoes in the world are **shield volcanoes**. They have gently sloping sides and broad summits. In profile, a shield volcano appears as a broad arc, like a warrior's shield (Figure 3.3). These volcanoes are among the tallest mountains on Earth when measured from their bases, often located on the ocean floor. They are common on the Hawaiian Islands, in Iceland, and on some islands in the Indian Ocean.

Shield volcanoes generally have nonexplosive eruptions of very hot, low-viscosity, basaltic magmas (Figure 3.4). These magmas come from the mantle and have not mixed with silica- and gas-rich magmas derived from continental crust. Basaltic magmas also have not undergone *fractionation*, a process by which magma chemistry slowly changes over time. Fractionation involves progressive crystallization of different

◀ **FIGURE 3.3 SHIELD VOLCANO** Mauna Loa, a classic shield volcano formed from countless eruptions of basalt. Note that the profile of the volcano is very gently curved, like that of a warrior's shield. The volcano's diameter is more than 80 km. *(John S. Shelton)*

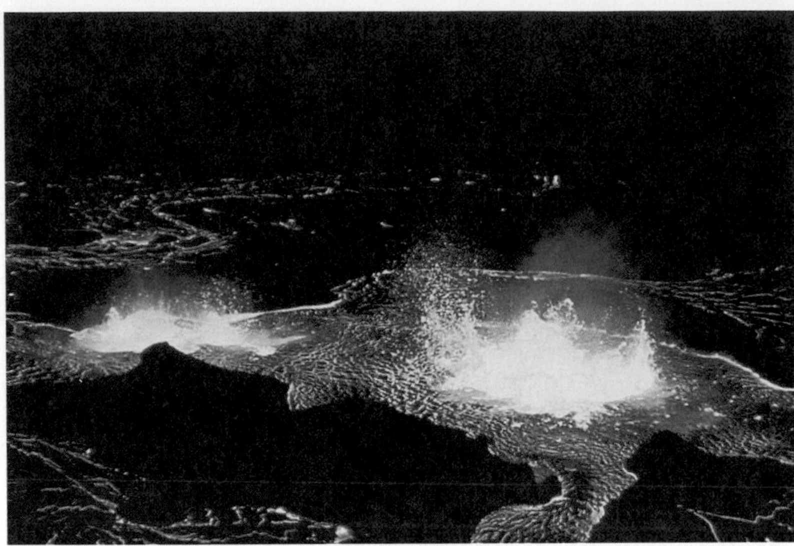

◄ **FIGURE 3.4 LAVA FOUNTAIN** Fiery fountain of lava erupting from Kilauea volcano on the Big Island of Hawaii. *(U.S. Geological Survey)*

minerals in a slowly cooling magma. The first minerals to crystallize are rich in the elements iron, calcium, and magnesium. Later, minerals with abundant sodium and aluminum crystallize at temperatures of 700°C–900°C, and, still later, silica crystallizes in the form of quartz at about 600°C–700°C. As fractionation proceeds, the remaining magma becomes progressively enriched in silica, alumina, and gases. The magma chemistry evolves from that of basalt, to andesite, then to dacite, and finally to rhyolite.

Magma of basaltic composition erupts as **lava** through openings, or *vents*, in the shield volcano and flows down the sides of the volcano, in some cases for dozens of kilometres. Examples of shield volcanoes in Canada include Mount Edziza in northern British Columbia and the Ilgachuz Range in central British Columbia.[4]

Shield volcanoes consist almost entirely of lava flows, but fragmented debris, termed **tephra**, can also be erupted from these volcanoes. Tephra particles range from fine dust, through gravel-sized *lapilli* (2 mm to 64 mm), to large angular *blocks* and smooth-surfaced **bombs** larger than 64 mm across. Accumulations of tephra are referred to as **pyroclastic deposits** (from the Greek *pyro*, meaning "fire," and *klastos*, meaning "broken"). If cemented or fused, the deposits are termed *pyroclastic rocks*.

Lava can flow many kilometres away from a vent through underground *lava tubes*. The walls of the tubes insulate the magma and keep it hot and fluid. Sometimes, lava completely drains from the tubes, leaving long, sinuous caverns. Lava tubes form natural conduits for the movement of groundwater and may cause engineering problems when they are encountered during construction projects.

Composite Volcanoes Mount Fuji, Mount Rainier, and Volcan Osorno (Figure 3.5) are examples of **stratovolcanoes**, also called *composite volcanoes*. The term *stratovolcano* is derived from the interlayered lavas and pyroclastic deposits that characterize these conical volcanoes. Stratovolcanoes erupt less frequently than do active shield volcanoes, but the eruptions involve andesitic or dacitic magmas and are explosive (Figure 3.6). Lavas are relatively silica rich and viscous, and thus they rarely flow more than a few kilometres from vents.

Many active volcanoes in Alaska, Washington, and Oregon are stratovolcanoes. British Columbia also has stratovolcanoes,

◄ **FIGURE 3.5 STRATOVOLCANO** Volcan Osorno in Chile is a beautiful, snow-clad composite volcano that last erupted in 1869. *(Copyright © 1997 Michael Levin. www.MikeLevin.com)*

including Mount Meager and Mount Garibaldi, but they are dormant or inactive, and their original conical forms have been destroyed by erosion.

Don't let the beauty of stratovolcanoes fool you; their eruptions tend to be deadly. Stratovolcanoes are responsible for most of the death and destruction caused by volcanoes throughout history. The 1980 eruption of Mount St. Helens in Washington State was accompanied by a huge landslide and a gigantic lateral blast, similar in form to the blast of a shotgun.[5] The famous eruption of Mount Vesuvius in A.D. 79 destroyed the Roman city of Pompeii (Figure 3.7). Today, 3 million people live within sight of this active volcano. We should consider Vesuvius and other active stratovolcanoes armed and dangerous.

Volcanic Domes Lassen Peak and Mono Craters in California are examples of **volcanic domes**, steep-sided mounds of lava that form around vents from the eruption of highly viscous, silica-rich magmas (Figure 3.8). The most recent series of eruptions from Lassen Peak, between 1914 and 1917, included a tremendous lateral blast that affected a large area.

Cinder Cones **Cinder cones** (also called *scoria cones*) are relatively small volcanoes made of nut- to boulder-sized pieces of red or black basalt (Figure 3.9).[6] The cones are round to oval in surface form and have a crater at their top. Tephra from extinct cinder cones is the "lava rock" used widely in commercial landscaping. Cinder cones are found on the flanks of larger volcanoes, along some normal faults, and along cracks or fissures.

Eruptions in 1943 in the Itzicuaro Valley of central Mexico, about 320 km west of Mexico City, offered a rare opportunity to observe the birth and rapid growth of a volcano at a location where none had existed before. An astounding event occurred on February 20, 1943, following several weeks of earthquakes and thunderous sounds coming from beneath the surface of Earth. As Dionisio Pulido was preparing his cornfield for planting, he noticed that a hole he had been trying to fill for years had reopened in the ground at the base of a knoll. As Señor Pulido watched, the surrounding ground swelled, rising more than 2 m, and sulphurous gases and ash began billowing from the hole. By that night, the hole was ejecting glowing-red rock fragments high into the air. After only five days, the cinder cone had grown to more than 100 m high, and blocks and ash continued to erupt from the

▲ **FIGURE 3.6 EXPLOSIVE ERUPTION** Mount St. Helens erupts violently on May 18, 1980, sending huge quantities of ash and gases high into the atmosphere. Explosive eruptions like this are characteristic of stratovolcanoes. *(Roger Werth, Long View Daily News/Woodfin Camp and Associates)*

▶ **FIGURE 3.7 DESTRUCTION OF POMPEII** The Roman city of Pompeii was buried in suffocating hot ash during an eruption of Mount Vesuvius (top of the photo) in A.D. 79. *(Copyright © BBC)*

◄ **FIGURE 3.8 VOLCANIC DOMES** Mono Craters in California are volcanic domes consisting of rhyolitic and dacitic lavas. The volcanoes range in age from about 40,000 to 600 years old. *(Long Valley Observatory, U.S. Geological Survey)*

vent. In June 1943, basaltic lava began to flow from a fissure at the base of the now 400 m high cone. The lava flow soon overran the nearby village of San Juan Parangaricutiro, leaving little but the church steeple exposed (Figure 3.10). No one was killed in these eruptions, and within a decade Paricutín became a dormant volcano. Nevertheless, during its nine years of eruption, more than 1 billion m^3 of ash and 700 million m^3 of lava erupted from Señor Pulido's cornfield. Crops failed and livestock became sick and died. Although several villages were relocated to other areas, some residents have moved back to the vicinity of Paricutín. Locating property boundaries proved to be difficult because everything was covered by ash and lava, resulting in land ownership disputes.[6]

Maars The violent interaction of magma and groundwater produces **maars**. The conversion of water into steam drives a violent explosion that forms a crater, similar to one made by a meteorite impact.

Ice-Contact Volcanoes Many volcanoes and lava flows erupt beneath or against glaciers. Several active volcanoes lie at the base of Vatnajökull, the largest ice cap in Iceland. These subglacial volcanoes periodically erupt, melting large quantities of ice and thus producing huge outburst floods, termed *jökulhlaups.* Ice-contact volcanoes are also common in some areas formerly covered by Pleistocene ice sheets. Many excellent examples are found in British Columbia, which was repeatedly covered by the *Cordilleran ice sheet.*[7] These ice-contact volcanoes have odd shapes that were produced by rapid chilling of lavas and pyroclastic material when they came in contact with water and ice. Rapid cooling of the lavas produced forms called *pillows,* which broke up as they rolled

◄ **FIGURE 3.9 CINDER CONE** This young cinder cone, which is part of the Mount Edziza shield volcano in northwest British Columbia, has a small crater at its summit. *(Reproduced with the permission of the Minister of Public Works and Government Services Canada, 2007, and courtesy of Natural Resources Canada, Geological Survey of Canada. GSC 2000-129)*

◄ **FIGURE 3.10 RAPID GROWTH OF A VOLCANO** In this 1943 photograph, the Paricutín cinder cone in central Mexico is erupting a cloud of volcanic ash and gases. A lava flow has nearly buried the village of San Juan Parangaricutiro. *(Courtesy of Tad Nichols)*

down the slopes of the submerged volcanoes, forming other types of volcanic deposits called *pillow breccias*. Where the eruptions did not melt through the overlying ice sheet, subglacial mounds were produced. In other cases, the eruptions melted through the ice, producing lava flows that covered the pillow breccias. Such steep-sided, flat-topped volcanoes have been termed *tuyas,* after Tuya Butte in northern British Columbia, where they were first recognized[7] (Figure 3.11). Similar mountains in Iceland are called table mountains because of their flat tops.

An interesting ice-contact lava flow of late Pleistocene age is found in Garibaldi Provincial Park, 65 km north of Vancouver, British Columbia (Figure 3.12). Mount Garibaldi is a deeply dissected, dormant volcano that has a long history of eruptions extending back more than 2 million years. At the end of the Pleistocene, about 12,000 years ago, a lava flow issued from a satellite cone on the flank of Mount Garibaldi. The flow came into contact with a decaying valley glacier in Cheakamus Valley at what is termed "The Barrier." There, the chilled front of the lava flow froze and formed a steep rock face several hundred metres high. Since the glacier in Cheakamus Valley disappeared about 11,000 years ago, the fractured face of The Barrier has repeatedly collapsed, producing large landslides in the valley below, the last of which was in the winter of 1855–1856. A future landslide from The Barrier could block an important highway and damage a dam.

Volcanic Features

A volcano is a complex system, much more than a mountain that simply expels lava and pyroclastic debris from its top. Volcanoes or volcanic areas commonly include craters, calderas, volcanic vents, geysers, and hot springs.

Craters, Calderas, and Vents **Craters** are depressions at the tops of volcanoes that form by explosion or collapse of the summit area. They are usually hundreds of metres to

◄ **FIGURE 3.11 ICE-CONTACT VOLCANO** This table mountain in Iceland, termed Hjorleifshofdi, is an example of a tuya. It formed when lavas erupted at the base of a glacier. The heat of the eruption melted ice, forming a subglacial lake. Lava flowing into the lake chilled in contact with the cold water and left a pile of pillows. As the lake expanded, explosive interactions of erupting magma and water blanketed the pillow lavas with thick pyroclastic material. Finally, when the lake melted through the surface of the glacier, lava flowed over the pyroclastic deposits and cooled as thick columnar-jointed flows. All three stages in the eruption are visible in this photograph. *(Mary Chapman, USGS)*

▲ **FIGURE 3.12 ICE-CONTACT LAVA FLOW IN BRITISH COLUMBIA** The Barrier is a steep, unstable face several hundred metres high that formed when the Clinker Peak lava flow came into contact with a late Pleistocene glacier in Cheakamus valley, north of Vancouver, British Columbia. The flat-topped table, in the background, is a pillar of flat-lying lava flows that erupted into the base of the ice sheet that covered British Columbia at the end of the Pleistocene, about 15,000 years ago. *(Austin Post/U.S. Geological Survey; from Clague, J., and B. Turner. 2003. Vancouver, city on the edge: Living with a dynamic geological landscape. Vancouver, BC: Tricouni Press)*

a couple of kilometres in diameter. Circular to oval depressions up to a few dozen kilometres in diameter that form during explosive ejection of magma and subsequent collapse of a volcano are termed **calderas** (Figure 3.13). Caldera-forming eruptions are the largest and most deadly types of volcanic eruptions, but fortunately they are rare; eruptions that pro-

◄ **FIGURE 3.13 CALDERA CRATER LAKE, OREGON** This water-filled caldera formed during a violent eruption of Mount Mazama volcano about 7700 years ago. *(QT Luong/terragalleria.com)*

◄ **FIGURE 3.14 FLOOD BASALTS** Pancake-like accumulation of nearly flat-lying basalt flows outcropping along the Columbia River in Washington. *(John J. Clague)*

duce calderas several kilometres in diameter occur, on average, once every 200 to 1000 years. The violent eruptions that form large *resurgent calderas* are discussed below.

Volcanic vents are openings through which lava and pyroclastic debris erupt. Some vents are roughly circular; others are elongated cracks called *fissures*. Extensive fissure eruptions have produced huge accumulations of nearly horizontal lava flows called *flood basalts*. Thick flood basalts underlie about 150,000 km^2 of the interior plateaus of southern British Columbia, Washington, Oregon, and Idaho, an area nearly three times the size of Switzerland (Figure 3.14). The lavas range in age from about 17 million to 6 million years old.

Hot Springs and Geysers Groundwater becomes heated when it comes into contact with hot rock. The hot water can discharge at the surface as a *hot spring,* or *thermal spring*. Less commonly, groundwater boils in an underground chamber to produce periodic, steam-driven releases of steam and hot water called *geysers*. World-famous geyser fields are found in Iceland, New Zealand, and Yellowstone National Park in Wyoming (Figure 3.15).

Resurgent Calderas Calderas many dozens of kilometres across are produced by very rare, but extremely violent, eruptions. At least 10 such eruptions have occurred in the last million years, three of which were in North America. A large caldera-forming eruption may produce up to 1000 km^3 of pyroclastic debris consisting mostly of ash—that's enough to cover the island of Manhattan to a depth of about 1.6 km, or four times the height of the Empire State Building. This volume is approximately 1000 times the amount of ash

◄ **FIGURE 3.15 OLD FAITHFUL AND ITS PLUMBING SYSTEM** An eruption of Old Faithful Geyser, Yellowstone National Park, Wyoming. Although the geyser's name implies predictability, eruption intervals vary from day to day and year to year and often change after earthquakes. *(John J. Clague)*

produced by the 1980 eruption of Mount St. Helens! Ash deposits from such an eruption can be 100 m thick near the crater's rim and a metre or so thick 100 km away.[8]

Toba caldera on the Indonesian island of Sumatra is the site of the largest eruption of the last 2 million years. The caldera is 30 km wide and 100 km long; it formed 75,000 years ago when about 2800 km^3 of pyroclastic material were blown high into the atmosphere. Sulphur aerosols produced by this cataclysmic eruption lowered sea-surface temperatures by 3°C–3.5°C for about six years and may have caused nearly complete deforestation of southeast Asia. Genetic evidence suggests that the human species nearly became extinct through the Toba eruption—the total number of people on Earth fell to about 10,000 immediately after the eruption, probably because of famine.

The largest caldera-forming eruptions in North America occurred about 600,000 years ago at Yellowstone National Park in Wyoming and about 700,000 years ago at Long Valley, California. The latter event produced the Long Valley caldera and covered a large area with ash (Figure 3.16). Measurable uplift of the land and a multitude of earthquakes up to **M** 6 in the early 1980s suggested that magma was moving upward beneath Long Valley, prompting the U.S. Geological Survey to issue a potential volcanic hazard warning that was subsequently lifted.

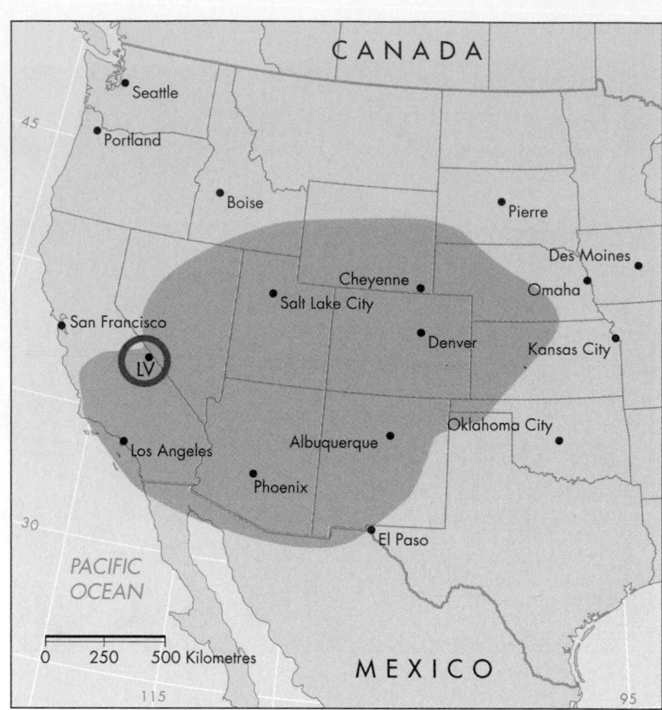

▲ **FIGURE 3.16 WIDESPREAD ASH FALL HAZARD** The area in orange was covered by ash from the Long Valley caldera eruption approximately 700,000 years ago. The red circle around Long Valley (LV) has a radius of 120 km and encloses the area that would receive more than 1 m of ash if a similar eruption were to occur again. *(From Miller, C. D., D. R. Mullineaux, D. R. Crandell, and R. A. Bailey. 1982. Potential hazards from future volcanic eruptions in the Long Valley–Mono Lake area, east-central California and southwest Nevada—A preliminary assessment. U.S. Geological Survey Circular 877)*

Volcano Origins

A caldera-producing eruption can develop quickly, in a few days to a few months. Subsequent, intermittent, lesser volcanic activity can linger for 1 million years. The Yellowstone event created hot springs and geysers, including Old Faithful, and sporadic eruptions occurred in the Long Valley caldera until very recently. Both sites are still capable of eruptions because magma is present at shallow depths beneath the caldera floors. Both are considered resurgent calderas because their floors have slowly domed upward since the explosive eruptions that formed them.

Volcanism is directly related to plate tectonics. More specifically, the tectonic setting determines the type of volcano that will be present (Figure 3.17):

1. ***Subduction zones.***
   In a subduction zone, oceanic crust, which is denser than continental crust and commonly covered by thick, wet sediments, is carried into Earth's mantle. Rising heat and pressure dry out the subducting crust in a process called *dehydration*. At depths of several dozen kilometres, the water expelled from the descending crust rises and changes the chemical composition of the overlying mantle. The presence of water lowers the melting temperature of the overlying mantle rocks and causes them to melt, forming magma that rises through the crust to erupt on the surface.

Stratovolcanoes occur at subduction zones and thus are the most common type found around the Pacific Rim. For example, volcanoes in southwest British Columbia, Washington, Oregon, and California are associated with the Cascadia subduction zone (Figure 3.18). More than 80 percent of terrestrial volcanic eruptions have come from volcanoes above subduction zones.[9] The dominant volcanic rock in this setting is andesite, which is produced by mixing of basaltic magmas with continental crust and fractionation. Continental crust has a higher silica content than basaltic magma; thus, andesite has a silica content between those of basalt and rhyolite.

2. ***Mid-ocean ridges.***
   In other areas, plates move away from one another instead of colliding. Commonly, this occurs in the oceans along mid-ocean spreading ridges, where basaltic magma derived directly from the asthenopshere, part of Earth's upper mantle (Chapter 1), rises to the ocean floor to create new crust. This magma mixes very little with other materials, therefore the lavas are made almost entirely of low-viscosity basalt. Where spreading ridges occur on land, such as in Iceland, shield volcanoes are formed.

3. ***Hot spots beneath the oceans.***
   Volcanoes are also found where hot mantle material wells up beneath a plate at a stationary point rather than at the boundary between two plates. The upwelling mantle material, focused on a single spot, creates a volcano. However, the plate continues to slowly move and a series of volcanoes form, becoming progressively older in the direction of plate movement. These chains of volcanoes

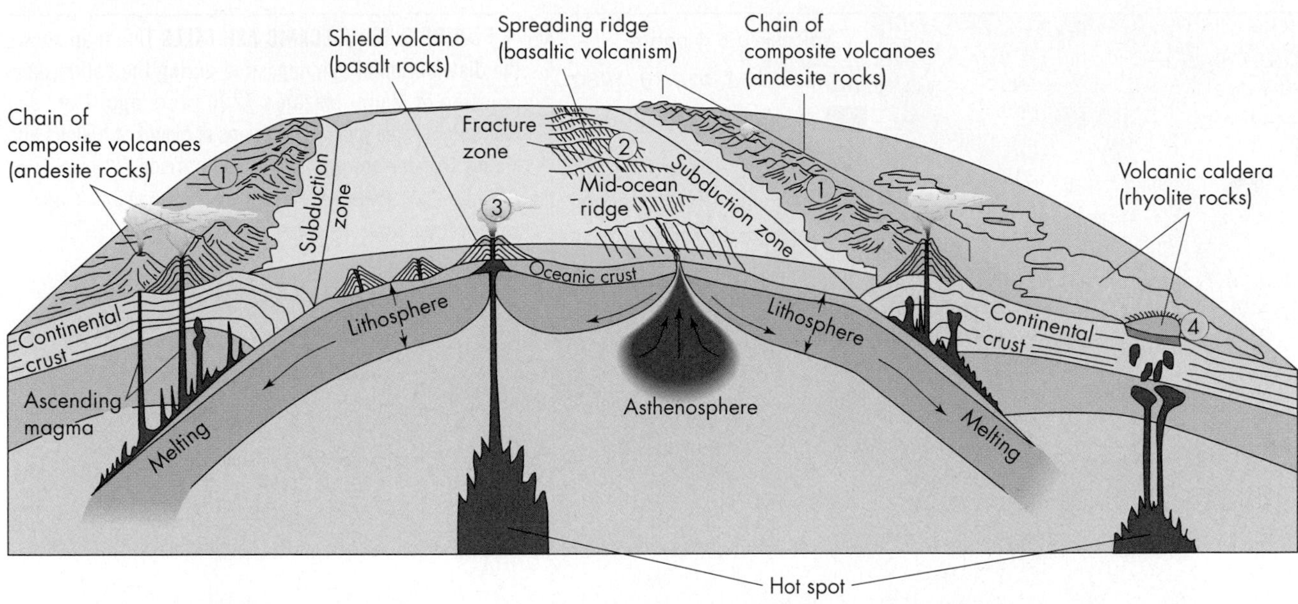

▲ **FIGURE 3.17 VOLCANIC ACTIVITY AND PLATE TECTONICS** An idealized diagram showing plate tectonic processes and their relation to volcanic activity. Numbers refer to explanations in text. *(Modified from Skinner, B. J., and S. C. Porter. 1992. The dynamic Earth, 2nd ed. New York: John Wiley)*

are termed *hot-spot* volcanoes. The most famous example is the Hawaiian Islands, located within the Pacific plate.[10] The Hawaiian Islands have been built up from the seafloor through submarine eruptions of basaltic lava similar to those at mid-ocean ridges. The source of the magma appears to be a hot spot that has been stationary for many millions of years. With time, plate motion has produced a chain of volcanic islands running southeast

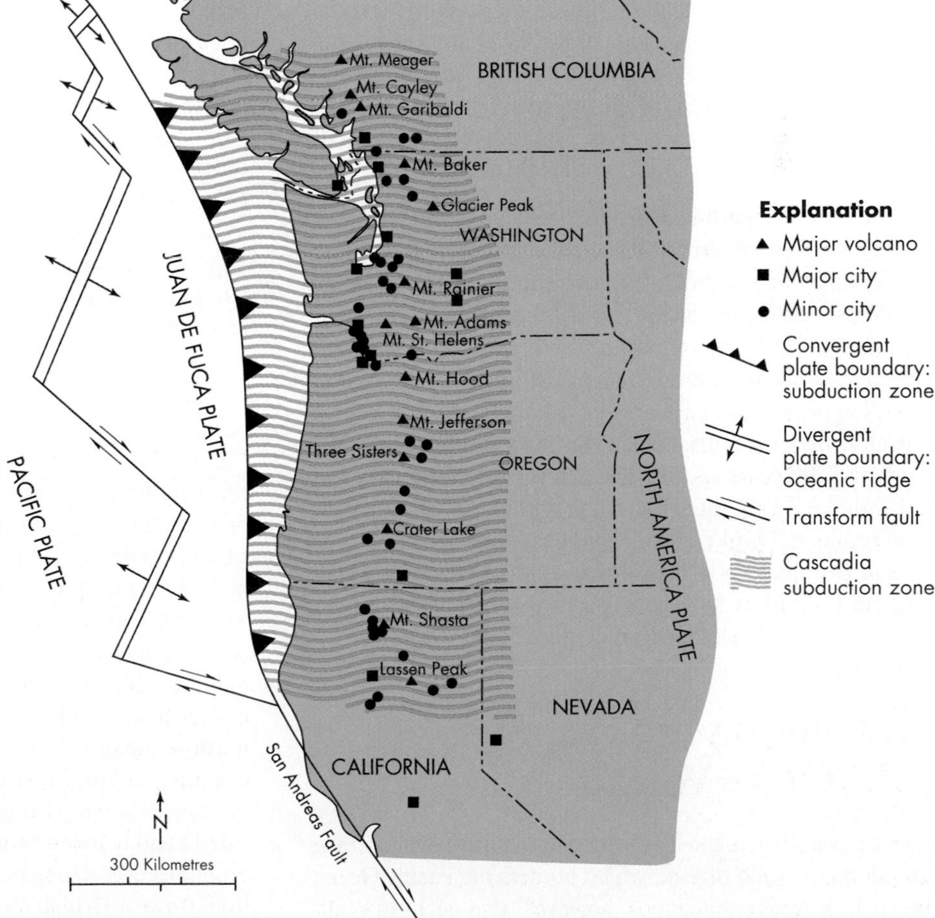

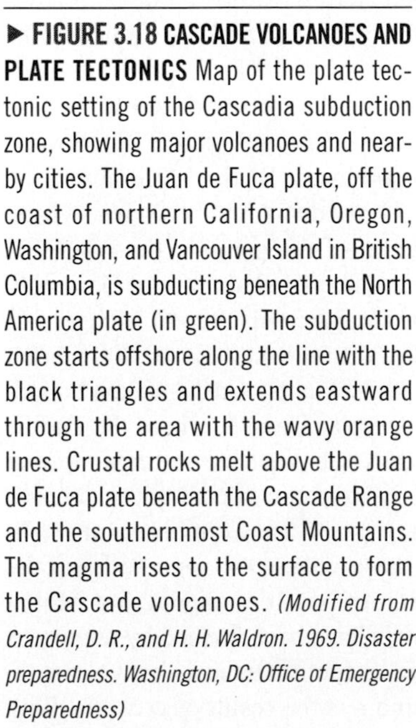
▶ **FIGURE 3.18 CASCADE VOLCANOES AND PLATE TECTONICS** Map of the plate tectonic setting of the Cascadia subduction zone, showing major volcanoes and nearby cities. The Juan de Fuca plate, off the coast of northern California, Oregon, Washington, and Vancouver Island in British Columbia, is subducting beneath the North America plate (in green). The subduction zone starts offshore along the line with the black triangles and extends eastward through the area with the wavy orange lines. Crustal rocks melt above the Juan de Fuca plate beneath the Cascade Range and the southernmost Coast Mountains. The magma rises to the surface to form the Cascade volcanoes. *(Modified from Crandell, D. R., and H. H. Waldron. 1969. Disaster preparedness. Washington, DC: Office of Emergency Preparedness)*

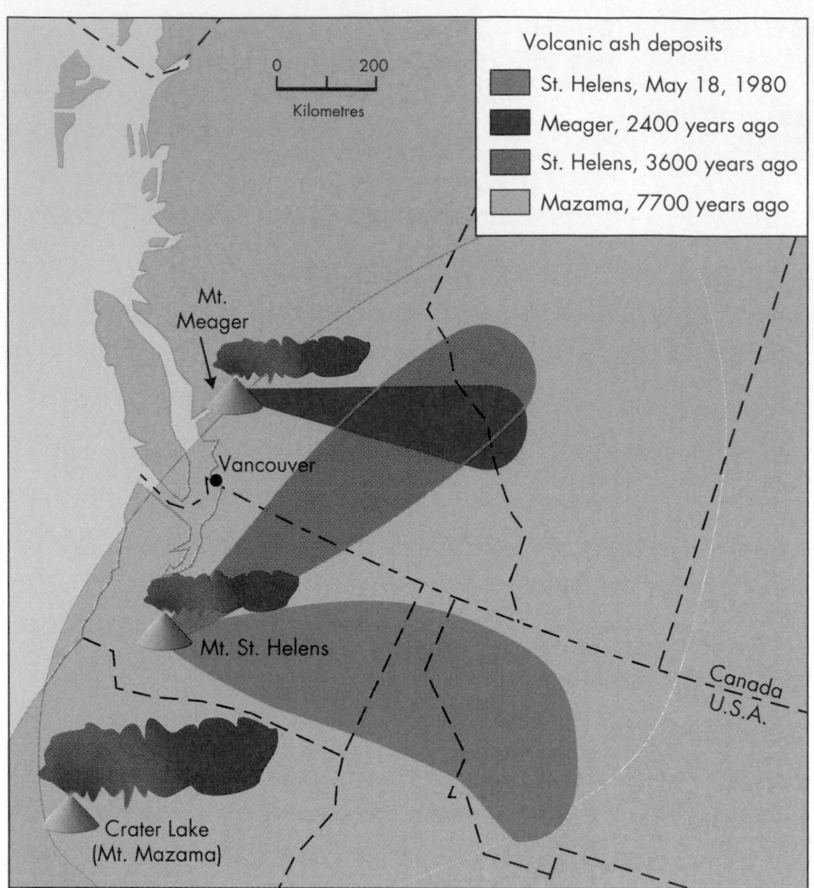

◄ **FIGURE 3.19 VOLCANIC ASH FALLS** This map shows the distribution of ash deposited during the cataclysmic eruption of Mount Mazama 7700 years ago. The "ash plumes" of three younger eruptions of Mount St. Helens and Mount Meager are plotted for comparison. *(Clague, J. and B. Turner. 2003. Vancouver, city on the edge: Living with a dynamic geological landscape. Vancouver, BC: Tricouni Press)*

to northwest. The island of Hawaii is presently near the hot spot and is experiencing active volcanism and growth. Islands to the northwest, such as Molokai and Oahu, appear to have moved off the hot spot, because their volcanoes are no longer active. The oldest volcanoes of the Hawaiian chain lie west of Kauai.

4. ***Hot spots beneath continents.***
Caldera-forming eruptions occur in this tectonic setting. They may be extremely explosive and violent, and they are associated with dacitic and rhyolitic magmas. As mentioned earlier, the largest of these eruptions in North America occurred more than a half million years ago at Yellowstone National Park, Wyoming; and Long Valley, California. A smaller, caldera-forming eruption happened about 7700 years ago at what is now Crater Lake, Oregon (Figure 3.13). Crater Lake lies within the caldera produced by the explosion of Mount Mazama. Ash from this eruption has been found throughout western North America and as far north as central British Columbia, Alberta, and Saskatchewan (Figure 3.19).[11]

3.2 Geographic Regions with Active Volcanoes

As we've established, most volcanoes on Earth's land surface occur along the Ring of Fire, which borders the Pacific Ocean (Figure 3.2). Active volcanoes, however, also occur in other settings: hot spots (Hawaii, Long Valley, Yellowstone), mid-ocean ridges (Iceland), and continental rift zones (East Africa). The highest risk of volcanic activity in Canada and the United States is in the mountainous regions of the Pacific Northwest, northwest and central British Columbia, the Aleutian Islands, and Yellowstone Park (Figure 3.20). More than 90 percent of North America is free of risk from local volcanic activity, but the effects of a large caldera explosion in the western United States would likely be felt far from the source in the form of ash fall and ash clouds in the atmosphere.

Young volcanoes in Canada are restricted to British Columbia and southern Yukon Territory (Figure 3.21). Several eroded stratovolcanoes in southwest British Columbia form the northern part of the Cascade volcanic chain, which owes its origin to subduction of the oceanic Juan de Fuca plate beneath North America. They include Mount Garibaldi, Mount Cayley, and Mount Meager; only Mount Meager has had an eruption in postglacial time (the past 10,000 years). Similar volcanoes are also present in the Alaska-Yukon boundary area and north of the Aleutian Trench, where the Pacific plate is subducting beneath North America. A large number of Pleistocene and postglacial volcanoes occur within a broad north-trending belt in northwest British Columbia and southernmost Yukon. Most of these volcanoes are small and the product of a single eruption of basaltic magma, but Mount Edziza and Hoodoo Mountain have been formed by numerous eruptions over a long period. Scientists believe that volcanism in northwest British Columbia is the result of crustal rifting

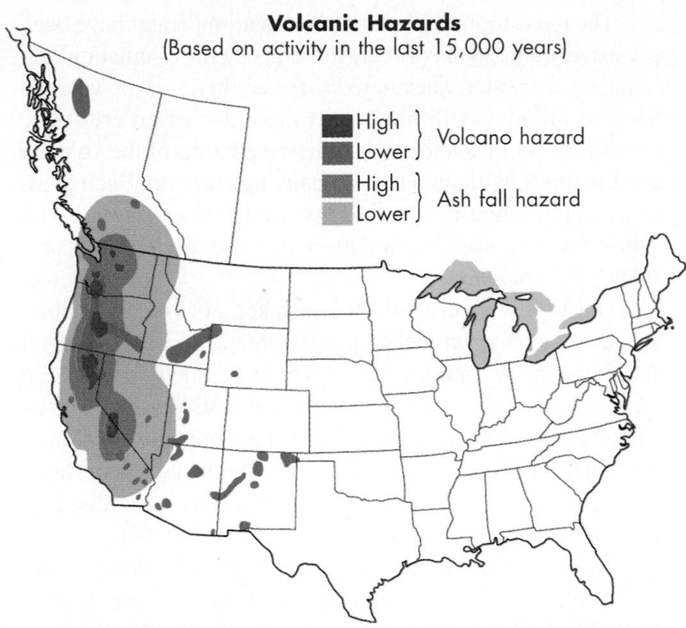

▲ **FIGURE 3.20 CANADIAN AND U.S. VOLCANIC HAZARD** Volcanic hazard for Canada and the contiguous United States based on activity during the last 15,000 years. The red colours show high and lower local volcanic hazard. The grey area is at risk of receiving 5 cm or more of ash fall from large explosive eruptions. *(Adapted from U.S. Geological Survey)*

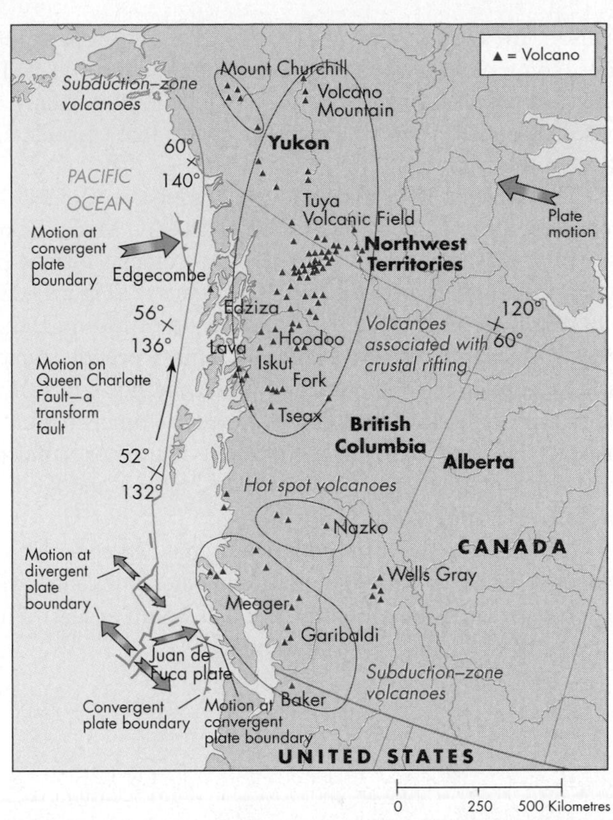

▲ **FIGURE 3.21 VOLCANOES AND THEIR TECTONIC ENVIRONMENT IN WESTERN CANADA** Recent volcanic activity in western Canada occurs in three tectonic settings: (1) along convergent plate boundaries, where one plate subducts beneath another (for example, Mount Garibaldi and Mount Meager); (2) in regions where the North America plate is rifting (for example, Mount Edziza and the Iskut River area); and (3) at hot spots where upwelling magma breaks through the crust (Nazko). The green lines delineate transform faults. Zones of different types of volcanism are circled. *(Reproduced with the permission of the Minister of Public Works and Government Services Canada, 2007, and courtesy of Natural Resources Canada, Geological Survey of Canada; as seen in Christoperhson, R. W., and M-L. Byrne. 2006. Geosystems: An introduction to physical geography. Toronto: Pearson Education Canada)*

caused by right-lateral faulting along the Pacific-North America plate boundary to the west (the Queen Charlotte and Fairweather faults). A third group of volcanoes extends in a westerly direction from Nazko in central British Columbia to the Pacific Coast near Bella Coola. The volcanoes increase in age to the west—Nazko volcano (Figure 3.22) is only 8000 years old, whereas the dykes that fed former volcanoes on the coast are up to 14 million years old. The simplest interpretation of this age trend is that the volcanoes formed over a hot spot in the mantle and moved to the west, in a conveyor-belt

◀ **FIGURE 3.22 NAZKO VOLCANO** This small volcano formed about 8000 years ago and is the youngest and easternmost volcano in a possible hot-spot chain of volcanoes that extends across the west half of central British Columbia. *(Catherine Hickson)*

fashion, off the hot spot.[12] Small, mainly basaltic volcanoes, some of which are postglacial in age, occur in Wells Gray Provincial Park in eastern British Columbia. Many of these volcanoes erupted beneath ice sheets that episodically covered the area.

The volcano that poses the greatest risk to Canada is, ironically, in the United States. Glacier-cloaked Mount Baker in northern Washington is a great stratovolcano formed by numerous eruptions over the past 30,000 years[13] (Figure 3.23). The relatively undissected conical shape of Mount Baker reflects its status as an active volcano. It most recently erupted in the mid-1800s, and venting of gases and hot fluids from the summit crater in the late 1970s provided a timely reminder that the volcano is active. The hazards of greatest concern at Mount Baker are ash fall, landslides, lahars, and the filling of river valleys with sediment.

A major eruption of Mount Baker could spread ash over Vancouver, Abbotsford, Chilliwack, and other cities and towns in southern British Columbia. The ash would at least temporarily paralyze air and ground traffic.

The rocks around Mount Baker's summit crater have been extensively altered to soft clay minerals by the circulating hot, acidic groundwater. The altered rocks could fail if the volcano became inflated with magma at the onset of an eruption. Landslides could also occur on the steep flanks of the volcano at other times, without an accompanying eruption. Such landslides could range in size from small debris avalanches and debris flows to massive collapses of the entire summit or a side of the volcano.

During an eruption of Mount Baker, hot volcanic debris would mix with water melted from snow and ice on the summit and flanks of the mountain to form large lahars that would rush down nearby river valleys. In the worst-case scenario, a large lahar might reach the Bellingham area, as apparently happened about 7000 years ago. Lahars might also enter Baker Lake, a reservoir near the base of Mount Baker, and displace enough water to overtop the dam or cause it to fail.

Failure of the dam would be catastrophic for downstream communities along the Skagit River in Washington. A lahar or series of lahars moving down the Nooksack River on the

◀ **FIGURE 3.23 MOUNT BAKER** This active volcano looms above the Vancouver skyline. A major eruption would melt the glaciers on Mount Baker, causing floods and lahars in the valleys that drain the mountain. *(C. J. Hickson [top], John J. Clague [bottom])*

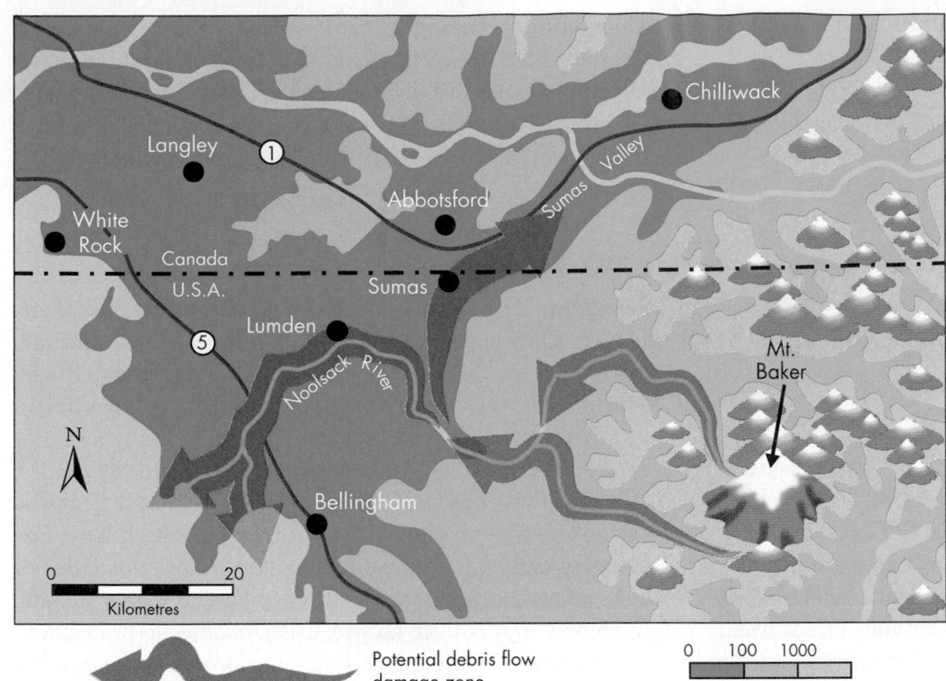

◀ **FIGURE 3.24 MOUNT BAKER LAHAR** A large volcanic debris flow (lahar) moving down the Nooksack River valley from Mount Baker might spill into British Columbia at Sumas. *(Clague, J., and B. Turner. 2003. Vancouver, city on the edge: Living with a dynamic geological landscape. Vancouver, BC: Tricouni Press)*

north side of Mount Baker could deposit enough material to force water or debris into British Columbia at Sumas (Figure 3.24).

Large landslides or lahars would increase sediment loads to rivers, such as the Skagit and Nooksack, and cause them to build up their beds. Settlements and other infrastructure on the valley floors might be buried or flooded as the level of the riverbeds rose.

3.3 Effects of Volcanoes

Worldwide, 50 to 60 volcanoes erupt each year, including 2 or 3 in the United States, mainly in Alaska.[1] Many eruptions are in sparsely populated areas, causing little, if any, loss of life or economic damage. In contrast, eruptions near densely populated areas can be catastrophic[14] (Table 3.3). Approximately

TABLE 3.3 Selected Historic Volcanic Eruptions

Volcano or City	Year	Effect
Vesuvius, Italy	A.D. 79	Destroyed Pompeii and killed 16,000 people; city was buried by volcanic ash and rediscovered in 1595
Skaptar Jökull, Iceland	1783	Killed 10,000 people (many died from famine) and most of the island's livestock; also killed crops as far away as Scotland
Tambora, Indonesia	1815	Global cooling; produced "year without a summer"
Krakatoa, Indonesia	1883	Tremendous explosion; 36,000 deaths from tsunami
Mount Pelée, Martinique	1902	Pyroclastic flow killed 30,000 people in a matter of minutes
La Soufrière, St. Vincent	1902	Killed 2000 people
Mount Lamington, Papua New Guinea	1951	Killed 6000 people
Villarica, Chile	1963–1964	Forced 30,000 people from their homes
Mount Helgafell, Heimaey Island, Iceland	1973	Forced 5200 people to evacuate their homes
Mount St. Helens, Washington	1980	Debris avalanche, lateral blast, and lahars killed 57 people and destroyed more than 100 homes
Nevado del Ruiz, Colombia	1985	Eruption generated lahar that killed at least 22,000 people
Mount Unzen, Japan	1991	Pyroclastic flows and lahars killed 41 people and burned more than 125 homes; more than 10,000 people evacuated
Mount Pinatubo, Philippines	1991	Tremendous explosions, pyroclastic flows, and lahars combined with a typhoon killed more than 300 people; several thousand people evacuated
Montserrat, Caribbean	1995	Explosive eruptions, pyroclastic flows; south side of island evacuated, including capital city of Plymouth; several hundred homes destroyed

Source: Data are partially derived from Ollier, C. 1969. Volcanoes. Cambridge, MA: MIT Press.

500 million people live close to volcanoes, and in the past 100 years nearly 100,000 people have been killed by volcanic eruptions, 28,500 in the 1980s alone.[1,14] Densely populated countries with many active volcanoes, such as Japan, Mexico, the Philippines, and Indonesia, are particularly vulnerable.[2] Several active or potentially active volcanoes in western North America are near cities with populations of more than 500,000 (Figure 3.18).

3.4 Hazards Associated with Volcanoes

Volcanic hazards can be subdivided into *primary* (or direct) *effects* of eruptions and *secondary* (or indirect) *effects*. Lava flows, ash fall, volcanic bombs, pyroclastic flows, pyroclastic surges, lateral blasts, and poisonous gases are primary effects (Figure 3.25). Secondary effects include lahars, debris avalanches, other landslides, groundwater and surface water contamination, floods, fires, and tsunami. Large eruptions can also cool Earth's atmosphere for a year or so.[8,15]

The size of a volcanic eruption can be quantified by using a scale called the Volcanic Explosivity Index (VEI), which takes into account the volume of material erupted, the height of the eruption cloud, the duration of the main eruptive phase, and other parameters to assign a number on a linear scale from 0 to 9. The May 1980 eruption of Mount St. Helens, which destroyed about 630 km^2 of land, expelled 1.4 km^3 of magma, and produced an eruption cloud 24 km high, has a value of 5 on the VEI. In contrast, the last large eruption from the Yellowstone caldera, which occurred about 600,000 years ago and expelled more than 1000 km^3 of magma, has a VEI value of 8.

Lava Flows

Lava flows are one of the most common products of volcanic activity. They happen when magma reaches the surface and flows out of the central crater or when it erupts from a fissure or vent on the flank of a volcano. The three major types of lava take their names from the volcanic rocks they form: basalt, by far the most abundant of the three; andesite; and rhyolite.

Lava flows can be fluid and move rapidly, or they can be viscous and move slowly. Basaltic lavas, which have low viscosity and high eruptive temperatures, have velocities of up to a few kilometres per hour. They harden with a smooth, commonly ropy surface texture, called *pahoehoe* (pronounced pa-hoy-hoy) (Figure 3.26). Cooler, more viscous, basaltic lava flows move at rates of as little as a few metres per day and harden with a rough, blocky surface texture, termed *aa* (pronounced ah-ah) (Figure 3.27). Most lava flows travel slowly enough that people and animals are able to move out of their way.[16] Property and environmental damage, however, can be extensive. For example, lava flows can dam rivers, kill resident fish, and form a barrier to migrating fish, as happened

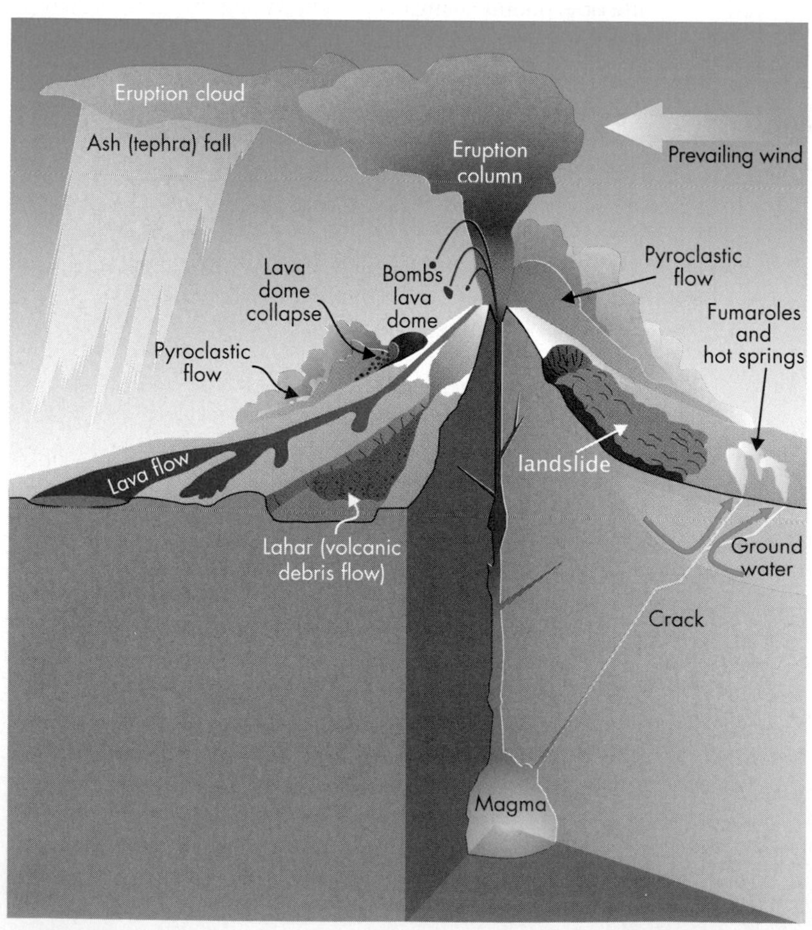

◄ **FIGURE 3.25 VOLCANIC HAZARDS** Hazards associated with explosive stratovolcanoes, such as Mount Meager, Mount St. Helens, and Mount Rainier. *(U.S. Geological Survey)*

▲ **FIGURE 3.26 PAHOEHOE LAVA FLOW** The ropy surface texture of a pahoehoe lava flow engulfing a home at Kalapana, Hawaii, in 1990. This flow and others produced by eruptions of Kilauea volcano destroyed more than 100 structures, including the Kilauea National Park Service Visitors Center. *(Paul Richards/© Bettmann/CORBIS)*

▲ **FIGURE 3.27 AA LAVA FLOW** A blocky aa lava flow engulfing a building during an eruption on the island of Heimaey, Iceland, in 1973. The blocky surface texture develops on cooler, slower-moving basaltic lava. *(Solarfilma ehf)*

along the Nass River in central British Columbia during an eruption of Tseax volcano a few hundred years ago.[17]

Lava flows from the flank of Kilauea volcano in Hawaii, which began in 1983 and continue sporadically to this day, have caused major property damage. This series of eruptions is the longest and largest in Kilauea's recent history.[3] By 1992, more than 50 structures in the village of Kalapana had been destroyed by lava flows, including the Kilauea National Park Visitors Center. The village of Kalapana has virtually disappeared, and it will be many decades before much of the land is productive again.

Pyroclastic Flows and Surges

The most lethal eruptive phenomena are **pyroclastic flows**, which are dense avalanches of hot gas, ash, and volcanic rock fragments that cascade down the slopes of a volcano during an explosive eruption (see the chapter-opening photograph on page 73). Pyroclastic flows are also known as ash flows or *nueé ardentes* (French for "glowing clouds"). Some pyroclastic flows form when the towering column of ash rising above the volcano collapses. Others form when a less energetic eruption boils over the edge of a crater or caldera, or when a lava flow or dome on a steep slope collapses. Large pyroclastic flows can move at speeds of up to 150 km/h and run dozens of kilometres from their source.[6] They destroy buildings and other objects in their paths by impact, burial, or incineration. People caught in a pyroclastic flow have no chance of survival.

Pyroclastic flows have killed more people than any other volcanic phenomenon in the past 2000 years.[18] The most deadly event in recent history occurred in 1902 on the Caribbean island of Martinique. On the morning of May 8, a pyroclastic flow roared down Mount Pelée and through the town of St. Pierre, killing an estimated 30,000 people[19] (Figure 3.28). The only two survivors were severely burned.

Pyroclastic surges are dense clouds of hot gas and rock debris produced by explosive interaction of water and magma. They are more violent and travel much faster than pyroclastic flows—pyroclastic surges have been clocked at more than 360 km/h.

▲ **FIGURE 3.28 PYROCLASTIC FLOW DESTROYS ST. PIERRE** The town of St. Pierre on the Caribbean island of Martinique was obliterated by an incandescent pyroclastic flow in May 1902. Only 2 of the town's 30,000 residents survived. *(Library of Congress, Prints & Photographs Division. LC-USZ62-25077)*

Lateral Blasts

Gas, ash, and rock fragments can be blown horizontally from the side of the mountain at the start of an eruption. These **lateral blasts** eject debris at tremendous speeds and can be very destructive. A lateral blast during the initial stage of the May 18, 1980, eruption of Mount St. Helens flattened forest up to 25 km from the vent.[5]

Ash Fall

A tremendous quantity of finely broken volcanic rock and gas is blown high into the atmosphere during many volcanic explosions (Figure 3.6). The particles are carried downwind and rain out to produce **ash fall**. Volcanic ash can carpet hundreds or even thousands of square kilometres of land around a volcano, creating several hazards:

- Vegetation, including crops and trees, may be destroyed. The long-term impact of ash on forestry and agriculture, however, can be beneficial because ash enriches the soil and increases soil moisture.
- Surface water may be contaminated. Very fine ash particles clog the gills of fish and kill other aquatic life. Ash can also temporarily increase the acidity of the water. Studies of steelhead and salmon in streams west of Mount St. Helens showed that fish populations suffered severely after the 1980 eruptions. In addition to the increased acidity of surface waters, many other lethal secondary effects occurred, including the loss of fish-spawning habitat and riparian vegetation.
- Buildings may be damaged as ash piles up on roofs (Figure 3.29). As little as 1 cm of ash adds an extra 2.5 t of weight on an average house with a 140 m^2 roof.
- Respiratory illnesses, such as asthma and bronchitis, are aggravated by contact with volcanic ash and associated aerosols.[16] Coarser particles can lodge in the nose and eyes. *Silicosis* has been attributed to long-term exposure to volcanic ash.
- Ash can damage mechanical and electrical equipment. It is abrasive and, at great distances from the volcano, is fine enough to work its way into the moving parts of machinery. Electrical power can be disrupted because transformers are poor conductors of heat and will overheat and explode when covered by only a few millimetres of ash.
- Ash can affect aircraft flying at high altitudes. The effect of ash on jet engines was discovered in 1982 when a Boeing 747 jet on a flight over Indonesia encountered ash erupted from Galunggung volcano. All four engines failed, but the plane was able to make a successful emergency landing in Jakarta. In 1989 a KLM 747 jet on its way to Japan flew through a cloud of volcanic ash from Redoubt Volcano in Alaska. Power to all four of its jet engines was lost and the plane began a silent, 4270 m fall toward the Talkeetna Mountains below.[20] The 231 passengers on board endured a tense five minutes before the captain was able to restart the engines. When engine power was regained, the aircraft was only 1220 m above the highest mountain peaks. Fortunately, the pilot was able to make an emergency landing in Anchorage, Alaska. Repairs to the aircraft cost an estimated $80 million.[6] Ash abrades the outer parts of jet engines and can melt inside the engines at the high temperatures at which they operate. Abrasion damages the engine fan blades and melting ash disrupts the mixing of air and fuel in the combustion chamber, leading to engine shutdown. The ash also abrades the exterior of the aircraft, frosting cockpit windows and landing lights.

Poisonous Gases

A number of gases, including water vapour (H_2O), carbon dioxide (CO_2), carbon monoxide (CO), sulphur dioxide (SO_2), hydrogen sulphide (H_2S), chlorine (Cl), and hydrofluoric acid (HF), are emitted during volcanic eruptions. In some cases, these gases reach toxic concentrations. A notable example occurred at Lake Nyos, a deep crater lake on a dormant volcano in the Cameroon highlands of West Africa. On an August night in 1986, with little warning other than a loud rumbling, Lake Nyos released a misty cloud of dense carbon dioxide gas. Nearly odourless, the gas cloud flowed from the volcano

◄ **FIGURE 3.29 VOLCANIC ASH ON ROOFS** Ash may increase the load on the roofs and walls of buildings by several tonnes. The building shown here collapsed and burned from hot ash and lava during an eruption in Iceland in 1973. *(Owen Franken/Stock Boston)*

into valleys below, displacing the air. It spread silently through five villages, suffocating 1742 people, an estimated 3000 cattle, and numerous other animals[21] (Figure 3.30a and 3.30b).

Carbon dioxide continues to accumulate at the base of Lake Nyos and another release could occur in the future.[21] Although the area around the lake was closed after the 1986 disaster to all but scientists studying the hazard, thousands of people have returned to farm the land. Scientists have installed an alarm system at the lake that will sound if carbon dioxide levels become high. A pipe extends from the lake bottom to a degassing fountain on the surface of the lake (Figure 3.30c), allowing carbon dioxide gas to escape slowly into the atmosphere. The fountain is releasing a little more carbon dioxide gas than is naturally seeping into the lake, thus the hazard is being slowly reduced. Additional pipes with degassing fountains will be necessary to completely eliminate the hazard.

Sulphur dioxide can react with water in the atmosphere to produce sulphuric acid and acid rain downwind of an eruption. Sulphuric acid damages crops, and the increased acidity of water collected in cisterns can leach heavy metals into drinking water. Sulphur dioxide vented from the Laki volcano in Iceland in 1783 killed people and livestock and damaged crops. Many of the survivors died from starvation.

Fluorine killed and disfigured livestock after the 1845 and 1970 eruptions of Hekla volcano in Iceland.[22] The 1783 Laki eruption contaminated pastures in Europe with fluorine and caused the death of grazing cattle in as little as two days.[23]

In Japan, volcanoes are monitored to detect releases of such poisonous gases as hydrogen sulphide. When high concentrations of gases are detected, sirens are sounded to advise people to evacuate to higher ground.

Volcanoes can also produce a type of smog known as *vog* (volcanic material, *v*, and fog, *og*). Eruptions of Kilauea have emitted sulphur dioxide, steam, and other volcanic gases, which at times react with water vapour to produce vog and acid rain. The southeast part of the island of Hawaii can be blanketed with a thick, blue acidic haze that far exceeds air quality standards for sulphur dioxide. Public health warnings have been issued because small, acidic aerosol particulates and sulphur dioxide can induce asthma attacks and cause other respiratory problems. Residents and visitors have reported breathing difficulties, headaches, sore throats, watery eyes, and flu-like symptoms when exposed to vog. In addition, acid

(a)

(b)

(c)

▲ **FIGURE 3.30 POISONOUS GAS FROM DORMANT VOLCANO** (a) In 1986 Lake Nyos released a large volume of carbon dioxide. *(T. Oban/Corbis/Sygma)* (b) The gas asphyxiated 1742 people and about 3000 cattle. *(© Peter Turnley/CORBIS)* (c) Gas being released from the bottom waters of Lake Nyos with a degassing fountain in 2001. *("Nyos degassing system conceived, designed and manufactured by a French company, Data Environment and the University of Savoie, France." Courtesy of J. C. Sabroux)*

rain has made the water in some shallow wells and household rainwater-collection systems undrinkable. Acidic rainwater extracts lead from metal roofing and water pipes and may have caused elevated lead levels in the blood of some residents.[24]

Edifice or Sector Collapse

The flank of a volcano may collapse during an eruption or even at times when there is no eruptive activity. Flank collapse can increase the size and strength of an eruption. A massive landslide during the early moments of the May 18, 1980, eruption of Mount St. Helens catastrophically depressurized the volcano and caused a very different eruption than had been predicted.[5] As magma moves up into the throat of a volcano from the magma chamber below, the volcano inflates, much like blowing up a balloon. The volcano's slopes become oversteepened and unstable during the magma's ascent. Ground shaking associated with steam venting, magma ascent, or an earthquake can trigger a collapse, which, if large enough, is called a *sector collapse.*

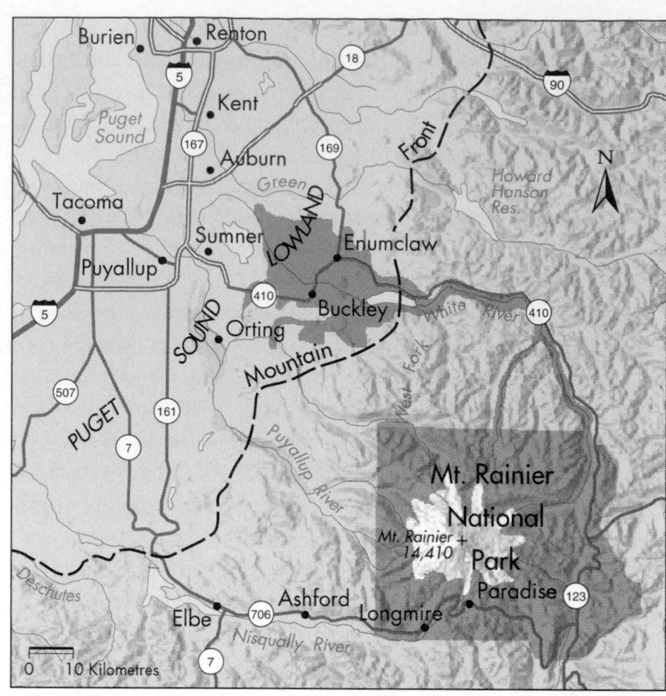

▲ **FIGURE 3.31 LAHARS** A map of Mount Rainier and vicinity showing the extent of the 5600-year-old Osceola mudflow in the White River valley (coloured orange) and the 500-year-old Electron mudflow (coloured beige) in the Puyallup River valley. *(From Crandell, D. R., and D. R. Mullineaux. U.S. Geological Survey Bulletin 1238)*

Debris Flows and Other Mass Movements

The most serious secondary effects of volcanic activity are **debris flows**, also known by their Indonesian name, *lahars.* Lahars are produced when large amounts of loose volcanic ash and other pyroclastic material become saturated with water and rapidly move downslope (Figure 3.31). Even relatively small eruptions of hot volcanic material may quickly melt large volumes of snow and ice on a volcano. The rapid melting produces a flood of meltwater that mixes with pyroclastic material eroded from the slope of the volcano to create a debris flow.

Volcanic debris flows are fast-moving mixtures of fine sediment and large rocks that have a consistency similar to wet concrete. Debris flows can travel many kilometres down valleys from the flanks of the volcano where they formed.[16] For example, early in 1990, a pyroclastic flow from Mount Redoubt, a volcano in Alaska, moved across Drift Glacier. It rapidly melted snow and ice and transformed into a debris flow with a discharge comparable to the Mississippi River at flood stage. Fortunately, the event was in an isolated area, so no lives were lost.[14]

Debris flows can occur days, weeks, or years after an eruption. Explosive eruptions may remove all vegetation from areas around a volcano, making them vulnerable to debris flows and other landslides. In addition, the flanks of the volcano may be covered with loose tephra, which is easily mobilized into debris flows by heavy rains or rapid snowmelt.

Gigantic lahars have moved down the flanks of volcanoes in the Pacific Northwest in both historic and prehistoric time. Two of these occurred on Mount Rainier (Figure 3.31). Approximately 5600 years ago, the "Osceola mudflow" moved 1.9 km^3 of sediment up to 80 km from the summit of the volcano.[25] Deposits of the younger, 500-year-old "Electron mudflow" reached about 56 km from the volcano into now-populated suburbs of Seattle.[25] Observers of a lahar the size of the Electron mudflow might see a wall of mud the height of a house moving toward them at close to 30 km/h. With the flow moving at 8.3 m/s, the observers would need a car headed in the right direction to escape being buried alive.[16] Hundreds of thousands of people now live on the deposits of the Osceola and Electron mudflows (Figure 3.32), and there is no guarantee that a similar flow will not occur again.

One of the world's worst historical volcanic disasters was a lahar. Nevado del Ruiz in Colombia erupted on November 13, 1985. In spite of the fact that the volcano was monitored and warnings were provided, a series of lahars killed 25,000 of the 30,000 residents of the town of Armerio.[26] A similar lahar in 1845 killed the same town's entire population of 1400 people.

Mount St. Helens 1980–2006: From Lateral Blasts to Lava Flows

The May 18, 1980, eruption of Mount St. Helens in Washington State (Figure 3.33) exemplifies the many types of things that happen during an explosive volcanic eruption. The eruption, like many natural events, was unique and complex, making generalizations somewhat difficult. Nevertheless, we have learned a great deal from Mount St. Helens, and the story is not yet over.

Mount St. Helens awoke in March 1980, after 120 years of dormancy, with earthquakes and small explosions created by the boiling of groundwater as it came in contact with hot rock. By May 1, a prominent bulge had developed on the north flank of the mountain (Figure 3.34a). The bulge grew at a rate of about 1.5 m per day until, at 8:32 A.M. on May 18, an **M** 5.1 earthquake triggered a huge debris avalanche (Figure 3.34b), causing 2.3 km^3 of rock, the entire area of the bulge, to break away and shoot down the north flank of the mountain, displacing water in nearby Spirit Lake (see Professional Profile). The avalanche then struck and overrode a ridge 8 km to the north and made an abrupt turn before moving 18 km down the Toutle River valley.

During the flank collapse, Mount St. Helens erupted with a lateral blast from the area of the former bulge (Figure 3.34b and c). The blast moved at speeds of more than 480 km/h, faster than a bullet train, and levelled timber over an area of about 600 km^2 (Figure 3.35a).[27] Shortly thereafter, pyroclastic flows began to sweep down the north slope of the volcano.

Within an hour of the lateral blast, a large column of ash and gases had reached an altitude of approximately 19 km, extending more than 4 km into the stratosphere (Figure 3.34d). The eruption continued for more than nine hours; in that time about 1 km^3 of volcanic ash was ejected from the volcano. The ash fell over a large area of Washington, northern Idaho, and western and central Montana; traces of ash were recorded in southwest Canada. The ash cloud drifted eastward to New England (Figure 3.35b), and in less than three weeks had circled Earth.

The entire northern slope of the volcano, which is the upper part of the North Fork of the Toutle River watershed, was devastated. Forested slopes were transformed into a grey barren landscape of volcanic ash, rocks, blocks of melting glacier ice, narrow gullies, and hot steaming pits[27] (Figure 3.36).

The first of several lahars occurred minutes after the start of the eruption. The lahars raced down the valleys of the north and south forks of the Toutle River at speeds of 29 km/h to

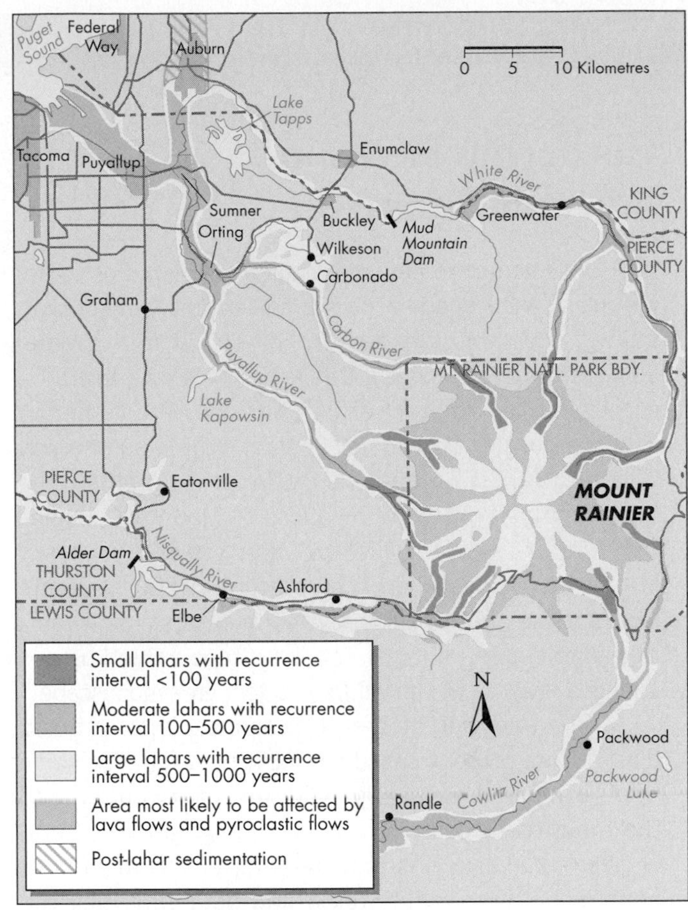

▲ **FIGURE 3.32 LAHAR HAZARD POTENTIAL** A map of Mount Rainier and vicinity showing areas at risk from lahars, lava flows, and pyroclastic flows. The Seattle and Tacoma suburbs of Puyallup, Sumner, Orting, and Auburn are at risk. *(Hoblitt et al. 1998. USGS Open-File Report 98-428)*

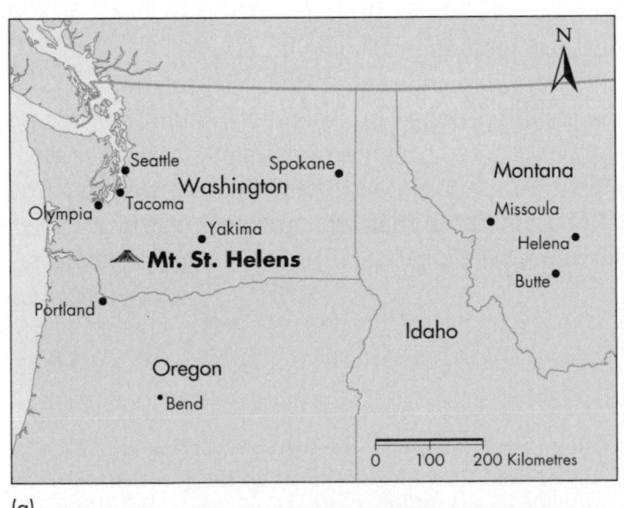

▲ **FIGURE 3.33 MOUNT ST. HELENS BEFORE AND AFTER** (a) Location of Mount St. Helens. (b) The volcano before (in photo held aloft) and after the May 18, 1980, eruption. Much of the north side of the volcano slid away during the eruption, and the summit was lowered by about 400 m. The lateral blast shown in Figure 3.34 originated in the amphitheatre-like area at the top centre of the photograph. *(Jim Richardson, National Geographic Image Collection)*

PROFESSIONAL PROFILE

Catherine Hickson, Volcano Scientist

Why does someone become a volcanologist? For some, it's an interest sparked by a grade-school project with baking soda and vinegar; for others, it is a special episode on the Discovery Channel. For a rare few, it is witnessing an eruption of historic size. Dr. Catherine Hickson got her start in volcanology in just such a way (Figure 3.A). "It was really a matter of luck rather than 'good' timing that found me close to Mount St. Helens that fateful day," says Hickson. She was 14 km east of Mount St. Helens when it erupted in 1980. "We were forced to flee, but I was captivated by the colossal events that unfolded in minutes. The landscape around us was changed from a pristine wilderness to a grey moonscape."

Of particular interest to Hickson was the "directed blast," more properly called a pyroclastic surge. The surge that devastated more than 360 km^2 of terrain around the mountain was driven by both magma and steam. Hickson explains: "As magma entered the volcano, it heated the surrounding rocks and began melting the capping glaciers. The mountain stewed in this acidified brew for weeks and then finally gave way." That fateful morning, the energy of the magma and the pressurized water was unleashed, taking 57 lives.

"Volcanoes and eruptions are a fascinating field of scientific study, but for me, the impact of eruptions on humans is equally important," says Hickson. Through her experiences at Mount St. Helens, she was given initial insight into the brutal reality of what happens when people are faced with a volcanic threat. "The eruption changed me. Since then I have tried to devote time and energy to making our scientific knowledge of natural hazards understandable to the public and policymakers. How do we make emergency and land-use planners listen to what geologists are saying and, most importantly, take action?" she asks.

Hickson has made countless presentations to professionals and nonprofessionals over the years. In 2002, she created a multinational project in South America with the help of funding from the Canadian International Development Agency and the governments of Argentina, Bolivia, Chile, Colombia, Ecuador, Peru, and Venezuela. This successful project is building capacity in Andean countries to reduce the risk of hazardous natural processes, including volcanic eruptions.

▲ **FIGURE 3.A CATHERINE HICKSON, VOLCANOLOGIST** Cathie Hickson was camping just east of Mount St. Helens when it erupted on May 18, 1980. The eruption was a life-defining moment for her—she subsequently trained for a career in volcanology and currently works to reduce the risk that people face from volcanic eruptions. *(Cathie Hickson)*

"What we really need to do," Hickson notes, "is to think about the long-term threat of natural hazards on not only our current built environment but also the environment our children and grandchildren will be living in—let's not leave them a legacy of destroyed cities because we were careless in our development practices."

—John J. Clague

55 km/h, threatening the lives of people camped along the river.[27]

On the morning of May 18, 1980, two young people on a fishing trip were sleeping about 36 km downstream from Spirit Lake in the Toutle Valley. They were awakened by a loud rumbling noise from the river, which was covered by felled trees. They attempted to run to their car, but water from the rising river poured over the road, preventing their escape. A mass of mud then crashed through the forest toward the car, and the couple climbed onto its roof to escape the mud. They were safe only momentarily, as the mud pushed the vehicle over the bank and into the river. Leaping off the roof, they fell into the river, which was by now a rolling mass of mud, logs, collapsed train trestles, and other debris. The two were

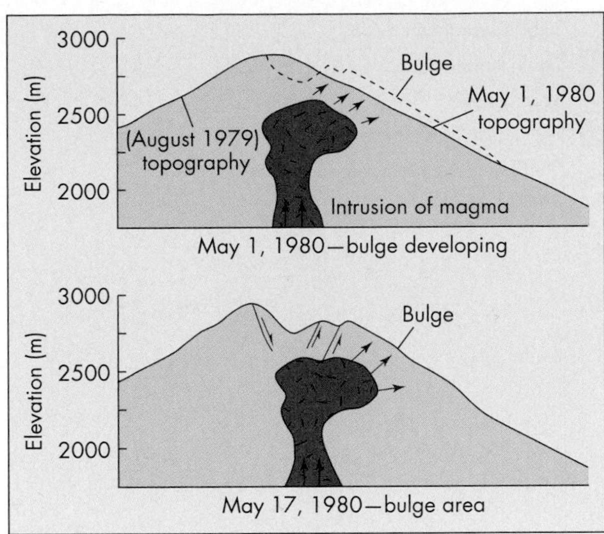

(a) Before eruption May 1 to 17, 1980

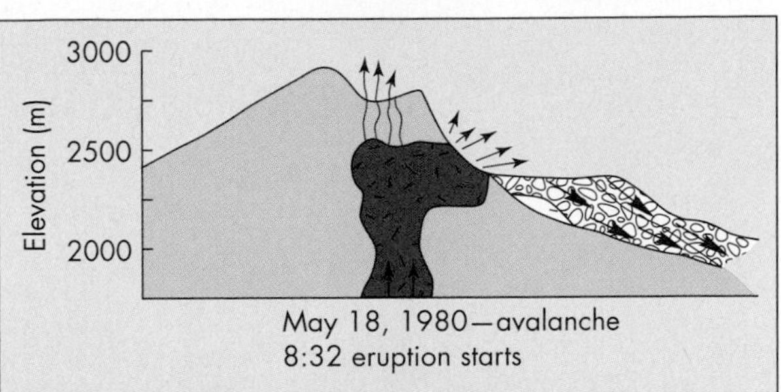

(b) Eruption starts May 18,1980

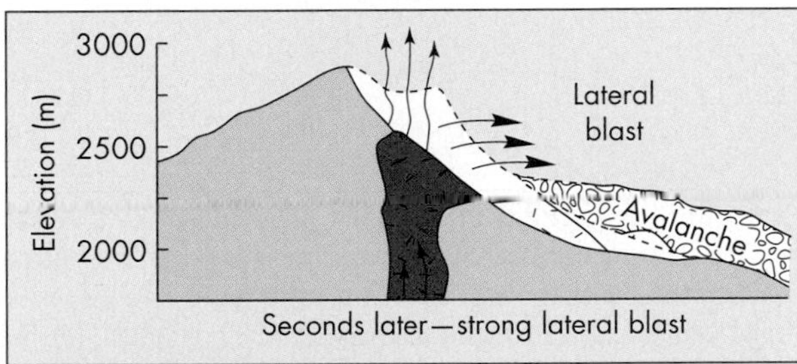

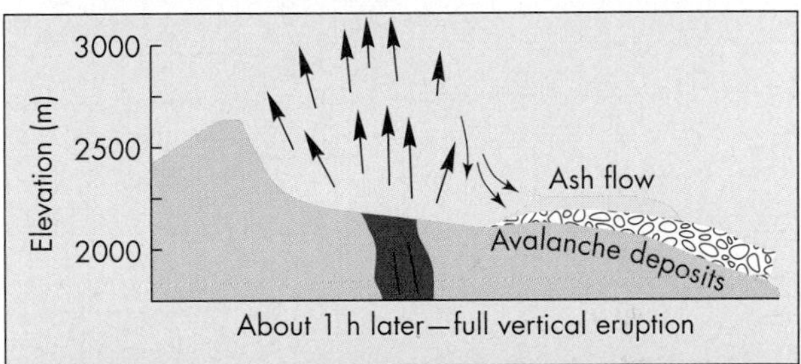

(c) Seconds after eruption starts

(d) About an hour after eruption starts

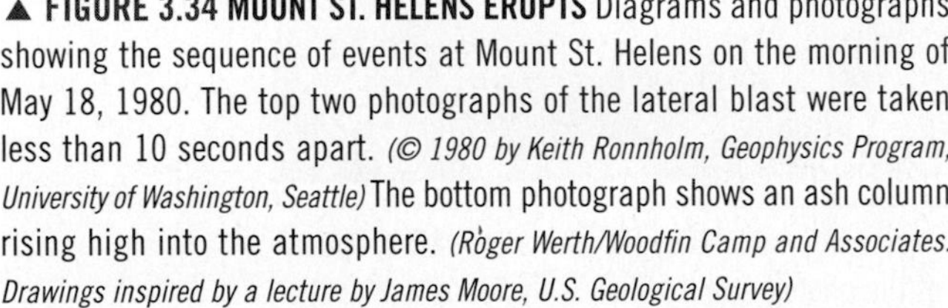

▲ **FIGURE 3.34 MOUNT ST. HELENS ERUPTS** Diagrams and photographs showing the sequence of events at Mount St. Helens on the morning of May 18, 1980. The top two photographs of the lateral blast were taken less than 10 seconds apart. *(© 1980 by Keith Ronnholm, Geophysics Program, University of Washington, Seattle)* The bottom photograph shows an ash column rising high into the atmosphere. *(Roger Werth/Woodfin Camp and Associates. Drawings inspired by a lecture by James Moore, U.S. Geological Survey)*

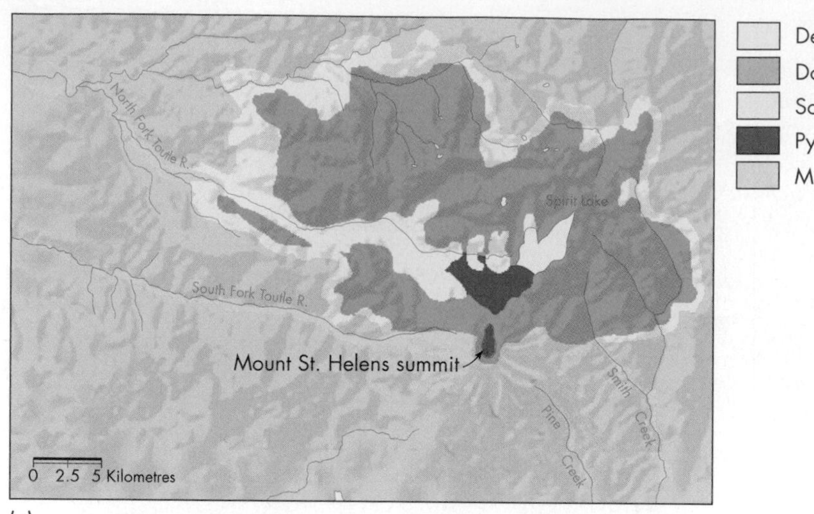

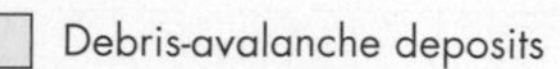

(a)

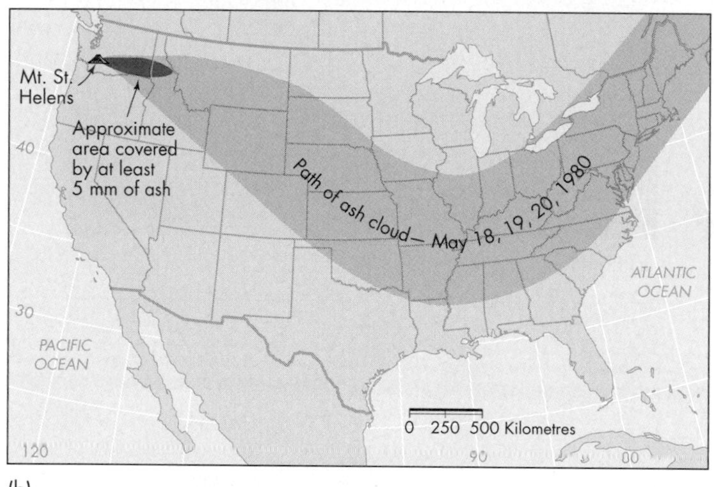

(b)

◀ **FIGURE 3.35 ERUPTION DEPOSITS AND ASH CLOUD** (a) A map of the area around Mount St. Helens, showing the extents of debris-avalanche deposits, tree blowdown, pyroclastic flow deposits, and lahars associated with the May 18, 1980, eruption. (b) The path of the ash cloud (orange) from the 1980 eruption. The area covered by at least 5 mm of ash is shown in red. *(Data are from U.S. Geological Survey publications)*

▲ **FIGURE 3.36 BARREN LANDSCAPE PRODUCED BY ERUPTION** The desolate landscape produced by the May 18, 1980, eruption of Mount St. Helens. The entire valley, from the centre left to lower right corner of the photograph, is filled with debris avalanche deposits. *(John J. Clague)*

carried downstream approximately 1.5 km, disappearing several times beneath the flow, before another family of campers spotted and rescued them.

When the volcano could be viewed again after the eruption, the top of the mountain was gone. What was originally a symmetrical snow-clad volcano was now a huge, steep-walled amphitheatre facing northward (Figure 3.33b), and what was originally Spirit Lake was now filled with sediment and trees. The horizontal blast, debris avalanche, pyroclastic flows, and lahars had devastated an area larger than Toronto, Ontario. The eruption killed 57 people, and associated flooding destroyed more than 100 homes. Enough timber to build 50,000 houses was flattened by the blast. The total damage from the eruption was estimated to exceed US$1 billion.

Nineteen small eruptions occurred during the first six years following the cataclysmic eruption in May 1980. Lava flows during these smaller eruptions built a lava dome to a height of approximately 267 m above the 1980 crater floor (Figure 3.37). Earthquake activity increased several times between 1989 and 2004, accompanied by small explosions, ash flows, and lahars.

On September 23, 2004, following a period of quiescence, Mount St. Helens returned to life when magma began moving up toward the crater floor. A subsequent eruption built a new lava dome south of the dome built between 1980 and 1986 (Figure 3.37). The eruption continued until mid-2005 and was observed continuously by the U.S. Geological Survey Cascades Volcano Observatory. The mountain is monitored with a network of automated seismographs and GPS satellite receivers to detect earthquakes and ground deformation, aircraft to collect gas samples, acoustic instruments to detect lahars, and video cameras to continuously record events.[28]

By 1998, 18 years after the main eruption, plants and animals had returned to Mount St. Helens, and parts of the mountain were green. However, the mounds of landslide deposits are still prominent, a reminder of the catastrophic event of 1980. Mount St. Helens National Monument has a new visitors' centre that has attracted more than 1 million visitors.[29] The volcano remains active.

3.5 Linkages between Volcanoes and Other Natural Hazards

Volcanoes are intimately linked to several other natural hazards. We have already stressed the relation between volcanoes and plate tectonics, specifically the relation between plate tectonic setting and types of eruptive activity. Volcanoes are also linked to fire, earthquakes, landslides, tsunami, floods, and climate change.

Volcanic eruptions are not a major cause of fire, but it isn't difficult to imagine the link between these phenomena. Plants and human-built structures commonly catch fire when they are struck by lava flows, pyroclastic flows, and superheated bombs. In January 2002, Africa's most destructive volcanic eruption in 25 years sent residents of the Democratic Republic of Congo fleeing raging fires ignited by lava flows (Figure 3.38). One flow sparked an explosion that killed 60 people.

Earthquakes commonly precede or accompany volcanic eruptions as magma rises through Earth's crust to the surface. Weeks of earthquakes preceded the first eruption at Paricutín volcano west of Mexico City. Some earthquakes preceding an eruption may be large enough to cause damage.

Landslides are possibly the most common side effect of volcanic activity. As discussed above and in Case Study 3.1, sector collapses and lahars can do great damage and take many lives.

Volcanic eruptions beneath glaciers commonly cause devastating floods, termed *jökulhlaups*. Iceland is at greatest

◄ **FIGURE 3.37 NEW DOME IN CRATER** Steam and volcanic gases rise from a new dome that formed in the crater of Mount St. Helens in 2004. Unlike the older snow-covered dome directly to the right (north), heat from the new dome melts snowfall. The opening in the crater wall at the right is where the lateral blast occurred in 1980 (Figure 3.34). *(Ken McGee/U.S. Geological Survey)*

risk from eruption-triggered floods. Recurrent floods from beneath the Vatnajökull ice cap have damaged highways, bridges, and farmland.

As mentioned previously, sector collapses at volcanoes can trigger tsunami. In extreme cases, waves can reach great heights close to the point of failure, but they attenuate rapidly as they move away from the volcano and are unlikely to cause catastrophic damage thousands of kilometres away.

Lastly, volcanic eruptions can affect climate. A cloud of ash and sulphur dioxide remained in the atmosphere for more than a year after the 1991 Mount Pinatubo eruption (Figure 3.39). The ash particles and aerosol droplets scattered incoming sunlight and slightly cooled the atmosphere during the year following the eruption.[2,31]

3.6 Natural Service Functions of Volcanoes

Although active volcanoes pose a serious threat to those who live near them, they provide important natural service functions. Perhaps their greatest gift to us occurred billions of years ago when gases and water vapour released from vol-

3.1 CASE STUDY

Volcanic Landslides and Tsunami

What may be the largest active landslides on Earth are located on Hawaii. They are up to 100 km wide and 20 km long and extend from a volcanic rift zone on land out to sea. These landslides creep at rates of about 10 cm per year and contain blocks the size of Manhattan Island. Some scientists worry that one of these creeping rock masses may fail catastrophically and generate a fast-moving submarine debris avalanche. The debris avalanche, in turn, could trigger a huge tsunami that would wash marine debris hundreds of metres above sea level onto nearby islands and cause damage along shores around the Pacific Basin. Fortunately, such events are rare; the average recurrence interval seems to be about 100,000 years or so.[3]

Other huge, volcano-related landslides have been documented on the Canary Islands in the Atlantic Ocean off the west coast of Africa. Six landslides occurred on Tenerife (Figure 3.B), the largest of these islands, during the past several million years, including one less than 150,000 years ago. The seafloor north of Tenerife is covered by 5500 km^2 of landslide deposits, an area nearly as large as the greater Toronto area.[30]

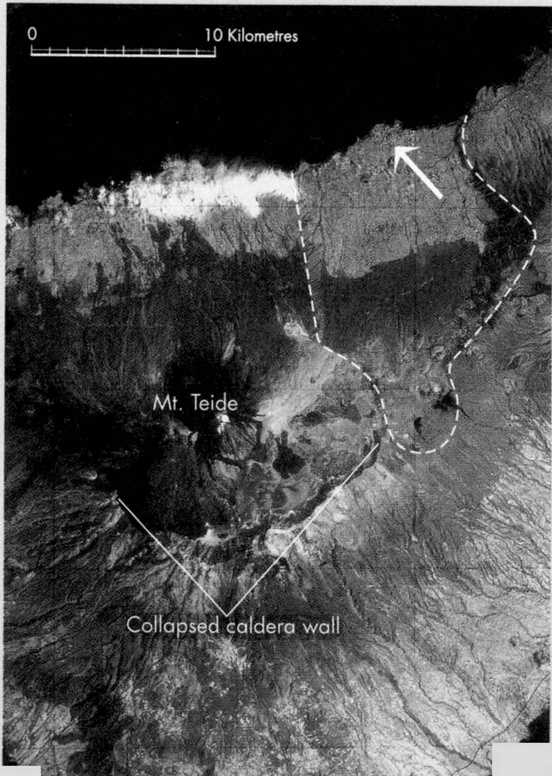

◄ **FIGURE 3.B GIANT LANDSLIDE ON TENERIFE** (a) An aerial view of part of the island of Tenerife, the largest island of the Canary Islands. La Cañadas caldera and Mount Teide (elevation 3700 m) are labelled. *(Espagna Instituto Geografico Nacional)* (b) The white dashed line outlines the extent of the Orotova landslide, one of many large landslides on the island. The white arrows in (a) and (b) point to the seaward end of the landslide. *(Jose Barea/Espagna Instituto Geografico Nacional)*

▲ **FIGURE 3.38 LAVA IGNITES FIRES IN GOMA** This fire was ignited by a lava flow from Nyiragongo volcano in the Democratic Republic of Congo in January 2002. More than 400,000 people in the city of Goma were displaced by fires and lava flows. *(Getty Images, Inc.)*

canoes began to form the atmospheric and hydrologic systems that allowed life to appear and evolve. Volcanoes also provide us with fertile soils, a source of power, recreational opportunities, and new land.

Volcanic Soils

Volcanic eruptions provide lavas and pyroclastic deposits, which, when weathered, are an excellent growth medium for plants. The nutrients produced by weathering of volcanic materials allow such crops as coffee, maize, pineapple, sugar cane, and grapes to thrive. However, these fertile soils encourage people to live in hazardous areas. So, although volcanic soils provide an important resource, nearby volcanic activity can make it difficult to safely use that resource.

Geothermal Power

The internal heat associated with volcanoes can be used to generate power for nearby urban areas. Geothermal electrical power is being generated in Hawaii, California, Nevada, Italy, New Zealand, and other areas, and much of the city of Reykjavík, Iceland, is heated with geothermal energy. An important benefit of geothermal energy is that it can be a renewable resource. However, the steam driving the system

(a)

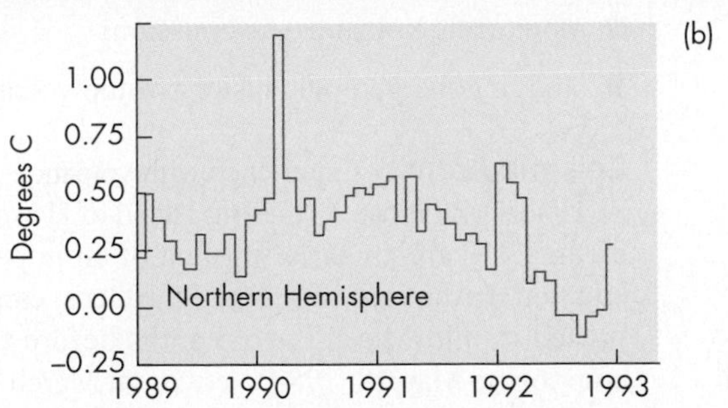

◄ **FIGURE 3.39 VOLCANIC ERUPTION TEMPORARILY COOLS CLIMATE** (a) An eruption of Mount Pinatubo in 1991 ejected huge amounts of volcanic ash and sulphur dioxide up to about 30 km into the atmosphere. Ash particles remained in the upper atmosphere and circled Earth for more than a year. (b) The sulphur dioxide and, to a lesser extent, ash temporarily lowered Earth's average surface temperature. The Mount Pinatubo eruption was the second largest in the twentieth century. *(Photo by D. Harlow/U.S. Geological Survey, Denver; graph courtesy of Climatic Research Unit)*

◀ **FIGURE 3.40 GEOTHERMAL POWER** The Wairakei geothermal field on the North Island of New Zealand was one of the first in the world to be developed. *(Copyright © 2002–2005 Ulrich Neumann—All Rights Reserved)*

cannot be removed faster than it is restored naturally or it will become depleted, as has happened at Rotorua in New Zealand. Although geothermal energy is a renewable resource, it cannot be exploited without some adverse environmental impacts. Collector wells, surface pipes, and electrical transmission lines can be unsightly and occupy large tracts of land (Figure 3.40), and the water produced by the conversion of steam to power may be acidic or contain high concentrations of heavy metals.

Recreation

Heat associated with volcanoes provides recreational opportunities. Health spas and hot springs are developed in volcanic areas. Volcanoes also provide opportunities for hiking, snow sports, and education. About 3 million tourists visit Yellowstone National Park each year to see its geysers and hot springs, and Kilauea volcano attracts more than 1 million visitors annually. Volcanoes in Wells Grey and Garibaldi provincial parks in British Columbia are also popular tourist attractions.

Creation of New Land

In our discussion of the benefits of volcanoes, we would be remiss not to mention that eruptions are responsible for creating some of the land we inhabit. Iceland, Hawaii, and many other oceanic islands would not exist without volcanoes!

3.7 Minimizing the Volcanic Hazard

Volcanic eruptions are beyond our control; there is nothing we can do to affect their timing and severity. Whereas deep-well disposal may increase the number of earthquakes in an area, and land clearing may worsen flooding, no human activity affects volcanoes. We can, however, take actions to minimize the loss of life and property from volcanic eruptions.

Forecasting

Forecasting volcanic eruptions is an important part of efforts to reduce volcanic risk. An eruption **forecast** is a statement of the probability that a volcano will erupt in a particular way and within a defined time. It is analogous to a weather forecast and is not as precise as a "prediction."[3]

Scientists gather information about precursor phenomena to improve their ability to forecast volcanic eruptions. One problem is that most forecasting techniques require experience with actual eruptions before precursor phenomena can be fully understood. Earth scientists have a good track record of predicting eruptions on the Hawaiian Islands because they have had so much experience with eruptions there.

Eruption forecasts rely on information gained by

- monitoring seismic activity
- monitoring thermal, magnetic, and hydrologic conditions at the volcano
- monitoring the land surface to detect tilting or swelling of the volcano
- monitoring volcanic gas emissions
- studying the geologic history of the volcano[14,31]

Seismic Activity Experience with volcanoes, such as Mount St. Helens and those on the Big Island of Hawaii, suggests that earthquakes are an early warning of an impending volcanic eruption. In the case of Mount St. Helens, earthquake activity started in mid-March, two months before the cataclysmic eruption on May 18, 1980. Activity in March began suddenly with nearly continuous, shallow earthquakes, but the frequency of earthquakes did not increase in the days and hours before the May 18 eruption. At Kilauea, earthquakes have been used to monitor the movement of magma as it approaches the surface. Magma bodies have also been mapped using geophysical techniques.

Small steam explosions and earthquakes began several months before the 1991 Mount Pinatubo eruption.[3] Mount Pinatubo, however, was an eroded ridge that did not have the classic shape of a stratovolcano, and it had not erupted in 500 years. Most people living near the mountain were unaware that it was a volcano, and they were not particularly concerned about the earthquakes. After the initial steam explosions, scientists began monitoring earthquakes on the volcano and studying past volcanic activity. Earthquakes increased in number and magnitude before the catastrophic eruption, and foci migrated from deep beneath the volcano to shallow depths beneath the summit.[3]

Thermal, Magnetic, and Hydrologic Monitoring Before an eruption, a large volume of magma moves into a holding reservoir beneath the volcano and changes the local magnetic, thermal, hydrologic, and geochemical conditions at the volcano. A rise in heat flow may be detected by satellite remote-sensing or infrared aerial photography. Increased heat may also melt snow or glaciers, which can be detected by remote sensing. This method was used with some success at Mount St. Helens before the main eruption on May 18, 1980.

When older volcanic rocks are heated by new magma, their original magnetic properties may change. Volcanic rocks lose their stable magnetization when they are heated above a certain temperature, known as the *Curie temperature*. Changes in rock magnetization can be detected by ground or aerial magnetic surveys.[14,32]

Land Surface Monitoring Some volcanic eruptions can be forecast by monitoring small changes in the volcano's surface. Hawaiian volcanoes, especially Kilauea, have supplied most of the data. The summit of Kilauea tilts and swells before an eruption and subsides during the eruption (Figure 3.41a and 3.41b). Tilting of the summit, in conjunction with an

◄ **FIGURE 3.41 INFLATION AND TILTING BEFORE ERUPTION** (a) An idealized diagram of Kilauea, showing inflation and surface tilting as magma moves up into the throat of the volcano. The red area is the underground magma chamber that fills before an eruption. *(1992. U.S. Geological Survey Circular 1073).* (b) Graphs showing tilting of the surface of Kilauea in two directions (east-west and north-south) from 1964 to 1966. Note the slow increase in tilting before eruptions and the rapid lowering of the surface during eruptions. *(From Fiske, R. S., and R. Y. Koyanagi. 1968. U.S. Geological Survey Professional Paper 607)*

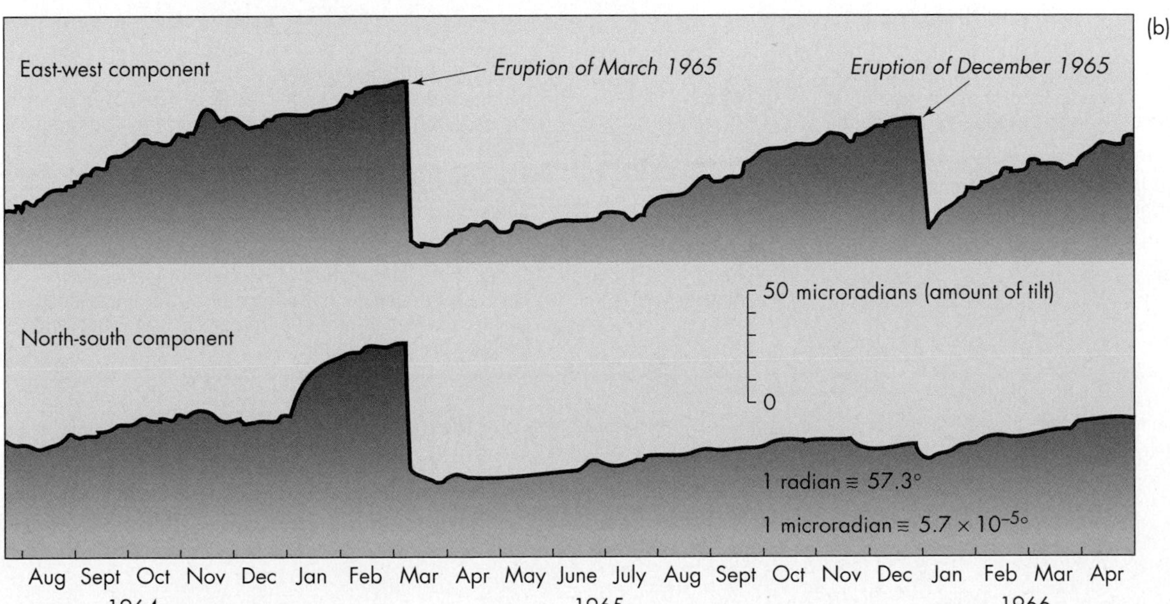

earthquake swarm, was used to predict an eruption near the farming community of Kapoho on the flank of the volcano, 45 km from the summit. As a result, the inhabitants were evacuated before lava overran and destroyed most of the village.[33] Because swelling and earthquakes have preceded past eruptions, scientists are able to reliably predict the activity of Hawaiian volcanoes. Monitoring of ground movements, such as tilting, swelling, and opening of cracks, or of changes in the water level of lakes on or near a volcano may indicate magma movements in advance of an eruption.[14] Today, satellite-based radar and GPS satellite receivers can be used to monitor changes in volcanoes, including surface deformation, without sending people into hazardous areas.[34]

Monitoring Volcanic Gas Emissions Changes in the relative amounts of carbon dioxide and sulphur dioxide or changes in gas emission rates may indicate movement of magma toward the surface. Measurements of volcanic gases proved useful in studying eruptions at Mount St. Helens and Mount Pinatubo. The volume of sulphur dioxide emitted from Mount Pinatubo increased by more than a million times two weeks before the eruption in 1991.

Geologic History An understanding of the recent geologic history of a volcano is helpful in predicting its future eruptive behaviour. The primary tools for reconstructing a volcano's history are geologic mapping and age dating of lava flows and pyroclastic deposits. Geologic mapping underpins the preparation of derived hazard maps that can assist in land-use planning and disaster preparedness.[14] Hazard maps are now available for a number of volcanoes around the world, including the Cascade volcanoes in the United States. Geologic mapping and dating of volcanic deposits at Kilauea led to the discovery that more than 90 percent of the surface of the volcano has been covered by lava in the past 1500 years. The town of Kalapana, destroyed by lava flows in 1990, might never have been built if this information had been available before development.

Volcanic Alert or Warning

At what point should the public be warned that a volcanic eruption may occur? This question is an important one being addressed by volcanologists and policymakers. At present no standard protocol exists, but a response plan has been developed by the U.S. Geological Survey. The plan involves the use of green, yellow, orange, and red codes to indicate an increasing level of concern. It is in use for the Long Valley caldera in California (Table 3.4). Similar systems have been, or are being, developed for other volcanic areas, such as Alaska and the Cascade Range in the Pacific Northwest. Although a colour-coded system is a good start, the hard questions remain: When should evacuation begin? When is it safe for people to return? Evacuation is recognized as necessary before condition red, but the need for evacuation at yellow or orange conditions is less well defined.

TABLE 3.4 Volcanic Hazards Response Plan for Long Valley Caldera, California

Geologic Behaviour	Condition	Response
Background: As many as 10 to 20 small earthquakes per day with magnitudes (**M**) less than 3 and uplift at an average rate of about 2.5 cm per year	*Green* No immediate risk	*Routine monitoring* plus *information calls* to U.S. Geological Survey personnel and town, county, state, and federal agencies about earthquakes and notable changes in ground deformation, fumarole activity, and gas emissions
Weak unrest: Increase in the number or strength of small earthquakes, or a single earthquake of **M** > 3		
Moderate unrest: An **M** > 4 earthquake or more than 300 earthquakes in a day		
Intense unrest: An earthquake swarm with at least one **M** 5 earthquake or evidence of magma movement at depth as indicated by an increased rate of ground deformation	*Yellow* **Watch**	*Intensified monitoring:* Set up emergency field headquarters at Long Valley caldera; initial *Watch* message sent by U.S. Geological Survey to California officials, who promptly inform local authorities
Eruption likely within hours or days; strong evidence of magma movement at shallow depth	*Orange* **Warning**	*Geologic Hazard Warning* issued by U.S. Geological Survey to governors of California and Nevada and local authorities; public informed
Eruption underway	*Red* **Alert**	*Sustained onsite monitoring and communication:* Maintain intensive monitoring and continuously keep civil authorities informed on progress of eruption and likely future developments

Notes:

Expiration of Watch, Warning, and Alert: The chart below shows the time in days that a given condition remains in effect, after the level of unrest drops below the threshold that initially triggered the condition.

Condition	Expires After	Subsequent Condition
Watch	*14 days*	*Green (no immediate risk)*
Warning	*14 days*	*Watch*
Alert	*1 day*	*Warning*

Source: Modified from the U.S. Geological Survey. 1997.

3.8 Perception of and Adjustment to the Volcanic Hazard

Perception of Volcanic Risk

Information about how people perceive volcanic risk is limited. People live near volcanoes for a variety of reasons: (1) they were born there and in the case of some islands, such as the Canary Islands, all land is volcanic; (2) the land is fertile and good for farming; (3) people are optimistic and believe an eruption is unlikely; (4) people are fatalistic or risk takers; (5) they are unaware of any risk; and (6) they cannot choose where they live; for example, they may be limited by economics. A study of risk perception in Hawaii found that a person's age and length of residence are significant factors in their knowledge of volcanic hazards and possible adjustments to them.[35] One reason the evacuation of 60,000 people before the 1991 eruption of Mount Pinatubo was successful was that the government had educated people about the dangers of violent *ash eruptions* and lahars. A video depicting these events was widely shown before the eruption and helped convince local officials and residents that they faced a real and immediate threat.[3]

Scientific understanding of volcanoes is constantly improving. However, good science is not sufficient (Survivor Story). Probably the greatest risk reduction will come from an increased understanding of human and societal issues that

SURVIVOR STORY

A Close Call with Mount St. Helens

Don Hamilton (Figure 3.C) was lucky to be nowhere near a telephone on the evening of May 17, 1980.

The next day, at 8:32 A.M., Mount St. Helens erupted, spewing enormous amounts of rock and ash into the atmosphere and covering the surrounding terrain with up to hundreds of metres of debris.

But that evening, Hamilton was sitting on the porch of a lodge at Spirit Lake, no more than 16 km from the peak of the mountain, visiting the lodge's resident, a local eccentric named Harry Truman. By that time, earthquakes and seismic observations had geologists clamouring about an imminent eruption, and Truman, then 84 years old, had become a minor celebrity for his stalwart refusal to evacuate.

Hamilton was working for the now-defunct *Oregon Journal*, and that night he might have stayed with Truman if he had had a telephone. But Hamilton needed some way to file his story, so he left for Portland.

As it turned out, leaving was the best decision of his life. When the volcano erupted the next morning, Hamilton was safely in bed in Portland. Truman and his lodge were buried in a massive landslide.

In the weeks leading up to the eruption, Hamilton had witnessed several earthquakes while visiting the old man. "I was up there a few times in his lodge, up on his front porch, when some pretty good quakes hit," Hamilton says. "I could see the road rippling. It was the weirdest thing I'd ever seen."

By this time, the media had already caught up with Truman, who had appeared on the *Today* show and in *The New York Times*. But for all his bravado, Hamilton notes, there were cracks in Truman's resolve. "I saw some genuine fear in his face. He looked drawn. His eyes were bugging out a little bit. The earthquakes made him stop and pay attention."

▲ **FIGURE 3.C OREGON REPORTER WHO ESCAPED DEATH ON MOUNT ST. HELENS** A fateful decision to leave Harry Truman's lodge on the slopes of Mount St. Helens on May 17, 1980, saved Don Hamilton's life. Don recounted his story 25 years later when Mount St. Helens erupted again in March 2005. *(Courtesy of Don Hamilton)*

But in spite of all the warnings, most people weren't prepared for the sheer magnitude of the eruption. "The geologists were certainly warning us that this was a very dangerous and unstable situation," he says. "But I don't think anybody really anticipated the enormity of what happened. There wasn't a lot of documented history of this kind of thing."

The morning of the eruption, Hamilton and his brother, a photographer for the *Oregon Journal,* chartered a flight to Mount St. Helens and were lucky enough to have a pilot who was willing to loosely interpret the FAA restrictions on the air space around the volcano.

Hamilton describes the view from the plane as utterly extraordinary. The peak of Mount St. Helens had

SURVIVOR STORY (Continued)

been blown off in the initial blast. A massive column of volcanic ash rose straight into the clouds above.

As they got closer they saw massive lahars as well as cars, trucks, and bridges that had been destroyed. "The road that I'd been going up for two weeks was completely washed out," Hamilton says.

For residents of Portland and many other areas near the volcano, ash from the eruption became a regular part of life that summer. "People were wearing surgical masks. Ash was piled up on the side of the road. It just stayed there all summer," Hamilton says. "For that whole summer you just lived with it."

For Hamilton, the timing couldn't have been worse. "It was the only summer I had a convertible," he says. "I kept the top up most of the time that summer."

—Chris Wilson

arise during an emerging **volcanic crisis**, when scientists predict that an eruption is likely in the near future. In such a crisis, improved communication among scientists, emergency managers, educators, media, and private citizens is particularly important. The goal is to prevent a volcanic crisis from becoming a disaster or catastrophe.[34]

Adjustments to Volcanic Hazards

Apart from evacuation, the primary human adjustments to volcanic eruptions are attempts to deflect lava flows from populated areas. Several methods, such as bombing, hydraulic chilling, and wall construction, have been employed to deflect lava flows away from populated or otherwise valuable areas. These methods have met with mixed success.

Bombing has proved most effective against flows in which fluid lava is confined to a relatively narrow channel bounded by solidified lava. The purpose of the bombing is to block the channel and cause the lava to pile up and break through upstream, where it will take a less damaging route. Successive bombing at higher and higher points on a flow may be necessary to control the threat. Poor weather conditions, abun-

(a)

(b)

(c)

◄ **FIGURE 3.42 FIGHTING LAVA FLOWS ON THE ISLAND OF HEIMAEY, ICELAND** (a) The lava fountain as seen from the harbour of Vestmannaeyjar *(Solarfilma ehf).* (b) An aerial view of Vestmannaeyjar. White steam appears above the advancing black lava flow. The steam comes from water being applied to cool and slow the front of the flow. An arcing stream of water from a water cannon is visible in the lower right corner of the photograph. *(James R. Andrews)* (c) An aerial view showing the front of the blocky lava flow moving into the harbour. *(James R. Andrews)*

dant smoke from burning vegetation, and falling ash reduce the effectiveness of bombing.[36] Overall, the results of bombing are unpredictable, and bombing is ineffective in the case of large, unconfined flows.

The world's most ambitious hydraulic chilling effort was initiated in January 1973 on the Icelandic island of Heimaey. Basaltic lava flows from Mount Helgafell nearly closed the harbour of Vestmannaeyjar, the island's main town and Iceland's main fishing port. The situation prompted immediate action.

Three favourable conditions existed: (1) the slow movement of the lava flows allowed time to initiate a control effort; (2) transport by sea and roads allowed for the delivery of pipes, pumps, and heavy equipment; and (3) water was readily available. Initially, the edges and surface of the flow were cooled with water discharged from numerous fire hoses (Figure 3.42). Then, bulldozers were moved up on the slowly advancing flow to make a path for a large water pipe. The plastic pipe did not melt because water was flowing in it. Small holes in the pipe accelerated cooling of hot spots along parts of the flow. Watering had little effect the first day, but the flow then began to slow down and stop.

These actions had a positive effect. They restricted lava movement, reduced property damage, and allowed the harbour to remain open. When the eruption stopped five months later, the harbour was still usable.[37] In fact, the shape of the harbour was actually improved because the front of the flow provided additional protection from the sea.

Summary

The viscosity of magma is related to its temperature and silica content and is important in determining the eruptive style of a volcano. Shield volcanoes are the largest volcanoes on Earth. They are common at mid-ocean ridges, such as Iceland, and over mid-plate hot spots, such as the Hawaiian Islands. Shield volcanoes are characterized by nonexplosive eruptions of basaltic lava flows. Stratovolcanoes occur at subduction zones, particularly around the Pacific Rim. Many of the volcanoes in Japan, the Aleutian Islands of Alaska, the Cascade Mountains of Canada and the United States, Central America, and the Andes of South America are of this type. These volcanoes are characterized by explosive eruptions and comprise mainly lava flows and pyroclastic deposits of andesite composition. Volcanic domes are smaller, highly explosive volcanoes that occur inland of subduction zones and comprise largely rhyolite and dacite.

Features of volcanoes include vents, craters, and calderas. Other features related to volcanic activity are hot springs and geysers. Calderas form from infrequent large and violent eruptions. They may present a volcanic hazard for a million years or more after they form. Recent uplift and earthquakes at the Long Valley caldera in eastern California and continuing thermal activity in Yellowstone National Park are reminders of this potential hazard.

Volcanic activity is directly related to plate tectonics. Most volcanoes are located at plate boundaries, where magma is produced by the spreading or subduction of lithospheric plates. Two-thirds of the volcanoes on land are associated with subduction of lithospheric plates along the "Ring of Fire" surrounding most of the Pacific Ocean. Specific geographic regions of North America at risk from volcanic eruptions include parts of British Columbia and Alaska, Long Valley, the Yellowstone area, and the northwest coast of California, Oregon, and Washington.

The primary effects of volcanic activity include lava flows, lateral blasts, pyroclastic surges and flows, ash fall and bombs, and emission of poisonous gases. Secondary effects include debris flows (lahars), which are generated when melting snow and ice or precipitation mix with ash and other pyroclastic material. Lahars can travel dozens of kilometres from their source and are extremely destructive. All these phenomena have occurred historically in Alaska and Washington and will occur there in the future.

Volcanoes are associated with other natural hazards, including fire, earthquakes, landslides, tsunami, and climate change. However, they also provide benefits, including fertile soils, a source of power, recreational opportunities, and new land.

Efforts to reduce volcanic risk must be centred on human and societal issues, including communication and education. The objective of these efforts is to prevent a volcanic crisis from becoming a disaster or catastrophe. Seismic, thermal, magnetic, hydrologic, and land surface monitoring of active volcanoes, combined with an improved understanding of their recent geologic history, may eventually result in reliable forecasting of volcanic activity.

Perception of the volcanic risk is a complex social and economic issue. Some people have little choice but to live near a volcano, and others ignore or downplay the risk. The primary human adjustment to an impending eruption is evacuation. Bombing, hydraulic chilling, and construction of barriers have been used in attempts to control lava flows, but these methods have had mixed success and require further evaluation. Community-based education plays an important role in informing people about the hazards of volcanoes.

Key Terms

ash fall (p. 90)
bomb (p. 76)
caldera (p. 80)
cinder cone (p. 77)
crater (p. 79)
debris flow (p. 92)
forecast (p. 100)
lahar (p. 72)
lateral blast (p. 90)
lava (p. 76)
lava flow (p. 88)
maar (p. 78)
magma (p. 72)
pyroclastic deposit (p. 76)
pyroclastic flow (p. 89)
pyroclastic surge (p. 89)
shield volcano (p. 75)

stratovolcano (or composite volcano) (p. 76)
tephra (p. 76)
volcanic crisis (p. 104)
volcanic dome (p. 77)
volcanic vent (p. 81)

Review Questions

1. How do magma chemistry, gas content, and viscosity contribute to volcano explosivity?
2. What determines the viscosity of magma?
3. List the major types of volcanoes and the characteristics of the magma associated with each.
4. List the major types of volcanoes and their eruption styles.
5. What is the relation between plate tectonics and volcanoes?
6. How do lava tubes help move magma far from the erupting vents?
7. What is the relation between the Hawaiian Islands and the hot spot below the Big Island of Hawaii?
8. What is a geyser and how does it operate?
9. Why are caldera eruptions so dangerous?
10. List the primary and secondary effects of volcanic eruptions.
11. What methods have been used to control lava flows?
12. Differentiate among ash falls, lateral blasts, pyroclastic flows, and pyroclastic surges.
13. What are the main gases emitted during a volcanic eruption?
14. How are volcanic eruptions able to produce gigantic debris flows?
15. How can forecasts of volcanic eruptions be improved?

Critical Thinking Questions

1. While looking through some boxes in your grandparents' house, you find a sample of volcanic rock that your grandfather collected. He cannot remember where he collected it. You take it to school, and your geology instructor tells you that it is a sample of andesite. What can you tell your grandparents about the type of volcano the rock probably came from, its geologic environment, and the type of volcanic activity that likely produced it?
2. People's perception of volcanic risk and what they will do in the event of an eruption depend on both their proximity to the volcano and their knowledge of volcanic processes and how to respond. With this knowledge in mind, develop a public relations program that could alert people to a potential volcanic eruption. Keep in mind that, in past tragedies, people have ignored hazard maps that show they live in dangerous areas.

Selected Web Resources

Volcanoes of Canada
http://gsc.nrcan.gc.ca/volcanoes/erupt_e.php From Natural Resources Canada

Hawaii Volcanoes National Park
www.nps.gov/havo/home.htm Safety considerations and pictures of an erupting volcano

How Volcanoes Work
www.geology.sdsu.edu/how_volcanoes_work General site on volcanoes from San Diego State University

Volcano Products
www.ssd.noaa.gov/VAAC Volcano links from the National Oceanic and Atmospheric Administration

U.S. Geological Survey Volcano Hazards Program
http://volcanoes.usgs.gov USGS site with general information on volcanic hazards, reducing risk, the Volcano Disaster Assistance Program, online USGS pamphlets and books, and links to sources of information at the five volcano observatories (Alaska, Cascades, Hawaii, Long Valley, and Yellowstone)

Weekly Volcano Activity Report
www.volcano.si.edu/reports/usgs Up-to-date reports on volcanic activity worldwide from the Smithsonian Institution and the U.S. Geological Survey

VolcanoCams of the World
vulcan.wr.usgs.gov/Photo/volcano_cams.html Links to near real-time pictures of volcanoes from the USGS Cascades Volcano Observatory

Volcanoes of the World
http://www.swisseduc.ch/stromboli General volcano site from Stromboli online

http://volcano.und.edu General site on volcanoes from the University of North Dakota

HAZARD CITY: ASSIGNMENTS IN APPLIED GEOLOGY

Volcanic Hazard Assessment

The Issue

Three small earthquakes have shaken Hazard City in the past two weeks. The epicentres of the earthquakes are at Lava Mountain, a dormant volcano that last erupted in the 1800s. The reactions of the citizens of Hazard City range from indifference to alarm. The mayor realizes that information is needed to develop an appropriate response.

Your Task

The mayor has hired you and two other geologists to investigate. Your job is to conduct a preliminary hazard assessment of the city. A good preliminary assessment must consider all potential hazards associated with a volcanic eruption, which for Lava Mountain include ash fall, lahars, pyroclastic flows, lava flows, and emission of poisonous volcanic gases. The assessment must also include an evaluation of the parts of Hazard City that are at risk from these different processes.

This is not a trivial assignment. Expect to do field work, learn about the different parts of Hazard City, and use web-based information to learn about different volcanic hazards. Because the geography of the town is important, you may want to print the maps and write notes on them while you do fieldwork and research.

Average Completion Time

2 hours

CHAPTER 4

Learning Objectives

Landslides, the downslope movement of Earth materials, constitute a serious natural hazard in many parts of the world. Landslides are commonly linked to other hazards, such as earthquakes and volcanoes. Most landslides are small and slow, but some are large and fast. Both may cause significant loss of life and damage to property, particularly in urban areas. Your goals in reading this chapter should be to

- Understand slope processes and the different types of landslides
- Know the forces that act on slopes and how they affect slope stability
- Know which geographic regions in North America are at risk from landslides
- Know the effects of landslides and their linkages with other hazardous natural processes
- Understand that landslides, although hazardous, can provide benefits
- Understand how people can affect the landslide hazard
- Be familiar with adjustments people can make to avoid death and damage caused by landslides

▶ **LIVING WITH LANDSLIDES**
Homes, roads, and streets were built at Portuguese Bend southwest of Los Angeles, despite the fact that geologic maps published in the 1940s revealed most of the area to be a landslide. Palos Verdes Drive South, shown in the photograph on the right, crosses the landslide and has been repaired repeatedly. *(Chris Cantelmo)*

Mass Wasting

Portuguese Bend, California

The Portuguese Bend landslide along the southern California coast in Los Angeles illustrates how people can increase the landslide hazard. This landslide, which destroyed more than 150 homes, is part of a larger ancient slide (Figure 4.1). Road-building and changes in subsurface drainage associated with urban development reactivated the ancient landslide.

Aerial photographs of the lower part of the reactivated landslide show evidence of its movement (Figure 4.2). The evidence includes bare ground west of the highway where recent movement destroyed homes and roads, and a kink in the pier caused by land sliding into the ocean.

Eventually, the slow-moving landslide destroyed the pier and the adjacent swim club. Recent movement of the slide started in 1956 when fill was placed over the upper part of the ancient slide during construction of a county road. During subsequent litigation, the County of Los Angeles was found responsible for the landslide.

From 1956 to 1978 the slide moved continually at an average rate of 0.3 cm to 1.3 cm per day. Several years of above-normal precipitation accelerated the movement to more than 2.5 cm per day in the late 1970s and early 1980s. Since 1956, the total displacement of the slide near the coast has been more than 200 m. Rainfall also reactivated a second part of the ancient slide to form the Abalone Cove landslide to the north (Figure 4.1). The second slide prompted additional geologic investigations, and a landslide-control program was initiated. Wells were drilled into the wet rocks of the Portuguese Bend landslide in 1980 to remove groundwater from the slide mass and thus dry out and stabilize the rocks. By 1985 the slide had apparently been stabilized. However, precipitation and groundwater conditions in the future will determine its fate.[1]

Homes on the Portuguese Bend landslide slowly moved during the 22-year period of activity. One home constantly shifted position as it moved more than 25 m. Homes that were not destroyed by the movement were adjusted every year or so with hydraulic jacks. Utility lines were placed on the surface to avoid breakage as the ground shifted. With one exception, no new homes have been constructed since movement began. The remaining occupants have chosen to adjust to the landslide rather than bear total loss of their property. Nevertheless, few geologists would choose to live there now.

PORTUGUESE BEND
LANDSLIDE AREA
CONSTANT LAND MOVEMENT
NEXT 0.8 MILES
USE EXTREME CAUTION

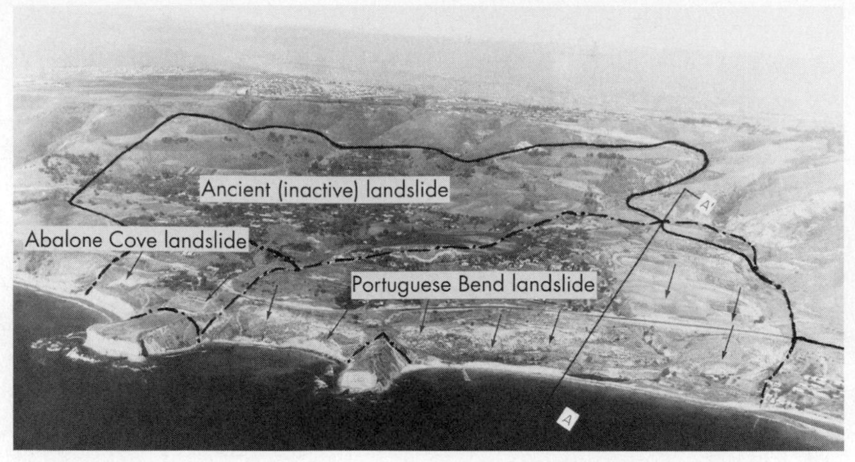

(a)

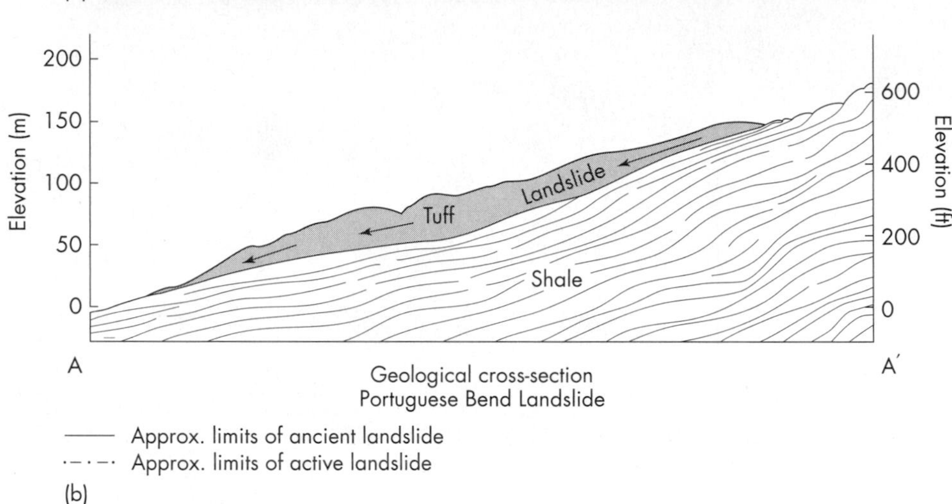

(b)

◄ **FIGURE 4.1 ANCIENT LANDSLIDES CAN BE REACTIVATED** (a) The extent of the ancient inactive landslide at Portuguese Bend, parts of which were reactivated in the 1950s and 1970s. The arrows show the direction of land movement toward the Pacific Ocean, shown in the foreground. (b) Cross-section A to A' on the right side of (a) passes through the Portuguese Bend landslide. The landslide involves sliding of volcanic tuff, a consolidated pyroclastic rock, over a weak layer of shale. *(Photograph and cross-section courtesy of Los Angeles County, Department of County Engineer)*

The story of the Portuguese Bend landslide illustrates the importance of a scientific understanding of landslides. Recognizing landslides and using land-use planning to avoid building on active slides is preferable to reacting to landslide movement after homes have been constructed.

◄ **FIGURE 4.2 HOMES DESTROYED** The kink in the pier in the upper left portion of this image shows initial damage from the Portuguese Bend landslide. Eventually most of the homes seen here, as well as the swim club and pier, were destroyed by the landslide. Look for the pier at the lower centre of Figure 4.1a to get a sense of the size of the landslide. *(John S. Shelton)*

4.1 An Introduction to Landslides

Mass wasting is a general term for any type of downslope movement of rock or sediment because of gravity. Mass wasting can be slow or fast and can involve small or large volumes of sediment or rock. Although some scientists limit use of the term **landslide** to rapid movements of soil or rock, we consider the term in its broadest sense to also include rock fall, debris flows, and slowly moving bodies of coherent rock.

Slope Processes

Slopes may appear stable and static, but they are actually dynamic, evolving systems. The processes that are active in these systems generally do not produce uniform slopes. Rather, most slopes comprise several segments that are either straight or curved.

Spectacular examples of segmented slopes can be seen at Moraine Lake in Banff National Park, Alberta (Figure 4.3). Steep faces regularly shed rock fragments to the apron of **talus** below. Both the rock face and the talus slope are segments of the overall slope.

Most slopes outside mountain ranges are gentle and lack a *free face.* They can be convex, concave, straight, or more commonly some combination of all three. The shape of a particular slope depends largely on the rock type and climate. Free-face development is more common in mountains, on hard rocks, and in arid environments. Convex and concave slopes are more common on softer rocks or in humid environments. However, there are many exceptions to these general rules, depending on local conditions. For example, steep slopes form the walls of some river valleys crossing the otherwise flat interior plains of western Canada.

Earth material on most slopes is constantly moving. Movements range from imperceptible creep to thundering avalanches of rock and soil at velocities of 160 km/h or more.

▲ **FIGURE 4.3 CONTRASTING SLOPES** Composite slope segments at Moraine Lake, Banff National Park, Alberta. The steep cliffs at the left side of the photograph are sharply bordered by a gentler apron of talus. *(Robert Berdan)*

Through time, mass wasting erodes valley walls and is one reason that nearly all valleys are much wider than the streams they contain.

Types of Landslides

Earth materials may fail and move downslope in many ways. Scientists classify landslides to reflect these differences (Table 4.1). Four important variables underpin most landslide classifications: (1) the mechanism of movement (fall, topple, slide, flow, or complex movement), (2) type of material (rock, consolidated sediment, or organic soil), (3) amount of water present, and (4) rate of movement.[2] In general, movement is considered rapid if it can be discerned with the naked eye; otherwise, it is classified as slow. Movement rates range from a few millimetres per year in the case of slow creep to many dozens of metres per second for some rockslides and rock avalanches.[3]

TABLE 4.1 Common Types of Mass Movements

Mechanism	Type of Mass Movement	Characteristics
Fall	Rock fall	Individual rocks bound downward or fall through the air.
	Slump	Coherent blocks of rock or sediment slide on an upward-curved surface; also called a rotational landslide.
Slide	Debris slide or avalanche	Sediment or soil slides on an inclined surface; also called an earth slide.
	Rockslide	Large blocks of bedrock slide on an inclined surface, typically bedding planes, foliation surfaces, or joints.
	Rock avalanche	A type of rockslide in which the fragmented rock mass flows at very high velocities, commonly for long distances.
	Creep	Very slow downslope movement of rock and soil. Sackung is deep-seated creep of large masses of fragmented rock along poorly defined slip surfaces.
Flow	Earthflow	A flow of wet, deformed soil and weathered rock.
	Debris flow	A cement-like mixture of rock, sand, mud, plant debris, and water travels rapidly down a stream channel or ravine; includes mudflows and lahars.
	Complex	A combination of two or more types of mass movement.

Falling refers to free fall and bounding of rock or blocks of sediment from the face of a cliff (Figures 4.4 and 4.5). **Sliding** is the downslope movement of a coherent block of rock or sediment along a discrete failure plane (Figures 4.4 and 4.6; see Case Study 4.1). **Slumping** is a particular type of sliding in which the failure plane is curved upward (Figures 4.4 and 4.7). **Flow** is the slow to rapid downslope movement of sediment in which particles move semi-independently of one another, commonly with the aid of water (Figure 4.4). Very slow flow of rock or sediment, at rates ranging from millimetres to dozens of centimetres per year, is termed **creep**. A special type of creep involves movement of large masses of rock, up to many billions of cubic metres, along ill-defined, deep failure planes. The German word **sackung** (loosely translated as "slope sag") has been applied to these huge, slow-moving landslides. Slow creep-like movements in which rock masses pivot about a point are termed **topples**. Topples are common in rocks with joints or bedding planes that dip steeply into the slope.

Many landslides are complex combinations of sliding and flowage. For example, a landslide may start out as a rock fall or slide but transform into a flow lower along its path (Figure 4.8). Most **subaqueous landslides** are of this type. A slump or slide on the submerged slope of a delta or at the edge of the continental shelf can change into a debris flow or a *turbidity current* that travels great distances from the point of failure (Figure 4.9). A famous example of a complex subaqueous landslide is the Grand Banks landslide off Newfoundland in 1929. A large earthquake triggered a huge (200 km^3) initial slump or slide on the seafloor at the edge of the *continental shelf*. The failed mass rapidly transformed into a turbid flow of mud, sand, and water (a turbidity current) that travelled hundreds of kilometres along the sea floor at speeds of 60 km/h–100 km/h, breaking 12 submarine telegraph

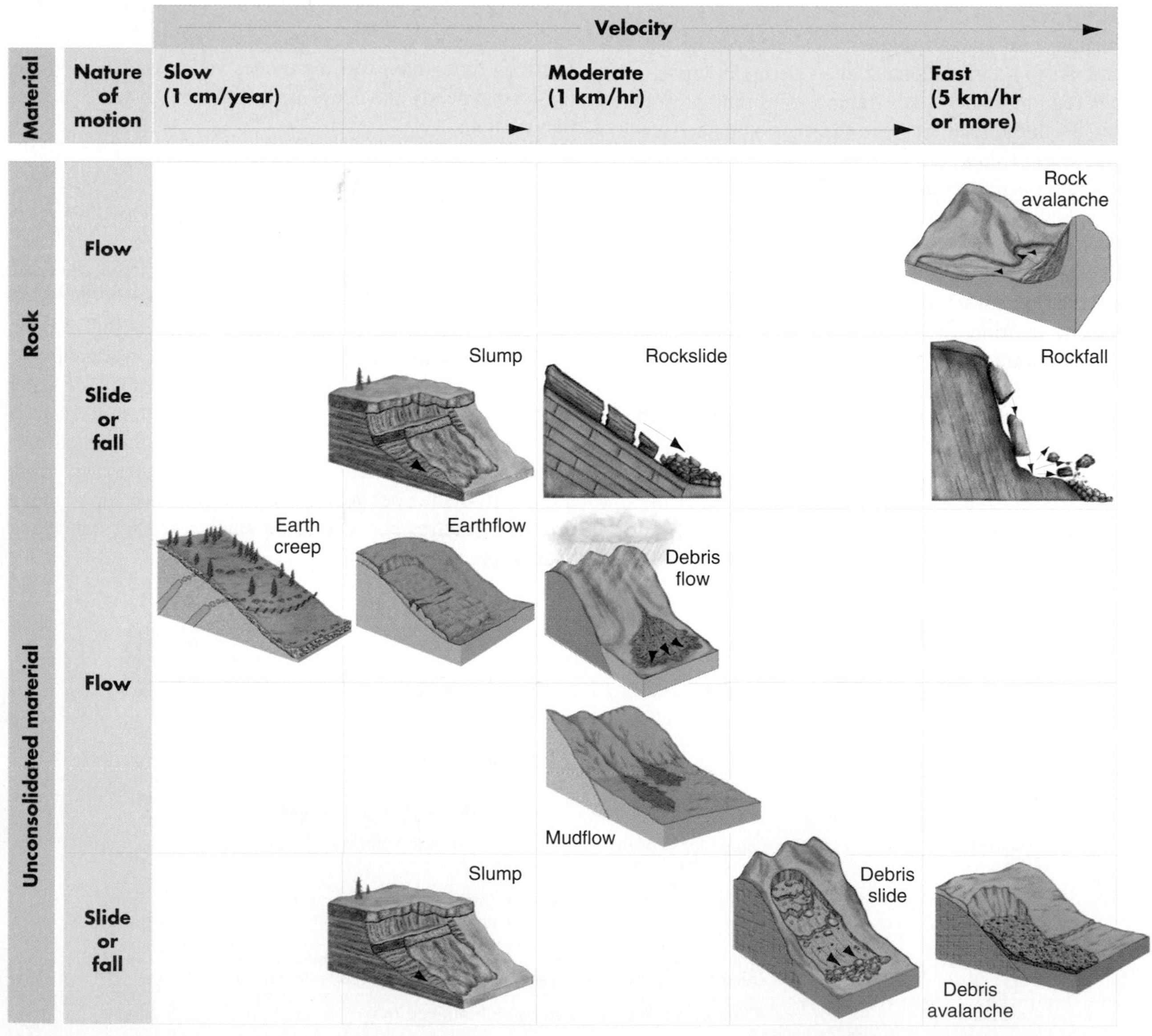

▲ **FIGURE 4.4 TYPES OF LANDSLIDES** Landslides are classified according to (1) type of movement (fall, slide, topple, flow), (2) type of material that fails (i.e., rock or unconsolidated sediment), (3) amount of water or air involved in the movement, and (4) velocity.

▲ **FIGURE 4.5 ROCKFALL** Rockfall on the Trans-Canada Highway near Yale, British Columbia. *(Duncan Wyllie)*

▲ **FIGURE 4.6 LARGE ROCKSLIDE BURIES HIGHWAY EAST OF VANCOUVER** A photograph of the Hope slide, which buried Highway 3 in southern British Columbia to a depth of up to 80 m on January 9, 1965. At 48 million m^3, the Hope slide is the largest historic rockslide in Canada. *(George Diack/ Vancouver Sun)*

cables.[5] Some complex landslides may form when water-saturated sediments flow from the lower part of a slope and undermine the upper part, causing *slump blocks* to form.

Forces on Slopes

To understand landslides, we must examine the forces that determine the stability of a slope. Slope stability can be evaluated by determining the relation between **driving forces** that move rock or sediment down a slope and **resisting forces** that oppose such movement (Figure 4.10). The largest driving force in the downslope component is the weight of the slope material and the water it contains. That weight can include anything placed on the slope by people, such as fill material and buildings. The resisting force is the **shear strength** of the slope material, that is, its resistance to failure by sliding or flow along potential slip planes. Potential slip planes are surfaces of weakness in the slope material, such as bedding planes in sedimentary rocks, foliation in metamorphic rocks, and fractures in all types of rock.

Slope stability is evaluated by computing a **factor of safety** (FS), defined as the ratio of the resisting forces to the driving forces. If the factor of safety is greater than 1, the resisting forces exceed the driving forces and the slope is considered stable. If the factor of safety is equal to 1, the driving forces equal the resisting forces and a slope failure can be expected. Driving and resisting forces are not static; as local conditions change, these forces may change, increasing or decreasing the factor of safety.

4.1 CASE STUDY

Hope Slide: Canada's Largest Historic Landslide

Late on the night of January 9, 1965, without warning, a huge mass of rock, enough to fill an indoor stadium several times over, slid away from the flank of Johnston Peak, 17 km southeast of Hope, British Columbia. The rock fragmented as it raced down the slope toward B.C. Highway 3 in the valley below. On reaching the valley floor, the debris obliterated Outram Lake and drove a wave of muddy sediment 150 m up the opposite valley wall. The muddy debris fell back down the slope and flowed both up and down the valley. When the dust settled, more than 3 km of Highway 3 was buried beneath as much as 80 m of debris (Figure 4.6) and four motorists were dead.

The *trigger* for the Hope slide is unknown—weather, human activity, and groundwater conditions apparently were not factors. For many years, it was thought that two small earthquakes, recorded on a seismograph at Penticton at the time of the slide, were the triggers. A reexamination of the seismograms, however, showed that the inferred earthquake traces were really the result of the landslide debris striking the valley floor.[4]

The *cause* of the landslide, however, is known. The metamorphosed volcanic rocks that slid off Johnston Peak are riddled with joints, some of which dip parallel to the steep mountain slope. In addition, the rupture surface partly coincides with one or more thin, weathered layers of volcanic rock that dip parallel to the slope.

◀ **FIGURE 4.7 SLUMP** A large coherent block of silt has slid on a curved failure plane near Quesnel, British Columbia. *(John J. Clague)*

◀ **FIGURE 4.8 ROCK AVALANCHE** A photo-draped digital elevation model (DEM) of a rock avalanche on the flank of Mount Munday in the Coast Mountains of British Columbia. The landslide began as a rockslide but rapidly evolved into a high-velocity flow that streamed across the glacier in the foreground. The distance from the top to the bottom of the photo is 4 km. *(Evans, S. G. 2006. Single-event landslides resulting from massive rock slope failure: characterizing their frequency and impact on society. In Landslides from massive rock slope failure. Edited by S. G. Evans, G. Scarascia-Mugnozza, A. L. Strom, and R. L. Hermanns, NATO Science Series IV, Vol. 49, Springer, Dordrecht, pp. 53–73)*

Driving and resisting forces on slopes are determined by the interrelations of the following variables:

- type of material
- slope angle and topography
- climate
- vegetation
- water
- time

The Role of Material Type Material composing a slope can affect both the type and the frequency of landslides. Important material characteristics include mineral composition, degree of cementation or consolidation, and the presence of planes of weakness. Planes of weakness may be sedimentary bedding planes, metamorphic foliation, secondary joints, or zones along which Earth has moved before, such as an old landslide slip surface or a fault. These planes can be especially hazardous if they are inclined more than about 15° and intersect or are parallel to the slope of a hill or mountain.

In the case of slides, the shape of the slip surface is strongly controlled by the type of material that fails. Slides have two basic patterns of movement, *rotational* and *translational*. Rotational slides, or slumps, have curved slip surfaces, whereas translational slides have planar slip surfaces (Figure 4.4).

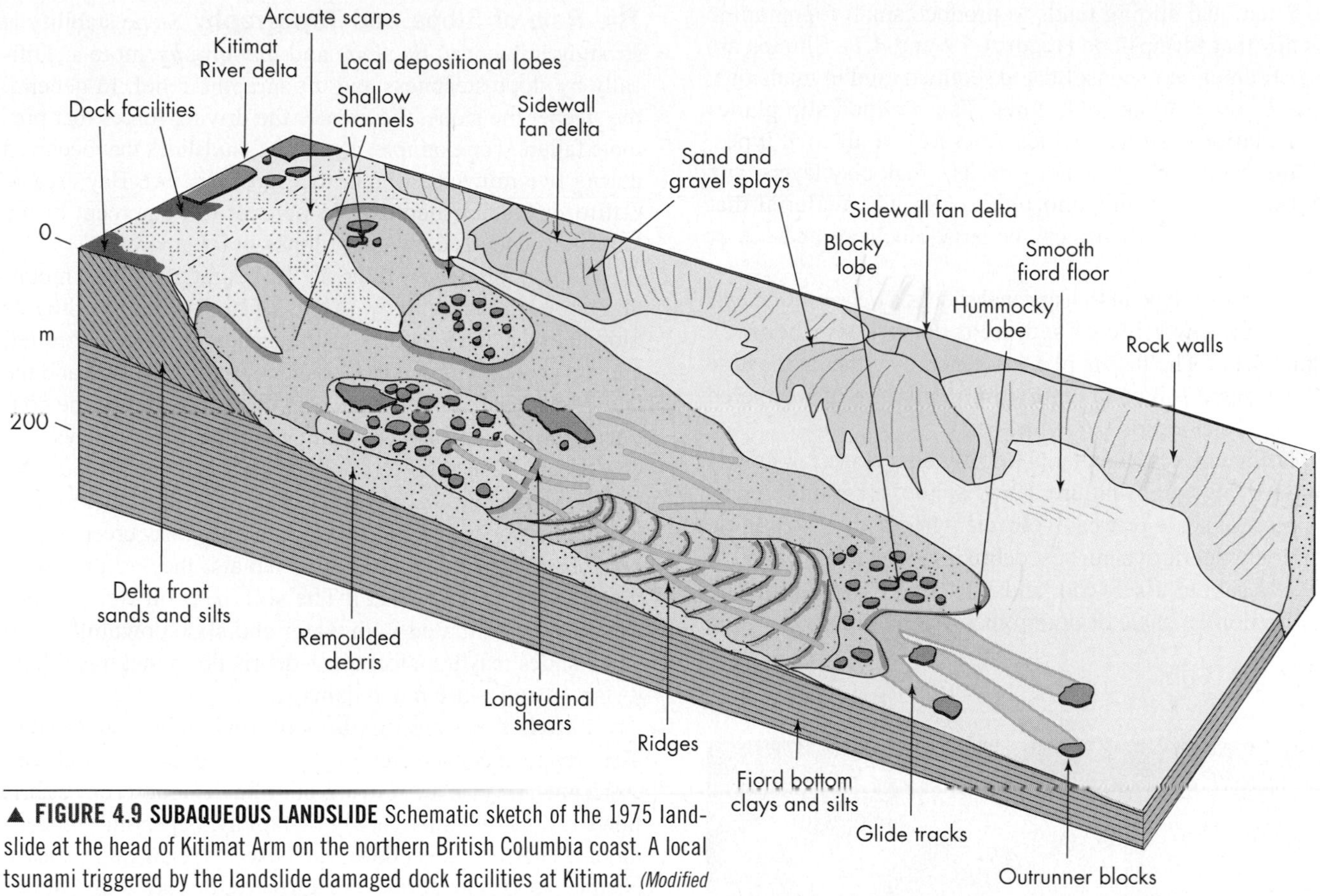

▲ **FIGURE 4.9 SUBAQUEOUS LANDSLIDE** Schematic sketch of the 1975 landslide at the head of Kitimat Arm on the northern British Columbia coast. A local tsunami triggered by the landslide damaged dock facilities at Kitimat. *(Modified from Prior/Bornhold/Johns, Journal of Geology, pp. 707–727, Figure 2, from "Depositional characteristics of a submarine debris flow" 92 (1984), Publisher University of Chicago)*

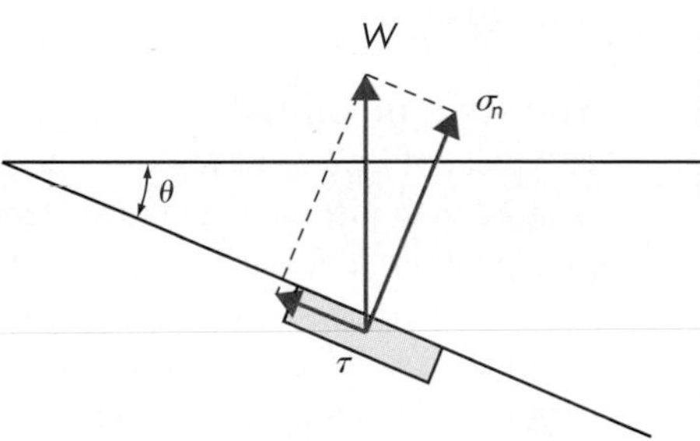

▲ **FIGURE 4.10 FORCES ACTING ON SLOPES** A rigid block resting on an inclined plane is a mechanical analog of a failing slope. The weight of the block, *W*, exerts a normal stress, σ_n, perpendicular to the inclined plane, and a shear stress, τ, parallel to the plane. The normal stress acts to hold the block in place, whereas the shear stress acts to move the block down the inclined plane. Movement of the block is restrained by frictional resistance along the contact zone between the block and the inclined plane. The critical shear stress, τ_{crit}, required to overcome the frictional resistance and cause failure is expressed by the formula

$$\tau_{crit} = (\sigma_n - \sigma_{pw}) \tan\theta + C$$

where σ_{pw} is the pore water pressure along the contact zone; θ is the *angle of friction; tan* θ is the coefficient of friction, a material constant that for most Earth materials ranges from 0.6 to 0.7; and *C* is the cohesion across the contact zone. In simple terms, this formula says that the shear stress necessary to overcome the resistance to sliding decreases with (1) decreasing normal stress, (2) increasing pore pressure (e.g., rising groundwater table), and (3) decreasing cohesion (e.g., removal of tree roots in surficial deposits. *(Evans, S. G. 2006. Single-event landslides resulting from massive rock slope failure: characterizing their frequency and impact on society. In Landslides from massive rock slope failure. Edited by S. G. Evans, G. Scarascia-Mugnozza, A. L. Strom, and R. L. Hermanns, NATO Science Series IV, Vol. 49, Springer, Dordrecht, pp. 53–73)*

Rotational sliding tends to produce small topographic benches that tilt upslope (Figures 4.4 and 4.7). Slumps are most common in unconsolidated sediment and in mudstone, shale, or other weak rock types. The inclined slip planes of translational slides include fractures in all rock types, bedding planes in sedimentary rocks, weak clay layers, and foliation planes in metamorphic rocks. The material that moves along these planes can be large blocks of bedrock or sediment.

A common type of translational slide is a *debris avalanche,* a very shallow slide of sediment or soil over bedrock (Figure 4.11). The failure plane is generally either at the base of the organic soil or in **colluvium**, a mixture of weathered rock and other debris below the soil.

The nature of the material underlying a slope can greatly influence the type of failure. For example, mass movements on slopes of shale or weak volcanic pyroclastic material are commonly debris avalanches, debris flows, slumps, or creep. Builders should assess the landslide hazard before starting construction on shale or other types of weak rock.

▲ **FIGURE 4.11 DEBRIS AVALANCHES** Numerous debris avalanches and debris flows occurred in a logged area in the southern Coast Mountains of British Columbia following heavy rains. Many of the landslides have sources along poorly engineered forestry roads. *(John J. Clague)*

The Role of Slope and Topography Slope stability is strongly influenced by *slope* and *topography,* more specifically by slope steepness and topographic relief. In general, the steeper the slope, the greater the driving forces that promote failure. For example, a study of landslides that occurred during two rainy seasons in the San Francisco Bay area of California established that 75 percent to 85 percent of the landslides occurred on steep slopes in urban areas.[6]

Topographic *relief* refers to the height of a hill or mountain above the land below. Areas of high relief are hilly or mountainous, have dozens to thousands of metres of relief, and are generally prone to landslides. Within Canada and the United States, the mountains of the western part of the continent, the Appalachian Mountains, walls of river valleys, and coastal bluffs have the greatest frequency of landslides. All types of landslides occur on steep slopes within these areas, and gentle slopes developed on some rocks may creep imperceptibly. Even small slides can be lethal if they occur in populated areas (Figure 4.12). The soil layer on steep slopes can become saturated with water and slide downhill. Such small slides may transform into debris flows that travel long distances and cause much damage.

Debris flows are mixtures of mud, debris, and water. They range in consistency from thick mud soups to wet concrete, such as you see flowing out of a cement truck. Debris flows can move either slowly or rapidly, depending on conditions. They can travel down established stream valleys, leave channels and flow across fan surfaces, or take long narrow tracks or *chutes* on steep hillsides. Debris flows can transport as little as a few hundred cubic metres of material; at the other end of the spectrum, cubic kilometres of material can be transported by debris flows following the failure of the flank of a volcano (see volcanic mudflows and debris flows discussed in Chapter 3).

The Role of Climate *Climate* is the characteristic weather typical of a place or region over years or decades. Climate is more than just the average air temperature and amount of precipitation. It also includes the type of precipitation and its seasonal patterns, such as winter rain and snow along the Pacific Coast, winter blizzards in the Arctic and Great Plains, summer thunderstorms in the southwestern United States, heavy snows along the shores of the Great Lakes, and hurricane activity on the Mexican and southeastern U.S. coasts. Temperate climates characterize much of the Atlantic and Pacific Coasts, whereas most of the continental interior has strong seasonal contrasts, with cold winters and hot summers. Climate influences the amount and timing of water that infiltrates or erodes a hillslope and the type and abundance of hillslope vegetation.

In arid and semi-arid climates, vegetation tends to be sparse, soils are thin, and bare rock is exposed in many areas. Free-face and talus slopes are common in these areas, and mass movements include rock falls, debris flows, and shallow soil slips.

In subhumid and humid climates, abundant vegetation and thick soil cover most slopes. Mass movements in these areas include deep complex landslides, soil creep, rockslides,

◀ FIGURE 4.12 EVEN SMALL LANDSLIDES CAN KILL A photograph of the 1889 Champlain Street landslide in Quebec City, Quebec. Fifty people were killed in houses at the base of the failed slope. *(William James Topley/ Bibliothèque et Archives Canada/PA-131073)*

slumps, and debris flows. We will now discuss the roles of vegetation and water on slopes in more detail.

The Role of Vegetation Vegetation has a complex role in the development of landslides. The nature of the vegetation in an area is a function of climate, soil type, topography, and fire history, each of which also independently influences what happens on slopes. Vegetation is a significant factor in slope stability for three reasons:

1. Vegetation provides a protective cover that reduces the impact of falling rain. It allows rainwater to infiltrate into the slope while retarding surface erosion.
2. Plant roots add strength and cohesion to slope materials. They act like steel rebar reinforcements in concrete and increase the resistance of a slope to landsliding.[7]
3. Vegetation adds weight to a slope, which can increase the likelihood that the slope will fail.

The Role of Water Water is nearly always involved with landslides, so its role is particularly important.[8] Water affects slope stability in three ways:

1. Many landslides, such as shallow *soil slips* and debris flows, happen during rainstorms when slope materials become saturated.
2. Other landslides, such as slumps, develop months or even years following deep infiltration of water into a slope.
3. Erosion of the toe of a slope by a stream reduces the mass of resisting material and thus decreases the slope's stability.

Stream or wave erosion reduces the factor of safety by removing material at the base of a slope (Figure 4.13). This problem is particularly critical if the base of the slope is an old, inactive landslide that is likely to move again (Figure 4.14). It is important to recognize old landslides when road cuts and other excavations are planned so that potential problems can be isolated and corrected before construction.

Water also contributes to the *liquefaction* of fine granular sediments. When disturbed, water-saturated silts and sands can lose their strength and flow as a liquid. The shaking of thick clays beneath Anchorage, Alaska, during a great earthquake in 1964 caused layers of sand at depth to liquefy, triggering large, destructive landslides.[9] Spontaneous liquefaction of *Leda clay* in the St. Lawrence Lowland in southern Quebec and Ontario triggered large landslides that destroyed many homes and killed more than 70 people in the twentieth century (Figure 4.15). Leda clay accumulated in a large marine embayment that extended up the St. Lawrence Valley at the end of the Pleistocene. At that time, low-lying areas up to about 200 m above present sea level were inundated by the sea and covered by silt and clay deposited by streams flowing from the wasting ice sheet that covered most of central and eastern Canada. Landslides in Leda clay occur on river valley slopes when initially solid material transforms into liquid mud (Figure 4.16).[10] Liquefaction starts in a small area and spreads to a much larger area. The *quick clay* failures in Quebec and Ontario are especially interesting because liquefaction can occur without earthquake shaking. The sensitivity of Leda clay to liquefaction stems from the structure of the sediment. In the natural state, the constituent mineral grains are loosely packed and the forces binding the grains are weak; an analogy is a "house of cards." When the sediment

(a)

(b)

◀ **FIGURE 4.13 WATER ERODING THE TOE OF A SLOPE CAUSES INSTABILITY** (a) Stream-bank erosion shown in the lower left corner of this photograph caused slope failure and damage to a road in the San Gabriel Mountains, California. *(Edward A. Keller)* (b) Wave erosion caused this landslide in Cove Beach, Oregon. Further movement threatens the homes above. *(Gary Braasch/Getty Images Inc.-Stone Allstock)*

is disturbed, the mineral binding forces drop to zero and the house of cards collapses.

The freezing of water in fractures in rock can destabilize slopes and trigger rock falls. Water increases about 10 percent in volume when it freezes and exerts large forces along fractures in rock. Monitoring of steep slopes along the Trans-Canada Highway in British Columbia has shown that rock fall is most common at times when temperatures fluctuate frequently above and below the freezing point[11] (Figure 4.17).

Water is also implicated in shallow landslides (**thaw flow slides**) in areas of *permafrost* (Figure 4.18). Thaw flow slides typically occur during warm spells in summer when the *active layer* (seasonal melted layer) is thickest. The skin of water-saturated sediment slides away from the frozen ground below and flows downhill.[12]

The Role of Time Forces acting on slopes change with time. For example, both driving and resisting forces change seasonally as the water table fluctuates. Much of the weather-

(a)

(b)

▲ **FIGURE 4.14 REACTIVATION OF A SLIDE** (a) Part of the beach (end of thin arrow) in Santa Barbara, California, was buried during a reactivation of an older landslide. (b) Close-up of the head of the landslide where it destroyed two homes. The thick black arrow in (a) points to the location of this picture. *(Courtesy of Don Weaver)*

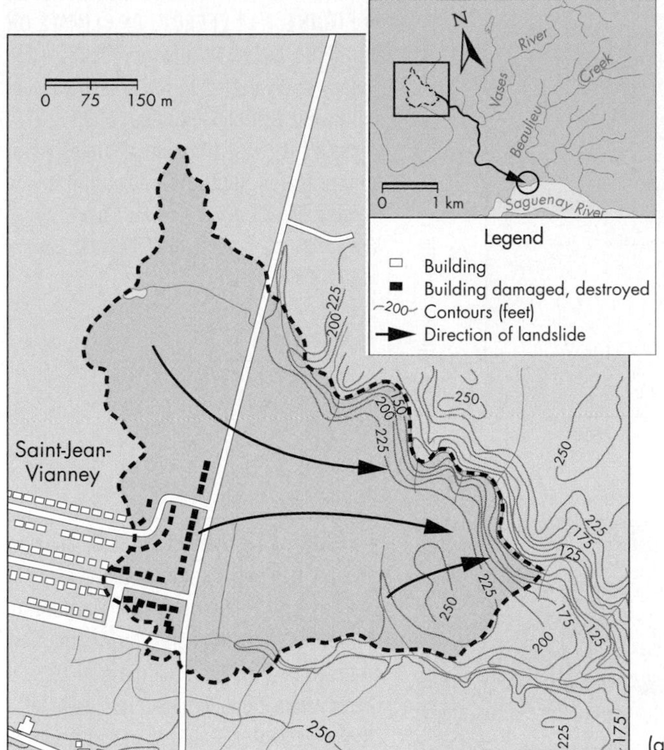

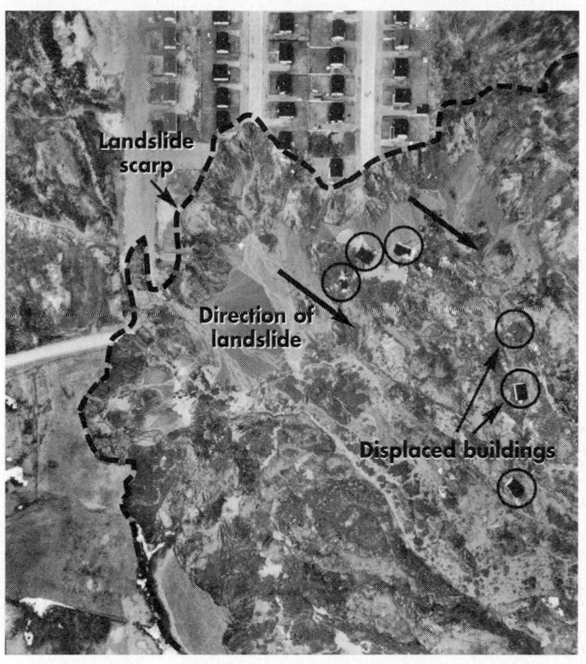

▲ **FIGURE 4.15 QUICK CLAY FAILURE** (a) A map and (b) oblique aerial view of the Saint-Jean-Vianney landslide, which happened in southern Quebec on May 4, 1971. Approximately 40 houses were engulfed by the landslide and 31 lives were lost. Some displaced houses can be seen in the debris below the scarp. *(© Gouvernement du Québec)*

ing of rocks, which slowly reduces their cohesion and strength, is caused by the chemical action of water in contact with soil and rock near Earth's surface. Soil water is commonly acidic because it reacts with carbon dioxide in the atmosphere and soil to produce weak carbonic acid. Slope failure may occur without an obvious trigger when the resisting forces finally fall below the driving forces. The failure may be preceded, over days or months, by an increase in the rate of creep.

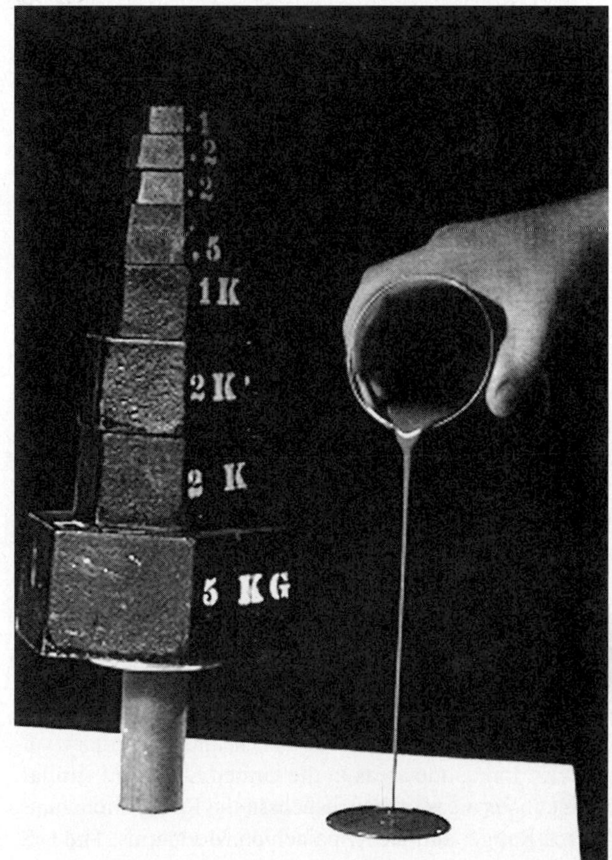

▶ **FIGURE 4.16 QUICK CLAY** The sensitivity of Leda clay to liquefaction is illustrated by a simple test on a sample from Ottawa, Ontario. The sample on the left is intact and strong enough to withstand a vertical load of 11 kg. After disturbance, a sample of the same material with the same moisture content behaves like a fluid. *(Reproduced with the permission of the Minister of Public Works and Government Services Canada, 2007, and courtesy of Natural Resources Canada, Geological Survey of Canada)*

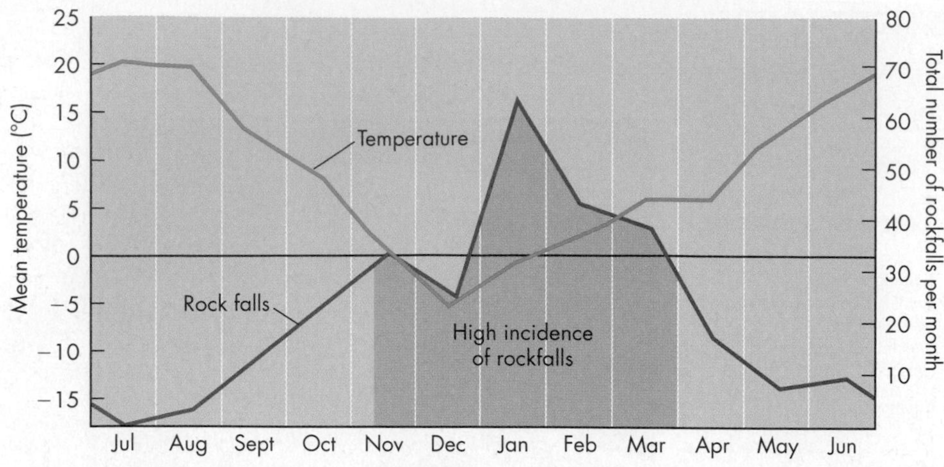

◀ **FIGURE 4.17 EFFECTS OF CLIMATE ON ROCKFALL ACTIVITY** A plot of rock fall frequency and weather in the Fraser Canyon, southwest British Columbia, 1933–1970. Rock fall is most frequent at times when temperatures fluctuate above and below freezing. *(Modified from Peckover, F. L., and J. W. G. Kerr. 1977. Canadian Geotechnical Journal 46:633–696)*

◀ **FIGURE 4.18 THAW FLOW SLIDE** The flow of water-rich sediment on a gentle slope in permafrost terrain in the Mackenzie Mountains, Northwest Territories. The flow came to rest on the floodplain of Dekale Creek, where it has formed a fan (lower left). *(Photographer S. G. Evans. Reproduced with the permission of the Minister of Public Works and Government Services Canada, 2007, and courtesy of Natural Resources Canada, Geological Survey of Canada. GSC 2000-094)*

4.2 Geographic Regions at Risk from Landslides

As you may imagine, landslides occur wherever there are significant slopes. Mountainous areas have a higher risk for landslides than most areas of low relief. The latter generalization is supported by a map of major landslide areas in Canada (Figure 4.19). Areas where landslides are most common are the western Cordillera of British Columbia, Yukon, and Alberta, and the Appalachian provinces of Quebec and New Brunswick. The landslide hazard in other parts of the country is more localized, notably in the St. Lawrence Valley where many slopes are developed in Leda clay, and along the valleys of the large rivers that cross the Prairies. Materials that are particularly prone to landsliding include lacustrine and marine silts and clays, Cretaceous shales, and Quaternary volcanic rocks. Landslide areas in the United States are similar: the mountainous areas of the west coast, the Rocky Mountains, the Alaska Range, and the Appalachian Mountains. The U.S. Plains are relatively free of landslides.

Three factors are expected to increase the incidence of landslides in some areas of the world in this century:

1. Urbanization and development will increasingly expand into landslide-prone areas.
2. Tree cutting will continue in landslide-prone areas.
3. Changing global climate patterns will result in increases in precipitation in some regions.[13]

4.3 Effects of Landslides and Linkages with Other Natural Hazards

Effects of Landslides

Landslides and related phenomena cause substantial damage and loss of life (Figure 4.20). In North America, 30 people, on average, are killed each year by landslides. The total cost

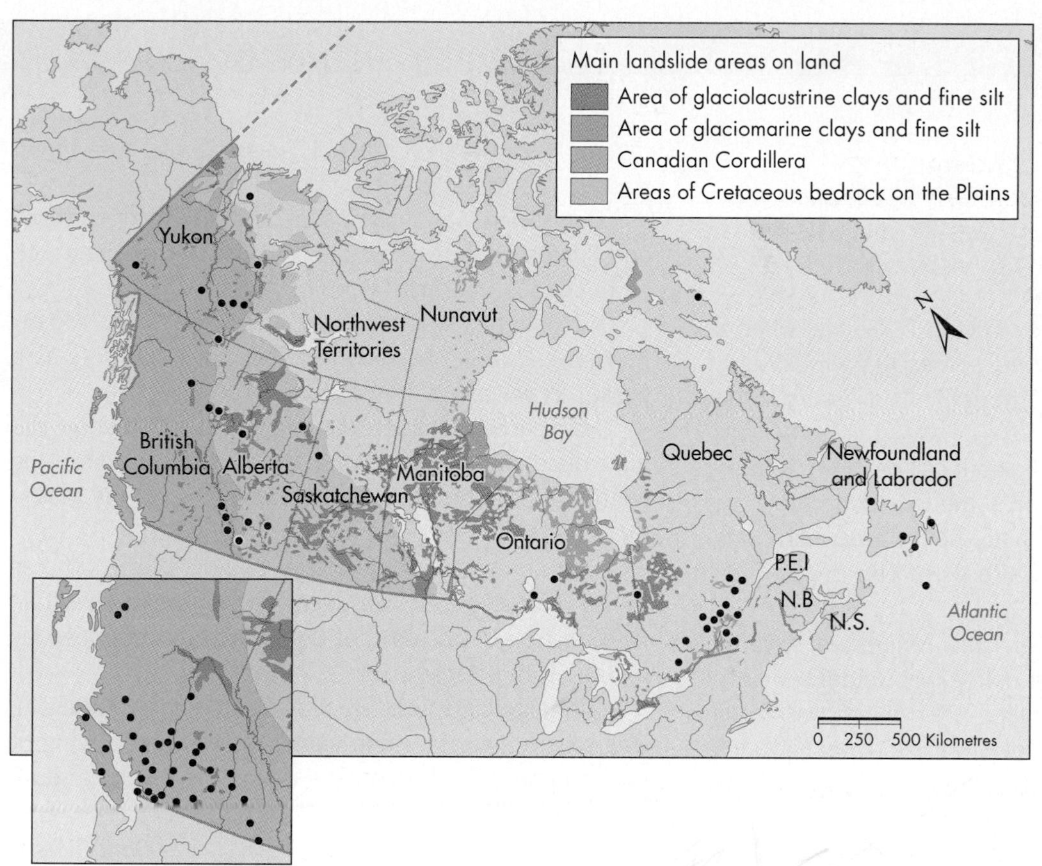

◄ FIGURE 4.19 LANDSLIDES IN CANADA This map shows locations of large historic landslides and the distribution of landslide-prone materials in Canada. Landslides are most common in mountainous areas, the St. Lawrence Lowland, and river valleys on the western interior plains. Materials particularly prone to landsliding include lacustrine and marine silts and clays and Cretaceous shales. *(After Evans, S. G. 2001. Geological Survey of Canada Bulletin 548:46–47; reproduced with the permission of the Minister of Public Works and Government Services Canada, 2007, and courtesy of Natural Resources Canada, Geological Survey of Canada)*

of landslide damage exceeds $1 billion per year and, in some years, is more than $3 billion.[14]

The direct, damaging effects of landslides include being struck by or buried in debris (see the Survivor Story). Landslides can damage homes, roads, and utilities that have been constructed at the top, base, or side of a hill (Figure 4.21; see Case Study 4.2). They regularly block roads and railroads, delaying travel for days or more. One massive landslide, the 1965 Hope slide, blocked a major highway in southern British Columbia for weeks and another in April 1903 buried part of the town of Frank, Alberta, killing about 75 people (Figure 4.22). Landslides may even block shipping lanes. In 1980 a debris flow from the Mount St. Helens volcanic eruption filled the Columbia River with more than 34 million m^3 of sediment. The sediment stopped cargo ships from reaching Portland, Oregon, until dredging was completed.

◄ FIGURE 4.20 KILLER LANDSLIDE On February 17, 2006, a landslide engulfed the farming village of Guinsaugon on the Philippine island of Leyte. The muddy debris killed more than 2000 people, nearly the entire population of the town. *(U.S. Navy Photo by Photographer's Mate 1st Class Michael D. Kennedy)*

SURVIVOR STORY

Landslide

Danny Ogg thought he was "a goner" when the first boulder hit his truck.

He was driving on Interstate 70 west of Denver when a giant granite boulder crashed across his windshield, leaving him with only one thought: "I'm going to be buried alive."

The boulder was one of about 20 or 30 that rocketed down the steep slope onto the interstate highway, which winds through the Rocky Mountains, early one spring morning in 2004 (Figure 4.A). The largest rock weighed 30 t.

Ogg, a 50-year-old driver from Tennessee, says he had no indication that a landslide was underway until the first rock hit his tractor-trailer. After that, it was "bang bang bang, crunch crunch," as he puts it, as his truck collided with the falling debris and eventually hit the median. The vehicle's fuel tank was torn open in the process, spilling hundreds of gallons of diesel fuel.

His sense of time was skewed in the terrifying moments of the landslide. "After I hit the first boulder, it took two, three minutes, I guess. It was fast but it wasn't," he remarks.

Ogg suffered an injured back and some torn cartilage and ligaments, but he was lucky, considering the much more serious injuries he could have incurred.

"I thought I was a goner," he says. "I don't know how long I was in there. It addled me. I was silly as a goose, as we say in Tennessee."

His sense of location was also askew: "You know you ain't dead yet, but you don't know where you are," he continues. "I didn't know if I was hanging off the mountain or what."

Ogg notes that some of the boulders left potholes in the road a foot or two deep, and a *Rocky Mountain News* article reported that some of them bounced as high as 6 m after impact.

Although landslides are difficult to predict and avoid, Ogg says he will be more vigilant now when driving in the mountains. "When you go around the mountain now, you look up."

—Chris Wilson

▲ **FIGURE 4.A BOULDERS ON U.S. INTERSTATE 70** Granite blocks, some as large as 4 m^3, line the shoulder of an interstate highway near Glenwood Springs, Colorado. Heavy rain and subsequent freezing conditions dislodged rock from a free face more than 100 m above the highway. One car-sized boulder bounced across the highway and landed in the nearby Colorado River. A highway crew had to drill or blast apart the largest blocks and push them over to the shoulder so that traffic could get through. *(U.S. Geological Survey)*

◄ **FIGURE 4.21 SHALLOW SOIL SLIPS CAN KILL** This southern California home, located at the base of an unstable slope, was destroyed in 1969 by a small debris flow. The landslide claimed two lives. *(Courtesy of John Sadle, Los Angeles Department of Building and Safety)*

▲ **FIGURE 4.22 FRANK SLIDE** The 1903 Frank slide is Canada's best-known landslide and a classic example of a *rock avalanche*. It travelled more than 3 km in 100 seconds (average velocity, 20 m/s) and buried part of the town of Frank, Alberta, killing about 75 people. Coal mining at the base of the mountain likely triggered the landslide. *(GeoSolutions Consulting Inc., Ottawa, www.geosolutions.com)*

4.2 CASE STUDY

Southern California Landslide Disaster of 2005: Lessons Learned

Monday, January 14, 2005, was a disaster for the small beachside community of La Conchita, 80 km northwest of Los Angeles. Ten people lost their lives and about 30 homes were destroyed or damaged when a fast-moving landslide tore through the upper part of the community (Figure 4.B). The earthflow was a partial reactivation of a 1995 landslide that destroyed several homes but caused no fatalities. Although it had been raining for days before the 2005 slide and the intensity of the rain was high at times, neither residents nor local officials recognized that another slide was imminent. As a result, some people were trapped in their homes and others ran for their lives.

Contributing Factors

The La Conchita coastline and others near Los Angeles are the "landslide capitals" of southern California for four reasons:

1. ***Presence of steep, high slopes.*** The steep slope above La Conchita is a 180 m high, prehistoric sea cliff. The face of the slope is almost vertical in places, in sharp contrast to the top, which is a gently sloping marine terrace planted with avocado orchards. Shells from ancient beach deposits near the top of the cliff indicate that the terrace was at sea level about 40,000 years ago. These observations and others nearby suggest that

(a)

(b)

▲ **FIGURE 4.B REACTIVATION OF A LANDSLIDE** (a) An aerial view of the 1995 La Conchita landslide with part of the community of La Conchita in the foreground. The cliff face is underlain mostly by older slide deposits, including a large slump block partially covered with vegetation on the left side of the photograph. The 1995 landslide buried or damaged several houses at the base of the slope. *(U.S. Geological Survey)* (b) An aerial view of the 2005 reactivation of the same landslide. For reference, the white arrow on the left side of each photograph points to the same building. The landslide started as a slump but changed into a flow that left two lobes at the base of the slope, a large one on the right side of the photograph and a much smaller one in the centre. Mud and debris covered parts of four streets and damaged or buried about 30 houses. The dotted line delineates the toe of the 1995 slide. *(AP Wide World Photos)*

the terrace was uplifted at a rate of 4 m to 6 m every thousand years. These uplift rates are among the highest in the world. Some of the uplift at La Conchita probably happens incrementally during large earthquakes every few hundred to thousand years on nearby geologic faults.

2. ***Presence of weak rocks.***
   Most of the La Conchita sea cliff comprises older landslide deposits and weakly cemented sedimentary rocks with little strength to resist mass wasting on steep slopes.

3. ***Presence of numerous historic and prehistoric landslides.***
   Landslide after landslide is visible for about 9 km of the prehistoric sea cliff along U.S. Highway 101 southeast of La Conchita. Some of these slides are recent, whereas others are probably thousands of years old. Every few years, including in 2005, mudflows cover or erode the highway, closing it for a day or so. On the same day as the 2005 La Conchita landslide, mudflows closed the highway 500 m north of La Conchita. Had homes been in the path of the flows, they would have been destroyed.

4. ***Periodic prolonged and intense rainfall.***
   Rainfall in southern California is highly variable and the amount of precipitation fluctuates widely from year to year. Both the 1995 and 2005 La Conchita landslides occurred after prolonged, often intense winter rains. The intensity of the rainfall was probably the major trigger of the 2005 landslide—more significant than land use or attempts to stabilize the slope after the 1995 landslide.

Solutions to the Landslide Problem

Possible solutions to the recurring problem of landslides at La Conchita include the following:

1. ***Stabilize the slope.***
   An engineering structure, consisting of benches and large retaining walls, could be designed for the hillslope above La Conchita. Similar structures have been built in the Los Angeles area, where a substantial landslide hazard threatens development. However, this solution is probably cost-prohibitive for La Conchita, because there are only about 100 standing structures in the community.

2. ***Change the land use.***
   The homes and buildings in La Conchita could be purchased at market value and the land converted into a park. This solution would require community support and a large fundraising effort by a nonprofit organization because county, state, or federal funds would, by themselves, be insufficient to purchase the property. This approach may not be feasible because, even after two major landslides in 10 years, some La Conchita residents like the community and want to remain, even with the knowledge that another potentially deadly landslide is possible. Some people who died in the 2005 slide had earlier stated they believed the area was safer after the 1995 slide. They willingly took the risk of staying.

3. ***Install an effective warning system.***
   Sensors to detect slope movement were installed following the 1995 slide. The 2005 slide either started above these sensors or moved too rapidly for a warning to be issued. In hindsight, observations of the amount, duration, and intensity of rainfall might have been helpful in providing a warning. In southern California, wildfire warnings, referred to as "Red Flag" days, are issued on the basis of air temperature and wind patterns. Perhaps similar warnings could be issued for landslides at La Conchita based on weather patterns. The downside to such a system is the likelihood of false alarms. A battery of instruments that measure rainfall and slope movement might be the best approach.

4. ***Do nothing substantial and bear future losses.***
   To a certain extent, "do nothing" was the course of action following the 1995 slide. Since 1995, residents have been repeatedly warned of the landslide risk, a small wall was constructed at the base of the cliff to prevent mud from covering the road, and the slope was monitored for movement. Some people moved away following the 1995 slide; however, others decided to stay and people new to the community bought property. These personal decisions were based on individual perceptions of risk. It is hoped that this time more will be done to reduce the continuing hazard. The question is not if another slide will occur, but when. Doing nothing is not an acceptable option for protecting lives and property.

Indirect damaging effects of landslides include floods upstream of landslide dams, downstream floods caused by the rapid breaching of landslide dams, and blockage of salmon migration routes. Partial blockage of the Fraser River in southern British Columbia by rockfall during construction of the Canadian National Railway in 1914 prevented salmon from reaching their spawning grounds. The runs still have not recovered to their pre-1914 levels, resulting in large economic losses to the Fraser River salmon fishery.[15]

Linkages between Landslides and Other Natural Hazards

Landslides are linked to just about every other natural hazard you can think of. Earthquakes, volcanoes, storms, and fires all can cause landslides; these relations are discussed in other chapters in this book. As mentioned above, landslides may be responsible for flooding if they form a debris dam across a river.

A large landslide can also trigger a tsunami or cause widespread flooding if it displaces water out of a lake or bay. In 1963 more than 240 million m^3 of rock slid into the Vaiont reservoir in northeastern Italy. The landslide displaced water over the dam, flooding the valley below and killing more than 2600 people.[16] Most of the deaths were in the town of Longarone, which was flooded with 70 m of water.

A spectacular landslide-triggered tsunami occurred in Lituya Bay, Alaska, on July 7, 1958. A strong earthquake triggered a rockslide on a steep slope high above the head of the bay. The rockslide plunged into the bay and displaced a huge mass of seawater that raced up the opposite valley wall to an elevation of 525 m, completely destroying the forest in its path (Figure 4.23). In four minutes, a 30 m high wave surged 11 km to the mouth of the bay, where it swept away two fishing boats anchored just inside a low forested spit. Remarkably, the crew of one of the boats survived and told a harrowing tale of their boat being swept over the tops of trees, across the spit toward the open Pacific Ocean. Smaller, although still damaging, landslide-triggered tsunami have occurred in *fiords* in Norway, Alaska, and British Columbia.

Earthquakes can trigger subaqueous landslides that, in turn, generate devastating tsunami. In 1988, a submarine landslide triggered by an **M** 7.1 earthquake caused a tsunami that killed more than 2200 people in several communities on the north coast of Papua-New Guinea.

The most destructive tsunami in Canadian history was triggered by a submarine landslide. On November 18, 1929, an **M** 7.2 earthquake occurred about 20 km beneath the seafloor at the southern edge of the Grand Banks, 250 km south of Newfoundland. The shaking triggered a huge submarine slump, which, in turn, set off a tsunami that propagated across the Atlantic Ocean, registering on tide gauges as far away as South Carolina and Portugal. The tsunami arrived in Bermuda about two hours after the earthquake, travelling at an average velocity of just more than 700 km/h. In contrast, it took about 2.5 hours to travel the much shorter distance to Newfoundland because of the drag exerted by the shallow continental shelf north and west of the earthquake epicentre.

Burin Peninsula was hardest hit by the tsunami. Three main waves thundered up narrow channels and into bays over a half-hour period on the evening of November 18. The tsunami lifted small boats and schooners 5 m high, snapping anchor chains and tossing the craft onshore or engulfing them. Houses floated from their foundations; some were splintered,

◄ **FIGURE 4.23 TSUNAMI IN LITUYA BAY** Lituya Bay, Alaska, shortly after the tsunami of July 7, 1958. A large landslide plunged into the bay at its head (red arrow), triggering the tsunami. The prominent trimline delineates the upper limit of the tsunami. Forest below this line was obliterated by the surging waters. *(From Clague, J., C. Yorath, R. Franklin, and B. Turner. 2006. At risk: Earthquakes and tsunamis on the west coast. Vancouver, BC: Tricouni Press)*

◄ **FIGURE 4.24 TSUNAMI STRIKES NEWFOUNDLAND** Coastal communities on Burin Peninsula bore the brunt of the 1929 tsunami. This photograph shows buildings in Lord's Cove that were tossed and smashed by the tsunami. *(Photo of 1929 tsunami damage in Lord's Cove, Burin Peninsula. Photo by Harris M. Mosdell, from the W. M. Chisholm collection, provided by A. Ruffman, GeoMarine Associates, Halifax)*

whereas others were swept back and forth by the flooding and ebbing waters (Figure 4.24). The tsunami damaged more than 40 coastal communities on Burin Peninsula and claimed 27 lives in Newfoundland and Labrador and one in Nova Scotia. Damage was made worse by the fact that the tsunami arrived near the peak of a very high tide.

4.4 Natural Service Functions of Landslides

Although most hazardous natural processes provide important natural service functions, the potential benefits of landslides are few. Benefits include the creation of new habitats in forests and aquatic ecosystems.

Landslides, like fire, are a major source of ecological disturbance in forests. For some old-growth forests, this disturbance can be beneficial by increasing both plant and animal diversity.[17] Landslide-dammed lakes provide new habitat for fish and other aquatic organisms, and large landslides provide open spaces in forests favoured by some animals and plants.

Mass wasting can produce sediments that contain valuable minerals. Weathering frees mineral grains from rocks, and mass wasting transports these minerals downslope. Heavier minerals, particularly gold and diamonds, can be concentrated at the base of the slope and in adjacent streams. Gold and diamonds have been mined from colluvial deposits, although they are much more common in fluvial sediments.

4.5 Human Interaction with Landslides

Mass wasting is a natural process, and landslides can happen without any human modification of the land. However, expansion of urban areas and transportation networks and exploitation of natural resources have increased the number and frequency of landslides in many areas. For example, grading of land surfaces for housing developments may initiate landslides on previously stable hillsides. However, people can reduce the incidence of landslides by taking preventative measures, for example improving surface drainage on naturally sensitive slopes.

The effect of human activities on the magnitude and frequency of landslides ranges from nearly insignificant to very significant. In instances where human activities, such as road construction and deforestation, increase the number and severity of landslides, we need to learn how our practices cause slides and how we can minimize their occurrence. Below are descriptions of some human activities that cause landslides.

Timber Harvesting

The possible cause-and-effect relation between timber harvesting and erosion is a major environmental and economic issue around the world. Two controversial practices are *clearcutting,* which involves harvesting all trees from large tracts of land, and the construction of logging roads to remove cut timber from the forest. Landslides, especially debris avalanches, debris flows, and earthflows, are responsible for much of the erosion in these areas.

One 20-year study in Oregon found that shallow slides are the dominant form of erosion. It also found that timber-harvesting activities, such as clearcutting and road building, did not significantly increase landslide-related erosion on geologically stable land. In contrast, logging on unstable slopes or weak rocks increased landslide erosion by several times compared with slopes that had not been logged.[18]

Road construction in timber harvesting areas can pose an especially serious problem because roads interrupt surface drainage, alter subsurface movement of water, and can adversely change the distribution of materials on a slope by cut-and-fill or grading operations.[18] Based in part on past errors, geologists, engineers, and foresters are developing improved management practices to minimize the adverse effects of logging. New forest-management practices include the harvesting of smaller cut blocks, selective logging of cut blocks, helicopter logging to minimize the number and length of access roads, and controlled surface drainage along roads. In spite of these advances, landslides continue to be associated with timber harvesting.

Urbanization

Human activities are most likely to cause destructive landslides in urbanized areas with high densities of people, roads, and buildings. Examples from Rio de Janeiro, Brazil, and Los Angeles, California, illustrate this point.

Rio de Janeiro, with a population of more than 6 million people, may have more problems with slope stability than any other city of its size.[19] Several factors contribute to the serious landslide problem in Rio: (1) the granite peaks that spectacularly frame the city (Figure 4.25) have steep slopes of fractured rock that are covered with thin soil, (2) the area is periodically inundated by torrential rains, (3) cut-and-fill construction has seriously destabilized many slopes, and (4) vegetation has been progressively removed from the slopes.

The landslide problem started early in the city's history, when many of the slopes were logged for lumber and fuel and to clear land for agriculture. Landslides associated with heavy rainfall followed this deforestation. More recently, a lack of building sites on flat ground has led to increased urban development on steep slopes. Excavations have undercut the base of many slopes and removed vegetation and soil at critical points. In addition, fill placed on slopes to expand the size of building sites has increased the load on already unstable land. When adding to these activities the fact that Rio de Janeiro experiences tremendous rainstorms, it becomes apparent that the city has a serious problem.

In February 1988, an intense rainstorm dumped more than 12 cm of rain on Rio de Janeiro in four hours. The storm caused flooding and debris flows that killed at least 90 people and left 3000 people homeless. Most of the deaths were caused by debris flows in hill-hugging shantytowns where housing is precarious and control of storm water runoff nonexistent. However, more affluent mountainside areas were not spared from destruction. In one area, a landslide destroyed a nursing home and killed 25 patients and staff. Restoration costs for the entire city exceeded $100 million. If future disasters are to be avoided, Rio de Janeiro must take extensive and decisive measures to control storm runoff, increase slope stability, and limit development on dangerous slopes.

Southern California has also experienced a large number of landslides associated with hillside development, and Los Angeles has the dubious honour of illustrating the economic importance of studying urban geology.[20] It took natural processes millions of years to produce the valleys, ridges, and hills of the Los Angeles basin. In a little more than a century, people have radically altered them. Forty years ago, F. B. Leighton, a geological consultant in southern California, wrote: "With modern engineering and grading practices and appropriate financial incentive, no hillside appears too rugged for future development."[20] People have become a more important agent of landscape change than rivers. Almost overnight, we can convert steep hills into flat lots and roads. The grading process, in which benches, referred to as pads, are cut into slopes for home sites, has been responsible for many landslides in southern California, and Los Angeles has led North America in developing codes for grading.

Grading codes that minimize landslide risk have been in effect in the Los Angeles area since 1963. The codes were adopted in the aftermath of destructive and deadly landslides in the 1950s and 1960s. Since these codes have been in effect and detailed engineering geology studies have been required before development, the number of hillside homes damaged by landslides and floods has been greatly reduced. Although initial building costs are greater because of the strict codes, the costs are more than offset by the reduction of losses in subsequent years.

People may destabilize formerly stable slopes by removing rock or sediment, watering lawns and gardens, installing septic systems, or adding fill and buildings (Figure 4.26). As a rule, any project that steepens or saturates a slope, increases its height, or places an extra load on it may cause a landslide.[20]

◄ **FIGURE 4.25 LANDSLIDES IN RIO DE JANEIRO** Panoramic view of Rio de Janeiro, Brazil, showing the steep "sugarloaf" mountains and hills (right centre of the image). Steep slopes, fractured rock, shallow soils, and intense rainfall contribute to the landslide problem in Rio, as do such human activities as urbanization, logging, and agriculture. Nearly all the bare rock slopes were at one time vegetated, and that vegetation has been removed by landslides and other erosional processes. *(Getty Images Inc.-Stone Allstock)*

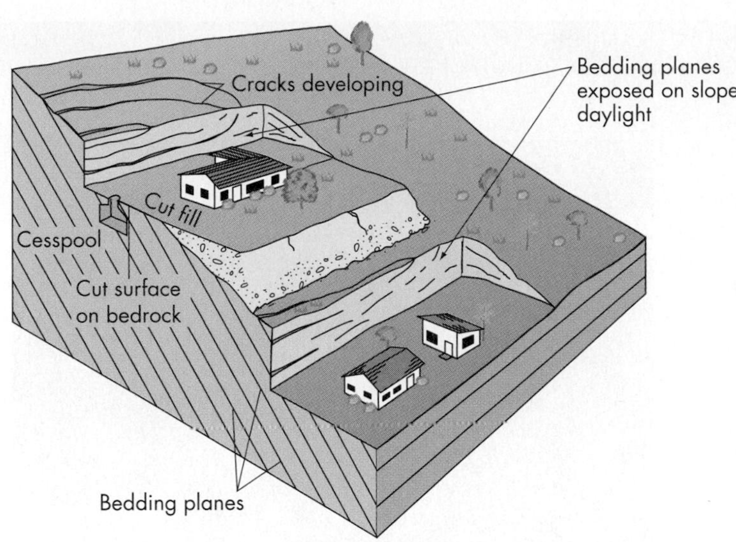

◀ **FIGURE 4.26 URBANIZATION AND LANDSLIDE POTENTIAL** The diagram shows how building on slopes can increase the chance of landslides. The diagonal lines at the left side of the block diagram are bedding planes in sedimentary rock. Excavation into the hillside behind the houses has removed support. Fill (yellow) used to extend the flat pad for building adds weight to the slope. Cracks shown in the upper part of the diagram are an early sign that a landslide is likely to occur. Wastewater from septic fields adds water to the hillslope. *(Reprinted, with permission, from Leighton, F. B. 1966. Landslides and urban development. In Engineering geology in southern California. Los Angeles: Los Angeles Section of the Association of Engineering Geologists)*

Landslides related to urbanization have been a problem in some areas of Canada. In Vancouver, most damaging slides have been debris avalanches and debris flows in glacial sediments, fill, and soils.[21] A typical example is a small debris avalanche that destroyed two homes and claimed one life in a North Vancouver neighbourhood on January 19, 2005. Fill in the backyard of a home at the top of a steep slope failed during heavy rain and swept down the slope and into the houses below. The landslide entrained soil and trees as it moved downslope, adding to the destruction. Another similar landslide had occurred in the same area and under similar circumstances in 1979. Landslides have also damaged and destroyed homes built too close to the edges of valley walls in Edmonton.

4.6 Minimizing Landslide Hazard and Risk

To minimize landslide risk, it is necessary to identify areas in which landslides are likely to occur, employ engineered structures to prevent landslides, warn people of impending failures, and control active slides (see Professional Profile). As discussed below, the preferred and least expensive option is to avoid developing sites where landslides are occurring or are likely to occur.

Identification of Potential Landslides

Recognizing areas with a high potential for landslides is the first step in minimizing the hazard. A variety of surface features indicate unstable or potentially unstable slopes:

- Crescent-shaped cracks or terraces on a hillside
- A scalloped or recessed crest of a valley wall
- A tongue-shaped area of bare soil or rock on a hillside
- Large boulders or piles of talus at the base of a cliff
- An area of tilted, or *jack-strawed*, trees
- Trees that are convex at their base but straight higher up
- Exposed bedrock with layering that is parallel to the slope
- Tongue-shaped masses of sediment at the base of a slope or at the mouth of a valley
- A hummocky, or irregular and undulating, land surface at the base of a slope

Earth scientists search for these indicators in the field and on aerial photographs. They then assess the hazard and produce several kinds of maps (Figure 4.27).

One type of map is the direct result of the landslide inventory described above. It may be a reconnaissance map showing areas that have experienced slope failure, or it may be a more detailed map discriminating landslide deposits of different age. Information concerning past landslides may be combined with land-use considerations to develop a *slope stability map* for use by engineering geologists or a *landslide hazard map* with recommended land uses for planners. Preparing a *landslide risk map* is more complicated, because it involves evaluating the probability that a landslide will occur and an assessment of potential losses.[22] In this context, it is important to reemphasize the difference between landslide *hazard* and *risk*. Hazard reflects the expected type, size, and likelihood of landslides in a particular area. Risk is the total vulnerability of the area to landslides and takes into account population and economic infrastructure. There is no risk if landslides occur in a natural area without people or development. In contrast, all other things being equal, risk increases as population and development grow.

Prevention of Landslides

Prevention of large, natural landslides is difficult or impossible, but common sense and good engineering practices help to minimize the hazard. For example, loading the top of slopes, cutting into sensitive slopes, or increasing the flow of water on slopes should be avoided or done with caution.[23] Common engineering techniques for landslide prevention include surface and subsurface drainage, removal of unstable slope materials, and construction of retaining walls or other supporting structures.[3]

PROFESSIONAL PROFILE

Matthias Jakob, Engineering Geologist

Matthias Jakob (Figure 4.C) has a passion for falling, bouncing, flowing, and creeping rock and soil. Born near the German Alps and now a senior geoscientist with a geotechnical consulting firm in Vancouver, British Columbia, Jakob is fascinated with the processes that form mountains and even more so with the processes that wear them down.

Jakob has studied landslides around the world, from North America to Italy, Germany, Bolivia, Ecuador, Argentina, Chile, and Venezuela. He has gained first-hand experience with a large variety of mass movements in a range of climates and geologic settings.

"Every time you work in a new region, you have to retrain yourself, understand the special local conditions, and adapt your methods and interpretations accordingly. A good landslide scientist is the one who constantly questions his or her hypotheses," Jakob insists. "Geological idiosyncrasies at any given site can be overwhelming at times and may lie outside one's expertise. Yet, time after time, ignorance of geological subtleties has led to catastrophic loss. A multidisciplinary approach, sometimes involving highly specialized scientists, is commonly needed to solve the geo-puzzle.

"In our business, you quickly realize that landslides are sometimes ignored. Landslides at any given location are rare events and human memory is short. Too often, I hear statements like 'I have lived here all my life and nothing has ever happened.' Such an assertion may not be true and, even if it is, it may be foolhardy to assume that an inhabited area is free of hazards."

Deciphering the history of landslides is a crucial part of Jakob's work. He is particularly interested in short- and long-term changes in the source area of landslides, which may alter hazard and risk. The source area can change because of human activity, such as mining and forestry, or indirectly from climate change. "We think that coastal British Columbia will get wetter in the future, but to conclude that more rain will cause more landslides is overly simplistic," Jakob explains. "Different types of landslide respond differently to changes in rainfall. An earthflow may move after one year of above-normal rainfall, whereas debris flows respond to a combination of higher antecedent rainfall and higher rainfall intensities."

▲ **FIGURE 4.C GEOLOGIST EXAMINES RECENT LANDSLIDE** Matthias Jakob, an engineering geologist based in Vancouver, British Columbia. *(Courtesy of Matthias Jakob)*

Jakob is a firm believer that climate is changing and that the changes will affect slope stability. He plans to focus much of his future research on the interplay between slope stability and hydrology. He notes that "increasingly warmer winters are responsible for severe insect damage to forests in British Columbia's interior, making the region more vulnerable to wildfires. Widespread burning commonly increases rates of natural erosion and may increase the size and frequency of debris flows."

Jakob states that "time is of the essence in this line of work." Steep slopes and mountain valleys in western Canada are under increasing development pressure. New development, in tandem with climate change, will augment landslide risk and pose a challenge for landslide specialists, particularly in British Columbia, where the number of lawsuits dealing with geotechnical practice exceeds those of all other Canadian provinces combined.

—John J. Clague

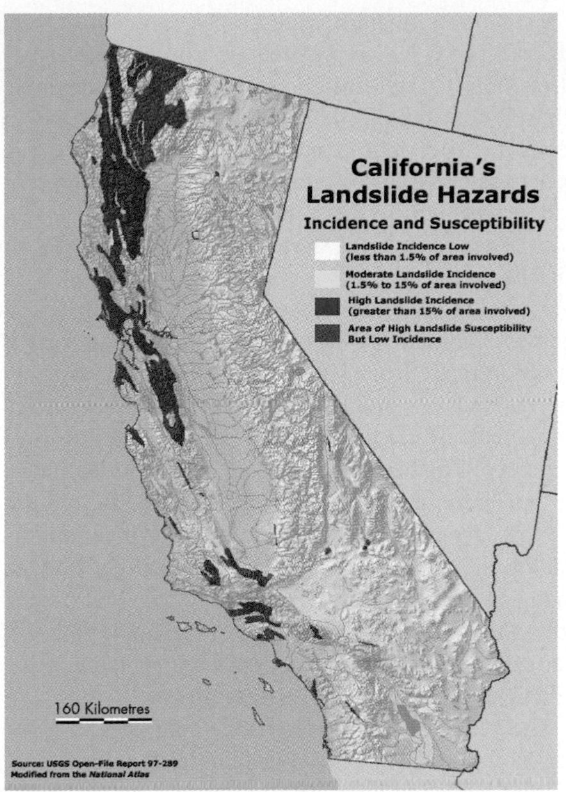

▲ **FIGURE 4.27 LANDSLIDE HAZARD MAP** A generalized map showing areas of different landslide incidence in California. *(U.S. Geological Survey)*

Drainage Control Surface and subsurface drainage control is generally effective in stabilizing a slope. The objective is to keep water from running across or infiltrating the slope. Surface runoff may be diverted around the slope by surface drains. Infiltration may also be controlled by covering the slope with an impermeable layer, such as soil-cement, asphalt, or plastic. Groundwater may be removed by installing subsurface drains. The simplest drains, which are commonly used in fractured bedrock, are horizontal or inclined drill holes or tunnels (Figure 4.28a). More complex drains, which are sometimes used in soft rocks or unconsolidated sediments, consist of pipes with holes along their length. The pipes are surrounded with permeable gravel or crushed rock and positioned underground to intercept and divert water away from a potentially unstable slope.[3]

Two examples from British Columbia illustrate the importance of drainage in stabilizing landslides. The Trans-Canada Highway crosses the Drynoch landslide, a large slow-moving earthflow in the Thompson River valley in southern B.C. For many years, slow movement of the earthflow displaced and damaged the highway, necessitating regular and costly repairs. The British Columbia Ministry of Highways and Transportation installed a system of surface and subsurface drains to reduce the amount of water infiltrating the slope. Soon thereafter, movement rates decreased substantially and, today, little maintenance of the highway is required where it crosses the landslide.

(a)

(b)

(c)

◀ **FIGURE 4.28 WAYS OF INCREASING SLOPE STABILITY** (a) Holes drilled in fractured rock to drain groundwater and thereby reduce water pressures. (b) Rock bolts anchoring fractured rock on a steep cut face, reducing the possibility of rock fall. (c) Metal mesh draped over a rock face to intercept small rockfall. *(John J. Clague)*

The Downie slide is a huge (1.4 km^3) sackung in the Columbia River valley north of Revelstoke, British Columbia. The toe of the landslide was inundated when Mica Dam was built in 1973. After dam construction, BC Hydro and Power Authority (BC Hydro) conducted an exhaustive study of the landslide to determine its three-dimensional geometry, its movement rates, and the effects of inundation of its toe beneath 100 m of water. BC Hydro staff decided that the best approach to ensure against catastrophic slope failure would be to drain water away from rocks at the base of the landslide. Work on the Downie slide was carried out between 1977 and 1982. A drainage system consisting of hundreds of metres of tunnels and thousands of metres of drill holes was established to drain the water away. Since 1982, when the work was completed, the landslide mass has practically stopped moving and is considered to be more stable than it was before the dam was built.

Grading Carefully planned grading can improve slope stability. In a cut-and-fill operation, material from the upper part of a slope is removed and placed near the base. The overall gradient of the slope is thus reduced, and placement of material at the toe of the slope increases the resisting force. However, this method is not practical on a very high, steep slope. Instead, the slope may be cut into a series of benches or steps, each of which contains surface drains to divert runoff. The benches reduce the overall slope and are good collection sites for falling rock and small slides (Figure 4.29).[3]

Slope Supports One of the most common stabilization strategies is to support slopes with retaining walls. Retaining walls can be constructed of concrete or brick, stone-filled wire baskets called *gabions*, or piles of long concrete, steel, or wooden beams driven into the ground (Figure 4.30). To function effectively, the walls must be anchored well below the base of the slope, be backfilled with permeable gravel or crushed rock (Figure 4.31), and contain drainage holes to reduce water pressure in the slope (Figure 4.30).

Potentially unstable rock slopes can also be secured with rock bolts, which are steel or iron pins up to several metres long inserted into holes drilled into the slope and anchored with facing plates (Figure 4.28b). Heavy metal screens and rock fences can also be placed over steep cut slopes to catch small rock fragments before they reach roads or railways (Figure 4.28c). Screens provide no protection against rockslides, but they may be effective for small rockfalls.

Preventing landslides can be expensive but well worth the effort. Estimates of the benefit-to-cost ratio for landslide prevention range from 10 to 2000. That is, for every dollar spent on landslide prevention, \$10 to \$2000 are saved.[24]

The cost of *not* preventing a landslide is illustrated by the massive Thistle landslide, which occurred southeast of Salt Lake City in April 1983. The landslide moved down a mountain slope and across a canyon to form a natural dam about 60 m high. The dam created a lake that flooded the community of Thistle, the Denver-Rio Grande Railroad switchyard and tracks, and two major U.S. highways (Figure 4.32).[24] The total direct and indirect costs of the landslide and associated flooding exceeded US\$400 million.[25]

The Thistle slide involved reactivation of a portion of an older, larger landslide. It had been known for many years that the older landslide mass moved during times of high precipitation. It thus came as no surprise that the 1983 landslide was triggered by extremely high amounts of precipitation during a strong El Niño year (see Chapter 11). A review of the evidence suggests the Thistle slide could have been predicted and prevented! The failure could have been prevented by installing a network of subsurface and surface drains at a cost of US\$300,000 to US\$500,000, a small amount compared to the cost of the damage the landslide caused.[24] Because the benefit-to-cost ratio in landslide prevention is so favourable, it seems prudent to evaluate active and potentially active landslides in areas where considerable damage may be expected and possibly prevented.

◄ **FIGURE 4.29 CUT BENCH IN ROCK ALONG A HIGHWAY** The stepped bench reduces the overall steepness of the slope and provides better drainage. Benches cut into bedrock can intercept rockfall before it reaches the highway. *(John J. Clague)*

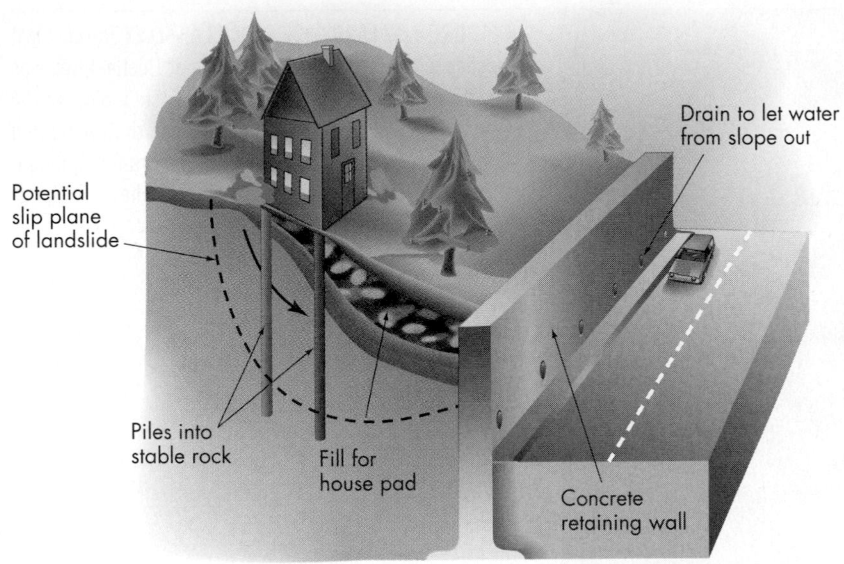

◀ **FIGURE 4.30 HOW TO SUPPORT A SLOPE** The types of slope support shown in this illustration include a deeply anchored, concrete retaining wall along a road, concrete piles sunk into stable rock, and subsurface drains that reduce water pressure in the slope.

Landslide Warning Systems

Landslide warning systems do not prevent landslides; rather they provide time to evacuate people and their possessions, stop trains, and reroute traffic. Hazardous areas can be visually inspected for surface changes, and small rockfalls on roads and other areas can be noted for quick removal. Human monitoring has the advantages of reliability and flexibility, but it becomes difficult during adverse weather and in hazardous areas.[26] Rockfall along transportation routes in British Columbia has been monitored for decades by the BC Ministry of Transportation and Highways, CP Railway, and CN Railway.

Other warning methods include electrical systems, tiltmeters, and geophones that pick up vibrations from moving rocks. Many Canadian and U.S. railways have rock fences on slopes above their tracks that are linked to signal systems. When a large rock hits the fence, a signal is sent and trains can be stopped before they are in danger. This and other mitigation measures have significantly reduced the number of railroad accidents, injuries, and fatalities in North America.[26] BC Hydro conducts regular surveys of slopes along its hydroelectric reservoirs to measure surface displacements and to ensure that movements in areas of known landslides, such as the Downie slide, are not accelerating.

A pilot landslide warning system is being developed in western Washington State by the U.S. Geological Survey and Pierce County. Acoustic flow monitors, which can detect the passage of a debris flow, have been installed in valleys draining Mount Rainier.[27] A large debris flow from the mountain, similar to one that occurred about 500 years ago, would devastate more than a dozen communities and kill thousands, or possibly tens of thousands, of people.

Shallow wells can be drilled into slopes and monitored to signal when slopes contain a dangerous amount of water. In some regions, a rain-gauge network is useful for warning when a precipitation threshold has been exceeded and debris

◀ **FIGURE 4.31 RETAINING WALL** This retaining wall of concrete cribbing was installed and then back-filled to help stabilize the roadcut. *(Edward A. Keller)*

◀ **FIGURE 4.32 LANDSLIDE BLOCKS A VALLEY** The costliest landslide in U.S. history, the 1983 slide at Thistle, Utah, was a reactivation of an older slide. The landslide blocked the Spanish Fork River and impounded a lake that inundated the community of Thistle, the Denver-Rio Grande Railroad, and two major American highways. Nearly the entire landslide deposit moved again in 1999. *(Michael Collier)*

avalanches or debris flows are likely to occur. Surface movements can be monitored through periodic surveying of benchmarks on landslides. It is now possible to detect changes in positions of surface points, with an accuracy of a few millimetres or less, by using satellite global positioning technology.

4.7 Perception of and Adjustment to Landslide Hazards

Perception of Landslide Hazards

The common reaction of homeowners, when asked about landslides, is "It could happen somewhere else, but not here."[20] Just as flood hazard mapping does not prevent development in flood-prone areas, landslide hazard maps do not prevent many people from moving into hazardous areas. Prospective hillside occupants who are initially unaware of the hazard may not be swayed by technical information. The infrequency of large landslides reduces awareness of the hazard, especially where evidence of past events is not readily visible. Unfortunately, it often takes a disaster to bring the problem to the attention of many people. In the meantime, people in many parts of North America and other areas continue to build homes in areas subject to future landslides.

Adjustments to the Landslide Hazard

The only fail-safe way of dealing with landslide hazards is to avoid landslide-prone areas, but many people still go ahead and build and live in dangerous situations. As long as people continue to live in homes "with a view," we will need to make adjustments to minimize death and damage from landslides. Adjustments include locating critical facilities outside landslide-prone areas and implementing remedial corrective measures.

Siting of Critical Facilities As in the case of earthquakes (Chapter 2), safely siting critical public facilities, such as hospitals, schools, electrical-generating facilities, and police stations, is crucial. Ensuring that these buildings are not located on or directly below hillsides is a simple way to guarantee that they will remain functional in the event of a landslide.

Remedial Corrective Measures The best way to stop a slow-moving landslide is to attack the process that caused it. In most cases, the culprit is high water pressure within or below the slide. The pressure can be reduced by installing an effective drainage system. A reduction in water pressure increases the resisting force of the slope material, thereby stabilizing the slope.[8]

Personal Adjustments: What You Can Do to Minimize Your Landslide Risk

Consider the following advice if purchasing property on a slope:

- Seek an evaluation of the property by a professional geologist or engineering geologist.
- Avoid homes at the mouth of a valley or canyon, even a small one, because such sites may be in the path of debris flows.
- Consult local agencies, such as city or county engineering departments, that may be aware of landslides in your area.
- Look out for "little landslides" on the property—they usually get larger with time.
- If purchasing a home, look for cracks in walls; also look for retaining walls that lean or are cracked. Be wary of doors or windows that stick or floors that are uneven. Foundations should be checked for cracks or tilting. If cracks in the walls of a house or foundation can be followed across the ground beyond the structure, be especially concerned that the ground may be moving.
- Be wary of leaks in a swimming pool or septic tank, trees or fences tilted downslope, or utility wires that are taut or sagging.
- Avoid slopes with small springs. Suspect ground that is wet or has unusually lush vegetation.
- Walk the property and, if possible, surrounding properties, looking for linear or curved cracks, even small ones, that might indicate instability.
- Look for the surface features that geologists use to identify potential landslides.
- Although it may be cost-effective to correct a potential landslide problem, the expense can still be considerable and much of the fix is below ground where you will never see the improvement. Overall, it is better not to purchase land that can move.

The presence of one or more of the above features does not prove that a landslide is present or that one will occur. For example, cracks in walls and foundations, doors or windows that stick, or floors that are uneven can be caused by soils that shrink and swell (see Chapter 6). However, further detailed investigation is warranted if the above features are present.

Summary

Slopes are dynamic, evolving systems. On some slopes, Earth materials move downward at rates ranging from millimetres per year to several dozen metres per second. Slope failure involves the falling, sliding, toppling, or flow of materials; most landslides are characterized by combinations of sliding and flow.

The stability of a slope is determined by its geology, slope angle and height, climate, vegetation, water, and time. The cause of a landslide can be determined by examining the relation between driving forces, which induce failure, and resisting forces, which oppose movement. The most important driving force is the weight of the slope materials, and the most important resisting force is the shear strength of the slope materials. The factor of safety of a slope is the ratio of resisting forces to driving forces. A ratio greater than one means that the slope is stable, whereas a ratio of one or less indicates that failure is likely. The type of rock, sediment, or soil forming a slope influences both the type and the frequency of landslides.

Water is an important factor in slope failure. Moving water in streams, lakes, or oceans erodes the base of slopes, increasing the driving forces. Excess groundwater increases both the weight of the slope material and the water pressure within the slope, which in turn decreases the resisting forces.

Landslides can occur anywhere there are slopes. In North America, they are most common in the mountainous areas of the west, the Appalachian Mountains, and the St. Lawrence Lowland. When landslides occur in populated areas, they can cause significant damage and loss of life. They are also linked to other hazards, especially floods, earthquakes, tsunami, volcanic eruptions, and wildfires.

The effects of land use on slope stability range from insignificant to very significant. We should avoid developing areas where landslides occur independently of human activity or, alternatively, use appropriate protective measures. Where land use has increased the number and severity of landslides, we need to learn how to minimize their recurrence. Filling large water reservoirs alters groundwater conditions along their shores and may cause slope failure. Logging operations on weak, unstable slopes may also increase the incidence of landslides. Grading of slopes for development has created or increased landslide problems in many urban areas of the world.

To minimize landslide hazard and risk, it is necessary to identify unstable and potentially unstable slopes, adopt preventative measures, and correct problems when they arise. Mapping and monitoring help identify hazardous sites. Grading codes, enacted in response to landslides triggered by cut-and-fill operations in urban areas, have reduced landslide damage in urban areas. Prevention of large natural landslides is difficult, but careful engineering practices can minimize the risk in places where such slides are possible. Engineering techniques for landslide prevention include drainage control, proper grading, and construction of retaining walls and other support structures. Efforts to stop or slow existing landslides must attack the processes that led to failure—usually by initiating a drainage program that lowers water pressure in the slope. Even with all these measures, losses from landslides are expected to increase through the twenty-first century.

Most people perceive landslide risk as minimal, unless they have prior experience with landslides. Furthermore, hillside residents, like floodplain occupants, are not easily swayed by technical information. Nevertheless, the wise person will have a geologist inspect property on a slope before purchasing it.

Key Terms

colluvium (p. 116)
creep (p. 112)
debris flow (p. 116)
driving forces (p. 113)
factor of safety (p. 113)
falling (p. 112)
flow (p. 112)
landslide (p. 111)
mass wasting (p. 111)
resisting forces (p. 113)
sackung (p. 112)
shear strength (p. 113)
sliding (p. 112)
slumping (p. 112)
subaqueous landslide (p. 112)
talus (p. 111)
thaw flow slide (p. 118)
topple (p. 112)

Review Questions

1. What is a landslide?
2. What are the three main ways that materials on a slope can fail?
3. What is the factor of safety and how is it defined?
4. How do slumps (rotational slides) differ from soil avalanches and rockslides (translational slides)?
5. How does the slope angle affect the incidence of landslides?
6. How and where do debris flows occur?
7. What are the three ways that vegetation is important in slope stability?
8. Why does time play an important role in slope stability?
9. What regions of North America have the highest incidence of landslides?
10. How might processes involved in urbanization increase or decrease the stability of slopes?
11. What types of surface features are associated with landslides?
12. What can be done to prevent landslides?

Critical Thinking Questions

1. Your consulting company is hired by Parks Canada to determine landslide risk in a national park. Develop a plan of attack that outlines what must be done to achieve this objective.
2. Why do you think that few people are concerned about landslides? Assume you have been hired by a municipality to make its citizens more aware of the landslide risk on the steep slopes in the community. Outline a plan of action and defend it.
3. The snow-clad Cascade volcanoes of western North America experience numerous landslides, most of which are not triggered by volcanic eruptions. You have been hired to establish a warning system for subdivisions, businesses, and highways in valleys flanking Mount Baker volcano, near the Washington–British Columbia border. How would you design a warning system that will alert citizens to evacuate hazardous areas?

Selected Web Resources

Canada Landslide Project
http://gsc.nrcan.gc.ca/landslides/clp/index_e.php
Comprehensive site on landslides from Natural Resources Canada

National Landslide Information Center
http://landslides.usgs.gov Information on landslides from the U.S. Geological Survey

Landslide hazards
www.fema.gov/hazards/landslide/index.shtm Information on landslide hazard and landslide mitigation from the U.S. Federal Emergency Management Agency

Landslides in California
www.consrv.ca.gov/cgs/geologic_hazards/landslides/index.htm Information on landslides and landslide maps from the California Geological Survey

Landslides in Oregon
www.oregongeology.com/sub/Landslide/Landslidehome.htm Information about debris flows and other landslides from the Oregon Department of Geology and Mineral Industries

Landslides in Colorado
http://geosurvey.state.co.us/Default.aspx?tabid=35 Information on landslides and landslide engineering from the Colorado Geological Survey

Puget Sound landslides
www.ecy.wa.gov/programs/sea/landslides Information on landslides and landslide prevention from the Washington Department of Ecology

HAZARD CITY: ASSIGNMENTS IN APPLIED GEOLOGY

Landslide Hazard Assessment

The Issue

Landslides are a significant cause of property damage. Damage or death from landslides can be nearly instantaneous, such as at La Conchita in January 2005. Conversely, slow-moving landslides can take place over many years, gradually destroying buildings located on them. In either case, the conditions conducive to landslides are generally readily identifiable. As part of choosing a site for residential and commercial development, a contractor should commission a landslide hazard assessment. Determining the potential for landslides is a very common job done by geologists and geological engineers. They use maps, field surveys, soil reports, and aerial photographs to accomplish the task.

Your Task

Your client, a housing contractor, is considering five sites for single-family residences. Your job is to determine the landslide hazard for each of the five sites based on airphoto interpretation, study of geologic and soil maps, and field investigation. You must be careful not to recommend any sites that will put your client at risk. Sites with even a small amount of risk should be avoided.

Average Completion Time

1 hour

CHAPTER 5

▶ **AVALANCHE!** A large snow avalanche races down a mountain slope in the Bow River Valley, Canadian Rockies. *(Clair Isrealson)*

Learning Objectives

Snow avalanche fatalities are increasing because more people are participating in winter recreational activities, notably skiing and snowboarding. Some roads and rail lines in mountains are also at risk from snow avalanches. Your goals in reading this chapter should be to

- Understand the causes of snow avalanches
- Know the different types of avalanches
- Know the geographic regions where avalanches occur
- Recognize links between avalanches and other hazards, as well as the natural service functions of avalanches
- Understand how humans interact with avalanche hazards
- Know what can be done to minimize the risk from avalanches

Snow Avalanches

The Chilkoot Disaster

The Klondike gold rush began in 1896 with the discovery of gold at Bonanza Creek, Yukon Territory. By 1898, thousands of prospectors were heading to the Klondike by almost every route imaginable. None of the routes, however, was shorter or cheaper than the Chilkoot Trail, which linked Skagway, Alaska, to Yukon. As a result, this trail became the most popular way for prospectors to reach the Klondike.

The Chilkoot Trail extends from tidewater at Skagway, Alaska, into northwest British Columbia. The most difficult stretch of the trail is the approach to Chilkoot Pass, which, at 1067 m above sea level, marks the boundary between the United States and Canada. The approach to the pass, although not long, is steep, in places nearly 40°. The pass was crossed by thousands of prospectors during the spring and summer of 1898 (Figure 5.1).

Disaster struck some of these prospectors on April 3, 1898. Heavy snow had fallen throughout February and March of that year, but warm weather at the beginning of April melted the surface of the snow-pack, producing icy conditions. Then, on April 2, it began to snow again. Guides knew conditions were perfect for avalanches and warned prospectors to stay away. The lure of gold was too strong, however, and some men continued up the pass in spite of the warnings. The first of a series of avalanches occurred at 2:00 A.M. on April 3, burying 20 prospectors. Another avalanche buried three more at 9:30 A.M. All were rescued, but fear of more avalanches convinced some 220 other people living and working on the trail to evacuate. Sometime between 11:00 A.M. and noon, a third massive avalanche thundered down the mountainside, covering an area of 4 ha, burying a group of evacuees under up to 9 m of snow.

About 1500 volunteers worked for four days to rescue the injured and recover bodies. The avalanche claimed 60 lives, making it one of most widely reported events of the Klondike gold rush and the deadliest avalanche in North American history.

◀ **FIGURE 5.1 FORTUNE SEEKERS ASCENDING CHILKOOT PASS** Heavily laden prospectors trudge toward the summit of Chilkoot Pass during the Klondike gold rush. Sixty of the fortune seekers were killed by a large avalanche on April 3, 1898. *(E. A. Hegg/Library and Archives Canada C-005142)*

5.1 Introduction to Snow Avalanches

As you learned in Chapter 4, avalanches are rapid downslope movements of snow, ice, rock, or soil. In this chapter, we are concerned with **snow avalanches**, which are masses of snow, generally more than a few cubic metres in volume, that separate from the intact snowpack and slide or flow downslope. For convenience in this chapter, we use the word "avalanche" as a short form for "snow avalanche," while recognizing that ice, rock, and soil can also avalanche down steep slopes.

An avalanche may travel as a coherent block, deforming and fragmenting to some degree, or it may rapidly disaggregate into small particles that move independently of one another. Some avalanches are too small to bury a person; some are larger than 1 million m^3 and are capable of destroying a village or many hectares of forest (Figure 5.2, Table 5.1). A 300,000 m^3 avalanche in Montroc, France, in 1999 crushed ski chalets under 100,000 t of snow 5 m deep, killing 12 people. During World War I, more than 60,000 soldiers died in avalanches during the mountain campaign in the Alps. Many of the avalanches were triggered by artillery fire.

Most avalanches occur in remote, uninhabited mountains during fall, winter, and spring, and consequently go unnoticed. Although generally not witnessed, avalanches are common—by one estimate, about 1.5 million avalanches large enough to bury a person occur annually in western Canada[1]; yet only about 100 avalanche accidents are reported in this region each year. If we assume that approximately 20 percent of all avalanche accidents are reported, it follows that only about 1 in 3000 potentially destructive avalanches injure people or damage property. This statistic, however, may increase in the future as areas in which avalanches happen are further developed and used by winter recreationists.

Avalanches, like landslides, are driven by gravity. They differ, however, in many important respects from landslides, for example, in the failure and transport mechanisms and the physical properties of the failed material. Our discussion of

▲ **FIGURE 5.2 LARGE AVALANCHE** A large avalanche moves down a chute in the San Juan Mountains, Colorado. It started when a large slab of snow near the ridge crest suddenly failed. The avalanche descended 830 m to the valley floor and then climbed up the opposite slope, burying 245 m of U.S. Highway 550 beneath 1 m of snow. *(Mark Rawsthorne)*

TABLE 5.1 Avalanche Size

Size	Run-Out	Potential Damage	Length and Volume
Sluff	Small snow slide that normally does not bury a person	Relatively harmless	Length < 50 m Volume < 100 m^3
Small	Avalanche stops on the slope	Can bury, injure, or kill a person	Length < 100 m Volume < 1000 m^3
Medium	Avalanche runs to the bottom of the slope	Can bury and destroy a car, damage a truck, destroy small buildings, or break trees	Length < 1000 m Volume < 10,000 m^3
Large	Avalanche runs out over areas significantly less steep than 30°; may reach the valley bottom and run up the lower part of the opposing slope	Can bury and destroy large trucks and trains, large buildings, and forested areas	Length > 1000 m Volume > 10,000 m^3

avalanches begins with a consideration of snow climatology, proceeds to avalanche initiation, and then to a discussion of avalanche motion.

Snow Climatology

The probability of snow falling and accumulating in an area depends on the season and on such geographic factors as latitude, altitude, and proximity to an ocean or large body of freshwater. Snow accumulates when temperatures are at or below freezing. The length of the snow season depends mainly on latitude and altitude. Snow may fall and remain on the ground for only a few weeks at low elevations in the mid-latitudes or for almost 12 months at high latitudes or in high mountains. In general, snowfall is rare south of 35° N latitude and north of 40° S latitude, except at high elevations. The west coasts of the Northern Hemisphere continents, however, are devoid of snow to much higher latitudes. Unusually heavy snowfalls occur around large lakes, notably the Great Lakes. Parts of southern Ontario and upstate New York are located in "snow belts" bordering the Great Lakes, which are the source of much of the precipitation that falls as snow.

The amount of snow on the ground depends on many factors, the most important of which are the slope of the land, elevation, amount of snowfall, and winds. Snow accumulates on slopes less than about 45°; it sluffs away on steeper slopes. Temperature decreases with altitude, thus high mountains, even near the Equator, have permanent snow cover. Examples include Mount Kilimanjaro in Tanzania and Volcán Cayambe in Ecuador. The cold air masses of the Arctic and Antarctic hold little water vapour, thus these regions receive little snowfall. The snow that is present, however, does not melt at sea level in parts of these regions. Similarly, some mountains in Bolivia, Chile, and Argentina are high (4500 m–6900 m above sea level) and cold, but they lie east of the Atacama Desert, are hyperarid, and consequently receive little snow. Winds redistribute snow, producing buildups, or *slabs*, that are unstable. Thus, the amount of snow on the ground can differ considerably over short distances.

Avalanche Initiation

Some avalanches, termed **point-release avalanches**, begin with failure of a small amount of loose fluffy snow and grow as they move downslope. The sliding slow causes failures in the adjacent snowpack, producing a distinctive, downslope-widening trough, like an inverted V (Figure 5.3). Point-release avalanches commonly happen after heavy snowfall. The thick, loose snow is unstable, both because of its mass and because the snow crystals have little time to bond.

▲ **FIGURE 5.3 POINT-RELEASE AVALANCHE** A point-release avalanche, as the name implies, results from initial failure of a small amount of snow. Progressively more snow becomes incorporated into the avalanche as it moves downslope, giving rise to the distinctive inverted-V shape seen in this example. *(Photographer B. Jamieson. Reproduced with the permission of the Minister of Public Works and Government Services Canada, 2007, and courtesy of Natural Resources Canada, Geological Survey of Canada. GSC 2000-102)*

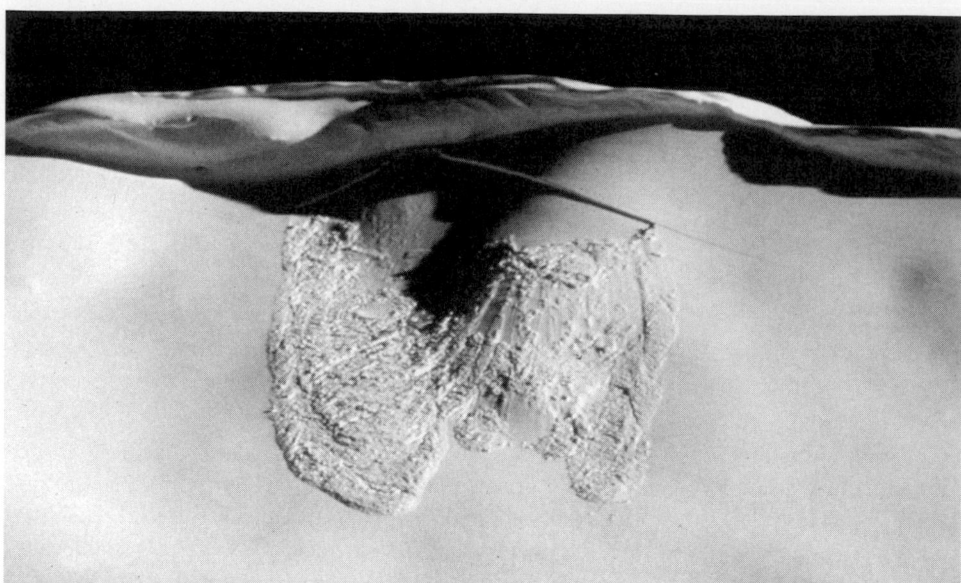

◄ **FIGURE 5.4 SLAB AVALANCHE** This avalanche occurred when a slab of snow slipped along a weak layer, shearing away from near-vertical crown and lateral scarps. The slab rapidly disintegrated as it moved downslope. *(Photographer B. Jamieson. Reproduced with the permission of the Minister of Public Works and Government Services Canada, 2007, and courtesy of Natural Resources Canada, Geological Survey of Canada. GSC 2000-103)*

Layers of cohesive snow can fail as a slab, leaving steep crown, lateral, and toe scarps and a smooth basal failure plane (Figure 5.4). A **slab avalanche** begins with fracturing of the snowpack along a weak layer at depth. Gravity causes the snowpack to creep downslope, with the top of the snowpack moving faster than the bottom. If a weak layer is present (Figure 5.5), it may deform, or shear, more than the layers above and below it. This weak horizon may slowly deform over hours or days and be followed by sudden failure. The initial point failure propagates along the weak surface, causing a slab to break away along bounding crown and lateral fractures[2] (Figure 5.4). Slab avalanches are very dangerous; thus, backcountry recreationists and avalanche forecasters look for weak layers when assessing local avalanche risk.

Weak Layers

The structure of the snowpack determines its potential to avalanche.[3,4,5] Slab avalanches require a buried weak layer and an overlying stronger slab. The relationship between avalanche potential and properties of snow that can be easily measured—strength, grain size, grain type, and temperature—are complex and not fully understood. Additional complexity results from the fact that the thickness and characteristics of the snow cover vary in both time and space. A few generalizations, however, can be made.

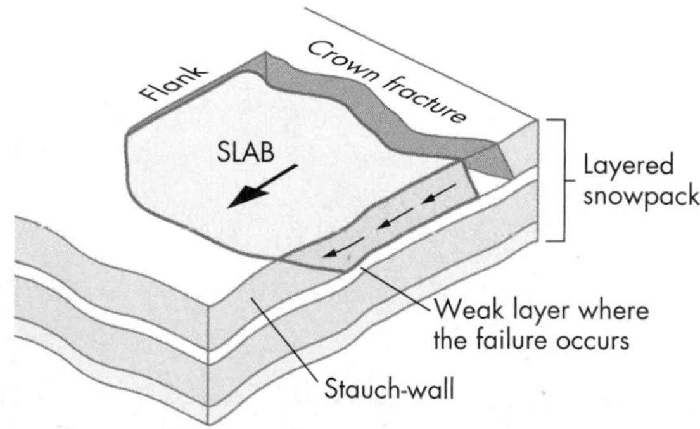

▲ **FIGURE 5.5 SLAB AVALANCHE WEAK LAYER** Slab avalanches begin when snow fails along a mechanically weak layer parallel to the surface. This diagram shows some of the terms used by avalanche scientists and safety personnel when referring to slab avalanches. *(Reproduced with the permission of the Minister of Public Works and Government Services Canada, 2007, and courtesy of Natural Resources Canada, Geological Survey of Canada)*

New snow that has not had time to bond to the layer below, especially if it is light and powdery, is susceptible to sliding. Compacted snow is less likely to move than light powdery snow. Snow that is above the level of boulders and plants on a slope has no natural objects to anchor it and is therefore more dangerous than thinner snow. Of course, snow that completely buries surface irregularities is just what skiers and snowboarders desire.

Weather determines the evolution of the snowpack. Important meteorological factors include heating by solar radiation, radiative cooling, temperature gradients in the snowpack, and snowfall amounts and type.[6] Most avalanches happen during or soon after a storm.

Weak layers in the snowpack can form in three main ways:

1. ***Wind.***
   Blowing snow can build up on sheltered lee slopes, and wind can stabilize the snowpack on other slopes. A **wind slab** is a body of thick, poorly bonded snow deposited by wind on a slope. Snow can be deposited by winds rising over the crest of a slope or the top of a mountain. The leeward slope, where the snow accumulates, is said to be *top-loaded*. Wind blowing parallel to a ridge crest can also deposit snow, producing *cross-loaded* wind slabs that are commonly difficult to spot and tend to be less stable than top-loaded wind slabs. Wind may increase during a snowstorm, depositing a dense layer of broken and packed snow crystals on a delicate layer of unbroken crystals. The layer of unbroken crystals becomes a buried weak surface along which failure may occur later.

2. ***Formation of hoar at depth in the snowpack.***
Hoar consists of ice crystals that are deposited on and within the snowpack when the air is moist and cold. Hoar forms when water vapour condenses directly into ice. Depth hoar forms from air occupying spaces between snow crystals. Its depth depends on the temperature profile in the snow, although most layers of depth hoar occur near the base of the snowpack. Cold air on a thin snowpack is a particularly favourable situation for developing depth hoar.

3. ***Formation of hoar at the surface.***
Surface hoar, also called *hoar frost*, forms at the surface of the snowpack on cold clear nights. Ice crystals, which may be feather-shaped and larger than snowflakes, change only very slowly once buried. The overlying and underlying snow layers commonly gain strength over days and weeks, leaving the buried surface hoar as a weak layer.

Avalanche Motion

During the first few seconds of a slab avalanche, the failed snow mass is a coherent slab comprising fractured blocks of snow that are accelerating downslope. Within a few tens of metres, the slab disintegrates into smaller fragments and then individual grains of snow.[2] At velocities above about 35 km/h, dry avalanches generate a cloud of powdered snow that billows above the flowing mass (Figure 5.2). The powder cloud is much less dense (3 kg/m^3–15 kg/m^3) than the flowing snow (50 kg/m^3–150 kg/m^3). Wet avalanches, unlike dry avalanches, contain intergranular liquid water and are denser than dry ones (300 kg/m^3–400 kg/m^3) but do not achieve the high velocities of some large dry avalanches.[1] Some dry avalanches have been clocked at 200 km/h, leaving almost no time for a person downslope to get out of the way. These avalanches may have sufficient momentum to climb opposing slopes and destroy the forest on them. They may also displace air, causing a damaging air blast that arrives seconds before the avalanche does.

Avalanche Triggering

Most avalanches occur naturally during or soon after snowstorms. Others happen when normal daytime heating or an inflow of warm air raises the temperature of the upper part of the snowpack.

In most recreational accidents, a person triggers the avalanche.[7] Field studies indicate that, in situations where the snowpack is near the threshold of failure, slab avalanches can be triggered simply by the extra weight of a person traversing the slope. The person's weight increases the shearing force in the weak layer, triggering failure.

Some avalanches are triggered intentionally, generally with explosives, as part of avalanche-control programs. Some skiers attempt to release unstable snow in a controlled manner, which is an inadvisable practice.

Terrain Factors

An avalanche path has three parts:

1. The **start zone**, where the snowpack fails
2. The **track**, along which the avalanche accelerates and achieves its highest velocity
3. The **run-out zone**, where the avalanche decelerates and snow is deposited

The three parts of the path are easy to identify when avalanches follow ravines, gullies, and *chutes* and when the tracks are on forested slopes (Figure 5.6). They are much more difficult to distinguish on slopes above the treeline or where the snow is not channelled.

Slope Angle The most important terrain factor for avalanche formation is slope steepness. Numerous, small, loose avalanches, called **sluffs**, occur on slopes steeper than 60° (Figure 5.7). Most sluffs are too small to bury a person, but

▲ **FIGURE 5.6 COMPONENTS OF AN AVALANCHE PATH** A large avalanche path with a start zone, a track extending through forest, and a run-out zone on the valley floor. *(Photographer B. Jamieson. Reproduced with the permission of the Minister of Public Works and Government Services Canada, 2007, and courtesy of Natural Resources Canada, Geological Survey of Canada. GSC 2000-105)*

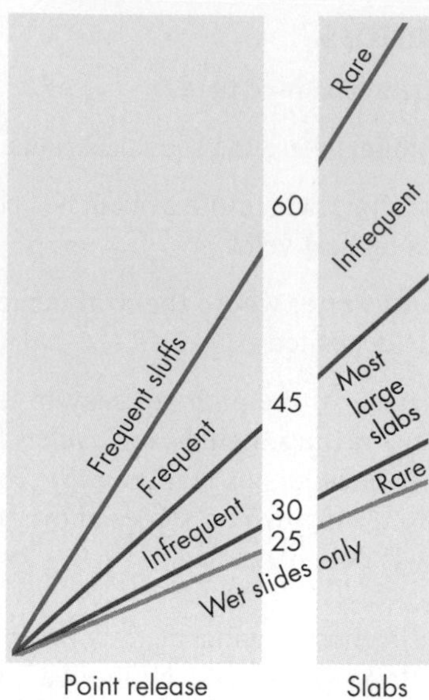

▲ **FIGURE 5.7 RELATION BETWEEN SLOPE ANGLE AND AVALANCHE TYPE AND FREQUENCY** Slopes less than 25° and steeper than 60° have a low avalanche risk. Little snow accumulates on steep slopes, and snow does not easily slide on gentle ones. Most large avalanches happen on slopes of 30° to 45°. Wet avalanches, however, are more common on slopes less than 30°. *(Modified from Jamieson, B. 2001. Snow avalanches. In A synthesis of geological hazards in Canada, ed. G. R. Brooks, p. 86. Reproduced with the permission of the Minister of Public Works and Government Services Canada, 2007, and courtesy of Natural Resources Canada, Geological Survey of Canada)*

they can cause climbers to fall or trigger larger avalanches on slopes below.

Most large avalanches are released from slopes between 30° and 45°, although some happen on slopes of 45° to 60°.[7] Slopes between 30° and 45° are favoured by skiers, snowboarders, and snowmobilers, which is why recreationists commonly trigger avalanches.

Fewer than 5 percent of dry avalanches occur on slopes lower than 30°. Wet snow slides, however, can happen on slopes that are less than 25°[1] (Figure 5.7). They contain liquid water between the grains of recrystallized snow.

Orientation of Slope The location of a slope with respect to wind and incident sunlight affects avalanche occurrence. Slopes in the lee of wind can accumulate large amounts of snow in wind slabs and cornices, increasing the avalanche danger. Deposits of wind-blown snow on leeward slopes commonly consist of interleaved stronger and weaker layers, reflecting variable wind speeds during deposition. This snow stratigraphy creates ideal conditions for slab avalanches. Slopes facing the Sun are commonly more prone to avalanches during sunny, warm weather, whereas shaded slopes are more likely to release avalanches in cold weather. In middle latitudes in the Northern Hemisphere, more avalanches happen on shady slopes with northern and northeastern aspects than on slopes with other orientations.

Other Terrain Factors Several other terrain factors play a role in triggering avalanches.[8,9] Convex slopes are statistically more dangerous than concave ones. The reasons for this difference lie partly in human behaviour—skiers and snowboarders favour convex slopes over concave ones—and partly in the fact that the *tensile strength* of snow is lower than the *compressive strength*. Avalanches are also more common on slopes with smooth surfaces, such as grass or smooth rock, than on treed or rough slopes. Rough surfaces, such as talus slopes, must accumulate enough snow to bury surface irregularities before dangerous avalanches will occur. Vegetation cover is important for anchoring the snowpack, although in some situations buried vegetation can create weak zones within the snowpack. Avalanches rarely initiate within tree-covered areas, but they do enter and destroy forests (Figure 5.8).

The avalanche hazard is commonly greater at high elevations because snowfall and winds are greater there and trees are fewer or absent. Gullies or ravines can have dangerous wind slabs at their heads or margins. These features also

◄ **FIGURE 5.8 TIMBER DAMAGED BY AN AVALANCHE** Avalanches generally initiate in non-forested areas, but they can run into and destroy mature forest. *(Photo by Chris Stethem)*

funnel avalanches, increasing their destructive force and making escape difficult.

5.2 Geographic Regions at Risk of Avalanches

Avalanches can occur almost anywhere that has sufficient snow and a slope steep enough for the snow to slide on. Generally, the snowpack must be at least 50 cm thick; areas with deeper snow will produce more and larger avalanches.[1]

Avalanche activity in Canada is greatest in the mountains of Alberta, British Columbia, and Yukon Territory (Figure 5.9). Avalanches are also common in parts of Newfoundland and Labrador, in the Gaspé region of Quebec, along the north shore of the St. Lawrence River, and along the eastern margin of the Arctic Islands. They are less common in central and eastern Canada and rare on the Prairies and in the Arctic. Most avalanches in the United States occur in the high mountains extending from the Sierra Nevada and Cascade ranges on the west to the Rocky Mountains on the east.

5.3 Effects of Avalanches and Links with Other Natural Hazards

Effects of Avalanches

More than 600 people have died in avalanches in Canada since the earliest reported accidents in the mid-nineteenth century.[1] Until the early twentieth century, most avalanche fatalities were people killed while building railways (see Case Study 5.1) or roads, or working at mine sites (Figure 5.10). The number of industrial and transportation fatalities, however, is now very low, largely because measures are routinely

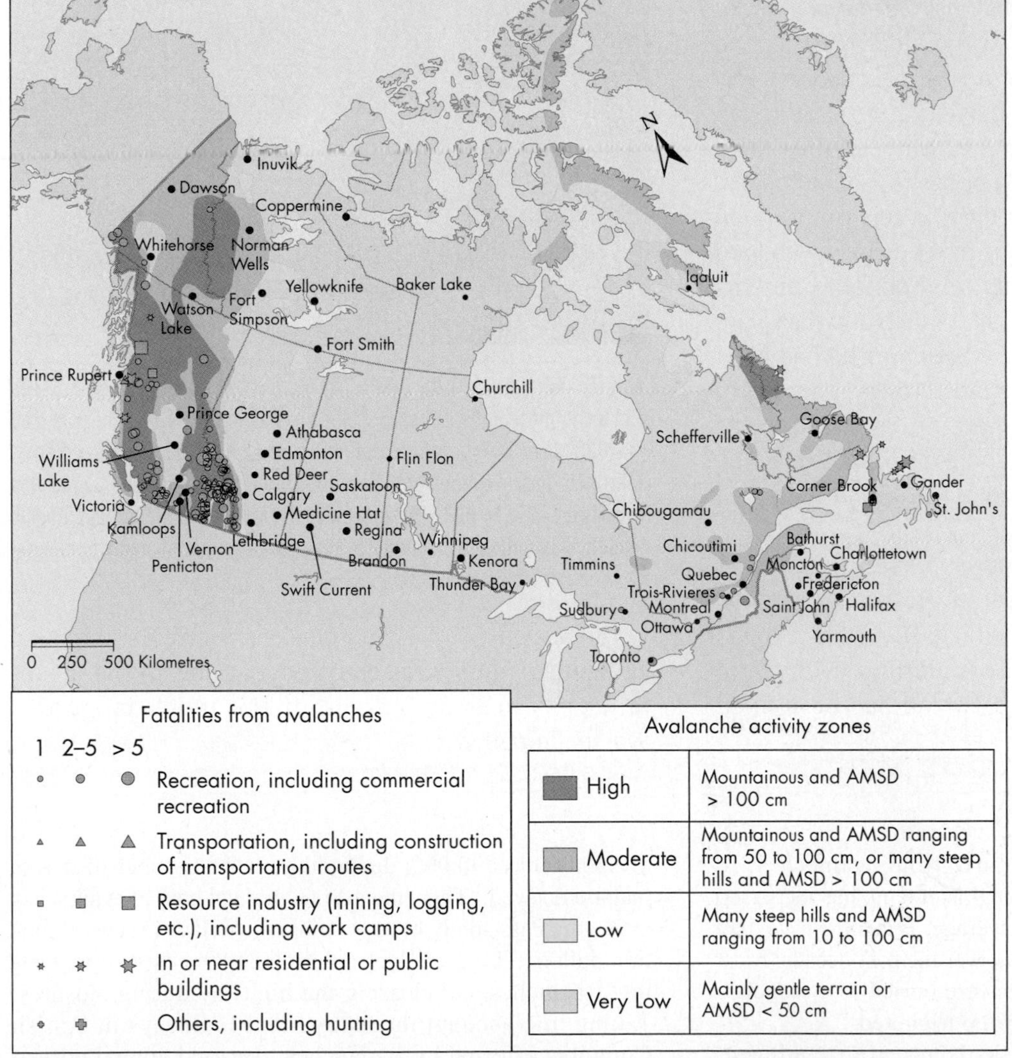

▲ **FIGURE 5.9 AVALANCHES IN CANADA** A map showing the regional occurrence of avalanches in Canada. The map is necessarily generalized. It does not take into account, for example, isolated steep areas and isolated areas of heavy snowfall or strong winds. *(Modified from Jamieson, B. 2001. Snow avalanches. In A synthesis of geological hazards in Canada, ed. G. R. Brooks, Fig. 12. Reproduced with the permission of the Minister of Public Works and Government Services Canada, 2007, and courtesy of Natural Resources Canada, Geological Survey of Canada)*

5.1 CASE STUDY

Disaster in Rogers Pass

The Canadian Pacific Railway line was the first transcontinental rail line in Canada. It opened for regular traffic in 1886. During construction of the line and in the early years of its operation, "White Death" avalanches claimed approximately 250 lives in Rogers Pass, in Glacier National Park, British Columbia (Figure 5.A).[10] The worst accident occurred in March 1910.

At 6:30 P.M. on March 4, 1910, a large avalanche swept down the flank of Mount Cheops and deposited about 7 m of heavy snow on the tracks in Rogers Pass. A rotary snowplow attached to a locomotive and carrying 64 workers was called in to clear the tracks. In spite of heavy snowfall, the work was considered safe because the Mount Cheops avalanche had just cleared snow from the slopes above and because the slope adjacent to the railway on the other side of the pass was mostly forested. The work crew was cutting a trench through the dense snow burying the tracks when another large avalanche raced down the slope opposite Mount Cheops.

The foreman of the work crew, after reporting on progress at the watchman's hut at 11:30 P.M., noticed that he could not see the lights from portable lanterns and the snowplow. He made a call for help and then went to investigate. He first located a fireman who had been sucked out of the locomotive and thrown about 30 m onto an unused snowshed, where he lay with serious internal injuries, a broken leg, and a dislocated shoulder. The foreman dragged him to a rail car and called Revelstoke for help.

Two hundred people, including nurses and doctors, arrived at the accident scene from Revelstoke, 70 km to the west, at dawn the next morning. Shovelling through the heavy snow, they found 62 victims in the 7 m deep trench that they had dug, which had been filled by the second avalanche.

▲ **FIGURE 5.A ROGERS PASS** The Trans-Canada Highway crosses avalanche-prone Rogers Pass in the Selkirk Mountains. Avalanches claimed about 250 lives in Rogers Pass during construction of the Canadian Pacific Railway in the late nineteenth century. The 8 km Connaught Tunnel was constructed in 1914 and 1915 to replace the railway's route through Rogers Pass. It was built at a cost of $5.5 million, equivalent today to several hundred million dollars. *(John J. Clague)*

In response to this and previous accidents, the 8 km Connaught Tunnel was constructed beneath the mountain pass to bypass some of the most dangerous avalanche paths.

taken to protect road and rail lines from avalanches. In contrast, the number of recreational accidents has increased dramatically since the 1930s. On average, 12 people have died in avalanches in Canada each year over the past decade; most of them were recreationists who were buried in avalanches that they or a member of their group triggered.

Avalanches also cause traffic delays, with significant economic losses.[11] For example, for about 100 hours each winter, the Trans-Canada Highway in Rogers Pass, British Columbia, is closed because of avalanches. A typical two-hour closure of the highway can result in monetary losses of $50,000 to $90,000, depending on the number of trucks that are delayed.[1] Thus, the average annual cost of avalanches at Rogers Pass solely because of traffic delays is several million dollars. This sum does not include the costs of preventing avalanches and clearing the highway during closures. Taking into account the many other highways in British Columbia affected by avalanches, the total annual cost of traffic delays in that province alone exceeds $5 million. This figure is conservative because it does not include railway delays or the effect of closures on timely deliveries and lost business.

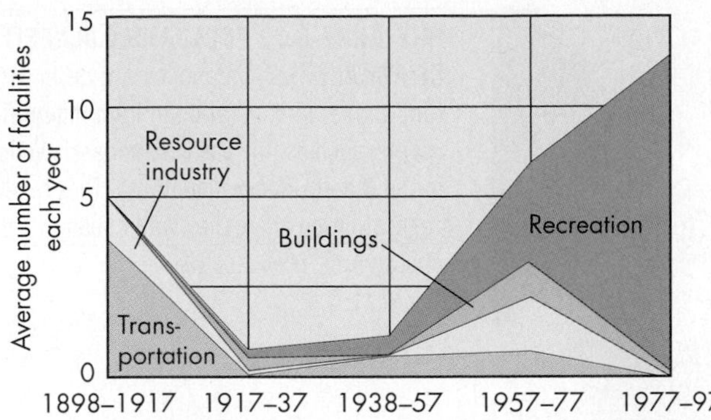

▲ **FIGURE 5.10 AVALANCHE DEATHS IN CANADA** The distribution of avalanche fatalities in Canada according to the activity of the victims at the time of the accident. Categories include recreation (skiing, snowboarding, and snowmobiling); transportation, including highway and railway construction; resource industry, including accidents at work camps; and residential and commercial buildings. Some accidents have been excluded because they do not fit any of these categories. In the past 50 years, the number of recreational accidents has increased dramatically, whereas the number of other accidents has decreased. *(Modified from Jamieson, B. 2001. Snow avalanches. In A synthesis of geological hazards in Canada, ed. G. R. Brooks, p. 82. Reproduced with the permission of the Minister of Public Works and Government Services Canada, 2007, and courtesy of Natural Resources Canada, Geological Survey of Canada)*

Property damage from avalanches in Canada in most years is less than $500,000, although much damage probably is unreported. Damage from avalanches in the European Alps in some winters is much larger. Typical infrastructure damage includes residential and commercial buildings at ski resorts, ski lifts, and vehicles.

Avalanches damage forests by uprooting, breaking, and injuring trees (Figure 5.8). They also remove soil required for forest regeneration. Individual avalanches can destroy or damage up to $500,000 worth of timber.[1] Clearcutting forestry practices can make the problem worse by creating new source areas; avalanches initiated in the cut-block run into commercially valuable forests. In some cases, structures can be installed to support the snowpack and thus inhibit avalanches, but this solution is expensive and not always successful.

An example of avalanche damage to forest occurred on March 14, 1996, near Revelstoke, British Columbia. On that day, a forest cut-block above Nagle Creek released a large avalanche that travelled 450 m down a 37° slope. Small gullies funnelled the avalanche into six lobes that continued several hundred metres through forest, destroying trees and depositing the broken trees and soil in a lower, older cut-block (Figure 5.11). The value of the destroyed timber was about $400,000.

Links between Avalanches and Other Natural Hazards

Avalanches have few direct links to other natural hazards. Earthquakes in mountainous areas in winter, however, can trigger numerous avalanches. Some of these avalanches may block roads and rail lines, impeding rescue and relief efforts. Perhaps of greater importance is the indirect link between changing climate and avalanche frequency. Climate change may increase winter snowfall in some areas or increase the severity of winter storms, which can alter avalanche frequency. Some areas may experience more variable winter weather, with frequent thaws that also can change avalanche frequency.

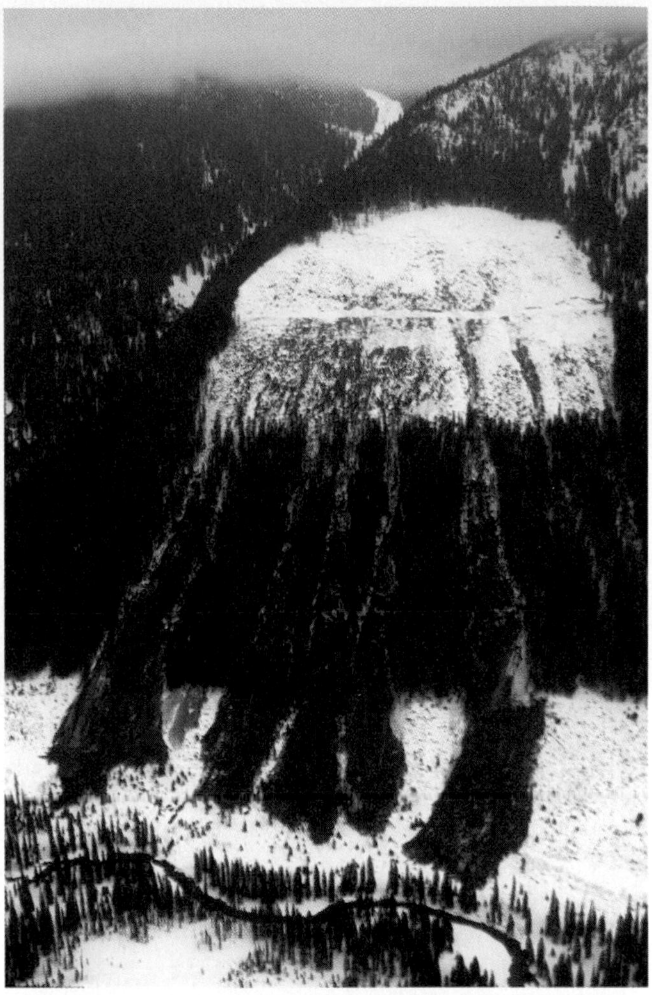

▲ **FIGURE 5.11 AVALANCHE DAMAGE TO FOREST** A photograph of a steep slope adjacent to Nagle Creek near Revelstoke, British Columbia, showing the aftermath of an avalanche that damaged the forest. The avalanche started in the cut-block just above the centre of the photo and split into six lobes that moved through the forest onto the lower cut-block near the base of the photo. *(Photo courtesy of Jim Bay)*

5.4 Natural Service Functions of Avalanches

Avalanches provide the same ecological benefits as landslides (Chapter 4). They are a source of ecological disturbance that can increase local plant and animal diversity. In many mountain valleys, avalanches maintain broad strips of herbaceous and shrub vegetation between closed subalpine forests

◄ **FIGURE 5.12 ECOLOGICAL BENEFITS OF AVALANCHES** Avalanches are an important shaper of vegetation in high mountain valleys, such as this one in Kananaskis Valley in the Alberta Rocky Mountains. They renew vegetation on the valley walls seen in this photograph. *(John J. Clague)*

that, collectively, can cover more than half the valley walls (Figure 5.12). These open areas are important to many animals, including grizzly bears, marmots, pikas, and ground squirrels, and to a variety of subalpine plants.

5.5 Human Interaction with Avalanches

Avalanches are common in all but the driest mountain ranges on Earth. They are a hazard only when humans share their space. In long-settled mountains, such as the European Alps, people have adjusted to avalanches by avoiding them as much as possible, such as by establishing settlements outside areas prone to avalanches. More recently, driven by the boom in leisure activities and tourism, settlement has greatly expanded in the Alps, encroaching into avalanche-prone areas, often with disastrous results. In less settled mountains, such as those of western North America and southern New Zealand, recreational avalanche accidents were at one time uncommon. That situation has changed with the rapid growth in outdoor winter recreation in these areas (see Case Study 5.2).

5.6 Minimizing Avalanche Risk

Avalanche risk can be reduced by placing buildings, roads, and other infrastructure beyond dangerous areas, by using engineered structures to slow or deflect avalanches, by reinforcing exposed structures, by triggering controlled avalanches with explosives, and with forecasting.

The first-line hazard mitigation measure is the appropriate location of permanent structures. If a risk remains after structures have been built, other measures must be taken. Secondary protection along vulnerable transportation corridors involves forecasting and a control program that includes temporary road and rail closures. Deflecting structures and reinforcement can provide additional protection for fixed structures.

Location of Infrastructure

Avalanche risk can be estimated by determining the distribution, frequency, and sizes of avalanches in a given area. Hazardous areas can be shown on maps (Figure 5.13), providing planners with the information they require to locate buildings, roads, and other structures in areas where the hazard is low or where mitigation measures can be taken to keep the risk low. Avalanche frequency, like the frequency of floods and earthquakes, is commonly described in terms of a *recurrence interval*, the time between avalanches of a particular size or extent.

In Switzerland and some places in the United States, new residential buildings are generally not allowed in the "red zone," defined as the area where avalanches capable of impact pressures of 30 kPa (kilopascals) or more occur, on average, once every 300 years. Some jurisdictions have a "blue zone," which lies outside the red zone and shows areas where avalanches with recurrence intervals of 30 to 300 years might produce impact forces of no more than 30 kPa. Legislation may require that buildings located in the blue zone have reinforced walls facing the avalanche path or that they be protected by deflection structures. No special engineering is required outside the blue zone.

In Canada, a single line is commonly drawn on a map to delineate areas at risk from avalanches. Areas inside this line are subject to avalanches with a specified recurrence interval, such as 300 years. Currently, however, Canada has no consistent policies for avalanche hazard zones.

5.2 CASE STUDY

Deadly Avalanche in Glacier National Park

A huge avalanche killed seven young backcountry skiers in Glacier National Park, British Columbia, on February 1, 2003 (Figure 5.B). The incident highlights the risks that even well-prepared people face when they venture into the backcountry during winter.

The skiers were a group of 14 grade-10 students and three adults from a private school south of Calgary, Alberta. The three adults included two teacher-guides and a volunteer; all three had backcountry experience.

The school group had spent the afternoon before the accident at an alpine cabin 20 minutes from the Trans-Canada Highway. They skied near the cabin and, supervised by Andrew Nicholson and Dale Roth, avalanche-certified teachers, dug avalanche pits, did snowpack testing, and performed compression tests on nearby slopes. They set out storm boards to collect the overnight snowfall and, in the morning, compared the samples with samples of old snow already on the ground. They then skied to the park visitor centre, where Nicholson talked with officials about snow conditions and was given a daily bulletin that included weather conditions, satellite imagery, and avalanche danger ratings. The report for February 1 stated that, below the treeline, where the group planned to stay, the avalanche danger was "Moderate—Natural avalanches are unlikely. Human triggers are possible." A snow layer deposited on December 6 suffered "compression test failures" according to the daily report. Another layer, deposited on January 20, "easily released" during tests. The deep November layer, comprising two laminated crusts of ice bounding a layer of unstable crystals, had worried avalanche forecasters all winter.

The group set out up a valley near Rogers Pass, one of the most avalanche-prone areas in western Canada. The Canadian army routinely fires howitzers in Rogers Pass in winter to trigger controlled avalanches and keep the highway and railway open. During the ascent, the group followed the standard practice for travelling in avalanche zones by maintaining 10 m to 15 m spacing between pairs of skiers. About 15 minutes into the trip, the guides stopped and quizzed each student on avalanche safety protocol. Their route, however, offered no protection if an avalanche occurred on the high slopes above them, which included the 2600 m peak of Mount Cheops. Aware of the considerable avalanche danger, the guides conferred with the students, who wanted to continue to ski for Balu Pass. Nicholson and Roth made the final decision to proceed.

▲ **FIGURE 5.B KILLER AVALANCHE** A view to the west up the valley of Connaught Creek in Glacier National Park, British Columbia. The site of the avalanche that killed seven young skiers from Alberta on February 1, 2003, is shown by the yellow arrow. *(Kip Wiley)*

Rich Marshall and his wife, Abby Watkins, professional guides from Golden, British Columbia, watched the group ski up the valley. They had stopped for tea in some trees at an elevation of about 1680 m and could see the students about 100 m below them. At 11:45 A.M., just as the group was passing Mount Cheops on the valley bottom, something, perhaps the weight of snow blown over the shoulder of the mountain, became too much for the January snow layer. It failed and avalanched down the mountain. This avalanche, by itself, would have just dusted the valley bottom. Unfortunately, it caused a slab about 0.5 km wide to fail along the weak November crust, and approximately 900 t of snow cascaded down the slope and onto the valley floor. "We see an avalanche of that magnitude [3.5 out of 5] at least once a year, but usually not in that pass," said Eric Dafoe, a public safety coordinator for Parks Canada, "and usually during a big storm period, when no one is around."

Marshall was closing his thermos at 11:45 when he heard a sharp crack from across the valley. He saw the snowpack at an elevation of approximately 2400 m, not far below the summit of Mount Cheops, give way and begin to descend toward the students and their guides. "Avalanche! Avalanche! Avalanche!" he yelled.

The students had only seconds before the avalanche, moving with enough force to flatten 4 ha of forest, struck them. First came a "wall of snow," one student later told

5.2 CASE STUDY *(Continued)*

wardens, and then "blackness." Marshall and Watkins were dusted by the avalanche and then sped toward the group. Investigators would later conclude that the couple saved at least five lives.

Each student carried a shovel and a probe and wore an *avalanche transceiver*, which emits a beeping signal that can be received by another beacon. The closer Watkins got to a buried student, the louder and more frequent were the beeps. She and Marshall moved quickly, but some of the group had been moved more than 200 m by the avalanche. Once free, some of the survivors tried to dig out their friends. Nicholson, who was carrying a satellite phone, called the Rogers Pass warden, and within 40 minutes, 10 rescuers were on the scene. The number grew quickly to 40 and included park staff, mountain guides, military personnel, and heli-ski guides. But seven of the students were too deeply buried. It would be 1 hour and 20 minutes from the time the avalanche hit before the last body was recovered.

In the days following the disaster, grieving parents questioned the decision to continue to Balu Pass. If the chances of an avalanche were "considerable" just above where the students were to ski, why take the risk? Strathcona-Tweedsmuir School head Tony Macoun insisted that the risks were weighed by the entire group and that every reasonable precaution had been taken. "They were as prepared as they could have been," said Ingrid Healy, an assistant head at the school, "as *anyone* could have been."

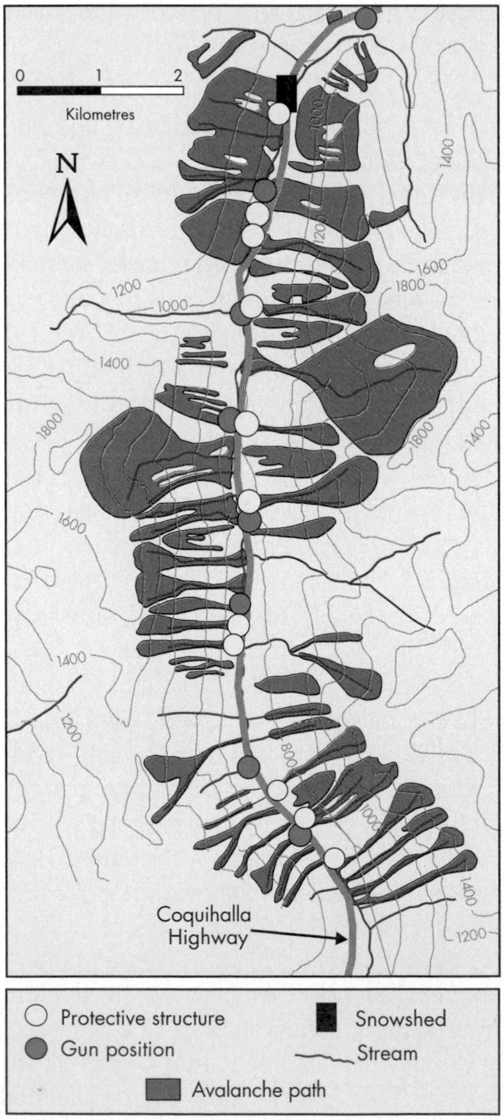

Structures in the Start Zone

Fences or nets are installed in some avalanche start zones to support the snowpack and prevent large avalanches (Figure 5.14). Such structures are considered unsightly by some people and also are very expensive. They are only practical for protecting inhabited structures, busy roads, and critical infrastructure. Smaller, less expensive structures may allow regrowth of forest along avalanche paths. Europeans have considerable experience with start-zone structures, but such structures are not commonly used in North America.

Where wind-blown snow is an important cause of avalanches, structures can be built that reduce the accumulation of snow in the avalanche start zone. These structures are sophisticated versions of snow fences seen in places along highways. Snowdrifts accumulate on the windward side of the fences, reducing the amount of snow deposited in the avalanche start zone. Other structures, resembling upward-sloping roofs, carry wind-blown snow below the normal start zone.

Structures in the Track and Run-Out Zone

A variety of structures are used to slow or deflect avalanches in the track and run-out zone. They include deflecting berms,

◄ **FIGURE 5.13 MAP OF AVALANCHE PATHS** Avalanche paths, shown in pink, along a section of Coquihalla Highway between Hope and Merritt, British Columbia. Protective structures were built to reduce the chance of avalanches reaching the highway. The green lines are contours, which are lines of equal elevation; in this case, the vertical spacing between contours is 200 m. *(From Clague, J., and B. Turner. 2003. Vancouver, city on the edge: Living with a dynamic geological landscape. Vancouver, BC: Tricouni Press)*

◄ **FIGURE 5.14 AVALANCHE SUPPORT STRUCTURE** Support structures in an avalanche start zone above Davos, Switzerland. Such structures prevent large avalanches from starting, but they are expensive and are generally used only where people and property are at high risk. *(Photographer B. Jamieson. Reproduced with the permission of the Minister of Public Works and Government Services Canada, 2007, and courtesy of Natural Resources Canada, Geological Survey of Canada. GSC 2000-107)*

splitting wedges, avalanche sheds, and mounds. *Berms* deflect avalanches away from buildings or parallel to roads. Soil or concrete *splitting wedges* are located on the exposed sides of buildings to force the avalanche around the structure. *Avalanche sheds*, or *galleries*, allow avalanches to run over roads or railways (Figure 5.15). *Mounds*, somewhat reminiscent of large "moguls" along ski runs, are constructed to slow avalanches and thus reduce their run-out. Unfortunately, mounds may become buried early in the winter, allowing subsequent avalanches to travel unimpeded over them.

▲ **FIGURE 5.15 AVALANCHE SHED** An avalanche shed on the Coquihalla Highway, west of Coquihalla Pass, British Columbia. The shed was constructed at a cost of $12 million to carry avalanches over the highway. *(John J. Clague)*

Control through the Use of Explosives

Explosives are used to test for unstable snow and to release accumulations of snow during temporary closures of highways, railroads, and ski runs. Explosive charges are projected from compressed-air cannons, fired by military artillery, or dropped from helicopters on ridges. Approximately 30,000 charges are used each year for avalanche control in Canada, about half in ski areas.[1]

Explosions in start zones usually, but not always, release avalanches. They are no guarantee that the snowpack will not fail naturally or be triggered by a person soon afterward.

Forecasting

An **avalanche forecast** is an assessment of the probability and size of avalanches within a defined area under existing or future conditions.[12,13] Forecasts are based on four types of information:

1. ***Occurrences of avalanches.***
   Observed occurrences of avalanches provide an indication of the likelihood that additional avalanches will occur under similar conditions.

2. ***Stability and strength tests.***
   Several field tests have been developed to assess snowpack stability. All these tests are subjective, and results will differ for different users. Nevertheless, they provide some indication of the likelihood that the snowpack may fail. The *shovel test* is a traditional field test that involves pulling the upper part of a column of undisturbed snow about 0.3 m^2 with a shovel. Fractures produced along weak snowpack layers by the force of the shovel identify potential failure planes for slab avalanches. The *compression test* involves the application of a vertical force, commonly with the back of a shovel blade, on a column of undisturbed snow similar to that used in shovel tests. Any weak layers will fracture along the exposed vertical face of the column (Figure 5.16). In the *rutschblock test*, a skier steps onto a column of undisturbed snow, 2 m across the slope and 1.5 m along the side. The skier pushes on the column with his or her skis and then jumps on it. A score of 1 to 7 is assigned to the snowpack based on the loading required to release a block from the upper part of the column.

3. ***Snowpack observations.***
   Forecasting also involves observations of snowpack characteristics, including the thickness and properties of visible weak layers.

4. ***Weather.***
   An important aspect of avalanche forecasting is tracking weather conditions, including temperature, precipitation, and wind.

Observations of recent avalanches provide the most direct evidence of avalanche risk. Weather observations provide the least direct evidence, and stability tests and snowpack observations lie somewhere between the two.

▲ **FIGURE 5.16 SNOW COMPRESSION TEST** A field compression test is used to locate weak layers in the snowpack and provide an index of stability. Note the weak layer that has fractured to the right of the man's elbow (dark band). *(Photographer B. Jamieson. Reproduced with the permission of the Minister of Public Works and Government Services Canada, 2007, and courtesy of Natural Resources Canada, Geological Survey of Canada. GSC 2000-108)*

Observations of recent avalanches, weak snowpack layers, heavy snowfall, and warming are important to forecasters because they are avalanche indicators. In contrast, if few or no avalanches have occurred, if field tests suggest the snowpack is stable, and if the weather is cold and clear, the danger of avalanches is low and a forecaster will probably allow a highway or ski area to remain open. These two examples are, of course, end members in a spectrum of conditions that a forecaster faces. Forecasters must commonly make decisions based on contradictory conditions—some suggesting stability and others indicating instability. They consider all the data, weigh some observations more than others, and assess uncertainties and the risk associated with different forecasts. Their decisions are ultimately based on experience and training. Forecasts are constantly revised as new information becomes available.

Recently, computer software has been developed to assist forecasters. Most algorithms compare current measurements of precipitation, temperature, wind, and other variables with average values of the same variables spanning many years. Avalanches would be considered unlikely if most past days with similar conditions were avalanche free.

Another method of forecasting involves rule-based or expert systems that incorporate the knowledge of avalanche experts.[14] Rules are constructed about the effects of snow stratigraphy, precipitation, wind, temperature, field tests, and other factors to establish a measure of avalanche danger. For example, the avalanche danger might be increased by one unit if wind speed exceeds 25 km/h or decreased by one unit if the temperature drops below 0°C. No prior data are required to apply such rules, but the rules must be tested with current data and revised if necessary.

5.7 Avalanche Safety

Winter travelling in the backcountry is never 100 percent safe. The practice of good avalanche safety is a process, involving route selection, examination of the snowpack and weather conditions, and human factors.[15] People involved in winter recreation in the mountains need to ask themselves the following three questions:

1. Is the slope to be crossed prone to avalanches?
2. Is the snowpack unstable?
3. What are the consequences of being caught in an avalanche in this terrain?

The first question can be answered by using such terrain factors as slope angle and orientation discussed earlier in the chapter. The second question can be answered by using public bulletins, observations of recent avalanches in the area, stability tests, and snowpack and weather observations. The Canadian Avalanche Association and the American Avalanche Association provide advice on avalanche dangers and appropriate human responses (Table 5.2; see Professional Profile). The third question requires an appreciation of snowpack and terrain factors. If an avalanche occurs, is it likely to be small or large? Is it likely to be a slab or point-release avalanche? Will the avalanche be in wet or dry snow? Could I be swept over a cliff or into trees or boulders?

Good Habits Minimize Risk Avalanche danger reports should be considered and all warnings heeded. Never follow in the tracks of others without making your own evaluation; snow conditions are almost certain to have changed since the tracks were made. Observe the terrain and note obvious avalanche paths where vegetation is missing or damaged, where there are few surface anchors, and below cornices or ice formations. Avoid travelling below others who might trigger an avalanche. Minimize traverses of steep slopes. Maintain separation—ideally one person should cross the slope and enter an area safe from avalanches before the next person crosses. Route selection should also consider what dangers lie above and below the traverse and the consequences of an unexpected avalanche. Stop or camp only in safe locations. Wear warm gear to delay hypothermia if buried. Plan escape routes. Never travel alone. The party should be large enough to perform a rescue, although additional people increase the disturbance to the slope. If you find yourself in a potentially dangerous avalanche situation, you should seriously question the choice of the route, ask why your safety is being put in jeopardy, and consider alternatives to pressing on.

Too often, inappropriate human factors enter into decisions about risk. Some people focus on a peak, an attractive slope, or other destination and continue in spite of strong evidence of avalanche danger. Groups may spread out, leaving slower but knowledgeable people out of decisions about the route or avalanche danger. Careful decision making may be abandoned at the end of the day, when people are tired and in a rush to reach their destinations. Many avalanches happen during clear weather when skiers, snowboarders, and snowmobilers are drawn to beautiful open slopes, high mountain passes, and peaks. Inexperienced winter recreationists can reduce their risk by travelling with more experienced people or by hiring a guide.

5.8 Avalanche Rescue and Survival

The motion of the snow during an avalanche kills about 25 percent of avalanche victims.[1] If the victim survives this battering, he or she must be quickly located and extracted

TABLE 5.2 Avalanche Danger Scale

Danger Level (Colour)	Avalanche Probability and Trigger	Recommended Action in Backcountry
Low (green)	Natural avalanches unlikely; human-triggered avalanches *unlikely*	Travel is generally safe; normal caution is advised.
Moderate (yellow)	Natural avalanches unlikely; human-triggered avalanches *possible*	Use caution in steeper terrain on certain slope aspects.
Considerable (orange)	Natural avalanches possible; human-triggered avalanches *probable*	Be cautious in steeper terrain.
High (red)	Natural and human-triggered avalanches *likely*	Travel in avalanche terrain is not recommended.
Extreme (red with black border)	Widespread natural or human-triggered avalanches *certain*	Travel in avalanche terrain should be avoided and travel should be confined to low-angle terrain well away from avalanche run-outs.

Source: Canadian Avalanche Association. 2006. http://www.avalanche.ca/default.aspx?DN=8,4,558,3,Documents. *Accessed November 4, 2006.*

PROFESSIONAL PROFILE

Clair Israelson, Executive Director of the Canadian Avalanche Association and the Canadian Avalanche Centre

Clair Israelson (Figure 5.C) is executive director of both the Canadian Avalanche Association and the Canadian Avalanche Centre. Since 1981, the Canadian Avalanche Association (CAA) has supported avalanche safety in Canada by developing national technical standards, training avalanche workers, and providing specialized support services for frontline avalanche operations. Its sister organization, the Canadian Avalanche Centre (CAC), was created in 2004 and has developed and delivered avalanche awareness programs, avalanche forecasts and warnings, and avalanche skills training programs for the public. "It is both a great privilege and a responsibility," Israelson says, "to serve these fine nongovernment organizations."

Israelson's first experience with avalanches was in 1968 when he was a high school student living near Vancouver. During the Christmas holidays, heavy snow fell in the mountains and he and a friend decided to snowshoe into a high alpine bowl in Golden Ears Provincial Park.

"As we plodded up through a forested access gully," he explains, "rain started to fall. When we reached the treeline, large wet avalanches began to rumble down from the cloud-shrouded, snow-covered peaks into the bowl in front of us. We knew nothing about avalanches but realized that we were in danger and needed to get out of harm's way."

Retracing their steps back down through the forested gully, Israelson and his friend were shocked to find a 100 m section of their tracks covered by an avalanche up to 3 m deep. "Had we been there an hour later, we could have been killed."

They realized that they needed to learn about avalanches, but the trip to the local library didn't help much. In 1968, not a lot was known or published about avalanches. In the winter of 1971, Israelson worked as a Park Warden in Yoho National Park. His job was to help evaluate and control avalanches that could threaten the Trans-Canada Highway and the Canadian Pacific Railway.

▲ **FIGURE 5.C CLAIR ISRAELSON** Clair Israelson is executive director of the Canadian Avalanche Association, a nonprofit, nongovernmental organization established in 1982 to support avalanche safety in Canada. CAA develops national standards, trains avalanche workers, and provides services for frontline avalanche operations. *(Clair Isrealson)*

It was a rare winter, with huge avalanches destroying mature forest, closing the highway and railway, destroying buildings, and forcing the evacuation of several homes and businesses in the town of Field. "The mystery and majesty of avalanches captured my imagination, and for the past 35 years avalanche protection has been my life's work," Israelson says.

He adds, "Although CAA and CAC work takes up most of my year, I'm still able to work part time in winter as a heli-ski guide, out in the mountains where avalanches are part of nature's annual cycle. It's good for the soul."

Over the past 35 years, incredible advances have been made in avalanche science and protection programs. Although the number of avalanche deaths each year continues to rise, the rate of growth in the recreational and commercial use of Canada's mountains in winter far outstrips the avalanche fatalities. The avalanche accident rate is going down. Avalanche education, awareness, and risk-control programs are preventing accidents and saving lives.

"Avalanches will continue to threaten human activities in Canada for as long as snow falls on mountains," says Israelson. "Skilled people are needed to protect Canadians from natural hazards such as avalanches."

—John J. Clague

from the snow. Between 55 percent and 65 percent of victims buried in the open are killed.[6] Survival depends mainly on the length of time the person is buried and the burial depth.

Research carried out in Italy on a sample of 422 buried skiers indicates how low the chances of survival can be.[16] Survival dropped very rapidly from 92 percent within 15 minutes of burial, to 30 percent in 35 minutes, to almost 0 percent in 2 hours. Buried victims die of suffocation, hypothermia, or injuries. In most backcountry situations, few victims survive long enough for other members of the group to get help. Reports of live recoveries by searchers called to the accident site are rare. Therefore, the victim's best, and generally only, chance of survival depends on an effective search by other members of the group. It is vital that everyone surviving an avalanche conduct an immediate search, rather than waiting for help to arrive. Help can be called once victims are located and dug out. Even in a well-equipped country, such as France, it typically takes 45 minutes for a helicopter rescue team to arrive, by which time most of the victims are likely to have died. In some cases, avalanche victims are not located until summer when the snow melts.

The chance of survival also depends on depth of burial. Only 5 percent to 10 percent of avalanche victims survive burial in more than 1.5 m of snow, and few survive deeper burial.

Chances of a buried victim being found alive and rescued are increased when everyone in the group carries standard avalanche safety equipment and has been trained in how to use it. Safety equipment includes avalanche cords, transceivers, probes, and shovels.[17]

Avalanche Cords

An **avalanche cord** is the oldest safety device and was largely used before transceivers became available. The principle is simple—an approximately 10 m red cord, similar to a parachute cord, is attached to a person's belt. While skiing, snowboarding, or snowshoeing, the cord is dragged along behind the person. In the event of an avalanche, the light cord remains on top of the snow and, being red, is easily visible to rescue personnel. Typically the cord has markings every metre, which indicate the distance to the victim.

Avalanche Transceivers

An avalanche may cover a large area, and if victims are completely covered by snow, the chances they will be found alive are low. Survival becomes much more likely if the victims are wearing **avalanche transceivers**, also referred to as beacons, beepers, ARVA (*Appareil de recherche de victimes en avalanche*, in French), and LVS (*Lawinen-Verschütteten-Suchgerät*, Swiss German). These portable devices emit a beep via a 457 kHz radio signal in normal use. They are switched to receive mode to locate a buried victim up to 80 m away, commonly in 5 to 15 minutes. Analog receivers provide audible beeps that rescuers interpret to estimate the distance to the victim. Digital models give visual indications of the direction and distance to victims and require little practice to use.

Probes

Collapsible rods can be extended to probe for victims up to several metres deep in snow. Probing can be done with sectional rods, skis, ski poles, or branches. It is a time-consuming process if a thorough search is done without a beacon. Five probers are about 100 times slower than one searcher with a transceiver. In the United States, 86 percent of the 140 victims found by probing since 1950 were already dead.[6] And of victims buried more than 2 m, only 4 percent are found and rescued alive.

Shovels

As an avalanche decelerates, the snow becomes compressed into a compact mass. Shovels are essential to dig through the snow to the victim, because the deposit is too dense to dig with hands or skis. Shovels are also useful for digging snow pits to evaluate snowpack stability.

Avalanche Dogs

When avalanche dogs are used the search times are similar to those achieved with transceivers, but a trained dog generally does not arrive at the accident scene in time to recover people alive. There are reports of buried avalanche victims being found alive by dogs in the United States but none in Canada.

Avalanche Survival

If you are ever caught in an avalanche, try to ski or board toward the side of the moving mass of snow. When you fall, jettison your equipment and attempt swimming motions. As the snow comes to rest, try to preserve an airspace in front of your mouth, and try to thrust an arm, leg, or object above the surface, assuming you are still conscious. Once the snow stops, enlarge the air space if you are able to move; however, limit movement to minimize oxygen consumption. Rapid breathing may cause the snow in your face to glaze, creating a seal that limits oxygen.

The low odds of surviving an avalanche emphasize the importance of the mitigation measures described above. Information on current weather and snow conditions, avalanche education, and a thoughtful decision-making process are essential to minimize personal avalanche risk.

Summary

An avalanche is the sudden failure and rapid movement of a mass of snow down a mountainside. The snow may move as a coherent block, or it may rapidly disaggregate into small particles that move independently of one another. Avalanches present obvious dangers to backcountry recreationists and to people working in resource industries in steep mountain areas. They also damage property and forest, and cause expensive rail and road traffic delays.

Avalanches are of two types. Point-release avalanches involve failures of small masses of snow; they grow in size as they travel downslope, producing a distinctive, downslope-widening trough, like an inverted V. Slab avalanches are failures of a mass of cohesive snow along a weak layer at depth. They leave steep crown, lateral, and toe scarps and a smooth planar basal failure plane.

Weather determines the evolution and stability of the snowpack. The most important weather-related factors are heating by solar radiation, radiative cooling, temperature gradients in the snowpack, and snowfall amounts and type.

Weak layers in the snowpack form in three main ways. First, wind contributes to the rapid buildup of snow on sheltered lee slopes. The resulting wind slabs consist of thick, poorly bonded snow that is susceptible to failure. Wind may also increase during a snowstorm, depositing a layer of broken and packed snow crystals on a delicate layer of unbroken snowflakes that fell earlier. The layer of broken crystals becomes a buried weak surface along which failure may later occur. Second, weak layers of crystals formed by the sublimation of water vapour (depth hoar) can form within the snowpack. Hoar can form at different depths, depending on the temperature profile in the snowpack. Third, large ice crystals (surface hoar) form on the surface on cold clear nights. The crystals may change only slowly once buried and become a weak layer within the snowpack.

Most avalanches start naturally during or soon after snowstorms. Others happen when normal daytime heating or the inflow of a warm air mass heats the upper layer of the snowpack. In most recreational accidents, a person triggers the avalanche.

An avalanche path consists of three parts—the start zone, where the snowpack fails; the track, along which the avalanche accelerates and achieves its highest velocity; and the run-out zone, where the avalanche decelerates and snow is deposited. The three zones are easy to identify where an avalanche follows gullies or chutes that have carried previous avalanches and where the tracks are on forested slopes. The zones are more difficult to distinguish on slopes above the treeline and where the snow is not channelled.

Large avalanches generally occur on slopes between 30° and 45°. These slopes are also popular with skiers, snowboarders, and snowmobilers, which is why recreationists commonly trigger avalanches.

Avalanches in Canada are most common in the mountains of Alberta, British Columbia, and Yukon Territory. They can occur, however, anywhere in Canada where there are slopes of sufficient steepness to accumulate and release snow. Most avalanches in the United States occur in the high mountains extending from the Sierra Nevada and Cascade ranges on the west to the Rocky Mountains on the east.

Avalanche risk can be reduced by locating infrastructure outside known danger zones, by placing defensive structures within avalanche tracks, by reinforcing exposed structures, by setting off controlled avalanches with explosives, and with forecasting. Defensive structures include fences and nets in the start zone, and berms, splitting wedges, avalanche sheds, and mounds in the run-out zone.

Avalanche forecasting is an assessment of the likelihood and size of avalanches under existing or future conditions. Forecasts are based on observed occurrences of avalanches, stability and strength tests, observations of snowpack characteristics, and observations of weather conditions. Numerical and rule-based computer software has been developed to assist forecasters. The computational algorithms compare current measurements of precipitation, temperature, wind, and other meteorological variables with average values of the same variables spanning many years.

Avalanche safety involves route selection, examination of the snowpack, consideration of weather conditions, and human factors. People involved in winter recreation in the mountains need to ask and answer the following three questions: Is the slope to be crossed prone to avalanches? Is the snowpack unstable? What are the consequences of being caught in an avalanche on the terrain to be crossed?

The chance of surviving an avalanche depends on the length of time and depth that a person is buried. The probability of a buried victim being found alive and rescued is increased when everyone in a group carries standard avalanche safety equipment and has been trained in how to use it. Safety equipment includes avalanche cords, transceivers, probes, and shovels.

Key Terms

avalanche cord (p. 155)
avalanche forecast (p. 152)
avalanche transceiver (p. 155)
hoar (p. 143)
point-release avalanche (p. 141)
run-out zone (p. 143)
slab avalanche (p. 142)
sluff (p. 143)
snow avalanche (p. 140)
start zone (p. 143)
track (p. 143)
wind slab (p. 142)

Review Questions

1. What are the two types of avalanches and how do they form?
2. How do weak layers form in a snowpack?
3. What role does wind play in avalanches?
4. Describe or sketch the three parts of an avalanche's path.
5. What is the most common trigger of avalanches?
6. Identify the factors that affect snowpack stability.
7. How does depth hoar form and what effect does it have on the stability of snow?
8. What is the relation between slope steepness and avalanches?
9. What are the two types of wind slabs and how do they form?
10. What regions in North America are most at risk from avalanches?
11. What are the natural service functions of avalanches?
12. Identify the types of engineered structures that are used to reduce avalanche risk.
13. What is an avalanche shed?
14. Describe the procedures used to forecast avalanches.
15. What is a snow compression test?
16. What percentage of avalanche victims survive 30 minutes of burial? 2 hours?
17. What safety and rescue equipment should every backcountry skier carry?

Critical Thinking Questions

1. You and a group of friends are preparing for a weekend ski trip to a remote mountain lake. What actions should you take before and during the trip to minimize the risk that someone in the group will be caught in an avalanche?
2. You have been hired by a ski resort to advise it on avalanche safety in an area that is slated for development. How would you identify areas that should be off-limits to skiing? How would you handle areas that are likely to be attractive to skiers but, under some circumstances, will have a high avalanche danger?
3. You are part of a ski party returning from a long, tiring day of skiing. Your party is properly dressed for severe winter conditions, has been trained in avalanche awareness, and is equipped with avalanche probes and transceivers. You are two hours from your vehicles and it has started to snow heavily, with strong gusty winds. To reach your cars, you must pass along a narrow section of valley with slopes rising at an angle of about 35° from the valley floor. You are aware that the avalanche danger has increased since the beginning of the day but are tired and anxious to reach your destination. What actions do you take?

Selected Web Resources

Avalanches, Avalanche Safety, and Avalanche Forecasting
www.avalanche.ca Canadian Avalanche Association

www.avalanche-center.org/Canada Avalanche Center

www.pc.gc.ca/pn-np/bc/glacier/activ/activ9_E.asp Parks Canada

www.americanavalancheassociation.org American Avalanche Association

www.slf.ch/welcome-en.html Swiss Federal Institute for Snow and Avalanche Research

European Avalanche Services
www.slf.ch/laworg/map.html Directory of avalanche services in Europe

Artificial Avalanche Release
www.elikos.com/en/artificial-avalanche-release-system.html Use of explosives to trigger avalanches

CHAPTER 6

Learning Objectives

Subsidence, or sinking of the land, is an important geologic process that causes extensive damage in some areas of the world. Your goals in reading this chapter should be to

- Understand the causes and effects of subsidence
- Know the geographic regions at risk from subsidence
- Understand the hazards associated with karst terrain
- Recognize links between subsidence and other hazards, as well as the natural service functions of karst
- Understand how people interact with subsidence hazards
- Know what can be done to minimize the risk of subsidence

▶ **FLOODING IN PIAZZA SAN MARCO, VENICE, ITALY**
A high tide on November 1, 2004, flooded 80 percent of Venice in northern Italy. Flooding is becoming more common as Venice subsides and sea level rises. *(AP Wide World Photos)*

Subsidence

Venice Is Sinking

Italy's beautiful and famous city of Venice faces a serious geologic problem. The city is sinking, or subsiding, up to 2 mm per year. Venice is built on 17 small islands connected by more than 400 bridges. The city's location and numerous canals are part of its attraction, but the presence of so much water and the ongoing slow subsidence of the city make it extremely prone to flooding.

The land on which Venice is built is only centimetres above sea level. Although subsidence has been occurring naturally for millions of years, pumping of groundwater from the 1930s to the 1960s significantly increased the rate at which the city is sinking.[1] The pumping and thus the human contribution to this natural hazard ended in the 1970s, but, unfortunately, natural subsidence is still occurring. The response has been to raise buildings and streets, but this solution is not viable in the long term. The Italian government has considered building a large and very expensive retractable dam across the mouth of the lagoon that separates Venice from the Adriatic Sea. The idea is to prevent water from flowing into the lagoon at times of high water.

6.1 Introduction to Subsidence

Subsidence is the slow or rapid downward movement of Earth's surface. The form of the subsiding area can be circular, linear, bead-like, or irregular. Subsidence can also involve an imperceptible lowering of the surface over a large area.

Subsidence is commonly associated with the dissolution of limestone, gypsum, or rock salt at depth. The resultant **karst** landscape is irregular in form and has closed depressions. Other natural causes of subsidence include thawing of frozen ground, compaction of recently deposited sediment, shrinking of expansive soils, earthquakes, and deflation of magma chambers. Human-induced subsidence, discussed in section 6.6, can result from withdrawal of fluids from subsurface reservoirs, collapse of soil and rock over mines and other subsurface excavations, and draining of wetlands.

Karst

Dissolution of limestone, gypsum, or rock salt occurs as groundwater moves through the rock. Rock salt and gypsum dissolve when they come in contact

with neutral waters, whereas limestone dissolves readily only in acidic waters. Rock salt is approximately 7500 times more soluble than limestone, and gypsum 150 times more soluble than limestone.[2]

Percolating water becomes acidic when carbon dioxide is dissolved in it. Acidification occurs in the atmosphere where rainfall is in equilibrium with carbon dioxide and in soil where carbon dioxide is produced by bacterial decomposition. The respiration of most soil bacteria is like respiration in humans—both involve consumption of oxygen and release of carbon dioxide. Dissolving carbon dioxide in water produces carbonic acid, the same weak acid that is present in carbonated soft drinks.

Areas underlain by thin-bedded, fractured, or well-jointed limestone are especially vulnerable to dissolution. Surface waters are easily diverted to depth in these rocks along fractures or cracks between sedimentary layers. Acidic percolating waters enlarge fractures by dissolving rock (Figure 6.1). The chemical reactions leading to limestone dissolution are the following:

water + carbon dioxide = carbonic acid

$$H_2O + CO_2 = H_2CO_3$$

carbonic acid + limestone = calcium + bicarbonate

$$H_2CO_3 + CaCO_3 = Ca^{++} + 2HCO_3^{-1}$$

The dissolution produces empty spaces, or voids, of a range of sizes beneath the land surface. The voids are produced preferentially in zones of mixing of waters near the water table. Over time, contiguous voids join to produce caves and caverns. Where these large openings are close to the surface, pits known as **sinkholes** may develop, either individually (Figure 6.2) or in large numbers. A surface pockmarked with a large number of sinkholes is termed a **karst plain**.

Many karst areas are characterized by beautiful rolling hills separated by areas of subsidence underlain by extensive cave systems (Figure 6.1). Cave openings can be sites of *disappearing streams* where surface water goes underground, or the place where groundwater emerges at the surface in springs. In humid tropical regions, extensive dissolution removes most of the soluble bedrock, leaving behind a landscape of steep hills known as *tower karst* (Figure 6.3).

Sinkholes In karst areas, sinkholes range from one to several hundred metres in diameter (Figure 6.4) and are of two basic types:

1. *Solution sinkholes.* These pits form by solution of buried bedrock. Acidic groundwater is concentrated in holes that develop along bedding planes, joints, and fractures.

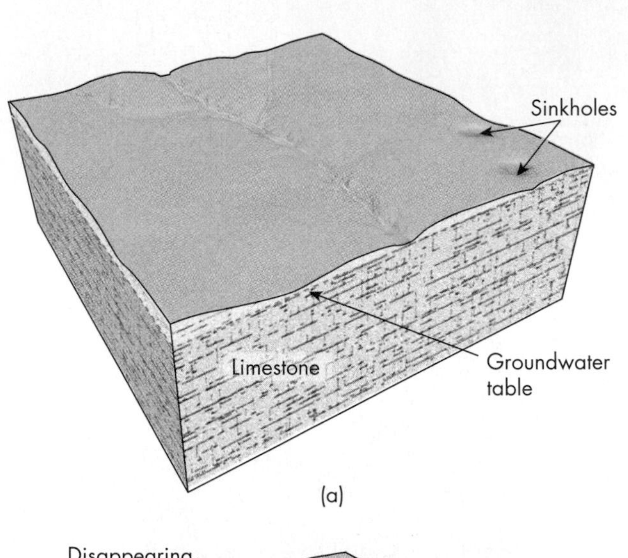

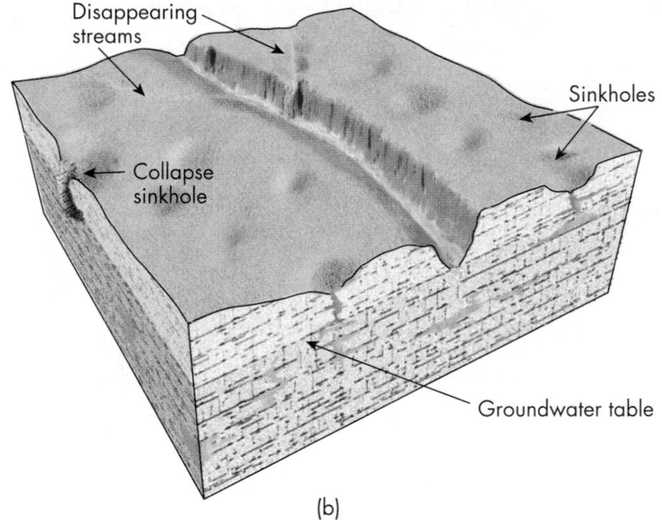

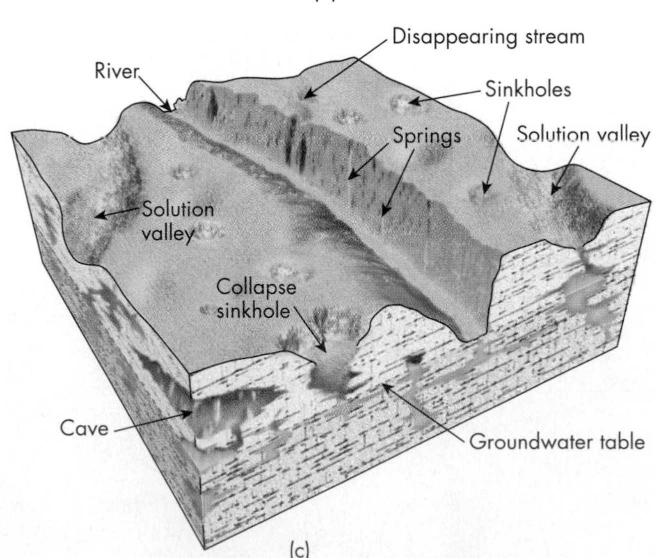

▶ **FIGURE 6.1 DEVELOPMENT OF KARST TOPOGRAPHY** (a) In the early stage of karst formation in a limestone terrain, water from the surface seeps through fractures and along layers in the soluble rock. Weak acid in the water slowly dissolves the rock. (b) The water table falls as a river incises into the rock. Caves begin to form and then collapse to become sinkholes. Some surface streams disappear underground. (c) In later stages of karst development, a downward-eroding river continues to lower the water table. Large caverns and sinkholes develop and eventually merge to form solution valleys and plains without surface streams. In humid tropical climates, intense dissolution removes nearly all the rock, leaving behind pillars of limestone referred to as tower karst. *(Modified from illustration by D. Tasa in Tarbuck, E. J., and F. K. Lutgens. 2005. Earth: An introduction to physical geology, 8th ed. Upper Saddle River, NJ: Pearson Prentice Hall)*

◄ **FIGURE 6.2 SMALL SINKHOLE** Most sinkholes, such as this one in Boyle County, Kentucky, are small. *(Photograph by Kentucky Geological Survey geologist Jim Currens)*

2. *Collapse sinkholes.* This type of sinkhole develops by the collapse of surface or near-surface rock or sediment into an underground cavern system.

Some sinkholes open into a subterranean passage, through which water escapes during rainstorms. Others are filled with rubble that blocks the flow of water to the subsurface. Blocked sinkholes may contain small lakes, but most such lakes eventually drain when the water seeps through the debris.[3] Artificial ponds and lakes constructed over sinkholes may drain suddenly into subterranean cavities (see Survivor Story).

Cave Systems As solution pits in limestone enlarge, a system of caves or larger caverns may form. Mammoth Cave in Kentucky, Carlsbad Caverns in New Mexico, and Castleguard Cave in the Alberta Rocky Mountains are three famous **cave systems** in North America. Caves develop at or near the groundwater table where water that is saturated with

◄ **FIGURE 6.3 TOWER KARST** (a) Painting of Chinese tower karst "Peach Garden Land of Immortals" by Qiu Ying. *(Asian Art and Archaeology, Inc./CORBIS-NY)* (b) Tower karst south of Guilin in South China's Guangxi Zhuang Autonomous Region. *(A C Waltham/Robert Harding World Imagery)*

◄ **FIGURE 6.4 COLLAPSE SINKHOLE** This large sinkhole in Winter Park, Florida, grew rapidly over three days in 1981. The sides of the sinkhole have since been stabilized and landscaped, and the site is now a park with a small lake. *(Leif Skoogfor/Woodfin Camp and Associates)*

calcium and bicarbonate from the chemical weathering of limestone is replaced with undersaturated water. Caves grow larger as groundwater moves through fractures in the rock or between sedimentary layers. Later, if the groundwater table falls, seeping water will deposit calcium carbonate on the sides, floor, and ceiling of the cave as *flowstone, stalagmites*, and *stalactites* (Figure 6.5).

Tower Karst Large, steep limestone pillars that rise above the surrounding landscape are known as tower karst. They are residual landforms of a highly eroded karst landscape and are common only in humid tropical regions, notably Cuba, Puerto Rico, and Southeast Asia. The most spectacular examples are near Guilin, China (Figure 6.3).

Disappearing Streams Karst regions are underlain by a complex network of subterranean channels. Surface streams may disappear into caves and continue underground as *disappearing streams*.

Springs Areas where groundwater naturally discharges at the surface are known as **springs**. Most springs in karst areas are highly productive, especially during rainy periods. They are an important resource, but many are drying up because

◄ **FIGURE 6.5 CAVE FORMATIONS** Carlsbad Caverns, New Mexico, contains stalactites, which hang from the ceiling, stalagmites, which grow up from the ground, and flowstone, which forms as water flows slowly down the walls or across an inclined surface. *(Bruce Roberts/Photo Researchers, Inc.)*

SURVIVOR STORY

Sinkholes

Lake Chesterfield was a pleasant 9.3 ha, human-made lake in a quiet suburb of St. Louis. That is, until it disappeared. Residents of the community of Wildwood say the entire lake drained in three days in early June 2004.

"It was like someone pulled the plug," says Donna Ripp, who lives across the street from the lake site (Figure 6.A). Two days after Ripp first noticed that the level of the lake was dropping, it was half-empty. After another day, the lake was gone entirely.

The culprit was clear: a gaping sinkhole at the north end of the lake that Ripp's husband, Eric, estimates to be about 20 m in diameter. What geologists are now investigating is what the larger subterranean network looks like.

This region of Missouri, which Ripp describes as "a beautiful area where we still have a lot of deer," is rife with underground caves and cavities, including many that are expansive enough for people to explore.

A geologist who inspected the lake shortly after the water drained found that the sinkhole consisted of two long but relatively narrow chimneys connected to a system of caves that extended laterally for many kilometres.

To develop a better picture of the subsurface plumbing system, the geologist drilled five test holes at 12 m intervals, two of which revealed empty cavities below. He estimated that 600 holes in a 12 m grid would be required to even begin to understand the region completely. He recommended filling the cavities with a cement-like substance so other sinkholes won't open and create a similar problem.

In the meantime, the residents of Wildwood are getting a crash course on karst topography. "I didn't even know there were underground caves here until all this happened," Donna Ripp says.

—Chris Wilson

◀ **FIGURE 6.A LAKE DRAINED BY SINKHOLE** Residents of Wildwood, Missouri, examine the mudflat that was the site of Lake Chesterfield, a 9.3 ha, human-made lake in suburban St. Louis, Missouri. The lake drained in three days after a sinkhole opened beneath it. About 340 million litres of water funnelled through the sinkhole in the lake bottom. *(Hillary Levin/Saint Louis Post-Dispatch)*

of overpumping of groundwater. Springs are also vulnerable to contamination; pollutants at the surface can relatively easily enter underground drainage systems and migrate to springs.

Thermokarst

In polar regions and at high elevations in mountains, subsurface materials remain frozen throughout the year (Figure 6.6). Permanently frozen ground, referred to as **permafrost**, may be continuous across the landscape and extend to depths of tens or even hundreds of metres. In slightly warmer climates, permafrost may exist as discontinuous patches or thin layers. To qualify as permafrost, soil or sediment must remain cemented with ice for at least two years.

Under normal conditions, frozen ground thaws to a depth of a few dozen centimetres to, at most, a few metres during summer. This *active layer* then refreezes in the winter. However, more extensive thawing of permafrost can occur when the ground is disturbed by human activity or when the climate warms. Thawing can produce subsidence, especially if the soil or sediment contains a large amount of ice. Land subsidence of several metres or more is possible from thawing of permafrost.[4] An irregular surface produced by permafrost

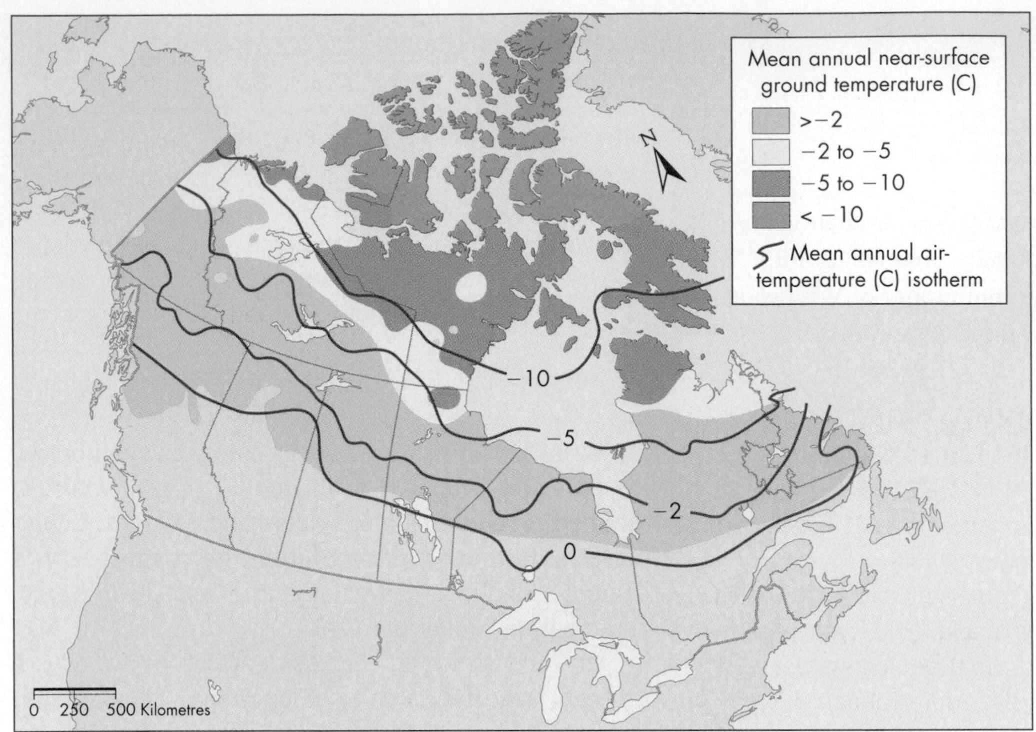

▲ **FIGURE 6.6 DISTRIBUTION OF PERMAFROST** Map showing spatial variations in mean annual air temperature and near-surface ground temperature within Canada's permafrost region. Permafrost is discontinuous within the zone of air temperatures between 0°C and −2°C, and is continuous in areas with mean air temperatures less than −2°C. *(Brooks, G. R. 2001. A synthesis of geological hazards in Canada. Geological Survey of Canada Bulletin 548, p. 245; reproduced with the permission of the Minister of Public Works and Government Services Canada, 2007, and courtesy of Natural Resources Canada, Geological Survey of Canada)*

thaw is known as *thermokarst*. Climatic warming over the past four decades has thawed large areas of Arctic permafrost in Canada, forming unstable, water-filled depressions (Figure 6.7). In some areas, the *permafrost table* is dropping at rates of close to 20 cm per year.[5]

Piping

As groundwater percolates slowly through loose sediments, it can pick up particles of silt and sand in the subsurface and slowly carry them laterally to a point of water discharge on a slope (a spring). Over time, shallow subterranean tunnels and cavities may develop in the sediments, which ultimately collapse to produce surface depressions and ravines.[6] This process is called **piping**. It is most common in silty and sandy sediments. Karst-like depressions formed by piping are present on inhabited benches underlain by glacial lake silts in Kamloops, British Columbia.[7] Occasionally, new depressions form, damaging structures that overlie the developing subterranean cavities.

◀ **FIGURE 6.7 THERMOKARST** These thermokarst ponds are in the lowlands bordering Hudson Bay, Manitoba. This scene shows a mosaic of frozen peat and shallow thermokarst ponds that occupy depressions where ice has thawed. The ponds range in size from several metres to several hundred metres. *(Lynda Dredge, Geological Survey of Canada Photo No. 2001-124; reproduced with the permission of the Minister of Public Works and Government Services Canada, 2007, and courtesy of Natural Resources Canada, Geological Survey of Canada)*

Sediment and Soil Compaction

Peat and other organic sediments, and loose clay, silt, and sand are susceptible to subsidence. Subsidence occurs as the sediment compacts or loses water. Sediment compaction can occur naturally or as the result of human activities.

Fine Sediment Clay, silt, and sand commonly contain abundant *pore water*—water occupying spaces among the particles that constitute the sediment. Over time, the amount of pore water decreases and the sediment compacts. Rapid deposition and compaction are especially common on river deltas. In a natural system, compaction of delta sediments is balanced by new sediment deposition, keeping the surface of the delta, called the *delta plain,* from sinking below sea or lake level. Most deltas, however, are favoured sites for cities, farms, and other infrastructure, all of which must be protected from flooding with *dykes*. Protective dykes, however, prevent new sediment from accumulating on the delta plain, thus the land surface gradually subsides. Sedimentation on the Mississippi River delta plain, for example, was stopped by levees built on both sides of the river by the U.S. Army Corps of Engineers. These levees have protected communities, like New Orleans, from river flooding, but they have also kept new sediment from being added to the delta plain. Similarly, dykes protect more than 200,000 people and billions of dollars of infrastructure on the Fraser River delta south of Vancouver, British Columbia. Much of the delta plain is at or just below mean sea level and is slowly subsiding because it is no longer being replenished with new sediment. Construction of the Aswan dam upstream of the Nile River delta and the diversion of two-thirds of the river water into canals have stopped sediment from reaching much of the delta plain.[8]

Organic Sediment Some of the sediment that accumulates in marshes, bogs, swamps, bayous, and other wetlands common on deltas contains large amounts of partially decayed leaves, stems, roots, and, in colder regions, moss, which soak up water like sponges (Figure 6.8). **Organic sediments**, especially *peat*, compact to a fraction of their original thickness when they lose their contained water.

Bacterial decomposition of peat and other organic sediments converts organic carbon compounds to carbon dioxide gas and water. Water and wind erosion and burning of peat lands also destroy dry organic sediments. The decomposition, erosion, and burning of organic sediments cause the irreversible subsidence of drained wetlands. Subsidence of New Orleans has been aggravated by draining of wetlands and destruction of organic sediments.[9]

A dramatic example of wetland subsidence is the Florida Everglades. Droughts combined with land drainage, primarily for agriculture and urban development, caused more than half of the Everglades to subside between 0.3 m and 3 m during the twentieth century.[10]

Expansive Soils

Some clay-rich soils, referred to as **expansive soils**, shrink significantly during dry periods and expand or swell during wet periods. Most of the swelling is caused by the chemical attraction of water molecules to surfaces of clay particles (Figure 6.9a).[11] It can also be caused by the attraction of water molecules to platy layers that form the crystalline structure of some clay minerals.

The *smectite* group of clay minerals has very small clay crystals and thus a very large surface area to attract water molecules. Smectites are abundant in many clay and shale deposits, and they are the primary constituents of *bentonite*, a rock that forms from the alteration of volcanic ash. Clay, shale, and soils containing smectite have the greatest potential for shrinking and swelling.

The presence of expansive soils can be inferred from surface features indicative of repeated shrinking and swelling. These features include *desiccation cracks* produced by

◄ **FIGURE 6.8 PEAT BOG** This bog near Portage, Prince Edward Island, contains almost 8 m of peat that has slowly accumulated over the past 10,000 years. *(Reproduced with the permission of the Minister of Public Works and Government Services Canada, 2007, and courtesy of Natural Resources Canada, Geological Survey of Canada)*

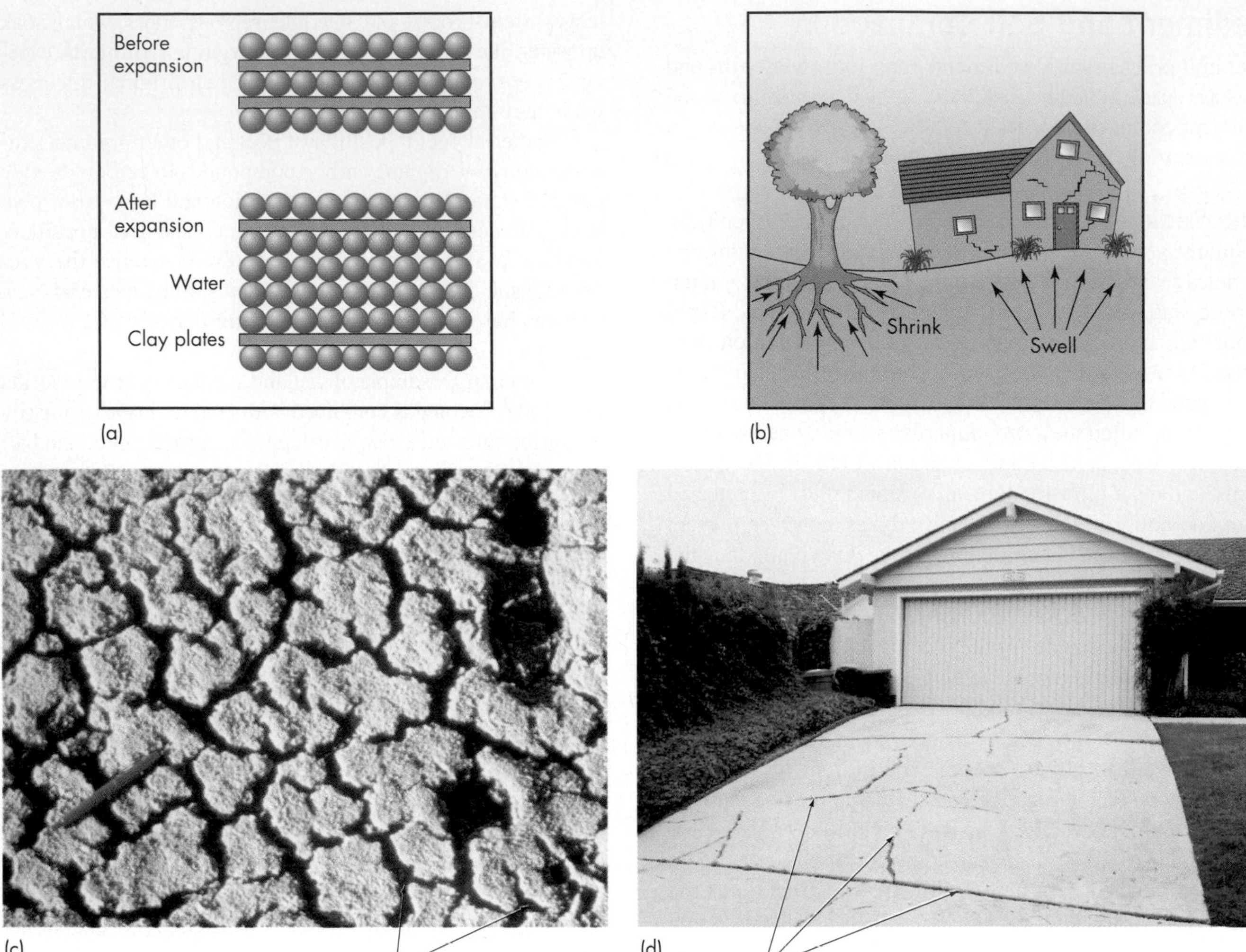

▲ **FIGURE 6.9 EXPANSIVE SOILS** (a) Smectite, a group of clay minerals, expands as water molecules are added to the clay particles. (b) Effects of the shrinking and swelling of clay at a home site. *(After Mathewson, C. C., and J. P. Castleberry, II. Expansive soils: Their engineering geology. Texas A&M University)* (c) Drying of an expansive soil produces this popcorn-like surface texture and a network of polygonal desiccation cracks. *(U.S. Geological Survey)* (d) Shrinking and swelling of expansive soil cracked the concrete in this driveway. *(Edward A. Keller)*

drying of the soil (Figure 6.9c), a popcorn-like weathering texture on bare patches of clay (Figure 6.9c), alternating small mounds and depressions, tilting and cracking of blocks of concrete in sidewalks and foundations (Figure 6.9d), wavy bumps in asphalt pavement (Figure 6.10), and random tilting of utility poles and gravestones.

Structural damage to buildings located on expansive soil is caused by changes in the moisture content and therefore the volume of the soil. Factors that affect the moisture content of an expansive soil include climate, vegetation, topography, and drainage.[12] Regions with a pronounced wet season followed by a dry season are more likely to experience problems than regions where precipitation is more evenly distributed throughout the year.

Vegetation exerts a strong influence on the moisture content of a soil. Trees use local soil moisture for respiration and photosynthesis. Withdrawal of water from the ground may produce soil shrinkage (Figure 6.9b).

Earthquakes

Earthquakes can lower ground over large areas. As mentioned in Chapter 2, the 1964 Alaskan earthquake produced subsidence over an area of several tens of thousands of square kilometres. Some coastal areas subsided up to 2 m, flooding some communities. The geologic record shows that similar great earthquakes at the Cascadia subduction zone in the Pacific Northwest have repeatedly lowered the outer coasts of Vancouver Island, Washington, and Oregon[13] (Figure 6.11). The model that explains these recurrent earthquakes postulates that a portion of the subduction zone is "locked," that is, the subducting and overriding plates are stuck against one another. Ongoing subduction causes the west edge of the North America plate to buckle. The underwater, seaward edge of the continent is dragged downward and a bulge appears along the coast (Figure 6.12). The accumulating strain is released when the two plates slip during a great earthquake. At that time, the edge of the North America plate elastically

▶ **FIGURE 6.10 DAMAGE FROM EXPANSIVE SOIL** Uneven shrinking and swelling of expansive clays in layers of steeply dipping bedrock produced the rolling surface of this road and sidewalk in Colorado. *(Courtesy of David C. Noe, Colorado Geological Survey)*

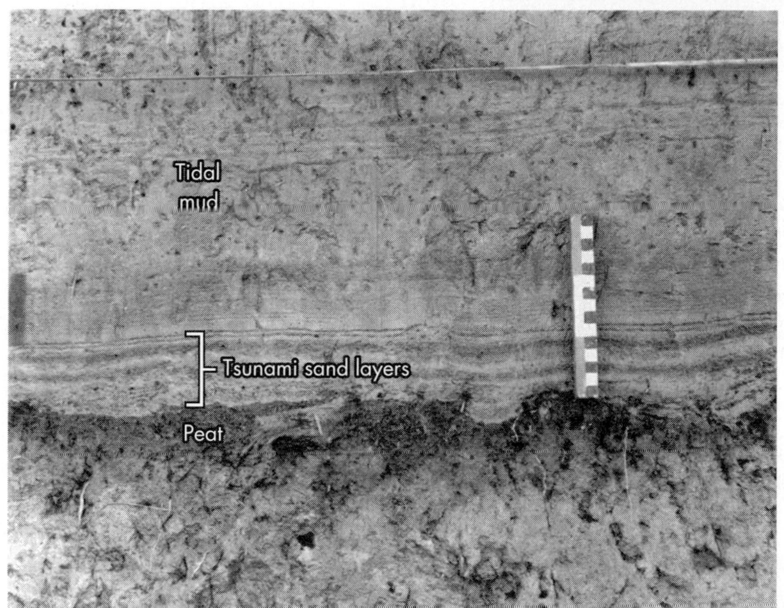

◀ **FIGURE 6.11 GEOLOGIC EVIDENCE OF SUBSIDENCE DURING AN EARTHQUAKE** The sediments seen in this photograph are exposed in the bank of the Niawiakum River in southwest Washington. A peat layer is abruptly overlain by tsunami sand and tidal mud. The peat records a former marsh that subsided 1–2 m during the last great earthquake in the Pacific Northwest in A.D. 1700. The down-dropped marsh was overrun by a tsunami, which deposited the sand. Later, mud gradually settled out of tidal waters onto the sand-blanketed marsh. Divisions on scale are 1 cm. *(Stein Bondevik)*

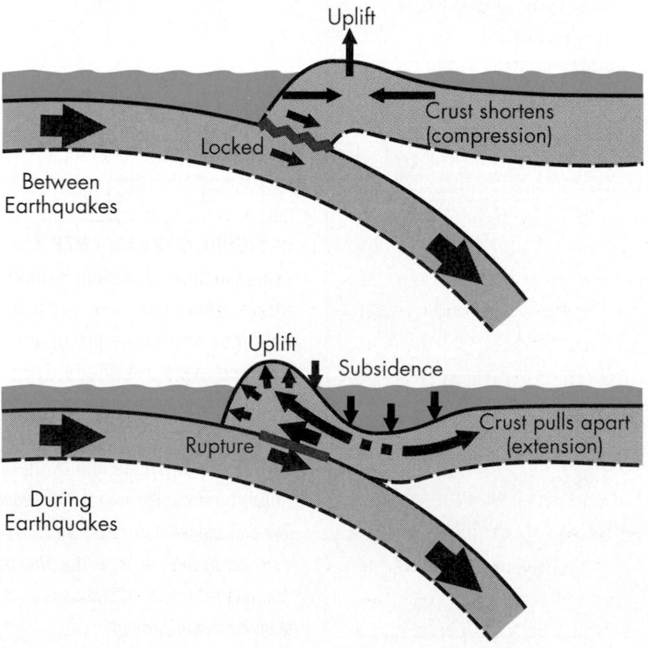

◀ **FIGURE 6.12 BUILDUP TO AN EARTHQUAKE** The oceanic Juan de Fuca plate is presently locked to the North America plate. Vancouver Island is being flexed upward because of compression and elastic shortening of the North America plate above the locked interface. This deformation has been detected from satellite measurements of small changes in the position of points on Earth's surface. Sometime within the next several hundred years the plates will suddenly unlock, triggering a great earthquake and causing the Pacific coast of Vancouver Island, Washington, and Oregon to subside. *(Clague, J., C. Yorath, R. Franklin, and B. Turner. 2006. At risk: Earthquakes and tsunamis on the west coast. Vancouver, BC: Tricouni Press)*

bounces back to its original undeformed position. This realignment results in the uplift of the previously downwarped area and subsidence of the coastal bulge. A similar cycle has been observed along subduction zones off Japan, Chile, and Indonesia.

Deflation of Magma Chambers

Subsidence can also result from volcanic activity. As magma moves upward underneath or into a volcano, the surface of the volcano may be forced upward. When the volcano erupts, the underground magma chamber is partly or completely emptied and the surface subsides. As mentioned in Chapter 3, cycles of uplift and subsidence are useful in predicting volcanic eruptions. Ground-level changes of up to several metres can occur over giant *resurgent calderas*, such as at Yellowstone Park, Wyoming, and Long Valley, California (Chapter 3). However, these changes are not noticeable because they happen over large areas.

6.2 Regions at Risk from Subsidence

Nearly 10 percent of Earth's land surface is karst, and approximately 25 percent of North America is underlain by limestone and other rocks susceptible to karst development (Figure 6.13). Karst in Canada occurs mainly on Vancouver Island; in the Rocky, Selwyn, and Mackenzie Mountains; in the Hudson Bay lowlands; locally in Arctic Canada; and in the Appalachian Mountains. In the United States, karst occurs in a region extending through the states of Tennessee, Virginia, Maryland, and Pennsylvania; in parts of Indiana, Kentucky, and Missouri; in central Florida; in the Edwards Plateau of central Texas; and in Puerto Rico. Subsidence and other karst-related phenomena are problems in these areas.

Permafrost covers more than 20 percent of the world's land surface.[5] Most of Alaska and more than half of Canada and Russia are underlain by permafrost. Many towns and settlements are threatened by thawing permafrost, including Barrow in Alaska; Inuvik in Canada; and Yakutsk, Norilsk, and Vorkuta in Russia.[5]

Subsidence caused by compaction of sediment is most pronounced on deltas, such as those of the Mississippi River in the United States, the Mackenzie and Fraser rivers in Canada, and the Nile River in Egypt.

Peat and other organic sediments underlie temperate- and cold-climate wetlands of Alaska, Canada, Siberia, and northern Europe. These wetlands are variously called "bogs," "fens," "moors," and "muskeg." Coastal wetlands are particularly vulnerable to subsidence.

Expansive soils are a problem primarily in parts of southern Canada and the western United States. Earthquake-related subsidence is a risk on the west coast of North America. Deflation of a magma chamber can cause subsidence in any area of active volcanism.

6.3 Effects of Subsidence

Karst and expansive soils cause much economic damage each year. Karst areas are subject to sinkhole collapse and groundwater pollution. Expansion and shrinkage of soils damage highways, buildings, pipelines, and other structures. Additional damage results from subsidence of delta plains, wetlands, and many areas underlain by thawing permafrost.

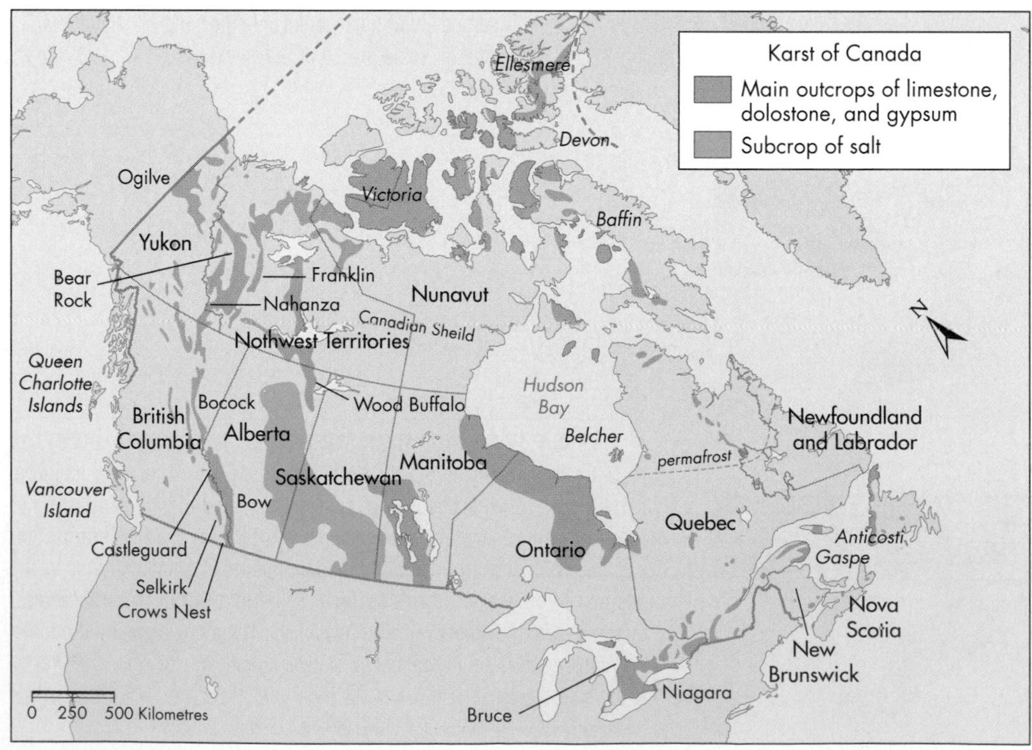

◀ **FIGURE 6.13 KARST MAP** Karst occurs in areas underlain by limestone, dolostone, and gypsum. This map shows the distribution of these rocks in Canada. Large areas of the conterminous United States, Alaska, Puerto Rico, and Hawaii also are underlain by these soluble rocks. *(Copyright 2004 from the Encyclopedia of caves and karst science, by John Gunn, editor. Reproduced by permission of Taylor & Francis, a division of Informa plc.)*

Sinkhole Collapse

Rapidly forming sinkholes have caused considerable damage to highways, homes, sewage lines, and other structures. Natural and artificial fluctuations in the water table are probably the trigger for sinkhole collapse. Dissolution of limestone takes place mainly near the water table, and near-surface caverns enlarge when the water table is high. As long as a cavern is filled with water, the buoyancy of the water helps support the weight of the overlying material. If, however, the water table drops, some of the buoyant support is lost and the cave roof may collapse. This situation was dramatically illustrated in Winter Park, Florida, on May 8, 1981, when a large collapse sinkhole began to develop. The sinkhole grew rapidly and within 24 hours had swallowed a house, part of a community swimming pool, half of a six-lane highway, parts of three businesses, and parking lots containing several vehicles (Figure 6.4).[14] Damage exceeded US$2 million.

Sinkhole hazards in urban and some rural areas may be masked by human activities. For example, a sinkhole near Allentown, Pennsylvania, marked by a 65 m pond in the 1940s, was subsequently filled with dead stumps, blocks of asphalt, and other fill. By 1969, the site was a nearly flat cornfield and was no longer recognizable as a sinkhole. Runoff from nearby paved areas, however, continued to flow into the swale, probably causing further dissolution of the limestone below the fill. Withdrawal of groundwater in the area also contributed to a lowering of the water table. These factors led to a catastrophic collapse of the land surface on June 23, 1986. A pit approximately 30 m in diameter and 14 m deep formed in only a few minutes. The damage was restricted to a street, parking lots, sidewalks, sewer lines, water lines, and other utilities, but subsequent stabilization and repair costs totalled nearly US$500,000.

Groundwater Use and Contamination

Areas of karst have abundant groundwater that is intensively used by people but is also easily polluted. Sinkholes and caves provide direct connections between surface water and groundwater (Figure 6.14). They make the groundwater vulnerable to pollution and to water-table lowering during droughts. One common source of pollution is waste carelessly discarded in sinkholes. Groundwater can also be contaminated where polluted water from surface streams flows into caves and fractures. Polluted surface water reaches the groundwater table without having been naturally filtered by sediment or rock.

Water-table fluctuations in karst areas affect people, plants, and wildlife. For example, groundwater is extracted from karst on the Edwards Plateau for use in towns and cities throughout central Texas. Frequent droughts in this region rapidly lower the water table and reduce or stop water flow from springs, threatening unique plants and animals that are found only in and around the springs.

Thawing Permafrost

Early settlers in Yukon Territory and Alaska built their homes directly on permafrost, only to find that heat from the floors of the buildings thawed the soil, causing irregular ground settlement. By the middle of the twentieth century, most buildings in these areas were placed on columns, or piles, sunk into the permafrost. By elevating the floors of the buildings, the piles kept the structures' heat away from the ground. Special precautions were taken to prevent melting of permafrost during construction of the pipeline from oil fields on the north slope of Alaska to tidewater at Valdez. The oil had to be heated to lower its viscosity sufficiently to be conveyed hundreds of kilometres in pipe, thus the pipeline had to be elevated or insulated to prevent the transfer of the heat to the frozen ground (Figure 6.15).[15] These protective strategies, however, assumed the climate would not change. That assumption has been proven wrong by developments over the past several decades.

Climate at high latitudes has warmed markedly in recent years, thawing some permafrost and causing roads to cave in,

◄ **FIGURE 6.14 WATER FROM A SUBTERRANEAN STREAM** Groundwater and surface water in karst areas are intimately connected. This waterfall discharges groundwater from Falling Spring northwest of West Union, Iowa. *(Kenneth Murray/Photo Researchers, Inc.)*

◄ **FIGURE 6.15 TRANS-ALASKA PIPELINE** The Trans-Alaska Pipeline was constructed between 1975 and 1977 to transport heated oil 1300 km from the North Slope of Alaska to a marine terminal at Valdez on Prince William Sound. The pipeline is above ground for more than half of its length. It rests on specially designed vertical supports with "heat pipes" that are 5 cm in diameter and contain anhydrous ammonia. Anhydrous ammonia is a gas when the ground is cold. It rises in the heat pipes and condenses above the surface when the ground warms, thus removing heat from the ground. The heat is transferred through the walls of the heat pipes to aluminum radiators at the tops of the supports. *(John J. Clague)*

airport runways to fracture, and buildings to crack, tilt, or collapse (Figure 6.16). About 300 apartment buildings have been damaged in two Siberian cities alone.[5] The State of Alaska now spends around 4 percent of its annual budget repairing damage caused by seasonal and permanent thawing of permafrost.[16]

Coastal Flooding and Loss of Wetlands

Flooding of low-lying coastal areas and destruction of wetlands are two major effects of ground subsidence. Subsidence of the Mississippi Delta during the past century has contributed to wetland loss and the sinking of New Orleans. Much of New Orleans is near or below the level of both the Gulf of Mexico and the adjacent Lake Pontchartrain. Only a ring of levees surrounding the city keeps it from being flooded by the river, the lake, and the Gulf. The progressive loss of wetlands through subsidence and draining contributed to the damage caused by Hurricane Katrina in 2005. Marshes on the delta plain are disappearing at rates of up to 80 km^2 per year because of submergence.[9] Without intervention, the remaining marshes will disappear by 2090 and New Orleans will be directly on the Gulf of Mexico.[9]

In late August 2005, Hurricane Katrina fluctuated between a Category 4 and Category 5 hurricane as it headed westward across Florida and then north toward Louisiana and Mississippi. Forecasters warned that it could directly hit New Orleans. Government officials ordered the evacuation of 1.2 million people in the metropolitan area. However, large numbers of people were still in New Orleans when the storm passed just east of the city on August 29. A 5 m high storm surge entered Lake Pontchartrain and topped New Orleans' levees, flooding parts of the city with water up to 6 m deep.[17] In places the hurricane pushed water more than 10 km inland.

◄ **FIGURE 6.16 THAWING PERMAFROST DESTROYS BUILDING** This apartment building in Cherskii in eastern Siberia partially collapsed because of the thaw of the permafrost on which it was built. Structural damage from thawing permafrost is becoming common in Canada, Russia, and Alaska. *(Photo by Professor V. E. Romanovsky, University of Alaska Fairbanks)*

More than 1800 people in New Orleans and surrounding areas perished.

Expansive Soils

Expansive soils are responsible for several billion dollars' damage annually to highways, buildings, and other structures in Canada and the United States. In many years this cost exceeds that of all other natural hazards combined. Every year more than 250,000 new houses are constructed on expansive soils in North America. About 60 percent of these will experience some minor damage, such as cracks in the foundation, walls, driveway, or walkway, and 10 percent will be seriously damaged, some beyond repair (Figures 6.9 and 6.10).[12,18] Underground water lines in expansive soils may rupture when there is a significant change in soil moisture, causing a loss of water pressure and a "boil water" advisory.

6.4 Linkages between Subsidence and Other Natural Hazards

As mentioned previously, subsidence can be a side effect of earthquakes, volcanic activity, and climate change. In addition, subsidence can amplify other hazardous processes. The link between subsidence and flooding, for example, is a common one.

Flooding can be a severe problem in areas that are rapidly subsiding, especially where subsidence is being caused by the overpumping of groundwater (see the opening to this chapter). In many cities, the demand for clean drinking water leads to depletion of the resource and subsidence.

Subsidence can also have a link to climate change. Drought conditions commonly lower the groundwater table, causing unconsolidated sediments to compact and shrink. In the deserts of the southwestern United States, drought is contributing to regional subsidence and to the formation of large, polygonal *desiccation cracks* (Figure 6.17). These cracks are the same size and depth as linear cracks, called *earth fissures*, produced by overpumping of groundwater.[19]

Global warming is the primary cause of thawing of permafrost in the Arctic and of the current global rise in sea level. In coastal areas, such as Venice, New Orleans, and the Nile River delta, subsidence adds to the rise of sea level caused by global warming, increasing the resulting rate of loss of land.

▲ **FIGURE 6.17 LARGE DESICCATION CRACK** This crack is part of a polygonal network of large desiccation cracks in southeastern Arizona that stem from natural lowering of the groundwater table because of drought. *(Mike Bryce/Graham County Highway Department)*

6.5 Natural Service Functions of Subsidence

Subsidence can cause many environmental and economic problems, but it also has some benefits. Karst formations are some of the world's most productive sources of clean water, and cavern systems and tower karst are important aesthetic and scientific resources (Figure 6.3). The caves of karst areas are home to rare, specially adapted creatures, some of which are found nowhere else. For example, caves beneath the Edwards Plateau in Texas are home to more than 40 unique species, eight of which are legally designated as endangered (Figure 6.18). In fact, karst regions provide so many benefits that the Karst Waters Institute maintains a "Top Ten List" of endangered karst ecosystems.[20]

▲ **FIGURE 6.18 CAVES ARE UNIQUE ECOSYSTEMS** Unique species, such as this endangered Texas blind salamander from Ezell's Cave National Natural Landmark in central Texas, have evolved to live in the total darkness of caves. *(Robert and Linda Mitchell Photography)*

Water Supply

About 25 percent of the world's population gets its drinking water from karst formations, and 40 percent of the U.S. population relies on water from karst terrains.[9] Carbonate rocks beneath the Edwards Plateau, discussed above, provide drinking water for more than 2 million people.

Aesthetic and Scientific Resources

Karst provides an important aesthetic resource. Rolling hills, extensive cave systems, and beautiful formations of tower karst are among the striking landscape features found in karst terrains (Figures 6.3 and 6.5). For example, the tower karst regions of China are areas of unparalleled beauty that offer stunning vistas. Caves are popular destinations for both spelunkers and tourists. Mammoth Cave National Park, Kentucky, contains the world's longest cave system and attracts about 2 million visitors each year.

Aesthetics aside, karst regions provide scientists with a natural laboratory in which to study climate change. Stalactites, stalagmites, and flowstone contain records of changes in the ratios of two important stable isotopes of oxygen (^{16}O and ^{18}O), from which changes in past cave temperatures and, therefore, climate can be reconstructed. The caves also provide an ideal environment for preserving animal remains, making them important resources to palaeontologists and archaeologists.

Unique Ecosystems

Caves are home to rare creatures that are adapted to live only in this environment. Karst-dependent species, known as *troglobites*, have evolved to live in the total darkness of caves; they include flatworms, beetles, and eyeless fish, shrimp, and salamanders (Figure 6.18). Other species, such as bats, rely on caves for shelter. Karst areas generally support a diverse ecosystem found nowhere else.

6.6 Human Interaction with Subsidence

When people live in areas of karst, subsiding ground, permafrost, or expansive soils, existing problems can be exacerbated and new ones created. People contribute to problems caused by subsidence by withdrawing subsurface fluids, excavating underground mines, thawing frozen ground, restricting deltaic sedimentation, draining wetlands, and using poor landscaping practices.

Withdrawal of Fluids

Withdrawal of subsurface fluids, such as oil, gas, and groundwater, can induce or increase subsidence.[21] Fluid pressures in sediment and rock help support the material above, much

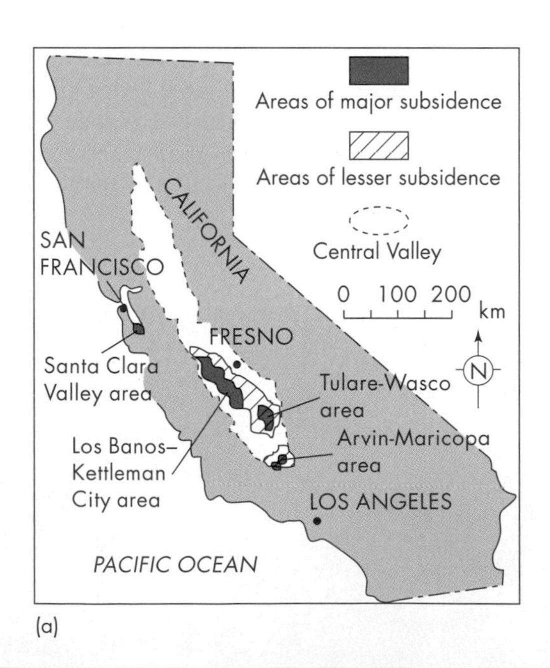

Areas of major subsidence
Areas of lesser subsidence
Central Valley
0 100 200 km
CALIFORNIA
SAN FRANCISCO
FRESNO
Santa Clara Valley area
Tulare-Wasco area
Arvin-Maricopa area
Los Banos–Kettleman City area
LOS ANGELES
PACIFIC OCEAN
(a)

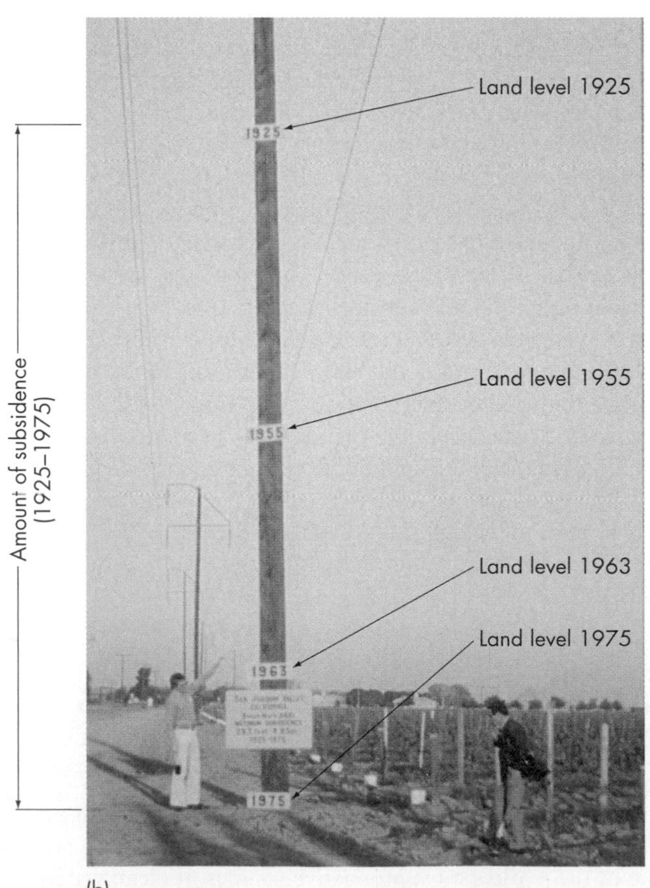

▲ **FIGURE 6.19 LAND SUBSIDENCE CAUSED BY GROUNDWATER EXTRACTION** (a) Areas of land subsidence in California resulting from groundwater removal. *(After Bull, W. B. 1973. Geological Society of America Bulletin 84. Reprinted by permission.)* (b) Subsidence in the San Joaquin Valley, California. The marks on the telephone pole are the positions of the ground surface in recent decades. The total amount of subsidence is nearly 8 m. *(Courtesy of Ray Kenny)*

as buoyancy makes a heavy object at the bottom of a swimming pool seem lighter. Removal of the fluid by pumping reduces support and causes surface subsidence.

A classic example of this phenomenon can be found in the Central Valley of California, where thousands of square kilometres of land have subsided because of the removal of groundwater for irrigation and other uses (Figure 6.19a). In one area, about 5000 km^2 of land has subsided more than 0.3 m, and the maximum subsidence is about 9 m (Figure 6.19b). As the water was mined, fluid pressure was reduced, sedimentary grains compacted, and the surface subsided (Figure 6.20).[22,23] Subsidence caused by overpumping has also been documented near Phoenix, Arizona; Las Vegas, Nevada; the Houston-Galveston area in Texas; San Jose, California; and Mexico City, Mexico.

Underground Mining

Sudden surface subsidence has accompanied or followed underground mining of coal, salt, and phosphate. Most subsidence over coal mines is caused by the failure of pillars of coal left behind to support the mine roof. With time, the pillars weather, weaken, and collapse. The roof then caves in and the land surface above the mine subsides (see the Professional Profile). In the United States more than 8000 km^2 of land, an area twice the size of Rhode Island, have subsided

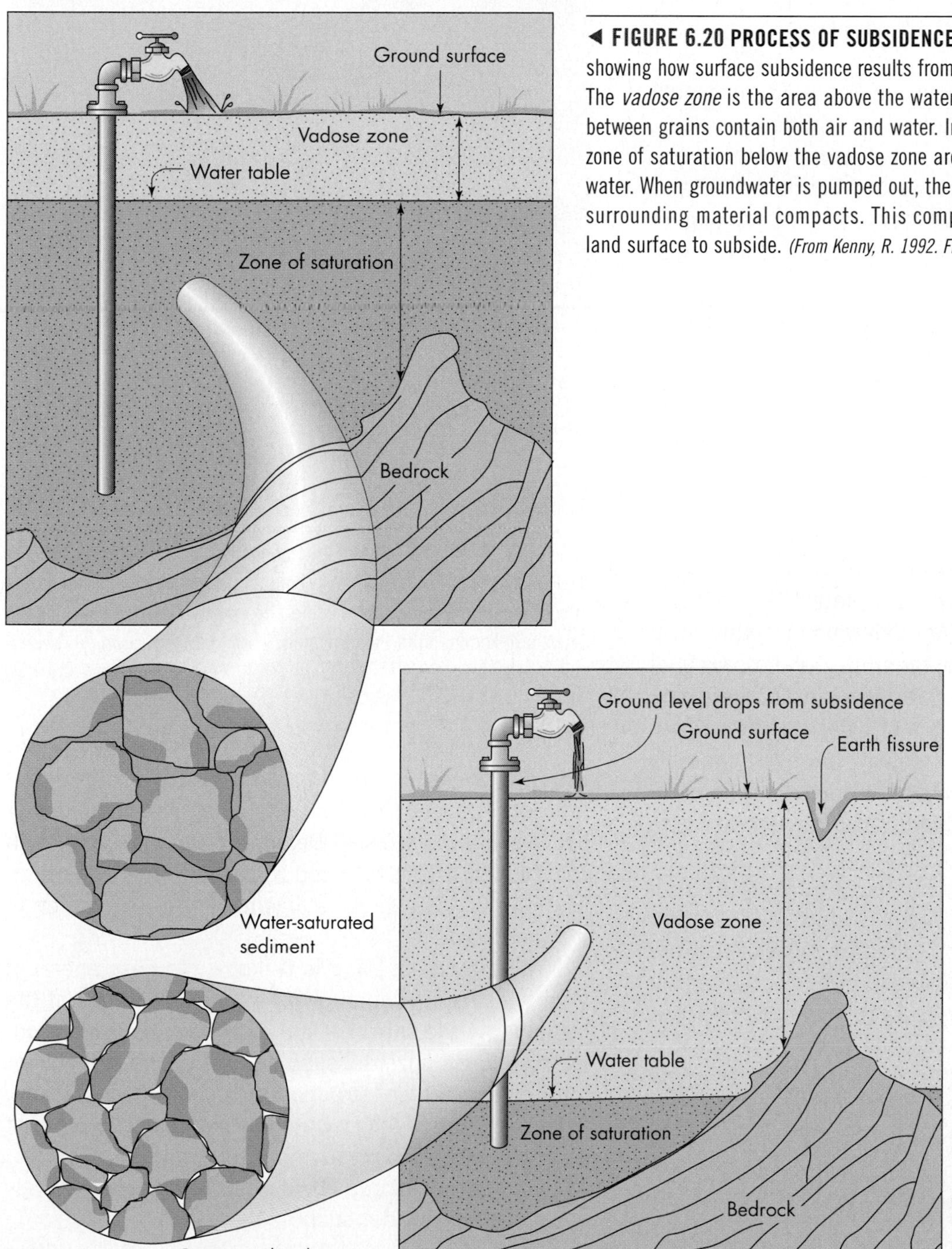

◄ **FIGURE 6.20 PROCESS OF SUBSIDENCE** An idealized diagram showing how surface subsidence results from pumping groundwater. The *vadose zone* is the area above the water table where the pores between grains contain both air and water. In contrast, pores in the zone of saturation below the vadose zone are completely filled with water. When groundwater is pumped out, the pores collapse and the surrounding material compacts. This compaction can cause the land surface to subside. *(From Kenny, R. 1992. Fissures. Earth 2[3]:34–41)*

because of underground coal mining. The subsidence continues today, long after mining ended. In 1995, a coal mine that last operated in the 1930s collapsed beneath a 600 m section of a highway in Ohio; repairs were completed three months later.[24] Although coal-mine subsidence most often affects farmland and rangeland, it has damaged buildings and other structures in urban areas, such as Scranton, Wilkes-Barre, and Pittsburgh, Pennsylvania; Youngstown, Ohio; and Farmington, West Virginia.[24,25]

Ground subsidence over mine workings is also an issue in some places in Canada, such as in Timmins, Ontario, where gold is still being mined. Many old mines, which closed long ago, were shallow but outside the town boundaries at the time. The town has since grown and expanded over the old shallow

PROFESSIONAL PROFILE

Helen Delano, Environmental Geologist

Anyone looking to build a house in Pennsylvania should carefully consider whether the site might be hazardous. "We have something for everyone," says Helen Delano, from the Pennsylvania Bureau of Topographic and Geologic Survey (Figure 6.B). "As geologists working for the State of Pennsylvania, one of our tasks is looking at where there are hazards."

One of the dangers is deadly gases, such as methane, which can migrate up from buried organic material. A more common hazard is sinkholes and subsidence related to past coal mining. Delano notes that the southwestern part of the state has been mined for coal since the mid-eighteenth century and that the shallower mines are only 15 m to 30 m below the surface.

Much information on this hazard is available from coal-mining maps, but when the maps do not provide a complete picture, relatively simple and inexpensive technology can help geologists determine whether there are any major cavities underground. Delano says that geologists sometimes insert a television camera into boreholes to get a better idea of what the subsurface geology looks like. This technology, however, can only be used at relatively shallow depths. Geophysical methods are suited for greater depths, but they are far more expensive.

Delano began her career by examining natural hazards in the Pittsburgh area. "When I first started working, I would go out and look at people's backyard problems and help them understand what was going on. I'd also collect data, trying to keep track of the scope of the problems for the state," she says.

Now she deals also with municipalities, advising them when natural hazards pose problems for building projects. "I have a folder on my desk right now for a rural community that has a proposal for a housing project over eighteenth- and nineteenth-century iron mines," Delano says.

▲ **FIGURE 6.B HELEN DELANO** Environmental geologist Helen Delano is the Pennsylvania Geological Survey contact person for local governments in southeastern Pennsylvania. Here she examines an exposure of the Gettysburg Formation in Pennsylvania. *(Photo by James Shaulis, Pennsylvania Geological Survey)*

Several options are available when a major construction project is slated for an area where subsidence is a risk. "Usually the cheapest thing to do is build your house somewhere else," Delano points out. "But when the location is just too good to pass up, there are engineering solutions, such as digging a deep foundation in firm bedrock."

The important thing is to know the risks ahead of time. "It's much, much cheaper to factor in risk at the beginning," she says. For the most part, however, studies of geologic hazards, such as subsidence, are not yet routine for small construction projects in Pennsylvania. "Most residential construction doesn't take into account geologic hazards, but as more and more of the safe, valuable land is occupied, it will become increasingly necessary to consider such dangers."

—***Chris Wilson***

mines. The collapse of old *adits* and shafts caused considerable damage to some of the newer parts of the town. The adits and shafts were filled with sand, but over the years some of the sand washed away and ceased to support the adit roofs. Subsequent mitigation involved bracing the adits with concrete. This example illustrates the danger of allowing urban expansion without recognizing a predictable hazard.

Subsidence has taken place over both solution and open-shaft salt mines. Solution mines are the source of most of our table salt. Shafts are drilled to inject fresh water into salt deposits. The dissolved salt is then pumped out of the shaft, leaving behind a cavity that may later collapse. Such collapses and subsequent surface subsidence have occurred at solution mines in Kansas, Michigan, and Texas.

Open-shaft mining is used to extract rock salt beneath Goderich, Ontario; Detroit, Michigan; and Cleveland, Ohio; and potash from sedimentary rocks beneath Saskatchewan. In the last three decades, two underground salt mines in the United States have flooded catastrophically, causing subsidence and surface damage. One, the Retsof Mine near Geneseo, New York, was once the largest salt mine in the world. Its roof collapsed in 1994, allowing groundwater to flood the mine. Two large sinkholes formed, damaging roads, utilities, and buildings.[26]

The second flooding event occurred at Jefferson Island in southern Louisiana in 1980, when an oil rig drilling for natural gas accidentally penetrated an underground salt mine. The rig was mounted on a floating barge in a small lake above a salt dome (Figure 6.21). After drilling into a mine shaft, the rig toppled over and disappeared as lake water began to drain into the mine. Within three hours, the entire lake had drained and a 90 m deep, 800 m wide subsidence crater had formed above the flooded mine. Fortunately, 50 underground miners and 7 people on the drilling rig escaped injury. The mine was a total loss, and buildings and gardens on Jefferson Island were damaged by subsidence. The structural integrity of salt mines is of concern because the U.S. Strategic Petroleum Reserve is stored in four Gulf Coast salt mines. A fifth mine below Weeks Island, Louisiana, was emptied of oil in 1999 because of groundwater seepage through a sinkhole.

Thawing Permafrost

People have contributed to the thawing of permafrost through poor building practices. Placement of poorly insulated buildings directly on frozen ground and burial of warm utility lines have locally thawed permafrost, causing considerable damage.[5,27]

Restricting Deltaic Sedimentation

Marine deltas require the continual addition of sediment to their surface to remain at or above sea level. People have reduced or stopped sedimentation on most delta plains by constructing upstream dams, by building levees at the sides of distributary channels, and by diverting sediment-laden river water into canals. All these practices can contribute to subsidence of the delta plain.

Draining Wetlands

People have drained wetlands for agriculture and settlement for centuries. Most of the western part of the Netherlands was drained for agriculture between the ninth and fourteenth centuries.[1] Draining of wetlands in the Untied States has caused or increased subsidence in the Florida Everglades and the Sacramento-San Joaquin Delta in California.

Some wetlands in Canada are drained to extract peat for horticultural use. The industry generates revenues of nearly $200 million per year, mainly in Alberta, Quebec, and New Brunswick. The total area of peat mined, about 17,000 ha, is small relative to the total area of wetlands in Canada (roughly 100 million ha), but the conventional mining

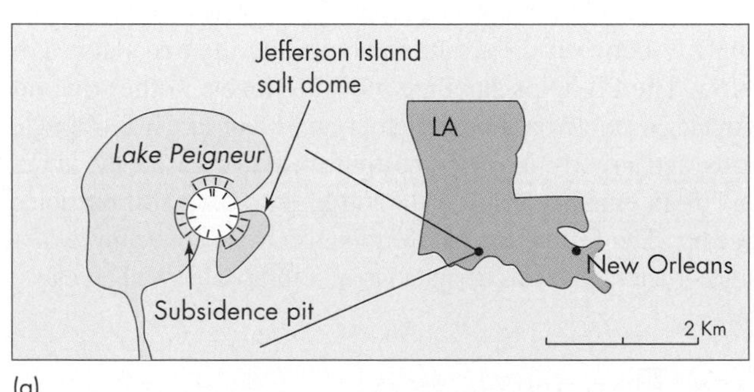

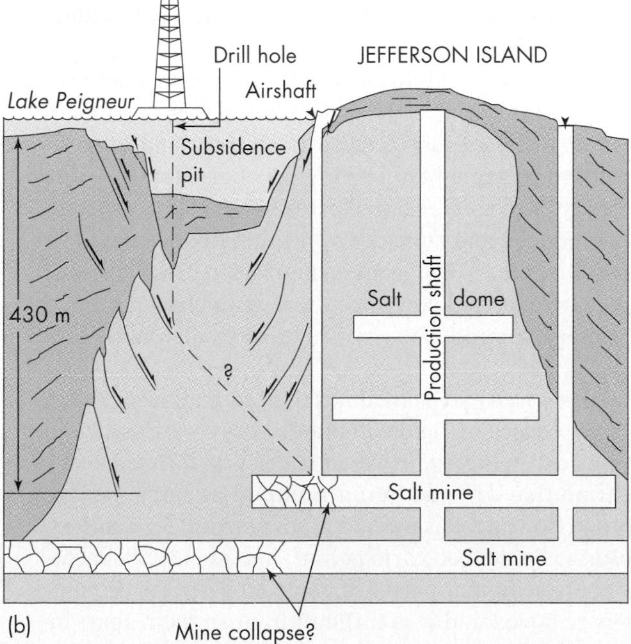

▲ **FIGURE 6.21 FLOODING AND COLLAPSE OF A SALT MINE** (a) The location of Lake Peigneur, Louisiana, and (b) an idealized diagram showing the Jefferson Island Salt Dome collapse. About 15 million m^3 of water flooded a salt mine when a shaft was penetrated during drilling.

practice is damaging and leads to a lowering of the wetland surface. A wetland to be mined is first drained. Then peat is sucked from the dry surface with a vacuum harvester. Lowering of the wetland surface results from both removal of peat and compaction of the remaining organic sediments after mining is finished.

Landscaping Expansive Soils

Problems related to shrinking and swelling of expansive soils can be amplified by poor landscaping practices. Planting trees and large shrubs close to buildings may cause damage from soil shrinkage during dry periods when plant roots pull moisture from the soil.[28] At the other extreme, planting a garden or grass that needs frequent watering close to a building can cause damage from soil swelling. Rather than maintaining the soil at a constant moisture level, watering systems commonly leave excess water in the soil. Excess water is the principal cause of damage from swelling soils.[28]

6.7 Minimizing Subsidence Hazards

It is difficult to prevent natural subsidence. However, people can take steps to minimize the risk of damage from this phenomenon.

Restricting Fluid Withdrawal We will always be faced with sinkholes in areas where carbonate bedrock is being aggressively dissolved or where groundwater levels are falling because of drought. We can, however, prevent human-caused subsidence through extraction of groundwater, oil, and gas.

Groundwater mining is the unsustainable extraction of groundwater—the removal of more groundwater by wells and springs than is replenished through infiltration of rain and surface water. The practice commonly causes irreversible subsidence. Further subsidence can be minimized only by reducing fluid withdrawals.

From the early 1900s to the mid-1970s, groundwater mining in the Houston-Galveston area of Texas was the primary cause of up to 3 m of subsidence over an area of 8300 km^2.[29] The problem prompted the 1975 Texas Legislature to create a regulatory district to issue well permits. Groundwater pumping was reduced and subsidence has greatly decreased or stopped altogether. The same cannot be said for parts of Florida, Arizona, and Nevada, where groundwater mining is continuing to produce subsidence, sinkholes, and earth fissures.

Injection wells are sometimes used to minimize or stop subsidence caused by fluid withdrawal. They were used with some success in the 1950s when water was injected at the same time that oil was being pumped at Long Beach, California. However, this method is not practical for **aquifers**, or subsurface water bodies, in porous, fine-grained sediments because the sediment particles compact after the groundwater is removed and it is difficult to push them apart by injecting fluid.[30] Further, it seems pointless to replace groundwater with water injected from the surface.

Regulating Mining The best way to prevent damage from mining-induced subsidence is to prevent mining in settled areas. Such laws are currently in place in many countries, but the old abandoned mines still pose a threat.

Preventing Damage from Thawing Permafrost Most engineering practices for building on permafrost presume the ground will remain frozen if heat from a building, pipeline, or other structure does not reach it. With recent thawing of permafrost caused by climate warming, new and more costly practices are being developed, such as placing buildings on adjustable screw jacks or lattice-like foundations to accommodate recurrent freezing and thawing of ground ice.[5]

Reducing Damage from Deltaic Subsidence Preventing subsidence of delta plains and restoring deltas to a natural state are not feasible plans. Levees will continue to prevent sediment-laden floodwaters from entering urbanized areas, and pumping systems will remove excess surface water from the areas protected by the levees. However, in undeveloped areas, levees could be removed or breached to restore the supply of sediment and freshwater necessary to reestablish marshes. Restored marshes may help protect subsided urban areas from storms and rising seas.

Stopping the Draining of Wetlands It is not possible to restore organic sediments that have dried out through the drainage of wetlands. Only proper water management of existing marshes and swamps will minimize their subsidence in the future.

Preventing Damage from Expansive Soils Proper design of subsurface drains, rain gutters, and foundations can minimize damage caused by expansive soils. These techniques improve drainage and allow foundations to accommodate some shrinking and swelling of the soil.[12] Another preventive method is to construct buildings on a layer of compacted fill that forms a barrier between the structure above and the expansive soil below. The fill helps stabilize moisture levels in the soil and provides a stable base on which to build. For larger buildings, roads, and airports, it may be cost-effective to excavate the upper part of an expansive soil or to add lime to bind soil particles together. The Edmonton Convention Centre is an example of a large structure that was designed to accommodate swelling clays.

6.8 Perception of and Adjustments to Subsidence Hazards

Perception of Subsidence Hazards

Few people living in Canada or the United States are concerned about subsidence. However, people living in areas of karst or permafrost, on deltas, or where groundwater is being mined are more likely to understand the hazard. People living in areas where sinkholes are common are generally well aware of the hazard and perceive it to pose a real risk to property.

Adjustments to Subsidence Hazards

The most appropriate adjustment to subsidence hazards is to avoid building in subsidence-prone regions. This approach is clearly not possible everywhere, because large areas of the Canadian Prairies and the western United States are underlain by swelling soil, much of Canada and Alaska has permafrost and organic sediments, and a significant portion of the eastern United States is underlain by karst. The best we can do is to identify high-risk areas in which construction should be prohibited or limited. Unfortunately, in many areas, subsidence is difficult or impossible to predict. Some methods are available, however, to identify areas of potential subsidence.

Geologic Mapping Detailed geologic maps can be made to accurately identify subsidence hazards. An understanding of the geology and surface and groundwater systems will greatly aid in determining the magnitude and areal extent of subsidence.

Surface Features In areas underlain by limestone, rock salt, and gypsum, such surface features as cracks, hummocky ground, and closed depressions should be noted. The appearance of cracks in the ground may indicate that collapse is imminent, and appropriate steps should be taken to avoid damage and injury. Cracks in the ground in arid areas may provide warning of damage from expansive soils or a falling water table.

Geophysical Surveys Knowledge of the subsurface environment is essential when decisions are to be made about where to build structures in karst terrain. The subsurface can be explored with *ground penetrating radar* (GPR) and other geophysical methods, and by drilling boreholes before construction begins. Additional geologic surveys may be needed to assess high-risk areas encountered during construction. In areas of expansive soils or permafrost, geotechnical borings and soil testing may be needed to properly design foundations.

Some American states, such as Colorado, require disclosure of the presence of expansive soils when houses are sold. Disclosure requirements apply to homebuilders, homeowners, and real estate brokers.[30] Homeowners who live in areas where subsidence has occurred in the past or is currently occurring should check the hazard coverage in their insurance policies; many insurers do not cover damage from sinkholes or mine subsidence.

Summary

Ground subsidence is caused by natural processes, human activities, or a combination of the two. Natural causes include dissolution of limestone, rock salt, or gypsum; lowering of the groundwater table or fluid pressures; thawing of permafrost; a reduction or cessation of sediment deposition on delta plains; draining of wetlands; shrinking of expansive soils; earthquakes; and deflation of magma chambers.

Solution of limestone by acidic groundwater creates a landscape of caves and sinkholes known as karst topography. Related features include disappearing streams, springs, and tower karst. Most sinkholes form by collapse of cavern roofs, often triggered by a falling water table or by groundwater mining.

During the past several decades, thawing of permafrost has become a major hazard in the Arctic. Most of the thawing is the result of twentieth-century climate warming. Thawing permafrost causes subsidence and can produce thermokarst, a terrain consisting of uneven ground with sinkholes, mounds, and lakes.

Saturated, loose sediment compacts when the water table falls or fluid pressure is reduced. A lowering of the water table may be natural or it may result from human activities, such as groundwater mining. Subsidence can be irreversible if the sediment compacts or dries out.

Surface features associated with compaction include large earth fissures and desiccation cracks.

Compaction and subsidence occur naturally on deltas. Sediment deposition during floods keeps pace with sediment compaction on deltas that are in a natural state. Construction of dams, levees, and canals interferes with sedimentation and can cause the delta surface to subside, aggravating flooding in urban areas that are not properly protected.

Expansive soils contain smectite, which swells when it becomes wet and shrinks when it dries. Wetting and drying of this clay cause the soil to expand and contract, which can cause extensive structural damage. Factors that affect the moisture content of an expansive soil include climate, vegetation, topography, and drainage.

Subsidence is a problem in most Canadian provinces, its three territories, and more than 45 states in the United States. Karst is common in many parts of Canada and the United States. Hazards include sinkhole collapse and groundwater pollution. Both permafrost and wetlands are common in Canada, Alaska, and Russia. Expansive soils are a problem primarily in the Canadian Prairies and in the western United States.

Although subsidence causes many problems, it also has benefits. About 25 percent of the world's population gets its drinking water from karst, and karst regions have important aesthetic and scientific value. Limestone caves, for example, are home to rare animals that are specially adapted to live underground.

Human beings can exacerbate subsidence problems by extracting subsurface fluids and rock, placing poorly insulated structures on frozen ground, preventing sedimentation on deltas, draining wetlands, and using poor landscaping and drainage practices on expansive soils. Natural subsidence is difficult to prevent, but human-induced subsidence may be minimized or prevented by injecting water during crude-oil production and regulating groundwater pumping and underground mining. Damage from expansive soils may be minimized by using sound construction and landscaping techniques. An understanding of the local geologic and hydrologic systems can help prevent groundwater contamination in karst areas.

Adjustments to subsidence hazards include identification of problem areas through geologic and subsurface mapping. Homeowners can protect themselves with insurance, but they must ensure that policies cover the subsidence hazards in their area.

Key Terms

aquifer (p. 176)
cave system (p. 161)
expansive soil (p. 165)
groundwater mining (p. 176)
karst (p. 158)
karst plain (p. 160)
organic sediment (p. 165)
permafrost (p. 163)
piping (p. 164)
sinkhole (p. 160)
spring (p. 162)
subsidence (p. 158)

Review Questions

1. How do caves and cave systems form?
2. What features are found in karst areas?
3. Describe the two processes by which sinkholes form.
4. What is permafrost and how has climate change affected it?
5. What keeps a delta plain from subsiding?
6. What happens to wetlands when they are drained of water?
7. Why do expansive soils shrink and swell?
8. What features might indicate the presence of expansive soils?
9. What factors influence the moisture content of expansive soils?
10. Explain how subsidence can occur during earthquakes at subduction zones.
11. Identify the types of subsidence hazards that are likely to be found in the (a) Canadian Prairies, (b) eastern United States, and (c) northern Canada and Alaska.
12. What subsidence process causes the most economic damage? Why is it so costly?
13. What factors contribute to the formation of sinkholes?
14. Why is groundwater sometimes polluted in karst terrains?
15. What conditions were responsible for the catastrophe caused by Hurricane Katrina in New Orleans?
16. How is subsidence linked to changes in climate?
17. Explain how fluid withdrawal and mining can increase subsidence.
18. How can we minimize and adjust to subsidence hazards?

Critical Thinking Questions

1. You are considering building a home in an area in British Columbia underlain by limestone and are concerned about possible karst hazards. What are some of your concerns? What might you do to determine where to build your home?
2. You work in the planning department in one of the parishes (counties) close to New Orleans. What would you advocate in the long term and in the short term to protect your community from flooding?
3. You have inherited a house built on a concrete slab in southern Saskatchewan. The soil outside the house contains smectite. What could you do to minimize damage from the shrinking and swelling of the soil?

Selected Web Resources

Karst
www.watersheds.org/earth/karst.htm Information about the relationship between water and karst

Foundations on Swelling or Shrinking Soils
http://irc.nrc-cnrc.gc.ca/pubs/cbd/cbd184_e.html From the National Research Council of Canada Institute for Research in Construction

Karst in British Columbia
www.for.gov.bc.ca/hfp/values/features/karst/index.htm From the British Columbia Ministry of Forests

Karst Waters Institute
www.karstwaters.org Information about karst water systems and the "Top Ten List" of endangered karst ecosystems

Sinkhole.org
www.sinkhole.org Information about sinkholes, with emphasis on those in Florida

Mine Subsidence Insurance
www.dep.state.pa.us/dep/deputate/minres/bmr/msipage/msi_info.htm From the Pennsylvania Department of Environmental Protection

Swelling Soil
http://geosurvey.state.co.us/Default.aspx?tabid=109 Abstracted from the Colorado Geological Survey special publication on swelling soils

Land Subsidence from Groundwater Pumping
http://geochange.er.usgs.gov/sw/changes/anthropogenic/subside From the U.S. Geological Survey, with emphasis on land subsidence in the southwestern United States

Land Subsidence
http://water.usgs.gov/pubs/circ/circ1182 Excellent U.S. Geological Survey publication on human interaction with subsidence

http://water.usgs.gov/ogw/subsidence.html Information on subsidence from the U.S. Geological Survey

Permafrost in Canada
http://gsc.nrcan.gc.ca/permafrost/index_e.php General information on permafrost from the Geological Survey of Canada

Permafrost: A Building Problem in Alaska
www.uaf.edu/coop-ext/publications/freepubs/HCM-00754.pdf Publication of the University of Alaska Fairbanks Cooperative Extension Service

CHAPTER 7

▶ **THE RED RIVER FLOOD OF 1997** Rural communities in southern Manitoba and North Dakota experienced their worst flooding in nearly 50 years in May 1997 when the Red River, swollen from melting snow, spilled over its banks and across the broad valley floor. Ring dykes were built around the town of Rosenort to keep it dry. *(Source image © Canadian Space Agency, 1997. Received by the Canada Centre for Remote Sensing. Processed and distributed by RADARSAT International under the ADRO. Interpretation by Vantage Point International in cooperation with CCRS; inset photo reproduced with the permission of the Minister of Public Works and Government Services Canada, 2007 and courtesy of Natural Resources Canada, Geological Survey of Canada. Photographer: Greg Brooks)*

River Flooding

Learning Objectives

Water covers about 70 percent of Earth's surface and is essential to life on the planet. However, water can injure and kill people and destroy property in certain situations, such as during a flood. Flooding is the most universally experienced natural hazard. Floodwaters have killed more than 10,000 people in North America since 1900, and during the past decade, property damage from flooding averaged more than $4 billion per year. Your goals in reading this chapter should be to

- Understand basic river processes
- Understand the process of river flooding and know the difference between upstream and downstream floods
- Know what geographic regions are at risk from river flooding
- Know the effects of flooding and the linkages with other natural hazards
- Recognize the benefits of periodic river flooding
- Understand how people affect the flood hazard and flood risk
- Be familiar with adjustments people can make to minimize injury and damage from river flooding

The Red River Flood of 1997

People are often surprised to learn that Winnipeg, Manitoba, has a significant flood hazard, since the Red River, which flows past the city, is normally calm and the valley is flat and distant from any mountainous area. Storms that bring precipitation to Manitoba in the fall and winter are formed thousands of kilometres away in the Gulf of Mexico and Pacific Ocean. The Red River basin, however, is large, and during some winters heavy snowpacks accumulate in the upper parts of the watershed.

The snowpack in the spring of 1997 was particularly heavy, and in May warming temperatures accompanied by rain melted the accumulated snow. The river rose slowly, but relentlessly. Despite frenzied efforts to strengthen and raise existing dykes and to build new ones, the river spilled across the broad valley floor to depths of many metres, creating a vast temporary lake nicknamed the "Red Sea." At the peak of the flood on May 4, the lake covered 2560 km^2 of southern Manitoba and extended across parts of North Dakota. In Canada, more than 7000 military personnel were mobilized for 36 days to assist in strengthening dykes and in relocating nearly 25,000 evacuees. Many communities were under water or cut off from surrounding areas. Some communities were spared, however, because the hastily raised dykes held the water out. Most important, Winnipeg stayed dry because the Red River Floodway, constructed at considerable cost after an earlier flood, routed the peak flows around the city.

The flooding was the worst in nearly 50 years; three people drowned and damage totalled $815 million. But the 1997 flood is only one of many damaging floods that have occurred in the Red River Valley in the past 100 years. A similar flood in the spring of 1950 lasted 51 days and forced the evacuation of 60,000 people in Manitoba; nearly 10 percent of Winnipeg was inundated during this event. Other damaging Red River floods occurred in 1904, 1916, 1922, 1923, 1960, 1966, 1969, 1970, 1974, 1979, 1984, 1986, and 2006.[1,2]

Geology plays an important role in Red River flooding. Most of the valley is underlain by clayey sediment deposited in a vast Pleistocene lake known as glacial Lake Agassiz. The *permeability* of the clay is low; consequently, rain and floodwaters do not seep into the ground as they would in other settings. Instead, water accumulates on the land surface.

Floodway
Canal d'évacuation

Winnipeg

Brunkild Dike Extention
Prolongement de la
digue Brunkild

Red River
Rivière Rouge

30 km

Pleistocene glaciation is responsible for another condition that makes the Red River Valley vulnerable to flooding. An ice sheet covered most of Canada, including Manitoba, and North Dakota as recently as 13,000 years ago, during the late *Pleistocene*. That ice sheet depressed the underlying crust by several hundred metres. The centre of loading, or *isostatic depression*, was north and northeast of southern Manitoba. The amount of crustal depression decreased in a southerly direction into the United States. The load imposed by the ice sheet was removed when Manitoba was deglaciated 11,000 to 13,000 years ago. Removal of this load caused the land to *rebound*, with progressively greater uplift to the north, toward the centre of loading of the former ice sheet. This process is still going on, although much more slowly than during deglaciation. The net effect of the rebound is a very small tilting of the land surface upward toward the north, in the direction the Red River flows. The gradient of the river is thus slowly decreasing with time, making it progressively more difficult for the river channel to contain floodwaters.

The 1997 Red River flood has great significance to Canada and other countries. Flooding is our most common natural hazard, yet we have been slow to recognize the benefits of restricting development on **floodplains**. Changes in land use, especially urbanization, have increased flood risk along thousands of streams and rivers in towns and cities across Canada. The best way to reduce and minimize this risk is simple: don't build on floodplains.

7.1 An Introduction to Rivers

Water evaporates from Earth's surface, primarily from the oceans; it exists as a gas in the atmosphere; and it precipitates on oceans and on the 30 percent of Earth's surface that is land. Some of the water that falls on land as rain and snow infiltrates into the ground or returns to the atmosphere through evaporation and transpiration by plants. Much of the water that falls on land, however, returns to the oceans via surface flow along paths determined by the local topography.

Surface flow, referred to as *runoff,* finds its way to small **streams**, which are *tributaries* of larger streams or **rivers**. Local usage differs as to what a creek, brook, stream, and river are. Geologists, however, commonly use the term *stream* for any body of water that flows in a channel. The region drained by a single stream is variously called a **drainage basin**, *watershed,* river basin, or *catchment* (Figure 7.1a).

One important characteristic of a river is the slope of the surface over which it flows, or its *gradient.* The gradient of a river is determined by calculating the drop in elevation of the channel over some horizontal distance and is commonly expressed in metres per kilometre or as a dimensionless number (elevation drop in metres divided by horizontal distance in metres). In general, the gradient of a river is greatest in its *headwaters*, decreases downstream, and is lowest at the river mouth, which is its *base level.* The base level of a river is the lowest elevation to which it may erode. Generally, this elevation is at or near sea level, although a river may have a temporary base level, such as a lake. A graph showing downstream changes in a river's elevation is called a *longitudinal profile* (Figure 7.1b).

The valley of a river is steeper-sided and narrower in its headwaters than near the river mouth, where a wide floodplain may be present (Figure 7.1c, 7.1d). At higher elevations, the steeper gradient of the river facilitates erosion and downstream transfer of sediment.

River valleys have different forms in formerly glaciated mountain areas than in mountains that have not been glaciated. Many valleys in glaciated mountains have a U-shaped cross-sectional profile—the equilibrium form that results from lengthy erosion by valley glaciers (Figure 7.2a). In contrast, most river valleys in nonglaciated mountain landscapes have V-shaped cross-sections produced by fluvial erosion and mass wasting (Figure 7.2b).

Material Transported by Rivers

Rivers move not only water but also a tremendous amount of material. This material, called the *total load,* consists of bed load, suspended load, and dissolved load. *Bed load* comprises particles of sand and gravel that slide, roll, and bounce along the channel bottom in rapidly moving water. It constitutes less than 10 percent of the total load of most rivers. *Suspended load* comprises mainly silt and clay particles carried in suspension above the riverbed. It accounts for nearly 90 percent of the total load of most rivers and gives them a muddy appearance during periods of high flow. *Dissolved load* comprises electrically charged atoms or molecules, called *ions,* that are carried in solution in the water. Most dissolved load is derived from chemical weathering of rock and sediment in the drainage basin. Ions in discharging underground springs, sewage, and chemical effluent can be a significant part of the dissolved load of some rivers.

River Velocity, Discharge, Erosion, and Sediment Deposition

Rivers are important agents of erosion and sediment deposition and play a major role in sculpting our landscape (Figure 7.2). The velocity of water changes along the length of a river, affecting channel characteristics and both erosion and sediment deposition. Hydrologists combine measurements of flow velocity and cross-sectional area of the flow (A) to determine **discharge** (Q), a more useful indicator of stream flow than velocity alone (Figure 7.3).

Discharge is the volume of water moving through a cross-section of a river per unit of time and is commonly reported in units of cubic metres per second. It is calculated by multiplying the cross-sectional area of the water in the channel by the flow velocity.

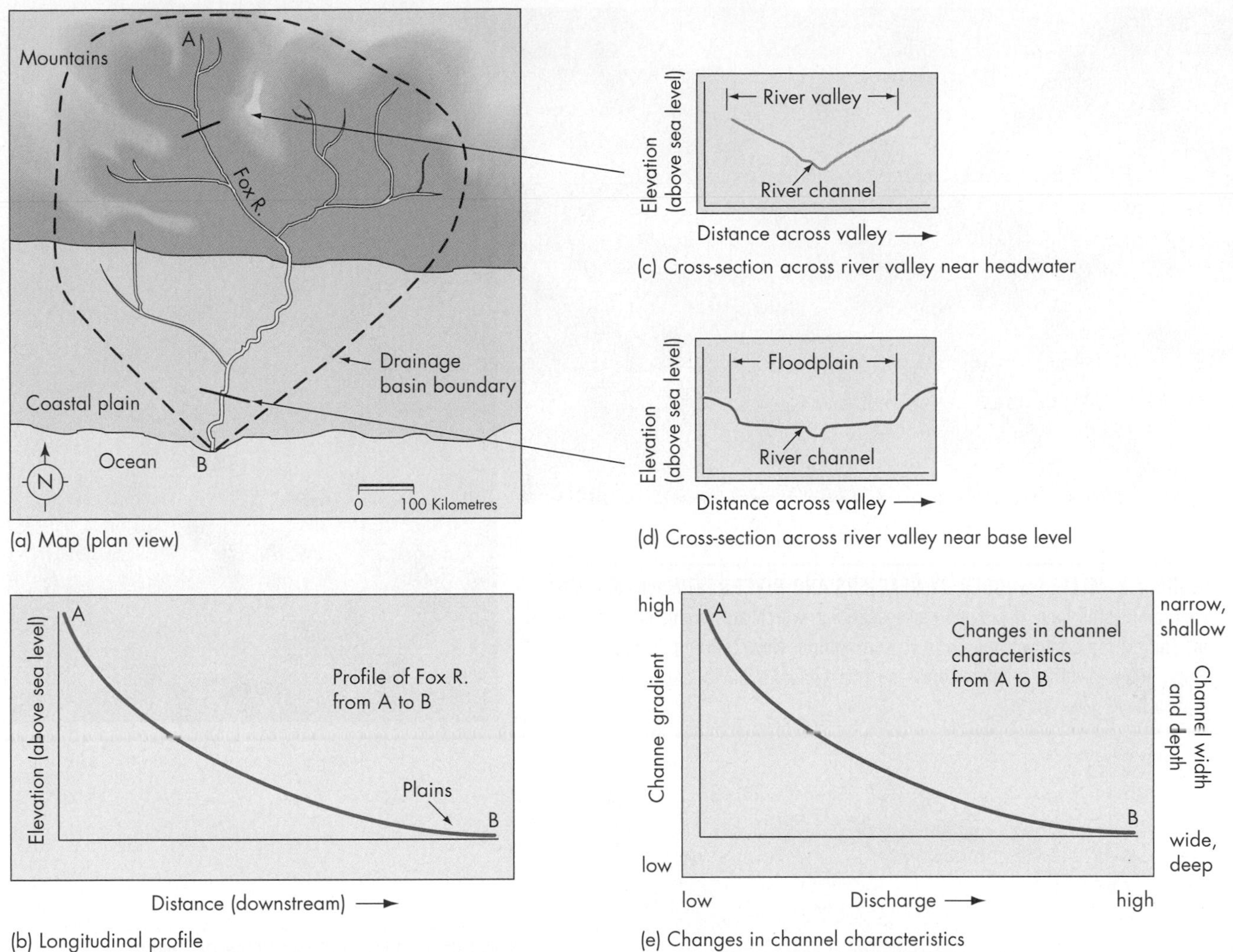

▲ **FIGURE 7.1 DRAINAGE BASIN MORPHOLOGY** (a) The drainage basin, or watershed, of the hypothetical Fox River is delineated by a black dashed line. (b) The longitudinal profile of Fox River from point A at the head of the river to point B at its mouth; note that the vertical scale is greatly exaggerated. (c) A cross-section of the river valley near its headwaters; the valley is steep-sided and the valley floor is narrow. (d) A cross-section of the valley on the coastal plain near the river mouth; the valley floor is broad and the valley walls more gentle than in the headwaters. (e) Empirical relations among channel width, channel depth, and discharge, which govern changes in channel form and discharge along a river.

Flow velocity and cross-sectional area are related. If the cross-sectional area decreases, the velocity of the water must increase for discharge to remain constant. You can prove this with a garden hose. Turn on the water and observe its velocity as it leaves the hose. Then put your thumb partly over the end of the hose, thereby reducing the area of outflow. You will observe an increase in flow velocity. This principle explains why the velocity of a river is higher in a deep narrow canyon than in an area where the flow is less confined.

The gradient of a river decreases where it flows from mountains onto a plain or into an ocean or lake. In these places, the river builds a fan-shaped body of sediment on land referred to as an *alluvial fan* (Figure 7.4), or a triangular or irregularly shaped deposit in water called a *delta* (Figure 7.5).

The flood hazard on alluvial fans and deltas is different from that on the floodplain of a river. At the head, or *apex*, of an alluvial fan or delta, the river commonly enters a system of *distributary channels* that carry parts of the discharge to different parts of the fan or delta. These channels may change position rapidly during a single flood or from one flood to the next, creating a hazard that is difficult to predict.[3] For example, a large recreational vehicle (RV) park on the delta of the Ventura River in southern California flooded four times in the 1990s (see Case Study 7.1). The RV park had been constructed across an old distributary channel. Engineers studying potential flood hazards at the site before the RV park was built had not recognized that the building site was located on a river delta.

Channel Patterns and Floodplain Formation

Most features of rivers result from the interaction of flowing water and moving sediment. As seen from an airplane, streams and rivers have different **channel patterns**. Three patterns are common: *braided,* with a large number of

(a)

(b)

▲ **FIGURE 7.2 VALLEYS ERODED BY GLACIERS AND RIVERS** (a) Most valleys in glaciated mountains have U-shaped cross-sections, which are produced by glacial erosion. The example shown here is in Milford Sound, New Zealand. *(John J. Clague)* (b) A valley in Nepal with a V-shaped cross-section, typical of fluvial erosion and mass wasting. *(© Gernot Koller 2003)*

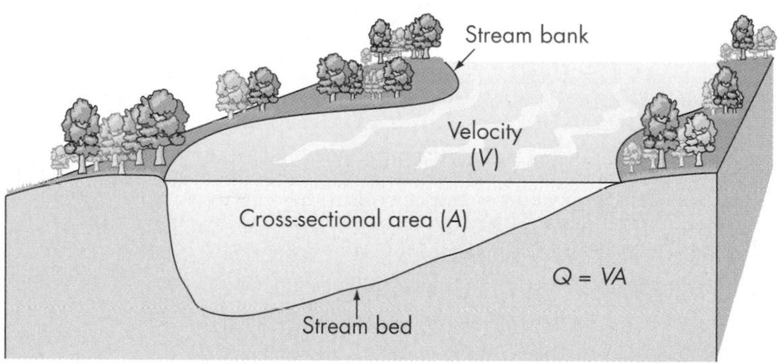

◄ **FIGURE 7.3 CALCULATING STREAM DISCHARGE** The discharge of a stream (*Q*) is determined by multiplying the velocity of the flow (*V*) times the cross-sectional area (*A*) of the water in the channel.

◄ **FIGURE 7.4 ALLUVIAL FAN IN DEATH VALLEY** This alluvial fan formed where a stream leaves a steep canyon and flows onto the floor of Death Valley. Infrequent floods discharge water onto the white salt flats seen in the upper left. *(Michael Collier)*

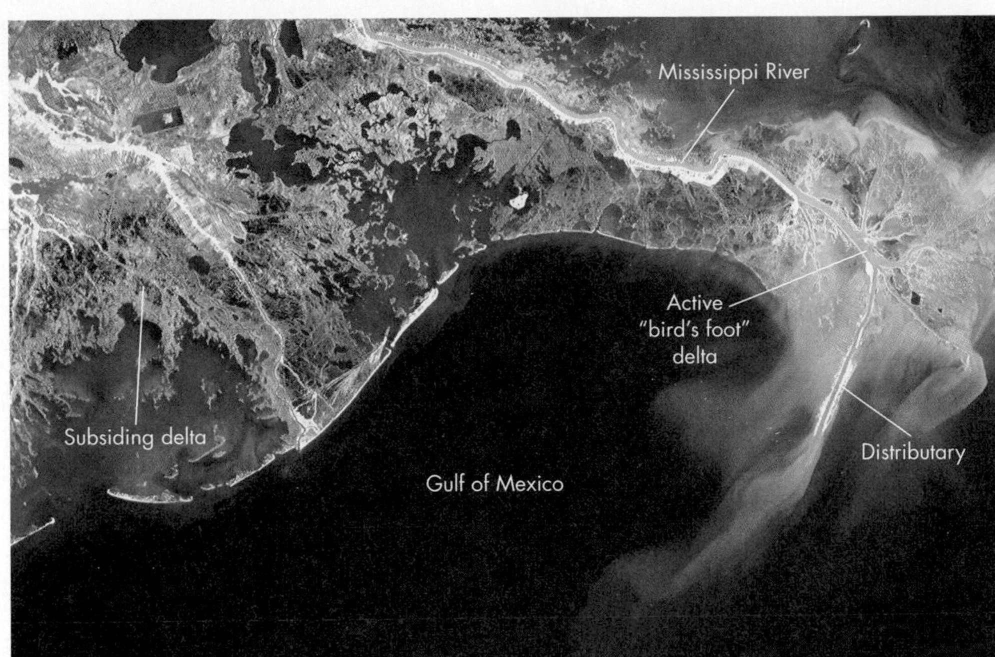

◄ **FIGURE 7.5 MISSISSIPPI DELTA** In this false-colour satellite image of the Mississippi River delta, vegetated areas are pink and grey, sediment-laden waters are white and light blue, and deep water is darker blue. The main, active distributary channel is the light-blue irregular line that extends from the top left centre of the image to the middle right edge. At the far right, the channel divides into several secondary distributaries that have the shape of a "bird's foot." The width of the image is about 180 km. *(LANDSAT image by U.S. Geological Survey/Courtesy of John S. Shelton)*

intersecting active channels; *anastomosing*, with two or more channels and intervening stable islands or bars; and *meandering*, with a single channel shaped like a snake. Braided floodplains (Figure 7.6) have numerous unvegetated sand and gravel bars that divide and reunite the main channel, especially during low flow. Overall, braided channels tend to be wide and shallow compared with meandering channels. A river is likely to have a braided pattern if it has an abundant coarse bed load and large diurnal variations in discharge. These conditions are found in areas where the land is rising because of tectonic processes and where rivers receive abundant water and sediment from glaciers.

(a)

(b)

◄ **FIGURE 7.6 BRAIDED RIVER** (a) The braided pattern of Hopkins River, near Lake Ohau on the South Island of New Zealand, is formed by shallow channels flowing around and across numerous gravel bars. The river's coarse bed load is derived from the Southern Alps, seen in the distance. *(© davidwallphoto.com)* (b) Surface view of a braided channel system below the toe of Fox Glacier in New Zealand, with intertwined gravelly channels. The distance across the channel in the lower left is about 15 m. *(John J. Clague)*

7.1 CASE STUDY

Flooding on the Delta of the Ventura River

In 1905 philosopher George Santayana said, "Those who cannot remember the past are condemned to repeat it." Scholars may debate the age-old question of whether or not cycles in human history repeat themselves, but the recurrent nature of such natural disasters as floods is beyond dispute.[4] Better understanding of the past behaviour of a river is therefore helpful in estimating its present and future flood potential. Consider the February 1992 Ventura River flood in southern California (Figure 7.A). The flood severely damaged the Ventura Beach Recreational Vehicle (RV) Resort, which had been constructed a few years earlier. Discharge increased from less than 25 m^3/s to a peak of 1322 m^3/s in only four hours. This rate of flow is approximately twice the daily peak summer discharge of the Colorado River through the Grand Canyon. It is an immense discharge for a normally small river with a drainage area of only about 585 km^2. The flood occurred during the day, and only one person was killed. Had it occurred at night, the death toll would likely have been much higher.

The *recurrence interval* of the 1992 flood is approximately 22 years, but earlier engineering studies had suggested that the RV park would not be inundated even by a flood with a recurrence interval of 100 years. What went wrong?

- Planners did not recognize that the RV park was constructed on a historically active distributary channel of the Ventura River delta. In fact, early reports did not even mention a delta.
- Engineering models that predict flood inundation are not applicable to river delta distributary channels, where natural channel erosion and shifting are likely to occur.
- Historical documents, such as maps dating back to 1855, and more recent aerial photographs showed that the channels were not properly evaluated. Maps rendered from these documents suggest that the distributary channel passing through the RV park was present in 1855 and that it carried water in 1969, 1978, and 1982 (Figure 7.B).[5]

Clearly, the history of the Ventura River was not considered when the engineering study was done. Had it

◄ **FIGURE 7.A FLOODING OF CALIFORNIA'S VENTURA BEACH RV RESORT IN FEBRUARY 1992** The RV park was built next to a historically active distributary channel of the Ventura River. Similar floods occurred again in 1995 and 1998. The highway on the left is impassable because of the floodwaters. *(Mark J. Terrell/AP/Wide World Photos)*

been, the site would have been deemed unsafe for development, given that a historically active channel was present. Nevertheless, development permits were issued, and, in fact, the RV park was rebuilt after the 1992 flood.

A warning system developed after the 1992 disaster has, so far, been effective in providing early warning of an impending flood. Winter floods again swept through the park in 1995 and 1998. Although the warning system worked and people were successfully evacuated, both floods caused severe damage. In effect, the RV park is a "sitting duck." A move is now afoot to purchase the park and restore the land to a more natural environment—a good move!

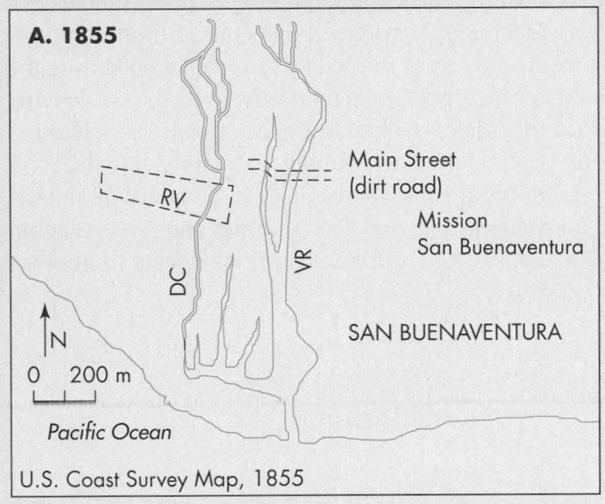

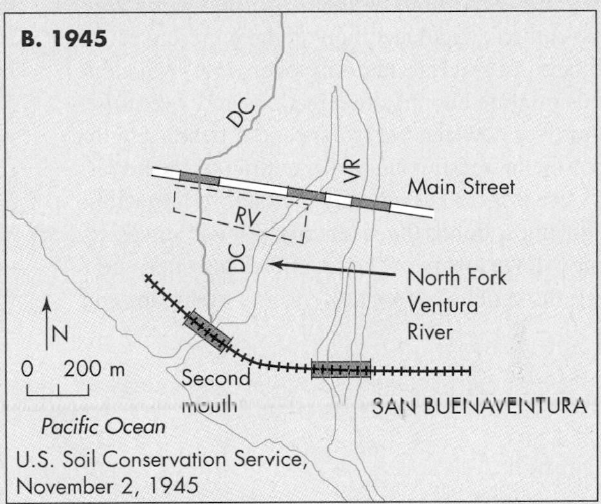

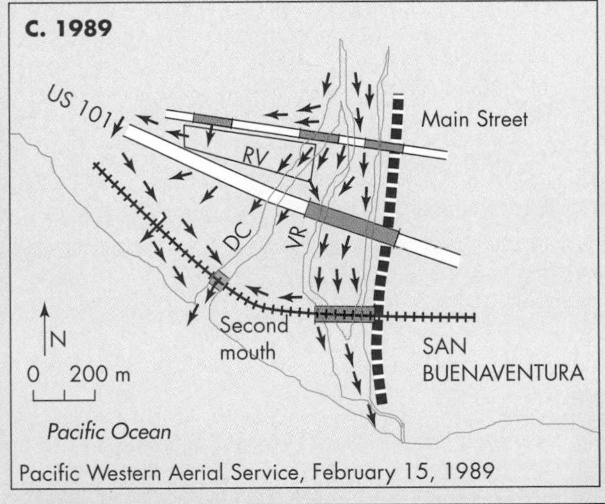

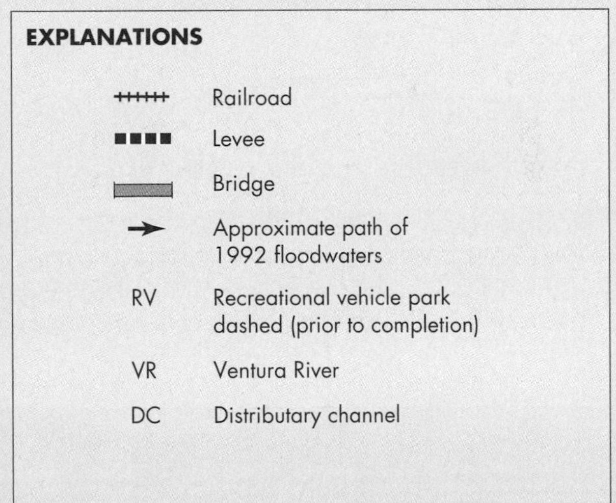

▲ **FIGURE 7.B HISTORICAL MAPS OF THE VENTURA RIVER DELTA** (a) In 1855, a small active distributary channel (DC) extended through the future site of the RV park (dashed box), joining the main Ventura River channel (VR) near the river mouth. (b) By 1945, the 1855 channel was wider and carried the flow of the North Fork of the Ventura River directly to the Pacific Ocean. A second distributary flowed through the western part of the future RV park and joined the North Fork upstream of its mouth. (c) In 1989, around the time the RV park was built, the original 1855 channel was still an active distributary. A levee had been built on the east side of the delta to protect San Buenaventura from flooding. The levee and an earthen fill elevating a rail line and U.S. Highway 101 acted as dams during the 1992 flood, increasing the depth and extent of flooding on the delta (arrows in c). *(From Keller, E. A., and M. H. Capelli. 1992. Ventura River flood of February, 1992: A lesson ignored? Water Resources Bulletin 25[5]:813–831)*

Many rivers have snaky, curving channel bends called *meanders* that migrate back and forth across the floodplain over years or centuries (Figure 7.7). Interestingly, although the meandering behaviour of rivers has been studied for a century by hydrologists, geologists, engineers, and physicists, no one is certain why rivers meander. We do, however, know a great deal about how water flows in a meandering channel.

Canoeists and rafters have long known that water moves faster along the outside of a meander bend than along the inside. The fast-moving water erodes the riverbank on the outside of the bend to form a steep slope known as a *cutbank*. In contrast, slower water on the inside of a meander bend deposits sand and sometimes gravel to form a *point bar*. Erosion of the cutbank and deposition on the point bar cause the meander bend to migrate laterally over time. Adjacent meander bends migrate in opposite directions and, over time, the path of the river between the two meander bends lengthens because of the increasing lateral separation of the bends. This process creates an increasingly unstable situation. Eventually, during a flood, the river *avulses*—it leaves its channel directly downstream of the first bend and cuts a new channel along the much shorter route to the upstream end of the second bend. During avulsion, the river abandons a looping section of the old channel, which is left as a *meander cutoff*. Lakes within the old abandoned channel are termed *oxbow lakes*. This process is important in constructing and maintaining some floodplains.

Floodplains are also built at times of *overbank flow,* when rising waters spill over the riverbank and onto the floodplain. The escaping waters deposit fine sand, silt, and clay, thus building up the floodplain. Much of the sediment transported by rivers is temporarily stored in a variety of types of bars within the channel.

Meandering and anastomosing channels commonly contain a series of regularly spaced pools and riffles (Figure 7.8). *Pools* are deep areas produced by scour at high flow, and *riffles* are shallow areas formed by sediment eroded from the pools. At low flow, pools contain relatively deep, slow-moving water and riffles have shallow, fast-moving water. Such changes in water depth and velocity along a stream create different *habitats* for organisms, increasing the diversity of aquatic life.[6] For example, fish may feed in riffles and seek shelter in pools, and pools have different types of insects from those found in riffles.

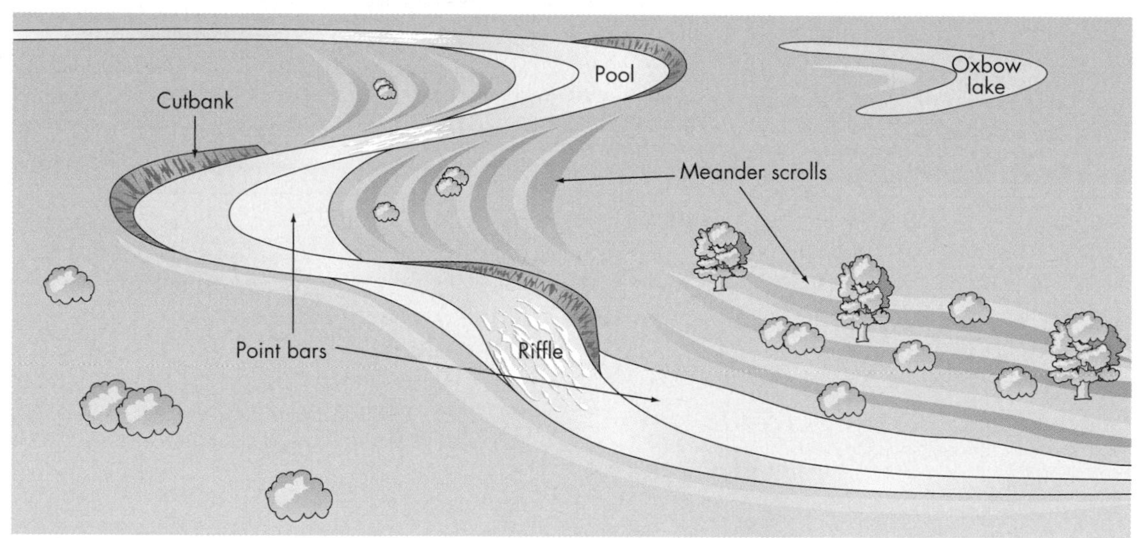

◀ **FIGURE 7.7 MEANDERING RIVER** (a) The important features of a meandering river. Migration of meander bends is commonly indicated by low, curving, vegetation-covered ridges, called *meander scrolls*. The scrolls adjacent to the point bar in the left centre of the figure indicate that the stream migrated from right to left. (b) The Waiau River, South Island New Zealand. Note the unvegetated point bars directly downstream of meander bends. *(© davidwallphoto.com)*

◄ **FIGURE 7.8 POOLS AND RIFFLES** A pool-riffle sequence in Sims Creek near Blowing Rock, North Carolina. Deep pools lie under the smooth, reflective water surface in the centre and lower right of the photograph; shallow riffles lie under the rough, nonreflective water in the far distance and left foreground. *(Edward A. Keller)*

Having presented some of the characteristics and processes of water flow and sediment transport in rivers, we will now discuss the process of flooding in greater detail.

7.2 Flooding

Overbank flow is termed **flooding** (Figure 7.9). The magnitude and duration of a flood are determined by the amount, areal distribution, and duration of precipitation in the drainage basin; the rate at which the precipitation soaks into the ground; the presence or absence of a snowpack; the air temperature; and the speed at which surface runoff reaches the river. The amount of moisture in the soil at the time precipitation starts also plays an important role in flooding. Water-saturated soil is like a wet sponge that cannot hold additional moisture. Flooding will probably occur if heavy rains fall on ground that is already saturated. Dry soil may be able to absorb considerable moisture and thus reduce or prevent flooding. Flooding can also result from the piling up of water behind ice jams on rivers, the damming of rivers by landslides, and the sudden draining of lakes impounded behind moraines, glaciers, and landslide deposits[1,7] (Figure 7.10).

Floods can happen at different times of the year. Their timing depends mainly on the size of the watershed and on regional climate. Many large rivers in North America, for example the Mississippi and Fraser, flood only in late spring following winters marked by abnormally heavy snowfall. Thick snowpacks melt rapidly during extended periods of unusually warm weather, sometimes accompanied by heavy rain. The watersheds of large rivers are too big to be significantly influenced by local thunderstorms or by single cyclonic storms that occur at other times of the year. Mid-size rivers also can carry peak flows during late spring, although those in wet temperate areas, such the Pacific Coast of northwestern North America, commonly flood in the fall during periods of

◄ **FIGURE 7.9 THE 1894 FRASER RIVER FLOOD** The town of Chilliwack, British Columbia, at the peak of the Fraser River flood in May 1894. The Fraser River has flooded many times, but the 1894 flood is the largest on record. It was caused by the melt of an unusually heavy snowpack in southern British Columbia during hot, wet spring weather. *(British Columbia Archives, A03900, S. J. Thompson, 1894)*

▲ **FIGURE 7.10 OUTBURST FLOOD FROM A MORAINE-DAMMED LAKE** Oblique aerial view of the breached moraine at Nostetuko Lake in the southern Coast Mountains of British Columbia. In 1983, an ice avalanche from the retreating toe of Cumberland Glacier plunged into Nostetuko Lake, generating waves that overtopped and breached the moraine. The sudden release of 6 million m^3 of water produced a short-lived although huge flood in the valley below. *(Stephen G. Evans)*

heavy rain after the first snow has fallen. Ice-jam floods are common in northern areas of Canada and occur when rivers freeze in the fall or, more commonly, during *break up* in spring (Figure 7.11). Small streams can flood at any time of the year: in early spring, during mid-winter thaws, or during summer thunderstorms. Small streams reach flood stage very quickly if heavy, warm rain falls on frozen ground or snow. Severe flooding can also result from the intense rainfall that accompanies hurricanes and cyclones and from the surges created by these severe storms (Chapter 9 and the Survivor Story). Human modification of rivers and floodplains, discussed in section 7.7, can also affect river processes and flooding.

A flood begins when a stream achieves *bankfull discharge*—the discharge at which water first flows out of the channel. *Flood discharge* can also be defined as the level of the river surface at a point, or its *stage*. A graph showing changes in discharge, water depth, or stage over time is called a *hydrograph* (Figure 7.12).

The term *flood stage* is frequently used to indicate that a river has reached a level likely to cause property damage. This definition is subjective—the elevation of a river at flood stage depends on human use of the floodplain.[8] The relations among stage, discharge, and recurrence interval of floods are described and illustrated in Case Study 7.2. The **recurrence interval** of a flood of a particular magnitude is the average time between events of that magnitude.

Upstream and Downstream Floods

Floods can be further characterized as upstream and downstream floods. *Upstream floods* occur in the upper parts of drainage basins and in small tributary basins of a larger river. They are generally produced by intense rainfall of short duration over a small area.

Floods that are sudden and involve a large increase in discharge are called *flash floods*. Peak discharge of flash floods can be reached in less than 10 minutes. This type of flooding is most common in arid and semi-arid environments, in areas with steep topography or little vegetation, and following breaks

◄ **FIGURE 7.11 ICE-JAM FLOODING** An upstream view of an ice jam along the Mackenzie River at Fort Simpson, Northwest Territories, on May 3, 1989. The ice jam is 1200 m wide at this site. It extended more than 30 km upstream along a tributary of the Mackenzie River. Note the flooding adjacent to the buildings along the riverbank. *(Courtesy of Water Survey of Canada, Fort Simpson, NWT)*

SURVIVOR STORY

Flooding from Hurricane Hazel

The worst flood disaster in Canadian history occurred in 1954, when Hurricane Hazel struck Toronto.

As the storm approached Ontario from the Caribbean on October 13, 1954, it showed signs of weakening. It had crossed the Allegheny Mountains and its wind velocities were rapidly falling off. However, the warm, moisture-laden air came in contact with a cold front lying over southern Ontario, producing record rainfall. From the morning of October 14 to midnight on October 15, about 210 mm of rain fell on the watersheds of several streams in Toronto.

Streams in the municipality are characterized by steep slopes with little natural storage capacity. Thus, even under the best of conditions, the intense rainfall from Hurricane Hazel would have caused flooding. In this case, the situation was made worse by already saturated soils. Autumn rainfall had been unusually heavy and had soaked the soils, thus preventing infiltration of any portion of the hurricane's downpour. Ninety percent of the rain that fell on the Humber River watershed during the hurricane left as runoff.

Hurricane Hazel caused the most severe flooding in Toronto in more than 200 years. Most of the affected floodplains had been developed by 1954, thus the flood damage was high. More than 20 bridges were destroyed or damaged beyond repair, 81 lives were lost, and nearly 1900 families were left homeless. The Humber River swept away a full block of houses on one drive alone, killing 32 residents in one hour (Figure 7.C). After the disaster, the

(a)

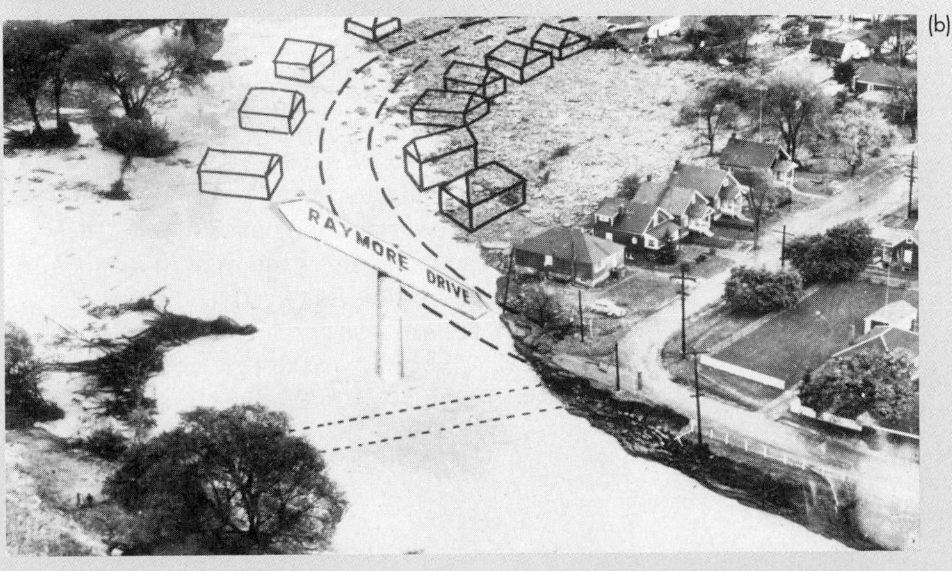

(b)

◄ **FIGURE 7.C FLOOD DAMAGE FROM HURRICANE HAZEL** The houses on Raymore Drive were destroyed by Humber River floodwaters during Hurricane Hazel on October 16, 1954. *(Courtesy of Toronto and Region Conservation Authority)*

SURVIVOR STORY *(Continued)*

Metropolitan Toronto and Region Conservation Authority undertook a comprehensive program of management of the watersheds under its jurisdiction. It acquired floodplain property and converted it to parkland.

The following account is one family's harrowing experience during the flood.

> Early in the evening of Hurricane Hazel the farm's foreman dropped in to warn them that the Marsh might flood, but that if so, they would be looked after. Like the rest of the family, 15-year-old Harry was not overly worried. "After all, we were 1500 miles away from the ocean, and the ocean was where the floods came from."
>
> Close to 9 o'clock, however, Harry, his elder brother, and a visiting friend were sent off to the local store to get candles in case the storm caused a power failure. When they reached the store they were astonished to find the doors wide open and everyone gone. They helped themselves to the candles (planning to pay later) and set out back home.
>
> At this point things became serious. The water was now running over the road, and the wind was so strong that the boys had to hold hands as they walked. They noticed that the only lights around came from their house, and realized that everyone else had cleared out.
>
> Back in the house they held a family conference and decided that with only five adults and twelve children they were not in a position to make a break for higher ground. Now the water was flowing into the house, and floating onion crates began to bang into the back door, forcing it open. Harry's father finally decided to nail the door shut with a board, which was "our first big mistake, since it meant that the water level rose higher outside the house than inside."
>
> There was two feet of water in the house and the furniture had been stacked on tables when from upstairs the family saw a neighbouring house start to move. Then as they felt a "terrific jolt" they realized that *they* were moving, floating off the pilings that formed the house's base. "The amazing part was," as Harry recalls, "all the lights in the house stayed on, because we were moving towards the power lines, and they were slackening."
>
> Then the house hit the road and a hydro pole, shearing it right off and dropping the wires on the roof, where they lay shooting sparks all over the place. For a while it seemed that the weight of the wires over one corner might tip the house over, but then, with another jolt, the house was free.
>
> "The house just took off like a boat, a real Noah's Ark. From 11:30 till 6:30 we floated aimless through the Marsh, bumping into houses, greenhouses, barns, hydro poles, everything. The area over by the Holland River had a faster current and somehow our house got caught in that current and starting spinning like a top, faster and faster, and rocking to and fro. We all would run from one side of the house to the other when it tilted, trying to balance it out. One of my younger brothers, Bastina, actually got violently sea-sick.
>
> "Until then we had been too busy to really worry and then one of the younger ones asked if we were all going to die. My mother said only one person knew that, the Lord, and we all knelt down and prayed, the Lord's Prayer. And we did get out of the current and finally came to rest against a service road near the 400, where a complete field of carrots had floated up to the surface and helped hold us in place. We were two and half miles away from where we started, with lots of side trips that had often taken us near our original place.
>
> "At that time there were still cars going along the 400 and we shouted and waved to attract their attention. I even fired off a .22, but with the noise of the wind and the water, it couldn't be heard. Then we waved bedsheets and motorists saw us, and soon an amphibious truck from Camp Borden came along. One man got out, tied a rope around his waist, and plunged in to swim towards our house. We were about 250 feet away and the water was pretty wild and cold but he made it. We knocked a window out downstairs and pulled him in. Then another man came along the rope in a canoe which kept tipping but he told us we'd be okay with the extra weight of two people in the canoe. So we made it out to the truck in seven trips, and were taken to Bradford Town Hall."

(From Hurricane Hazel by Betty Kennedy. 1979 Macmillan of Canada.)

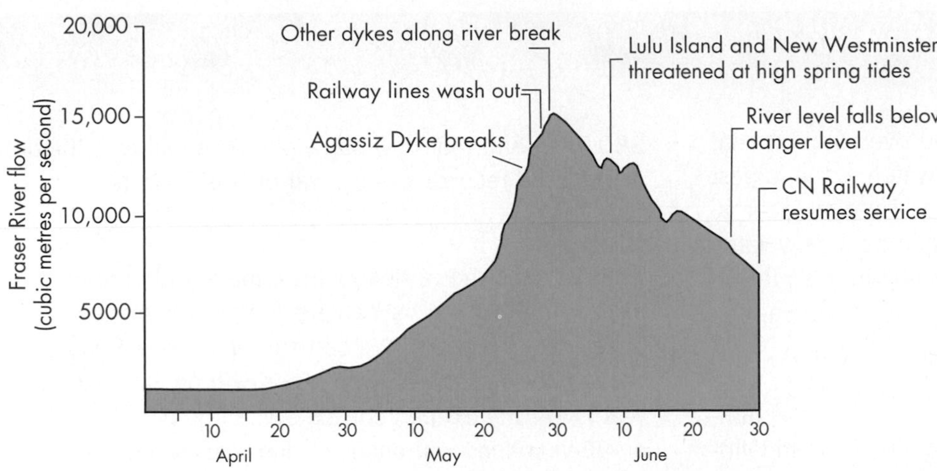

◀ **FIGURE 7.12 HYDROGRAPH** A hydrograph showing changes in the discharge of the Fraser River during its flood in 1948. The 1948 flood is the second largest on record, exceeded only by a flood in 1894 (Figure 7.9). *(After Clague, J., and R. Turner. 2003. Vancouver, city on the edge: Living with a dynamic geological landscape. Vancouver, BC: Tricouni Press)*

7.2 CASE STUDY

Magnitude and Frequency of Floods

Catastrophic floods reported on television and in newspapers are produced by infrequent, large, intense storms. Smaller floods may be produced by less intense storms that occur more frequently. All floods can be measured or estimated from data collected at stream-gauging stations (Figure 7.D). Such data show that there is a relation between the peak discharge of a flood and its average recurrence. Flood peak discharge at any station can be

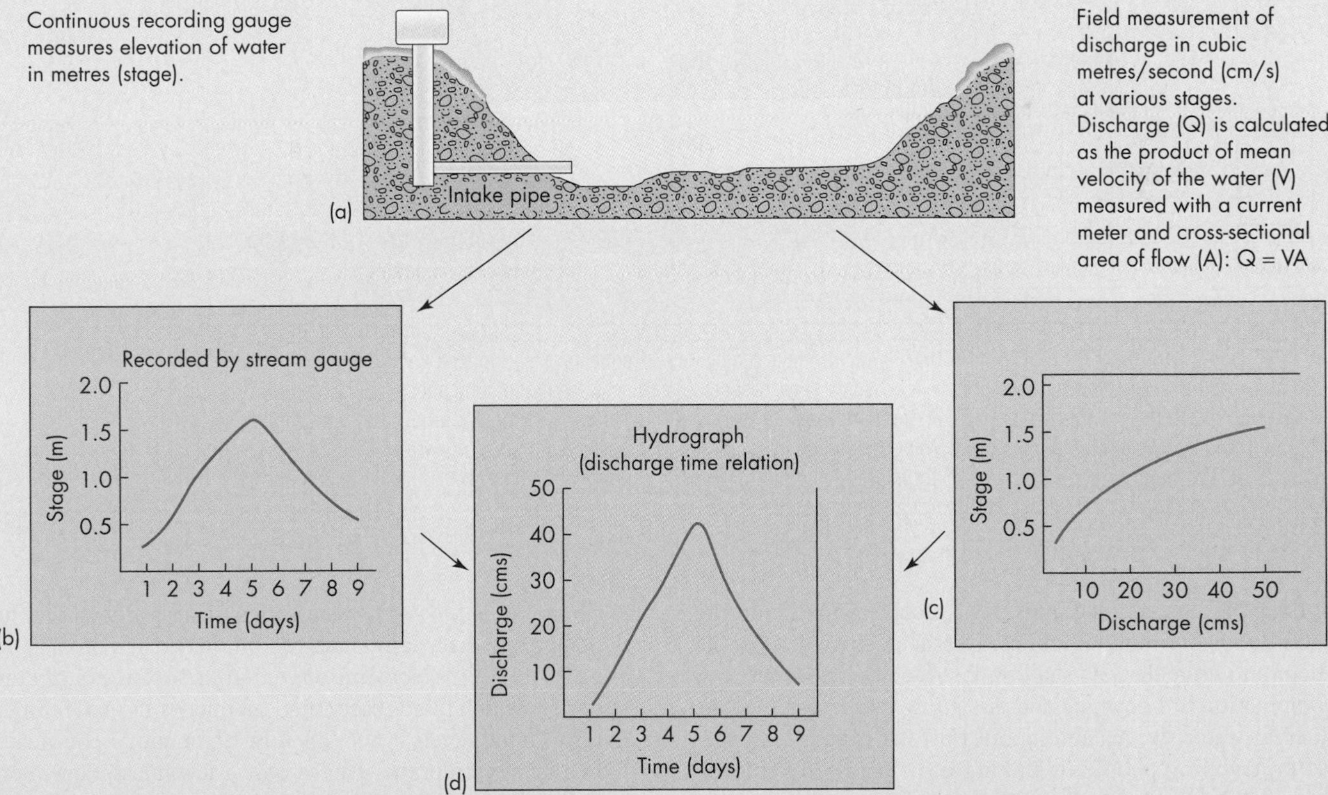

▲ **FIGURE 7.D HOW A HYDROGRAPH IS PRODUCED** A hydrograph is made by installing a recording gauge (a) to obtain a continuous record of the water level, or stage. This record is then used to produce a stage-time graph (b). Field measurements at various flows provide a stage-discharge graph (c). Graphs (b) and (c) are then combined to make the final hydrograph (d).

7.2 CASE STUDY *(Continued)*

compared with discharges measured over time at that station. Values of annual peak flow, which is the largest flow of the year, are calculated from the station records. An average recurrence interval for each peak flow value is then determined by using the following equation and plotted to create a discharge-frequency curve:

$$R = (N + 1) \div M$$

where R is the recurrence interval in years, N is the number of years of record, and M is the rank of the individual flow within the recorded years.[9] Turning to Figure 7.E, for example, we see that the highest flow for nine years of data for the Patrick River is approximately 280 m^3/s, and that flow has a rank M equal to 1 (Figure 7.E).[10] The recurrence interval of this flood is

$$R = (N + 1) \div M = (9 + 1) \div 1 = 10,$$

which means that a flood with a magnitude equal to or exceeding 280 m^3/s can be expected, on average, once every 10 years. We call this a 10-year flood. The probability that the 10-year flood will occur in any one year is 1/10 or 10 percent. Likewise, the probability that a **100-year flood** will occur in any year is 1 percent.

Extrapolating discharge-frequency curves is risky. A curve shouldn't be extended much beyond twice the number of years for which there are discharge records.

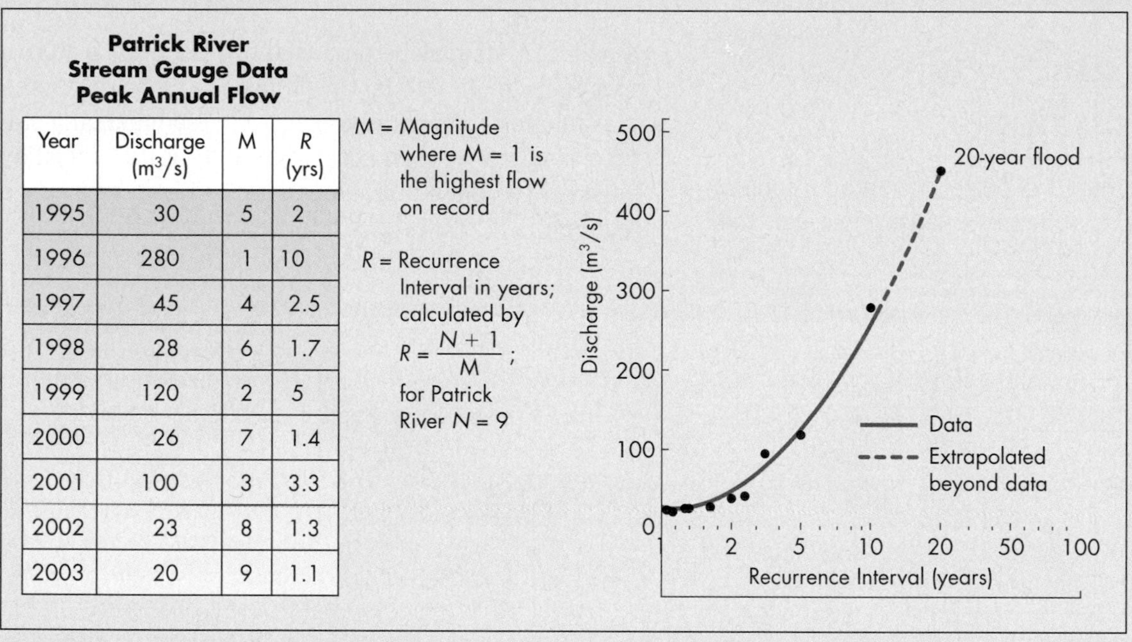

Patrick River
Stream Gauge Data
Peak Annual Flow

Year	Discharge (m^3/s)	M	R (yrs)
1995	30	5	2
1996	280	1	10
1997	45	4	2.5
1998	28	6	1.7
1999	120	2	5
2000	26	7	1.4
2001	100	3	3.3
2002	23	8	1.3
2003	20	9	1.1

▲ **FIGURE 7.E DISCHARGE-FREQUENCY CURVE** We can make a discharge-frequency graph for the Patrick River by ranking (1 through 9) the largest flow for each of nine successive years of discharge measurements in cubic metres per second (m^3/s). We then calculate the recurrence interval, or frequency, of the largest annual flow by using the formula shown above and tabulated in the table on the left. Finally, we plot the discharges as a function of the recurrence interval to produce the graph on the right. The curve can be extended or extrapolated to estimate a peak discharge of 450 m^3 per second for a 20-year flood. *(After Leopold, L. B. 1968. U.S. Geological Survey Circular 554)*

of dams, levees, and ice jams. Most people who die during flash floods are in automobiles. Deaths occur when people attempt to drive through shallow, fast-moving floodwaters. A combination of buoyancy and the strong lateral force of the rushing water sweeps automobiles off the road into deeper water, trapping people in sinking or overturned vehicles. Automobiles can be carried in water that is only 0.6 m deep.

Upstream floods can be very damaging, as illustrated by two disasters in North America during the late twentieth century, one in southern Quebec in 1996 and another in the Colorado Front Range in 1976. The Saguenay flood (in French, *le déluge du Saguenay*) was a series of flash floods that hit the Saguenay-Lac-Saint-Jean region of Quebec on July 19 and 20, 1996.[11,13] Problems started after two weeks of constant rain, which filled reservoirs, saturated soils, and brought rivers to flood levels. Then, on July 19, about 27 cm of rain fell on the region in the span of only a few hours, equivalent to the total normal monthly rainfall. More than 2 m of water ran through parts of Chicoutimi and La Baie, completely levelling an entire neighbourhood. More than 16,000 people were evacuated. Ten people died, more than 2600 homes and cottages were destroyed, and total damage exceeded $800

For example, the discharge-frequency curve for the Red River shown in Figure 7.F is based on more than 105 years of records, including the largest flood of the twentieth century in 1997. It has been extended to predict that the 200-year flood should have a peak discharge of about 5500 m^3/s, which is more than 20 percent larger than the peak discharge of the 1997 event.[11]

Data from many streams and rivers show that channels are formed and maintained by bankfull discharge, which occurs on average once every 1.5 to 2 years. In other words, a stream in a natural state overflows its banks and covers part of the floodplain with water and sediment once every year or two.

As more river flow data are collected, we can more accurately predict floods. However, designing structures for any flow with a long return period is a calculated risk because the predictions are commonly based on extrapolation of data. For many streams, the flow record is far too short to accurately predict the magnitude and frequency of large floods. Furthermore, a 50-year flood happens on the average of once every 50 years in the long term, but two 50-year floods could occur in successive years, as could two 100-year floods![12] As long as people build highways, bridges, homes, and other structures on floodplains, we should expect loss of life and property.

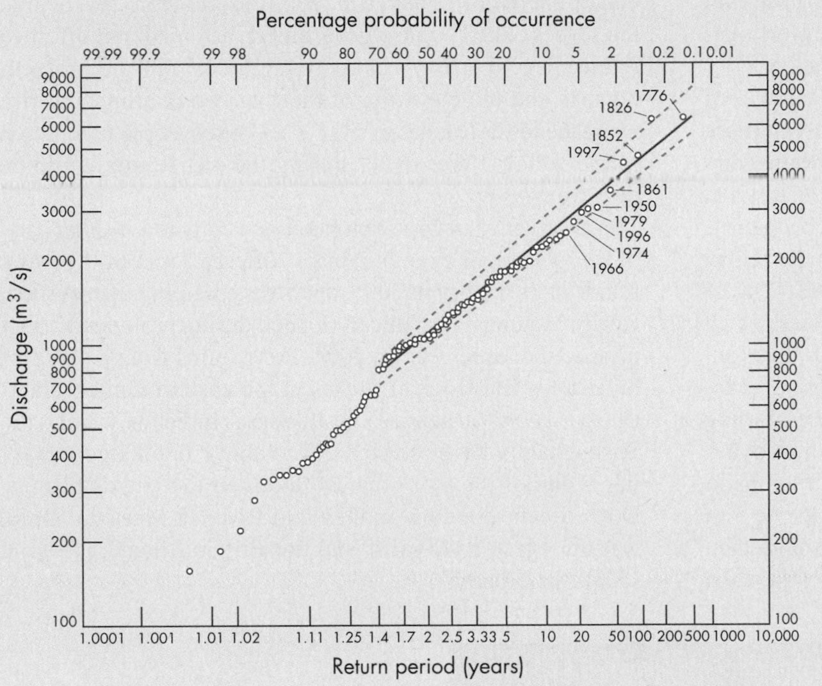

◀ **FIGURE 7.F RED RIVER DISCHARGE** Discharge-frequency curve of annual peak flows of the Red River, Manitoba, for 1776, 1826, 1851, 1875–1878, 1880–1885, and 1892–1997. A best-fit line and 95 percent confidence limits have been fitted to the data. The 10 highest flows in the record are labelled by year. Peak discharges of the four oldest floods are estimates based on historic accounts; discharges in the other years are measured flows. The 1997 flood is the fourth largest on record and has a recurrence interval of 62 years on the basis of this data set. *(After Brooks, G. R. et al. 2001. Floods. Geological Survey of Canada Bulletin 548:101–143; reproduced with the permission of the Minister of Public Works and Government Services Canada, 2007, and courtesy of Natural Resources Canada, Geological Survey of Canada)*

million; the flood was the worst in Quebec's history. A small white house in Chicoutimi (Figure 7.13) that stood unharmed while torrents of water flowed around it became the symbol of the flood. It was preserved and, despite a fire in 2002, remains standing today. An unexpected effect of the flood was the thick blanket of new clean sediments deposited over the heavily contaminated sediments at the bottom of the Saguenay and Ha! Ha! rivers. Research has shown that these contaminated sediments are no longer a threat to ecosystems.

Large flash floods occurred in July 1976 in the Colorado Front Range. They were caused by a system of thunderstorms that swept through several canyons west of Loveland and delivered up to 25 cm of rain in a few hours. The floods killed 139 people and caused more than US$35 million in damage to highways, roads, bridges, homes, and small businesses. Most of the damage and all the loss of life was in Big Thompson Canyon, where hundreds of residents, campers, and tourists were caught with little or no warning (Figure 7.14). Although the storms and floods were rare events in these Front Range canyons, comparable floods have occurred in the past and others can be expected in the future.[14,15,16]

◀ **FIGURE 7.13 FLOODING IN CHICOUTIMI** Flooding in downtown Chicoutimi, Quebec, triggered by heavy rainfall in July 1996. The floodwaters overtopped a small dam and spilled through the city. *(CP/Jacques Boissinot)*

Downstream floods affect larger areas than upstream floods and are commonly much more deadly. The worst natural disaster in human history was a flood on the Yellow River (Huang He) in China in 1931. Estimates of the number of people killed by this flood range from 850,000 to 4 million; the higher estimates include deaths caused by drowning, disease, and ensuing famines and droughts. Flooding on the same river in 1887 killed another 900,000 to 2 million people.

The root cause of the severe flood problem on the Yellow River is geologic.[17] The river carries an average of 37 kg of sediment per cubic metre of water in its lower reaches, which is a very large sediment load. A substantial amount of this silt is deposited in the lower reaches of the river where the channel becomes wider and the river's velocity decreases. Silting of the river channel has led to the construction of high dykes and levees to protect one of the most populous regions in China. Today, in some areas, the river bottom is 3 m to 5 m higher than the surrounding floodplain. Its bed is more than 10 m above the city of Kaifeng in Henan Province; there the bed of the river lies above the rooftops of the houses behind the levees. The Chinese government has made an effort to reduce severe erosion in upstream areas, but the problem persists and the elevation of the riverbed continues to rise along the lower reaches of river. The consequences of a breach in the Yellow River dykes during the wet season could be disastrous.

Destructive downstream floods are common in other parts of the world. For example, India suffered some of the worst floods in its history in 2005, and rivers draining the southern Rocky Mountains in Alberta flooded during prolonged heavy rains in the same year. In 2004, heavy rains from a series of hurricanes and tropical storms in the eastern United States caused record or near-record flooding. In Pennsylvania, the Susquehanna River crested 2.5 m above flood stage, making it one of the five greatest floods in the river's history. Downstream flooding on the Ohio River in Marietta, Ohio, was the worst in 40 years, and flooding in Atlanta, Georgia, set all-time records.

◀ **FIGURE 7.14 FLASH FLOOD IN BIG THOMPSON CANYON** Heavy rains in the Colorado Front Range in July 1976 caused a flash flood in Big Thompson Canyon that claimed 139 lives. *(U.S. Geological Survey Photographic Library, photo by R. R. Shroba)*

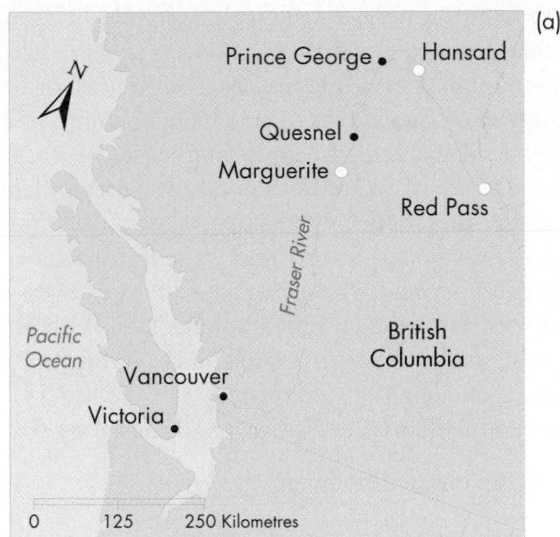

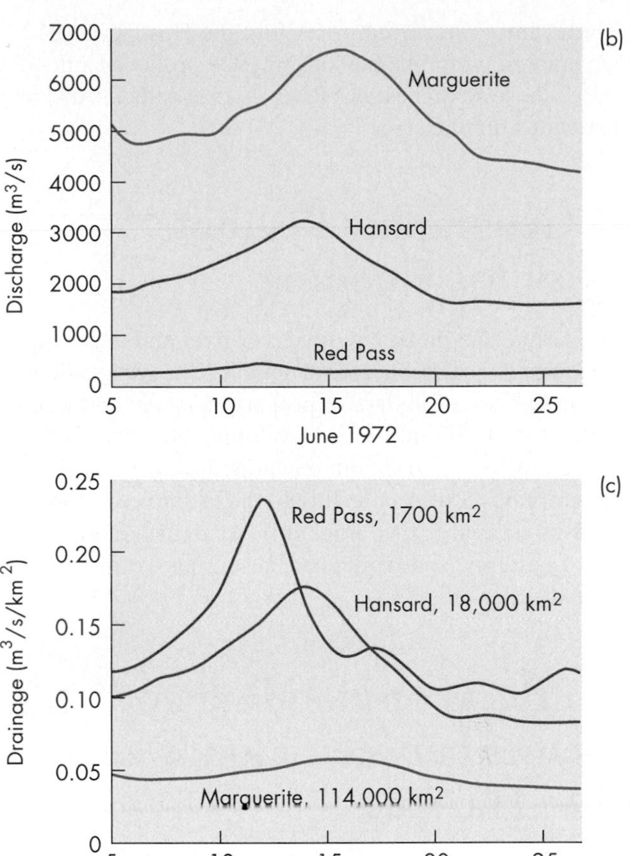

▲ **FIGURE 7.15 DOWNSTREAM MOVEMENT OF A FLOOD CREST** The floodwaters as they moved downstream along the Fraser River in southern British Columbia in June 1972. (a) A map of the area. (b) The volume of water passing Red Pass, Hansard, and Marguerite; the volume and duration of the flood increased as tributaries added more water. (c) The volume of water per unit area at the same points; flooding at Marguerite lasts much longer than flooding at Red Pass, in the headwaters of the basin.

Downstream floods inundate large areas and are produced by storms of long duration or by rapid melting of snowpacks. Flooding in small tributary basins is generally limited, but the combined runoff from thousands of slopes in tributary basins produces a large flood downstream. A flood of this kind is characterized by a large, slow rise in discharge at a particular location.[18] An example is the 1972 flood on the Fraser River in southern British Columbia (Figure 7.15a). As the flood crest migrated downstream, its peak discharge and duration increased (Figure 7.15b). Another way of looking at the flood is to examine downstream changes in discharge per unit area of the drainage basin (Figure 7.15c). This approach eliminates the effect of downstream increases in discharge and better illustrates the shape and form of the flood peak as it moves downstream.[19]

Very large, short-lived floods result from the sudden draining of glacier-, moraine-, and landslide-dammed lakes. Many of these "outburst" floods have peak discharges many times larger than normal rainfall- or snowmelt-triggered floods in the same basin (Figure 7.16). Glacier dams are notoriously unstable and can fail because of flotation of part of the dam or by drainage through tunnels at the base of the glacier. A moraine dam may fail when overtopped by waves triggered by a landslide or ice avalanche. Outburst floods and associated debris flows can be deadly when people live along their paths. A flood of debris and water caused by the failure of a moraine dam in the Cordillera Blanca of Peru in 1941 killed about 5000 people in the city of Huaraz.[20] Perhaps the largest outburst flood from a glacier-dammed lake in the

▲ **FIGURE 7.16 OUTBURST FLOOD DEVASTATION** A flood produced by the sudden draining of moraine-dammed Queen Bess Lake in British Columbia in July 1997 devastated the Nostetuko valley below the lake. The peak discharge of the flood had orders of magnitude larger than its bankfull discharge, which occurs on average about once every year or two. *(John J. Clague)*

twentieth century occurred in 1929 in the Himalayas. The sudden emptying of Lake Shyloch in 1929 produced a flood that raised the level of the Indus River 29 m at Attock, 700 km downstream from the lake.[21]

7.3 Geographic Regions at Risk for Flooding

Flooding can occur along any stream or river and thus is the most widespread natural hazard (Figure 7.17). A single flood can cause billions of dollars of property damage and large numbers of deaths (Table 7.1). Developing countries suffer much greater loss of life than developed ones because of the larger numbers of people at risk, the lack of monitoring and warning capabilities, poor infrastructure and transportation systems, and inadequate resources available for effective disaster relief.[8,22]

7.4 Effects of Flooding and Linkages between Floods and Other Hazards

Flood damage may be primary (that is, caused directly by the flood), or secondary, resulting from disruption of services and systems.[22] Primary effects include loss of life; injury; and damage to farms, homes, buildings, railroads, bridges, roads, and other engineered works from flowing water, debris, sediment, and inundation. Floods can also remove or bury soil and vegetation. Secondary effects include pollution, hunger, disease, displacement of people, and losses of services and income. Failure of wastewater ponds, treatment plants, sanitary sewers, and septic systems may contaminate floodwaters with disease-causing microorganisms. For instance, record rainfall in southern New England in June 1998 caused partially treated sewage to float into Boston Harbor, forcing closure of many areas of Rhode Island's Narragansett Bay to swimming and shellfish harvesting.

Several factors affect the damage caused by floods:

- Land use on the floodplain
- Extent, height, and strength of dykes
- Depth and velocity of floodwaters
- Rate of rise and duration of flooding
- Season of the year of flooding
- Amount and type of sediment deposited by floodwaters
- Effectiveness of flood forecasting, warning, and evacuation

Damage is far greater on floodplains that have commercial and residential development than on floodplains that are used for farming, ranching, and recreation. Flooding during the growing season may damage or destroy crops, whereas the same flooding during winter months will be less damaging. Along large rivers, flood forecasts by Environment Canada

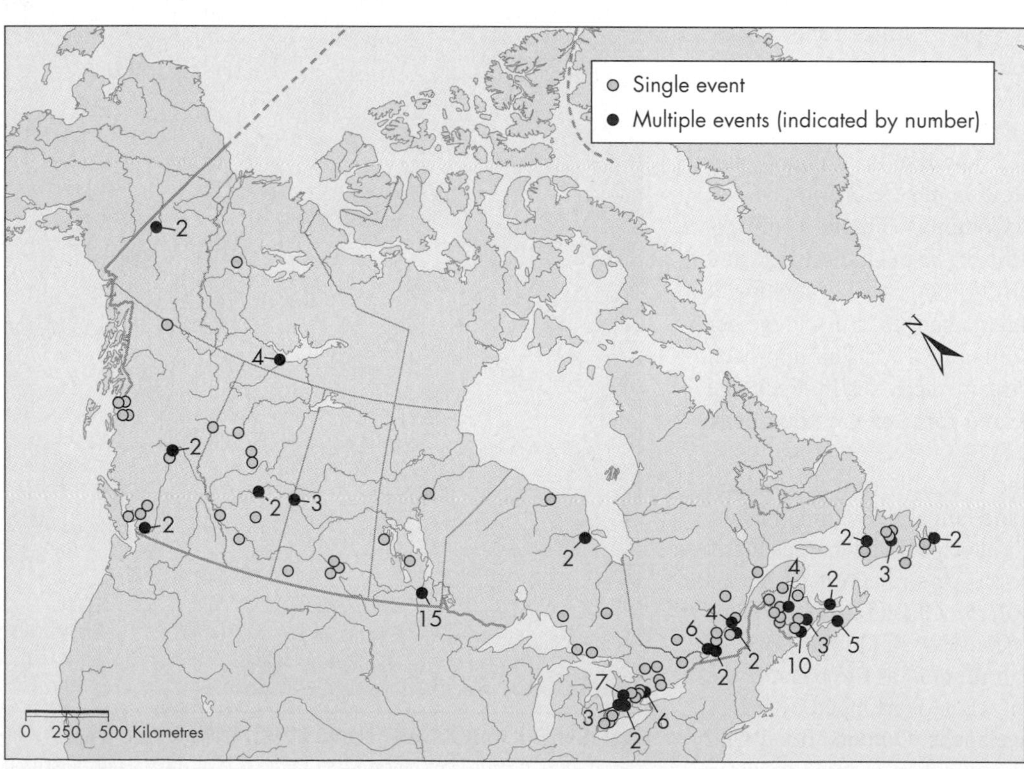

▲ **FIGURE 7.17 FLOOD DISASTERS IN CANADA IN THE TWENTIETH CENTURY** Locations of major historic floods in Canada. Symbols depict the general location of floods; most affected areas, however, were much larger than the symbol itself. *(After Brooks, G. R. et al. 2001. Floods. Geological Survey of Canada Bulletin 548:101–143; reproduced with the permission of the Minister of Public Works and Government Services Canada, 2007, and courtesy of Natural Resources Canada, Geological Survey of Canada)*

TABLE 7.1 Selected Floods in the United States and Canada

Year	Month	Location	Lives Lost	Property Damage ($millions)*
1933	May	Southern New Brunswick	7	Unknown
1937	January–February	Ohio and lower Mississippi River basins	137	418
1938	March	Southern California	79	25
1940	August	Southern Virginia and Carolinas and eastern Tennessee	40	12
1947	May–July	Lower Missouri and middle Mississippi River basins	29	235
1948	May–June	Lower Fraser River	10	15
1950	May	Red River basin, Manitoba	1	> 100
1951	June–July	Kansas and Missouri	28	923
1954	October	Southern Ontario	81	100
1955	December	West coast of United States	61	155
1963	March	Ohio River basin	26	98
1964	June	Montana	31	54
1964	December	California and Oregon	40	416
1965	June	Sanderson, Texas (flash flood)	26	3
1969	January–February	California	60	399
1969	August	James River basin, Virginia	154	116
1971	August	New Jersey	3	139
1972	June	Rapid City, South Dakota (flash flood)	242	163
1972	June	Eastern United States	113	3000
1973	March–June	Mississippi River	0	1200
1974	January	Southern Quebec	0	60
1976	July	Big Thompson River, Colorado (flash flood)	139	35
1977	July	Johnstown, Pennsylvania	76	330
1977	September	Kansas City, Missouri, and Kansas	25	80
1979	April	Mississippi and Alabama	10	500
1983	January	Newfoundland and Labrador	0	34
1983	June	Regina, Saskatchewan	0	60
1983	September	Arizona	13	416
1986	Winter	Western states, especially California	17	270
1986	July	Saskatchewan, Alberta	1	28
1987	July	Montreal	2	94
1990	January–May	Trinity River, Texas	0	1000
1990	June	Eastern Ohio (flash flood)	21	Several
1993	June–August	Mississippi River and tributaries		16,000
1993	July	Winnipeg, Manitoba	0	> 500
1997	January	Sierra Nevada, Central Valley, California	23	Several hundred
1997	May	Red River basin, Manitoba	3	4000
2001	June	Houston, Texas, Buffalo Bayou (coastal river)	22	2000
2004	August–September	Georgia to New York and the Appalachian Mountains	ca.13	400

Damages relate to the year of the disaster and are not adjusted for inflation.

and the U.S. National Weather Service provide the warning time needed to build temporary levees or remove property from vulnerable areas.

As discussed in other chapters, floods can be a primary effect of hurricanes and a secondary effect of earthquakes and landslides. Although seemingly counterintuitive, floods can also cause fires in populated areas. Floodwaters can produce shorts in electric circuits or erode and break gas lines, sparking dangerous fires.[22] For example, the 1997 Red River flood caused a fire in Grand Forks, North Dakota, that burned part of the city centre (Figure 7.18). River erosion during floods can also trigger landslides.

◄ **FIGURE 7.18 FLOODED CITY** These buildings in Grand Forks, North Dakota, were burned by a fire caused by the Red River flood in 1997. The flood forced the evacuation of 50,000 people in Grand Forks. *(Eric Hylden/Grand Forks Herald)*

7.5 Natural Service Functions

Flooding is a risk only when people live or have property on a floodplain or when they try to cross a flood-swollen river. In fact, periodic flooding has many benefits. Floods provide fertile sediment for farming; they benefit aquatic ecosystems; and in some areas they keep the surface of the land above sea level.

Fertile Land

When a river overflows its banks, the velocity of flow decreases, and the suspended load of fine sand, silt, clay, and organic matter is deposited on the floodplain. These periodic additions of nutrient-rich sediment are the reason that floodplains are some of the most fertile and productive agricultural areas in the world. Ancient Egyptians planned their farming around regular flooding of the Nile River. They understood that good harvests followed large floods, and they referred to flooding as "The Gift of the Nile." Unfortunately, with completion of the Aswan Dam in 1970, Egypt's annual floods have been effectively stopped. Now farmers must use fertilizer to successfully grow crops on what was once naturally fertile land.

Aquatic Ecosystems

Floods also flush out stream channels and remove accumulated debris, such as logs and tree branches. These flushing events have a generally positive effect on fish and other aquatic animals, and they may translate into a societal benefit in areas where fishing is important. Floods also carry nutrients downstream and into estuaries, increasing the food supply of aquatic organisms.

Sediment Supply

In some cases, flooding keeps the surface of a delta plain above sea level. For example, the Mississippi Delta in southeastern Louisiana is built of sediment that has been deposited by countless Mississippi River floods. Construction of levees along the Mississippi has all but eliminated flood sedimentation, with the result that much of the delta is now slowly subsiding. Some areas, including parts of New Orleans, are below sea level. As shown by Hurricane Katrina in 2005, this subsidence is a very big problem indeed!

A flood experiment carried out below a dam on the Colorado River in the Grand Canyon during 1996 provides an excellent example of the natural service functions of floods (see Case Study 7.3).

7.6 Human Interaction with Flooding

Human activity can significantly affect river processes and alter the magnitude and frequency of flooding. Land-use changes can increase or decrease sediment supply to a stream, which can, in turn, change the gradient and shape of the channel. Urbanization, especially increases in the number of paved areas, buildings, and storm sewers, changes runoff and, in some places, the risk of local flooding. Dyking of rivers to lower flood risk may, ironically, increase it because floodwaters can no longer spread out over the floodplain and are confined to a restricted space.

Land-Use Changes

Rivers are open systems that generally maintain a *dynamic equilibrium;* that is, an overall balance between the work the river does and the sediment load it receives. Sediment is supplied by tributaries, landslides, and erosion of bank materials. A river tends to maintain the gradient and cross-sectional shape that provide the flow velocity it needs to move its sediment load.[27]

A change in the amount of water or sediment carried by a river brings about changes in channel gradient or cross-sectional shape, effectively changing the velocity of the water. The change in velocity may, in turn, increase or decrease the amount of transported sediment. Land-use changes that alter a stream's sediment or water supply may set into motion a series of events that bring about a new dynamic equilibrium.

7.3 CASE STUDY

The Grand Canyon Flood of 1996

In 1963, the Glen Canyon Dam was built on the Colorado River upstream of the Grand Canyon. The dam tamed the river but drastically altered both the natural pattern of flow and the channel processes downstream.

Before the dam was built, the Colorado River achieved its peak flow in May or June when snow melted, and decreased through the summer and fall. During periods of high discharge, the river transported large amounts of sediment, including boulders in reaches with rapids, and it vigorously scoured its channel. Later, during the summer, the river deposited sand and gravel in large bars, called "beaches" by rafters (Figure 7.G).

After the dam was built, the size of the average annual flood dropped by about 66 percent and the size of the 10-year flood was reduced by about 75 percent. The dam controlled the flow to such an extent that the median discharge actually increased by 66 percent. The amount of sediment transported by the river immediately downstream of the dam fell to about 0.5 percent of pre-1963 values. The sediment load farther downstream was less affected because tributaries continued to add sediment to the river.[23]

The changes in flow in the Grand Canyon have greatly altered the Colorado River channel and its banks. Rapids may be getting more dangerous because large floods no longer move many of the boulders from shallow areas of the channel. Some of the large sandbars are disappearing through river erosion.

The loss of flood flows has also affected riparian vegetation. Before the dam was built, three nearly parallel belts of vegetation were present on the slopes above the river. Nearest the river and on sandbars, plants were removed by spring floods. Clumps of thorned trees, such as mesquite, acacia, cactus, and Apache plume, formed a belt directly above the flood limit. Widely spaced brittle brush and barrel cactus formed the uppermost belt.[24] The dam significantly reduced spring floods from 1963 until 1983. The absence of erosive high flows allowed plants not formerly found in the canyon, including tamarisk and willow, to become established in a belt along the riverbanks.

In June 1983, rapid snowmelt in the Rocky Mountains forced the release of about three times the normal amount of water from Lake Powell, the reservoir impounded by the Glen Canyon Dam. The volume of this release was about the same as an average spring flood before construction of the dam. The flood scoured sediment from the riverbed and banks, which replenished the sandbars, and it removed or broke off some of the tamarisk and willow trees. The large release of water was beneficial to the river and demonstrated the importance of floods in maintaining the system in a more natural state.

▲ **FIGURE 7.G THE COLORADO RIVER IN THE GRAND CANYON** The "beach" in the lower left is being used by river rafters. *(Larry Minden/Minden Pictures)*

In 1996, large amounts of water were purposely released from Lake Powell in a controlled experiment. The "test flood" formed 55 new beaches and added sand to 75 percent of the existing beaches. It also helped rejuvenate marshes and backwaters, which are important habitats for native fish and some endangered species. The experimental flood was hailed a success,[25] although some of the new sand was subsequently eroded.[26]

The 1996 test flood redistributed sand from the Colorado River channel bottom and banks to sandbars, but it did not introduce new sediment into the system. Little new sand was added by tributary streams because

7.3 CASE STUDY (Continued)

they were not in flood. The sand scoured from the river below the dam is thus a limited, nonrenewable resource that can't resupply sandbars on a sustainable basis.

Recognizing this, scientists have come up with a new plan to maintain the sandbars and their ecosystems.[26] The plan is to use sand delivered to the Grand Canyon by the Little Colorado River, a large tributary with a drainage area of 67,340 km^2 that joins the Colorado downstream of the Glen Canyon Dam (Figure 7.H). In 1993, a flood on the Little Colorado River carried a large volume of sand into the Colorado River, creating prominent beaches in the Grand Canyon. The beaches, however, were nearly removed by the Colorado River the following year because they were not high enough to survive erosion by normal flows released from Lake Powell.

The new plan involves timing floods from Glen Canyon Dam, when possible, to coincide with the sand-rich spring floods of the Little Colorado River. The resulting combined flow of the two rivers would be larger than normal, and the new sand from the Little Colorado would be deposited higher above the channel bed, where it is less likely to be removed by lower summer flows of the Colorado. Analysis of the hydrology of the Little Colorado River suggests that the opportunity to "piggyback" releases of water from Lake Powell on Little Colorado River floods, and thus replenish sand on the beaches, occurs, on average, once every eight years. The proposed plan would produce river flow and sediment transport conditions similar to those that existed before construction of the Glen Canyon Dam.[26]

Another effect of the Glen Canyon Dam has been to increase the number of people who raft the Colorado River through the Grand Canyon. Before 1950, fewer than 100 explorers and river runners had made the trip through the canyon. Today, rafting is limited to 15,000 people annually, with appreciable effects on canyon and river resources (Figure 7.G).

The Colorado River has been irreversibly changed by the Glen Canyon Dam. Despite the 1983 and 1996 floods, which pushed back some of the changes, river restoration efforts cannot be expected to return the river to what it was before construction of the dam.[23,24,26] However, better management of the flows and sediment transport will improve and help maintain the river ecosystem.

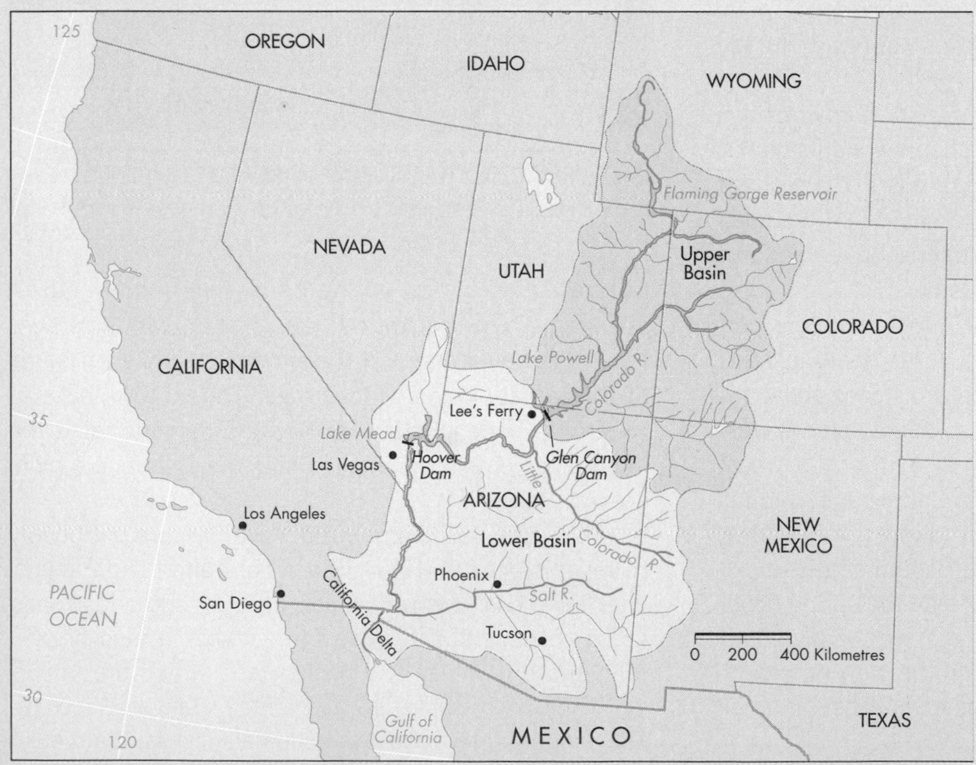

▲ **FIGURE 7.H THE COLORADO RIVER BASIN** Glen Canyon Dam divides the Colorado River basin (shaded areas) into two parts for management purposes. Flaming Gorge Reservoir in Wyoming and Lake Powell in Utah store runoff in the Upper Basin, and Lake Mead at the boundary between Nevada and Arizona stores runoff in the Lower Basin. The Colorado River delta, at the head of the Gulf of California, was once a large wetland area in Mexico, but today it is severely degraded because of diversion of river water for other uses in the United States.

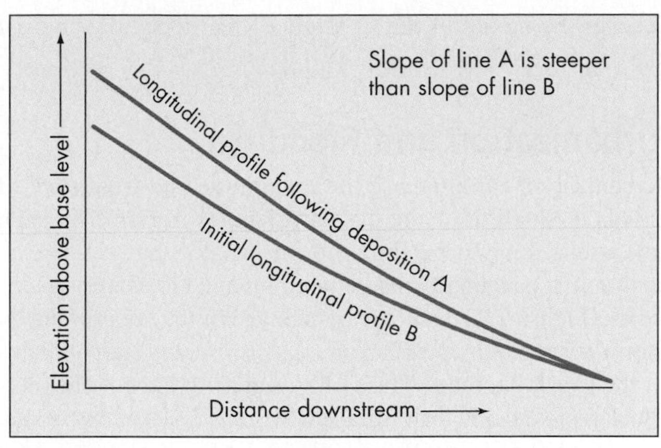

▲ **FIGURE 7.19 EFFECT OF DEPOSITION ON RIVER SLOPE** An idealized diagram illustrating that deposition in a stream channel increases the channel gradient; the slope of longitudinal profile A is steeper than that of longitudinal profile B.

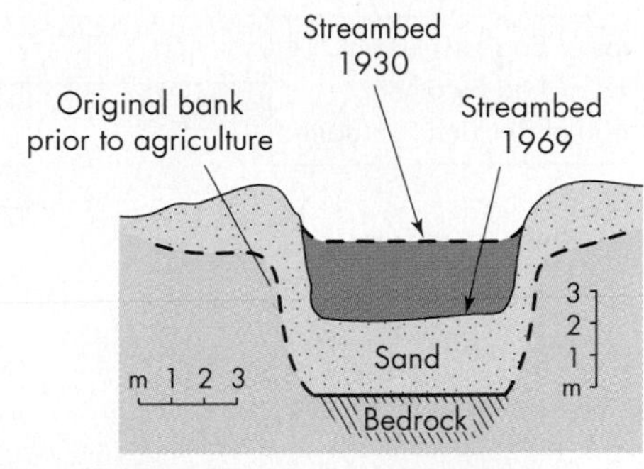

▲ **FIGURE 7.20 RESPONSE OF A STREAM TO CHANGES IN LAND USE** A cross-section of a stream at the Mauldin Millsite, Georgia, showing channel changes through time. Clearing of forest for agriculture increased sediment deposition in the channel until 1930. A return to woodland after 1930 increased stream erosion, thus lowering the channel. *(After Trimble, S. W. 1969. Culturally accelerated sedimentation on the middle Georgia Piedmont. Master's thesis, Athens, Georgia: University of Georgia. Reproduced by permission)*

Consider, for example, a land-use change from forest to an agricultural row crop, such as corn, that increases the amount of sediment delivered to a stream. At first, the stream will be unable to transport the additional load and will deposit some of the sediment, increasing the channel gradient. As the channel steepens, flow velocity increases, allowing the stream to move more sediment. If we assume that base level remains constant, this process will continue until the stream is flowing fast enough to carry the new load. If the concept that sediment deposition increases channel gradient seems counterintuitive, study the longitudinal profiles in Figure 7.19. A new dynamic equilibrium can be reached, provided the increase in sediment supply levels off and the channel gradient and shape can adjust before another change occurs.

Suppose the reverse situation now occurs; that is, farmland is converted to forest. Surface erosion will decrease and less sediment will be deposited in the stream channel. Erosion of the channel will eventually lower the gradient, which in turn will lower the velocity of the water. Erosion will continue until a new equilibrium is achieved between sediment supply and work done.

The sequence of events just described occurred in parts of the southeastern United States over the past 250 years. Most forests between the Appalachian Mountains and the Atlantic coastal plain were cleared for farming by the 1800s. The change from forest to farming accelerated soil erosion and triggered deposition of sediment in local streams (Figure 7.20). Channels that existed before farming began to fill with sediment. After 1930, the land reverted to pine forest. This change, in conjunction with soil-conservation measures, reduced the quantity of sediment delivered to streams. By 1969, formerly muddy, sediment-choked streams had cleared and eroded their channels (Figure 7.20).

Dam Construction

Consider now the effects of building a dam on a river. Upstream of the dam, the river enters the reservoir and deposits much of its sediment on a growing delta (Figure 7.21). Downstream of the dam, the river carries little sediment because most of its load has been deposited in the reservoir. As a result, the river can transport additional sediment and the channel is

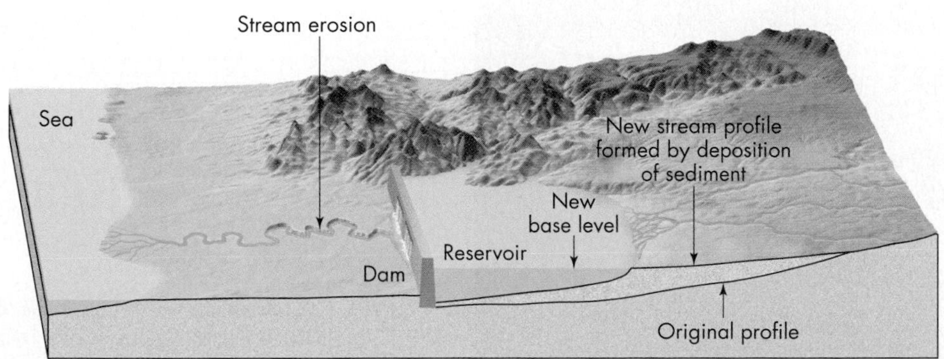

▲ **FIGURE 7.21 EROSION AND DEPOSITION CAUSED BY A DAM** Following dam construction, sediment accumulates within and upstream of the reservoir. Erosion occurs downstream of the dam because water leaving the reservoir carries much less sediment than the stream is capable of transporting. *(Modified after Tasa, D., in Tarbuck, E. J., and F. K. Lutgens. 2005. Earth: An introduction to physical geology, 8th ed. Upper Saddle River, NJ: Pearson Prentice Hall)*

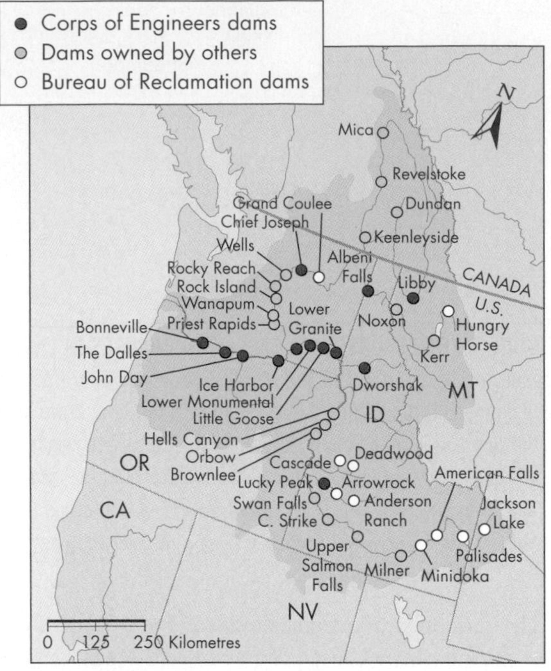

▲ **FIGURE 7.22 TAMING OF A RIVER** Much of the Columbia River upstream of Portland, Oregon, is a series of reservoirs impounded by dams built between 1933 and 1984. Sediment transported to the Pacific Ocean before dam construction now accumulates in the reservoirs.

eroded. The gradient of the river downstream of the dam will decrease until a new equilibrium is attained.

Dam construction has radically altered sediment and water flow on the Columbia River in British Columbia and Washington. A series of dams built in the past century for irrigation, electrical power generation, and flood control has left the Columbia with few free-flowing reaches (Figure 7.22). Most of the sediment transported by the river, as well as sediment introduced by tributary streams, accumulates in the reservoirs, which are gradually filling in. Much less sediment reaches the mouth of the Columbia River today than before the dams were constructed.

Urbanization and Flooding

Urbanization can increase the magnitude and frequency of floods in small drainage basins. Changes in runoff in such situations depend on the amount of land that is covered with roofs, pavement, and cement, referred to as *impervious cover* (Figure 7.23), and the percentage of the area served by storm sewers. In most urban areas, storm sewers start at drains at the sides of streets. They carry runoff to stream channels much more quickly than surface flow in natural settings would. An urban area with 40 percent impervious cover and 40 percent of its area served by storm sewers may experience up to about three times as many floods of a given magnitude as before urbanization (Figure 7.24). However, floods are less affected by urbanization as the size of the drainage basin increases.

Urban flooding can also result from poorly constructed or maintained drains. Long periods of only moderate rainfall can cause flooding if storm drains become blocked with sediment and storm debris. Water begins to pond behind debris in the drains, overflowing into low areas.

Urbanization also changes how rapidly floods develop. Comparison of hydrographs before and after urbanization shows a significant reduction in the time between peak rainfall and the flood crest after urbanization (Figure 7.25). A short *lag time*, referred to as *flashy discharge,* is characterized by a rapid rise and fall in discharge.

Urbanization also greatly reduces stream flow during the dry season. Normally, small streams continue to flow during dry periods because groundwater discharges into channels. However, because urbanization significantly reduces infiltration, less groundwater is available to recharge streams. This reduced flow affects both water quality and the appearance of a stream. Urban streams with low discharges may carry heavy loads of pollutants.[10] Some of the pollutants, such

◀ **FIGURE 7.23 URBANIZATION INCREASES IMPERVIOUS COVER** Aerial view of Toronto, Ontario, which, like all North American cities, has much of its land surface covered by paved streets, sidewalks, parking lots, and buildings. This impervious land cover greatly reduces infiltration of rainwater and increases surface runoff. *(Pavel Baudis/Czech Republic)*

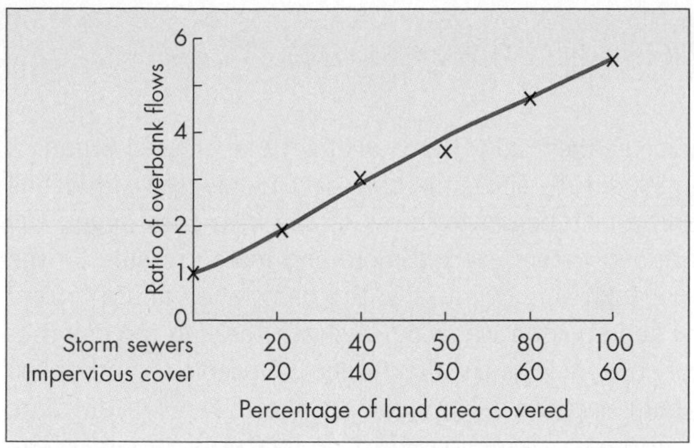

▲ **FIGURE 7.24 EFFECT OF URBANIZATION ON THE FREQUENCY OF FLOODS** The relation between the increase in overbank flows and the percentage of area with impervious cover and with storm sewers. A ratio of three, for example, means that three floods occurred after urbanization for every one that took place before urbanization, or that flooding was three times more frequent after urbanization. The graph shows that the frequency of floods increases with increasing urbanization. *(After Leopold, L. B. 1968. U.S. Geological Survey Circular 559)*

as nitrogen and phosphorus derived from fertilizer, can stimulate the growth of algae, which reduces the dissolved oxygen content of the water and harms aquatic life.

Impervious cover and storm sewers are not the only types of construction that increase flooding. Some flash floods occur because bridges built across small streams block the passage of floating debris, which then forms a temporary dam. If the dam fails, a destructive wave of water and debris moves downstream (see Case Study 7.4). Destructive floods may also result from the failure of constructed dams.

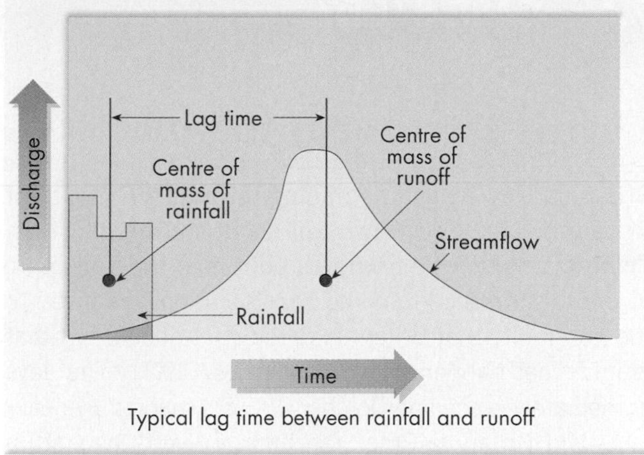

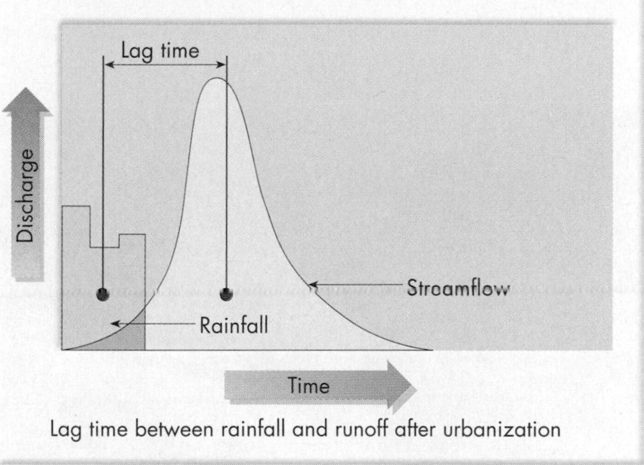

▲ **FIGURE 7.25 URBANIZATION SHORTENS LAG TIME** (a) A generalized hydrograph showing the lag between the time of peak rainfall and the time of flooding. (b) A hydrograph showing the decrease in lag time and more rapid rise and fall of discharge caused by urbanization. *(Modified from Tarbuck, E. J., and F. K. Lutgens. 2005. Earth: An introduction to physical geology, 8th ed. Upper Saddle River, NJ: Pearson Prentice Hall)*

7.7 Minimizing the Flood Hazard

Historically, and particularly in the nineteenth century, people responded to floods by attempting to prevent them. Physical barriers, such as dams and levees, have been built, and stream channels have been by widened, deepened, or straightened to more efficiently carry floodwaters. Flood-control measures are essential, but they can lure people onto floodplains in the false hope that flooding is no longer an issue. It is worth remembering that no dam or channel can handle the largest runoff that a river can deliver and that extensive flooding can occur when the flow ultimately exceeds the capacity of the structure.[22,29]

The Structural Approach

Physical Barriers Engineered structures constructed to reduce the risk of flooding include earthen **levees** (Figure 7.26), concrete floodwalls, dams to store water for later release, floodways that bypass populated areas, and storm-water-retention basins. Unfortunately, the benefits of these physical barriers are often lost because they encourage development on the floodplains they are intended to protect. For example, the winters of 1986 and 1997 brought tremendous storms and flooding to the western American states, particularly California, Nevada, and Utah. In all, damage exceeded several hundred million dollars and several people died. During one of the floods in 1986, a levee on the Yuba River in California broke, causing more than 20,000 people to flee their homes. An important lesson learned from this flood is that levees constructed long ago may be in poor condition and may fail during floods (Figure 7.27).

Some engineered structures designed to prevent flooding have actually increased the long-term flood risk.[30] For example, floodwalls at St. Louis, Missouri, produced a flow bottleneck during the 1993 Mississippi River flood, increasing the severity of flooding upstream (Figure 7.28). As the Mississippi floodwaters rose to record levels, the St. Louis floodwalls began to leak and required round-the-clock efforts to keep them from failing. Some towns were relocated after the 1993 flood, but weak floodplain regulations

7.4 CASE STUDY

Debris Flood at Britannia

Britannia was a bustling mining town at the mouth of Britannia Creek on Howe Sound in southern British Columbia. When the town was built near the beginning of the twentieth century, no consideration was given to the possibility that Britannia Creek might flood, but that is just what happened on October 28, 1921. The days immediately preceding October 28 were marked by heavy rain, and Britannia Creek ran high. Culverts beneath a large earthen railway embankment that crossed Britannia Creek directly above the town became plugged with debris and a lake began to form. As the lake grew larger, the trapped waters exerted more and more pressure on the embankment. Eventually, the dam failed and a torrent of debris-laden water cut a swath through the community (Figure 7.I). The flood killed 37 people and destroyed about half the 170 houses in the town.[28] A few large boulders carried by the floodwaters remain in the town, silent reminders of this past catastrophe.

◄ **FIGURE 7.I DISASTER AT BRITANNIA** The mining community of Britannia, built on the floodplain of Britannia Creek, before and after the catastrophic flood of October 1921. *(Britannia Beach Historical Society)*

and government subsidies allowed the construction of more than 25,000 new homes and other buildings on the floodplain behind new, higher levees in the St. Louis area.[30] Other communities, however, have learned that strong floodplain regulations and structural controls go hand in hand.[31,32,33,34]

◄ **FIGURE 7.26 MISSISSIPPI RIVER LEVEE** Earthen or concrete levees border the lower Mississippi River in Louisiana. A road on the top of this levee appears as a curving white line. This levee protects farms, homes, and businesses along the highway on the left. *(Comstock Images)*

Channelization Straightening, deepening, widening, clearing, and lining existing stream channels are all methods of **channelization** (Figure 7.29). Channelization is used to control floods, drain wetlands, and maintain navigable river channels.[35] Thousands of kilometres of streams in Canada and the United States have been channelized without adequate consideration of the adverse effects of the practice. Thousands of additional kilometres of channelization projects are planned or in progress.

Opponents of channelizing streams emphasize that the practice degrades river and wetland ecosystems (Figure 7.30). Their arguments are as follows:

- Draining wetlands adversely affects plants and animals by eliminating habitats necessary for their survival.
- Removal of trees along riverbanks eliminates shade and cover for fish and exposes the stream to the sun, which may damage plant life and heat-sensitive aquatic organisms.
- Cutting trees on floodplains eliminates many animal habitats, while increasing sediment delivery to the stream.
- Straightening a river channel destroys the diversity of natural flow conditions and feeding and breeding areas for aquatic life.
- Conversion of a meandering stream to a straight channel seriously degrades the aesthetic value of a natural area.[35]

▲ **FIGURE 7.27 LEVEE FAILURE** A breach of this levee in Illinois in 1993 flooded the town of Valmeyer. Water can be seen rushing through the breach in the grass-covered earthen levee. *(Comstock Images)*

Some drainage projects are beneficial. The benefits are probably greatest in urban areas with a high flood risk and in rural areas where previous land use has created drainage problems. In some areas, channel modification has improved navigation or reduced flooding without significant environmental degradation.

The largest flood channelization project in Canadian history was construction of the Red River Floodway between 1962 and 1968.[36] The floodway consists of four elements: the floodway channel, an inlet control structure, dykes, and an outlet structure (Figure 7.31). The floodway channel is 48 km long and has a designated flow depth of 8 m. The width of the top of the channel ranges from 213 m to 305 m. Material excavated from the channel was deposited along the channel sides to form an embankment 6 m high. The inlet control structure is located on the Red River just downstream from

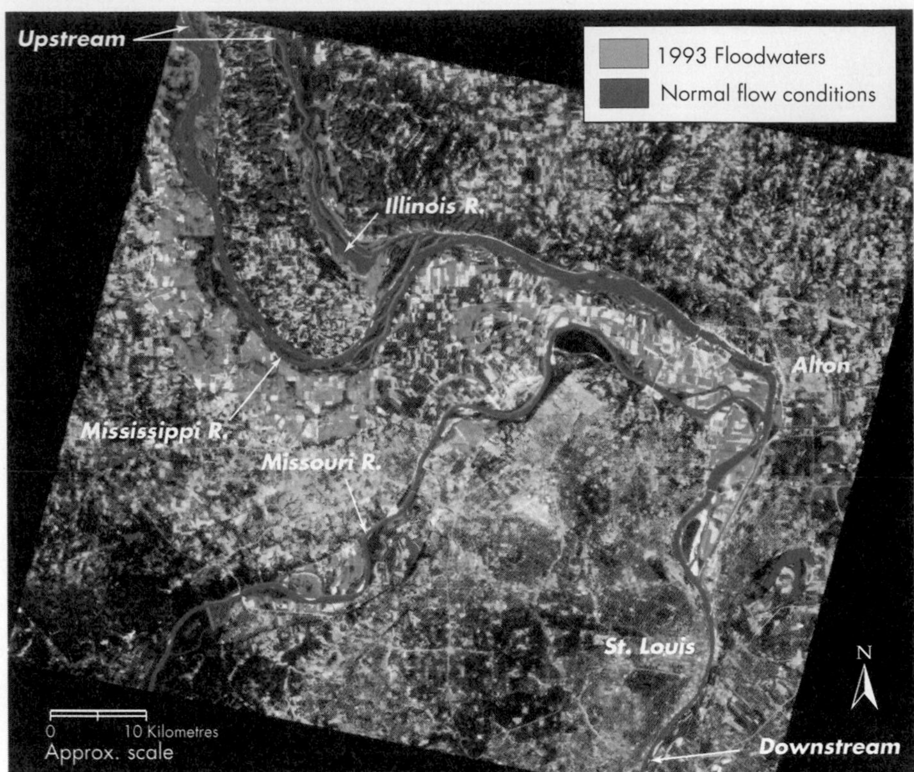

◄ **FIGURE 7.28 MISSISSIPPI RIVER FLOOD OF 1993** A satellite view of the area inundated by floodwaters upstream of St. Louis, where the Illinois and Missouri rivers join the Mississippi. The flooded area is light blue. Floodwalls built to protect St. Louis constrict the Mississippi River at the lower right. This flow bottleneck was responsible for widespread flooding upstream of St. Louis. *(© Cindy Brown/CORBIS/SYGMA)*

the floodway inlet near St. Norbert, Manitoba. Its purpose is to regulate the flow between the natural channel of the Red River and the floodway channel during periods of high flow. Dykes upstream of the inlet control structure prevent floodwaters from bypassing it. The vertical drop over the entire length of the floodway is 5 m, only half the corresponding drop of the Red River. The purpose of the outlet structure is to dissipate the potential energy in the water at its point of reentry into the Red River near Lockport, thereby preventing damage to the floodway.

The Red River Floodway was extensively criticized when it was planned and constructed. Its benefits, however, have been considerable. Had the floodway not existed during the great flood of 1997, Winnipeg would have been flooded. Damage to Winnipeg that might have occurred during Red River floods in 1969, 1970, 1974, 1979, and 1987 is in excess of $2 billion. The total cost of the Red River floodway and two other flood control structures was $94 million at the time of construction, equivalent to about $500 million today.

Channel Restoration: An Alternative to Channelization

Most streams in urban areas are no longer natural. **Channel restoration**[37] is a suite of measures that attempts to return severely modified streams to a more natural state. These measures include (1) removing urban waste from stream channels, (2) protecting existing channel banks by planting native trees and other vegetation, and (3) reestablishing deeper pools and shallower riffles within channels. Trees are

◄ **FIGURE 7.29 STREAM CHANNELIZATION** An extreme case of stream channelization: a concrete-lined channel in Los Angeles, California. *(Edward A. Keller)*

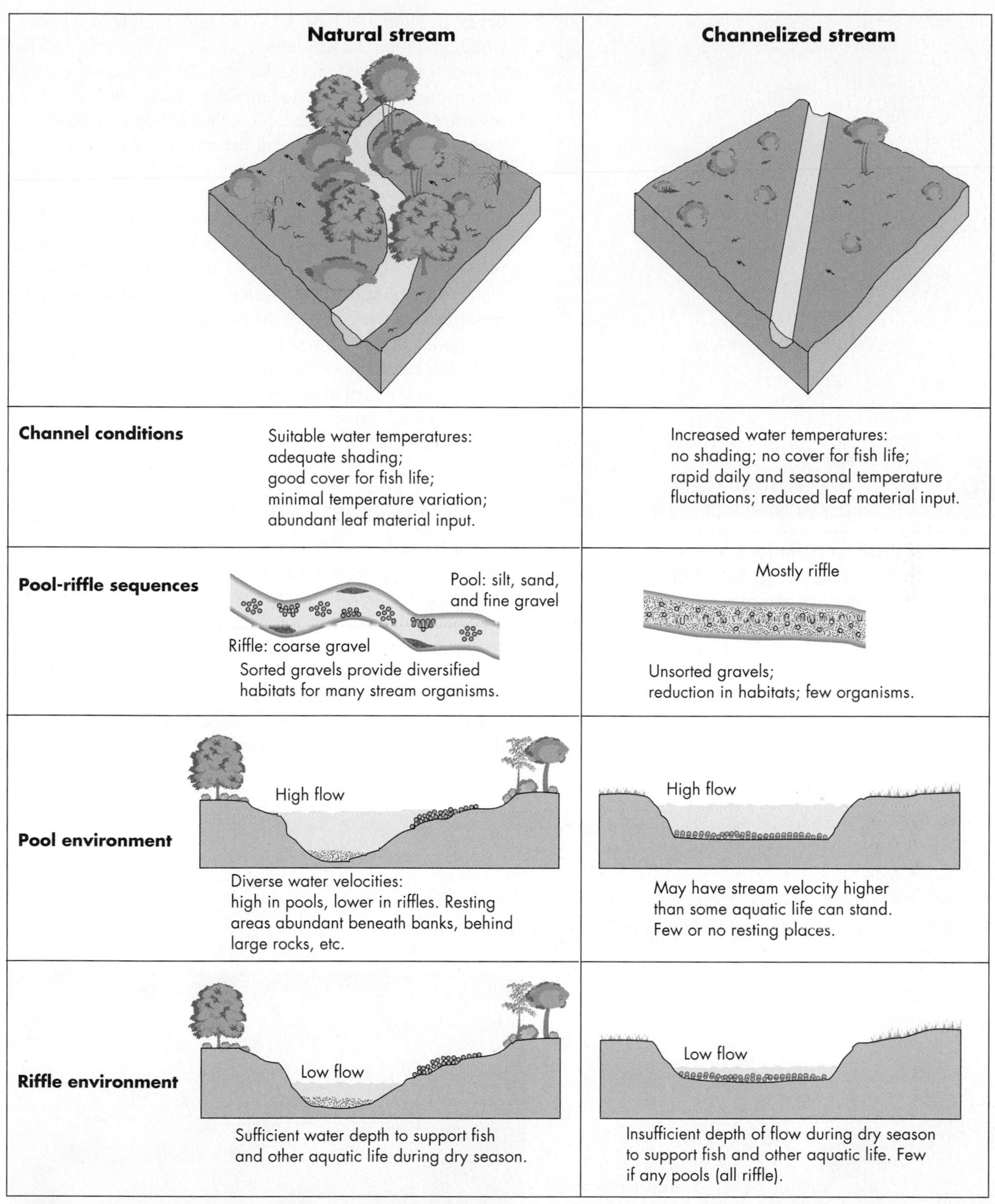

▲ **FIGURE 7.30 COMPARISON OF NATURAL AND CHANNELIZED STREAMS** The channelization of a stream significantly alters flow conditions, pool and riffle development, and aquatic ecosystems. *(Modified after Corning, Virginia Wildlife, February 1975)*

important because they provide shade for a stream and their root systems protect stream banks from erosion.

The objective of channel restoration is to create a more natural channel by allowing the stream to meander and develop variable water-flow conditions. Where lateral bank erosion must be controlled, the outsides of bends may be defended with large stones known as *riprap* or with wire baskets filled with rocks, known as *gabions* (Figure 7.32).

Kissimmee River Restoration Restoration of the Kissimmee River in Florida may be the most ambitious project of its kind attempted in the United States. Channelization of the river

▲ **FIGURE 7.31 RED RIVER FLOODWAY** The floodway diverts some of the flow of the swollen Red River during the 1997 flood, reducing the discharge of the river downstream in Winnipeg. *(Reproduced with the permission of the Minister of Public Works and Government Services Canada, 2005, and courtesy of Natural Resources Canada, Geological Survey of Canada. Photographer: Steve Solomon)*

began in 1960 and took 10 years to complete at a cost of US$32 million. The Kissimmee was changed from a 165 km meandering river into an 83 km straight ditch. As a result of the channelization, water quality decreased and numbers of waterfowl and fish declined. More than 800 km^2 of floodplain wetlands were drained during the project. Ironically, channelization increased the flood hazard because the floodplain wetlands no longer stored runoff.

Within a year after the project was completed, the State of Florida called for the river to be restored. The U.S. Congress in 1991 mandated the U.S. Army Corps of Engineers, which was responsible for the original channelization, to begin restoring about one-third of the river at a cost of US$400 million, more than 10 times the cost of the original project! Although restoration is certainly the right thing to do, more careful environmental evaluation before the original project would have revealed the potential damage that necessitated the restoration.[38]

Flood Forecasts and Advisories

The specific dates and magnitudes of floods cannot be predicted over long periods. For some watersheds, however, spring discharges can be estimated several days in advance by using models that incorporate snowpack depths, stream and lake levels, ground moisture, temperature, wind, evaporation, and weather forecasts. *Outlooks* of peak spring discharge can be made weeks in advance by using similar models with a variety of scenarios of melt rates and rainfall. Potential peak discharges of floods are expressed in terms of probability

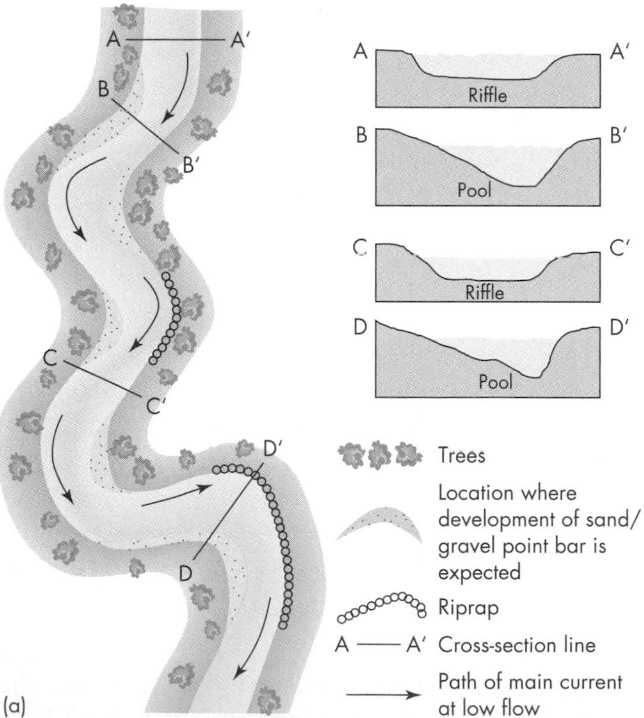

▲ **FIGURE 7.32 URBAN STREAM RESTORATION** (a) A channel restoration strategy that uses changes in channel shape to cause scour and deposition at desired locations. *(Modified after Keller, E. A., and E. K. Hoffman. 1977. Journal of Soil and Water Conservation 32:237–240).* (b) Dump truck placing riprap to defend the bank of Briar Creek in Charlotte, North Carolina. Grass was planted and covered with straw mulch (to the left of men) to help stabilize the stream bank. *(Edward A. Keller)*

of occurrence, but the actual peak runoff is dependent on climatic events that are yet to occur and thus inherently uncertain. Nevertheless, worst-case scenarios can be identified and planned for well in advance of the actual flooding.

Flood advisories or warnings are issued in anticipation of severe weather conditions, such as convective storms, thunderstorms, and hurricanes. Although the advisories are generally issued only hours in advance of the storm, they can provide sufficient time to mobilize resources for flood control and, in extreme cases, to evacuate people, livestock, or property from areas likely to be affected.

Northward-flowing rivers in Canada, such as the Moose and Mackenzie rivers, routinely produce ice-jam flooding in the spring. Residents know when the flooding is likely to occur and are generally well prepared for it. Historical data can be used to relate the time and magnitude of the peak water level during breakup to current conditions. Further, once an ice jam has formed somewhere along a river, empirical methods can be used to predict the rise in water level.

Forecasting floods caused by the failure of natural dams is a problem of timing rather than of magnitude. Moraine and glacier dam bursts are highly unpredictable, although they generally occur in the summer following a period of warm weather. A number of empirical formulas have been developed to estimate peak discharges of outburst floods from lakes impounded by glaciers, moraines, or landslides. The formulas express peak discharge as a function of the potential energy or volume of the impounded water. In addition, outburst floods can be predicted by using dam-break models, provided that the initial water volume and the topography of the flood path are known.

When a landslide dam forms, the extent of the resulting reservoir may be estimated from the elevation of the debris crest. Warnings can be given to people downstream from the dam of a possible outburst flood, if one is expected. An estimate of the time of filling of the reservoir can also be made from the volume of the impoundment and the rate of filling.

7.8 Perception of and Adjustment to Flood Hazards

Perception of Flood Hazards

Most governmental agencies, planners, and policymakers have an adequate perception and understanding of flooding (see Professional Profile), but many individuals do not. Public knowledge of floods, an understanding of future flooding risk, and a willingness to adjust to the hazard are highly variable.

Progress in reducing flood risk at the institutional level requires preparation of hazard maps of flood-prone areas. Flood-hazard maps show areas that are susceptible to flooding along streams, lakes, and coastlines, and areas where urbanization is likely to cause problems in the future. In addition, federal, provincial, territorial, and state governments have encouraged local communities to adopt floodplain management plans.[39] Still, the idea of restricting or prohibiting development on floodplains or of relocating present development to sites off the floodplain is problematic; extensive community discussion is needed before the general population will accept such measures.

Adjustments to the Flood Hazard

In recent decades, scientists and planners have increasingly recognized the advantages of alternatives to structural flood control measures. Alternatives include flood insurance and strict control of land use on floodplains. Planners, policymakers, and hydrologists generally agree that no single adjustment is best in all cases. An integrated approach that incorporates adjustments appropriate for a particular situation is a more effective strategy.

Floodplain Regulation From an environmental perspective, the best adjustment that can be made to flood hazards is through **floodplain regulation**. The goal of floodplain regulation is to maximize the benefit from floodplains while minimizing flood damage and the cost of flood protection.[40] This approach is a compromise between the indiscriminate development of floodplains, which results in loss of life and tremendous property damage, and the complete abandonment of floodplains, which gives up a valuable natural resource.

Engineered structures are necessary to protect lives and property on floodplains that have extensive development. We must recognize, however, that the floodplain is part of the river system and that any encroachment that reduces the cross-sectional area of the floodplain increases flood risk. One approach to reducing flood risk is to disallow new development that would lessen a river's access to its floodplain, in other words, to design with, rather than against, nature. Realistically, the most practical approach is a combination of physical barriers and floodplain regulations that minimize physical modification of the river system. For example, reasonable floodplain zoning may reduce the size of a floodwater diversion channel or an upstream reservoir required to produce a prescribed level of flood protection.

A preliminary step in floodplain regulation is flood-hazard mapping. Flood-hazard maps may delineate past floods or floods of a particular return period, for example the 100-year flood. They are useful in regulating development, purchasing land for parks and other public use, and creating guidelines for future land use on floodplains.

Flood-hazard evaluation may be accomplished in a general way by direct observation and measurement. For example, extensive flooding in the Mississippi River valley in the summer of 1993 was clearly mapped by using satellite imagery (Figure 7.28) and aerial photographs. The flood hazard can also be assessed from field measurement of high-water lines, flood sediments, scour marks, and the distribution of woody debris on the floodplain after water has receded.[39] Once flood-hazard maps have been produced, planners can modify zoning maps, regulations, and building codes (Figure 7.33).

PROFESSIONAL PROFILE

Walter Green, III, Emergency Operations Director

"If you can see water," says Dr. Walter G. Green, III (Figure 7.J), "it can come visit you." He offers this warning to anyone looking to buy property or build a house near water. "Water is very beautiful," he notes, "but at some point, it gets full."

As the former director of emergency operations for the Virginia Office of Emergency Medical Services, Green has seen his share of floods and is quick to point out the warning signs suggesting an area may eventually be flooded.

Green, now a professor at the University of Richmond, Virginia, says that his former position included the task of planning for a range of natural disasters and for coordinating appropriate responses. Among other things, he examined how well state and local emergency response services cooperate in preparing for disasters.

Green points out that flooding is becoming a more severe problem in urban areas because expanding development is decreasing the ground's ability to absorb water. Hurricanes are another major worry for emergency managers. "I start worrying about hurricanes when they're off the African coast," he says, adding that most people don't worry about hurricanes until they are in immediate danger.

The most dramatic flooding Green had to deal with was a flash flood in the wake of Hurricane Fran in 1996. Franklin County in Virginia suffered a great deal of damage when the Blackwater River overtopped its banks. "Water went up extraordinarily rapidly," he recalls. "It was literally coming out of the banks."

▲ **FIGURE 7.J VIRGINIA EMERGENCY OPERATIONS DIRECTOR** As director of emergency operations for the Virginia Office of Emergency Medical Services, Dr. Walter Green, III, coordinated responses to flooding. *(Courtesy of Gretchen R. Brooks)*

However, Green says the flood was not entirely unexpected. "There were some precursor signs, but at the time they weren't recognized." Flooding farther upstream on the Blackwater River should have been recognized as such a sign.

Green recommends contacting the local emergency management office before purchasing property near water. "The possibility of flooding is not to be taken lightly. These are extraordinarily powerful forces."

—Chris Wilson

Flood-Proofing Several methods of flood-proofing are currently available:

- Raising the foundation of a building above the anticipated level of flooding by using piles or columns or by extending foundation walls or earth fill[41]
- Constructing flood walls or earthen mounds around buildings to isolate them from floodwaters
- Using waterproofed doors, basement walls, and windows
- Installing drains with pumps to remove water

Other structural modifications can reduce damage when floodwaters enter a building. For example, ground floors of expensive riverfront properties in some communities in Germany are designed to withstand the forces of floodwaters and can be easily cleaned following a flood.[41]

Different Approaches Canada and the United States have adopted different approaches to managing their flood hazards. The Canadian approach involves planning, regulations to discourage new development on floodplains, and government flood damage compensation.[42] The U.S. approach includes some of these elements but places importance on private and public flood insurance.

The Canada Water Conservation Assistance Act of 1953 was the first federal legislation directly concerned with water resource management. It enabled the federal government to provide financial assistance to the provinces and territories for construction of works to conserve and control water. Under

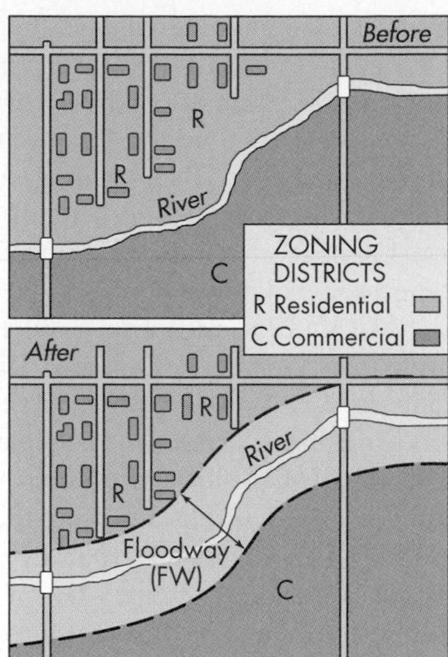

▲ **FIGURE 7.33 FLOODPLAIN ZONING** Zoning map before and after the implementation of flood regulations *(From Water Resources Council. 1971. Regulation of flood hazard areas, vol. 1)*

the act, the federal government contributed 37.5 percent of the cost of such works.

The Canada Water Act, passed in 1970, superseded the Canada Water Conservation Assistance Act. It allowed the federal government to participate with the provinces and territories in water-management programs. The philosophy behind the act was that

- Planning should be comprehensive and include all water uses and their economic, social, and environmental importance.
- Views of the people affected by the programs should be sought.
- Nonstructural flood control alternatives should be considered.
- Planning should take place on a watershed scale.

Flooding was recognized as a problem that required a new approach, beyond the traditional structural approach and providing disaster assistance. This approach was born of dissatisfaction with many aspects of the structure approach, the issue of "income transfer" from the general public to the minority of floodplain residents, changing social values, increased urbanization, economic conditions, and the seemingly endless escalation in flood damage costs, even with structure controls. The new approach was embodied in the federal Flood Damage Reduction Program established in 1975.

The Flood Damage Reduction Program operates under a series of federal-provincial and federal-territorial cost-sharing agreements. The two levels of government agree to the following policies:

- They will not build, approve, or finance flood-prone development in designated flood-risk areas.
- They will not provide flood disaster assistance for any development built after an area is designated to have a flood risk, except for flood-proofed structures.
- The provinces and territories will encourage local authorities to zone on the basis of flood risk.

Agreements between the two levels of government differ across provinces and territories, but normally a General Agreement outlining policies of the Flood Damage Reduction Program is supplemented by a subsidiary agreement on mapping. Additional agreements may be made on flood forecasting, structure controls, and research. The General Agreement sets out the basic approach, which is to consider all applicable structural and nonstructural measures to reduce flood risk. Effectiveness, costs, benefits, and environmental impacts are considered. The mapping agreements provide for a program to delineate and designate areas at risk from flooding. The federal criterion for defining the flood risk area is the 1-in-100-year flood, although this is not applied across the country. For example, the Canada-British Columbia Flood Damage Reduction Agreement uses the 1-in-200-year instead of the 1-in-100-year flood.

Areas in Canada at risk from flooding are commonly subdivided into two zones: the *floodway* and the *flood fringe*. The floodway is the portion of a river's floodplain with the deepest, fastest, and most destructive waters. Flood-vulnerable infrastructure is discouraged in the floodway because of the danger to life and potential property damage. New development may be permitted within the flood fringe, where water is shallower and slower, provided that it is adequately flood-proofed.

Local governments play an important role in floodplain management in Canada, because they are generally responsible for land-use planning and regulation of new development. The federal-provincial and federal-territorial agreements require that local authorities be encouraged to zone designated areas on floodplains according to the flood risk. In some provinces and territories, local governments are required to incorporate flood hazard information into municipal planning through official plans, zoning bylaws, subdivision plans, and flood regulations.

Provinces and territories have primary jurisdiction for responding to disasters, but the federal government will assist the provinces and territories if the cost of a disaster is larger than a province or territory can reasonably be expected to bear on its own. The federal financial contribution is determined by a formula based on provincial/territorial population and federal guidelines for defining eligible costs. Public Safety and Emergency Preparedness Canada (PSEPC) administers the Disaster Financial Arrangements on behalf of the Government of Canada. Not all damage is eligible for cost-sharing. For example, the program does not cover damage to large businesses, industries, crops, or summer cottages.

As mentioned, an important element of the United States' flood-management program is private and public insurance. In 1968 the U.S. Congress established the U.S. National Flood Insurance Program to make flood insurance available at subsidized rates. This program is administered by the Federal Emergency Management Agency (FEMA) and requires mapping of special Flood Hazard Areas, defined as areas that would be inundated by a 100-year flood. As discussed above, a 100-year flood is a flood that has a 1 percent chance of occurring in any given year. Flood hazard areas are designated along streams, rivers, lakes, alluvial fans, deltas, and low-lying coastal areas.

New property owners in areas that might be flooded must buy insurance at rates determined by the risk they face. In this case, risk is evaluated by using the flood-hazard maps. The insurance program is intended to provide short-term financial aid to victims of floods and to establish long-term land-use regulations that discourage development of floodplains. Part of this program involves revising building codes to limit new construction in a flood hazard area to flood-proofed buildings (Figure 7.34) and to prohibit all new construction in areas that would be inundated by a 20-year flood. Before joining the National Flood Insurance Program, a community must have FEMA prepare maps of the 100-year floodplain, and it must adopt minimum standards of land-use regulation within identified flood hazard areas. Nearly all U.S. communities with a significant flood risk have basic flood-hazard maps and have initiated some form of floodplain regulation. Several million property owners in the United States presently have flood insurance policies.[41]

By the early 1990s, policymakers and flood control professionals recognized that the flood insurance program was in need of reform. In response, in 1994, U.S. Congress passed the National Flood Insurance Reform Act, with provisions to further mitigate flood risk through flood-proofing, relocation, and buyouts of properties likely to be frequently flooded.[41]

Relocating People from Floodplains

To reduce future losses from flooding in the United States, local, state, and federal governments have been selectively purchasing and removing homes damaged by floodwaters. The following are two examples of voluntary relocation. In September 1999, nearly 50 cm of rain from Hurricane Floyd flooded many areas in North Carolina. Floodwaters damaged approximately 700 homes in Rocky Mount, and state and federal governments later decided to spend nearly $50 million to remove 430 of these homes, the largest single home buyout ever approved. Following purchase, the homes were demolished and the land was preserved as open space.

A wet cycle that began in 1993 caused Devils Lake in North Dakota to rise 8 m. With no natural outlet and flat land surrounding its shore, the lake more than doubled in size and inundated the land around the town of Churchs Ferry. By late June 2000, the town was all but deserted, the population having dropped from approximately 100 to 7 people. Most residents took advantage of a voluntary federal buyout plan and moved to higher ground. They were offered as compensation the appraised value of their homes plus an incentive; most considered the offer too good to turn down. They also recognized that the town eventually would have been destroyed by flooding anyway. Nevertheless, there was some bitterness among the town's population and not everyone participated. The mayor and the fire chief were among the seven people who decided to stay. The buyout program demonstrated how emotional such a process can be. It is difficult for people to leave their homes, even though they know floodwaters will eventually destroy them.

Personal Adjustments: What to Do and What Not to Do

We can't prevent floods, but we can prepare for them by learning what to do and what not to do before, during, and after floods (Table 7.2).

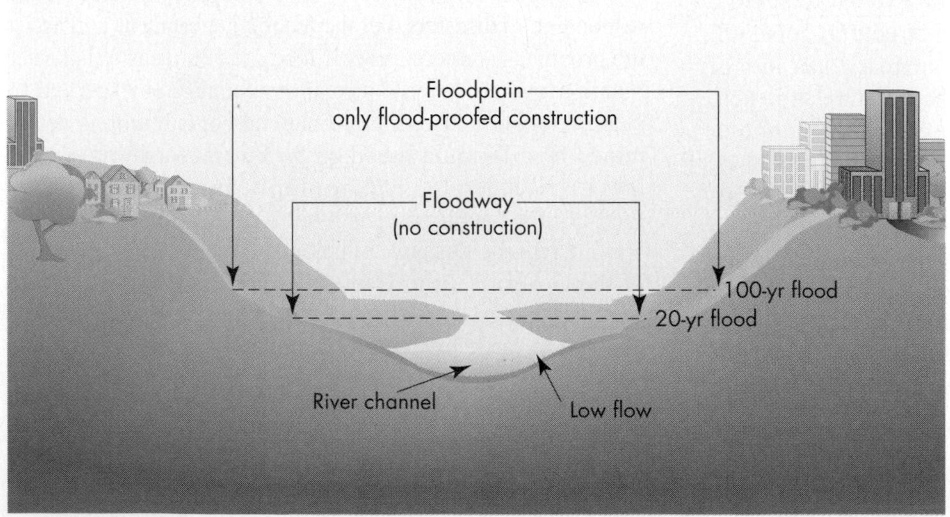

▲ **FIGURE 7.34 FLOODPLAIN REGULATION** Schematic diagram showing areas inundated by 100- and 20-year floods, which are the floods used for regulation under the U.S. National Flood Insurance Program.

TABLE 7.2 What to Do and What Not to Do before and after a Flood

What to Do	**PREPARING FOR A FLOOD** • Enquire about the risk of flooding where you live. • If your property is at risk, purchase flood insurance if you can and be sure that you know how to file a claim. • Buy sandbags or flood boards to block doors. • Assemble a flood kit, including a flashlight, blankets, raingear, battery-powered radio, first-aid kit, rubber gloves, key personal documents, and medication. Keep the kit upstairs if possible. • Find out where to turn off your gas and electricity. If you are not sure, ask your utility company. • Talk to your family or housemates about the possibility of flooding. Consider writing a flood plan and store it with your flood kit.
What Not to Do	• Never underestimate the damage a flood can do.
What to Do	**WHEN A FLOOD WARNING HAS BEEN ISSUED** • Be prepared to evacuate. • Observe water levels and monitor radio and television news and weather reports. • Move people, pets, and valuables upstairs or to higher ground. • Move your car to higher ground. It takes only 0.6 m of fast-flowing water to wash it away. • Check on your neighbours. Do they need help? They may not be able to escape upstairs or may need help moving furniture. • Do as much as you can in daylight. If the electricity fails, it will be hard to do anything at night. • Keep warm and dry. A flood can last longer than you think, and you can get cold. If you are forced out of your home, take warm clothes, blankets, a Thermos, and food supplies.
What Not to Do	• Don't walk in floodwater above knee level; the flowing water can easily knock you off your feet, and sewer-access holes, road works, and other hazards may be hidden beneath the water.
What to Do	**AFTER A FLOOD** • Check your home for damage and photograph any damage. • If insured, file a claim for the damage. • Obtain professional help in removing or drying carpets and furniture as well as cleaning walls and floors. • Contact gas, electricity, and water companies. You will need to have your utilities checked before you turn them back on. • Open doors and windows to ventilate your home. • Wash water taps and run them for a few minutes before use. Your water supply may be contaminated; check if you are concerned.
What Not to Do	• Don't touch items that have been in contact with the water. Floodwater may be contaminated and could contain sewage. Disinfect and thoroughly clean everything that became wet.

Source: Modified after Environment Agency, United Kingdom. 2004. Floodline: Prepare for flooding. www.environment-agency.gov.uk/subjects/flood/826674/830330. *Accessed January 15, 2004.*

Summary

The region drained by a river and its tributaries is called a drainage basin or watershed. Streams carry chemicals in their dissolved load and sediment in their suspended and bed loads. Discharge refers to the volume of water moving past a particular location per unit time.

Sediment accumulates on the floodplain when a stream migrates laterally or when it overtops its banks during floods. Streams can be braided, anastomosing, or meandering.

Flooding happens when a stream overtops its banks. Upstream floods and floods in small drainage basins are commonly produced by intense rain falling over a small area. Downstream floods are produced by rapid snowmelt and by storms of long duration or high intensity that affect a large area.

Flood magnitude and frequency are difficult to predict for many streams because of changing land use and short historical records. This difficulty is especially acute for extreme events, such as 100-year floods. The probability that a 100-year or greater flood will take place each year is the same, regardless of when the last 100-year flood occurred.

River flooding is the most universally experienced natural hazard. Floods can occur anywhere there are streams, and all regions of Canada and the United States face some threat of flooding. Flooding causes much death and damage, but it also maintains fertile lands, provides benefits to aquatic ecosystems, and deposits sediment on delta plains, countering the subsidence that may occur there.

Urbanization has increased flooding in small drainage basins by covering much of the ground with buildings, parking lots, and roads, thereby increasing runoff of storm water.

Loss of life from flooding is relatively low in developed countries, which have monitoring and warning systems and adequate resources for recovery. Property damage, however, is much greater in developed countries than in developing ones because floodplains are often extensively developed and have more infrastructure at risk.

Perhaps the best strategy for minimizing flood damage is floodplain regulation. However, engineered structures are required to protect existing development on floodplains. These structures include physical barriers, such as levees and flood walls, and dams that regulate the release of water from reservoirs.

Channelization is the straightening, deepening, widening, cleaning, or lining of existing streams, with the goal of controlling floods or improving drainage. Many channelization schemes have caused serious environmental damage, thus new projects must be carefully evaluated. New approaches to channel modification mimic natural processes, and some channelized streams are being restored to a more natural state.

Flood hazards and risk are generally understood at the institutional level but not necessarily at the individual level. More educational programs are needed to help people understand the risk of living in flood-prone areas.

Adjustments to flood hazards include flood insurance, floodproofing, and floodplain regulation. Dykes and other protective structures tend to encourage further development of floodplains by providing a false sense of security, thereby increasing risk. The first step in floodplain regulation is flood-hazard mapping. Planners use flood-hazard maps to zone flood-prone areas for appropriate uses. In some cases, homes in flood-prone areas have been purchased and demolished by governments and people have relocated to safe ground.

Key Terms

100-year flood (p. 194)
channel pattern (p. 183)
channel restoration (p. 208)
channelization (p. 206)
discharge (p. 182)
drainage basin (p. 182)
flooding (p. 189)
floodplain (p. 182)
floodplain regulation (p. 211)
levee (p. 205)
recurrence interval (p. 190)
river (p. 182)
stream (p. 182)

Review Questions

1. What is a drainage basin?
2. What are the three components that constitute the total load of a stream?
3. What were the lessons learned from the 1992 flood of the Ventura River?
4. Differentiate among braided, anastomosing, and meandering rivers.
5. What is the difference between pools and riffles?
6. How do upstream and downstream floods differ?
7. What are the primary and secondary effects of flooding?
8. What are the major factors that determine the amount of damage a flood causes?
9. How does urbanization affect flood hazard?
10. What is meant by floodplain regulation?
11. What is channelization?
12. What is channel restoration?
13. Describe the techniques used to flood-proof structures.
14. What do we mean when we say that a 10-year flood has occurred?
15. What are the differences between the Canadian and American flood-damage-reduction programs?

Critical Thinking Questions

1. You are a planner working for a community that is planning to put new subdivisions in the headwaters of a drainage basin. You are aware of the effects of urbanization on flooding and want to make recommendations to avoid some of these effects. Outline a plan of action.
2. You work for a local government that has been channelizing streams for many years. Bulldozers are used to straighten and widen channels, and the agency has been criticized for causing extensive environmental damage. You have been asked to develop new plans for channel restoration as part of a stream-maintenance program. Devise a plan that will convince the official in charge of the channelization program that your ideas will improve the urban stream environment while reducing flood risk.
3. What is your personal opinion about development on floodplains? What type of development, if any, should be allowed? What measures should be taken to protect structures on or near the floodplain? Formulate an argument to support your views.

Selected Web Resources

PSEPC
www.psepc.gc.ca Flood information from Public Safety and Emergency Preparedness Canada

Flood-Hazard Management
www.env.gov.bc.ca/wsd Flood information from the government of British Columbia

USGS
www.usgs.gov/themes/flood.html Flood information from the U.S. Geological Survey

NOVA Online: Flood!
www.pbs.org/wgbh/nova/flood Flood information from the Public Broadcasting System program NOVA

FEMA
www.fema.gov/about/divisions/mitigationmitigation.shtm Information about flood mapping, flood insurance, and flood mitigation from the Federal Emergency Management Agency

Coping with Floods
www.ag.ndsu.nodak.edu/flood From North Dakota State University

Dartmouth Flood Observatory
www.dartmouth.edu/~floods Information about detection, mapping, measurement, and analysis of extreme flood events

Flash Floods and Flood Safety
www.floodsafety.com Texas Environmental Center project to promote flood safety; emphasis on flash floods

HAZARD CITY: ASSIGNMENTS IN APPLIED GEOLOGY

Flood Insurance Rate Maps

The Issue

The Federal Emergency Management Agency has prepared flood maps for most river valleys in the United States. These maps show areas that would be inundated during a 100-year flood. Insurance rates differ widely depending on the map zone within which a property is located. For example, the owner of a $200,000 house located in a zone determined to be 30 cm or more *above* base flood elevation may pay $600 per year for flood insurance. Were the same house in a zone 30 cm or more *below* base flood elevation, the owner may pay up to $2500 per year for flood insurance.

Your Task

You are working as a geologist for an insurance company and you use FEMA flood maps daily. Today, your job is to assess the flood risk for three residential properties and to determine how much the homeowners will have to pay for flood insurance. To complete your work, you will use a Flood Insurance Rate Map (FIRM), a map that shows the different flood hazard zones within the community; and detailed descriptions of each property, with historical flood information.

Average Completion Time

1 hour

CHAPTER 8

▶ **TORNADO IN DOWNTOWN MIAMI, FLORIDA**
This tornado struck downtown Miami with winds between 160 km/h and 180 km/h at 2:00 P.M. on May 12, 1997. It lasted only 15 minutes but caused more than $500,000 damage.
(Photo by Arthur Harvey, courtesy of the Miami Herald)

Learning Objectives

Atmospheric processes and energy exchanges are driven mainly by energy reaching Earth from the Sun and are linked to climate and weather. Hurricanes, thunderstorms, tornadoes, blizzards, dust storms, heat waves, and flash floods resulting from intense precipitation are natural processes that are hazardous to people and are responsible for significant destruction and many deaths each year throughout the world. Your goals in reading this chapter should be to

- Understand Earth's energy balance and energy exchanges that produce climate and weather
- Know the different types of severe weather events
- Know the main effects of severe weather events and their relations to other natural hazards
- Understand how people interact with severe weather
- Understand how to minimize the adverse effects of severe weather
- Recognize the natural service functions of severe weather

Severe Weather

Tri-State Tornado, March 18, 1925

Although the majority of weather-related deaths in North America are the result of blizzards and heat waves, tornadoes are feared most by many people living in the mid-continent area of the United States and parts of Canada. This fear is well founded—a **tornado**, defined as a violently rotating column of air carrying extreme winds, can cause tremendous property damage and loss of life.

In just three and one-half hours on March 18, 1925, the Tri-State tornado killed more people and destroyed more property than any other tornado in historic time. The tornado was unique in several ways. First, it was in contact with the ground for 350 km, more than 180 km longer than any other tornado to date.[1] Second, the average width of the tornado was more than 1 km and its maximum width was 1.6 km. Only 73 of the more than 35,000 tornadoes reported in the United States have been as wide or wider than the Tri-State tornado.[1] Its width contributed to extreme damage over at least 425 km^2 (Figure 8.1). Third, the tornado had a straight path, in contrast to the curved track of most tornadoes. Fourth, the tornado's average forward speed of 100 km/h is one of the greatest ever reported. Most tornadoes travel at about half this speed.[2] People in the tornado's path assumed they were dealing with a thunderstorm because it was so broad, and, in fact, there were associated thunderstorms. The violent winds killed at least 695 people and injured more than 2000 others. Total damage, expressed in year 2007 dollars, was about US$200 million.

Topography had no effect on the tornado; it traversed hills as high as 425 m and crossed valleys and lowlands. The tornado's rotational winds had velocities of up to 290 km/h. Much of the death and damage resulted from the collapse of buildings, but flying debris was also responsible for much destruction (Figure 8.2).

Five factors account for the unprecedented death and damage caused by the Tri-State tornado: (1) no tornado forecasts or warnings were issued because the technology for them did not exist in 1925, (2) the tornado destroyed telephone lines that would have been used to warn people along its path, (3) it was exceptionally large and strong, (4) massive amounts of flying debris and dust masked the funnel shape and made it hard to recognize the storm as a tornado, and (5) many of the homes and farms of the time were poorly constructed and unable to withstand the strong winds.[3] If a similar tornado occurs in the future,

Barnett Bank
SunTrust
First Union

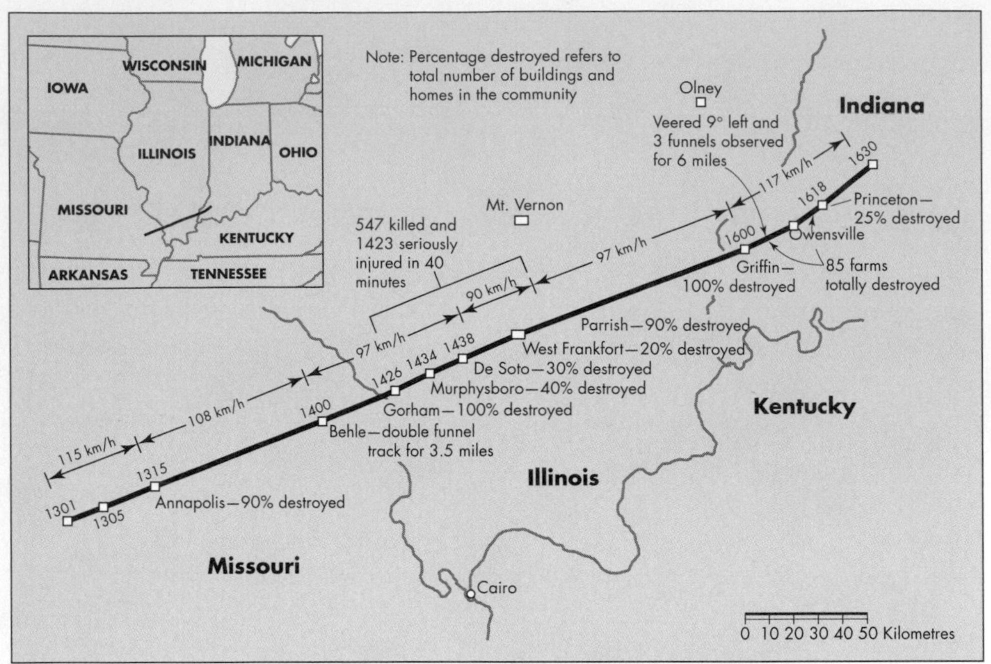

◄ **FIGURE 8.1 PATH OF A TORNADO** In three and one-half hours the Tri-State tornado of March 18, 1925, travelled 350 km from Reynolds County, Missouri, across Illinois, to near Princeton, Indiana. The tornado travelled at an average speed of 100 km/h and varied in width from 1 km to 1.5 km. The numbers from 1301 to 1630 along the tornado track refer to the time of day. *(Modified from Wilson, J. W., and S. A. Changnon, Jr. Illinois tornadoes. Illinois State Water Survey Circular 103. Urbana, IL)*

successful forecasting and warning, along with better construction techniques, will save many lives.

8.1 Energy

The concept of energy is fundamental to understanding severe weather. Energy is an abstract concept because we cannot see or feel it. It can, however, be quantified. The energy of moving objects can be approximated by the equation

$$E = mv^2/2,$$

where E is the energy of the moving body, m is its mass, and v is its velocity.

Another important concept is *force*. We experience force when we push or pull an object. For example, when we pull a box along the floor, or push our car after it has stalled, we exert a force in a specific direction. The strength or magnitude of this force can be measured by how much the force accelerates the motion of the box or car. Mathematically, force is expressed by the equation

$$F = ma,$$

where F is force, m is the mass of the moving body, and a is acceleration, or the change in velocity of the object per unit time. A newton (N) is defined as the force required to accelerate a 1 kg mass 1 m/s each second that it is in motion.

Another important concept in understanding energy is *work*. Work is done when energy is expended. In physics, work is the energy expended in applying a force to move an object a specific distance. Work is calculated by multiplying the force times the distance over which it is applied. It is measured in *joules* (J), defined as a force of 1 N applied over a distance of 1 m. The work done by a typical thunderstorm is approximately 10 trillion J. In contrast, an average hurricane does approximately 100,000 times that amount of work.

◄ **FIGURE 8.2 THE MOST DESTRUCTIVE TORNADO IN HISTORY** These are the ruins of the Longfellow School in Murphysboro, Illinois, where 17 children were killed by the Tri-State Tornado. The tornado struck the school at 2:34 P.M. on March 19, 1925. Most of the children were killed by the collapse of the school's un-reinforced brick walls. Trees surrounding the school were also destroyed. In Murphysboro, 234 people were killed, the largest number of tornado deaths in a single town in U.S. history. *(National Oceanic and Atmospheric Administration)*

The rate at which work is done is *power*—energy divided by time. Power is expressed as joules per second, or *watts* (W), where 1 J/s = 1 W. Many people associate watts with the power used by appliances and light bulbs. A light bulb, for example, may have a rated power of 100 W.

Atmospheric processes involve huge amounts of energy and power. The amounts of energy are so large that they may be expressed in terawatts (tW). One tW = 1 trillion W = 1 million megawatts (MW). The total solar energy absorbed at Earth's surface is approximately 120,000 tW per year, and it is mainly this power that heats our planet, evaporates water, and produces the differential heating that causes air masses to move. In comparison, current global energy consumption by people is less than 0.01 percent of this value, about 13 tW per year.

Types of Energy

The three main types of energy are potential energy, kinetic energy, and heat energy. *Potential energy* is stored energy. For example, the water held behind a dam contains potential energy that may be used to produce electricity. *Kinetic energy* is the energy of motion. A book on a shelf contains potential energy based on its height above the ground. If it falls from the shelf to the ground, it loses potential energy and gains kinetic energy.

Heat energy is the energy of the random motion of atoms and molecules and can be defined as the kinetic energy of atoms or molecules within a substance. Heat may also be thought of as energy transferred from one body to another because of the temperature difference between the two bodies.[4] The two types of heat that are important in atmospheric processes are sensible heat and latent heat. As the name suggests, *sensible heat* is heat that may be sensed or measured by a thermometer. It is the sensible heat that we feel in the air. *Latent heat* is heat that is either absorbed or released when a substance changes phase, for example, from a solid to a liquid or from a liquid to a gas. Latent heat in the atmosphere is related to the three phases of water: ice, liquid water, and water vapour. The evaporation of water involves a phase change from liquid water to water vapour and the expenditure of energy. The energy required for this transformation is called the *latent heat of vaporization*. It is recovered when water vapour changes back into liquid water through condensation in the atmosphere, producing rain.[4]

Heat Transfer

To complete our discussion of energy, work, and power, we now consider how heat energy is transferred in the atmosphere. The three major processes of atmospheric heat—conduction, convection, and radiation—can be understood by observing a pot of boiling water on an electric stove (Figure 8.3).

Conduction is the transfer of heat through a substance by means of atomic or molecular interactions. It requires a difference in temperature within the substance; heat will move from an area of greater temperature to one of lesser temperature. In our example, conduction of heat through the metal pot causes the handle to heat up. Conduction also occurs in the atmosphere, on land, and in bodies of water, such as the ocean. For example, warm surface ocean water may lose heat by conduction to the cooler air above.

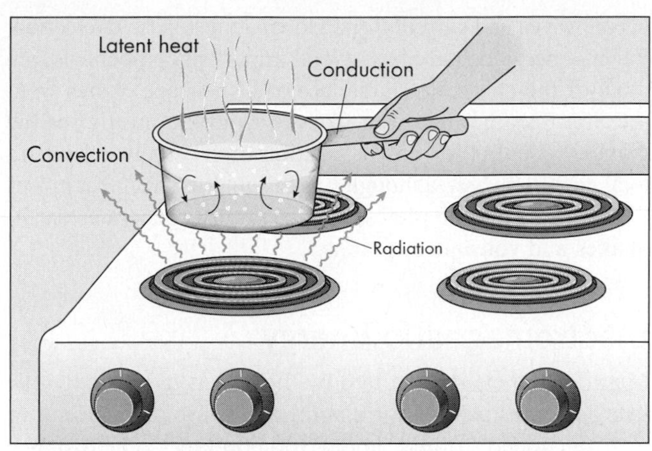

▲ **FIGURE 8.3 HEAT TRANSFER PROCESSES** Heat is transferred by conduction, convection, and radiation when water is boiled on an electric stove. *(Modified from Christopherson, R. W. 2003. Geosystems, 5th ed. Upper Saddle River, NJ: Prentice Hall)*

Convection is the transfer of heat by the movement of a fluid, such as water or air. In our example, water at the bottom of the pot warms and rises upward to displace the cooler water at the surface. The cooler water sinks to the bottom of the pot. This process physically mixes the water by creating a circulation loop known as a *convection cell*. Convection is an important process in transferring heat in thunderstorms.

Radiation is wave-like energy emitted by a substance that possesses heat. The transfer of energy by radiation occurs by oscillations in electric and magnetic fields; thus, the waves are called *electromagnetic waves*. In our example, heat energy radiates from the heating element in the electric stove to the pot on the stove. Some of these electromagnetic waves are visible to the eye—light emanating from the glowing coil on the stove—but most are not.

Summarizing our example, heat is transferred from the electric stove first by radiation from the glowing heating coil on the stove, then by conduction through the metal pot, and finally by convection, which moves warm water upward from the bottom to the top of the pot.

8.2 Earth's Energy Balance

The energy that reaches Earth from the Sun affects the atmosphere, oceans, land, and living things before being radiated back into space. *Earth's energy balance* is the equilibrium between incoming and outgoing energy (Figure 8.4). Energy changes form repeatedly and in a complex manner from the time it reaches Earth to the time it leaves, but it is neither created nor destroyed.

Earth intercepts only a tiny fraction of the total energy emitted by the Sun, but the intercepted energy is adequate to sustain life. Solar energy also drives the hydrologic cycle, ocean waves and currents, and global atmospheric circulation. Earth's energy balance has several important components, but most of the energy available at Earth's surface comes from the Sun. Geothermal heat, derived from the interior of the planet, accounts for only a fraction of 1 percent of Earth's total energy budget, although it is this internal heat that moves Earth's lithospheric plates, which, in turn, generates earthquakes and volcanic eruptions.

Electromagnetic Energy

Much of the energy emitted by the Sun is *electromagnetic energy*. It has a wave form and travels through space at or near the speed of light, about 300,000 km/s. The distance between the crests or troughs of two successive waves is referred to as the *wavelength* (Figure 8.5). The various types of electromagnetic radiation are distinguished by their wavelengths, and the collection of all possible wavelengths is known as the *electromagnetic spectrum* (Figure 8.6). Electromagnetic waves with long wavelengths (greater than 1 m) include radio waves and microwaves. At the other end of the spectrum, waves with very short wavelengths of less than 0.01 microns (μm) are X-rays and gamma rays. Visible electromagnetic radiation, referred to as light, makes up only a very small fraction of the total electromagnetic spectrum. Other significant types of electromagnetic radiation include infrared (IR) and ultraviolet (UV) waves. Infrared radiation plays an important role in maintaining temperatures in Earth's atmosphere that allow the planet to support life. Levels of UV radiation at Earth's surface are influenced by the planet's magnetic field and by ozone in the upper atmosphere.

Radiation, Absorption, and Temperature

Radiation and absorption of electromagnetic energy are affected by both temperature and reflectivity. An object's temperature influences the amount and type of electromagnetic radiation it emits. As you might expect, hot objects emit more electromagnetic energy than cool objects do. The amount of energy radiated from an object each second is proportional to the fourth power of the object's surface absolute temperature (kelvins or K). Thus, if the surface temperature of the object doubles, the radiated energy increases 16 times. As a consequence, the Sun, with a surface temperature of 5800°C (about 6100 K), radiates much more energy per unit area than does Earth, which has an average surface temperature of 15°C (about 290 K).

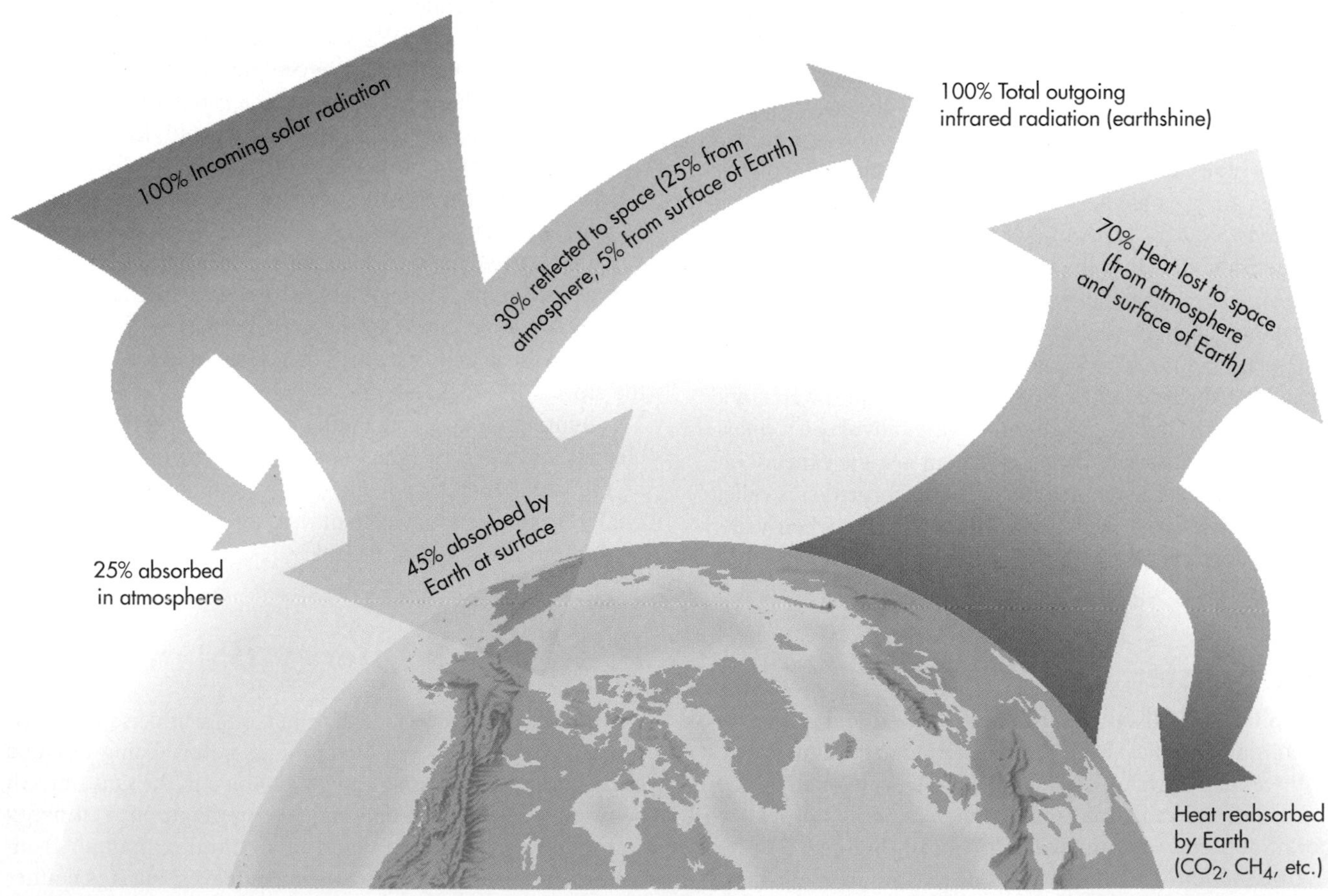

▲ **FIGURE 8.4 EARTH'S ENERGY BALANCE** Most of the energy flow to Earth from the Sun is either reflected or radiated back into space. Only a small proportion of the heat at Earth's surface comes from the interior of the planet. *(Modified after Pruitt, N. L., L. S. Underwood, and W. Surver. 1999. Bioinquiry learning system 1.0: Making connections in biology. Toronto: John Wiley & Sons)*

An object's temperature also affects the wavelength of the electromagnetic radiation it emits. Hot objects radiate energy more rapidly and at shorter wavelengths than do cool objects. The Sun emits mainly short-wave radiation, such as gamma rays, X-rays, and visible and ultraviolet light. In contrast, Earth's land surface, oceans, and clouds are so cool that they emit mainly longer wavelength infrared radiation.

Absorption of energy is similarly affected by surface temperature. A cold object on Earth's surface will initially absorb a large amount of incoming solar energy and therefore warm up. As it warms, however, the object begins to radiate more energy. With a constant input of energy, the object will eventually reach an equilibrium temperature that allows it to absorb and radiate energy at the same rate. Earth receives approximately 5.5 million exajoules (EJ) (1 EJ = 10^{18} J) of energy from the Sun, and it radiates the same amount of energy back into space (Figure 8.4).

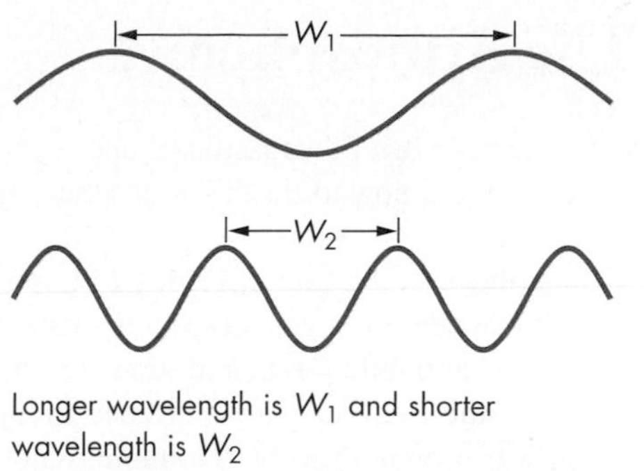

▲ **FIGURE 8.5 WAVELENGTH** Wavelength (W) is the distance between one wave crest and the next.

Reflectivity The colour of an object also plays a role in absorbing and radiating energy. **Albedo** is an object's ability to reflect electromagnetic energy. Dark or black surfaces absorb and radiate electromagnetic energy readily and thus have low albedos. In contrast, light-coloured or white surfaces, such as the upper surfaces of clouds, reflect electromagnetic energy rather than absorb it, and they have relatively high albedos. The proportion of solar energy reflected from clouds ranges from 30 percent for thin clouds to 90 percent for thick clouds. The proportion of solar energy reflected from vegetation is 30 percent to 40 percent for light-coloured dry grassland and 5 percent to 15 percent for darker coniferous pine forests. Snow and ice have the highest albedo of all naturally occurring materials at Earth's surface.

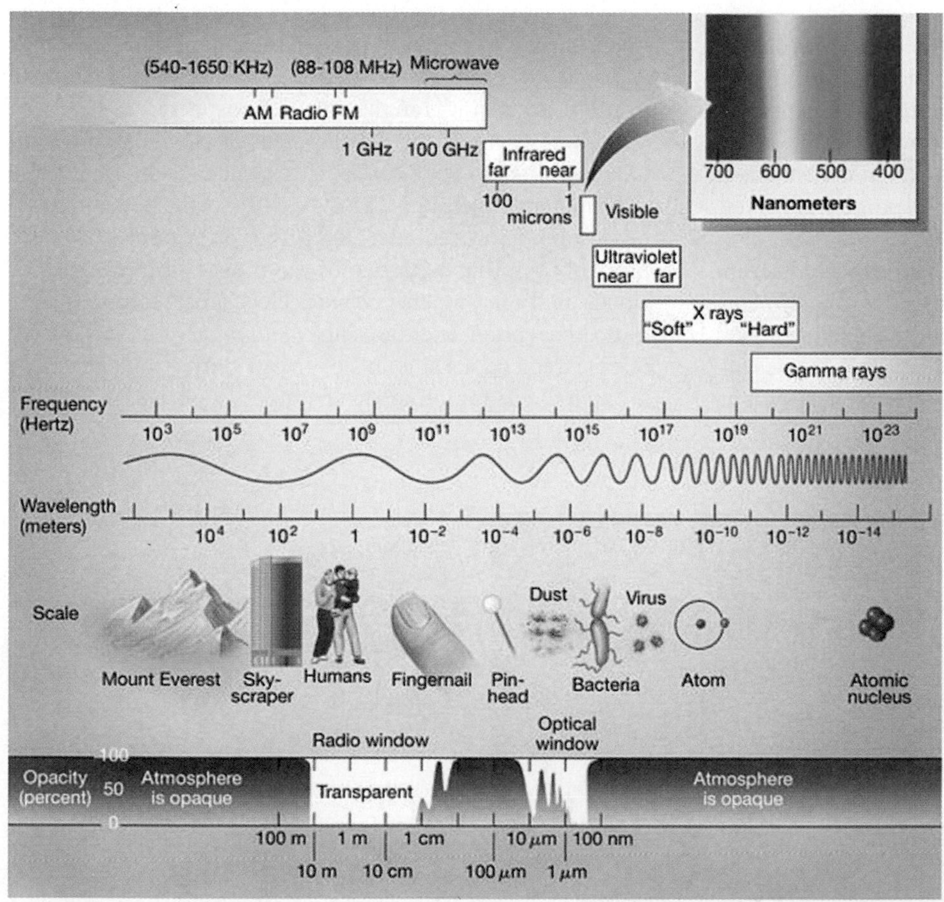

▲ **FIGURE 8.6 THE ELECTROMAGNETIC SPECTRUM** Wavelengths in the electromagnetic spectrum range from fractions of a micron in the case of X-rays and gamma rays to thousands of metres for long radio waves. Electromagnetic waves travel at the speed of light in a vacuum, about 300,000 km/s. *(Chaisson, Eric and McMillan, Steve, Astronomy Today, Fifth Edition, © 2005. Adapted by permission of Pearson Education, Inc., Upper Saddle River, NJ.)*

8.3 The Atmosphere

Having completed our brief discussion of energy and Earth's energy balance, we turn now to Earth's atmosphere and atmospheric circulation.

The **atmosphere** is the thin envelope of gases that surrounds Earth. It is made up of gas molecules, suspended solid and liquid particles, and falling rain and snow. The atmosphere is responsible for the weather we experience every day and it keeps Earth warm enough to be habitable. Knowledge of the structure and dynamics of the atmosphere is critical to understanding severe weather, as well as the mechanism and causes of global warming, which will be covered in Chapter 11.

Composition of the Atmosphere

Earth's atmosphere is mainly made up of nitrogen and oxygen, but it contains smaller amounts of argon, water vapour, and carbon dioxide, as well as traces of a host of other elements and compounds. With the exception of water vapour, we will discuss these gases in greater detail in Chapter 11.

Water vapour plays an important role in cloud formation and atmospheric circulation. We use the term *humidity* to describe the amount of water vapour, or moisture, in the atmosphere at a specific temperature. Humidity commonly changes with temperature, because warm air can hold more moisture than cold air. The amount of moisture in the air is expressed as **relative humidity**, the ratio, or percentage, of the water vapour present in the atmosphere to the maximum amount of water vapour that could be there. Values range from a few percent to 100 percent.

Almost all the water vapour in the atmosphere is evaporated from water at Earth's surface. Water is constantly being exchanged between the atmosphere on the one hand, and oceans, lakes, and continents on the other. Sleet, snow, hail, and rain remove water from the atmosphere and deposit it on Earth, where it may enter groundwater, rivers, lakes, oceans, and glaciers. Eventually this water evaporates and returns to the atmosphere to begin the cycle again. This constant cycling of water between the atmosphere and Earth's surface is a major part of the hydrologic cycle (see Chapter 1).

Structure of the Atmosphere

Images from orbiting satellites show that Earth's atmosphere is very thin compared with the diameter of the planet and that its upper limit is indistinct (Figure 8.7). Essentially the entire atmosphere lies below an altitude of 100 km.

Earth's atmosphere consists of four major layers or spheres (Figure 8.8). Here we focus on the lowest layer, the **troposphere**, which extends about 8 km to 16 km above the surface of the planet. We will discuss the other layers of the atmosphere in Chapter 11. Except during some jet airplane flights, we spend our entire lives within the troposphere. Not even the highest mountains breach the upper boundary of the troposphere, known as the *tropopause*. The defining characteristic of the troposphere is a rapid decrease in temperature upward, but the most visible feature is abundant condensed water vapour in the form of clouds. Clouds and the weather that directly affects us are in the troposphere.

Most water vapour condenses in the troposphere, leaving very little water in the higher layers of the atmosphere. The troposphere contains most of the atmospheric carbon dioxide and methane. Only ozone is significantly less abundant in the troposphere than it is in the upper atmosphere.

The formation and development of clouds are particularly important to our discussion of weather. Clouds comprise small water droplets or ice crystals; without them, there would be no rain, snow, thunder, lightning, or rainbows. You are probably familiar with two of the most common types of clouds: puffy fair-weather *cumulus* clouds that resemble pieces of floating cotton, and towering *cumulonimbus* clouds, which release tremendous amounts of energy during thunderstorms through condensation of water vapour (Figure 8.9).

◄ **FIGURE 8.7 EARTH'S THIN ATMOSPHERE** Viewed from space, the atmosphere appears as a thin layer surrounding Earth. *(NASA)*

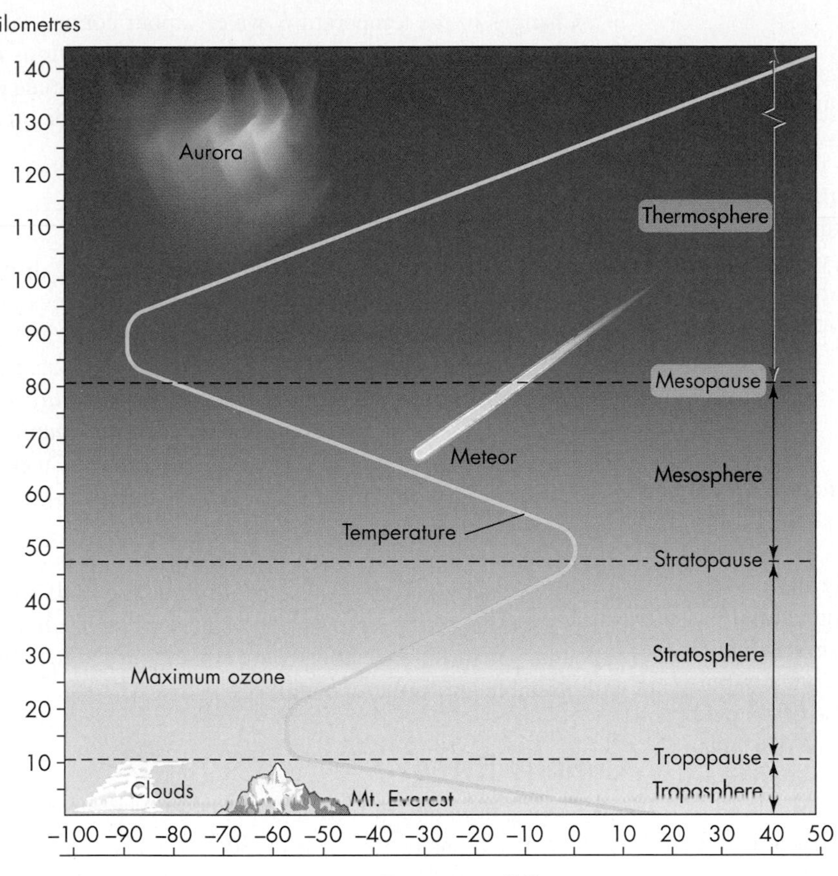

◀ **FIGURE 8.8 STRUCTURE OF EARTH'S ATMOSPHERE** Five atmospheric layers are defined on the basis of vertical changes in air temperature. The yellow line shows the change in air temperature with height above the surface of Earth. Weather develops in the lowest layer, the troposphere. *(Modified from Lutgens, F. K., and E. J. Tarbuck. 2004. The atmosphere: An introduction to meteorology, 9th ed. Upper Saddle River, NJ: Pearson Prentice Hall, with data from the National Weather Service)*

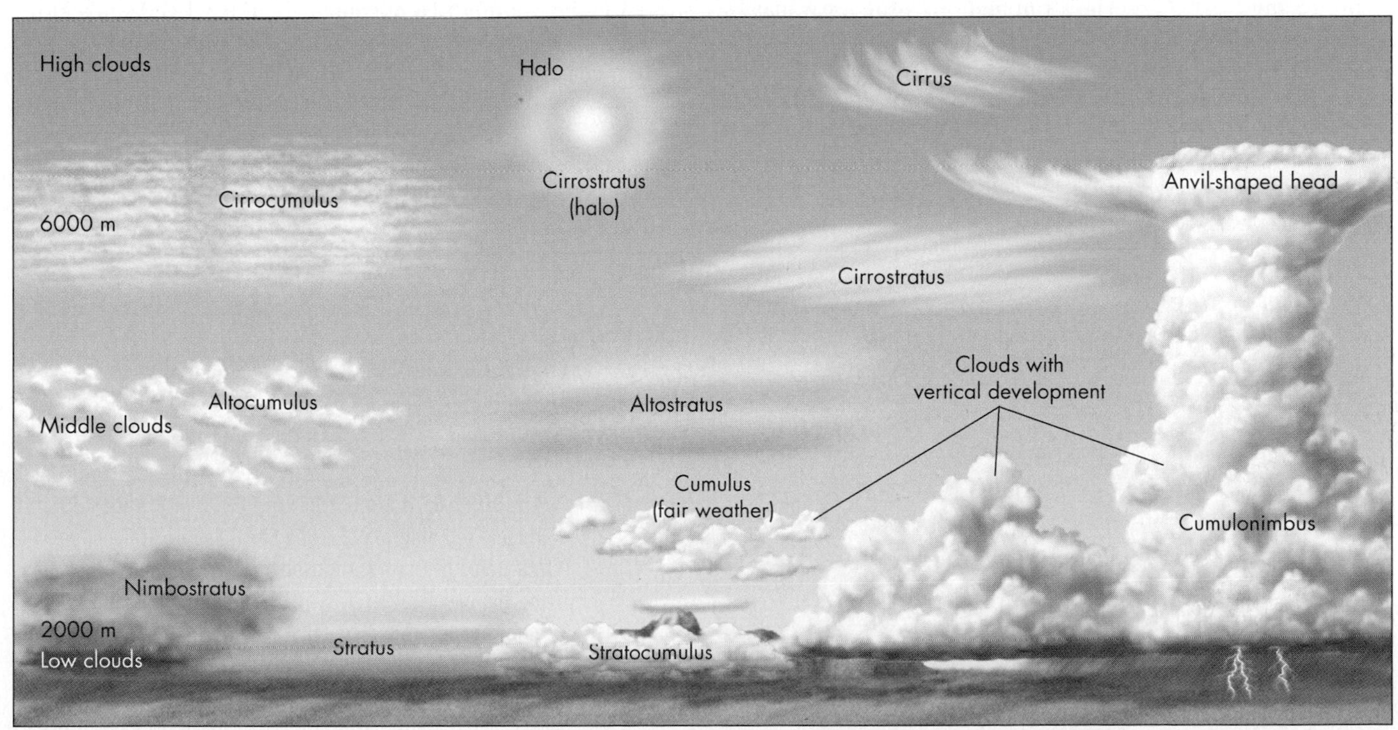

▲ **FIGURE 8.9 COMMON CLOUD TYPES** Clouds consist of very small water droplets and are classified on the basis of altitude (low, middle, and high) and form (cirriform, cumuliform, and stratiform). Cumulonimbus clouds are associated with severe thunderstorms and tornadoes. *(Modified from Christopherson, R. W. 2003. Geosystems, 5th ed. Upper Saddle River, NJ: Prentice Hall)*

8.4 Weather Processes

A complete discussion of atmospheric conditions and processes associated with severe weather is beyond the scope of this book. Students especially interested in this topic should pursue coursework in meteorology, the scientific study of weather. Here we focus on four aspects of the atmosphere that are important for understanding severe weather: atmospheric pressure, vertical stability of the atmosphere, the Coriolis effect, and the movement of air masses (fronts).

Atmospheric Pressure

Atmospheric pressure, also known as *barometric pressure*, is the weight of a column of air at a point on or above Earth's surface (Figure 8.10). It can also be thought of as the force exerted by gas molecules on a surface (Figure 8.11a). Atmospheric pressure is greater at sea level than at the top of a mountain, where there is less air above the surface (Figure 8.11b). Your ears "pop" during a drive up or down a mountain or when you take off in an airplane because of changes in atmospheric pressure. Nearly all the weight, and thus pressure, of the atmosphere is below an altitude of 50 km (Figure 8.11b).

Atmospheric pressure also differs over distances of tens to hundreds of kilometres across Earth's surface, and these differences strongly affect weather. Air rises and cools in areas of low atmospheric pressure; as the air cools, water vapour condenses to form clouds and precipitation. In contrast, in areas of high pressure, drier air slowly descends, producing clear skies. The air in high-pressure areas may be cold or hot depending on such factors as the time of year.

Changes in the temperature, water vapour content, and movement of air are responsible for horizontal variations in atmospheric pressure. Air flows horizontally from areas of high pressure to areas of low pressure; thus, atmospheric pressure differences are a major driving force for wind.

Unstable Air

Air also moves because of the vertical heterogeneity of the troposphere. We can understand these movements by examining the behaviour of a small volume or *parcel* of air. The tendency of a parcel of air to remain in place or to change its vertical position is referred to as *atmospheric stability*. An air mass is stable if its parcels resist vertical movement or return to their original position after they have moved. In contrast, an air mass is said to be unstable if its parcels rise until they reach air of similar temperature and density.[5] The atmosphere becomes unstable when lighter warm air is overlain by denser cold air. Under these conditions, the instability causes some parcels of air to sink and others to rise like hot air balloons. Air turbulence and severe weather are associated with unstable atmospheric conditions.

Coriolis Effect

Air moving from a high-pressure area to a low-pressure area tends to flow along a straight path. So why are wind patterns across Earth's surface curved? The answer is that the planet, our frame of reference, rotates beneath the flowing air masses, causing the winds to take a curved path. This change in motion or deflection is known as the **Coriolis effect.** Winds are deflected to the right in the Northern Hemisphere and to the left in the Southern Hemisphere (Figure 8.12). Winds along the Equator are not affected by the Coriolis effect.

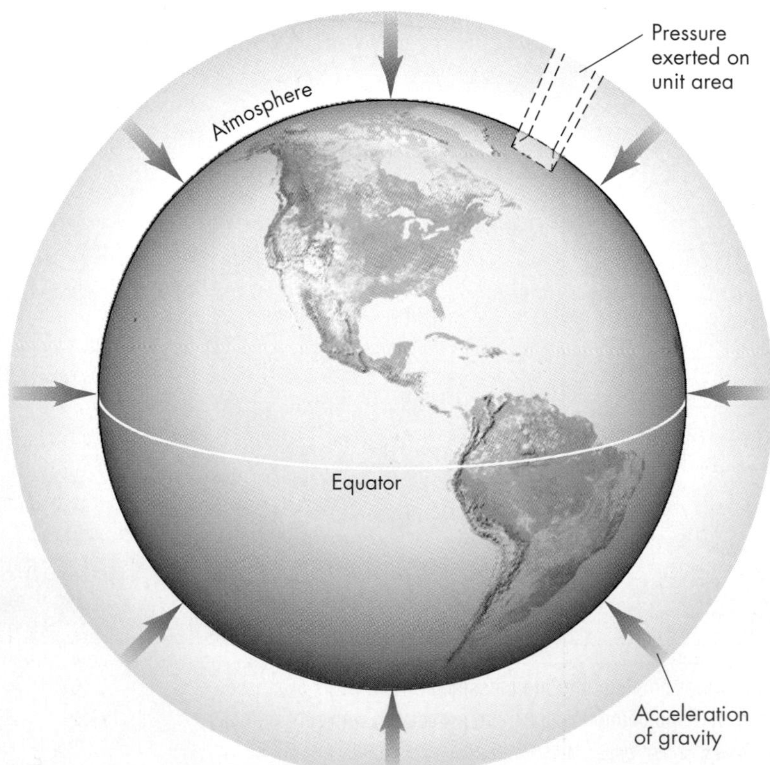

◄ **FIGURE 8.10 ATMOSPHERIC FORCE AND AIR PRESSURE** An idealized diagram showing Earth and its atmosphere. The total force of Earth's atmosphere is the product of its mass and the acceleration of gravity. Both the mass and gravitational acceleration are constant; therefore, the total force exerted by the atmosphere is also constant. However, atmospheric pressure at Earth's surface, which is expressed as force per unit area, differs from place to place because of differences in the temperature and density of the air. *(Modified from Aguado, E., and J. E. Burt. 2002. Understanding weather and climate, 2nd ed. Upper Saddle River, NJ: Prentice Hall)*

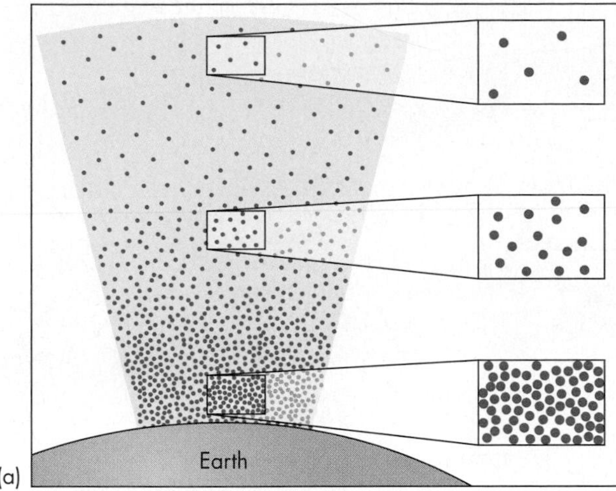

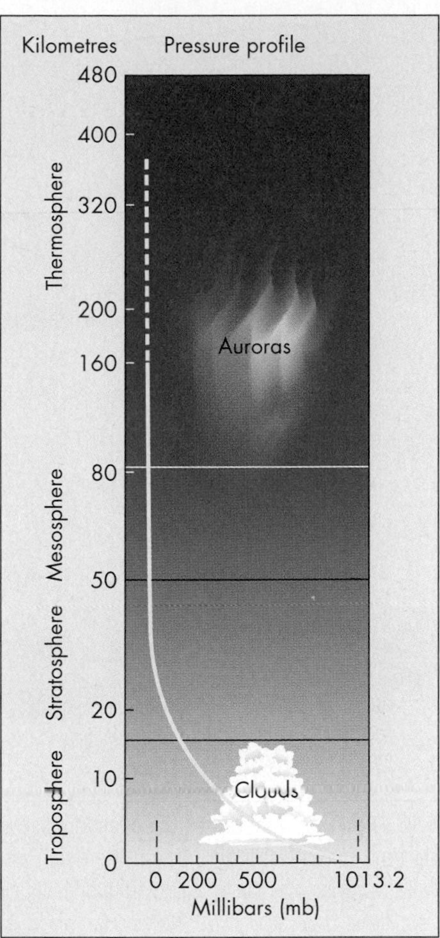

▲ **FIGURE 8.11 AIR PRESSURE** Both the density (a) and the pressure (b) of Earth's atmosphere decrease with altitude. The dots in (a) represent gas molecules in the air. Air pressure in (b) is measured in millibars. One atmosphere of pressure equals 1 bar or 1000 millibars. *(Modified from Christopherson, R. W. 2003. Geosystems, 5th ed. Upper Saddle River, NJ: Prentice Hall)*

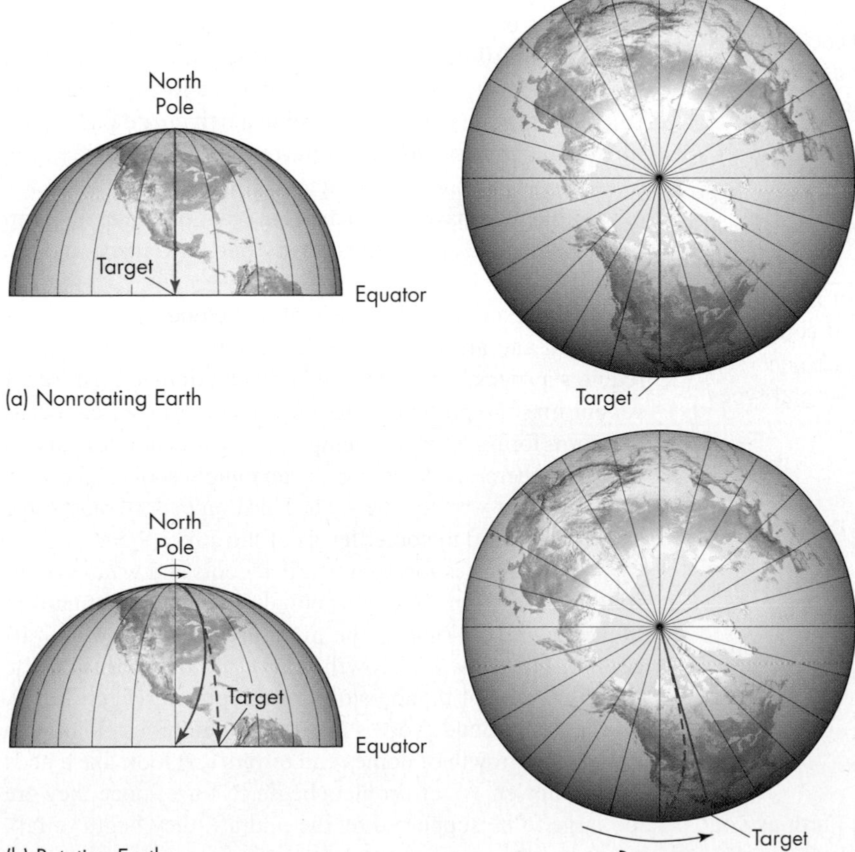

◄ **FIGURE 8.12 CORIOLIS EFFECT** The Coriolis effect can be demonstrated by using the hypothetical scenario of a one-hour flight of a rocket from the North Pole to the Equator. (a) If Earth were not rotating, the rocket would travel straight to the Equator. (b) However, because the planet is rotating about 15° per hour, the rocket appears to follow a curved path on Earth's surface, which is our reference plane. A rocket flying from the South Pole to the Equator would follow a curved path opposite to that shown here. *(Modified from Lutgens, F. K., and E. J. Tarbuck. 2004. The atmosphere: An introduction to meteorology, 9th ed. Upper Saddle River, NJ: Pearson Prentice Hall)*

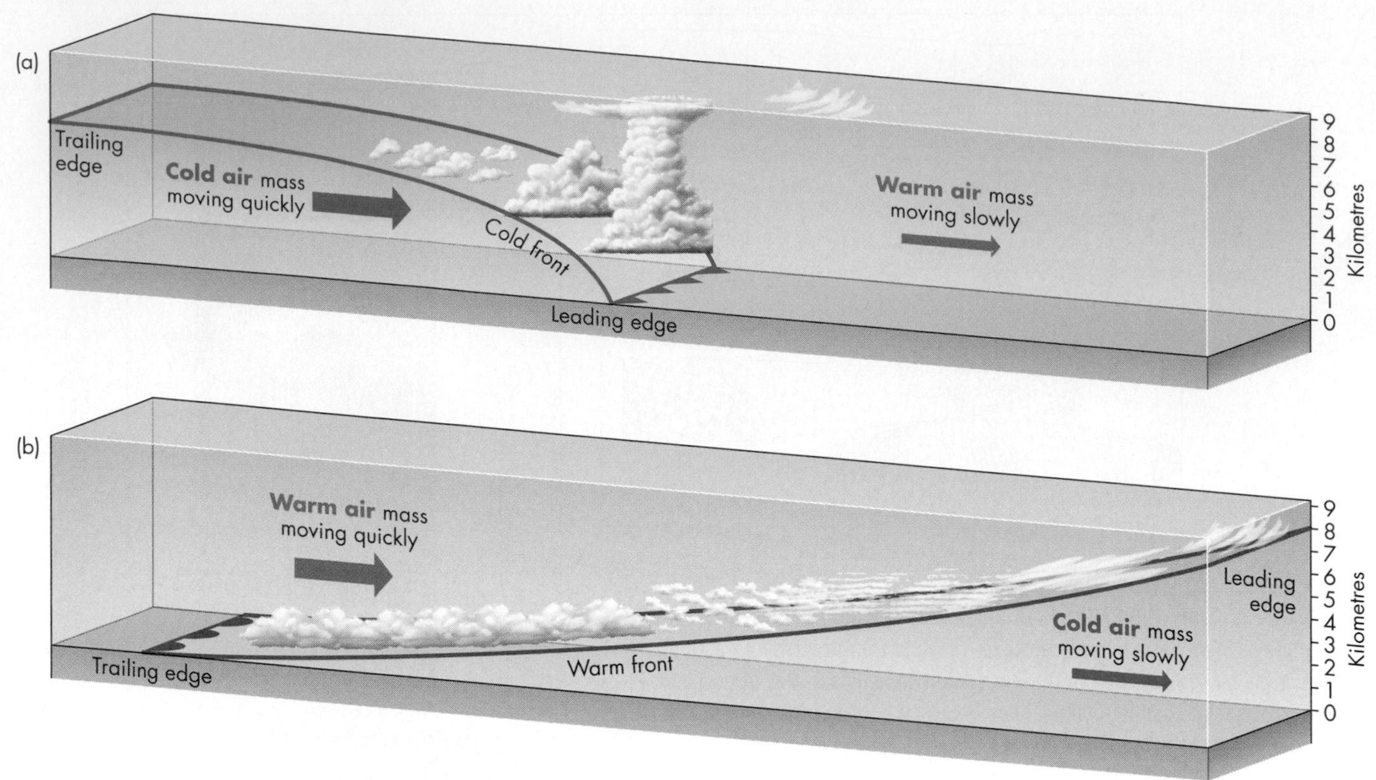

▲ **FIGURE 8.13 FRONTS** A front marks the boundary between two air masses of different density and temperature. (a) An advancing cold front forces warm air upward. The rising warm air creates clouds and heavy precipitation. (b) An advancing warm front forces warm air over cooler air, again producing clouds and precipitation. *(Modified from McKnight, T. L., and D. Hess. 2004. Physical geography, 8th ed. Upper Saddle River, NJ: Pearson Prentice Hall)*

Fronts

Meteorologists refer to the boundary between a cool air mass and a warm air mass as a *front*. A cold front forms when cool air moves into a mass of warm air; the opposite is true for a warm front (Figure 8.13). A *stationary front* is one with a boundary that does not move much. All three types of fronts can cause severe weather. A developing storm typically has a preceding warm front and a faster-moving cold front. North of the warm front is a mass of cooler air that was in place before the storm entered the area. As the storm intensifies, its cold front may overtake the warm front and come into contact with the older cool air mass, forming an *occluded front*. Figure 8.14 is a weather map that shows several types of fronts as well as areas of high and low pressure.

8.5 Hazardous Weather

The basic principles of atmospheric physics described above help us understand severe weather and its associated hazards. Severe weather events include thunderstorms, tornadoes, blizzards, heat waves, dust storms, and hurricanes (hurricanes are discussed separately in Chapter 9).

Thunderstorms

Thousands of thunderstorms are occurring on Earth as you read this chapter. Most of them are in equatorial regions. For example, the city of Kampala, Uganda, near the Equator in East Africa experiences thunderstorms, on average, nearly 7 out of every 10 days. In North America, thunderstorms are most frequent along the Front Range of the Rocky Mountains in Colorado and New Mexico and in a belt encompassing all of Florida and the southern parts of Georgia, Alabama, Mississippi, and Louisiana (Figure 8.15). However, most readers are likely to have experienced at least one thunderstorm because they occur in almost every part of Canada and the United States.

Although rain falls anywhere that clouds become oversaturated and are forced to release water, a thunderstorm requires a special set of atmospheric conditions. First, water vapour must be present in the troposphere to feed clouds as the storm forms. Second, a temperature gradient must exist in the troposphere, so that rising air can rapidly cool and become emplaced over warmer, moist air. Third, an updraft must force moist air upward to cooler levels of the atmosphere.

As moist air is forced upward, it cools and water vapour condenses to form a cumulus cloud. The cloud continues to grow upward as long as the moisture supply and updraft persist. This upward growth marks the beginning of the *cumulus stage* of thunderstorm development (Figure 8.16). The cumulus cloud evolves into a cumulonimbus cloud with the upward growth of domes and towers that look like a head of cauliflower. Water droplets begin to form; once they are too large to be supported by the updraft, they begin to fall, creating a downdraft.

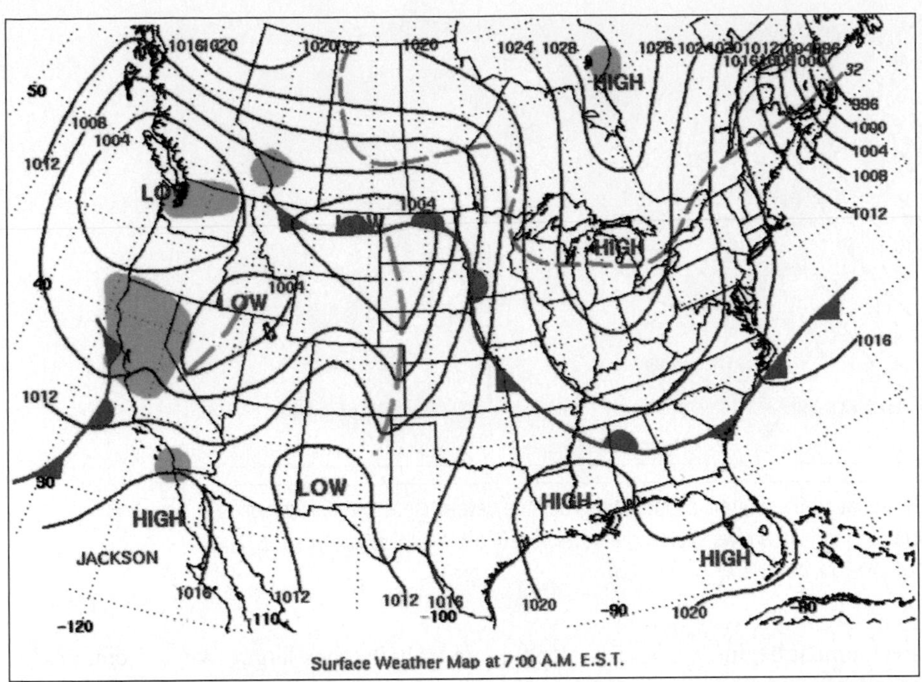

▲ **FIGURE 8.14 WEATHER MAP** This map depicts surface weather over the United States and southern Canada on April 13, 2003. It shows positions of high and low pressure centres (HIGH and LOW), two low-pressure troughs (orange dashed lines), a cold front extending east into the Atlantic Ocean (blue line with triangles), a warm front in North Dakota (red line with half circles), a stationary front in the lower Mississippi Valley (cold and warm front symbols on opposite sides of the alternating red and purple line), an occluded front off the California coast (alternating cold and warm front symbols on the same side of the purple line), a line delineating a surface temperature of 0°C (dashed blue line over central and eastern Canada), and areas of precipitation (green). The reddish brown contour lines show atmospheric pressure in millibars. *(U.S. National Weather Service)*

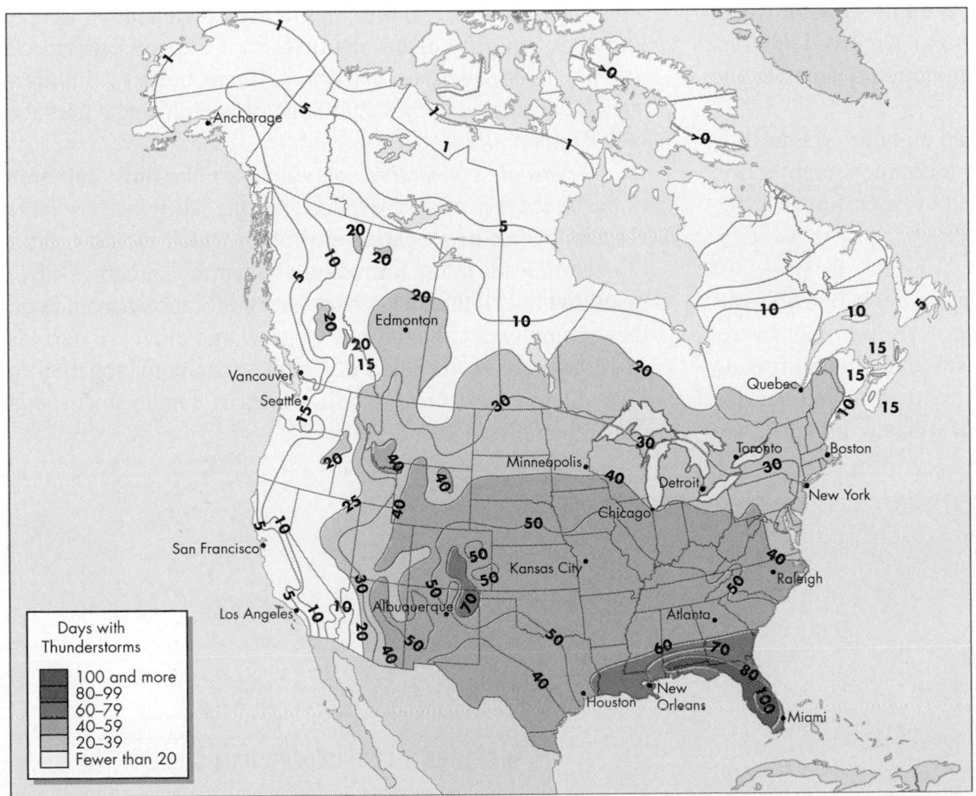

▲ **FIGURE 8.15 THUNDERSTORM OCCURRENCE IN NORTH AMERICA** This map of Canada and the United States shows the average number of days per year with thunderstorms. *(From Christopherson, R. W. 2003. Geosystems, 5th ed. Upper Saddle River, NJ: Prentice Hall, with data from the National Weather Service and Map Series 3, Climate Atlas of Canada)*

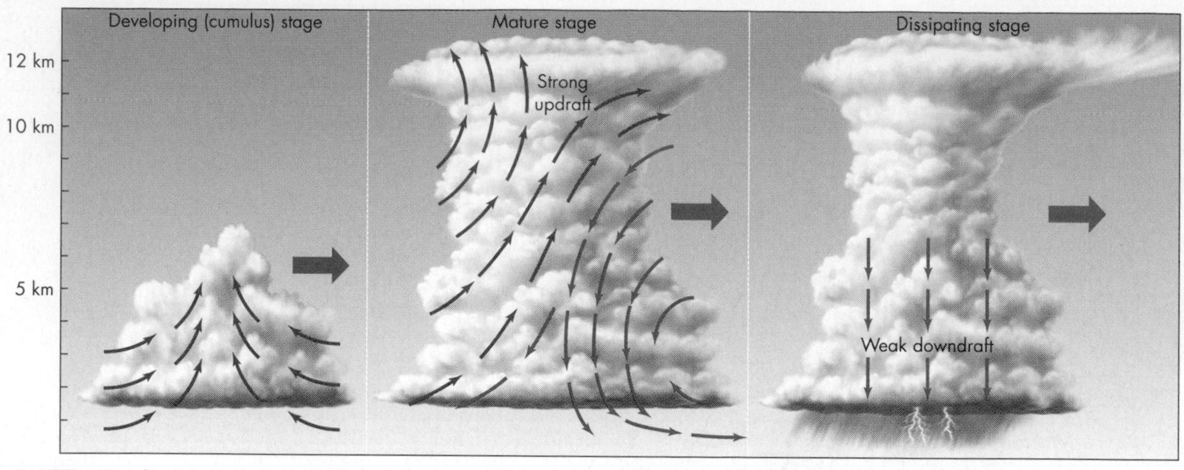

▲ **FIGURE 8.16 LIFE CYCLE OF A THUNDERSTORM** An idealized diagram showing stages in the development and dissipation of a thunderstorm. Red arrows show updrafts of warm air and blue arrows show downdrafts of cold air. *(Modified from Aguado, E., and J. E. Burt. 2001. Understanding weather and climate, 2nd ed. Upper Saddle River, NJ: Prentice Hall)*

The *mature stage* of thunderstorm development begins when the downdraft and falling precipitation leave the base of the cloud (Figure 8.16). At this time, the storm has both updrafts and downdrafts, and it continues to grow until it reaches the top of the unstable atmosphere near the tropopause. Updrafts may continue to build the cloud outward to form a characteristic anvil shape (Figure 8.17). The storm produces its most intense precipitation, thunder, and lightning during the mature stage (Case Study 8.1).

The final, or *dissipative*, stage of a thunderstorm begins when the supply of moist air is blocked by downdrafts at the lower levels of the cloud (Figure 8.16). Deprived of moisture, the thunderstorm weakens, precipitation decreases, and the cloud dissipates.

Most thunderstorms last less than an hour and do little damage. They can form any time, but are most common in North America during afternoon and evening hours in the spring and summer.

Severe Thunderstorms The scenario described above is typical of most thunderstorms, which never become severe. However, under certain conditions, some thunderstorms do become severe. Canada's Atmospheric Environment Service classifies a thunderstorm as severe if it has wind speeds in excess of 90 km/h or hailstones larger than 1.5 cm, or if it generates a tornado.[2] Severe thunderstorms require favourable atmospheric conditions over a large area and the ability to perpetuate themselves. They commonly appear in groups and can last from several hours to several days.

Conditions required to form a severe thunderstorm include wind shear produced by winds blowing in different directions, high water-vapour content in the lower troposphere, uplift of air, and the existence of a dry air mass above a moist air mass.[2] Three types of severe thunderstorms have been identified on the basis of their organization, shape, and size: roughly circular clusters of storm cells called *mesoscale convective complexes,* linear belts of thunderstorms called *squall lines,* and large cells with single updrafts called *supercells*.

Mesoscale convective complexes are the most common of the three types of severe thunderstorms. They are very large clusters of self-propagating storms in which the downdraft of one cell leads to the formation of a new cell nearby. Unlike many single-cell thunderstorms that last for less than an hour, these complexes can continue to grow and move for periods of 12 hours or more. Their downdrafts can come together to form *outflow boundaries,* arcuate lines of thunderstorms that travel long distances.

◀ **FIGURE 8.17 THUNDERSTORM CLOUD** Mature cumulonimbus thunderstorm clouds have anvil-shaped tops. Updrafts are deflected by a stable layer in the atmosphere that prevents further vertical growth of the cloud. *(Arjen and Jerrine Verkaik/Skyart Productions)*

Squall lines average 500 km in length and are lines of individual storm cells.[2] They commonly develop parallel to, and 300 km to 500 km ahead of, cold fronts.[2] Updrafts in the advancing squall line typically form anvil-shaped clouds whose tops extend ahead of the line. Downdrafts originating on the back side of the storms may surge forward as a *gust* front of cold air in advance of precipitation. Squall lines can also develop along *drylines,* an air mass boundary similar to a front, but along which the air masses differ in moisture content rather than in temperature. Drylines develop in the southwestern United States during the spring and summer, sometimes producing daily squall lines.

The most damaging of all severe thunderstorms are *supercell storms*. A supercell is a thunderstorm with a deeply rotating updraft flanked by smaller updraft elements. The flanking rising air masses usually merge with and augment the main rotating updraft, rather than developing into separate and competing thunderstorm cells. Although smaller than mesoscale convective complexes and squall lines, supercell storms are extremely violent and are the breeding ground for most large

8.1 CASE STUDY

Lightning

Lightning consists of flashes of light produced by the discharge of millions of volts of electricity (Figure 8.A) and is common during thunderstorms. The discharges momentarily heat the air in their paths to temperatures as high as 30,000°C, much hotter than the surface of the Sun.[5] Most lightning bolts travel from cloud to cloud, that is, they start and end in clouds. Cloud-to-ground lightning is less common, but many tens of millions of lightning bolts strike Canada and the United States each year.[6] Cloud-to-ground lightning is more complex than it appears to an observer (Figure 8.B). Each lightning strike begins when a column of electrically charged air, called a *step-leader,* advances downward from the base of a cloud. Within milliseconds, this column branches downward until it is close to the ground. A spark then surges upward to meet the leader. Once it makes contact, the column becomes the path for a brilliant *return stroke*. Thus, although a lightning strike appears to come down from the base of the cloud, the electrical discharge actually moves upward from the ground toward the cloud.[2]

Lightning strikes are a serious hazard, although the number of annual lightning deaths in North America has decreased as more people leave rural areas to live in cities. Lightning kills about 7 people in Canada each year and injures 60 to 70 more; in the United States, it kills about 100 people and injures more than 300 each year.[6,7,8] Seventy percent of survivors of a lightning strike suffer serious long-term health effects (see Survivor Story).[9] The chances of being struck by lightning in the United States are estimated to be 1 in 240,000 each year.[6] Over an average lifespan of 80 years, an individual's risk is 1 in 3000. An individual's risk, however, may be much higher or lower depending on where he or she lives and works.

To reduce the risk of being struck by lightning, avoid golfing, swimming, or boating during storms. Second, if in the open during a storm, do not take refuge under a

◀ **FIGURE 8.A LIGHTNING** A nighttime photograph of cloud-to-ground and cloud-to-cloud lightning strokes. *(NOAA Photo Library, NOAA Central Library; OAR/ERL/National Severe Storms Laboratory)*

8.1 CASE STUDY *(Continued)*

tree, tower, or any other object that extends high above the ground. Third, if a storm is approaching and lightning is visible, enter a building and stay there until the storm passes.

◀ **FIGURE 8.B DEVELOPMENT OF CLOUD-TO-GROUND LIGHTNING** (a) An electrical charge develops in a cloud. (b) An invisible step-leader forms a column of electrically charged air that branches downward toward the ground. (c) A spark jumps from an object on the ground, such as a tree, to the base of the step-leader. (d) Electrons flow back up to the cloud to produce the lightning strike.

tornadoes. They are typically 20 km to 50 km in diameter and last from two to four hours.

Hail Many large thunderstorms produce hard, rounded, or irregular pieces of ice called *hailstones*. Large hailstones from severe thunderstorms can cause much damage. You can infer how hailstones form by cutting one in half to reveal its bull's-eye pattern of concentric rings of ice. The rings form when a hailstone moves up and down in the turbulent air of a thunderstorm. Starting with a small ice pellet as a nucleus, a hailstone gets a coating of liquid water in the lower part of the storm that freezes when a strong updraft carries the stone upward into cold air. This process is repeated many times to form a large piece of hail. The largest authenticated hailstone in North America fell from a severe thunderstorm in Aurora, Nebraska, in June 2003. It was 18 cm in diameter, nearly the size of a volleyball, weighed 800 g, and was estimated to have hit the ground at a velocity of more than 160 km/h![10]

Damage caused by hail in Canada and the United States averages more than $1 billion per year.[10] In North America,

SURVIVOR STORY

Struck by Lightning

Michael Utley came within inches of death when he was struck by lightning on a Cape Cod golf course.

Like most of us, Michael Utley didn't worry much about being struck by lightning. The odds, after all, are very low. And so, at a charity golf tournament to benefit a local YMCA near his Cape Cod home, he was not concerned about a looming thunderstorm. "I didn't pay attention to it," he says.

Four holes into the game, a horn blasted, warning golfers to seek shelter. Utley replaced the flag in the hole and was several yards behind his three companions when he was struck by lightning.

Utley's friends heard a thunderous crack behind them, and when they turned around, they saw smoke coming from Utley's body, his shoes torn from his feet, and his zipper blown open.

Luckily, Utley remembers none of this. In fact, he remembered nothing for the next 38 days, which he spent in an intensive-care unit. Fortunately for Utley, one of his companions had recently been retrained in CPR, which may have saved his life.

Utley comments that some of the ideas we have about people struck by lightning are accurate and some are not. "The hair standing up, that's real. When that happens, you're pretty close to being dead," he says. But "I didn't see a white light at the end of the tunnel. I don't burn clocks off the wall when I touch them."

Utley, like many victims of lightning, had, in his words, "a variety of ups and downs" after the accident. His wife, Tamara, recalls that he did not slip into a coma-like state for several days. "It was very, very strange," she says. "When he first got to the ICU, he was able to move and he was very lucid." But within a few days he began to lose consciousness for extended periods. Utley remembers none of this either.

The road to recovery is not over for Utley. He still bumps into walls when he walks and has had to relearn many basic activities. Since the accident, he has spent a great deal of time working to educate the community, including the Professional Golfers' Association (PGA) (Figure 8.C), about the perils of lightning. He sums up his message to golfers with this slogan: "If you see it, flee it; if you hear it, clear it."

—***Chris Wilson***

▲ **FIGURE 8.C LIGHTNING SAFETY** This National Weather Service poster featuring professional golfer Vijay Singh reminds people to be careful outdoors during a thunderstorm. *(NOAA Photo Library)*

damaging hailstorms are most common on the Prairies, particularly in northeastern Colorado, southeastern Wyoming, and southern Alberta. North-central India, Bangladesh, Kenya, and Australia also experience frequent damaging hailstorms. Although rare in North America, deaths from hailstones are common in areas of high population density and poorly constructed dwellings, notably Bangladesh and India.[10]

Tornadoes

A tornado, or "twister," is one of nature's most violent natural processes. From 1992 to 2002, tornadoes in the United States killed an average of 57 people per year. Parts of Canada also experience deadly tornadoes: one in Edmonton in 1987 killed 27 people (Figure 8.18 and Case Study 8.2) and another in southern Ontario in 1985 claimed 8 lives. These spinning columns of wind range in shape from ropes to funnels and are capable of inflicting tremendous damage. To be called a tornado, a spinning column of wind or *vortex* must extend downward from a cloud and touch the ground. Funnel-shaped vortices that do not touch the ground are called *funnel clouds* (Figure 8.19b). The number of funnel clouds that develop each year far exceeds the number of tornadoes.

Tornadoes form where there are large differences in atmospheric pressure over short distances, most commonly during a severe thunderstorm. Although meteorologists do

◀ **FIGURE 8.18 TORNADO DAMAGE** This trailer park in Edmonton, Alberta, was severely damaged by a tornado in July 1987. *(CP Photo/Edmonton Sun/Brendon Dlouhy)*

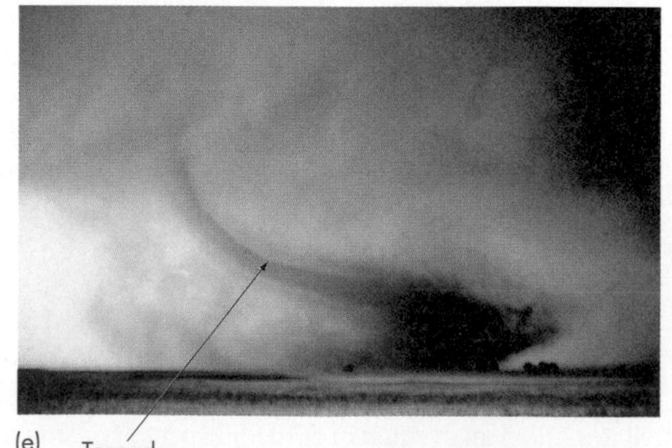

▲ **FIGURE 8.19 STAGES IN TORNADO DEVELOPMENT** (a) A wall cloud near Miami, Texas. Wall clouds extend downward during a severe thunderstorm and are commonly where tornadoes form. *(NOAA Photo Library, NOAA Central Library; OAR/ERL/National Severe Storms Laboratory)* (b) A funnel cloud over the state capitol buildings in Austin, Texas. *(Austin Public Library)* (c) A tornado in the organizational stage of development near Enid, Oklahoma. The funnel cloud extends downward from the thunderstorm and debris is beginning to rotate on the ground below the funnel. *(NOAA Photo Library, NOAA Central Library; OAR/ERL/National Severe Storms Laboratory)* (d) A tornado in the mature stage of development near Seymour, Texas. *(NOAA Photo Library, NOAA Central Library; OAR/ERL/National Severe Storms Laboratory)* (e) A tornado in the shrinking, rope stage near Cordell, Oklahoma. *(NOAA Photo Library, NOAA Central Library; OAR/ERL/National Severe Storms Laboratory)*

8.2 CASE STUDY

The Edmonton Tornado

On the afternoon of July 31, 1987, a tornado rated F4 on the Fujita scale ripped through Edmonton (Figure 8.D). Twenty-seven people were killed, more than 300 were injured, and property damage amounted to more than $330 million. The tornado remained on the ground for an hour, cutting a path of destruction 40 km long and up to 1 km wide. It achieved wind speeds of up to 460 km/h. The loss of life, injuries, and destruction of property made this tornado the worst natural disaster in Alberta's history and one of the worst in Canada's history.[11]

Weather forecasts issued for Edmonton by Environment Canada during the morning and early afternoon of July 31, 1987, warned of a high potential for severe thunderstorms that afternoon. Environment Canada responded swiftly on receipt of the first report of a tornado touching down adjacent to Edmonton's southern boundary. It issued a tornado warning over weather radio five minutes after the report.

While municipal emergency agencies, fire departments, ambulance, and police were responding, the Canadian Department of National Defence placed helicopters and ambulances on standby at Canadian Forces Base Edmonton and provided reconnaissance flights for the City of Edmonton and the deputy prime minister. During the storm, Emergency Preparedness Canada established contact with the Alberta Government Emergency Response Centre and established a liaison office at the response centre later that day.

The post-disaster response period lasted approximately three weeks, during which immediate disaster assistance was provided to victims. At the end of August 1987, the Government of Alberta announced a disaster-recovery program with assistance from the Government of Canada.

▲ **FIGURE 8.D EDMONTON TORNADO** On July 31, 1987, a tornado sliced through Edmonton, Alberta, killing 27 people and injuring more than 300 others. *(Photo courtesy of Robert den Hartigh)*

The Alberta Emergency Public Warning System was developed as a result of the disaster. It interrupts private and public broadcasts on radio, television, and cable systems, alerting the public to imminent potential disasters.

Other deadly tornadoes in Canada include an F3 event that travelled across Pine Lake, Alberta, and into a trailer park on July 14, 2000 (11 people killed, 132 injured), and an F4 tornado that struck Barrie, Ontario, on May 31, 1985 (8 people killed, 60 injured, and more than 800 left homeless).

not completely understand how tornadoes form, they know that most tornadoes go through similar stages in development (Figure 8.19).

In the initial, *organizational stage* of a tornado, wind shear causes air to begin to rotate within the thunderstorm. Winds that turn from south to west as they carry moist air aloft increase rapidly with height and initiate rotation of the air mass. If the updraft and the wind shear are strong enough, a large rotating column of air known as a *mesocyclone* forms. Updrafts, commonly in the rear of the storm, lower a portion of the cumulonimbus cloud to form a *wall cloud* (Figure 8.19a). The wall cloud may itself begin to slowly rotate, and a short funnel cloud may descend from it (Figure 8.19b). At the same time, dust and debris on the ground begin to swirl below the funnel (Figure 8.19c). If the two rotating columns of air join, the funnel cloud becomes a tornado. Not all wall clouds and mesocyclones produce tornadoes, and a tornado can develop without the presence of a wall cloud or mesocyclone.

In the second, *mature* stage of a tornado, a visible funnel extends from the thunderstorm cloud to the ground and moist air is drawn upward (Figure 8.19d). Small intense whirls, called *suction vortices,* may form within larger tornadoes (Figure 8.20a). They orbit the centre of the vortex and may be responsible for the tornado's greatest damage.[1]

The tornado enters the *shrinking stage* when the supply of warm moist air is reduced. The funnel begins to tilt and becomes narrower. Winds can increase at this stage, making the tornado even more dangerous.

In the final, *rope stage* (Figure 8.19e), the upward-spiralling air comes in contact with downdrafts and the tornado begins to move erratically. This behaviour marks the beginning of the end for the tornado, but it can still be

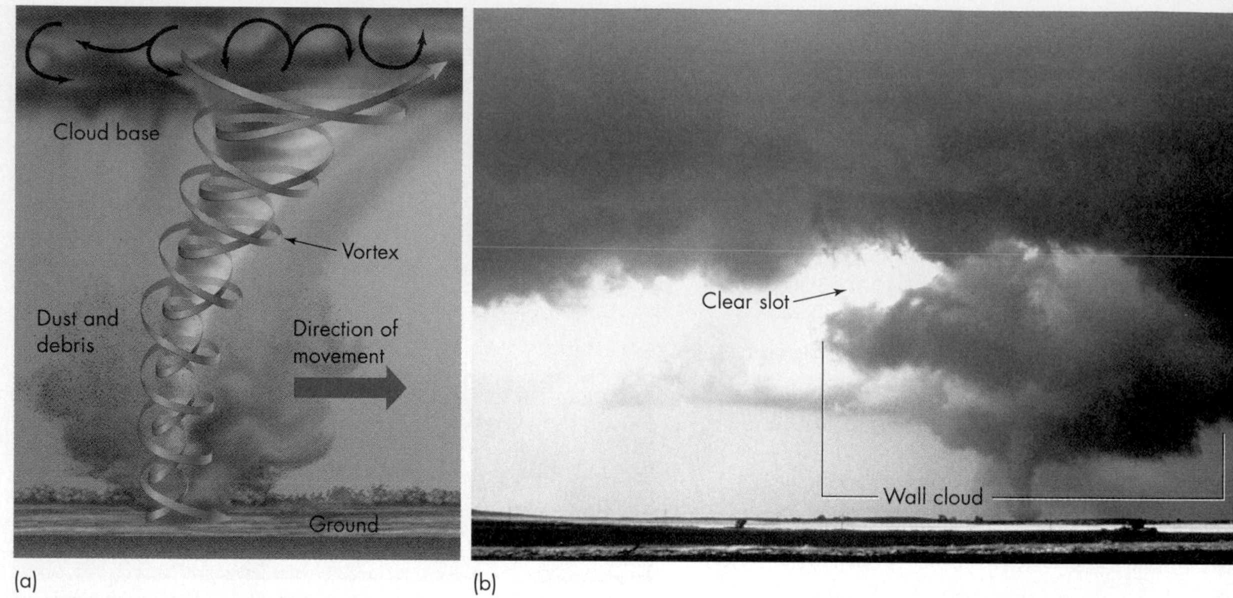

▲ **FIGURE 8.20 AIR MOVEMENT DURING A TORNADO** (a) An idealized diagram of a tornado vortex showing air movement. *(Modified from Whittow, J. 1980. Disasters: The anatomy of environmental hazards. London: Penguin Books)* (b) A classic tornado extending from the wall cloud of a supercell thunderstorm near Alfalfa, Oklahoma. A clear slot immediately in front of the wall cloud has formed by a downdraft that may have contributed to the formation of the tornado. The wall cloud itself was formed by an updraft. Both the wall cloud and the tornado are silhouetted against lighter sky where very little rain is falling. *(NOAA Photo Library, NOAA Central Library; OAR/ERL/National Severe Storms Laboratory)*

extremely dangerous. Tornadoes may go through all the stages described above or they may skip stages, and new tornadoes can form nearby as older tornadoes dissipate.

Tornadoes pick up soil, vegetation, and debris as they move across land. This material gives the tornado cloud its characteristic dark appearance (Figure 8.20b). Tornadoes typically have diameters of tens of metres and wind speeds of 65 km/h to more than 450 km/h.[2] Most tornadoes travel fewer than 10 km and last only a few minutes before weakening and disappearing. However, as mentioned in the case history that opened this chapter, the largest and most damaging tornadoes may have widths of hundreds of metres and paths a few hundred kilometres long.

Classification of Tornadoes Tornadoes are classified according to their maximum wind speeds and the damage they produce. They are assigned values on the *Fujita* or **F-scale** (Table 8.1) on the basis of post-storm damage surveys. The F-scale has six categories, F0 to F5. Although F6 tornadoes, with winds more than 511 km/h, can occur, their winds leave no structures standing, thus it is almost impossible to recognize them.

Two types of tornadoes develop over water: *tornadic waterspouts*, which descend from storm clouds (Figure 8.21), and *fair weather waterspouts,* which develop upward from the water surface. Tornadic waterspouts are larger and more intense than are fair weather waterspouts, and they form in

TABLE 8.1 Fujita Scale for Tornadoes

Scale	Wind Speeds (Estimated)	Typical Damage
F0	<117 km/h	*Light damage:* Some damage to chimneys; branches broken off trees; shallow-rooted trees pushed over; sign boards damaged
F1	117–180 km/h	*Moderate damage:* Winds peel surface off roofs; mobile homes pushed off foundations or overturned; moving automobiles blown off roads
F2	182–252 km/h	*Considerable damage:* Roofs torn off frame houses; mobile homes demolished; boxcars overturned; large trees snapped or uprooted; light-object missiles generated; cars lifted off ground
F3	254–331 km/h	*Severe damage:* Roofs and some walls torn off well-constructed houses; trains overturned; most trees in forests uprooted; heavy cars lifted off the ground and thrown
F4	333–418 km/h	*Devastating damage:* Well-constructed houses levelled; structures with weak foundations blown some distance; cars thrown and large missiles generated
F5	420–511 km/h	*Incredible damage:* Strong frame houses levelled or blown away; automobile-sized missiles fly through the air in excess of 100 m; trees debarked; incredible phenomena will occur

Source: Based on National Oceanic and Atmospheric Administration (NOAA), Storm Prediction Center. 2006. "Fujita Tornado Damage Scale," The Online Tornado FAQs. www.spc.noaa.gov/faq/tornado/f-scale.html. *Accessed November 2, 2006.*

much the same way as tornadoes do on land. Waterspouts form from downdrafts or from the movement of air down from a tropical disturbance to the water surface. Both types of waterspouts can move on shore and "touch down" on land, although they rarely cause damage greater than an F1 tornado.[12]

Occurrence of Tornadoes Although tornadoes occur throughout the world, they are much more common in the United States than in any other country. The United States has just the right combination of weather, topography, and geographic location to make it the perfect spawning ground for tornadoes.[1] Most U.S. tornadoes happen in the spring and summer in the region extending from Florida to Texas and north to the Dakotas, Indiana, and Ohio. The area at highest risk on the Great Plains is called "Tornado Alley." Canada experiences far fewer tornadoes than the United States does, but it has several tornado-prone regions, including southern Alberta, southern Ontario, southeastern Quebec, and an area extending from southern Saskatchewan through southern Manitoba to Thunder Bay, Ontario (Figure 8.22).[13]

Tornadoes are also common in Bangladesh, Australia, New Zealand, northern India, South Africa, Argentina, Japan, eastern China, and central Europe from France and Great Britain eastward to Russia and Ukraine. However, violent tornadoes (F4 and F5) are rare or nonexistent outside North America, with the possible exception of Bangladesh.[1]

Most waterspouts occur in tropical and subtropical waters, but they have been reported off the New England and California coasts, on the Great Lakes, and on Lake Winnipeg.[1] They are especially common along the Gulf Coast of the United States, in the Caribbean Sea, in the Bay of Bengal, and in the South Atlantic Ocean. A study conducted in the Florida Keys reported 390 waterspouts within 80 km of Key West during a five-month period.[1]

▲ **FIGURE 8.21 TORNADIC WATERSPOUTS** Two tornadic waterspouts over Lake Winnipeg, Manitoba. Tornadic waterspouts extend downward from storm clouds and can move onshore as weak tornadoes. *(Dr. Scott Norquay/Tom Stack & Associates, Inc.)*

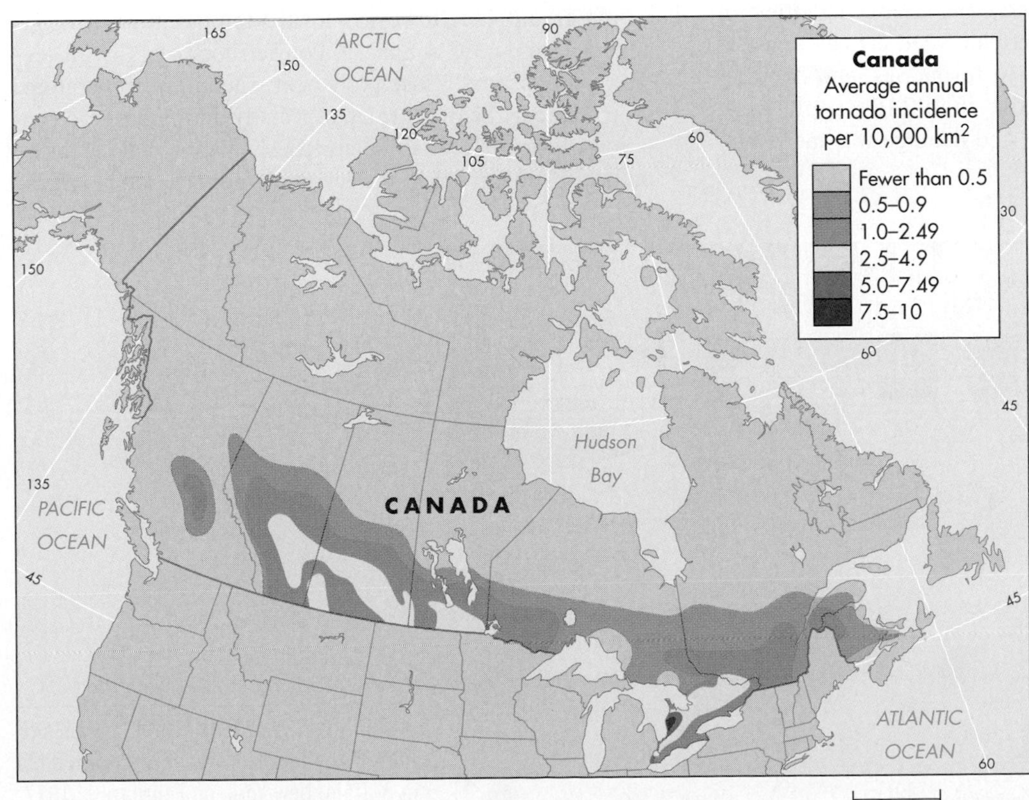

◀ **FIGURE 8.22 TORNADO OCCURRENCE IN CANADA** Average annual number of tornadoes per 10,000 km^2 in Canada based on data from 1950 to 1997. *(Reprinted by permission of David Eitken)*

Blizzards, Extreme Cold, and Ice Storms

Blizzards are severe winter storms characterized by high winds, blowing snow, and low visibility for an extended period. The official threshold for blizzard conditions differs in Canada and the United States. In Canada, winds must exceed 40 km/h with visibilities of less than 1 km for at least 4 hours, whereas in the United States winds must exceed 56 km/h with visibilities of less than 400 m for at least 3 hours.[14,15]

Blizzards can produce heavy snowfall, wind damage, and large snowdrifts (Figure 8.23). The Saskatchewan blizzard of 1947 lasted for 10 days and buried an entire train in a snowdrift 8 m deep and 1 km long.[16] Another famous storm, the "Blizzard of 1888," killed more than 400 people and paralyzed the northeastern United States for three days with snow drifts that reportedly covered the first floors of buildings.

Storms that produce heavy snowfall and blizzards form when upper-level winds associated with a low-pressure trough interact with a surface low-pressure system.[17] Blizzards typically occur on the northwest side of these storms as they move north along the east side of a low-pressure trough.[17]

Blizzards associated with heavy snowfall are common through much of Canada, the American Great Plains and northeastern states, and in areas around the Great Lakes. Blizzards on the east coast of Canada and the United States commonly occur during *nor'easters*, which derive their name from continuously blowing northeasterly winds just ahead of the storms. Nor'easters wreak havoc with hurricane-force winds, heavy snowfall, and high waves that damage coastal infrastructure. These storms are most common between September and April and can create blizzard conditions in Halifax, New York, Boston, and other east coast cities. In March 1993, a severe nor'easter paralyzed the east coast of the United States, causing snow, tornadoes, and flooding from Alabama to Maine. More than 240 people were killed in the "Blizzard of '93," and damage was more than US$1 billion.

Less than three years later, in January 1996, a strong winter storm brought another massive blizzard to the east coast. The storm crippled the eastern United States for several days and produced record-breaking snowfall in Philadelphia and parts of New Jersey; it dropped 51 cm of snow in New York City's Central Park. The blizzard killed at least 100 people and caused an estimated US$2 billion in damage.

A blizzard can also occur without snowfall. "Ground blizzards" in Antarctica, Alaska, Canada, and on the American Great Plains rework existing snow to produce whiteout conditions with visibility limited to a few metres or less.

The **wind chill** effect makes blizzards more dangerous than other snow storms. Moving air rapidly cools exposed skin by evaporating moisture and removing warm air next to the body. This chilling reduces the time it takes for *frostbite* to develop. In blizzards, the wind chill temperature (WCT) is a more important measure of possible effects on the body than is the air temperature (Figure 8.24).

Blizzards and outbreaks of Arctic air can produce *extreme cold*. What constitutes extreme cold, however, depends on climate averages and on personal and community preparedness. In regions relatively unaccustomed to winter weather, near-freezing temperatures are considered "extreme cold." During the winter of 1989–1990, 26 people died of hypothermia in Florida, even though the weather would not have been considered extreme by the standards of people living in Canada and the northern United States. Because of normally mild temperatures, many Florida homes lack adequate heating and insulation, and the outdoor lifestyle in the state leads to danger for those who are not prepared for freezing temperatures. In the far north of Canada, where people are accustomed to cold winters, temperatures below about –45°C are considered extreme cold. The lowest recorded temperature in North America was –63°C at Snag, Yukon Territory, in 1947. In general, people rapidly lose body heat whenever temperatures drop markedly below normal, especially during blizzard conditions. Extreme cold is a dangerous situation that can bring on health emergencies in susceptible people, such as those

◀ FIGURE 8.23 AFTERMATH OF A BLIZZARD These cars were abandoned in deep snow drifts in Buffalo, New York, on February 1, 1977. *(Ira Block/National Geographic Image Collection)*

Wind speed, kmph	Actual Air Temperature in °C								
Calm	4°	−1°	−7°	−12°	−18°	−23°	−29°	−34°	−40°
8	2°	−4°	−11°	−17°	−24°	−30°	−37°	−43°	−49°
16	1°	−6°	−13°	−20°	−27°	−33°	−41°	−47°	−54°
24	0°	−7°	−14°	−22°	−28°	−36°	−43°	−50°	−57°
32	−1°	−8°	−16°	−23°	−30°	−37°	−44°	−52°	−59°
40	−2°	−9°	−16°	−24°	−31°	−38°	−46°	−53°	−61°
48	−2°	−9°	−17°	−24°	−32°	−39°	−47°	−55°	−62°
56	−2°	−10°	−18°	−26°	−33°	−41°	−48°	−56°	−63°
64	−3°	−11°	−18°	−26°	−34°	−42°	−49°	−57°	−64°
72	−3°	−11°	−19°	−27°	−34°	−42°	−50°	−58°	−66°
80	−3°	−11°	−19°	−27°	−35°	−43°	−51°	−59°	−67°

Frostbite times: 30 min. 10 min. 5 min.

◄ **FIGURE 8.24 WIND CHILL CHART** Table of equivalent temperatures felt by the body for different wind speeds. *(Adapted from the National Weather Service and Meteorological Services of Canada, version 11/01/01)*

without shelter, stranded motorists, and people who live in homes that are poorly insulated or without heat. Environment Canada and the U.S. Department of Health and Human Services provide suggestions and information to help people minimize the risk of death or injury from extreme cold.

Ice storms are prolonged periods of freezing rain. They can be more damaging than, and just as dangerous as, blizzards. During an ice storm, rain at a temperature near 0°C freezes when it comes into contact with cold surfaces. Heavy accumulations of ice are especially harmful to utility lines and trees, and can make driving treacherous. Ice storms typically occur during the winter on the north side of a stationary or warm front when three conditions are met: (1) ample moisture is present in the warm air mass south of the front, (2) warm air overlies a shallow layer of cold air, and (3) objects on the ground are at or below the freezing temperature. Snow begins to fall from the cooled top of the warm air mass and melts as it passes through the warm air. The resulting raindrops become supercooled as they descend through near-surface cold air. When they strike cold objects on the ground, such as roads, trees, and utility lines, the raindrops immediately freeze, forming a coating of ice. Layers of ice up to 20 cm thick have been produced by prolonged ice storms. Areas in North America most prone to ice storms include southern Ontario, southern Quebec, the mid-Atlantic and new England states, the Ohio River Valley, the south-central Great Plains, and the Columbia River Valley in the Pacific Northwest (Case Study 8.3).[10]

Drought

Drought is defined as an extended period of unusually low precipitation that produces a shortage of water for people, animals, and plants. More than 1 billion people live in semi-arid regions where droughts are common, and more than 100 million people can suffer malnutrition or death if drought causes crops to fail. Droughts commonly contribute to regional food shortages, but today widespread famine can be eased or prevented through relief efforts and the global food distribution system.

Droughts affect more people in Canada and the United States than any other natural hazard. Droughts on the Canadian Prairies from 1999 to 2002 caused losses in grain production of $3.6 billion. Losses in the United States from drought typically total US$6 billion to US$8 billion each year.[19] Droughts can cause serious water and power shortages, as well as agricultural problems (Figure 8.25).

The effects of a drought in the western United States in 1977 illustrate the impact these events can have. The 1977 drought brought crop failures, domestic water shortages, and a decrease in industrial productivity from a loss of hydroelectric power.[20] Stream flows in most large rivers in Washington state were 30 percent to 70 percent of normal, and many small streams and springs were dry. Low water flows increased water temperatures and caused algae blooms that depleted the waters of oxygen and killed fish. The drought resulted in a US$330 million to US$410 million loss to Washington state's economy alone, principally to the aluminum and fruit industries. As many as 10,000 jobs were temporarily lost.

In 2004, drought conditions in western North America again caused water shortages. After more than five years of low precipitation, water levels in major reservoirs from Alberta to Arizona were at their lowest points in decades.

Droughts are linked to global and regional weather patterns and ocean circulation. There may be a relation between drought in some areas of North America and ocean circulation in the equatorial Pacific (see Chapter 9). La Niña events, during which cool waters well up off the west coast of South America and flow westward along the Equator toward Australia and New Guinea, may lead to dry warm weather through much of the United States.

Whatever the cause, droughts are a normal part of the climate system. The droughts of the Dust Bowl period in the 1930s and droughts during the past several decades should not be thought of as unusual. In fact, historic droughts are not the most severe that are possible. Geologic studies of past vegetation and climate suggest that severe droughts lasting several decades have occurred at times during the past millennium in North America. The possibility of such droughts in the future demands that we prepare for them.

8.3 CASE STUDY

The 1998 Ice Storm

The worst North American ice storm of the twentieth century began on January 5, 1998. By January 10, parts of Quebec, Ontario, and the northeastern United States were gripped by up to 10 cm of accumulated ice. Fifty-seven communities in Ontario and 200 in Quebec were declared disaster areas. About 130 steel transmission towers (Figure 8.E), 30,000 utility poles, and millions of trees collapsed under the weight of the ice. More than 3 million people in Quebec and 1.5 million in eastern Ontario were without power. At least 35 people were killed as a result of house fires, falling ice, carbon monoxide poisoning, and hypothermia, and almost 1000 people were injured. About 100,000 people were evacuated to shelters. The estimated cost of the ice storm was $5.5 billion.[18]

On January 8, the military was brought in to help clear debris, provide medical assistance, evacuate residents, and canvass door to door to make sure people were safe. They also helped to restore power. Power was restored in most urban areas in a matter of days, but 700,000 people in rural communities were still without power three weeks after the beginning of the storm.

Ontario's and Quebec's economies were hit hard. Nearly one-quarter of Canada's dairy cows, one-third of the crop land in Quebec, and one-quarter of the farmland in Ontario were in the affected area. Milk-processing plants were closed, and about 10 million L of milk had to be dumped. Most of the maples used by Quebec maple syrup producers were killed. It was estimated that syrup production in the province will not return to normal levels for several decades.

The 1998 ice storm was the most expensive natural disaster in Canadian history. According to Environment Canada, the storm directly affected more people than any other previous weather event in Canada.

◄ **FIGURE 8.E ICE STORM** Supercooled rain can turn to clear ice when it falls on a surface that is at or below freezing. An ice storm in January 1998 downed electrical transmission lines that provide electricity to southern Quebec and Ontario. *(CP Photo/Jacques Boissinot)*

(a)

(b)

◀ **FIGURE 8.25 UNITED STATES "DUST BOWL"** (a) Dust storm caused by a cold front at Manter, Kansas, in 1935. (b) Sometimes called "black blizzards" because of their colour, these storms eroded topsoil from agricultural lands in the southern U.S. Great Plains. *(U.S. Department of Commerce)*

Dust and Sand Storms

Dust storms are strong windstorms that transport large amounts of fine sediment. Wind velocities in these storms exceed 48 km/h and visibility is less than 800 m.[4] A typical dust storm is several hundred kilometres wide and may carry more than 100 million t of dust. Television weather reporters may mistakenly call these events "sand storms." Most dust particles are mineral and rock grains less than about 60 μm (0.6 mm) in diameter. Natural dust also contains small amounts of fine biological material, notably spores and pollen. Dust storms remove valuable topsoil and disrupt transportation and commerce. Airborne dust particles can also affect human health. Fine dust particles can be carried long distances in the upper atmosphere. Satellite images show dust storms from West Africa crossing the Atlantic Ocean to Florida, and dust from Asia occasionally reaches western North America.

Sand storms, like dust storms, are strong windstorms that move large amounts of sediment. They differ from dust storms in transporting sand rather than silt. During a sandstorm, countless grains of sand are moved near the ground surface. Sand, unlike silt, is not transported long distances and is concentrated in a layer close to the ground surface. Blowing sand is very abrasive, as one author of this textbook learned firsthand when his windshield was frosted by blowing sand while driving in Colorado.

Dust and sand storms occur mostly in mid-latitude, semi-arid and arid regions. Huge dust storms in the southern U.S. Plains during the 1930s produced conditions known as the "Dust Bowl." A combination of drought and poor agricultural practices during the Great Depression caused severe soil erosion in parts of five states. Frequent, sometimes daily, dust storms in this area destroyed crops and pastureland (Figure 8.25). Drought extended into Alberta and Saskatchewan, causing severe hardship for farmers and ranchers.

Heat Waves

Much of the world is vulnerable to heat waves, which are periods of heat that are longer and hotter than normal. In recent years, heat waves have killed an average of about 220 people per year in Canada and the United States, about the same as the combined number of deaths from flooding, lightning, tornadoes, and hurricanes.

The threshold ambient temperature at which people are at risk from heat differs with location, but when summer temperatures reach about 5°C above the norm for a lengthy period, incidences of heat-related illness increase dramatically. High humidity compounds the effects of the heat by reducing evaporation, rendering perspiration less effective as a cooling mechanism. Under normal circumstances, people maintain a body temperature of about 37°C. When subject to extreme heat, the body tries to maintain this temperature by changing blood circulation and perspiring. At a temperature of 40°C, vital organs are at risk and, if the body's temperature is not reduced, death follows.

Heat waves take their greatest toll in cities. Urban centres, where the area of heat-absorbing dark roofs and pavement exceeds the vegetated area, are "heat islands" and can be as much as 5°C warmer than the surrounding countryside. People in rural areas generally get some relief from the heat when temperatures fall at night, but cities remain warm because of radiation from warm buildings and roads. Air pollution is generally worse in cities than in rural areas, exacerbating the effects of high temperatures by further stressing the body's respiratory and circulatory systems.

A record heat wave claimed about 35,000 lives in Europe in August 2003. That August was the warmest on record in the Northern Hemisphere. In France alone, nearly 15,000 people died from temperatures that reached 40°C and remained unusually high for two weeks. Germany lost some 7000 people from the heat, and Spain and Italy each suffered about 4200 heat-related deaths. On August 10, London recorded its first triple-digit Fahrenheit temperature; 900 people died from the heat there. The large number of deaths was due to the extreme temperatures that developed in poorly ventilated apartments and houses without central air-conditioning or even window units.

Heat-related fatalities are common in parts of India because of the high temperatures that hit before the monsoon, the large population, and the lack of means of protecting people. In May 2003, peak temperatures between 45°C and 49°C claimed more than 1600 lives throughout the country. In the state of Andhra Pradesh alone, 1200 people died from the heat. A year earlier, a one-week heat wave with temperatures topping 50°C claimed 1000 lives.

Several of the worst heat waves of the twentieth century occurred in Canadian and American cities. A heat wave in July 1936 set all-time records in Manitoba and Ontario: temperatures reached 40°C in Toronto and 42°C in Winnipeg. Nearly 800 Canadians died during this heat wave. In 1972, New York City experienced a two-week heat wave that claimed 891 lives, and in 1995, an extreme heat wave in Chicago killed 739 people.

Most heat waves in Canada and the United States are associated with elongate areas of high pressure, called *ridges*. Conditions west of the ridge are generally wet, whereas sunny and dry weather prevails to the east. If the ridge remains stationary for several days, air temperatures below the ridge may rise, triggering a heat wave.

The air can be either humid or extremely dry during heat waves. In either case, it is important to monitor the

RH (%) T (°C)	100	95	90	85	80	75	70	65	60	55	50	45	40	35	30	25	20
21	29	29	28	27	27	26	26	24	24	23	23	22					
22	31	29	29	58	28	27	26	26	24	24	23	23					
23	33	32	32	31	30	29	28	27	27	26	25	24	23				
24	35	34	33	33	32	31	30	29	28	28	27	26	26	25			
25	37	36	35	34	33	33	32	31	30	29	28	27	27	26			
26	39	38	37	36	35	34	33	32	31	31	29	28	28	27			
27	41	40	39	38	37	36	35	34	33	32	31	30	29	28	28		
28	43	42	41	41	39	38	37	36	35	34	33	32	31	29	28		
29	46	45	44	43	42	41	39	38	37	36	34	33	32	31	30		
30	48	47	46	44	43	42	41	40	38	37	36	35	34	33	31	31	
31	50	49	48	46	45	44	43	41	40	39	38	36	35	34	33	31	
32	52	51	50	49	47	46	45	43	42	41	39	38	37	36	34	33	
33	55	54	52	51	50	48	47	46	44	43	42	40	38	37	36	34	
34	58	57	55	53	52	51	49	48	47	45	43	42	41	39	37	36	
35		58	57	56	54	52	51	49	48	47	45	43	42	41	38	37	
36			58	57	56	54	53	51	50	48	47	45	43	42	40	38	
37					58	57	55	53	51	50	49	47	45	43	42	40	
38							57	56	54	52	51	49	47	46	43	42	40
									56	54	53	51	49	47	45	43	41
										57	54	52	51	49	47	44	43
											56	54	52	50	48	46	44
												56	54	52	50	48	46
													56	54	51	49	47

RH = relative humidity

Humidex (°C)	Degree of comfort
20–29	No discomfort
30–39	Some discomfort
40–45	Great discomfort; avoid exertion
46 and over	Dangerous; probable heat stroke

▲ **FIGURE 8.26 HUMIDEX CHART** The humidex index combines air temperature and relative humidity to provide a numerical measure of the body's perception of air temperature. A similar "heat index" chart is used by the National Weather Service in the United States.

humidex, or heat, **index** (Figure 8.26). This index measures the body's perception of air temperature, which is greatly influenced by humidity. For example, a temperature of 35°C will feel significantly hotter in Toronto where the relative humidity might be greater than 70 percent than in Las Vegas where the humidity is much lower. In the Toronto example, the combination of high temperature and high humidity produces a humidex temperature of 51°C, which is dangerous.

Heat waves cause other problems. In the summer of 2006, a heat wave strained electrical grids in Ontario to their limits. Electricity suppliers were barely able to meet increased demand from people cooling homes and workplaces with fans and air conditioners. The province of Ontario was not able to generate enough power to meet its demand during the heat wave and had to ask people to cut back. It also had to import electricity from Quebec, New York, and Michigan. Power imports, however, may not be assured. The electricity that Quebec sells to Ontario is hydroelectric power produced from dammed lakes and rivers. Drought preceding or accompanying heat waves lowers reservoirs in Quebec and reduces its power production and the amount of energy it can export. Ontario's only other option would have been to cut power to certain areas. But power cuts would have had a considerable impact on the province's economy, forcing work slowdowns at Ontario's big steel plants and automakers.

8.6 Human Interaction with Weather

We have discussed how changes in land use affect flooding and landslides, and how deep-well disposal and the filling of large water reservoirs may trigger earthquakes. Human activities can also have an impact on weather events. For example, the practice of plowing cropland after fall harvest and leaving the topsoil exposed to wind significantly increased the size of the dust storms in the Dust Bowl during the 1930s. Placing mobile homes in areas that are subject to frequent high winds and tornadoes greatly increases damage and loss of life from this type of severe weather.

Concern has been expressed that global warming is increasing the size and frequency of severe weather events. On the basis of computer models, some atmospheric scientists conclude that global warming is likely to increase the humidex index and the number of heat waves in continental interiors, as well as the intensity of precipitation in many areas.[21] Computer models also indicate that global warming is likely to increase the frequency of drought in mid-latitude continental interiors and may increase the number and strength of hurricanes, typhoons, and other tropical cyclones.[21] Other scientists, however, argue that these conclusions are premature based on current knowledge. The effects of global warming on tornadoes, thunderstorms, hailstorms, and lightning are still being studied but, overall, global warming will likely increase the incidence of severe weather.[22]

8.7 Natural Service Functions of Severe Weather

It might seem that severe weather has no benefits, but it does have several. Lightning starts wildfires, which are important in maintaining prairie and forest ecosystems (see Chapter 10). Windstorms help maintain the health of forests by toppling dead and diseased trees, which then are recycled in the soil. Fallen trees also create clearings that become new habitats for many plants and animals.

Blizzards and other snowstorms, thunderstorms, and tropical storms are important sources of water. Water derived from snowmelt and seasonal storms reduces a region's vulnerability to drought. Snowfall, clouds, and lightning also have an aesthetic value. Thanks to movies and television programs, tornado chasing has become a new form of tourism. Guided tours in specially equipped vehicles are offered in Tornado Alley to chase and photograph tornadoes (see Professional Profile). Tornado chasing, however, can be extremely dangerous; injury, even death, can occur if people are caught in a vehicle by a tornado.

8.8 Minimizing Severe Weather Hazards

Thunderstorms, tornadoes, droughts, and other severe weather events cannot be prevented and will continue to claim lives and destroy property. We can, however, take steps to minimize loss of life and damage from severe weather events if we can better predict and prepare for them.

Forecasting and Predicting Weather Hazards

Timely and accurate prediction of severe weather events is essential if human lives are to be saved. Even with improvements in satellite sensors and computer modelling, severe weather events are still difficult to forecast, and their behaviour is unpredictable.

Installation of a network of *Doppler radar* stations across North America has significantly improved our ability to predict the paths of severe storms. Doppler radar antennas send out electromagnetic waves with a wavelength a little longer than microwaves (Figure 8.6). Clouds, raindrops, ice particles, and other objects in the sky reflect the electromagnetic waves. The wavelength of the reflected waves differs depending on whether the objects are moving toward or away from the antenna. The change in wavelength, called the *Doppler effect,* is similar to the difference in pitch of a siren's sound waves as an ambulance approaches you and then goes away. The changes in radar wavelength are analyzed and can be used to make short-term predictions about weather, on the scale of hours. For example, Doppler radar can detect

PROFESSIONAL PROFILE

Warren Faidley, Tornado Chaser

Warren Faidley, tornado chaser extraordinaire, has seen tornado-damaged cars that "you couldn't even tell was a car until you got close and you started seeing parts that you recognized."

A veteran of tracking tornadoes, Faidley can recount any number of stories about the wrath of a twister (Figure 8.F). He recalls watching a woman search in the aftermath of a tornado and discover a fork from her kitchen lodged solidly in the trunk of a tree, bent almost sideways from the impact. Her home was a kilometre away.

"Tornadoes can knock over a boxcar," he says. "They'll pick up a car and toss it like a toy."

But Faidley describes tornadoes with a great deal of love and reverence. "Every tornado is different," he says, adding that they can take many forms, largely depending on the nature of the surface where they touch down.

To the experienced eyes of tornado chasers like Faidley, the storm that precedes a twister has a certain character. "Tornadic storms have a certain look and feel about them," Faidley says. "The way the clouds are billowing; they have a sculpted look, a determined look."

Faidley characterizes the sound of a tornado as "like a waterfall, where the closer you are, the louder it is," though at very close distances the sound can be obscured by the flying dust and debris.

For all their destructive potential, Faidley argues that the experienced chaser is not in much danger if he or she knows where it is safe to stand. "You can actually get pretty close to a tornado," he says.

▲ **FIGURE 8.F STORM CHASER** Warren Faidley with a newly formed tornado in the background. *(Warren Faidley)*

But given the effort that goes into tracking a good twister, a chaser rarely gets to observe one for very long—an average of less than five minutes, according to Faidley.

Although he says that the 1996 blockbuster film *Twister,* which features a tornado-hunting team, is inaccurate, the movie has done some good in fostering an interest in severe weather. "I actually know kids who saw that movie and are now becoming meteorologists," Faidley says.

—Chris Wilson

a mesocyclone within a thunderstorm, allowing meteorologists to issue some warnings up to 30 minutes in advance of the touchdown of a tornado.

Tornado Watches and Warnings A tornado **watch** is a public advisory that one or more tornadoes may develop in a specified area in the near future. A typical tornado watch covers an area of 50,000 km^2 to 100,000 km^2 and lasts four to six hours.[23] A watch does not guarantee that a tornado will happen; rather, it alerts the public to the possibility of a tornado and suggests they monitor local radio or television stations for more information.

When a tornado has been sighted or detected by Doppler radar, the watch is upgraded to a **warning**. A warning indicates that the affected area is in danger and that people should take immediate action to protect themselves and others. Watches can be upgraded to warnings, or warnings can be issued for an area not previously under a watch. Both watches and warnings can be issued not only for tornadoes but also for any type of severe weather: thunderstorms, tropical storms, hurricanes, heat waves, and blizzards, with some differences in the area covered and the duration of the watch or warning.

People's perception of the risk they face from severe weather hazards differs according to their experience. Someone who has survived a tornado will more likely perceive the hazard as real than will a person who has lived in a tornado-prone region but has never experienced one. Incorrect predictions of where or when a severe weather event will strike can also affect people's perception of risk. For example, if people are repeatedly warned of severe thunderstorms that never arrive, they may become complacent and ignore future warnings. An accurate understanding and perception of risk by planners and the public alike is key to reducing injury and death from severe weather events.

Adjustment to Severe Weather Hazards

Steps that can be taken to reduce death and damage from severe weather events include changes to a community's infrastructure and planning at the individual and community level. Actions taken to prevent or minimize death and damage are termed *mitigation*. They include the engineering and building of structures with safety in mind, installation of warning systems, and provision of hazard insurance. Establishing community and individual plans and procedures to deal with a possible natural disaster is considered *preparedness*.[24]

Mitigation Mitigation methods differ for each weather hazard, but some general statements can be made. Building new wind-resistant structures and upgrading existing ones can save lives and lessen property damage during severe storms, such as tornadoes and thunderstorms. In the United States, the Federal Emergency Management Agency (FEMA) offers grants and architectural plans to establish community shelters and safe rooms in buildings for tornado protection.[25]

Ensuring that electric, gas, water, and wastewater systems can function following severe storms is an important part of weather-hazard mitigation. This need was painfully apparent after the 1998 ice storm in Canada and the United States, when 60,000 people were still without power nearly three weeks after the storm ended.[26]

Other mitigation techniques include developing and installing warning systems and making hazard insurance widely available. The purpose of warning systems is to give the public the earliest possible notification of impending severe weather. Announcements can be made by radio, television, and the internet. Sirens can be installed in communities and used to issue tornado warnings. Insurance can be purchased by property owners in regions at risk of severe weather. Basic policies cover damage from water and wind, but residents should determine whether extra coverage is required for tornadoes, hurricanes, blizzards, or hailstorms.

Mitigation strategies for droughts and heat waves are more complicated and much more difficult to implement. Droughts lower reservoir levels and the capacity to generate hydroelectric power; they also reduce stream flow. Reduced water storage and stream flow may limit water availability for personal, agricultural, and industrial use. Mitigation and adaptation measures that can be taken to deal with drought include increasing the capacity of reservoirs, exploiting groundwater resources, desalinization, and water conservation. With the exception of conservation, these measures are expensive and they take time to implement. Governments may find it difficult to convince the public to spend funds in anticipation of droughts that might occur at some unknown time in the future.

Preparedness and Personal Adjustments People can take steps to prepare for severe weather. Some of the steps should be taken before a watch or warning is issued, whereas others are more appropriate when the danger is imminent. Persons living in areas prone to severe weather should be aware of the times of year that the risk is greatest and prepare themselves, their families, and their homes. Information about how to prepare for weather-related disasters is available from Environment Canada and its subsidiary, the Meteorological Service of Canada, from the U.S. National Oceanic and Atmospheric Administration (NOAA) and its subsidiary, the National Weather Service, and from the U.S. Federal Emergency Management Agency (FEMA).

Summary

Although Earth intercepts only a tiny fraction of the total energy emitted by the Sun, this energy sustains life and drives many processes at or near Earth's surface, such as atmospheric and oceanic circulation. Energy is transferred in the atmosphere by convection, conduction, and radiation. Of these three mechanisms, convection is the most dynamic and significant in producing severe weather.

Severe weather produces much-feared tornadoes and hurricanes, but drought is more damaging and heat waves and blizzards cause the majority of weather-related human deaths and injuries.

People interact with hazardous weather in numerous ways. At the local level, such land-use practices as housing and agricultural processes may increase the impact of severe weather. On the global scale, atmospheric warming in response to burning of fossil fuels and land clearing may be changing climate and weather. Warming of both the atmosphere and the oceans may feed more energy into storms, potentially increasing the incidence of severe weather events.

Minimizing injury and damage from thunderstorms, tornadoes, hurricanes, heat waves, and blizzards requires (1) better forecasting and warning of severe weather events, (2) construction practices that prevent or minimize death and loss of property, (3) hazard preparedness, including actions that individuals and communities can take once they have been warned of severe weather, and (4) education and insurance programs to reduce risk.

Key Terms

albedo (p. 223)
atmosphere (p. 224)
blizzard (p. 238)
Coriolis effect (p. 226)
drought (p. 239)
dust storm (p. 239)
F-scale (p. 236)
humidex index (p. 243)
ice storm (p. 239)
lightning (p. 231)
relative humidity (p. 224)
tornado (p. 218)
troposphere (p. 224)
warning (p. 244)
watch (p. 244)
wind chill (p. 238)

Review Questions

1. Describe the differences among force, work, and power.
2. What are the three types of energy and how do they differ?
3. What is the difference between sensible heat and latent heat?
4. What are the three types of heat transfer? How do they differ from one another?
5. Describe Earth's energy balance.
6. What is electromagnetic energy and how are its different types distinguished?
7. List in order the following types of electromagnetic energy from shortest wavelength to longest wavelength: radio waves, ultraviolet radiation, gamma radiation, visible light, infrared radiation, X-rays, and microwaves.
8. What is the relation between colour and energy absorption?
9. Describe the characteristics of the troposphere. How do meteorologists identify the top of the troposphere?
10. What is the tropopause? How high is it above Earth's surface?
11. Why does atmospheric pressure decrease with increasing altitude?
12. Explain the Coriolis effect. How does it influence weather?
13. What conditions are necessary for a severe thunderstorm to form?
14. Describe the three stages of thunderstorm development.
15. What are supercells, mesoscale convective complexes, and squall lines? How do they differ?
16. What is hail and how does it form?
17. Characterize a tornado in terms of wind speed, size, typical speed of movement, duration, and length of travel.
18. Describe the stages of tornado development.
19. How are waterspouts and tornadoes related? What are their differences?
20. What is a blizzard and how does it develop?
21. What is a nor'easter? How is it related to blizzards?
22. Describe the weather conditions that cause an ice storm.
23. How are the humidex index and wind chill temperature alike? How are they different?
24. How could global warming affect severe weather?
25. What are the natural service functions of severe weather?
26. What is the difference between a severe weather watch and a severe weather warning?
27. What is the difference between preparedness and mitigation?

Critical Thinking Questions

1. What severe weather events occur where you live? What steps might you take to protect yourself from these hazards?
2. Use the web resources listed below to determine what behaviour outside and inside your house increases the possibility that you might be struck by lightning.
3. Tornadoes can generally be spotted on weather radar, whereas many clouds cannot. What makes tornadoes visible?
4. Study the diagrams of cold fronts and warm fronts, and read the description about the development of ice storms. Explain why sleet (small pellets of ice) is more likely than freezing rain to accompany cold fronts.
5. Why does hail form in thunderstorms and not in other rainstorms or snowstorms?

Selected Web Resources

Weather
www.msc-smc.ec.gc.ca/weather/contents_e.html Fact sheets about lightning, blizzards, hailstorms, tornadoes, waterspouts, humidity, and wind chill from the Meteorological Service of Canada

Canada Online
http://canadaonline.about.com/od/extremeweather Articles and resources on extreme weather conditions in Canada

Atlantic Storm Prediction Centre
www.atl.ec.gc.ca/weather/aspc.html Information on the Atlantic Storm Prediction Centre/Canadian Hurricane Centre in Dartmouth, Nova Scotia

National Weather Service Storm Prediction Center
www.spc.noaa.gov Current severe weather information from NOAA

National Severe Storms Laboratory's Weather Room
www.nssl.noaa.gov/edu Questions and answers about tornadoes, thunderstorms, lightning, and hurricanes from the NOAA National Severe Storms Laboratory

National Climatic Data Center
http://lwf.ncdc.noaa.gov/oa/ncdc.html Weather data from NOAA

Hazards: Informing the Public About Hazards
www.fema.gov Background information about thunderstorms, tornadoes, heat waves, and winter storms from the U.S. Federal Emergency Management Agency

U.S. Hazards Assessment
www.cpc.noaa.gov/products/expert_assessment/threats.html Current U.S. weather hazards from the National Weather Service Climate Prediction Center

NOAA and American Red Cross Publications on Weather Hazards
http://weather.gov/om/brochures.shtml From the National Weather Service Office of Climate, Water, and Weather Services

Weather Safety
http://weather.gov/safety.php Links to NOAA web pages on weather safety from the National Weather Service

The Weather World 2010 Project
http://ww2010.atmos.uiuc.edu Multimedia guide to meteorology linked to current weather conditions from the University of Illinois

The Tornado Project Online!
www.tornadoproject.com A comprehensive website on tornadoes from a small company that has been collecting information since 1970

Extreme Weather Sourcebook 2001
http://sciencepolicy.colorado.edu/sourcebook Economic and societal aspects of severe weather from the National Center for Atmospheric Research

CHAPTER 9

▶ **HURRICANE KATRINA** Satellite image of Hurricane Katrina on August 28, 2005, as it heads north toward landfall near the Louisiana-Mississippi border. Spiralling bands of heavy rain and ferocious winds fill much of the eastern Gulf of Mexico, from Yucatan Peninsula at the bottom to Florida at the top. A pronounced eye marks the centre of this Category 5 storm, which was one of the strongest hurricanes in U.S. history and by far the most damaging. *(NASA/Jeff Schmaltz, MODIS Land Rapid Response Team)*

Coastal Hazards

Learning Objectives

In this chapter we focus on one of the most dynamic environments on Earth—the coast, where the sea meets the land. Large numbers of people live and visit beaches and rocky coastlines, but most of us have little understanding of how ocean waves and currents form and change coastlines. This chapter explains the processes at work in coastal areas and the hazards that result from wind and waves. Your goals in reading this chapter should be to

- Understand waves, currents, and beach forms and processes
- Understand coastal hazards, such as hurricanes, rip currents, tsunami, and erosion
- Understand the effects of coastal processes
- Know what coastal regions are at risk from these hazards
- Recognize the linkages between coastal processes and other natural hazards
- Know the benefits of coastal processes
- Understand how our use of the coastal zone affects coastal processes
- Understand the measures that can be taken to avoid damage and injury from coastal erosion, hurricanes, and tsunami

Hurricane Katrina

The 2005 hurricane season was the worst in the history of the United States. Four Category 5 hurricanes formed in the South Atlantic that year, two of which caused tremendous damage in the United States. Hurricane Katrina was the worst. It was the second Category 5 hurricane of the 2005 season and the sixth-strongest Atlantic hurricane ever recorded. Notably, three of these six storms occurred in 2005.

Hurricane Katrina formed over the Bahamas on August 23, 2005, and crossed southern Florida as a moderate Category 1 hurricane. It weakened as it crossed land but rapidly regained strength in the warm waters of the Gulf of Mexico, soon becoming one of the strongest hurricanes ever recorded in the Gulf. At its peak, the storm carried sustained wind speeds of up to 280 km/h. It is possible that Katrina was the largest hurricane of its strength to approach the United States in recorded history; its sheer size caused devastation more than 160 km from its centre.

Katrina made landfall near the Louisiana-Mississippi border on the morning of August 29 as a somewhat weakened Category 3 hurricane. The *storm surge*, which ranged from 4 m to 12 m high, caused catastrophic damage along parts of the coastlines of Louisiana, Mississippi, and Alabama (Figure 9.1). Levees separating Lake Pontchartrain from New Orleans were breached by the surge, inundating about 80 percent of the city and many neighbouring parishes (Figure 9.1b). Katrina maintained hurricane strength well inland, finally losing it more than 240 km from the coast, near Jackson, Mississippi. It was downgraded further to a tropical depression in Tennessee, where it broke in half. One half of the storm continued northward as far as the eastern Great Lakes, while the other half slowly dissipated over the southeastern United States, producing tornadoes from Georgia to Pennsylvania. On August 31, Katrina was absorbed by a frontal boundary and became a powerful extratropical low, causing moderate rain and gale-force winds in southeastern Quebec.

Hurricane Katrina was responsible for more than US$115 billion in damage, making it the costliest disaster in U.S. history. It was also the deadliest hurricane in the United States since 1928, taking at least 2140 lives.

More than a year after Hurricane Katrina, recovery was far from complete. Areas of New Orleans that were most severely flooded have

(a)

(b)

(c)

◀ **FIGURE 9.1 EFFECTS OF HURRICANE KATRINA** (a) A destroyed apartment building along Highway I-90 (the Gulf Coast Highway) in Long Beach, Mississippi. The destruction resulted from winds and the accompanying storm surge. *(John Fleck, FEMA)* (b) New Orleans on Monday, August 29, 2005. The photograph shows widespread flooding resulting from breached levees. *(illinoisphoto.com enhanced FEMA photo)* (c) A view of a section of the Mississippi coast showing the extensive damage caused by the Katrina storm surge. *(illinoisphoto.com enhanced FEMA photo)*

not been rebuilt, and the population of the city has not returned to its pre-Katrina level. Large numbers of people have been displaced permanently, and no clear plan is in place to return the people who want to do so. The costs of temporary shelter and the social and physical services required to maintain the displaced are huge and ongoing. We have much to learn about managing recovery from natural disasters and catastrophes.

9.1 Introduction to Coastal Processes

Waves

Waves are generated by wind, in some cases thousands of kilometres from the coast. Wind blowing over the ocean or a lake transfers some of its energy to the water, producing waves. The waves, in turn, travel through the water and eventually expend their energy at the shoreline.

Waves have a range of sizes and shapes. The size of waves depends on a combination of the following:

- The velocity of the wind; the stronger the wind, the larger the waves.
- The duration of the wind. Winds that last longer, such as those during storms, have more time to impart energy to the water, thereby producing larger waves.
- The distance the wind blows across the water, which is referred to as the *fetch*. A longer fetch allows larger waves to form, thus waves in the ocean are generally larger than those in a lake.

As waves move away from their source, they become organized into groups, or *sets*, of similar size and shape. Sets of waves may travel long distances across the ocean and arrive at distant shores with little loss of energy. Sets with different characteristics arrive at coastlines at different times. An alternation of small and large sets allows surfers to wait and take advantage of the sets of larger waves that they know will eventually arrive. You can often see these sets if you watch the surf from a beach or coastal cliff. Interactions among different sets from different sources produce a regular pattern, or "surf beat." Unexpected, unusually large **rogue waves**, occasionally arrive at the shore, sometimes with disastrous results (see Case Study 9.1).

Waves moving across deep water have a similar basic shape, or wave form (Figure 9.2a). Three parameters describe the size and movement of a wave: *wave height* (*H*), which is the difference in height between the trough and the crest of a wave; *wavelength* (*L*), the distance between successive wave crests; and *wave period* (*P*), the time in seconds for successive waves to pass a reference point. The reference point used to determine wave period could be a pier or another object anchored on the seafloor or lake bottom.

You can understand how waves transmit energy through the water by studying the motion of an object on the water surface and one below the surface. When a wave moves

9.1 CASE STUDY

Rogue Waves

Rogue waves form when a series of similar-size waves meet and coalesce to produce a much larger wave; this process is known as *constructive interference*. The new wave may be as high as the sum of the waves that coalesced. Seafloor irregularities and currents may also be important in forming rogue waves.

Rogue waves can be extremely dangerous. They can appear out of nowhere, crashing over a pier or a rocky headland and sweeping unsuspecting people to their deaths. Each summer several beachgoers in Canada and the United States are swept into the ocean by rogue waves. Shores, however, are not the only areas at risk from rogue waves. These waves can appear in the open ocean in otherwise fairly calm water (Figure 9.A). They may be large enough to break in open water and can threaten ships or offshore drilling platforms, such as those on the continental shelf off Atlantic Canada. In stormy seas, where all waves are large, rogue waves can reach 30 m in height. A rogue wave 20 m high struck the cruise ship *Norwegian Dawn* about 400 km off the coast of Georgia in April 2005, damaging the ship and ending the cruise. Ten separate rogue waves more than 25 m high were identified in the world's oceans in a study of three weeks of global satellite radar data.[1] This information is important to the shipping industry because most ships are designed to withstand waves only 15 m high.[1]

Rogue waves can develop almost anywhere in the world's oceans, but they are most common where local or regional conditions favour the constructive interference that permits them to form. One such place is off the southern tip of Africa where the southwest-flowing Agulhas Current, the eastward-flowing Antarctic Circumpolar Current, and the swell from Antarctic storms interact.

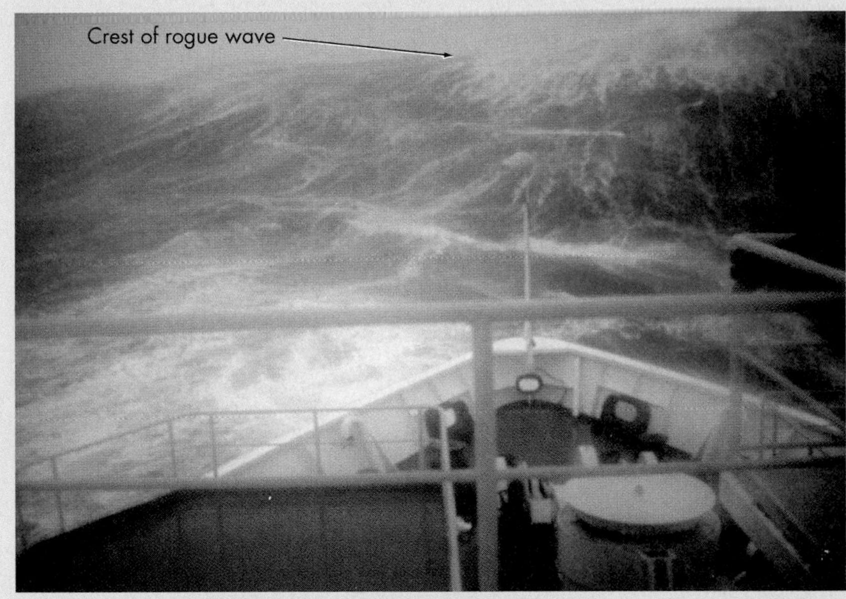

◄ **FIGURE 9.A ROGUE WAVE** This huge rogue wave is approaching the bow of the *JOIDES Resolution,* the scientific drilling ship of the Ocean Drilling Program. Rogue waves have sunk supertankers and large cargo ships. *(Ocean Drilling Program, Texas A&M University).*

through the area, an object 20 m below the surface moves up, forward, down, and back in a circular orbit, always returning to the same place (Figure 9.2b). An object nearer the water surface also moves in circles, but the circles are larger (Figure 9.2b).

The shape of the orbital motions changes as waves enter shallow water. At a depth of less than about one-half their wavelength (i.e., depth $\leq 0.5\ L$), the waves begin to "feel the bottom," causing the circular orbits to become ellipses (Figure 9.2c). In very shallow water (i.e., depth $\leq 0.05\ L$), motion at the bottom may be nearly horizontal, with only a small vertical component. You probably have experienced this while standing or swimming in shallow water; the water repeatedly pushes you toward the shore and then away from it.

Wave sets generated by storms far out at sea are called *swell*. Wave height, period, and velocity of the swell can be predicted by using equations based on the fetch, wind velocity, and the length of time the wind blows over the water. These predictions are important: by knowing the velocity and height of the waves generated by a distant storm, we can estimate when the waves will strike the shore and how erosive they will be.

As waves approach the coast, they become unstable and break. Wavelength and velocity decrease and wave height

► **FIGURE 9.2 WAVES AND BEACHES** (a) A wave form in deep water where the water depth is greater than one-half of the wavelength (*L*). The curving black line is the water surface and the thick vertical black line is a pier or some other reference point for determining the wave period (*T*). The black dashed line connecting the bottom of the troughs is the reference line for calculating wave height (*H*). (b) Motion of water particles associated with the movement of a wave in deep water. The water particles follow the path of the arrows in the black circles. (c) The motion of water particles in shallow water at a depth less than 0.25 *L*. The water particles follow the path of the arrows in the white circles. The small black arrows show that water moves forward and back in the swash zone on the beach. The waves are approaching the shore from right to left in (b) and (c).

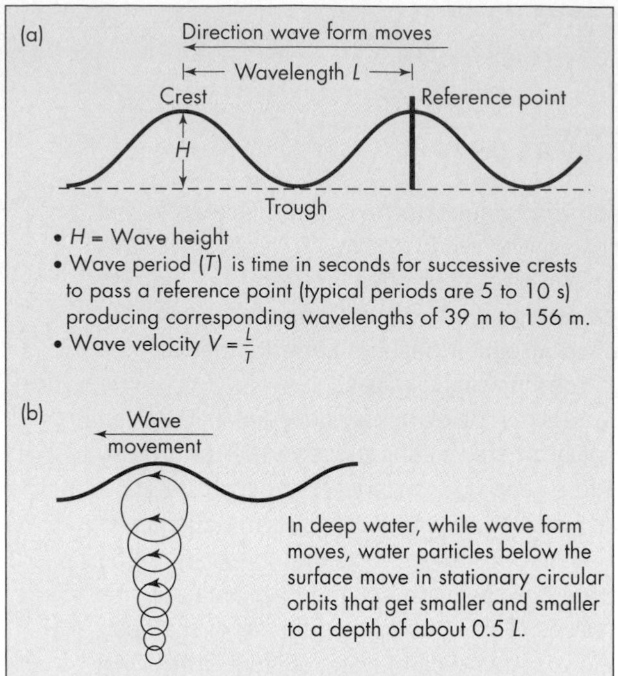

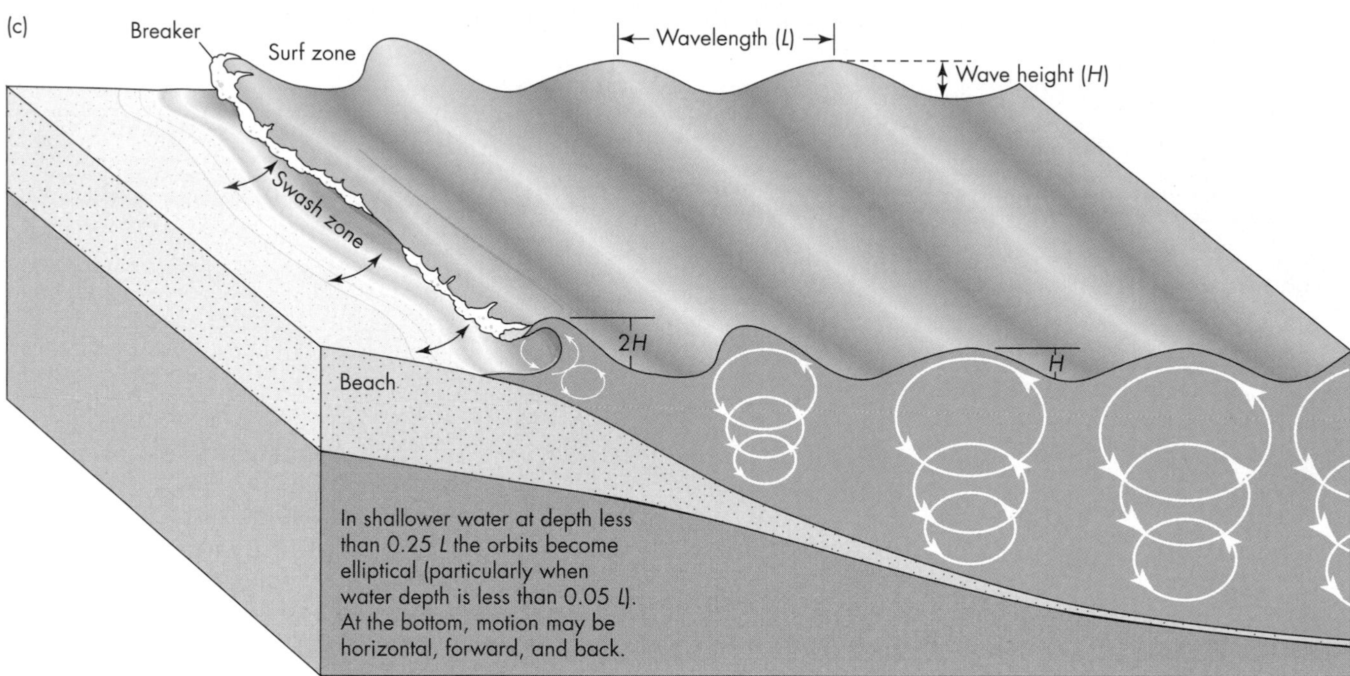

increases; only the wave period remains constant. The waves also change shape—the rounded crests and troughs found in deep water are replaced by peaked crests with relatively flat troughs in shallow water. Perhaps the most dramatic change is the rapid increase in wave height. As waves approach their breaking point in shallow water, their height may increase to twice that in deep water (Figure 9.2c). The waves collapse, or break, toward the beach because the wave crest keeps moving forward while the lower part of the wave slows down.

Waves release a large amount of energy as they rush ashore. Wave energy is approximately proportional to the square of wave height. Thus, if wave height increases from 1 m to 2 m, the wave energy, or wave power, increases by a factor of 4. Waves 5 m high, which are common in large storms, expend about 25 times the energy of waves 1 m high. The energy spent on a 400 km length of open coastline by waves about 1 m high is approximately the same as the energy produced by an average nuclear power plant over the same period.[2] The energy released by larger storm waves along the same stretch of coast is commonly many times this amount.

Variations along a Coastline Wave heights along a coast may increase or decrease as waves approach the shore. These variations are caused by irregularities in near-shore bathymetry and the shape of the coastline. Consider, for example,

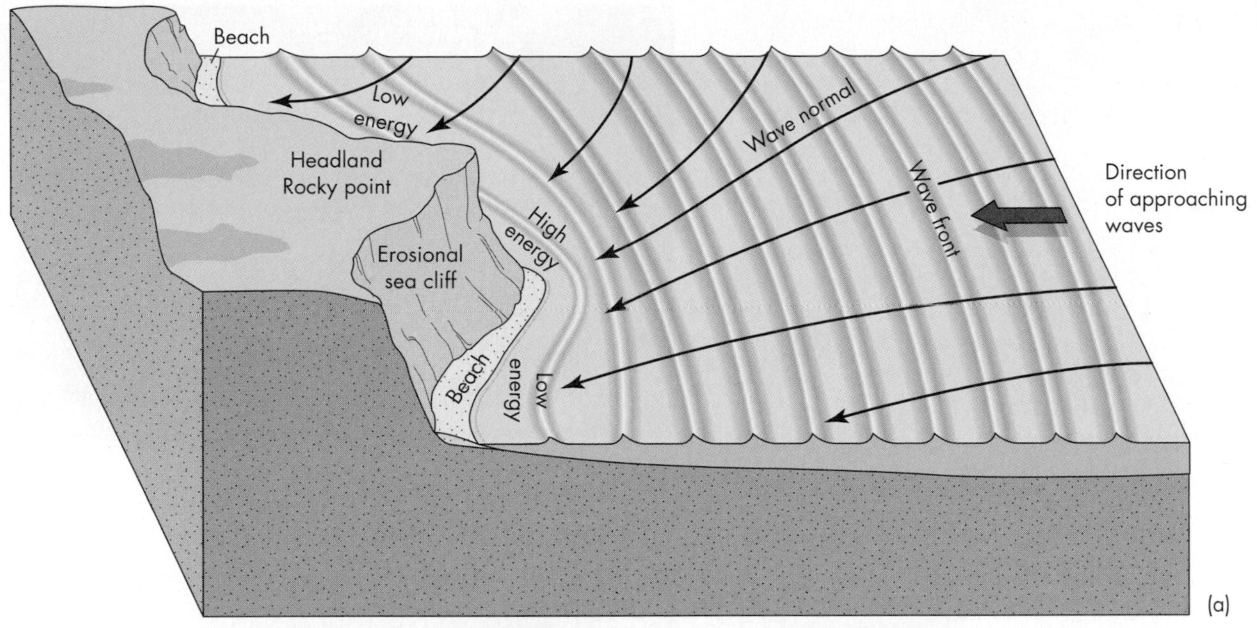

▲ **FIGURE 9.3 CONVERGENCE AND DIVERGENCE OF WAVE ENERGY** (a) A schematic diagram showing wave refraction and concentration of wave energy at headlands. Refraction, the bending of wave fronts, causes convergence of wave normals on headlands and divergence along indented reaches of the coast. Wave normals are the imaginary long curving black arrows. (b) Large waves striking a rocky headland along the Pacific Coast at Pebble Beach, California. *(Robert H. Blodgett)*

the behaviour of the crest of a single wave as it approaches an irregularly shaped coastline (Figure 9.3a).

Irregular coastlines commonly have small rocky peninsulas known as *headlands*. The shoreline between headlands may be relatively straight or somewhat curved. A long wave approaching the coast will first slow down in the shallow water off the headland. The slowdown causes the wave to bend, or *refract*, around the headland and thus to become more parallel to the shoreline (Figure 9.3a).

Effects of Wave Refraction To visualize the effects of wave refraction, draw a series of imaginary lines, called *wave normals*, perpendicular to the wave fronts, with arrows pointing toward the shoreline. These imaginary lines show the direction the waves are travelling. The resulting diagram (Figure 9.3a) shows that wave refraction causes *convergence* of wave normals at the headland and *divergence* along the shoreline away from the headland. Where wave normals converge, the height and energy of the waves increase. Thus, the largest waves along a shoreline are generally found along rocky headlands (Figure 9.3b). The long-term effect of greater energy expenditure on protruding areas, such as headlands, is that the shoreline tends to become straightened.

Breaking Waves Waves also differ in how they break along a shore. **Breaking waves** may plunge or surge, or they may gently spill onto the shore, depending on local conditions. *Plunging breakers* (Figure 9.4a) typically form on steep beaches and can be very erosive. *Spilling breakers* (Figure 9.4b) commonly develop on wide, gently sloping, sandy beaches and are less erosive than plunging breakers. In estuaries subject to large tides, inflowing tidal waters may be slowed by outflowing river water to produce **tidal bores**.[3] Tidal bores have very steep fronts, in rare cases up to several

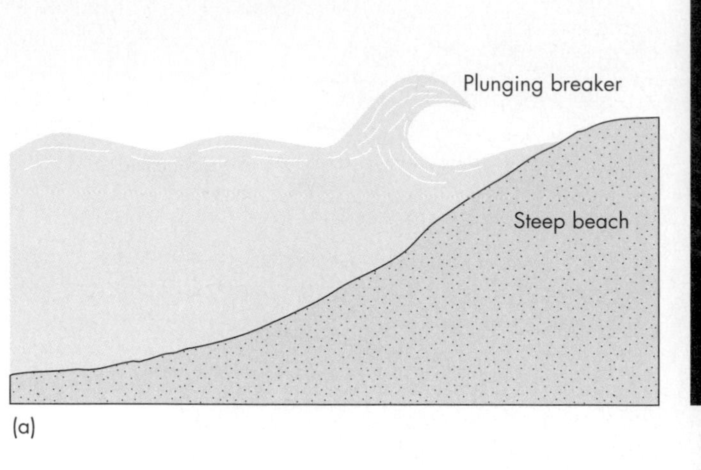

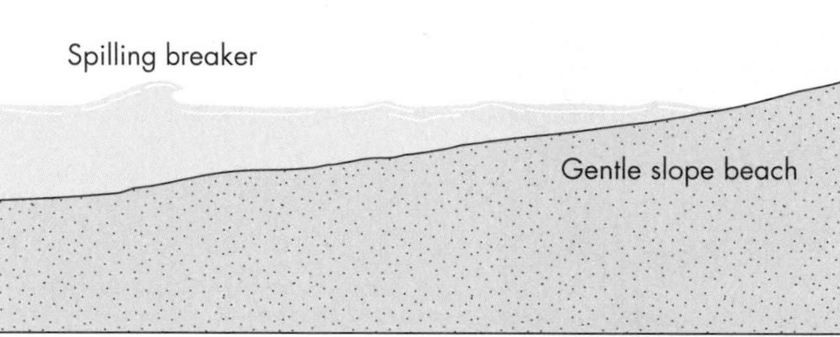

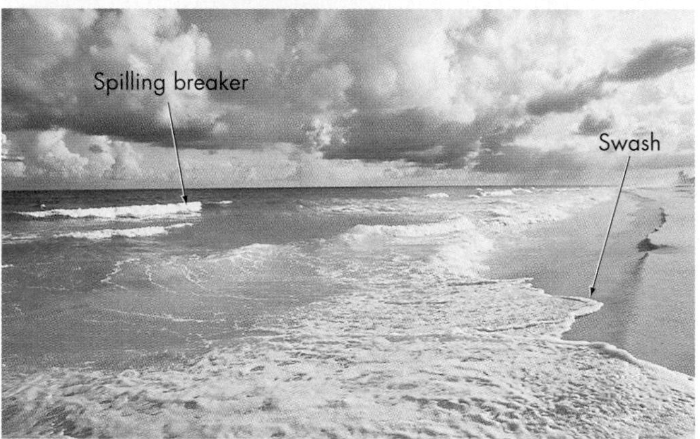

▲ **FIGURE 9.4 TYPES OF BREAKERS** A schematic diagram and photographs showing (a) plunging breakers on a steep beach and (b) spilling breakers on a gently sloping beach. *([a] Peter Cade/Getty Images, Inc.-Stone Allstock; [b] Penny Tweedie/Getty Images, Inc., Stone Allstock)*

metres high, and surge forward like broken waves (Figure 9.5). They occur at the mouths of the Amazon, Hooghly, Meghna, Indus, Severn, and Yangtse rivers, within the Bay of Fundy in Nova Scotia, and in Ungava Bay in Quebec. Breakers along a particular reach of the coast can also change seasonally and with changes in underwater slope and topography.

Beach Form and Processes

A **beach** consists of loose material, such as sand or gravel, that has accumulated by wave action at the shoreline. The sand and gravel are derived from a wide variety of rocks and, therefore, differ in colour and composition. The white beaches of South Pacific islands, for example, are made of

◄ **FIGURE 9.5 TIDAL BORE** Steep landward-moving wave produced by retardation of inflowing tidal water by outward-flowing river water in upper Cook Inlet, Alaska. *(Photographer: Archival photography by Mr. Steve Nicklas, NGS/RSD)*

broken bits of shell and coral, and Hawaii's black sand beaches are made from fragments of basalt. Wave energy and beach shape are other factors affecting beach materials. Most steep, high-energy beaches are gravel, whereas gently sloping, lower-energy beaches commonly consist of sand.

The Beach Onshore An understanding of beach processes requires knowledge of beach forms (Figure 9.6). The landward boundary of the beach can be a cliff, called a **sea cliff** along a seashore and a **bluff** along a lakeshore, one or more sand dunes, or terrestrial vegetation. Sea cliffs and lakeside bluffs are erosional landforms produced by waves, currents, and, in some cases, landslides. In contrast, coastal sand dunes form by deposition of wind-blown beach sand.

The onshore portion of many beaches can be divided into two zones that parallel the shoreline, one that is flat or slopes gently landward, called the *berm*, and another that slopes seaward, called the *beach face*. The berm is located at the backshore of a beach and consists of sand deposited by waves as they rush up and expend the last of their energy. Beaches may have more than one berm or none at all. The beach face is located seaward of the berm, where the beach slope steepens toward the water. It lies in part within the **swash zone**, which experiences the repeated up-rush and backwash of waves. The swash zone shifts seaward or landward because of changes in water level resulting from storms or tides.

The Beach Offshore The surf zone and the breaker zone lie directly offshore of the swash zone (Figure 9.6). The **surf zone** is located just seaward of the swash zone and is the place where waves move turbulently toward the shore after they break. Beyond the surf zone is the **breaker zone**, where incoming waves peak and break. A low ridge consisting of sand or gravel, called a *longshore bar*, occurs on the seafloor or lake floor in the breaker zone (Figure 9.6). A *longshore trough* may form by wave and current action landward of the longshore bar. Both the bar and the trough are elongate parallel to the crests of the breaking waves. Wide and gently sloping beaches may have several lines of breakers and longshore bars.[4]

Sand Transport Beach sand is not static; wave action constantly moves the sand in the surf and swash zones. Storms erode sand from the beach and redeposit it either offshore or landward in dunes. Most of the sand moved offshore during a storm returns to the beach later, during fair weather.

Sand also is carried parallel to the shore in the swash and surf zones by a process termed **littoral transport** (Figure 9.7). Littoral transport consists of two processes, beach drift and longshore drift. In *beach drift*, the repeated shoreward and seaward movement of sand in the swash zone produces a sinuous or zigzag transport path (Figure 9.7). The shoreward component of the movement is an angle to the shoreline, whereas the seaward component is nearly perpendicular to the shoreline. *Longshore drift* is the transport of sediment by currents that flow parallel to the shoreline, called *longshore currents* (Figure 9.7). Both types of drift occur where waves strike the coast at an angle other than 90 degrees (Figure 9.7). The terms *updrift* and *downdrift* refer to the direction that sediment is moving or accumulating relative to the direction of the incoming waves. For example, downdrift in Figure 9.7 is toward the lower right of the diagram.

The direction of littoral transport differs markedly along the Pacific, Atlantic, and Arctic coasts of Canada, primarily because of the complex shape of the coastline. Significant littoral transport is restricted to those parts of the Canadian coast with broad sandy beaches, largely on the Pacific and Atlantic Coasts. Littoral transport is limited or does not occur on the steep, rocky shorelines that form much of the Canadian coast and also on those parts of the Arctic coast where sea ice limits wave formation during much of the year. Broad sandy beaches are less common in Canada than in the United States. Rates of longshore drift for some U.S. beaches range from 150,000 m^3 to 300,000 m^3 of sediment per year.[5] Rates of

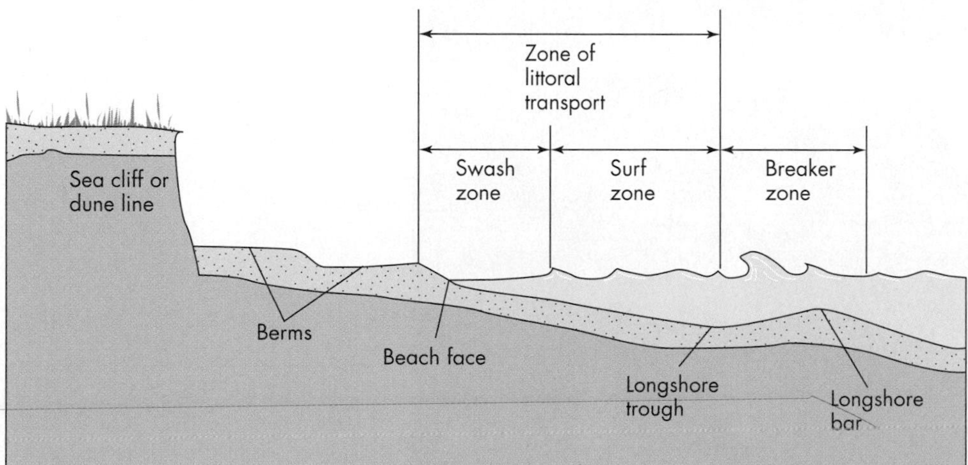

▲ **FIGURE 9.6 BEACH TERMINOLOGY** Basic terms for landforms and wave action in the beach and nearshore environment. A sea cliff or line of coastal sand dunes marks the landward limit of the beach. Two berms slope gently toward the cliff. The beach face slopes toward the water. A longshore trough and longshore bar are seaward of the beach face; the longshore bar forms within the breaker zone. The zone of littoral transport includes the swash and surf zones.

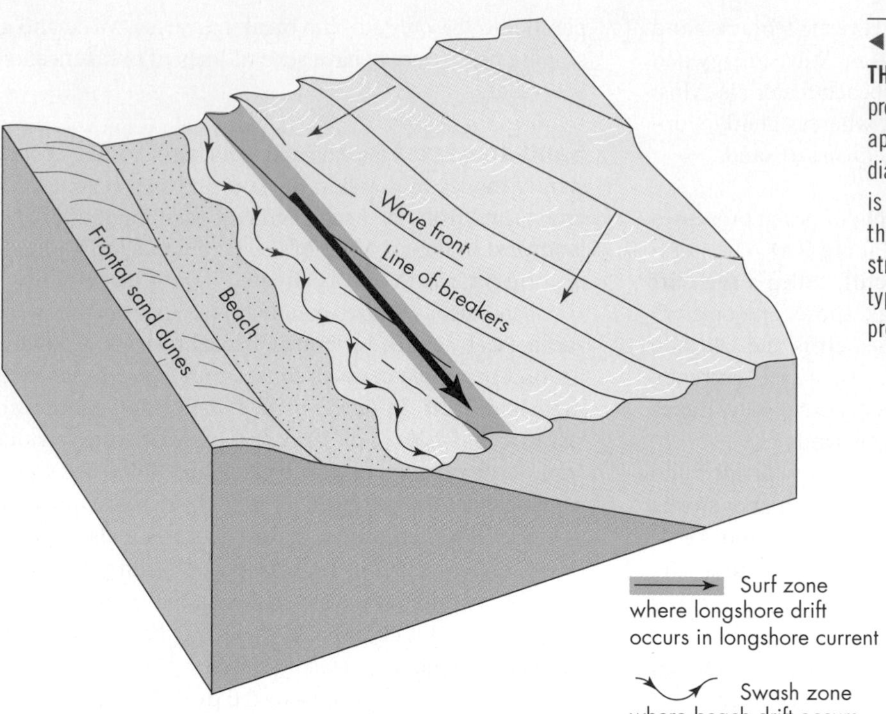

◄ **FIGURE 9.7 TRANSPORT OF SEDIMENT ALONG THE SHORE** A block diagram illustrating the processes of beach drift and longshore drift. Waves approach the coast from the upper right in this diagram (thin arrows). The direction of beach drift is shown by the wavy line in the swash zone, and the longshore drift direction is shown by the straight thick arrow in the surf zone. These two types of drift move sand along the coast; the process is termed littoral transport.

longshore drift for sandy shorelines of the Great Lakes are much less, about 6000 m^3 to 69,000 m^3 per year. Even these rates, however, are still substantial when you consider that a typical dump truck carries a meagre 8 m^3 of sand.[5]

Landforms Produced by Littoral Drift Beaches are not the only features produced by waves, currents, and longshore drift. Other landforms produced by these processes include spits, barrier islands, and tombolos. A **spit** is a long, narrow, low-lying ridge of sand or gravel that extends parallel to the shore from a point of land on the coast, commonly a headland or a cliff or bluff that is being eroded by waves (Figure 9.8). Spits taper to a point, but their foundations continue below water level farther in the direction of longshore drift. **Tombolos** are spits that are attached to the coast at both ends. They enclose brackish or freshwater ponds or lakes. **Barrier islands** are similar in form to spits but are wider and commonly extend for long distances along seacoasts. Except for the tidal and storm channels that breach them, barrier islands isolate bays and coastal waterways from the open ocean. Barrier islands are common features on the Atlantic coast of the United States (Figure 9.9).

◄ **FIGURE 9.8 SPIT** Goose Spit on the east coast of Vancouver Island, British Columbia. Goose Spit has formed over the past several thousand years from sand and gravel carried by south-flowing longshore currents. The source of the sediment is eroding sea cliffs at Willemar Bluff (top centre). *(Waite Air Photos Inc.)*

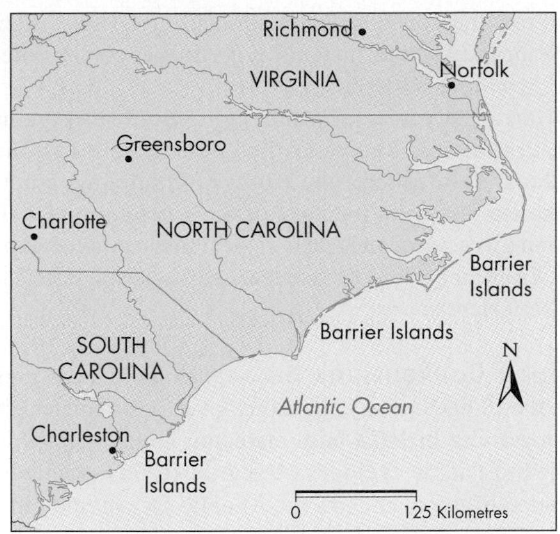

▲ **FIGURE 9.9 BARRIER ISLANDS ALONG THE U.S. ATLANTIC COAST** A map of parts of North and South Carolina, showing the extensive barrier island systems that separate the Atlantic Ocean from the U.S. mainland. Similar barrier islands are common along the Atlantic Coast from Massachusetts to Florida.

Rip Currents

Under some conditions, powerful **rip currents** carry large amounts of water directly away from the shore. They develop when a series of waves pile up water between the longshore bar and the swash zone. This water moves seaward in narrow zones, commonly metres to dozens of metres wide (Figure 9.10). Rip currents can extend seaward perpendicular to the shoreline for distances of hundreds of metres. They widen and dissipate once they have passed the line of breaking waves.

Rip currents may erode a channel through a longshore bar and thus become fixed in position for hours or days. Many beachgoers and lifeguards incorrectly call these currents "riptides" or "undertow." The currents are not tidal and they don't pull people under water; however, they do carry people away from shore into deeper water.

On average,100 people drown in rip currents each year in the United States. There are few fatalities in Canada, not because rip currents are any less common there, but because Canadian waters are too cold for most swimmers. On an annual basis, the number of deaths in the United States from rip currents is about the same as from river flooding and is greater than deaths from hurricanes or earthquakes. People drown in rip currents because they panic and struggle to swim directly back to shore. Rip currents, however, can exceed 6 km per hour, which even strong swimmers can't maintain for long. A swimmer trying to fight a rip current soon becomes exhausted and may not have the energy to stay afloat.

9.2 Tropical Cyclones

Tropical cyclone is a general term applied to large cells of moisture-laden air that rotate around an area of low pressure. They form over warm tropical or subtropical oceans and have a variety of names depending on their intensity and location. Low-intensity tropical cyclones are called tropical depressions and tropical storms. High-intensity tropical cyclones in the Indian Ocean and most of the Pacific Ocean are termed typhoons, tropical cyclones, or cyclonic storms. Similar storms in the Atlantic and northeastern Pacific Ocean are called **hurricanes**. We will use the term *hurricane*, because our emphasis is on cyclones affecting Canada and the United States.

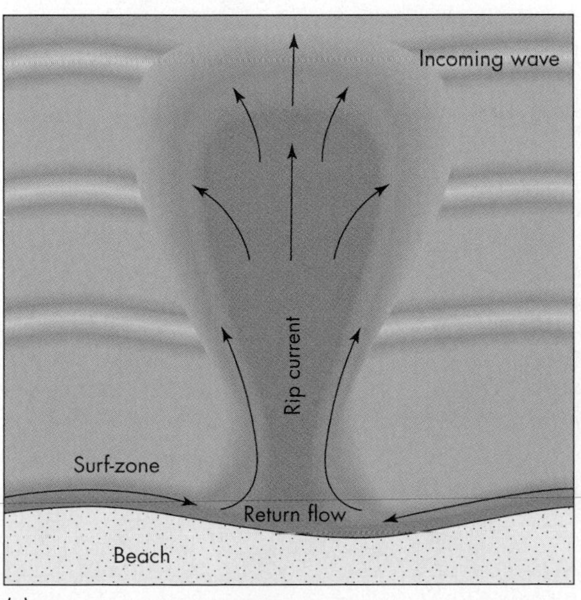

▲ **FIGURE 9.10 RIP CURRENT** (a) A bird's-eye view of the surf zone showing a rip current. The return flow of the current starts in the surf zone and extends through a low area in the longshore bar. The flow expands and dissipates beyond the breaker zone. (b) The area of relatively smooth water off this sandy beach marks a rip current. *(Edward A. Keller)*

Hurricane Formation The word *hurricane* is derived from a Caribbean Indian word meaning "evil spirit and big wind." To be termed a hurricane, some part of the storm must have sustained winds of at least 119 km/h.[6] Hurricanes require tremendous amounts of energy, which they acquire by evaporating tropical or subtropical ocean water. They form only in oceans that are warmer than 26.5°C.

Most hurricanes start out as *tropical disturbances,* which are large areas of unsettled weather with organized thunderstorms that persist for more than 24 hours. A tropical disturbance is associated with an elongated area of low pressure called a *trough*. Air in the disturbance is weakly rotating because of the Coriolis effect.

A low-pressure cell forms when winds increase and rotate around the area of disturbed weather. Low-pressure cells are areas of lower than normal atmospheric pressure that are typically associated with cloudy and rainy weather. At this time, the disturbance is classified as a *tropical depression*. Warm moist air is drawn into the depression and begins to spin faster, much as spinning ice skaters increase their rate of rotation by bringing in their arms. Once maximum sustained wind speeds reach 63 km/h, the depression is upgraded to a *tropical storm* and receives a name. It may then increase further in intensity to become a hurricane. Most tropical storms, however, never become hurricanes.

Hurricane Characteristics Hurricanes require a supply of warm water to sustain them. If the supply of warm water is cut off, the storm will weaken and die. Thus, Atlantic hurricanes weaken as they move north over cooler water or after they move onshore.

Hurricane winds blow in a large spiral surrounding a calm central area known as the *eye* (Figure 9.11). In the Northern Hemisphere, the winds circulate in a counterclockwise direction because of the *Coriolis effect*. This rotation gives hurricanes their characteristic circular appearance. Tropical cyclones rotate in a clockwise direction in the Southern Hemisphere.

Naming Conventions Hurricanes have been named since the 1940s. Initially, they were given only female names, but beginning in 1978 both male and female names were applied to Pacific cyclones. A year later, this practice was extended to hurricanes in the Atlantic Ocean and Gulf of Mexico. Six standard lists of hurricane names are used for the Atlantic Ocean. Each list is used alphabetically in sequence and then reused six years later. Similar lists have been created for other ocean basins subject to cyclones. The names of some particularly intense and destructive Atlantic hurricanes have been retired and replaced with new names. For example, the name "Mitch" was retired after a Category 5 hurricane of that name devastated several countries in Central America and killed more than 11,000 people.[6]

Classification of Hurricanes In a manner similar to those for earthquakes and tornadoes, hurricanes are ranked accord-

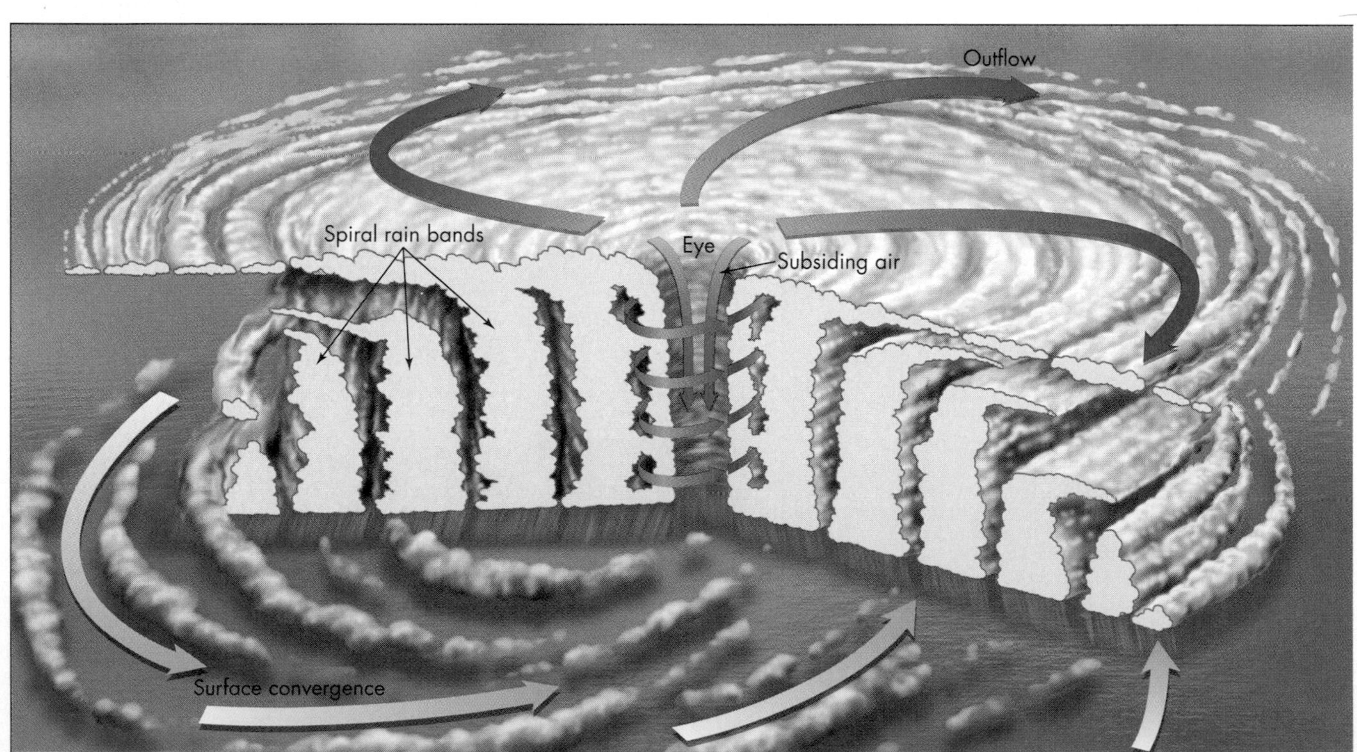

▲ **FIGURE 9.11 CROSS-SECTION OF A HURRICANE** The cloudless eye of a hurricane is surrounded by upward-spiralling winds and rain. Sinking dry air in the eye warms by compression, giving the storm its characteristic warm core. Tropical moisture spiralling toward the centre of the low-pressure area produces the rain bands. The vertical dimension of this diagram is greatly exaggerated. *(NOAA)*

TABLE 9.1 The Saffir-Simpson Hurricane Scale

The Saffir-Simpson Hurricane Scale is a five-point scale based on hurricane wind speed and the size of the associated storm surge. It is used to give an estimate of the potential property damage and flooding along the coast when a hurricane makes landfall.

Category 1 Hurricane

Winds 119 km/h to 153 km/h. Storm surge generally 1.2 m to 1.5 m above normal. No major damage to structures. Damage primarily to unanchored mobile homes, shrubs, and trees. Some damage to poorly constructed signs. Some flooding of coastal roads and minor pier damage. At their peak, hurricanes Allison (1995) and Danny (1997) were Category 1 hurricanes.

Category 2 Hurricane

Winds 154 km/h to 177 km/h. Storm surge generally 1.8 m to 2.4 m above normal. Some roof, door, and window damage. Considerable damage to shrubs and trees; some trees blown down. Considerable damage to mobile homes, poorly constructed signs, and piers. Coastal and low-lying escape routes flooded two to four hours before arrival of the eye of the hurricane. Small craft in unprotected anchorages break moorings. Hurricanes Bonnie (1998), George (1998), and Juan (2003) are examples of Category 2 hurricanes.

Category 3 Hurricane

Winds 178 km/h to 209 km/h. Storm surge generally 2.7 m to 3.7 m above normal. Some structural damage to small residences and utility buildings, including wall failures. Foliage blown off trees and large trees blown down. Mobile homes and poorly constructed signs destroyed. Low-lying escape routes cut off by rising water three to five hours before arrival of the eye of the hurricane. Flooding near the coast destroys smaller structures, and larger structures are damaged by floating debris. Land lower than 1.5 m above mean sea level may be flooded as far as 13 km inland. Evacuation of low-lying residences within several blocks of the shoreline may be required. Hurricanes Roxanne (1995) and Fran (1996) were Category 3 hurricanes at landfall.

Category 4 Hurricane

Winds 210 km/h to 249 km/h. Storm surge generally 4.0 m to 5.5 m above normal. Some roofs blown off residences, and extensive wall failures. Shrubs, trees, and all signs are blown down. Complete destruction of mobile homes. Extensive damage to doors and windows. Low-lying escape routes may be cut off by rising water three to five hours before arrival of the eye of the hurricane. Major damage to lower floors of structures near the shore. Terrain lower than 3.1 m above sea level may be flooded, requiring evacuation of residential areas as far as 10 km inland. Hurricanes Luis, Felix, and Opal (1995) were Category 4 hurricanes.

Category 5 Hurricane

Winds greater than 249 km/h. Storm surge generally greater than 5.5 m above normal. Complete roof failure on many residential and industrial buildings. Many complete building failures. All shrubs, trees, and signs blown down. Complete destruction of mobile homes. Severe and extensive window and door damage. Low-lying escape routes are cut off by rising water three to five hours before arrival of the eye of the hurricane. Major damage to lower floors of all structures located less than 4.6 m above sea level within many hundreds of metres of the shoreline. Evacuation of residential areas on low ground within 16 km of the shoreline may be required. Hurricane Mitch (1998) was a Category 5 hurricane at its peak over the western Caribbean. Hurricane Gilbert (1988) was a Category 5 hurricane at its peak and is the strongest Atlantic tropical cyclone of record. Hurricanes Rita and Katrina (2005) were also Category 5 hurricanes at their peak; they were, respectively, the fourth- and sixth-strongest Atlantic hurricanes ever recorded.

Source: Modified after Spindler, T., and J. Beven. 1999. NOAA, Saffir-Simpson Hurricane Scale. www.nhc.noaa.gov/aboutsshs.shtml. *Accessed January 4, 2005.*

ing to their potential for wind damage and flooding. The Saffir-Simpson Hurricane Scale has five categories, from Category 1, the lowest, to Category 5, the highest (Table 9.1). A Category 5 hurricane is a massive storm capable of catastrophic damage and loss of life. A record four Category 5 hurricanes occurred in the Atlantic Ocean and Gulf of Mexico in 2005: Emily, Katrina, Rita, and Wilma.

9.3 Tsunami

In winter tourists flock to the west coast of Vancouver Island, British Columbia, or the ocean beaches of Oregon and Washington to witness the full fury of a Pacific storm. Waves, metres high, rush ashore in turbulent fury, driven by storm-force winds blowing off the ocean. Yet, these waves pale in comparison to a different type of ocean wave—**tsunami** (Figure 9.12).

Tsunami Basics *Tsunami* is a Japanese word meaning "harbour wave." A more commonly used term is "tidal wave," but that is a misnomer because these waves have nothing to do with tides. Rather, they are triggered by cataclysmic events, mainly large earthquakes beneath the ocean floor (Figure 9.13), although they can also be caused by other phenomena. Unlike wind-driven waves, which affect only the uppermost few dozen metres of the ocean, tsunami involve the entire vertical column of ocean water.

A large tsunami can surge several kilometres inland and reach heights of 30 m or more, smashing everything in its path. It may surprise you that tsunami are imperceptible in the deep open ocean. Passengers on a ship crossing a tsunami would not even know they had done so. In the deep ocean, tsunami waves, travelling at speeds of hundreds of kilometres per hour, have heights of less than 1 m and wavelengths of up to 100 km. A large tsunami, however, can travel many thousand kilometres without losing much energy (see Case Study 9.2). As the waves approach shallow water near a coast, the waves begin to decelerate, become more closely spaced, and grow taller. They eventually break and surge ashore with exceptional force (Figure 9.14).

A popular misconception, reinforced by the Hollywood disaster movie *Deep Impact*, is that a tsunami consists of a single immense wave that curls over and crashes on the shore. A tsunami, however, is not a single breaker, but rather a series of waves separated by minutes to more than an hour.[13] Generally, the second or third wave is the largest of the wave train, and in many instances the first wave is preceded by a

◀ **FIGURE 9.12 TSUNAMI** Three sequential photographs show the arrival of a tsunami at Laie Point on the island of Oahu, Hawaii, on March 9, 1957. The tsunami was triggered by a magnitude 8.6 earthquake centred just south of the Aleutian Islands, about 3600 km from Oahu. The blue arrows indicate the direction of the onrushing waters. *(Henry Helbush, NOAA, National Geophysical Data Center; as seen in Clague, J., C. Yorath, R. Franklin, and B. Turner. 2006. At risk: Earthquakes and tsunamis on the west coast. Vancouver, BC: Tricouni Press)*

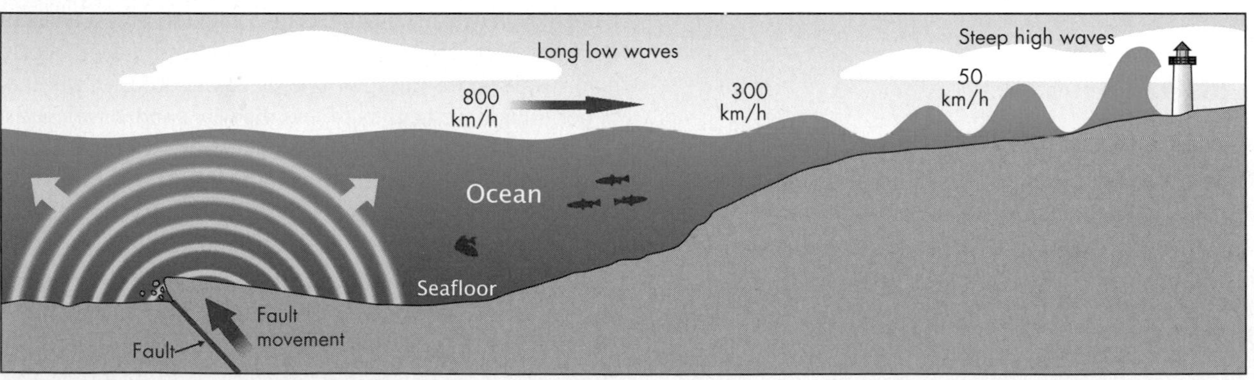

▲ **FIGURE 9.13 EARTHQUAKE TRIGGERS A TSUNAMI** A simplified diagram showing a tsunami triggered by rupture of the seafloor along a fault during an earthquake. The sudden upward displacement of the seafloor initiates waves of energy that move upward and outward from the source. As the waves shoal, they slow down, move closer together, and become higher. They then transform into turbulent, landward-surging masses of water that may run kilometres inland. *(Clague, J., C. Yorath, R. Franklin, and B. Turner. 2006. At risk: Earthquakes and tsunamis on the west coast. Vancouver, BC: Tricouni Press)*

▲ **FIGURE 9.14 TSUNAMI DAMAGE IN BANDA ACEH** This photo shows the near-total devastation of part of the capital of Aceh province, Sumatra, by the catastrophic Indian Ocean tsunami on December 26, 2004. *(Kazuhiro Nogi/AFP/Getty Images)*

recession of the sea. Rather than being curling breakers, the waves are typically turbulent, onrushing surges of debris-laden water (Figure 9.15). When one wave overtakes another, however, a steep wall of water, or bore, can be created.

Tsunami Causes Tsunami can be triggered by several types of catastrophic events:

- The rapid uplift or subsidence of the seafloor during a large earthquake
- A large underwater landslide
- The collapse of the flank of a volcano into the ocean
- A submarine volcanic explosion
- The impact of an asteroid or other large extraterrestrial object in the ocean

9.2 CASE STUDY

2004 Indian Ocean Tsunami

The second-largest earthquake in recorded history, with a moment magnitude of 9.3, struck just off the Indonesian island of Sumatra on Sunday morning, December 26, 2004. Aftershocks as large as magnitude 7.2 occurred for months after the main quake, and a magnitude 8.7 quake ruptured another section of the fault on March 26, 2005. The December earthquake was noteworthy for another reason—it triggered the most deadly tsunami of all time.

The December 26 earthquake was a subduction event, similar to quakes that happen off the coasts of British Columbia, Washington, and Oregon. It occurred along the fault that separates the Indo-Australia and Burma plates, west and northwest of the island of Sumatra. There, the Indo-Australia plate slowly moves eastward at an angle of about 10 degrees beneath the Burma plate along the Sunda Trench west of Thailand and Indonesia.

The Indo-Australia and Burma plates had been locked before the earthquake of December 26, 2004. Strain had accumulated along the subduction zone for more than 150 years because of the convergence of the two plates, and the accumulated strain was released within less than a minute by the earthquake.

The fault separating the two plates ruptured over more than 1200 km. Measurements and computer models indicate that the seafloor slipped up to 5 m vertically and up to 15 m horizontally along the fault. Parts of the Andaman and Nicobar islands were elevated by these movements, whereas land along the western coast

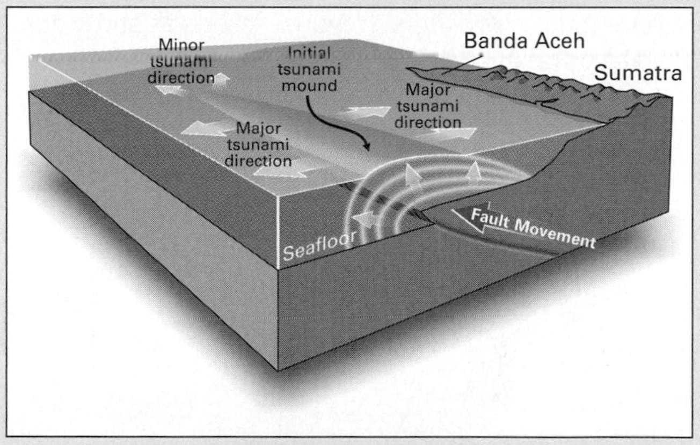

▲ **FIGURE 9.B THE INDIAN OCEAN TSUNAMI** A block diagram showing the generation of the tsunami in the Indian Ocean during the giant earthquake of December 26, 2004. The seaward edge of the Burma plate moves forward and upward, displacing the entire mass of ocean water above it. A series of tsunami waves radiates outward from the area where the seafloor has been uplifted. The largest and most energetic waves travel in opposite directions away from the rupture. Smaller waves move away from the fault in other directions. *(Clague, J., C. Yorath, R. Franklin, and B. Turner. 2006. At risk: Earthquakes and tsunamis on the west coast. Vancouver, BC: Tricouni Press)*

of Sumatra subsided up to 2 m, moving parts of the coastline below sea level.

The movement on this fault displaced the entire mass of overlying water and produced a series of waves that moved rapidly away from the seafloor (Figure 9.B). The waves reached nearby Indonesian islands within minutes and other countries hours later (Figure 9.C).

Countries bordering the Indian Ocean did not have a tsunami warning system like the one in the Pacific, and people were, for the most part, caught by surprise.

9.2 CASE STUDY *(Continued)*

Scientists at the Pacific Tsunami Warning Center in Hawaii immediately identified the earthquake that triggered the tsunami and tried to warn Indonesian colleagues and several United States embassies. Their attempts, however, were either unsuccessful or did not reach officials in time. Had an effective Indian Ocean warning system been in place, tens of thousands of lives could have been saved; the tsunami waves took more than seven hours to cross the entire Indian Ocean (Figure 9.C).[7]

Deaths from the Indian Ocean tsunami probably exceeded 228,000, but the exact number will never be known. More than three-quarters of these deaths were in Indonesia, which suffered from both intense earthquake ground shaking and the tsunami. Other countries with catastrophic loss of life include Sri Lanka, India, and Thailand. All houses, businesses, and other buildings in some areas were completely destroyed (Figure 9.D). Tourist areas of Thailand were also hit hard—several thousand visitors in tourist resorts at and around Phuket were killed (Figure 9.E).

People reacted differently to the approaching waves. Some seemed mesmerized by them, whereas others recognized the danger and ran in panic. In most cases, however, it was too late. About 100 tourists and employees at a hotel in Phuket were saved when 10-year-old Tilly Smith sounded the warning. Tilly was on vacation with her family and recognized the signs of a tsunami from a lesson at her school in Oxshott, England, only two weeks before. She had learned that the sea sometimes recedes before the arrival of the first tsunami wave. Tilly observed an unprecedented withdrawal of the sea from the shore near her hotel and told her mother. When her mother didn't react, she started screaming that they were in danger and should get off the beach. Tilly finally convinced her family, as well as others, to return to the hotel. Shortly thereafter, the beach and hotel were hit by powerful waves. Her mother later admitted that she didn't know what a tsunami was. Her daughter's school lesson had saved her life and the lives of others.[8]

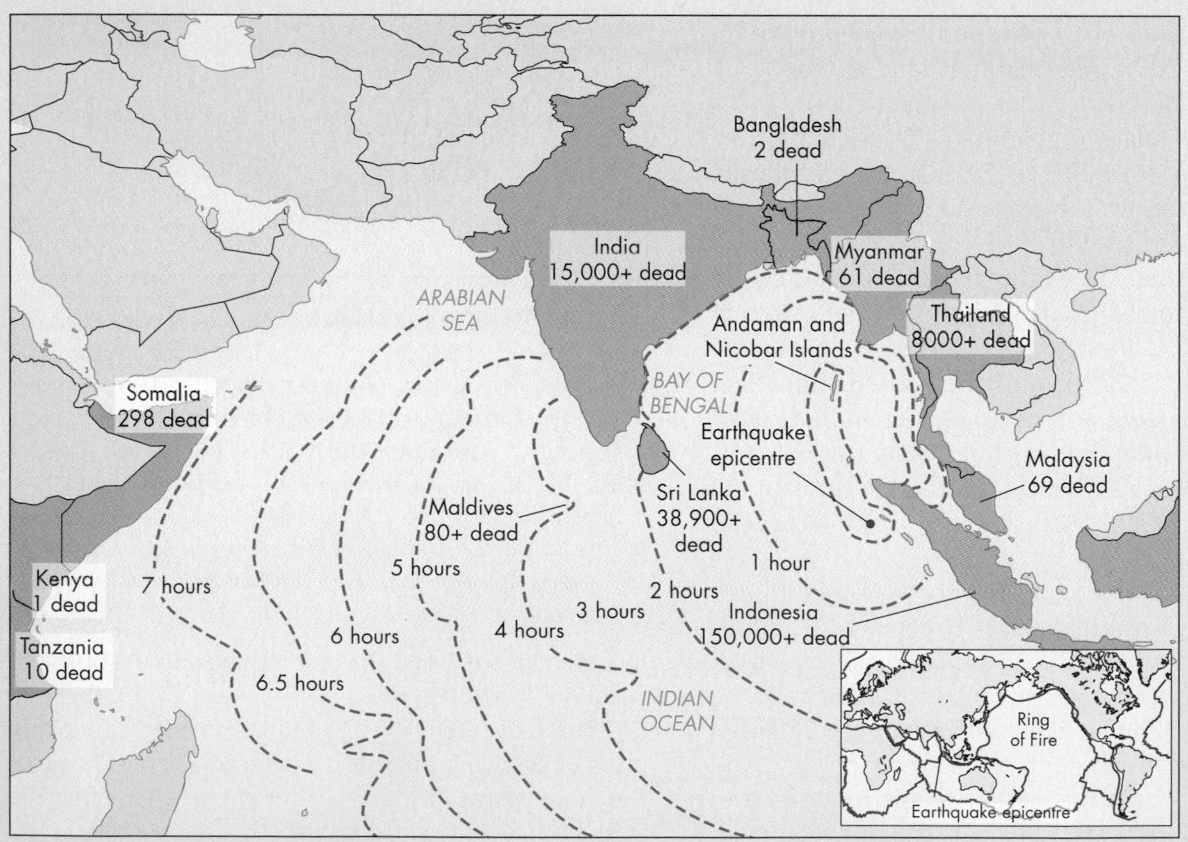

▲ **FIGURE 9.C DEADLIEST TSUNAMI IN HISTORY** The Indian Ocean tsunami of December 26, 2004, was by far the deadliest tsunami in history. It formed off the northwest coast of the island of Sumatra and spread damage and destruction across the Indian Ocean to the east coast of Africa. The exact death toll is unknown but likely is greater than 228,000. Dashed lines are the approximate positions of the lead wave or trough of the wave train at different times after the earthquake. *(Modified from NOAA National Weather Service)*

A scientist and his wife were staying at a beach hotel in Sri Lanka when they witnessed a small wave rise up and inundate the swimming pool. This wave was followed by a 7 m drop in sea level over the next 20 minutes. The scientist recognized that a big wave was coming and he and his wife sounded the alarm. A hotel employee then used a megaphone to warn people to get off the beach. Many people had gone to the beach to see the seafloor, which had never been exposed before. A 7 m wave arrived a few minutes later, but most people had climbed stairs to higher hotel floors. No employees or guests were killed. Two receptionists on the ground floor were swept out of the lobby but survived by clinging to palm trees.[9]

On the Nicobar Islands near the epicentre (Figure 9.C), Abdul Razzak, a port official, was awakened by the earthquake. He remembered from a *National Geographic* television program that tsunami were often produced by undersea earthquakes. Razzak sent two co-workers on a motorcycle to warn villages, and he ran to nearby areas yelling to people to go to the hills. About 1500 people obeyed the warnings and evacuated to the hillsides where they watched in horror as the waves rolled in and destroyed their villages.[10]

◀ **FIGURE 9.D BANDA ACEH BEFORE AND AFTER THE 2004 TSUNAMI** QuickBird satellite images of Banda Aceh, a provincial capital on Sumatra (a) on June 23, 2004, before the tsunami, and (b) on December 28, 2004, two days after the tsunami. All the buildings in this area were destroyed, including part of the bridge at the lower right. *(DigitalGlobe)*

9.2 CASE STUDY *(Continued)*

▲ **FIGURE 9.E TSUNAMI STRIKES THAILAND** A huge wave surges into the tourist resort of Phuket on the morning of December 29, 2004. The tsunami killed nearly 10,000 people in Thailand, including almost 1000 foreign tourists and Thai citizens in Phuket. *(AP Photo/APTN)*

On the Andaman Islands to the north, about 840 people in five Aboriginal tribes escaped injury. They had knowledge, passed on from their ancestors, about the relation between strong earthquakes and tsunami. In one instance, a Jarawa tribal elder led his people to the safety of a hilltop following the earthquake tremors. The elder said that he had been taught as a child to follow this procedure. Members of the Onge tribe also fled to the hills because their ancestors had taught them that if the level of the stream in their village suddenly dropped, it meant that the sea was pulling back and was "preparing to strike like a fist." In contrast, at least 48 recent settlers from the Indian mainland were killed on the Andaman Islands by the tsunami.[11] Long-time residents had a cultural memory of the natural hazard, whereas more recent immigrants did not.

The Indian Ocean tsunami taught us several lessons:

- Tsunami are much less common in the Indian Ocean than in the Pacific Ocean, but the December 2004 event demonstrated that they can have catastrophic consequences. The estimated return period for a 10 m tsunami in the Indian Ocean, Atlantic Ocean, and Caribbean Sea is about 1000 years, compared with less than 200 years in Hawaii.[12]
- Effective tsunami warning systems are needed in all ocean basins where tsunami can occur: the Pacific Ocean, the Indian Ocean, the Atlantic Ocean, and the Caribbean, Mediterranean, and Black seas. These systems must be well funded and well maintained. They also must be reliable; at the time of the Indian Ocean tsunami, three of the six warning buoys in the Pacific were inoperative. In 2006, a new warning system became operational in the Indian Ocean.
- A high-tech tsunami warning system alone is not enough. Once a warning is issued, emergency officials must rapidly and accurately transmit information and instructions to people in communities that may be affected. In addition, the residents of those communities must respond in an appropriate way. The responses of public officials and individuals to tsunami warnings that were issued following large earthquakes off northern California in 2005 and Tonga in 2006 show that much more work needs to be done in regional and local planning for tsunami.
- Earthquake and tsunami education is necessary for people who live on or visit coastlines that are vulnerable to tsunami. Warning systems, without education, are of limited value.

Like the port official on the Nicobar Islands, other people experiencing a large earthquake must understand that a tsunami could be coming, and they must immediately move to higher ground. Hundreds of kilometres away, in places where the earthquake was not felt, Earth still provided a signal of what was about to happen. The British schoolgirl in Thailand, the scientist in Sri Lanka, and people on the Andaman Islands realized that the sudden retreat of the sea is a signal of an impending tsunami. People must recognize these signs as warnings to move to higher ground immediately. Coastal residents and visitors must also understand that tsunami are seldom one wave; they are a train of many separate waves that can arrive over several hours. Most of the deaths in Crescent City, California, during the great Pacific tsunami of 1964 occurred when residents who had returned to their homes after the first wave had withdrawn were swept away by a second larger wave.

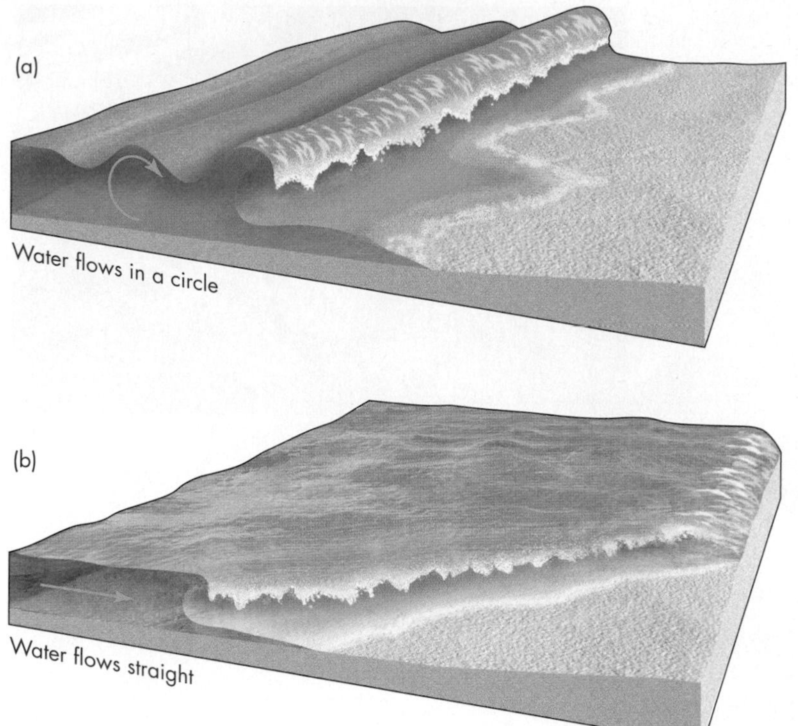

◄ **FIGURE 9.15 TSUNAMI WAVES DIFFER FROM WIND-DRIVEN WAVES** (a) Wind-driven waves wash up and down a beach without flooding higher areas. Water particles within a wind-driven wave have a circular or elliptical motion. (b) A tsunami wave surges over the beach and inland. The water flows straight forward in a highly turbulent state. People who do not drown in a tsunami can be severely injured by impacts with stationary objects and floating debris. *(Modified after Department of Earth and Space Sciences, University of Washington)*

Most destructive tsunami in historic times have been triggered by earthquakes. Tsunami generated by nearby earthquakes are especially deadly. In 1993, an **M** 7.8 earthquake in the Sea of Japan triggered a tsunami that struck a small town on Okushiri Island, Japan, killing 120 people and causing $500 million in property damage (Figure 9.16). The *run-up*, or elevation the waves reached, ranged from 15 m to 30 m.[14] The tsunami arrived only two to five minutes after the earthquake; thus, no warning could be issued.

Volcanic eruptions and large landslides have also caused destructive tsunami in historic time. The famous Krakatoa volcanic eruption in 1883 triggered a tsunami that killed about 36,000 people in southeast Asia.[15] An **M** 7.1 earthquake in July 1998 caused a large submarine landslide, which in turn produced a tsunami that destroyed coastal villages along a 30 km stretch of the north coast of Papua New Guinea, killing more than 2100 people. The residents of these villages had no warning of the impending disaster.[16]

A similar event occurred on the east coast of Canada in November 1929. An **M** 7.2 earthquake at the southern edge of the Grand Banks, 250 km south of Newfoundland, triggered a huge submarine slump that, in turn, set off a tsunami.[17,18] The tsunami propagated across the Atlantic Ocean, registering on tide gauges as far away as South Carolina and Portugal. It damaged more than 40 coastal communities and claimed 27 lives on Burin Peninsula in Newfoundland. Damage was made worse by the fact that the tsunami arrived near the peak of a very high tide. Maximum wave heights in communities that suffered the greatest damage ranged from 3 m to about 7.5 m.

The most spectacular landslide-generated tsunami of the twentieth century occurred on July 10, 1958, at Lituya Bay,

◄ **FIGURE 9.16 TSUNAMI AFTERMATH** Damage in Aonae on Okushiri Island, Japan, caused by a tsunami on July 12, 1993. The tsunami was triggered by a magnitude 7.8 earthquake off the west coast of Hokkaido and was one of the largest in Japan's history. It engulfed the coast of Okushiri Island and the adjacent coast of Hokkaido, killing 120 people. *(NOAA, National Geophysical Data Center)*

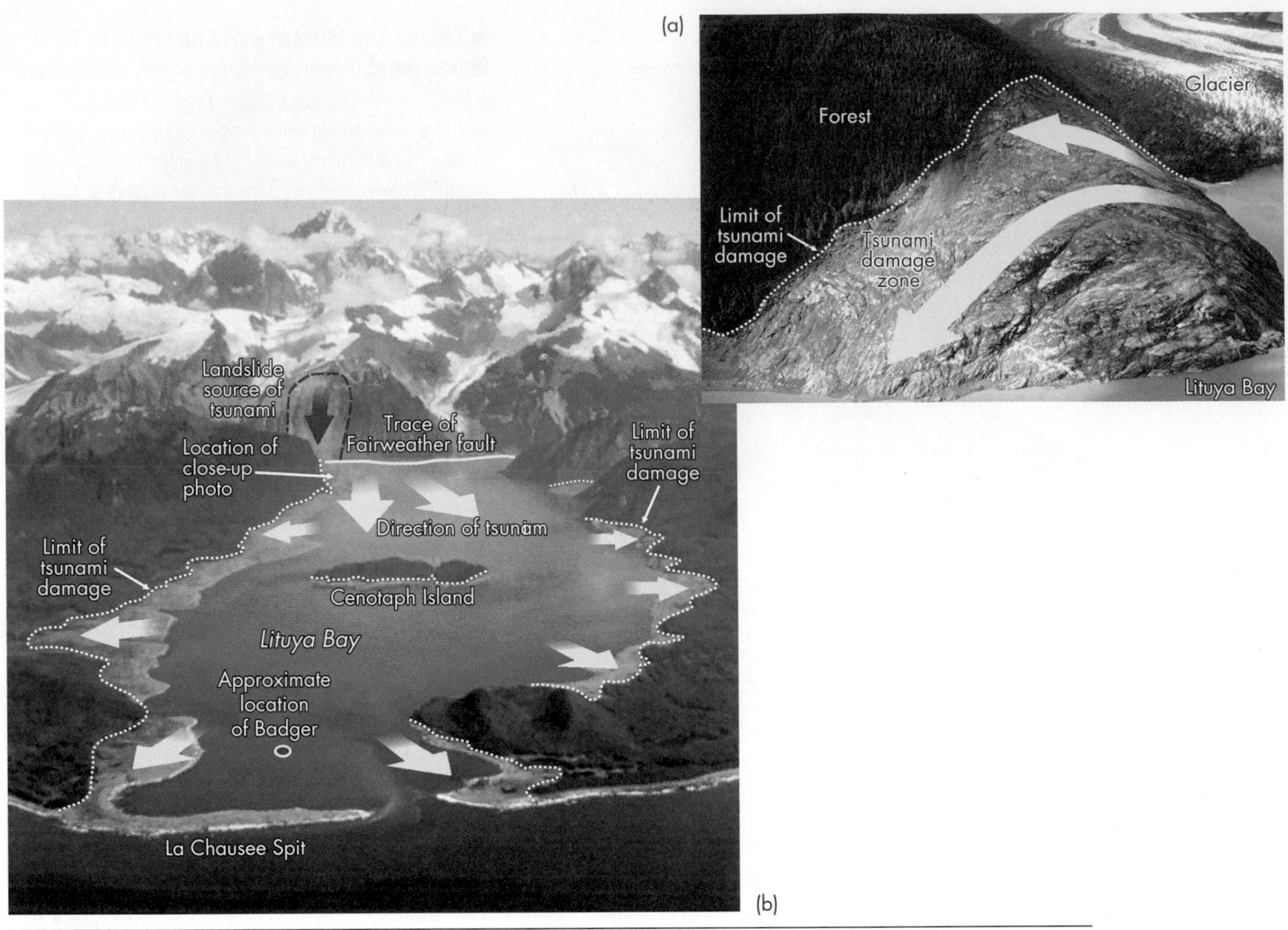

▲ **FIGURE 9.17 LITUYA BAY TSUNAMI** (a) The rocky headland directly west of the landslide at the head of Lituya Bay. Water displaced by the landslide surged up this slope, removing the forest to more than 500 m above sea level. (b) Photograph of Lituya Bay, Alaska, taken shortly after the tsunami of July 7, 1958. The prominent trimline (dotted line) delineates the upper limit of the tsunami. Forest below this line was obliterated by the surging waters. *(Clague, J., C. Yorath, R. Franklin, and B. Turner. 2006. At risk: Earthquakes and tsunamis on the west coast. Vancouver, BC: Tricouni Press; photos by U.S. Geological Survey, Donald Miller)*

Alaska (Figure 9.17).[19] A large earthquake triggered a rockslide at the head of the bay. The rockslide plunged into the bay and displaced seawater that ran up the opposite valley wall to an elevation of 525 m, destroying the forest in its path (Figure 9.17a). A 30-m high wave surged 11 km to the mouth of the bay, where it swept away two fishing boats anchored inside a low, forested spit (Figure 9.17b).

Geologists have suggested that even larger tsunami than the 1958 Lituya Bay event have been caused by collapses of the flanks of volcanoes on Hawaii in the Pacific Ocean and the Canary Islands in the Atlantic Ocean.[20,21] Massive hummocky landslide deposits have been mapped on the seafloor adjacent to the Hawaiian Islands; some of them extend dozens of kilometres from the shore. The deposits were probably emplaced during the collapse of the flanks of Mauna Loa and Kohala, two of the large volcanoes on Hawaii. Geologists infer that these collapses triggered large tsunami. In support of this idea, they note possible tsunami deposits on the slopes of Hawaii and Lanai, far above the present shore. The deposits contain fragments of coralline limestone that otherwise occur only at and below sea level. The inference is that the fragments were deposited by waves up to several hundred metres high. The Hawaiian Islands would be devastated if an event of this type were to occur today. It is unlikely, however, that distant parts of the Pacific Rim would be affected in the same way. A tsunami generated by a landslide, even a very large one, attenuates significantly over distances of thousands of kilometres, and wave run-ups on the west coast of North America would not be catastrophic.

Let's turn our attention to the apocalyptic scenario so adored by Hollywood—a large meteorite or asteroid striking the North Pacific, as apparently happened on the west coast of the Gulf of Mexico 65 million years ago, causing the extinction of the dinosaurs. If a meteorite 1 km in diameter were to strike the Pacific Ocean, it might produce waves dozens of metres high that would run up some Pacific shorelines to elevations of more than 100 m. Not a pretty picture for the hundreds of millions of people living along the coasts of the Pacific Ocean! Fortunately, the chance of such an event in our lifetimes is extremely low. Smaller meteorite impacts, however, are more common, as are the smaller tsunami they would trigger.

SURVIVOR STORY

Tsunami in the Lowest Country on Earth

Boxing Day, December 26, 2004, was hot and sunny in the Maldives, a beautiful group of atolls in the Indian Ocean. The Republic of Maldives is the lowest country on Earth; its highest point is only 2.4 m above sea level. Dave Lowe was working in his office at a resort on South Ari Atoll when he heard people screaming. He opened the door and to his horror saw a boiling, frothing wall of water bearing down on him.

"There was a strange mist that looked like a fog so I stopped breathing and tried to decide where to run," he said.

The resort had no two-storey buildings and was just 1 m above sea level. Lowe ran to the reception area where there were pillars that he could hold onto. Other people in the room were screaming when the first wave struck. "Three glass windows exploded and within seconds the water was up to my waist," he says. "I couldn't tell if the island was sinking or if the sea was rising."

Dave struggled to the reception desk to grab two children who were being swept out to sea and placed them on the counter. The surging water passed over his head. "I knew I was going to die and blacked out from fear. I regained consciousness when a receptionist yelled 'What is happening?'"

The water receded as quickly as it arrived, leaving fish flopping on the lobby floor and seaweed covering everything. The resort guests regrouped. Then Dave saw a second, even larger wave coming. People desperately hung onto anything they could. Wave after wave arrived and receded over the next six hours, gradually decreasing in size. There was debris everywhere, and guests suffered in the hot sun. Resort staff built a shelter for 15 children whose parents were missing. When darkness came, people stood watch, looking for more waves under a full moon. No one slept that night. "It looked like *Titanic, Lost, Lord of the Flies,* and *Survivor* all rolled into one," Dave comments.

He and other employees were evacuated by seaplane two days later. Several staff broke down crying when they flew over the Islands and saw the unbelievable devastation the tsunami had wrought. They had survived, but they didn't know how.

Most people imagine a tsunami to be a single, huge wave crashing onto the shore. This view is a dangerous misconception (Survivor Story). A tsunami is a series of large waves, the first of which may not be the largest. The first indication of the tsunami may be the arrival of a leading trough, not a wave crest. The arrival of a trough causes water to recede a considerable distance from the shore before the first wave arrives. On many occasions, people have drowned because they came down to the shore to witness the water withdraw just before the first wave struck. Many other people have died because they falsely assumed that the first wave would not be followed by a larger one.

9.4 Geographic Regions at Risk from Coastal Hazards

Many towns and cities are located on or near coasts and are vulnerable to the hazardous processes discussed in this chapter. Vancouver, Toronto, and Halifax, which are three of the largest cities in Canada, are coastal (Toronto is located on the shore of Lake Ontario). Similarly, the largest cities in the United States are coastal, and approximately 75 percent of that country's population lives in coastal states.[22] Demographic trends indicate that more than half of Canada's population and most of the U.S. population will eventually be concentrated along the Pacific, Gulf, and Atlantic seacoasts and along the shorelines of the Great Lakes. Disasters will inevitably increase as more people move into hazardous areas. Global warming will also cause problems for people living near the coast. The sea level will rise as our planet warms, increasing shoreline erosion and flooding.

Coastal Erosion

Coastal erosion is a near-universal hazard. Most Canadian provinces and territories and the 30 U.S. states that border oceans or the Great Lakes have problems with coastal erosion. Average local erosion rates along some barrier islands in the United States approach 8 m per year (or 8 m/y), and some Great Lakes shorelines have retreated at rates up to 15 m/y![22] These are extreme examples; generally, rates of coastal erosion are much lower, ranging from less than 1 cm/y to about 50 cm/y. Stable, steep rocky shorelines are common along the Pacific coast north of southern California; they form about 85 percent of the British Columbia coastline.[23] The coastal zone of central and northern British Columbia and

◄ **FIGURE 9.18 ROCKY COASTLINE** Steep, rocky coastlines like this one on the South Island of New Zealand erode relatively slowly and will not be greatly affected by sea-level rise. *(John J. Clague)*

Alaska is studded with rocky islands, some as large as U.S. states. Steep rocky shorelines are also common in other tectonically active areas around the world (Figure 9.18).

Erosion is a periodic problem along the coasts of the Great Lakes. It is most severe during extended periods of high lake level caused by above-normal precipitation. Measurements by the U.S. Army Corps of Engineers show that the level of Lake Michigan has fluctuated about 2 m since 1860. During periods of below-average lake level, wide beaches dissipate energy from storm waves and protect the shore. However, as lake levels rise, beaches become narrower and storm waves expend considerable energy against the shoreline. Even a small rise in water level will inundate a wide section of a gently sloping beach.[24] During periods of high water level, storm waves have eroded some lakeshore bluffs at an average rate of 0.4 m/y,[25] destroying many buildings, roads, retaining walls, and other structures (Figure 9.19).[24] Storms in the fall of 1985, for example, caused an estimated US$15 million to US$20 million in damage along shorelines of Lake Michigan.

Fewer than 30,000 people live on the Arctic coast of North America, thus coastal hazards are much less of a problem there than elsewhere on the continent. Sea ice limits fetch and therefore wave erosion throughout much of the central and northern Arctic. However, erosion rates of up to 2 m/y have been observed in the western Arctic, for example, along parts of the Beaufort Sea shoreline.[26] A problem in the Arctic that is not an issue elsewhere is thawing of permafrost. The Arctic climate has warmed significantly over the past several decades. This warming, together with wave erosion and sea-level rise, has eroded ice-rich coastal sediments (Figure 9.20). Some Inuit villages are threatened by the erosion and may have to be relocated at considerable cost.

Hurricanes

Hurricanes are a serious threat to the Atlantic coast of Canada and the Atlantic and Gulf coasts of the United States in summer and early fall. The Atlantic and Gulf coasts have the

◄ **FIGURE 9.19 LAKESHORE EROSION** Coastal erosion has destroyed this home at the shore of Lake Michigan. *(Steve Leonard/Getty Images, Inc.-Stone Allstock)*

▲ **FIGURE 9.20 COASTAL EROSION IN THE ARCTIC** Waves have attacked ice-rich sediments that form the shore along this part of Canada's Arctic Coast. *(Reproduced with the permission of the Minister of Public Works and Government Services Canada, 2005, and courtesy of Natural Resources Canada, Geological Survey of Canada. Photographer: Steve Solomon)*

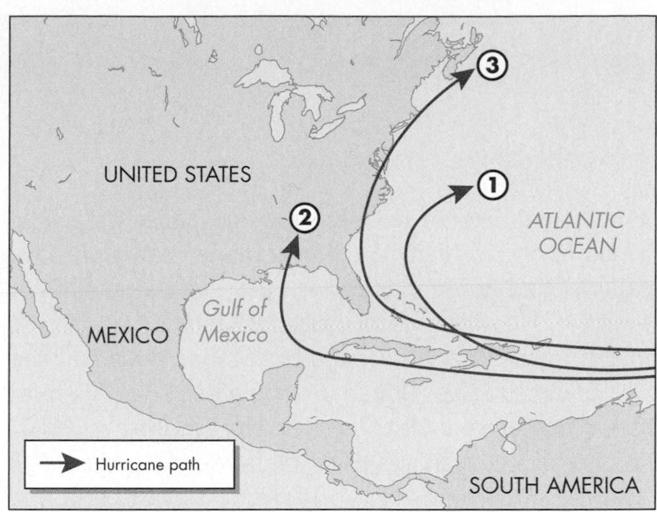

▲ **FIGURE 9.21 HURRICANE PATHS** The three common paths of hurricanes generated in the Atlantic Ocean. Each path, marked by a curving red arrow, starts in the central Atlantic Ocean east (right) of the map. Hurricanes that follow all three paths threaten Caribbean islands; hurricanes that take path 2 threaten the southeastern United States; and those that take path 3 threaten the Atlantic coast of the United States and Canada.

highest risk of hurricanes in North America; they experience, on average, five hurricanes each year. These hurricanes form off the west coast of Africa and take one of three tracks (Figure 9.21):

1. Westward across the eastern Caribbean, possibly passing over Caribbean islands, such as Puerto Rico, but then changing direction and moving northeast into the Atlantic Ocean without making landfall on the Atlantic coast of the United States.
2. Westward over Cuba and into the Gulf of Mexico, where they threaten the U.S. Gulf Coast.
3. Westward across the eastern Caribbean and then northeastward along the Atlantic coast, threatening the coast from central Florida to New York. A few hurricanes continue north as far as coastal New England and Atlantic Canada (Case Study 9.3).

Some hurricanes also form in the Gulf of Mexico, the Caribbean Sea, and the east Pacific Ocean. With the exception of the east Pacific hurricanes, they threaten the same areas as hurricanes generated in the Atlantic Ocean (Figure 9.22). Hurricanes that form in the east Pacific Ocean are a serious hazard to the Pacific Coast of Mexico, as far north as the city of Guaymas.

Hurricane risk can be assessed from maps that show the probability that a hurricane will strike a particular coastal reach in a single year. Hurricane-strike probabilities are highest along the coasts of southern Florida, Louisiana, and eastern Texas (Figure 9.23).

Tsunami

Tsunami can occur in any of the world's oceans or seas, although none are known to have occurred in the Arctic Ocean. About 85 percent of recorded tsunami have been in the Pacific Ocean because of their association with large earthquakes at subduction zones that surround much of the Pacific.[27] Areas at greatest risk from tsunami in the Pacific Basin are Japan, Kamchatka, Hawaii, islands in the southern and western Pacific, Chile, Peru, Mexico, and the northeastern Pacific Coast from Alaska to northern California. Tsunami generated

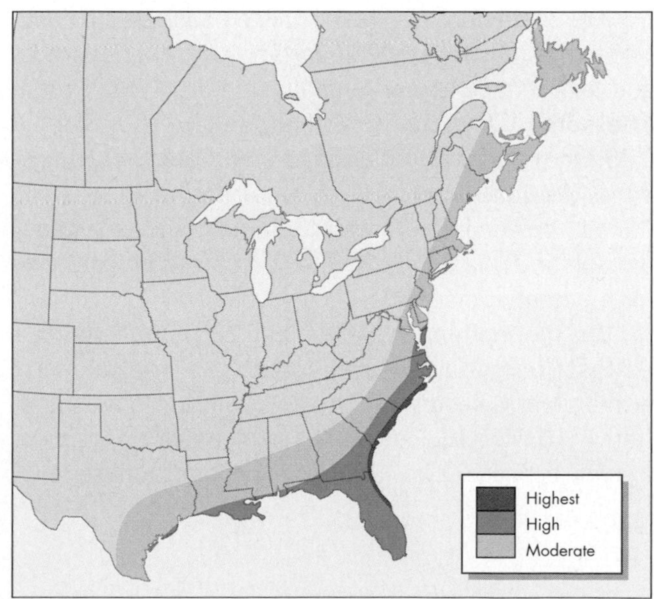

▲ **FIGURE 9.22 NORTH AMERICAN REGIONS AT RISK FROM HURRICANES** The highest-risk area (red band) is likely to experience 60 hurricanes in a 100-year period (the word "experience" here means that the hurricanes will pass within 160 km of the indicated area). The high-risk area (dark blue) can expect 40 to 60 hurricanes in 100 years, and the moderate risk area (light blue) will likely experience fewer than 40 hurricanes in 100 years. The map is based on observations from 1888 to 1998. *(Modified from U.S. Geological Survey and Atlas of Canada)*

9.3 CASE STUDY

Hurricane Juan

Most Canadians do not perceive hurricanes as posing a risk to them. Many parts of Canada, however, have experienced hurricanes in the past and will again. For example, Hurricane Hazel caused 81 fatalities in Toronto in 1954 (see Chapter 7), and Hurricane Frieda claimed 6 lives in southwest British Columbia in 1962. The most recent hurricane to hit a Canadian city was Juan in 2003.

Hurricane Juan was the sixth hurricane of the 2003 Atlantic hurricane season. It struck Nova Scotia and Prince Edward Island as a Category 2 hurricane, causing major damage to trees and property, especially within the urban core of Halifax (Figure 9.F). The storm killed eight people and caused more than $200 million in damage. It was the region's most powerful hurricane since 1873.

The tropical depression that would become Juan formed on September 24, 2003, northeast of the Bahamas. On September 25, the depression began to organize and it turned to the northwest. As the storm crossed the waters of the Gulf Stream, which were unusually warm for that time of year, it intensified and, on September 26, became a Category 1 hurricane on the Saffir-Simpson Hurricane Scale.

On September 27, Juan changed course as it came under the influence of the northerly flowing jetstream and took a track toward landfall in central Nova Scotia. The same day, it achieved a peak wind speed of 175 km/h and was reclassified as a Category 2 hurricane. As Juan approached, local media in Atlantic Canada broadcast warnings; the public and emergency officials in Nova Scotia were told to make preparations for a potential disaster.

On the morning of September 28, reports indicated that Juan would weaken to either a tropical storm or marginal Category 1 hurricane before it made landfall. By 6:00 P.M., however, hurricane warnings were issued, because Juan now was expected to make landfall as a strong Category 1 or weak Category 2 hurricane. At this point, it was too late for much of the general public to make necessary preparations.

The storm made landfall on September 29 with peak winds of 170 km/h and moved directly north toward Halifax. It continued north, crossing Nova Scotia and Prince Edward Island within hours before diminishing to a strong Category 1 hurricane. By midday the storm was centred over the Gulf of St. Lawrence and was downgraded to a tropical storm.

Hurricane Juan caused widespread damage in central Nova Scotia and Prince Edward Island. Most property damage was in the western urban core of Halifax. Truro, Nova Scotia, and Charlottetown, Prince Edward Island, also experienced significant property damage. Wave-rider weather buoys off the entrance to Halifax Harbour snapped their moorings after recording waves in excess of 20 m. Some of the harbour's populated shorelines, especially in Bedford Basin, were severely eroded by waves. The hurricane left more than 300,000 people without power, and it took a week and a half to restore power to the hardest hit rural areas of Nova Scotia's Eastern Shore and the Musquodoboit River valley. Seventy percent of the trees in Halifax's Point Pleasant Park were destroyed, fundamentally changing the character of the park. The Halifax Public Gardens was also badly damaged. Boats and seawalls along Charlottetown's waterfront sustained heavy wave damage, and the forest in that city's downtown core was heavily damaged.

Hurricane Juan resulted in several changes to the Meteorological Service of the Canadian Hurricane Centre (CHC). The centre was relocated from a vulnerable and exposed office building in Dartmouth, Nova Scotia, to a location that can withstand hurricane winds. CHC's hurricane warning system has also been improved. Traditionally, CHC issued only high wind and heavy rainfall warnings, not standard hurricane or tropical storm watches or warnings. Wind and heavy rainfall warnings were not heeded by local residents. Since 2004, CHC

by underwater landslides unrelated to earthquakes and by the flank collapse of volcanoes are less common, but they still represent a hazard to the east and west coasts of the United States and Canada, and to Hawaii and Alaska.

The Pacific Coast of North America has been struck by one large tsunami during historic time, and geological research has provided evidence for many others over the past few thousand years. The Alaska earthquake of March 27, 1964, the third largest of the twentieth century (**M** 9.2), triggered a tsunami that killed 130 people, some as far away as California. The main tsunami swept southward across the Pacific Ocean at a velocity of about 830 km/h, reaching Antarctica in only 16 hours (Figure 9.24). It caused extensive damage on Vancouver Island, British Columbia, and claimed lives as far south as Crescent City in northern California. The town of Port Alberni, at the head of Alberni Inlet on Vancouver Island, was particularly hard hit.[28] Three main waves struck Port Alberni over a three-hour period on the morning of March

has issued standard hurricane warnings for storms that could potentially affect Canada.

The name Juan was retired from the hurricane list in April 2004 and will never again be used for an Atlantic hurricane. It was the first time that the Meteorological Service of Canada had specifically requested that a hurricane name be retired. The name Juan was replaced by Joaquin.

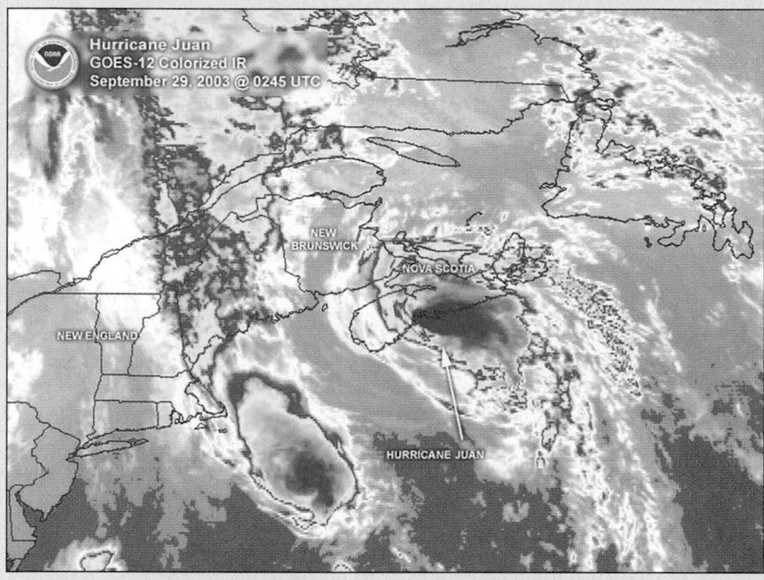

◄ **FIGURE 9.F DAMAGE FROM HURRICANE JUAN** Hurricane Juan caused more than $200 million damage when it crossed Nova Scotia and Prince Edward Island on September 29, 2003. The damage was caused by winds up to 170 km/h and a storm surge. This photo shows damage to the coastal community of Prospect, Nova Scotia. *(Top: NOAA; bottom: CP Photo/Halifax Chronicle Herald-Tim Krochak)*

28. The second and most destructive wave surged 1 km inland, forcing the police to use boats to rescue guests from the upper floor of a local hotel. About 260 homes in Port Alberni were damaged by this tsunami, 60 extensively.

The risk that residents of the west coast of Canada and the United States face from tsunami has been investigated by geologists and geophysicists in both countries. Their research has involved excavation and radiocarbon dating of tsunami deposits, dating of the rings of trees killed by tsunami, computer modelling of tsunami propagation and run-up, searches of historical records in Japan, and oral histories of aboriginal peoples. Geological studies in Washington State and a search of historical records in Japan showed that the source of a huge tsunami on the evening of January 26, 1700, was an **M** 9 earthquake at the *Cascadia subduction zone*, just off the west coast of British Columbia, Washington, and Oregon.[29] The earthquake and ensuing tsunami were eerily similar to the events in the Indian Ocean on December 26, 2004.

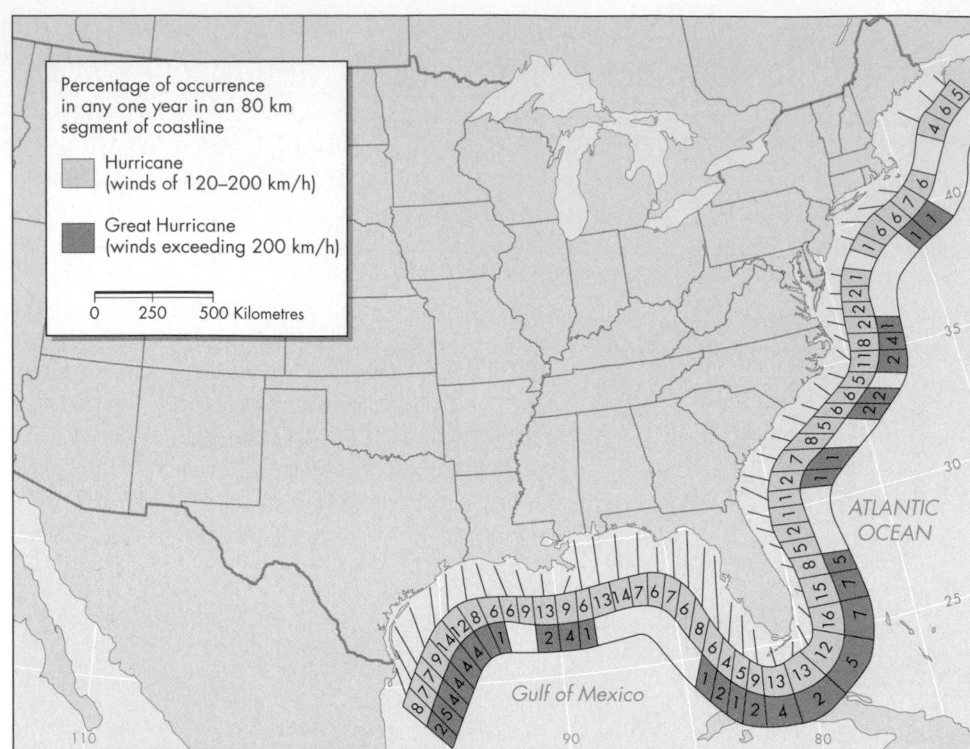

◄ **FIGURE 9.23 HURRICANE HAZARD MAP** The probability that a hurricane will strike a particular 80 km section of the U.S. Gulf and Atlantic Coasts in a given year. *(From Council on Environmental Quality, 1981. Environmental trends)*

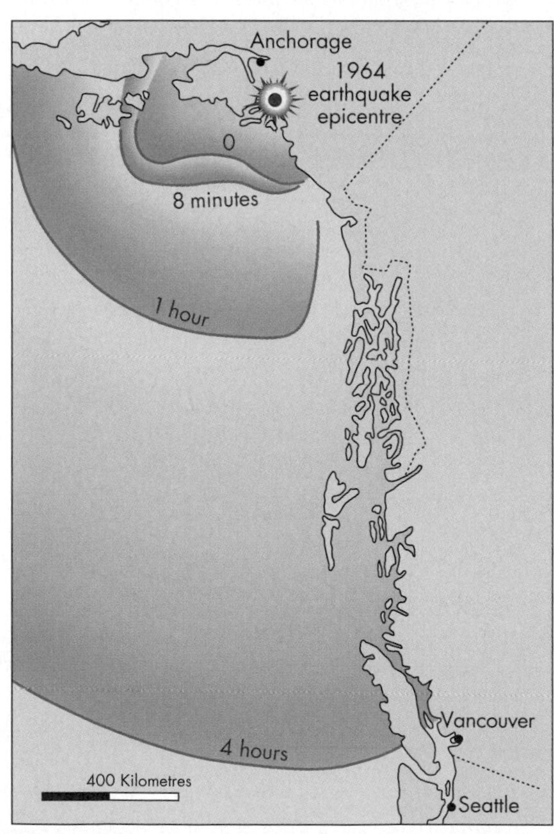

▲ **FIGURE 9.24 1964 ALASKA TSUNAMI** The tsunami generated by the 1964 Alaska earthquake moved rapidly across the Pacific Ocean from its source. The lines show the positions of the leading wave of the tsunami during the earthquake (time 0) and 8 minutes, 1 hour, and 4 hours later. *(U.S. Department of Commerce, National Oceanic and Atmospheric Administration, National Geophysical Data Center; as seen in Clague, J., C. Yorath, R. Franklin, and B. Turner. 2006. At risk: Earthquakes and tsunamis on the west coast. Vancouver, BC: Tricouni Press)*

Some places, such as Japan and Hawaii, experience frequent tsunami. Honshu, the largest of the Japanese islands, experiences a 10 m tsunami, on average, once every 10 years.[30] Historical records in Hawaii dating back to 1813 indicate that a measurable tsunami occurs there, on average, once every two years.[13] Other areas, such as the Gulf of Mexico and the Atlantic coast of the United States, have had no significant tsunami in historic time.

9.5 Effects of Coastal Processes

Coastal Erosion

Coastal erosion is becoming a serious global problem because of sea-level rise and the increasing development on shorelines. Large sums of money are spent to control erosion, but many of the benefits are temporary and much of the money is wasted.

Beach Erosion Beaches both gain and lose material. Sand is added from updrift sources, such as rivers and eroding cliffs, and is lost through littoral transport, return flow to deep water during storms, and wind erosion. When more sediment is lost than is gained, the beach will erode. The severity of erosion depends on many factors, such as the following:

- *The existence of coastal dunes:* shorelines with dunes erode at a slower rate than shorelines without dunes.
- *The orientation of the shoreline*: sites exposed to storm waves erode faster than those protected from them.
- *Groundwater seepage*: seepage at the base of a bluff causes slope instability and increases erosion.

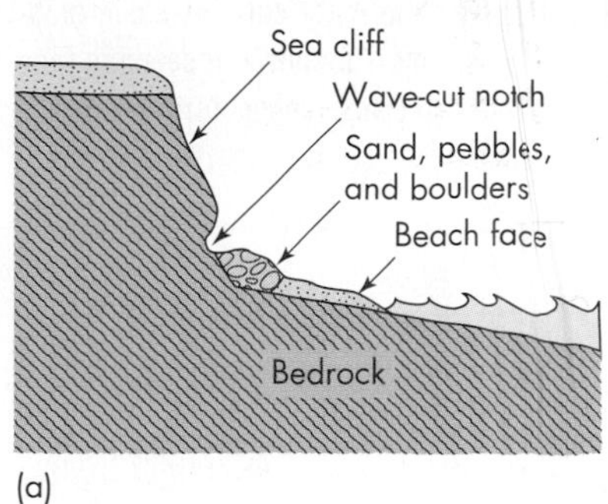

▲ **FIGURE 9.25 SEA CLIFF AND BEACH** (a) A generalized cross-section and (b) photograph of a sea cliff, beach, and intertidal rock platform at Santa Barbara, California. *(Courtesy of Donald Weaver)*

- *The existence of protective structures*: engineered structures are locally beneficial but may accelerate erosion in adjacent areas.[24,25]

The sand on many beaches is supplied by rivers. Dams built across rivers trap the sediment and, as a result, deprive beaches of sand.

Erosion on the Atlantic coast is caused by hurricanes and by other severe storms known as nor'easters,[1] by sea-level rise, and by human interference with natural shore processes.[31] Rising sea level contributes to coastal erosion because it allows storm waves to erode farther inland.

Some shorelines in Atlantic Canada, where sea level is rising more rapidly than elsewhere in North America,[32] are retreating at rates of up to 10 m/y. Even at close to the average rate of erosion, entire islands off Nova Scotia have disappeared in the recent geological past. Sea-level rise in this region is due, in part, to continuing crustal subsidence associated with the disappearance of the *Laurentide ice sheet*, which covered central and eastern Canada as recently as about 12,000 years ago. The ice sheet depressed the land on which it lay by several hundred metres, displacing viscous *mantle* material laterally within Earth to and beyond the ice margins. This lateral displacement of mantle material created an uplifted "bulge" beneath Atlantic Canada. When the ice sheet melted, the uplifted bulge collapsed and the land beneath Atlantic Canada subsided. This process continues today at a low rate and is augmenting the rise in sea level caused by melting of glaciers and thermal expansion of ocean waters. Rapid sea-level rise is contributing to coastal erosion in some areas of Atlantic Canada.

Worldwide, sea level is rising at a rate of about 2 mm/y. This global rise is due to melting of glaciers and thermal expansion of upper ocean waters (see Chapter 11). Scientists predict that sea level will rise between a few dozen centimetres and about 2 m over the remainder of the twenty-first century. Whatever the exact amount, coastal erosion will become an even greater problem than it is today. Engineered works designed to protect beaches interrupt longshore drift and cause erosion farther along the shore.

Cliff Erosion Sea cliffs and lakeshore bluffs can be eroded by waves and landslides. The problem can be aggravated when people alter cliffs during development.

Storm waves erode many sea cliffs and lakeshore bluffs, thus moving the shoreline landward (Figure 9.25). This possibility may not be apparent during periods of fair weather when a beach is present at the base of the cliff. Beach sediment protects the cliff from wave erosion during periods between storms. During fall and winter, however, successive storms remove much sand from beaches, leaving cliffs vulnerable to erosion (Figure 9.26). Most sea-cliff erosion on the west coast of North America happens during severe winter storms. Sea cliffs on the Atlantic coast of the northeast United States and Canada may be severely eroded during nor'easters. Storm waves also are responsible for most of the erosion of lakeshore bluffs along the Great Lakes.

Rates of cliff erosion range from millimetres per year to several metres per year. Measurements are sparse along most coasts, but are increasing through the use of remote sensing instruments, such as an aircraft-mounted laser system called LIDAR (Light Detection and Ranging). A LIDAR system records several thousand precise elevation measurements per second, from which accurate images and maps of the coastline can be constructed. Subsequent flights can detect changes, such as the shape of the beach and coastal dunes and the amount of retreat of a lakeside bluff or sea cliff. For example, two LIDAR flights, six months apart, along the coast near Pacifica, California, showed sea cliff retreat of up to 10 m.

Rates of erosion of 15 cm/y to 30 cm/y have been documented along parts of the Pacific Coast from British Columbia

◀ **FIGURE 9.26 SEA CLIFF EROSION** Steep, eroded sea cliff at Vancouver, British Columbia. Loose Pleistocene sands, which form the cliff, are easily eroded by waves during storms. Groundwater seepage from the lower part of the cliff (dark zone) contributes to the problem. *(John J Clague)*

to California. Even higher rates have been recorded in other areas, such as 2 m/y along parts of the English Norfolk coast and up to 4.6 m/y along the east side of Cape Cod. Erosion rates depend primarily on the strength of the cliff materials and wave energy.[33]

Erosion at any site varies over time. It will be more rapid during one or more years of weather that is stormier than normal. Also, erosion may be reduced by building *seawalls* or *groins* at the base of a cliff, by pumping groundwater from slopes, and by diverting surface runoff from the cliff top.

Coastal erosion is a natural process that cannot be completely stopped even with investments of large amounts of money. Therefore, we must learn to live with some erosion.

Hurricanes

Hurricane damage and fatalities are caused by winds, a storm surge, and freshwater flooding. Storm surges cause the greatest damage and contribute to 90 percent of all hurricane-related fatalities.[34]

A **storm surge** is a rapid local rise in sea level that happens when hurricane winds push water onto the coast. Tropical cyclones commonly generate storm surges of more than 3 m, and surges of 12 m or more have been recorded in Bangladesh and Australia.[35] Larger and faster-moving hurricanes create higher storm surges than do smaller, slower-moving hurricanes. High storm surges also develop on broad, shallow coastlines where the forward motion of wind-driven water is impeded because of friction. Storm surge and wind damage in the Northern Hemisphere are greatest in the forward right quadrant of the storm as it makes landfall—this is the direction in which the storm is both travelling and rotating; thus, the wind speed at the ground is higher there. The height of the surge will also be greater if the hurricane comes onto land at high tide.

A storm surge is not an advancing wall of water, but rather a steady increase in sea level. Large storm waves are superimposed on the surge and, together with the water itself, are responsible for much of the damage of a hurricane. The storm waves also erode beaches, islands, and roads.

Sand eroded from beaches and coastal dunes is carried landward by the storm surge and deposited as *overwash*. Overwash may occur in *washover channels* cut through the beach, sand dunes, or a barrier island. Washover channels can form during a single hurricane and, on islands and peninsulas, isolate one area from another. Most of the channels are naturally filled by littoral drift and wave action in the months following the storm.

To most people, the damage caused by wind is more obvious than that caused by the storm surge, in part because of the larger affected area. The type and magnitude of wind damage during hurricanes are summarized in the Saffir-Simpson Hurricane Scale (Table 9.1). Winds attain their greatest velocity, and precipitation is most intense, in the *eye wall* of the hurricane. The eye wall comprises clouds and rain that surround the calm eye of the storm. Rainfall rates of 10 cm/h are common in the eye wall. Because the storm is most intense in the eye wall, forecasters try to predict where the eye of the hurricane will make landfall.

A third hazard associated with hurricanes is inland flooding. Hurricanes produce heavy rains over large areas as they move inland, forcing streams over their banks. Hurricane Hazel, for example, caused severe flooding in Toronto (Chapter 7). In some hurricanes, the damage from inland flooding exceeds that of wind and the storm surge in the coastal zone. The flooding can last for days as waters slowly return to the sea.

▲ **FIGURE 9.27 ROOM WITH A VIEW** These homes, perched on a sea cliff along Puget Sound west of Port Townsend, Washington, were not damaged by this landslide in 1997. They could be destroyed, however, in a future landslide. *(Photo by Gerald W. Thorsen, courtesy of the Washington Division of Geology and Earth Resources)*

Tsunami

A tsunami can cause coastal flooding and catastrophic damage thousands of kilometres from its source. For example, a giant earthquake off the coast of Chile in 1960 triggered a tsunami that killed 61 people in Hawaii 15 hours later.

The majority of tsunami deaths are from drowning. Death and injury also result from physical impacts, either from floating debris or by being washed into stationary objects, such as buildings and trees. Flooding from tsunami can pose health risks from contaminated water and food supplies. Outbreaks of infectious disease are uncommon, but loss of shelter exposes people to insects, extreme weather, and other environmental hazards.[36] The trauma of a tsunami can produce long-lasting mental health problems in survivors.

9.6 Linkages between Coastal Processes and Other Natural Hazards

Coastal processes can injure or kill people and destroy property. They have links to other natural hazards, including earthquakes, flooding, landslides, volcanoes, subsidence, tornadoes, rising sea level, and asteroid impacts.

Intense precipitation associated with hurricanes causes flooding, erosion, and landslides. A hurricane's storm surge and heavy rainfall produce widespread coastal flooding. Coastal areas that have subsided because of, for example, an earthquake, soil compaction, or groundwater withdrawal are highly vulnerable to both river flooding and storm surges.

Coastal flooding is also linked to tsunami, which in turn are associated with some earthquakes, volcanic eruptions, and asteroid impacts. A large tsunami can sweep an area clear of buildings and vegetation and reach a kilometre or more inland (Figure 9.D). Unlike river flooding, a tsunami surge is bidirectional—landward with the arrival of each large wave and seaward with its withdrawal. This bidirectional flow creates tremendous turbulence and large spiralling eddies in coastal waters.

Wind damage from hurricanes is not limited to the winds circulating around the eye of the storm. About half of all hurricanes generate tornadoes or *downbursts* of precipitation-driven winds with speeds of more than 160 km/h.[6] Tornadoes are most common in the forward right quadrant of the hurricane.[6]

Another common hazard associated with coastal processes is landslides. Wave erosion undercuts or steepens sea cliffs and lakeside bluffs, triggering landslides (Figure 9.27).

9.7 Natural Service Functions of Coastal Processes

As is true of many of the other hazards we have discussed, it is difficult to imagine any benefits of coastal erosion, hurricanes, and tsunami. Some coastal processes, however, do provide benefits. Erosion is a problem for property owners in coastal areas, but the beauty of the coastal zone largely results from wave action and erosion (Figure 9.28). The stunning cliffs, rocky headlands, and sandy beaches of British Columbia and Atlantic Canada are the result of erosion and are important

◄ **FIGURE 9.28 SCENIC HEADLAND** This beautiful rock formation on the west coast of the South Island of New Zealand was formed by wave erosion. It is a popular tourist attraction and an important aesthetic resource. *(John J. Clague)*

aesthetic resources. Longshore drift maintains sandy beaches on all coasts, including lakeshores.

Hurricanes may provide much-needed precipitation to parts of North America stricken by drought. The moisture comes from tropical cyclones in the Atlantic Ocean and Gulf of Mexico, or is carried by upper-level winds from hurricanes along the Pacific Coast of Mexico. Most coastal and nearshore ecosystems require storms for healthy maintenance and renewal.

9.8 Human Interaction with Coastal Processes

Human interference with natural shore processes is a major cause of coastal erosion. Most problems arise in populated areas, where efforts to stop coastal erosion have interrupted the natural longshore movement of sand. Engineered structures may help beaches to grow in some areas, but they can cause downdrift erosion that damages valuable beachfront property. This type of interference is common on all coasts of North America, with the exception of the Arctic coast.

The Atlantic coast of the United States is fringed by barrier islands, which are separated from the mainland by a lagoon or bay (Figure 9.29). Most of the barrier islands have been altered by people.

The history of barrier islands along the Maryland coast of the United States illustrates the interplay between people and coastal processes in this area. Demand for the 50 km of oceanfront in Maryland is very high. The barrier islands are used seasonally by residents of the Washington and Baltimore metropolitan areas, and Ocean City, located on Fenwick Island, has experienced particularly rapid growth (Figure 9.30). Since the early 1970s, high-rise condominiums and hotels have been built on Ocean City's waterfront. Coastal dunes were removed to make space for new construction. This activity and serious beach erosion have increased the vulnerability of the island to hurricanes. Coastal dunes act as natural barriers to storm waves and partially protect structures built behind them. Ocean City experienced a hurricane in 1933. The hurricane's storm surge formed Ocean City inlet directly south of the city (Figure 9.30). This event indicates that Ocean City could be damaged or destroyed by the storm surge of a future hurricane.[37]

Assateague Island is located south of Ocean City, just across the inlet. It spans two-thirds of the Maryland coastline and is mostly undeveloped, in contrast to highly urbanized Fenwick Island. Both islands, however, share the same sand supply. At least that was the case until 1935, when *jetties* were constructed to stabilize Ocean City inlet (Figure 9.30). Since construction of the jetties, beaches at the north end of Assateague Island have receded about 11 m/y, nearly 20 times the long-term rate of shoreline retreat for the Maryland coast. During the same period, beaches directly north of the inlet, in Ocean City, became considerably wider, requiring lengthening of a recreational pier.[38]

Historic changes to Maryland's outer coast are clearly linked to human interference with the natural movement of sand along the shore. Construction of the Ocean City inlet jetties interfered with the southward drift of sand. The jetties diverted sand offshore, preventing it from continuing southward to nourish the beaches on Assateague Island.

Erosion is also a problem along the densely populated and extensively modified Gulf of Mexico coastline, which, like the Atlantic coast, has numerous barrier islands. A study of the Texas coastal zone suggests that, in the past 100 years, human modification of the coastline has accelerated erosion by 30 percent to 40 percent.[39] Much of the accelerated erosion stems from coastal development, subsidence because of

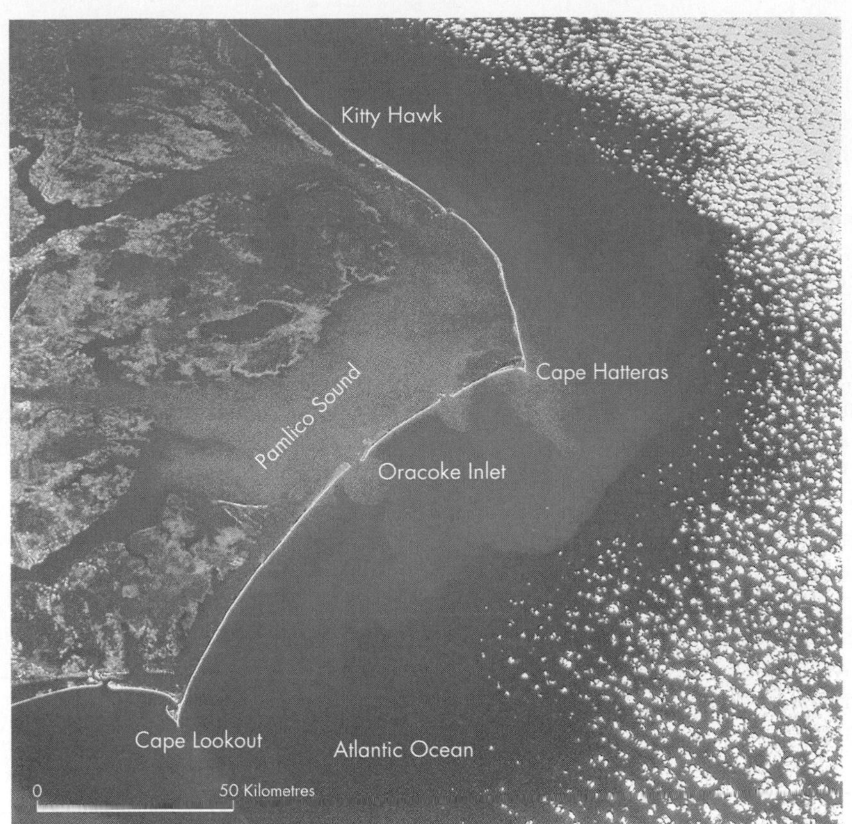

◄ **FIGURE 9.29 BARRIER ISLANDS OF NORTH CAROLINA** A view looking north from the *Apollo 9* spacecraft. Barrier islands appear as thin white ribbons of sand separating the Atlantic Ocean from Pamlico Sound. The yellowish-brown colour of Pamlico Sound is due to silt and clay suspended in the water. The suspended sediment is entering the Atlantic Ocean at Ocracoke Inlet and the inlet to the northeast. *(NASA)*

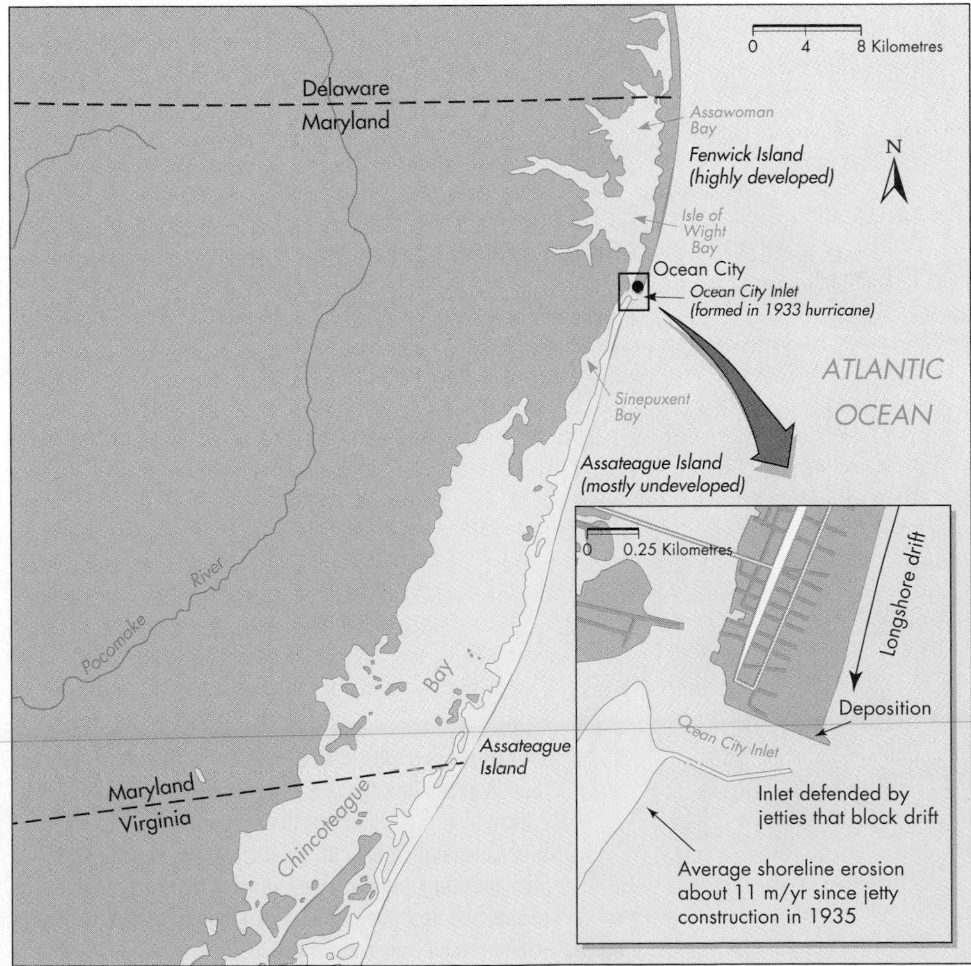

◄ **FIGURE 9.30 JETTY INCREASES BEACH EROSION** Fenwick Island, a barrier island on the Maryland coast in the United States, is experiencing rapid urban development. Potential hurricane damage is a concern. The inset is a map of Ocean City and a washover channel that formed during a hurricane in 1933. The north end of Assateague Island, shown in yellow, is relatively undeveloped and has experienced rapid shoreline erosion since a jetty was constructed in 1935.

groundwater and hydrocarbon withdrawal, and damming of rivers that supply sand to beaches.

The coastline of southern California is heavily populated and has been extensively altered by people. Winter storms during El Niño years have eroded beaches and sea cliffs, causing large amounts of property damage. Jetties and groins, built to improve beaches and to prevent infilling of the mouths of rivers with sediment, have in some instances produced severe downdrift erosion problems. Much of the California shoreline is developed in Tertiary mudstone and sandstone. These rocks erode more slowly than sandy shorelines, but structures built too close to cliff tops are at risk (Figure 9.31).

Some coastal residents of Washington and British Columbia live too close to the tops of sea cliffs. The problem is particularly acute in parts of the Strait of Georgia and Puget Sound (Figure 9.27), where homes are located at the tops of cliffs formed of loose Pleistocene sediments. Storm waves that would not be considered noteworthy on the exposed Pacific Coast can severely erode these cliffs.[23,40]

Activities that increase surface runoff or groundwater, remove vegetation from the cliff face, or increase the steepness of a sea cliff may trigger landslides that accelerate erosion. Urbanization at the top of a cliff or bluff may increase surface runoff. Watering lawns and gardens can add much water to the materials forming the slope, lowering the strength of the materials and increasing the chance of landslides.[33] Landfill, buildings, swimming pools, and patios may also decrease the stability of a coastal cliff by increasing the driving forces on slope materials (Figure 9.31). Coastal development is now strictly regulated in much of North America, but we continue to live with our past mistakes.

9.9 Minimizing Damage from Coastal Hazards

Coastal Erosion

Coastal erosion might appear easier to control than most other natural hazards. For example, we can do nothing to prevent earthquakes or volcanic eruptions; we can only prepare for them. There are things we can do, however, to control coastal erosion:[41]

- Shoreline stabilization with such structures as groins and seawalls—the "hard solution"
- Beach nourishment—the "soft solution"
- Land-use changes—avoid the problem by not building in hazardous areas or by relocating threatened buildings

One of the first tasks in minimizing and managing coastal erosion is to estimate future erosion. Estimates are based on

◄ **FIGURE 9.31 RETREAT OF SEA CLIFF IN ROCK** Apartment buildings at the edge of a sea cliff in Isla Vista, California. The outdoor deck may be "open," but it is unsafe because it is overhanging the cliff by at least 1 m. Note the exposed cement pilings that provide support for the buildings. The decks and apartment buildings are in imminent danger of collapse and were condemned in 2004. *(Edward A. Keller)*

historic shoreline change or on analysis of waves, wind, and sediment supply. Setback recommendations can then be made. A setback is the distance from the shoreline beyond which development, such as of houses and roads, is allowed. The setback concept is at the heart of coastal zone erosion management (Case Study 9.4).

Hard Solutions Structures built along the shoreline to slow erosion and protect buildings from damage are called **seawalls**. (Figure 9.32). They are made of concrete, large stone blocks called *riprap,* wood or steel pilings, cemented sandbags, or other materials. Seawalls have been criticized because they redirect the energy of incoming storm waves back onto

9.4 CASE STUDY

E-Lines and E-Zones

Recently, the U.S. National Research Council (NRC), at the request of the U.S. Federal Emergency Management Agency (FEMA), developed coastal zone management recommendations, some of which are listed below:[41]

- Estimates of future erosion should be based on historic changes to the shoreline or on statistical analysis of local wave and wind conditions and sediment supply.
- After average local erosion rates have been determined, maps should be made showing erosion lines and zones, which are referred to, respectively, as E-lines and E-zones (Figure 9.G). An **E-line** is the expected position of the shoreline after a specified number of years; for example, the E-10 line is the expected shoreline in 10 years. **E-zones** are the areas between the present shoreline and the E-line; the E-10 zone, for example, is the area between the shoreline and the E-10 line.
- No new habitable structures should be allowed in the E-10 zone.
- Movable structures are allowed in the E-10 to E-60 zones, which are deemed to be at intermediate and long-term risk.
- Permanent large structures must have setbacks to beyond the E-60 line.
- All new structures built seaward of the E-60 line, with the exception of those on high bluffs or sea cliffs, should be built on pilings. They should be designed to withstand erosion that could be caused by a storm that recurs, on average, once every 100 years.

NRC recommendations on setbacks are considered to be minimum standards for state and local coastal erosion management programs. At present, only a small number of states use a setback based on erosion rates.

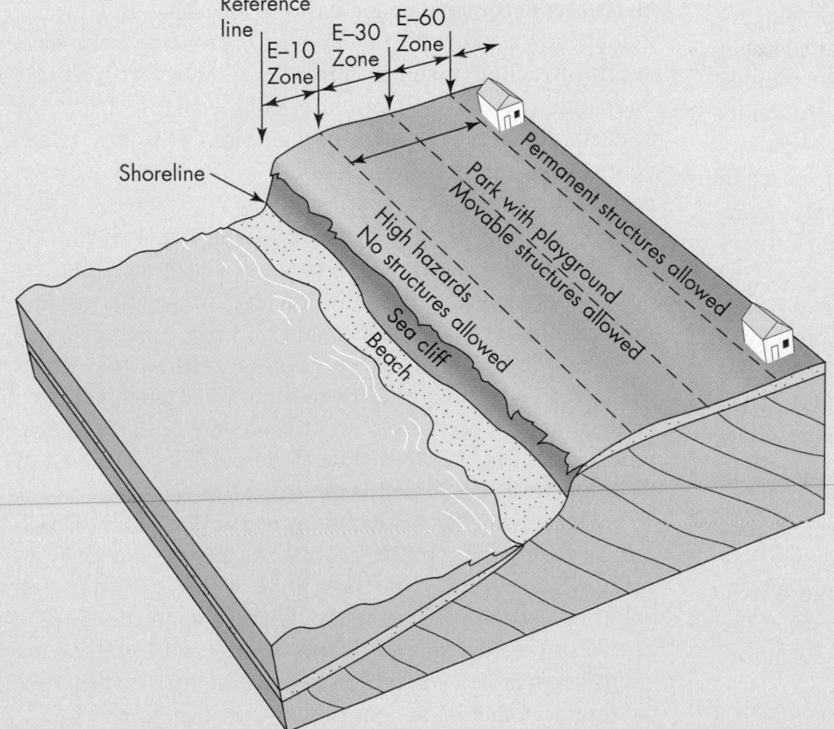

◀ **FIGURE 9.G E-LINES AND E-ZONES** A conceptual diagram illustrating E-lines and E-zones. Widths of E-zones depend on the rate of erosion and can be used to define setback distances. *(Modified from National Research Council. 1990. Managing coastal erosion. Washington, DC: National Academy Press)*

◄ **FIGURE 9.32 SEAWALL** This part of West Vancouver, British Columbia, is protected from wave erosion by a seawall and riprap. A popular pedestrian path is located on the seawall. *(Bob Turner)*

the beach. They may thus promote beach erosion and produce a narrower beach with less sand. Furthermore, seawalls are frequently damaged during severe storms and require costly repairs. Design and construction of seawalls thus must be carefully tailored to specific sites and needs. Because of these problems, some geologists believe that seawalls cause more problems than they solve and should rarely, if ever, be used.

Groins are linear structures placed perpendicular to the shore, commonly in groups called *groin fields* (Figure 9.33). Each groin in a groin field traps a portion of the sand carried by longshore drift. A small amount of sand accumulates updrift of each groin, contributing to an irregular but wider beach. The wider beach protects the shoreline from erosion.

However, groins, like seawalls, can create problems—sand is deposited updrift of the structure, but erosion can occur downdrift of it. Thus, a groin or groin field will produce a wider, more protected beach in a desired area, but at a cost to the adjacent shoreline. Once a groin has trapped all the sediment it can hold, sand is transported around its offshore end to continue its journey along the beach. Therefore, erosion may be minimized by artificially filling the space in front of each groin with sand. Despite such precautions, groins may cause undesirable erosion in the downdrift area; therefore, their use should be carefully evaluated.

Breakwaters and **jetties** are linear structures of riprap or concrete that protect limited stretches of the shoreline from waves. The purpose of a breakwater is to intercept waves and provide a protected area, or harbour, for mooring boats. They may be attached to, or separated from, the beach (Figure 9.34a, 9.34b). Jetties extend perpendicular to the shore at the mouth of a river or at the entrance to a bay or lagoon (Figure 9.34c). They are commonly built in pairs and are designed to prevent sediment from accumulating at the river mouth or bay entrance. Jetties also shelter the channel from large waves. Like groins, jetties block littoral transport and thus cause the updrift beach adjacent to one jetty to widen and downdrift beaches to erode.

Breakwaters and jetties block, or interfere with, littoral transport and alter the shape of the shoreline as new areas of deposition and erosion develop. The result can be serious erosion, or the harbour entrance can be blocked with newly deposited sand. Therefore, these structures must be carefully designed and constructed to minimize adverse effects. The sand may have to be moved by *artificial bypass,* that is, by dredging and pumping the sand adjacent to the breakwater and redepositing it downdrift of the harbour mouth. Other measures that can be taken to minimize adverse effects of breakwaters and jetties include beach nourishment, construction of a seawall, and emplacement of riprap.[4]

Soft Solutions Sometimes **beach nourishment** can be used in place of such "hard" engineered structures as groins and jetties to control erosion. It involves artificially placing sand on beaches to compensate for losses by longshore drift. Ideally, a nourished beach will protect coastal property from wave attack.[4] Beach nourishment provides a beach for recreation and some protection from shoreline erosion. It is also aesthetically preferable to many engineered structures. Beach nourishment can be helpful, but the sand generally requires periodic replenishment.

In the mid-1970s, the City of Miami Beach in Florida and the U.S. Army Corps of Engineers began an ambitious beach-nourishment program to reverse the serious erosion that had plagued the area since the 1950s. The program aimed to widen the beach and protect coastal resorts from storm damage.[42] By 1980, about 18 million m^3 of sand had been dredged and pumped from an offshore site onto the beach, producing a beach 200 m wide (Figure 9.35).[34] The cost of the project was US$62 million.

Vegetated dunes were built as part of the Miami Beach project to provide a buffer against wave erosion and storm surge (Figure 9.36). Specially built walkways allow the public access to the beach without damaging the dunes. The beaches survived major hurricanes in 1979 and 1992, and the nourishment project has proven to be a vast improvement over the fragmented erosion-control measures that preceded it.[4]

(a)

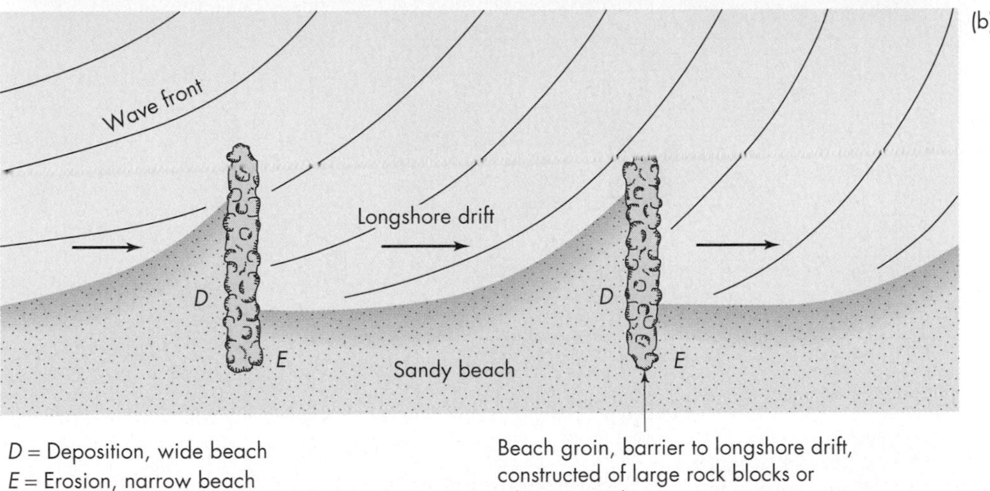

(b)

▲ **FIGURE 9.33 BEACH GROINS** (a) Several groins and breakwaters were built along the shoreline at Vancouver, British Columbia, to minimize the loss of beach sand through erosion. *(John J. Clague)* (b) Two groins trap sand at D, updrift of the structures. Erosion occurs at E.

More than 600 km of the U.S. coastline have received some beach nourishment, but not all the projects have been successful. A stretch of beach at Ocean City, New Jersey, was nourished in 1982 at a cost of about US$5 million. However, the sand that was placed on the beach was removed in less than three months by a series of storms. Beach nourishment remains controversial; some scientists consider sediment added during beach nourishment projects to be nothing more than "sacrificial sand" that will eventually be removed by coastal erosion.[34] Most beaches require frequent replenishment to remain intact.[43] Nevertheless, beach nourishment has become a commonly used method of restoring or creating beaches and protecting shorelines from erosion around the world.

Coastal erosion can be triggered or aggravated by removing vegetation from the shore. Removal of vegetation along the shoreline may destabilize sea cliffs, causing landslides. It may also reduce the resistance of the shore to erosion by storm waves, thus increasing the rate of shoreline retreat. Intertidal plants and animals and plants on the beach berm give shore materials greater resistance to erosion. Beach nourishment plans should include considerations of both physical and ecological aspects of the area that is to be protected.

Hurricanes

We cannot prevent hurricanes; thus, we attempt to reduce the damage they cause by accurately predicting their behaviour as they approach landfall and by evacuating people from their paths. However, the public must be given adequate warning of an approaching hurricane to prepare their homes or to evacuate.

Hurricanes can be difficult to forecast because they involve many different weather processes and they develop far from shore where there are few or no observers.[6] Once a

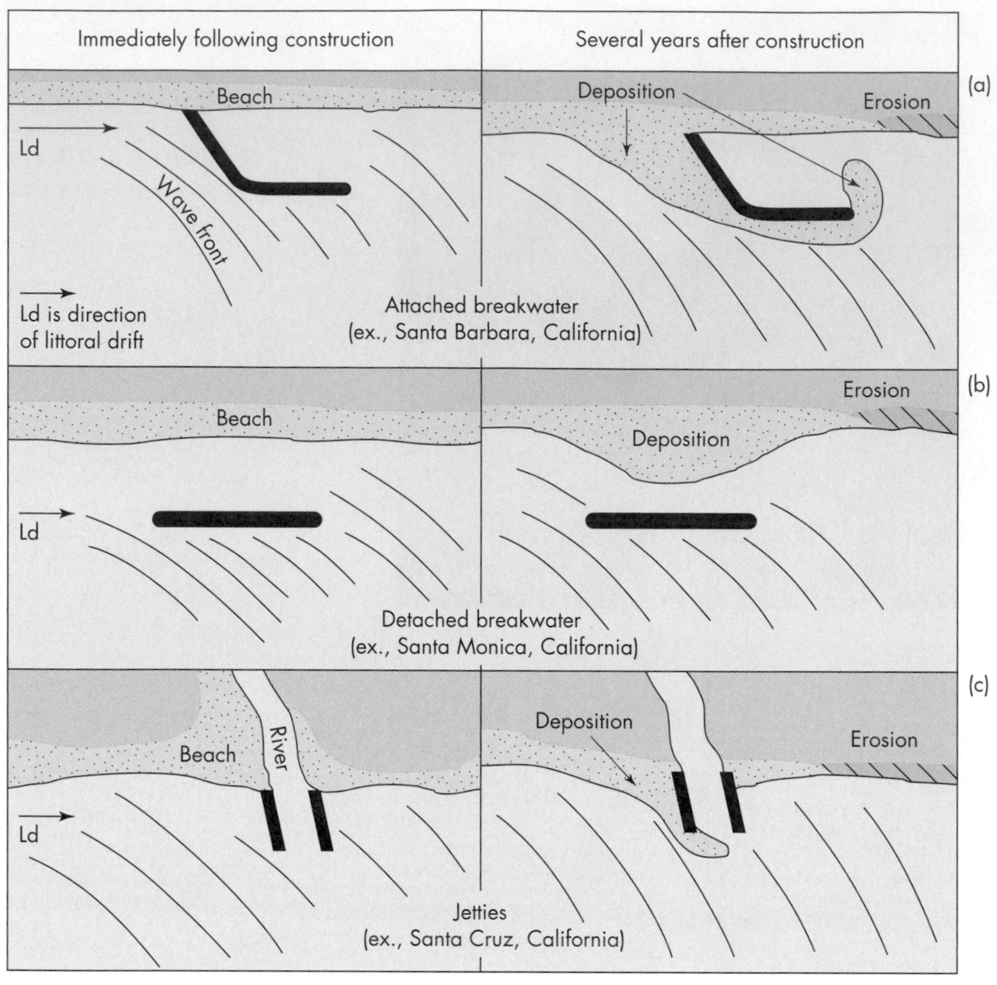

◄ **FIGURE 9.34 EFFECTS OF ENGINEERED COASTAL STRUCTURES ON SEDIMENTATION AND EROSION** Breakwaters, the thick black lines in (a) and (b), and jetties, the thick black lines in (c), alter deposition (yellow) and erosion (brown). Each row shows conditions immediately after construction of a structure (left) and later, following a period of deposition and erosion (right). Thin, curved black lines show the wave direction, and the arrows indicate the direction of littoral transport.

(a)

(b)

▲ **FIGURE 9.35 BEACH NOURISHMENT** Miami Beach (a) before and (b) after beach nourishment in the mid-1970s. *(Courtesy of U.S. Army Corps of Engineers, Headquarters)*

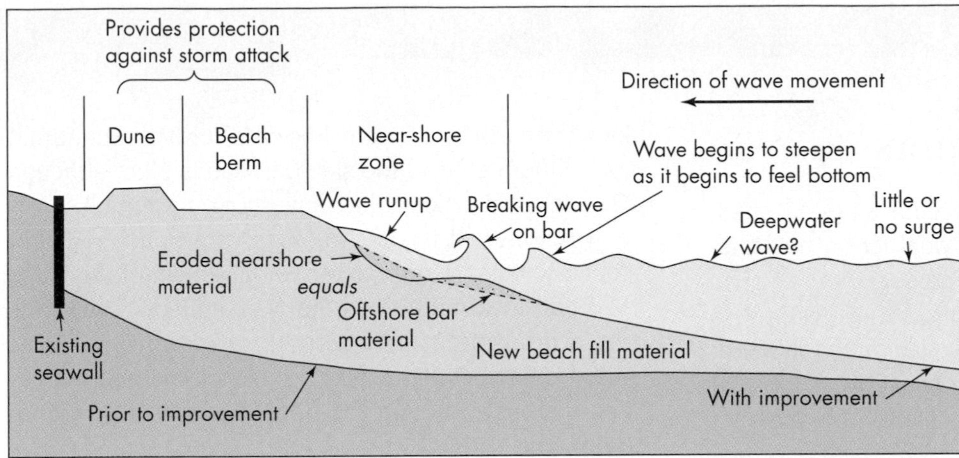

◀ **FIGURE 9.36 MIAMI BEACH AFTER NOURISHMENT** A diagrammatic cross-section of Miami Beach after the beach nourishment project in the mid-1970s. The constructed dune and the beach berm protect the shore against erosion by waves during severe storms. A pre-existing seawall is indicated by the thick black vertical line on the left. Added beach sand is light grey. The orange areas are sand that may be eroded and deposited during a storm; the dashed line shows the pre-storm profile of the beach. *(Courtesy of U.S. Army Corps of Engineers)*

hurricane has formed, meteorologists must try to predict if it will reach land, when and where it will strike, how strong the winds will be, how large an area will be affected, how much rain will fall, and how high the storm surge will be. They use many different tools to answer these questions.

Hurricane forecast centres are located around the world and include the Canadian Hurricane Centre in Dartmouth, Nova Scotia, and the U.S. National Hurricane Center in Miami, Florida. The Canadian Hurricane Centre monitors tropical cyclones and severe North Atlantic storms that might affect Atlantic Canada.[44] The U.S. National Hurricane Center monitors the Atlantic Ocean, Caribbean Sea, Gulf of Mexico, and eastern Pacific Ocean during the hurricane season, which extends from May 15 to November 30.[45] Both centres use information obtained from weather satellites, hurricane-hunter aircraft, Doppler radar, weather buoys, reports from ships, and computers to detect and forecast hurricanes. They issue watches and warnings to the public and support hurricane research. In Canada, a *hurricane watch* is issued when a hurricane approaches land and could be a threat to coastal and inland regions.[44] It provides people time to plan in the event that a warning is issued. A watch does not mean that a hurricane will definitely strike, but rather that everyone within the watch area should be prepared to act quickly if a warning is issued. The U.S. National Hurricane Center issues similar watches and warnings.[46]

Hurricane Forecasting Tools Weather satellites are valuable tools for detecting and tracking hurricanes. They acquire and transmit images of atmospheric systems that might develop into hurricanes, thus alerting meteorologists to areas that should be watched closely.[47] Satellites, however, cannot provide accurate information about wind speed and other aspects of storms. Thus, once a hurricane is detected, other tools are used to refine predictions about the storm's behaviour.

Special aircraft are flown directly into a hurricane to gather data about the storm, especially its intensity. U.S. Air Force Hurricane Hunter aircraft perform most of these missions. They can begin to collect data when Atlantic tropical cyclones move to within about 2600 km of Miami, Florida (see Professional Profile).

Doppler radar is another tool used to collect data on hurricanes, but only when the storms are within about 320 km of the radar station. Radar can provide information on rainfall, wind speed, and the direction in which the storm is moving (Figure 9.37).

Weather buoys are also used to track storms in the Atlantic Ocean and Gulf of Mexico. The buoys are automated weather stations that continuously record and transmit data to the Meteorological Service of Canada or the U.S. National Weather Service. Information is also obtained from ships near hurricanes.

Meteorologists use computers to integrate and model climate data and to make predictions about hurricane paths and intensity. Computer modelling has vastly improved our ability to predict when and where a storm will strike, but it does not do a good job of predicting the intensity of the storm. Reconnaissance flights thus remain an important element of hurricane prediction,[6] although they are dangerous and expensive. Currently, only the United States government conducts such flights, and only in the western Atlantic Ocean, Caribbean Sea, Gulf of Mexico, and an area around Hawaii.[6,48]

Hurricane risk can be further reduced by action at the community and personal levels. The public must be provided accurate and timely information on hurricanes that might make landfall. Television and radio are used to broadcast hurricane watches and warnings. Effective evacuation plans must be developed and publicized before the hurricane season to ensure that large numbers of people can move to safety as rapidly as possible. Public transportation must be provided, shelters opened, and the number of outbound traffic lanes increased along evacuation routes. Relief supplies and personnel must be marshalled close to affected areas before hurricanes strike. Property owners living in hurricane-prone regions should have access to insurance. Buildings can be constructed to withstand hurricane-force winds and elevated to allow the passage of a storm surge (Figure 9.38).

Before the hurricane season starts, coastal residents should prepare their homes and property by trimming dead or dying branches from trees and installing heavy-duty shutters that can be closed to protect windows. They should review evacuation routes and discuss emergency plans with family members. Everyone should have access to an emergency kit

PROFESSIONAL PROFILE

The Hurricane Hunters

Although amateur tornado chasers occupy an established, if eccentric, niche in the world of weather enthusiasts, hurricane hunting is a job for the pros.

Major Chad "Hoot" Gibson boasts that his crew is the only "weather reconnaissance" squadron in the world. The aptly named "Hurricane Hunters" are a crew of Air Force personnel who fly planes directly into the centre of hurricanes while the storms are still over the ocean. During their wild rides, they gather important data about the strength of hurricanes, which the U.S. National Weather Services use to forecast the hurricanes' intensity if they make landfall.

The crew begins to collect data 170 km from the eye of the hurricane at an altitude of about 16,000 m. They attempt to fly in a straight line through the hurricane to its eye. In the course of doing so, Gibson says they've encountered just about every form of severe weather possible: hail, updrafts and downdrafts, turbulence, even tornadoes. "We avoid those," he notes.

Near the centre of the hurricane is the furious eye wall, whose winds commonly move at about 225 km/h. Breaching the wall is no smooth ride. "There are times when the plane vibrates so badly that you can't read your computer screen," Gibson says.

But when they've made it through, the view from the eye is awe-inspiring. "Amazing, fantastic," he says. "It's like sitting at the 50-yard line of a football stadium." In a well-formed eye, the sky overhead is blue, although the water below "looks like a washing machine."

The winds at the centre of the storm are so calm, about 3 km/h to 8 km/h, that the movement of the plane itself can invalidate the data they collect. They thus drop a dropsonde, a "weather station in a can," as Gibson describes it, to take necessary measurements. Then it's back through the opposite wall and another bumpy ride.

Gibson recalls a mission through Hurricane Floyd in September 1999, when they entered the eye wall of the storm with winds of 220 km/h, reached the eye four minutes later where the winds were only 8 km/h, and then, five minutes later, were confronted with winds of 225 km/h as they passed through the eye wall again.

Not all hurricane eyes are perfectly formed, and some storms have several smaller centres. The hurricane hunters use the telltale 180-degree shift in winds, the trademark of the centre of a vortex, to mark the official storm centre.

The planes the squadron flies are Lockheed-Martin WC-130 aircraft, built between 1960 and 1964 and modified to carry the complex data-gathering equipment required for the missions (Figure 9.H). "Our youngest plane just turned 40," Gibson says.

—Chris Wilson

◄ FIGURE 9.H HURRICANE HUNTER AIRCRAFT This U.S. Air Force Reserve Lockheed-Martin WC-130 aircraft is specially equipped for collecting weather data in hurricanes for the U.S. National Hurricane Center. *(George Hall/CORBIS-NY)*

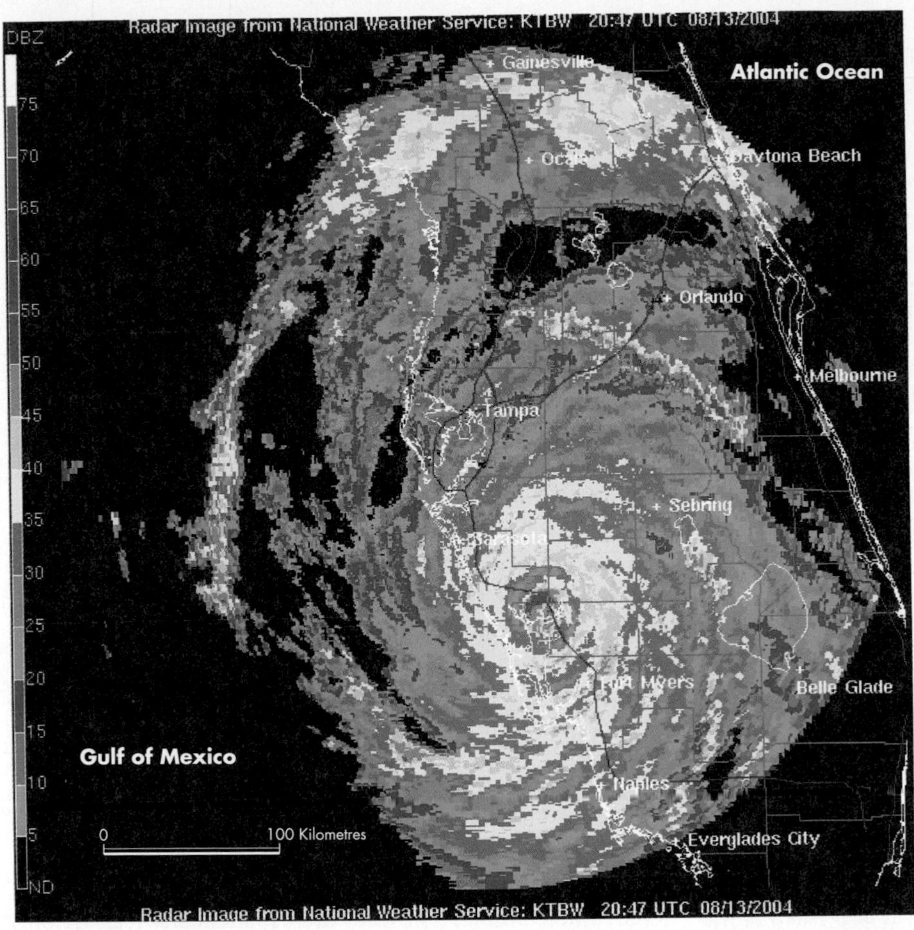

◀ **FIGURE 9.37 RADAR IMAGE OF HURRICANE CHARLEY** A Doppler radar image of Hurricane Charley, a Category 4 storm, just after it made landfall between Fort Myers and Sarasota on the west coast of Florida in the United States on August 13, 2004. The strongest winds coincide with the red and orange spiralling rain bands. *(Courtesy of the National Weather Service)*

that includes flashlights, a radio, spare batteries, a first-aid kit, emergency food and water, a can opener, cash, essential medicines, and sturdy shoes.[49] Once a hurricane warning has been issued, people who might be affected should stay tuned to local radio or TV stations. If an evacuation order is given, gather emergency supplies and leave by the assigned evacuation route.

Hurricane Opal We have made great strides in predicting the behaviour of hurricanes once they form, but there are still problems. Hurricanes may suddenly veer off their predicted path, as was dramatically illustrated by Hurricane Opal in the fall of 1995. Opal formed in the Gulf of Mexico and was predicted to remain a Category 1 or 2 storm (Table 9.1) as it slowly moved toward Florida. In fact, forecasters weren't sure that it would maintain hurricane strength until landfall. The U.S. National Hurricane Center decided that a hurricane warning was not necessary for the Florida Panhandle. The decision was made at 5:00 P.M. the day before the hurricane struck. Later, in the middle of the night, Opal crossed an isolated pool of warm Gulf water. It suddenly intensified to nearly a Category 5 storm and accelerated toward the Florida

◀ **FIGURE 9.38 HURRICANE-RESISTANT HOUSE** This house in the Florida Keys was built with strong blocks and space below the living area to allow a hurricane storm surge to pass through the building. *(Edward A. Keller)*

coast.[6] The National Hurricane Center hurriedly issued a hurricane warning, but most people did not receive it until they awoke the next morning when the violent hurricane was just offshore. Last-minute evacuations caused massive traffic jams that further endangered lives. Fortunately, Opal lost strength and dropped back to Category 3 intensity before it made landfall.[6] Nine people were killed by the hurricane, but the death toll would have been much higher had the storm not weakened at the last moment. This close call emphasizes the need for accurate predictions of the intensity and paths of hurricanes.

Hurricane Prediction and the Future Before 2005, deaths from hurricanes in the United States had been dropping, largely because of better forecasting, improved evacuation, and greater public awareness.[6] However, Hurricane Katrina, which killed 2140 people in New Orleans, Biloxi, and other communities in southern Louisiana and Mississippi, highlighted the extreme vulnerability of people on the Atlantic and Gulf coasts of the United States to severe tropical storms. Coastal populations are skyrocketing, so hurricane risk is increasing rapidly in the United States. Katrina also pointed out weaknesses in hurricane preparedness at all levels of government. Catastrophes like Hurricane Katrina will recur if coastal residents fail to prepare for tropical storms or ignore evacuation warnings.[6] They will also happen again if governments do not properly plan for hurricanes.

Hurricane-related property damage has increased dramatically in the last 50 years (Table 9.2). Losses will continue to mount as more and more people build homes and businesses in the coastal zone.

Tsunami

Like hurricanes, tsunami cannot be prevented. The damage they cause, however, can be greatly reduced through a variety of actions, including land-use controls (zoning, relocation, and property acquisition), emergency preparedness, dyking, barrier construction, flood proofing, tsunami-resistant construction, warning systems, and public education.[50] Public safety may require that certain uses of land in high-hazard areas be restricted through zoning regulations or by relocating property to higher ground. However, these types of actions are strongly resisted by residents who would be affected by them.

TABLE 9.2 Property Damage from Hurricanes on the Atlantic and Gulf Coasts

Decade	Property Damage (in 2000 US$)
1900–1909	$1.5 billion
1910–1919	$3.5 billion
1920–1929	$2.2 billion
1930–1939	$6.1 billion
1940–1949	$5.5 billion
1950–1959	$13.4 billion
1960–1969	$25.2 billion
1970–1979	$20.6 billion
1980–1989	$21.4 billion
1990–1999	$56.7 billion

Source: Jarrell, J. D., M. Mayfield, E. N. Rappaport, and C. W. Landsea. 2001. The deadliest, costliest, and most intense United States hurricanes from 1900 to 2000 (and other frequently requested hurricane facts). NOAA Technical Memorandum NWS TPC-1. Miami: National Hurricane Center. www.aoml.noaa.gov/hrd/Landsea/deadly. *Accessed May 14, 2005.*

Risk to coastal communities can be assessed by determining the frequency and size of past tsunami from historical records and geological data. Maximum tsunami heights along a reach of the coast are estimated by using computer-generated models and from the distribution of historic and prehistoric tsunami deposits. Maps can then be produced showing areas likely to be inundated by tsunami of different sizes. The maps may be used to guide or restrict development in tsunami-prone areas and to educate people living in these areas about the risk they face. Computer models also provide estimates of tsunami arrival times, currents, and forces on structures.

Dykes and walls can be constructed to prevent waves from reaching threatened residential and commercial areas. However, these barriers are expensive and should be built to the highest possible elevation that can be reached by a tsunami.[28] In some cases, offshore barriers can deflect tsunami waves or lessen their energy before they reach the shore. Again, these are expensive structures and may provide only limited protection. They are economically feasible only where large populations are at risk and where the threatened shoreline is at the head of a bay or inlet. Japan has constructed offshore breakwaters and onshore concrete walls to protect many of its coastal towns and cities from tsunami.

Buildings in areas of high tsunami risk can be designed or protected to reduce water damage. Elevation of buildings and other types of flood proofing (for example, installing seals for basement windows and bolting houses to their foundations) provide protection where water depths are 1 m or less and currents are not strong. Structures can be elevated to higher levels to provide greater protection, but the cost may be prohibitive. Some houses near the coast on the Hawaiian Islands have been built on pilings, their floors elevated 2 m to 3 m above ground level to allow water to move freely beneath them.

Protection of life also requires effective tsunami warning systems (Figure 9.39). Such systems, however, are useful only when the tsunami originates far from populated shores. The travel times of tsunami produced by earthquakes off Japan, Kamchatka, and Alaska are sufficiently long that low-lying coastal areas of British Columbia, Washington, and Oregon can be evacuated following alerts. When the source of the tsunami is less than about 100 km away, there generally is insufficient time to warn and safely evacuate people, and no warning is possible when a local landslide triggers a tsunami. The shaking caused by a local strong earthquake, however, is a good warning of a possible tsunami.

Three types of warning systems exist for tsunami in the Pacific Ocean: a Pacific-wide system (the Pacific Tsunami

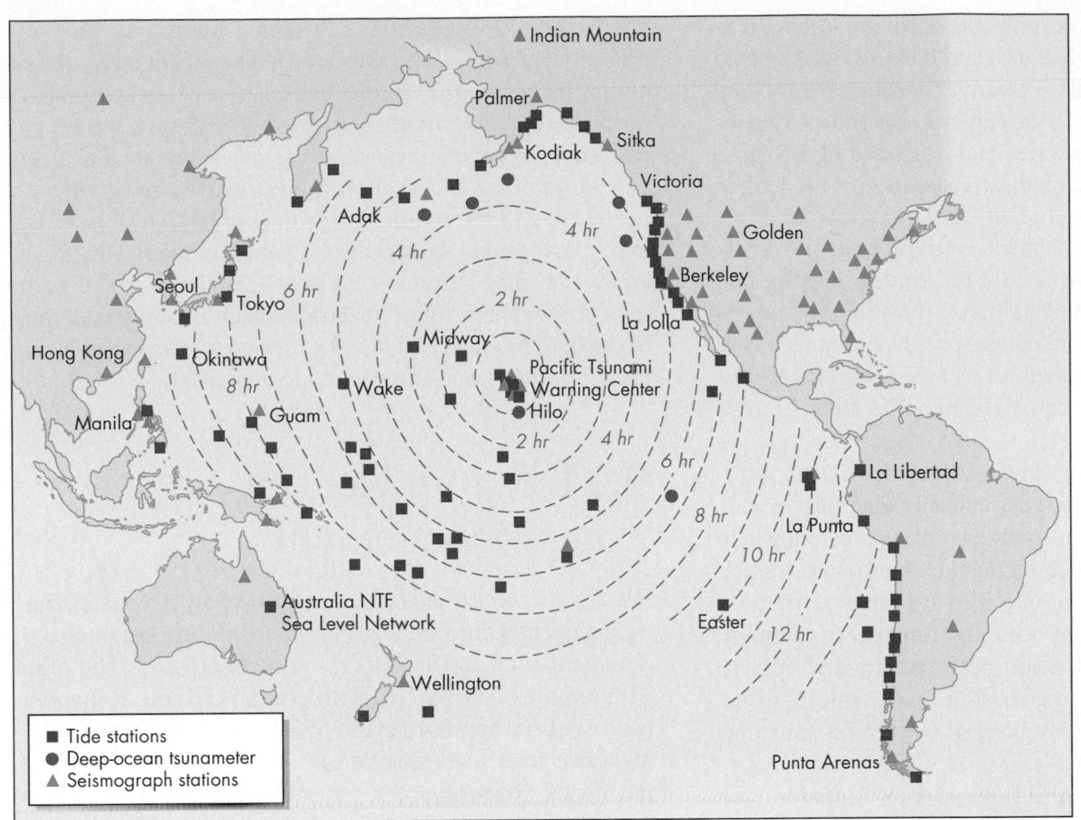

◄ **FIGURE 9.39 TSUNAMI WARNING SYSTEM IN THE PACIFIC** Information arrives at the Pacific Tsunami Warning Center in Hawaii from three sources: a network of seismographs, more than 100 tide gauges, and ocean-bottom pressure sensors linked to surface buoys. The dashed lines show the time it would take a tsunami to reach Hawaii from locations in the Pacific Ocean. *(Modified after NOAA National Weather Service)*

Warning Center) located in Hawaii; regional systems, including the West Coast and Alaska Tsunami Warning System, located in Alaska; and local systems in Chile and Japan.[28,50] The three systems use a network of seismographs located throughout the Pacific basin to provide real-time estimates of earthquake magnitude and location before issuing a tsunami warning. The warning centres then use more than 100 coastal tidal gauges to verify that a tsunami indeed was produced.

In recent years, interest has grown in using seafloor sensors to record the passage of tsunami in deep water. The U.S. National Oceanographic and Atmospheric Association (NOAA) has developed a network of deep-ocean reporting stations that can track tsunami and report them in real time, a project known as Deep-Ocean Assessment and Reporting of Tsunami (DART) (Figure 9.40). The network includes sensitive ocean-bottom sensors that detect the increased pressure from the additional volume of water produced when a tsunami wave passes over them. The sensors transmit the pressure measurements to buoys at the ocean surface, which transmit the data to NOAA's Geostationary Operational Environmental Satellite (GOES). The satellite, in turn, relays the information back to Earth where it is sent through NOAA communications systems to warning centres. The six DART buoys in the Pacific Ocean are anchored in about 6000 m of water. Following the 2004 Indian Ocean tsunami, NOAA announced that it would deploy 32 new DART buoys in the Pacific and Atlantic oceans and in the Caribbean Sea.

Tsunami risk can also be reduced through actions at the provincial, state, and local levels. (Tsunami in the territories are very unlikely.) Some communities in British Columbia, Hawaii, Alaska, Washington, Oregon, and California have

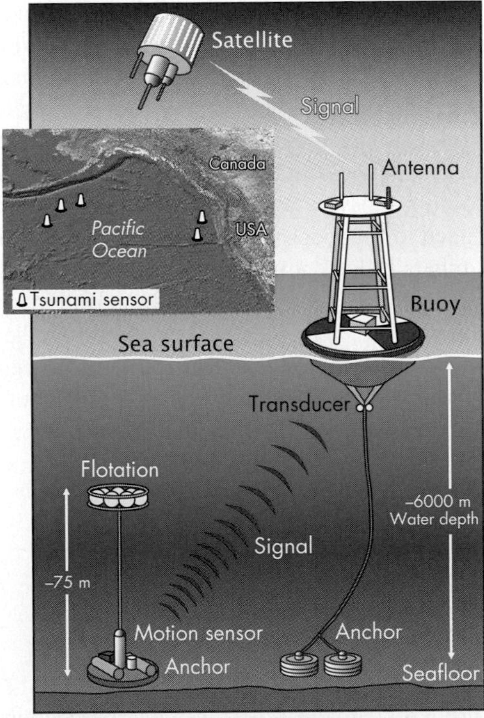

▲ **FIGURE 9.40 DART SYSTEM** The Deep-Ocean Assessment and Reporting of Tsunami (DART) system comprises a series of pressure sensors on the ocean floor in water depths of about 6000 m. The sensors measure changes in water pressure produced by a passing tsunami. They send data to buoys at the ocean surface. The data are relayed from the buoys to a satellite and from there back to Earth to a tsunami warning centre. *(Clague, J., C. Yorath, R. Franklin, and B. Turner. 2006. At risk: Earthquakes and tsunamis on the west coast. Vancouver, BC: Tricouni Press; modified from NOAA)*

developed local tsunami warning and evacuation plans. The plans include signs along beaches and harbours, designated evacuation routes, and sirens. Tsunami inundation maps based on computer models have been prepared for some communities in Washington, Oregon, and northern California. Additional mapping is planned for coastlines in the United States, spurred by the 2004 Indian Ocean tsunami.

Even the most reliable tsunami warning system is likely to be ineffective if people do not respond in orderly and intelligent ways. Because tsunami are infrequent, people's recollections, as with any rare natural phenomenon, fade with time, leading some communities into a false sense of security. Education is therefore essential if communities are to become more resilient to tsunami.

A public education program must provide tsunami information at regular intervals, perhaps annually, and must include instructions on how to get information during an alert, where to go, and what things to take. Educational initiatives should be included in school curricula to ensure that future generations understand the hazards and potential impacts of tsunami. Education about tsunami should not be limited only to those living on or near the coast but to all communities, because people from inland regions often travel to tsunami-prone areas (Case Study 9.2).

A range of educational initiatives can be undertaken in coastal communities. Activity sheets containing graphics, pictures, data, questions, and other relevant information can be used in schools to educate students about tsunami hazards. Tsunami evacuation routes can be publicized and marked by signs. Citizens should be consulted about land use in the tsunami inundation zone before decisions are made about siting or relocating critical facilities, such as hospitals and police stations, schools and other high-occupancy buildings, and petroleum-storage tank farms. Tsunami information can be printed in newspapers and telephone books, along with phone numbers of local emergency service offices. Citizens should also be regularly informed about local warning systems.

By international agreement, information from the United States' warning system is shared with warning centres in 23 other countries. In Canada, tsunami information is disseminated through the British Columbia Provincial Emergency Program.

9.10 Perception of Coastal Hazards

Past experience, proximity to the coastline, and the possibility of property damage affect a person's perception of risk from hazardous coastal processes. One study of sea-cliff erosion near Bolinas, California, found that shoreline residents in an area likely to experience damage in the near future were generally well informed and saw the erosion as a direct and serious threat.[51] People living a few hundred metres from the shore, although aware of the erosion problem, knew little about its severity. Still farther inland, people were aware that the coast was eroding but did not consider it a hazard.

Residents of the Gulf and Atlantic coasts may have significant experience with hurricanes but, surprisingly, do not always recognize the danger. During every hurricane, some people do not obey evacuation orders. People who have experienced a few small hurricanes may underestimate the effects of a large one. Incorrect predictions of when or where a hurricane will strike also lower the perception of risk. For example, if people are repeatedly warned of storms that never arrive, they may become complacent and ignore future warnings. As with any other hazard, an accurate understanding of coastal processes and the risk they pose is key to reducing loss of property and life when disaster strikes.

9.11 Future Coastal Zone Management

We are at a crossroads today with respect to coastal zone management. One path leads to the increasing use of coastal defences, such as seawalls, to control erosion. The other path requires that we live with coastal erosion; it involves controlled and appropriate use of land in the coastal zone.[41,43] Most structures in the coastal zone should be considered temporary and expendable; few critical facilities should be placed near a shore that is retreating because of erosion. Development in the coastal zone must be in the best interest of the general public rather than the few who profit from it. In other words, the shoreline belongs to all people, not just those fortunate enough to purchase beachfront property. This concept is at odds with the attitude of developers who consider the coastal zone "too valuable not to develop." In Canada, all beaches are public property and local property owners can't deny others access to the beach. Likewise in some U.S. states, such as Texas and Oregon, almost all beaches are public property and coastal zoning now requires avenues for public access.

The idea that, with minor exceptions, coastal zone development is temporary and expendable and that the general public should be given first consideration is founded on five principles:[43]

1. *Coastal erosion is a natural process.*
2. *Any shore construction causes change.* Shore structures interfere with natural processes and may produce adverse effects.
3. *Stabilization of beaches with dykes, groins, jetties, and other engineered structures protects property, not the beach itself.* Most protected property belongs to a small number of people, whereas the costs commonly are borne by the general public.
4. *Engineered structures designed to protect a beach may eventually destroy it.*
5. *Once built, defensive structures lead to further coastal development, a trend that is difficult, if not impossible, to reverse.*

Remember these guidelines if you plan to purchase land in the coastal zone: (1) allow for a sufficient setback from the beach, sea cliff, or lakeshore bluff; (2) ensure that the property is above the possible limit of flooding; (3) construct buildings to withstand high winds; and (4) if hurricanes are a possibility, be sure that the property has an adequate evacuation route.[43]

Summary

Waves are generated by storms at sea or on large lakes; they expend their energy at the shoreline. Irregularities in the shoreline and differences in coastal geology account for local differences in wave erosion. Most beaches consist of sand or gravel that has been carried to the coast by rivers or eroded from rocky headlands. Some beaches consist of locally derived broken shells and coral fragments. Waves striking a beach at an angle cause sediment to be transported parallel to the coast.

Almost all shorelines, including those of large inland lakes, are at risk from one or more coastal hazards, including rip currents generated in the surf zone, erosion, tsunami, rogue waves, and tropical cyclones. Coastal erosion is less damaging than river flooding, earthquakes, and tropical cyclones, but it is a serious problem along parts of Canadian and U.S. coasts and Great Lakes shorelines. Coastal erosion can be caused by river damming, construction of dykes, jetties, and other shoreline defences, severe storms, and a rise in sea level. Hurricanes pose a serious threat to the Atlantic and Gulf coasts of North America. Strong winds, storm surges, and heavy rainfall cause most of the damage. Although infrequent, large tsunami can be devastating. Tsunami are triggered by earthquakes, landslides, and, less commonly, volcanic eruptions and meteorite impacts. A tsunami is a train of waves, the first of which may not be the largest. In extreme cases, waves may reach elevations of more than 30 m in coastal areas.

Most coastal erosion problems are in populated areas. Seawalls, groins, breakwaters, jetties, and, more recently, beach nourishment have been used to combat beach erosion where property is at risk. These approaches have had mixed success and may cause additional problems in adjacent areas. Engineering structures are very expensive, require maintenance, and, once in place, are difficult to remove. The cost of engineering structures may eventually exceed the value of the properties they protect. Some structures may even destroy the beaches they were intended to save. Beach nourishment has been successfully used to restore and widen beaches, but it remains to be seen whether this "soft solution" to coastal erosion will be effective in the long term.

People can adjust to hurricanes by stocking emergency supplies, preparing once a warning has been issued, and, if required, evacuating before the storm hits. Houses can be constructed to withstand hurricane-force winds and can also be elevated to allow the passage of storm surges. Preparations for a tsunami are similar to those for a hurricane, except that immediate evacuation from threatened coastal areas is necessary.

Risk perception depends mainly on an individual's experience with, and proximity to, the hazard. Hurricane, tsunami, and erosion risks in wealthy countries are reduced through protective structures, land-use zoning, warning systems, education, and government and individual emergency planning.

Key Terms

barrier island (p. 256)
beach (p. 254)
beach nourishment (p. 280)
bluff (p. 255)
breaker zone (p. 255)
breaking wave (p. 253)
breakwater (p. 280)
E-line (p. 279)
E-zone (p. 279)
groin (p. 280)
hurricane (p. 257)
jetty (p. 280)
littoral transport (p. 255)
rip current (p. 257)
rogue wave (p. 250)
sea cliff (p. 255)
seawall (p. 279)
spit (p. 256)
storm surge (p. 274)
surf zone (p. 255)
swash zone (p. 255)
tidal bore (p. 253)
tombolo (p. 256)
tropical cyclone (p. 257)
tsunami (p. 259)

Review Questions

1. How do waves form on the ocean or a lake?
2. What factors affect the size of waves on the ocean or a lake?
3. Describe how water particles behave in the open ocean when a wind-driven wave passes. How does this behaviour change in shallow water?
4. Explain why waves converge at a coastal headland.
5. What are the two main types of breaking waves and where do they form?
6. Explain how littoral transport takes place. How is longshore drift related to the direction of wave approach?
7. What are the most serious coastal hazards?

8. How do tropical cyclones, hurricanes, tropical storms, tropical depressions, tropical disturbances, and typhoons differ?
9. Explain how and where hurricanes form.
10. How are hurricanes classified? What category is the most intense?
11. Describe the three common paths taken by North Atlantic hurricanes.
12. Describe the three major causes of hurricane damage.
13. How do tsunami waves differ from wind-driven waves?
14. What are the causes of tsunami?
15. What happens to a tsunami when it enters shallow water?
16. What are the common misconceptions that people have about tsunami?
17. Under what circumstances is it difficult to warn people of an impending tsunami?
18. What are the primary causes of death and injury in a tsunami?
19. Which areas of the United States and Canada have the highest risk for hurricanes and tsunami?
20. In what part of the world are tsunami most common? Why?
21. Describe how rip currents form.
22. What are the primary causes of coastal erosion? Why is coastal erosion becoming more of a problem?
23. Describe the processes that cause sea cliffs and lakeshore bluffs to retreat.
24. What are the relationships between coastal processes and flooding, landslides, subsidence, and tornadoes?
25. What are the natural service functions of coastal processes?
26. Explain the purpose of seawalls, groins, breakwaters, and jetties.
27. List arguments for and against beach nourishment.
28. Explain how hurricane watches and warnings differ.
29. What are the tools that are used to forecast hurricanes?
30. Describe the tools used to provide tsunami warnings.
31. What affects a person's perception of coastal hazards?
32. What are the five principles that should be accepted if we choose to live with, rather than control, coastal erosion?
33. Describe the adjustments that people need to make to survive hurricanes and tsunami.

Critical Thinking Questions

1. Has human activity increased coastal erosion? Outline a research program that could address this question.
2. Do you agree or disagree with the following statements: (1) All structures in the coastal zone, with the exception of critical facilities, should be considered temporary and expendable. (2) A balance of public and private interests is required for any development in the coastal zone. Explain your position on both statements.
3. Where would you go if you had to evacuate your home immediately? Where would you go if you had to evacuate your home and travel at least 100 km from where you live? What would you take with you in both cases? What problems might you or your community face in an evacuation? What would be your concerns?

Selected Web Resources

Canada's Coastline
http://gsca.nrcan.gc.ca/coastweb/facts_e.php Facts about Canada's coastline from Natural Resources Canada

USGS Coastal and Marine Geology Program
http://marine.usgs.gov U.S. Geological Survey Coastal and Marine Geology Program homepage

Coasts in Crisis
http://pubs.usgs.gov/circ/c1075 Online version of a U.S. Geological Survey Circular

Coastal and Nearshore Erosion and Storm Events
http://walrus.wr.usgs.gov/hazards/erosion.html From the U.S. Geological Survey

Erosion and Development in Coastal Regions and on Small Islands
www.unesco.org/csi Beach erosion and coastal zone management from Coastal Regions and Small Islands (CSI), United Nations Educational, Scientific, and Cultural Organization (UNESCO)

Twenty Frequently Asked Questions about Great Lakes Water Levels and Coastal Erosion
www.seagrant.wisc.edu/communications/LakeLevels From the University of Wisconsin Sea Grant Program

Rip Currents: Break the Grip
www.ripcurrents.noaa.gov From the National Weather Service

Canadian Hurricane Centre
www.ns.ec.gc.ca/weather/hurricane Information about hurricanes from the Meteorological Service of Canada

Hurricanes in Canada
http://atlas.nrcan.gc.ca/site/english/maps/environment/naturalhazards/majorhurricanes/1 A catalogue of major hurricanes that have affected Canada from Natural Resources Canada

Hurricanes and Hurricane Preparedness
http://hurricanes.noaa.gov Information about hurricanes and hurricane preparedness from the National Oceanic and Atmospheric Administration

Hurricanes and Hurricane Tracking
http://weather.gov/om/hurricane Hurricane information and tracking charts from the U.S. National Weather Service

Tsunami in Canada
http://atlas.nrcan.gc.ca/site/english/maps/environment/naturalhazards/tsunamis A catalogue of major tsunami that have struck Canada from Natural Resources Canada

Tsunami Research in Canada
www.pac.dfo-mpo.gc.ca/sci/OSAP/projects/tsunami/default_e.htm Research on the observation and modelling of tsunami from the Institute of Ocean Sciences, Fisheries and Oceans Canada

NOAA Tsunami Research
www.pmel.noaa.gov/tsunami Computer simulations and information about mitigation, inundation mapping, and the tsunami warning system from the NOAA Pacific Marine Environmental Laboratory

International Tsunami Information Center
www.tsunamiwave.info Tsunami information and resource tool kit (*TsunamiTeacher*)

Pacific Tsunami Warning Center
www.prh.noaa.gov/ptwc A wide range of information from the Pacific Tsunami Warning Center

Preparing for Tsunami
www.pep.bc.ca/hazard_preparedness/Tsunami_Brochure/Prepare_for_Tsunami.html Information on how you can protect yourself from tsunami from the British Columbia Provincial Emergency Program

HAZARD CITY: ASSIGNMENTS IN APPLIED GEOLOGY

Shoreline Property Assessment

The Issue

Shorelines are among the most dynamic places on our planet, with erosion and deposition occurring constantly through the actions of winds, waves, and currents. Severe storms can produce dramatic changes in just a few hours.

Shorelines also attract people. Their scenic beauty and recreational opportunities make them highly desirable sites for housing and other development. However, the dynamic and sometimes violent processes that operate at shorelines make them risky locations for development.

Shoreline erosion is a significant problem. Each year, it destroys or damages property in North America worth millions of dollars. It is possible to determine if a coastal property is at risk by becoming informed about erosion and by studying the prior history of the site. These studies enable citizens and communities to avoid developing or investing in risky areas, saving millions of dollars and possibly lives.

Your Task

Hazard City is about 50 km from the coast, and its residents enjoy visiting the beach. Many people have purchased second homes, beachfront cottages, or timeshares. Most of the properties are along the ocean shoreline and the banks of the Clearwater River, close to where it enters the ocean. Care must be taken when building houses in these areas because shoreline erosion can be a significant problem. Prudent buyers seek professional advicc before they make such an important purchase. A Hazard City developer has asked you to assess several properties and report on how they might be affected by shoreline erosion. Your task is to inspect the properties, determine whether or not they can be safely developed, and prepare a report for the developer.

Average Completion Time

1 hour

CHAPTER 10

▶ **OKANAGAN MOUNTAIN FIRE** This image from the Advanced Spaceborne Thermal Emission and Reflection (ASTER) radiometer on the *Terra* satellite was taken on September 2, 2003. It shows the widespread devastation left by the Okanagan Mountain fire in southern British Columbia. The pink area to the east (right) of the bend in Okanagan Lake is the burned area. Smoke (light blue) and areas of active burning (pinkish-white) are visible at the northeast perimeter of the fire. The city of Kelowna is north of the fire. *(NASA's Earth Observatory)*

Wildfires

Learning Objectives

As Earth's population grows, more people are living in and near scrublands and forests where wildfires occur. This trend increases the risk of property damage and loss of life from fires. Your goals in reading this chapter should be to

- Understand wildfire as a natural process
- Understand the effects of fires
- Know how wildfires are linked to other natural hazards
- Know the potential benefits of wildfires
- Know the methods employed to reduce wildfire hazard
- Understand how people adjust to the threat of wildfires

Wildfires in British Columbia in 2003

Hundreds of thousands of North Americans, seeking a more relaxed lifestyle, have moved into the forested fringes of cities in Canada and the United States. The lives of thousands of those Canadians changed abruptly in July and August 2003, when wildfires—ignited by careless smokers and lightning strikes—exploded out of control in southern British Columbia (Figure 10.1). These wildfires were the most damaging the region had ever endured.

The worst of the wildfires was the Okanagan Mountain fire, which burned approximately 250 km^2 of forest over a three-week period in August and September 2003 (Figure 10.2). It began on August 16 with a lightning strike in Okanagan Mountain Provincial Park, south of Kelowna. The fire rapidly spread and became an unstoppable firestorm. In just four days, it destroyed the park, jumped a 50 m wide fireguard, and approached the outskirts of Kelowna, a city of about 150,000 people. On one night at the height of the fire, a tongue of flames moved into a forested suburb of Kelowna and destroyed 239 homes. More than 45,000 people had to be evacuated in Kelowna and many other towns in southern British Columbia that summer. Property losses totalled more than $250 million, making it the most costly wildfire in Canadian history.[1]

The Kelowna fire was only one of many wildfires in British Columbia in 2003; other fires were even larger. In total, more than 2500 km^2 of the province's forests burned that summer. The total area burned was not of unprecedented size—more forest land was burned during the 1971 and 1983 fire seasons than in 2003. What made 2003 different from any other year were the number of people and amount of property in the paths of the fires.

Two factors contributed to the severity of the fires in southern British Columbia in 2003: (1) a prolonged drought combined with a hot, very dry summer left the forests and soils tinder dry; and (2) the forest floor had an overabundance of deadfall and other fuel, the result of decades of effective fire suppression.

This disaster and other similar wildfire disasters in Canada and the United States have made it clear that past fire-suppression policies in both countries have not reduced wildfire risk. A wind-driven fire with temperatures as high as 1000°C, moving through dry forest with abundant forest-floor fuel, cannot be stopped.

Kelowna
Westbank
Okanagan Lake
Okanagan
Mountain Park
0
5 Kilometres

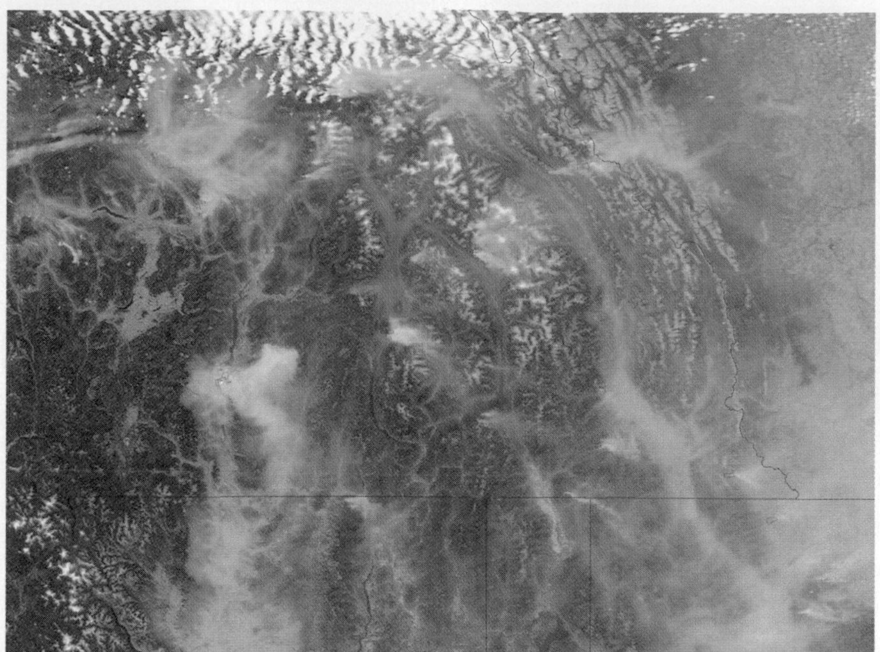

◄ **FIGURE 10.1 WILDFIRES AND SMOKE IN BRITISH COLUMBIA** A satellite image of southern British Columbia, showing major forest fires (red rectangles) and their plumes of smoke. The area shown in this image is 600 km across. *(Image courtesy of MODIS Rapid Response Project at NASA/GSFC)*

▲ **FIGURE 10.2 THE OKANAGAN MOUNTAIN FIRE** The Okanagan Mountain fire in southern British Columbia in August and September 2003 was the most damaging of nearly 2500 wildfires that burned in southern British Columbia that summer. Dry fuel, high winds, and low humidity hampered efforts to contain the fire, which burned for three weeks, destroyed hundreds of homes, and caused more than $250 million in damage. Nearly 45,000 people, one-third of Kelowna's residents, were evacuated from their homes, and in a single night, 239 houses in the city were lost. *(© 2003 Kevin Davies/AAA Photography)*

The wildfires in British Columbia in 2003 pointed out some fundamental principles involved in living with this natural hazard: First, large wildfires require abundant fuel; second, wildfires are becoming more disastrous because more and more people are moving into scrublands and forest lands at the *rural-urban interface*; and third, our fire management policies need to be reevaluated to minimize future damage by wildfires.

10.1 Introduction to Wildfire

Wildfire is an ancient phenomenon, dating back more than 350 million years to the time trees evolved and spread across the land. Grasses appeared about 20 million years ago, providing fuel for other types of wildfire. Much more recently, at the end of Pleistocene Epoch, the climate became warmer and perhaps drier than it is today, leading to a marked increase in wildfires, at least in the Northern Hemisphere.[2] The geologic record shows a significant increase in the amount of charcoal in sediment dating from the first several thousand years of the Holocene Epoch in western North America, indicating high wildfire frequency at this time. Part of this increase may be due to humans' use of fire to clear land and assist in hunting.[3,4,5]

After a fire, colonizing plants become established on the burned landscape. The vegetation goes through a post-fire cycle from early colonization to a mature ecosystem adapted to the climate at that particular location and particular time. This cycle, which operates today, is so ancient that some plants have evolved to rely on and use fire to their advantage. For example, oak and redwood trees have bark that resists fire damage, and some species of pine trees have seed cones that open only after a fire. Native eucalyptus trees in southeast Australia, which is regularly swept by bush fires in summer, sprout new leaves after the trees are charred. Often within a year or two, the "bush" has grown back to such an extent that it's not easy to see where it had burned.

Natural fires started by lightning strikes and volcanic eruptions allowed early humans to harness fire for heat, light, and cooking. The benefits of fire allowed humans to broaden their diet, settle in colder areas, and spread across all continents except Antarctica.[4] Aboriginal peoples used fire as a tool in hunting, warfare, and agriculture. Early Europeans commented on the many fires set by Aboriginal peoples for a variety of purposes. This practice continues today in parts of the world, occasionally with serious negative consequences (see Case Study 10.1).

10.2 Wildfire as a Process

Wildfire is a self-sustaining, rapid, high temperature biochemical oxidation reaction that releases heat, light, carbon dioxide, and other products.[4,5] During a wildfire, plant tissue and other organic material is rapidly oxidized by combustion, or burning. Grasslands, scrublands, and forest lands burn because, over long periods, these systems establish a balance between carbon production and decomposition. Plants remove carbon dioxide from the atmosphere by photosynthesis and temporarily sequester carbon in their tissues. Microbes alone do not decompose plant material fast enough to balance the addition of carbon through continued plant growth. Wildfires help to restore this balance. In this simplified view of wildfire, carbon dioxide, water vapour, and heat are released when plants burn. The combustion process, however, is complex—numerous chemical compounds are released in solid, liquid, and gaseous form. Common trace gases include nitrogen oxides, carbonyl sulphide, carbon monoxide, methyl chloride, and hydrocarbons, such as methane.[9] These gases, along with solid particles of ash and soot, form the smoke observed during a wildfire. Both ash and soot are powdery residues that accumulate after burning. Ash consists primarily of mineral compounds and soot is made of unburned carbon.

Flames and smoke provide an accurate mental picture of wildfire, but they do not capture fire's complexity. Wildfires have three phases, all of which operate continuously:[5] (1) pre-ignition, (2) combustion, and (3) extinction.

In the first or **pre-ignition** phase, vegetation is brought to a temperature and water content at which it can ignite and burn. Pre-ignition involves two processes, preheating and pyrolysis.

As vegetation is *preheated*, it looses a great deal of water and other volatile chemical compounds. A volatile compound is one that is easily vaporized. Gasoline, for example, contains many volatile chemical compounds and, when spilled, evaporates quickly to a gas that you can smell.

The other important process of pre-ignition is **pyrolysis**, which literally means "heat divided." Pyrolysis is actually a group of processes that chemically degrade the preheated fuel. Degradation takes place as heat splits large hydrocarbon molecules into smaller ones. Products of pyrolysis include volatile gases, mineral ash, tars, and carbonaceous char.[10] Pyrolysis takes place when you scorch a piece of toast, turning it black. The burnt toast is covered with char, and smoke coming out of the toaster contains small black droplets of tar. A similar thing happens when you scorch cotton fabric with a hot iron.

The two processes of pre-ignition—preheating and pyrolysis—operate continuously in a wildfire. Heat radiating from flames causes both preheating and pyrolysis in advance of the fire. These processes produce the first fuel gases that ignite in the next phase of the fire.

The second phase of a wildfire, **combustion**, begins with ignition and marks the start of a set of processes that are completely different from those related to pre-ignition. Pre-ignition processes absorb energy, whereas combustion involves external reactions that liberate energy in the form of heat and light.[5] Ignition does not necessarily lead to a wildfire. In fact, ignitions, both natural and human-caused, are far more numerous than full-blown wildfires. Wildfires develop only when the vegetation is dry and has accumulated in sufficient quantities to carry fire across the land.[10]

Once an area has burned, the low fuel supply prevents future wildfires. Fire will not threaten again until there is sufficient new fuel. These facts are contrary to past fire-management philosophy that only people can prevent forest fires. On ecologically important time scales—several decades to centuries—fires will occur whether people start them or not; the role of humans in triggering large wildfires is secondary to that of lightning.

Most people think that a wildfire involves a single ignition. Actually, the process is more complex. Ignition repeats time and time again as a fire moves across the land, like sparks and embers popping out of a fireplace, campfire, or barbecue grill. The dominant types of combustion are flaming combustion and glowing or smouldering combustion (Figure 10.3). These two types of combustion differ in that they proceed by different chemical reactions and have different appearances. Flaming combustion is the rapid, high-temperature conversion of fuel to thermal energy by oxidation reactions. It leaves a large amount of residual unburned material. This form of combustion sustains flames as the fire advances across the landscape. As volatile gases are removed from the fuel, woody material continues to burn, but the amount of fuel is less and ash begins to cover new fuel. The ash is noncombustible and may hinder flaming combustion. These processes lead to glowing or smouldering combustion, which can take place at lower temperatures and does not require rapid pyrolysis.

Three primary processes control the transfer of heat as a wildfire moves across the land: *conduction,* which is the transmission of heat through molecular contact; *radiation,* heat transfer by electromagnetic waves; and *convection,* heat transfer by the movement of heated gases driven by

10.1 CASE STUDY

Indonesian Fires of 1997–1998

Severe wildfires on the islands of Borneo and Sumatra during 1997 and 1998 bought international attention to Indonesia (Figure 10.A). Many of the fires were deliberately set to clear land, but they were made worse by a long drought caused by a strong El Niño event. The fires spread rapidly during the 1997 dry season and by September were beyond firefighters' control.[6] Although some rain fell in November, dry conditions returned in late 1997 and the fires raged again in early 1998. They were not extinguished until May 1998, when the drought finally broke and heavy rains fell. Over the two-year period, the wildfires burned between 80,000 km^2 and 100,000 km^2 of forest, an area larger than the province of New Brunswick.[7]

The wildfires released so much smoke that Indonesia, Malaysia, and Singapore were blanketed in what was euphemistically called "haze." The smoke reached as far north as southern Thailand and the Philippines (Figure 10.A), causing health and economic problems throughout the region. Visibility in parts of Indonesia, Malaysia, and Singapore was reduced to less than 50 m,[6] and many people were forced to wear masks to protect themselves from the smoke. In the most severely affected areas, people developed chronic respiratory, eye, and skin ailments; schools and businesses were forced to close for days to weeks; and many people died prematurely because of the pollution.[8] Low visibility is thought to have been partly responsible for the crash of a Garuda Airlines jet into a mountainside in northern Sumatra, killing all 236 people on board. The fires released about 2.57 Gt (gigatonnes) of carbon dioxide, equal to about 40 percent of the average annual emissions of CO_2 from all sources, including consumption of fossil fuels.

The fires also harmed Borneo's orangutans. Some orangutans, forced out of the forest by the fires, were killed by villagers when they raided fields for food. Large areas of the orangutans' preferred habitat were burned, forcing them to adapt to poorer conditions.[8]

The fires caused economic losses of $10 billion, including health care costs and lost tourism revenues in Indonesia. Malaysia and Singapore suffered declines in industrial production and lost tourism revenues, making the problem political.[8] Economic concerns aside, the effects of the wildfires on tropical forest ecosystems, biodiversity, and the atmosphere were so severe that some observers called them a global natural disaster.

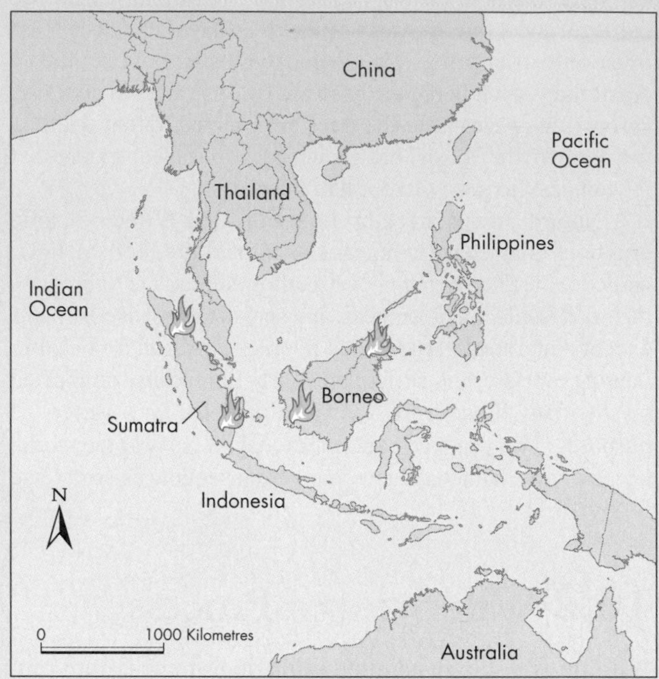

▲ **FIGURE 10.A INDONESIAN WILDFIRES OF 1997–1998** A map showing the locations of the disastrous wildfires in Indonesia in 1997–1998. The worst fires were on the islands of Borneo and Sumatra.

So what caused these fires to rage out of control? Rain forests cover most of Indonesia's 13,500 islands, but they are generally damp, and fire is uncommon in them. For thousands of years, farmers have used slash-and-burn methods to clear land for cultivation. More recently, large companies have employed the same methods on a much larger scale, and oil, lumber, and mining companies have used fire to clear land for development. In all of these cases, the intention is to burn only the land that is needed. However, in 1997, a severe drought caused by a strong El Niño caused the set fires to spark much larger wildfires that could not be contained. This was the fifth time that wildfires had become unmanageable in Indonesia since El Niño-related fires in 1983.

temperature differences in a liquid or gas. Wildfires transfer heat mainly by convection, although radiation also plays a role. Convective and radiant heating by the fire increases the surface temperature of the fuel. As heat is released, air and other gases become less dense and rise. The rising air removes both heat and combustion products from the zone of flaming. This process shapes the fire as it pulls in the fresh air required to sustain combustion.[5]

Finally, **extinction** is the point at which combustion, including smouldering, ceases. A fire is considered extinct when it no longer has sufficient heat and fuel to sustain combustion.

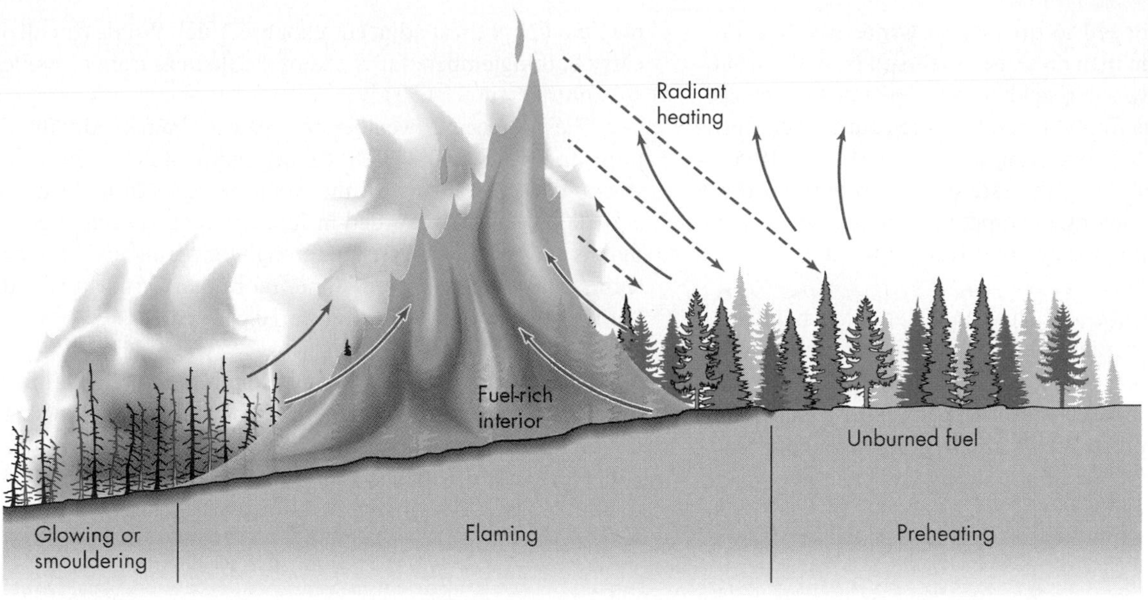

▲ **FIGURE 10.3 PARTS OF A WILDFIRE** Schematic diagram of an advancing wildfire showing its three phases: (1) an unburned area where vegetation is being preheated, (2) an area of flaming combustion with rising air currents, and (3) an area of glowing or smouldering combustion. The fire is advancing from left to right. Solid arrows indicate the motion of the air, and dashed lines show radiant heating from the fire. *(Modified after Ward, D. 2001. Combustion chemistry and smoke. In Forest fires: Behavior and ecological effects, eds. E. A. Johnson and K. Miyanishi, pp. 55–77, Chapter 3. San Diego, CA: Academic Press)*

Fire Environment

The behaviour of a large wildfire can be explained by three factors: fuel, topography, and weather. With sufficient information about these three factors, we can understand and predict wildfire behaviour.[10,11]

Fuel Wildfire fuels are complex and differ in type, size, quantity, arrangement, and moisture content. Types of fuel include leaves, woody debris and decaying material on the forest floor, grasses, mosses, ferns, shrubs, small and large living trees, and standing dead or dying trees. Smaller, finer fuels burn most readily and most vigorously, but large woody materials also contribute to fires. If disease or a storm downs a large number of trees, the wood will eventually dry and decay, allowing it to more easily burn during a wildfire. Fuel arrangement can also be important. Forests may consist of trees that are relatively uniformly spaced or that differ considerably in spacing. Most forests have one or more canopies of trees at different heights, as well as shrubs and other plants on the ground. In contrast, some forests may have little ground cover. The density of the trees in a forest is also important. Dense stands of lodgepole and jack pine in parts of temperate North America and stands of spruce forming the vast boreal forest of Canada and Eurasia contain abundant fuel and easily sustain wildfires once they start (Figure 10.4).

Topography Topography affects fire in several ways. First, in the Northern Hemisphere, south-facing slopes are relatively warm and dry, and fuel on these slopes has a lower moisture content and burns more readily than fuel on north-facing

◄ **FIGURE 10.4 CONIFEROUS FOREST** This mixed forest of lodgepole pine and white spruce in northern British Columbia contains abundant fuel required to sustain a rapidly moving wildfire during dry, hot weather. *(US Photo Services Photo)*

slopes. Slopes exposed to prevailing winds also tend to have drier vegetation than do slopes sheltered from the wind. In mountainous areas, winds tend to move up or down canyons, providing easy paths for wildfires. Wildfires burning on steep slopes preheat fuel upslope from the flames (Figure 10.5c). This preheating increases the rate of movement and thus spreading of a fire moving upslope. Fires may also advance downslope, especially if they are driven by wind.[11]

Weather Weather exerts a strong influence on wildfires. Large wildfires are particularly common following droughts that reduce fuel moisture content. Fires spread more rapidly under hot, dry conditions when humidity is low than when the air is cool and moist. Winds greatly influence the spread, intensity, and form of a wildfire. Strong and changing winds help the fire preheat adjacent unburned fuel. Winds can also carry burning embers far ahead of the flaming front to ignite *spot fires* (Figure 10.5b).[11]

The influence of weather on fires was dramatically illustrated in Florida in 2001. By the beginning of 2001, the state was in the midst of one of the worst droughts in its history, and 800 fires were recorded in January alone. Drought conditions and wildfires persisted through the spring and into the summer. By the middle of June, more than 3500 fires had burned at least 1500 km^2 (Figure 10.6).[12]

Types of Fires Wildfire scientists and firefighters classify fire behaviour according to the layer of fuel that is allowing the fire to spread: surface or crown. Most wildfires involve both types of fire. **Surface fires** move close to the ground and

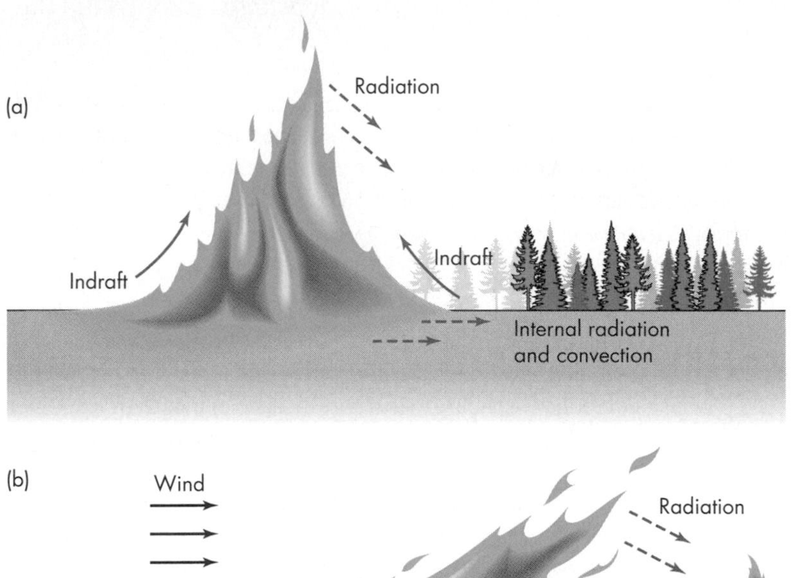

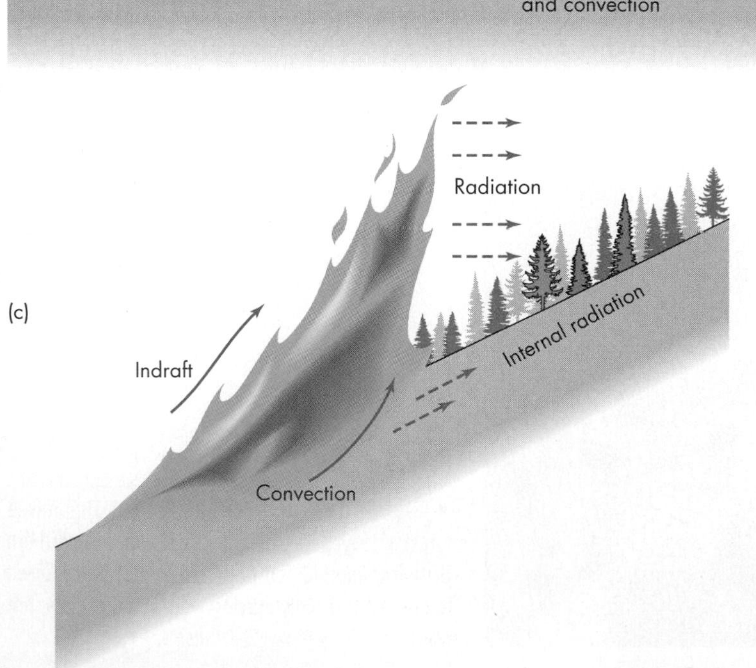

◄ **FIGURE 10.5 WILDFIRES ARE INFLUENCED BY WIND AND TOPOGRAPHY** Idealized diagrams of flame shape and processes associated with a spreading fire under three conditions: (a) flat ground and no wind, (b) flat ground with wind, and (c) a slope with wind driving the fire uphill. *(Modified after Rothermel, R. C. 1972. A mathematical model for predicting fire spread in wildland fuels. U.S. Forest Service Research Paper INT-10.5)*

involve shrubs, dead leaves, twigs, fallen trees, and grass (Figure 10.7). Some surface fires also burn the soil just under the ground surface (Figure 10.8). Surface fires differ greatly in their intensity. Low-intensity surface fires advance relatively slowly with glowing or smouldering combustion and limited flaming. Other surface fires, such as those in the scrublands of southern California and in the grasslands of Africa, can be extremely intense and release large amounts of heat as they move swiftly across the land (Figure 10.9). Some grass fires have been clocked at more than 300 m/min.[13] **Crown fires** move rapidly through the forest canopy by flaming combustion (Figure 10.10). *Intermittent crown fires* consume the tops of some trees, whereas *continuous crown* fires consume the tops of all or most of the trees. Crown fires are common in the mixed coniferous forests of western North America and the vast boreal forests of Canada and Siberia. They can be fed by surface fires that move up stems into the limbs of trees, or they can spread independently of surface fires. Large crown fires are generally driven by strong winds and can be aided by steep slopes. Such fires will grow and expand as long as conditions for combustion are favourable. They can advance at rates of up to 100 m/min and can also spread by throwing out fire brands that can be carried by the wind to start new fires up to several kilometres from the fire front.[11] Large wind-driven crown fires are nearly impossible to stop; people and animals must evacuate threatened areas.

▲ **FIGURE 10.6 DROUGHT CONTRIBUTES TO FLORIDA WILDFIRES** In the first half of 2001, about 3500 wildfires burned more than 1500 km^2 of Florida. Such roads as this had to be closed and people evacuated. *(Charlotte Sun)*

◀ **FIGURE 10.7 HIGH-INTENSITY SURFACE FIRE** A surface fire in a ponderosa pine forest burns shrubs and the lower storey of the forest. *(Kent & Donna Dennen/Photo Researchers, Inc.)*

◀ **FIGURE 10.8 LOW-INTENSITY SURFACE FIRE** This surface fire is burning soil and some surface vegetation and is characterized by smouldering and glowing combustion. *(Dr. Florian Siegert/Remote Sensing Solutions GmbH)*

◄ **FIGURE 10.9 SURFACE FIRE IN A GRASSLAND** A surface fire in the western United States. Wildfires can spread rapidly in grasslands when driven by strong winds. *(Mark Thiessen/National Geographic Image Collection)*

10.3 Effects of Wildfires and Linkages with Other Natural Hazards

Wildfires affect many aspects of the local environment: they burn vegetation, harm wildlife, release smoke into the atmosphere, char soil, increase erosion and runoff, and cause landslides.

Effects on the Geological Environment

Wildfires affect soils differently depending on the type and moisture content of the soil and the duration and intensity of the fire. The amount and intensity of precipitation after a fire also influence how a wildfire affects soil.[14]

Hot fires that scorch dry, coarse soil may leave a near-surface, water-repellent layer, called a *hydrophobic layer*. Water repellency is caused by the accumulation of chemicals derived from burning vegetation.[5] The water-repellent layer increases surface runoff and erosion because the burned surface lacks vegetation to hold the loose soil above the layer. Water flows over a hydrophobic soil layer, much as rain runs off a water-repellent raincoat. Soil above the hydrophobic layer quickly becomes saturated during rains and may wash downslope.[15] Hydrophobic layers may persist in soils for several years following a fire.

Heavy rains can significantly increase the incidence of erosion and landslides in burned areas. Wildfires in California in 1997 denuded vegetation from steep slopes just before the winter rains. Of 25 burned areas mapped by the U.S. Geological Survey, 10 produced debris flows during the first winter storm.[16] Sediment washed from the burned slopes choked swollen streams and rivers (see Case Study 10.2).

◄ **FIGURE 10.10 CONTINUOUS CROWN FIRE** Crown fires spread rapidly in the upper canopy of coniferous forests. They may move ahead of the fire on the surface. In 1995, high winds turned this crown fire, on Mount Lemmon outside Tucson, Arizona, into a firestorm. *(A. T. Willett/Alamy Images)*

10.2 CASE STUDY

Wildfires in Canada

Wildfires are a significant agent of change in the vast Canadian forest. They have played a major role in forming and maintaining the boreal forest ecosystem. Large fires in Canada have high rates of fuel consumption, spread rapidly, and release large amounts of energy. The standard measure of fire intensity in the Canadian Forest Fire Behaviour Prediction System is the energy release per unit length of fire front, measured in kilowatts per metre (kW/m). Typical fire intensities are 100 kW/m for surface fires, 2000 kW/m for intermittent crown fires, and 10,000 kW/m or more for continuous crown fires.[13] By one estimate, the amount of energy released annually by fires in Canada is enough to supply the electricity needs of the entire country for six months.[13]

On average, 8000 fires burn 2.5 million ha of forest in Canada each year. Only 3 percent of wildfires in Canada are larger than 200 ha, but these fires are responsible for 97 percent of the total area burned. The number of fires and the area burned differ widely across the country and from year to year; the largest total area burned, some 7.5 million ha, was in 1989 (Table 10.1). In comparison, Canada has about 400 million ha of

TABLE 10.1 Total Forest Land Burned in Canada, 1970–2004 (in km²)

Year	Atlantic Canada	Quebec	Ontario	Man.	Sask.	Alberta	B.C.	YT and NWT	Canada[1]
1970	112	312	227	371	5318	524	1056	1885	10,588
1971	45	2621	420	85	862	631	3513	7054	16,951
1972	504	1053	320	187	2068	493	261	2911	7802
1973	117	30	36	234	2386	107	334	8572	11,844
1974	561	30	5239	1612	260	184	210	387	8486
1975	1802	171	169	233	950	58	243	6690	10,317
1976	2187	569	5441	1281	910	225	570	6952	18,138
1977	42	319	4163	2316	1301	157	38	5989	14,379
1978	83	65	75	246	927	78	501	864	2892
1979	346	32	637	824	2297	1946	294	19,965	27,007
1980	46	316	5603	5143	13,488	6272	656	13,452	47,767
1981	140	25	1795	3762	16,480	13,656	1066	10,201	53,931
1982	117	80	39	154	646	6884	3487	5570	17,063
1983	194	2389	4437	992	522	28	674	2698	11,942
1984	91	31	1204	1302	3212	790	199	610	7654
1985	1566	27	10	118	1101	129	2346	2199	7552
1986	1493	1972	1456	103	132	27	169	4123	9501
1987	190	368	756	1695	2265	361	345	4874	10,856
1988	41	2757	3907	4857	811	145	115	724	13,361
1989	692	21,095	4039	35,679	4705	64	254	9059	75,596
1990	546	833	1837	164	1873	340	758	2742	9344
1991	700	4383	3188	1273	2394	62	247	3582	15,847
1992	81	271	1760	4575	970	35	305	671	8687
1993	280	1282	1047	673	6606	261	52	9447	19,677
1994	1114	1160	835	14,288	9949	296	303	34,251	62,960
1995	17	7277	6124	8892	13,870	3361	481	30,858	70,951
1996	849	6916	4488	1253	97	20	150	4777	18,549
1997	98	3931	385	418	39	47	19	1367	6307
1998	410	4183	1583	4506	9610	7270	437	18,145	46,143
1999	424	977	3283	1105	1737	1205	117	7399	6246
2000	1496	392	67	1109	1410	147	177	1855	6653
2001	24	331	107	789	1843	1541	97	1290	16,264
2002	361	10,138	1721	946	8790	4965	86	628	27,704
2003	380	879	3142	5479	1266	745	2647	1766	17,434
2004	30	30	16	260	2589	2361	2205	22,359	31,838

Note: Areas in hectares can be calculated by multiplying values in table by 100.

[1]Includes areas burned in national parks, which are not listed separately under provinces and territories.

Source: Data are based on Canadian Council of Forest Ministers, National Forestry Database Program. 2006. 3.1 Forest Fire Statistics by Province/Territory/Agency, 1970–2005, Table B. Area burned. http://nfdp.ccfm.org/compendium/data/2006_10/tables/com31e.htm. *Accessed November 12, 2006.*

10.2 CASE STUDY (*Continued*)

forested land, which is about 10 percent of the world's forests.[13] About 1 million ha are harvested each year.

On average, lightning strikes cause about 45 percent of the forest fires in Canada, but they result in 85 percent of the total area burned.[17] Typically, lightning-caused fires occur in remote areas where detection is more difficult and wildfires are not fought as aggressively as in populated regions. People are responsible for the remaining 55 percent of forest fires in Canada. Most of these fires result from recreational, residential, and industrial activities, but more than 10 percent of human-caused fires are intentionally set.

The Canadian Forest Service has nearly a century of data on forest fires. The data indicate that both the number of forest fires and the total area burned were greater in the second half of the twentieth century than in the first half (Figure 10.B). The total area burned began to increase in the late 1950s but has decreased slightly since about 1990. In comparison, in six separate years since 1980 new records have been set for the number of fires. The reasons for these differences are not clear, although climate change, population growth, and increased recreational and industrial use of wildlands could be factors.

Fire-suppression costs in Canada average approximately $400 million per year. Property damage averages more than $10 million per year. In comparison, forestry in Canada is a $60 billion per year industry.[17]

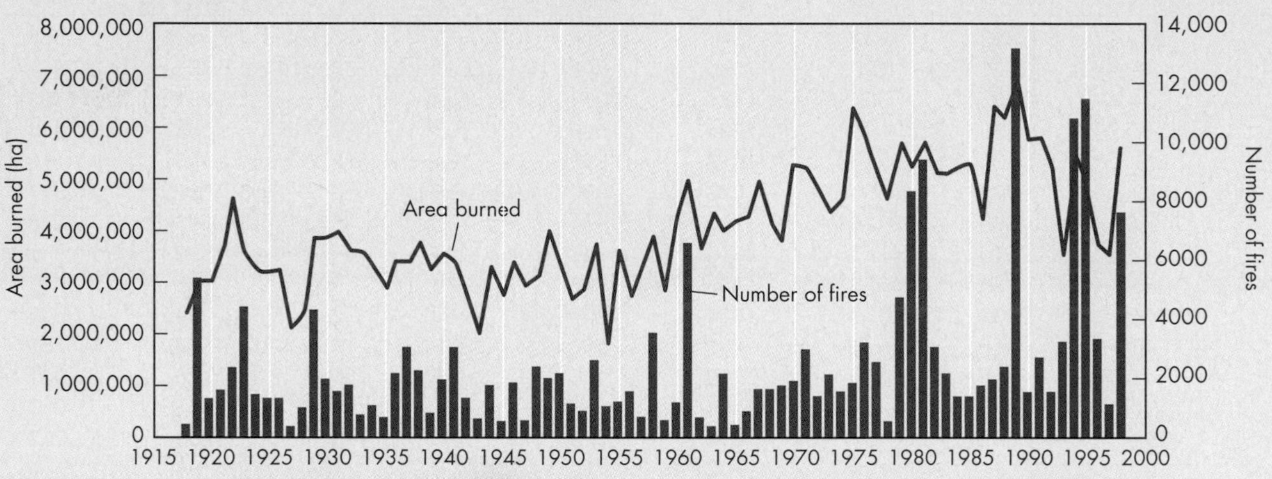

▲ **FIGURE 10.B ANNUAL VARIABILITY OF FOREST FIRES IN CANADA** The number of forest fires and total area burned in Canada have increased since the 1950s. *(Original map data provided by The Atlas of Canada, http://atlas.gc.ca/ © 2007. Produced under licence from Her Majesty the Queen in Right of Canada, with permission of Natural Resources Canada)*

Effects on the Atmosphere

Wildfires significantly increase the concentration of particulates in the atmosphere for weeks, even months (Figure 10.11). Increases of airborne particulates can be observed thousands of kilometres downwind of large, long-lasting fires. During the past decade, fires in Mexico, Guatemala, and other countries in Central America raised atmospheric particulates in some cities in the southern United States to levels exceeding Clean Air standards. Fires burning in Indonesia and Malaysia in 1997 and 1998 affected people in many other countries in the region (see Case Study 10.1).

Linkages with Climate Change

A possible consequence of climate warming expected later in this century is an increase in the intensity and frequency of wildfires brought about by changes in air temperature, precipitation, and the frequency of severe storms. Related biological changes may affect the type and quantity of fuel available for wildfires. Some of these changes may already be underway.

In late October 2003, wildfires in southern California burned about 6000 km^2 of forest and scrubland, destroyed several thousand homes, and killed 24 people. Twelve major fires started in a single week. Catastrophic "runaway" fires could not initially be contained by firefighters and spread rapidly to damage large areas (see Professional Profile). Autumn and winter are particularly hazardous seasons for wildfires in southern California. Hot, dry "Santa Ana" winds, which result from large-scale atmospheric circulation, produce dangerous conditions over all of southern California.[18,19]

Although the number of large wildfires in southern California hasn't changed significantly in the past few hundred years, their size and intensity and their effect on people certainly have. The population of southern California has doubled

◄ **FIGURE 10.11 SMOKE, GASES, AND PARTICULATES FROM WILDFIRES** Wildfires introduce large amounts of ash, soot, carbon dioxide, water vapour, and other gases into the atmosphere. *(CP Photo/Kelowna Daily Courier/Kip Frasz)*

PROFESSIONAL PROFILE

Bob Krans, Fire Division Chief

The Cedar fire in southern California began on October 25, 2003, when a lost hunter lit a signal fire in the Cleveland National Forest. By the time it was extinguished in November, the Cedar fire had become the worst fire in California history.

Bob Krans, fire division chief in Poway, California, had been in the firefighting business for 30 years and had never seen anything like it. "I saw conditions that I'd never seen before," Krans says. "It was extremely frustrating to deal with."

The smoke appeared orange because the blaze was lighting the smoke from within. Krans describes the fire as sounding like a freight train because of the strong accompanying wind, some of which was being generated by the fire itself because it was consuming huge amounts of oxygen.

Fighting a wildfire has hazards beyond the obvious ones of intense heat and quickly changing conditions. Krans says that firefighters near the blaze can suffer third-degree "steam burns" when the heat vaporizes the sweat inside their protective suits.

Krans recalls that the Cedar fire at times was consuming up to 5000 ha/h, whipped by winds blowing 105 km/h. At that rate, it is easy to observe the movement of the fire as it draws closer (Figure 10.C).

Although fire departments take extensive safety precautions, one firefighter perished and several others were badly injured while battling the Cedar fire when a second blaze closed off their escape route. The smoke can be so thick that vehicles require headlights and firefighters can become disoriented. "Daytime literally turns to nighttime," Krans notes.

—Chris Wilson

▲ **FIGURE 10.C FIRE DIVISION CHIEF BOB KRANS** Chief Krans examines the Cedar fire as it moves rapidly toward him. The fire reached the spot where Krans is standing in three minutes, destroying the house directly behind him. *(Photo courtesy of Chris Thompson, Poway Reserve firefighter)*

in the past 50 years, and fire suppression has increased natural fuels in forests and scrublands. As a result, the severity and intensity of fires are increasing, as are their human and ecological consequences.[18] The association of wildfire and Santa Ana winds is well known, but the exact timing of fires is controlled by rainfall during winter and the weather the summer before. The relation of the seasonal Santa Ana winds to projected climate warming has not been studied and isn't understood. However, if the trend toward drier, windier conditions in southern California continues, wildfires will likely become larger and more intense.[19,20]

The concentration of carbon dioxide in the atmosphere is expected to be twice the pre-Industrial Revolution value before the twenty-first century ends. Increases in temperature in most areas may make the wildfire hazard worse. For example, the climate of western North America from California to Alaska is likely to become warmer, drier, and windier—three factors that promote wildfires. Both the number and the intensity of wildfires will probably increase in this region. More property will be destroyed, more lives lost, and more floods and landslides will follow the fires. In addition, the costs of suppressing fires and of fire insurance will increase.[19] Similarly, warmer springs and summers over much of sub-Arctic Canada may increase the incidence of large wildfires in the boreal forest that covers much of this huge region.

Increases in fire frequency and intensity may also change the vegetation of semi-arid areas that presently have limited moisture. Grasslands will expand at the expense of dry coniferous forests in places like southern British Columbia and California. The boundary between the boreal forest and prairie grasslands in Canada may move north as climate warms and wildfires become more common.

Warmer and drier conditions can make trees more susceptible to beetle infestations, weakening them and rendering them more vulnerable to fire. An example is the current mountain pine beetle infestation in western Canada. Larvae of mountain pine beetle (*Dendroctonus ponderosae*) mature just inside the bark of lodgepole pine (*Pinus contorta*), an important forest tree in interior British Columbia, western Alberta, and southern Yukon Territory.[21,22] The adult beetles (Figure 10.12a) emerge from pine trees in early summer. After mating, the females lay their eggs in healthy trees. As the larvae develop, they mine the living part of the tree beneath the bark and eventually cut off the tree's supply of water and nutrients. The beetles also introduce a bluestain fungus that defeats the tree's natural defences against the attack by killing living cells in the inner bark and sapwood. The combination of larvae and fungus girdles and thus kills most affected trees. The beetle larvae can be killed by extreme and prolonged winter temperatures (–40°C) or by cold snaps of –25°C in

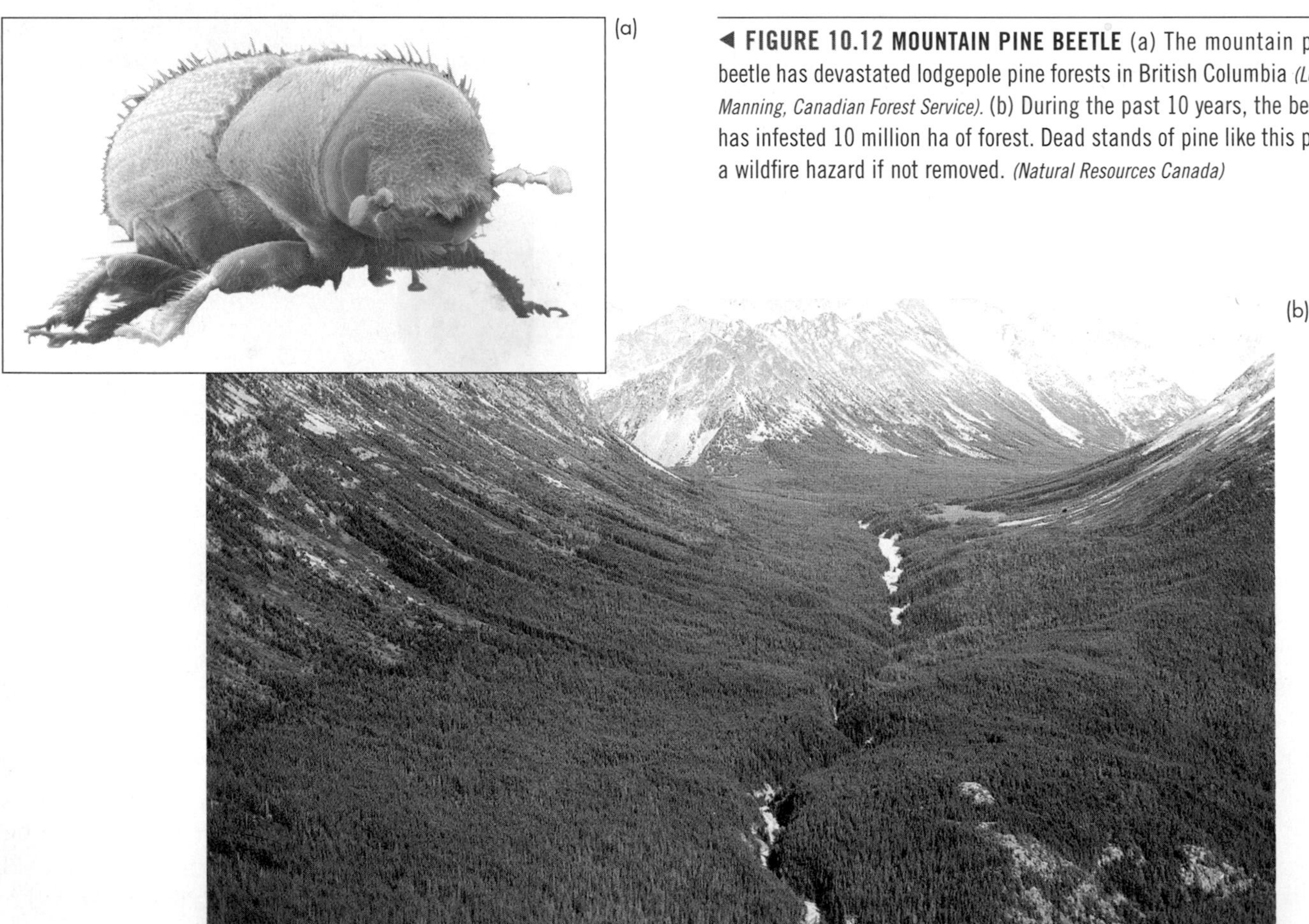

◄ **FIGURE 10.12 MOUNTAIN PINE BEETLE** (a) The mountain pine beetle has devastated lodgepole pine forests in British Columbia *(Leslie Manning, Canadian Forest Service)*. (b) During the past 10 years, the beetle has infested 10 million ha of forest. Dead stands of pine like this pose a wildfire hazard if not removed. *(Natural Resources Canada)*

early fall or late spring. However, over the past century, western Canada has warmed considerably, and large areas of lodgepole pine forest have not experienced such cold in more than a decade. Partly as a result of this warming, the mountain pine beetle has affected almost 10 million ha of forest; the most severe infestations are in central British Columbia, where up to 80 percent of all pines are expected to die within the next five years. The beetle has now spread into the Rocky Mountains of Alberta. The infestation may well be the largest ever recorded, and the extensive stands of dead trees (Figure 10.12b) are a serious fire hazard.

Other damaging insect infestations have occurred in western North America in recent years. Warmer temperatures on Alaska's Kenai Peninsula have led to a large infestation of another species of beetle there. An estimated 40 million trees have been killed in an area nearly three times the size of Prince Edward Island. As the trees die and desiccate, catastrophic wildfire will be much more likely.[19]

An increase in wildfires because of climate warming will affect human health. As mentioned previously, increases in airborne particulates from wildfires lower air quality and can harm people with breathing disorders. For example, wildfires in Florida in 1998 greatly increased the number of people seeking emergency treatment for asthma, bronchitis, and chest pain.[19]

10.4 Impacts of Wildfires

Fire affects people, property, companies, and the environments in a variety of ways. The level of impact depends largely on fire intensity and size. A large fire can result in town evacuations, road and airport closures, property loss, timber loss, habitat loss for some plants and animals, an increase in habitat for others, removal of the vegetation, and consumption of the forest floor.

Impacts on Plants and Animals

The effects of wildfire on plants and animals can be positive or negative depending on the type, size, location, and intensity of the fire. A wildfire reduces the number of individuals of each species of plant and animal living in the affected area, but the result may be beneficial to the community as a whole.

Vegetation Fire is an important element of many ecosystems. It temporarily reduces competition for moisture, nutrients, and light, allowing both the surviving and the new species to thrive, thus maintaining biodiversity. It maintains stand age diversity in forests by opening gaps in the canopy, allowing more sunlight to reach the forest floor. Fire also acts a regulator; where a fire has burned, the amount of fuel is reduced and the fire risk is decreased.

Fire triggers the release of seeds or stimulates flowering of species that depend on it for reproduction. Species with such reproductive adaptations live mainly in environments where fire is frequent. If wildfires were eliminated, these species would decrease and perhaps even disappear from these environments. Lodgepole pine and fireweed are examples of plants that require abundant sunlight and are common pioneer species after forest fires in North America. Lodgepole pine cones open after the tree has been burned, and the seeds germinate in the well-lit soils. Grasslands also require periodic fire to maintain themselves. Fire is also important to ecosystems as a whole. Following a fire, colonization and replacement of species follows a regular pattern known as *secondary succession*.

Fire increases the nutrient content of a soil, leaving an accumulation of carbon on the surface in the form of ash. If the ash is not removed by erosion, it forms a nutrient reservoir that is beneficial to local plants. Fires can also reduce populations of soil microorganisms, which may benefit the plants that compete with them for nutrients. Some microorganisms are parasites or carry diseases.[5]

Humans and Animals Timely evacuations have greatly reduced the number of deaths from wildfires in North America, but several large fires caused by land clearing and slash burning killed many people in the nineteenth century. A wildfire in 1825 burned more than 1,214,000 ha of forest in New Brunswick and Maine, killing 160 people. Another fire in 1871 in Wisconsin and Michigan charred more than 1 million ha and claimed 1500 lives. Ten years later, in 1881, a fire in eastern Michigan burned more than 400,000 ha and killed 169 people.[23]

Rains have a much greater erosive impact on an area after a fire. For example, in May 1996, a 48 km^2 fire burned two of the watersheds that supply drinking water for Denver, Colorado. Two months after the fire, a storm caused flooding that delivered large amounts of floating debris and high concentrations of manganese to the reservoir from which Denver draws its water. Two years after the fire, water quality was still poorer than it had been before the fire.[16]

Smoke and haze produced by fires can harm human health (see Case Study 10.1). As mentioned previously, exposure to smoke and haze produces eye, respiratory, and skin problems. Firefighters and others who have experienced prolonged exposure to smoke can experience chronic, sometimes fatal, respiratory problems.

Wildfire can, of course, destroy personal property. More and more people are living in densely vegetated areas at the fringes of cities. As a result, property losses because of wildfires are increasing dramatically. When a wildfire occurs in scrubland or forest near Victoria, Los Angeles, or Sydney, Australia, thousands of homes may be at risk.

Large intense wildfires can kill even the fastest-running animals, but animals generally are able to escape advancing fire. Even rodents have a good chance of survival because the ground in which they take refuge is a good insulator. Fish and other aquatic species may suffer from increased sedimentation, and stream temperatures may increase because plants along their banks have been destroyed.[14] However, many species of birds, insects, reptiles, and mammals benefit from wildfire (Case Study 10.3). Forest fires produce open areas suited for grazing mammals, including deer, moose, and bison, while maintaining grasslands required by some birds and rodents.

10.3 CASE STUDY

Yellowstone Fires of 1988

Because wildfires benefit ecosystems, many scientists believe that natural fires in forested areas should not be suppressed. In 1976 officials in Yellowstone National Park in Wyoming and Montana instituted a policy of allowing natural fires to burn in areas of the park managed as wilderness, provided they did not endanger human life, threaten visitor areas, such as Old Faithful, or spread to areas outside the park. Any human-caused fire, however, would be extinguished immediately. Before the summer of 1988, the worst fire in the park's history had burned only about 100 km^2 of forest. This figure stands in stark contrast to almost 3000 km^2 of forest consumed during the 1988 fire season, nearly one-third of Yellowstone's total area. The 1988 fires led to a major controversy over the National Park Service natural-burn policy.

The problem started when lightning strikes ignited 50 fires in the park in the early summer of 1988. Twenty-eight of the 50 fires were allowed to burn according to the natural-burn policy. These fires quickly expanded under the hot, dry, summer conditions, fuelled by high winds in mid-July. On July 17, Yellowstone officials bowed to political pressure and sent fire crews in to fight one of the natural fires. Within four days, many natural fires in and around Yellowstone were being fought, but it was clear that they were beyond the control of the crews. The fires did not slow until September 10, when rains fell throughout the area. Snows in November finally extinguished the flames.

Yellowstone's natural-burn policy was severely criticized during and after the 1988 fires. Although most scientists agree that fire is good for the natural environment, it was difficult for people to sit and watch the park burn. Eventually, 9500 firefighters were deployed at a cost of US$120 million dollars. Critics claimed that the fires would not have been so big if park officials had fought them from the beginning. Others argued, however, that the fires would not have been so severe if prior fire-suppression policies hadn't allowed fuel to accumulate to dangerous levels in the area. Post-fire studies in Yellowstone and elsewhere have shown that natural wildfires are beneficial to the environment (Figure 10.D). Yellowstone park officials still adhere to a natural-burn policy. This policy is correct because Yellowstone's ecosystems have, through geologic time, adapted to and become dependent on wildfire. The fires of 1988 did not destroy the park; on the contrary, they revitalized ecosystems through natural transformations that cycle energy and nutrients through solids, plants, and animals.

▲ **FIGURE 10.D RENEWAL AFTER FIRE** Fireweed and young conifers have become established on a burned landscape in southwest Yukon Territory. *(John J. Clague)*

10.5 Fire Management

The danger that wildfire poses to humans and property is minimized through *fire management*. The elimination of wildfire is not possible, nor is it economically feasible or ecologically desirable. A wildfire, however, cannot be allowed to run its natural course when it threatens lives, property, or valuable resources. The aim of fire management is to control wildfires for the benefit of ecosystems while preventing them from harming people and destroying property.

The fire season in Canada extends from April through October, whereas in parts of the United States, it is nearly year-round. In Canada, there typically is no winter wildfire activity, a flurry of spring fires after the snow melts, followed by a decline as forests green up in early summer, a peak of fires in mid-summer, and then decreasing activity in the fall. Characteristics of Canada's environment, society, and geography that have shaped fire management include (1) a sparse population concentrated along the U.S. border, (2) large areas with few roads, (3) both high- and low-value property and resources to protect, (4) limited, high-cost labour, (5) excellent technological infrastructure, (6) a short fire season, and (7) typical stand-replacing fires.[24]

Fire management in Canada is a provincial and territorial responsibility, except on federal lands. Fourteen provincial and territorial agencies set their own fire policies depending on local and regional fire regimes, forest types, and infrastructure at risk. Funding for fire management in Canada comes from general tax revenues, timber sale revenues, or levies based on land ownership.

The main elements of fire management in North America are scientific research, data collection, education, and fire suppression, including the use of prescribed burns.

Science Scientific research on wildfire and, especially, the role of fire in ecosystems is critical to fire management; we cannot manage what we do not understand. Further research is needed to better understand the **fire regime**, or pattern of fire activity of an area, including, for example, (1) the types of fuel present in plant communities, (2) typical fire behaviour, characterized by the size and intensity of the fire and the amount of biomass removed, and (3) the fire history of the area, including fire frequency and size. Reconstruction of natural fire histories is difficult in many areas because fires have been suppressed for nearly 100 years.[25,26] Nevertheless, fire management is more likely to be successful if fire regimes can be defined for specific ecosystems.

Data Collection Remote sensing has become an important tool for fire management. Satellite imagery, for example, is now routinely used to map vegetation and determine fire potential (Figure 10.13). Since the early 1990s, the U.S. Geological Survey, in cooperation with the National Oceanographic and Atmospheric Administration (NOAA), has prepared weekly and biweekly maps of parts of the contiguous United States and Alaska illustrating vegetation cover and biomass production. The maps, combined with field measurements of the moisture content of vegetation, are an invaluable resource for fire managers. A management tool called the Fire Potential Index was developed in the United States to characterize the fire potential of forests, rangelands, and grasslands. It takes into account the total amount of burnable plant material, or fuel load, the water content of dead vegetation, and the percentage of the fuel load that is living vegetation. Regional and local fire-potential maps are prepared daily in a geographic information system (GIS) to help land managers develop plans to minimize the threat of fires.

Education Public education is an integral part of fire management. People should be taught about wildfire and what they can do to minimize their personal risk.

Fire Suppression For the past century, fire management in Canada and the United States has been guided by a policy of wildfire suppression, mainly to protect human interests. Four principles underlie fire suppression in Canada: (1) reliance on information about fire danger, risk assessment, and resource allocation; (2) reliance on equipment, including vehicles, pumps and hoses, and communications; (3) reliance on aircraft to detect and suppress fires and to transport firefighters; and (4) rapid mobilization, both within and across agencies. Fire suppression is a provincial and territorial responsibility in Canada. A typical provincial or territorial fire management agency has four components.[24] An executive unit prepares plans and budgets and evaluates fire programs, such as for prevention, suppression, and training. A strategic unit monitors fire danger and fire activity, deploys resources across the agency, and authorizes interagency movement of resources.

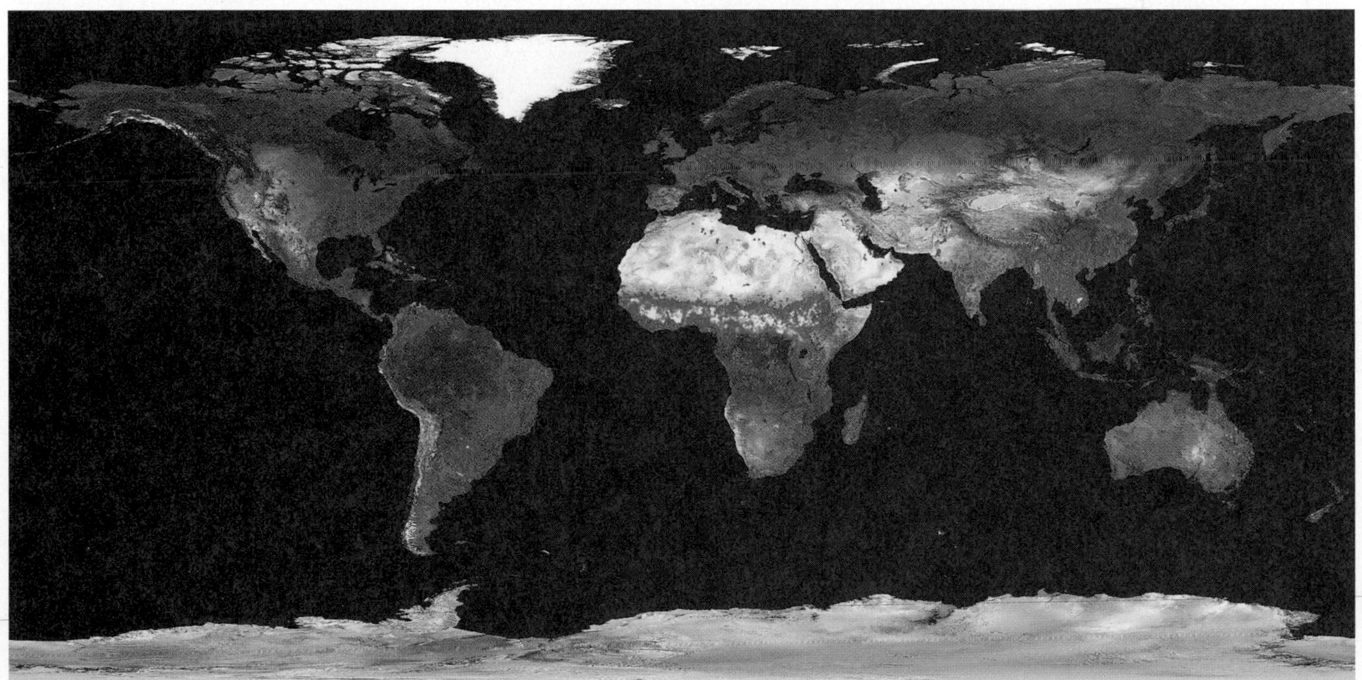

▲ **FIGURE 10.13 GLOBAL FIRE MAP** A map showing fires detected by the MODIS sensor on the Terra satellite from January 1 to 10, 2006. Each coloured dot is a location where MODIS detected at least one fire during the 10-day period. Colour ranges from red where the number of fires is small to yellow where the count is large. NASA has produced 10-day composite global fire maps like this since 2000. *(NASA)*

A management unit is responsible for day-to-day activities, including readiness, detection, and initial attack dispatches. An operational unit transports crews and equipment to fires, provides logistical support, and is directly responsible for fire suppression. A common operational practice is to steer the fire into an area with no fuel, termed a *fire break*. Natural fire breaks include rivers, lakes, and roads. Where no natural fire breaks exist, one can be made by using bulldozers to create a corridor through scrub or forest or by burning ahead of the fire.

Reliance on fire suppression in North America has led to a buildup of fuel in forests and an increased potential for large, high-intensity fires. One way to counter the buildup of fuel is to ignite controlled fires, also termed **prescribed burns**. The use of prescribed burns for forest management is not new; such fires have been used for years as an alternative to total fire suppression.[26]

The purpose of controlled burning is to reduce the amount of fuel in forests and thus the likelihood of a catastrophic wildfire.[16] Fire ecologists have found that more-frequent, smaller fires result in fewer large, dangerous fires.

Each prescribed burn has a written plan that outlines the objectives, where and how it will be carried out, under whose authority, and how the burn will be monitored and evaluated. Those in charge of a prescribed burn take on a great deal of responsibility—they have to predict the natural behaviour of the fire and successfully keep it under control. They face the difficult task of predicting the fuel and weather conditions under which they can safely control the fire. Such factors as temperature, humidity, and wind all must be taken into account.

Changes in winds during a prescribed burn can have disastrous results. On May 4, 2000, fire managers lost control of a prescribed burn in Bandelier National Monument in New Mexico, when the winds unexpectedly changed direction. After two weeks, the fire had burned 190 km^2 of forest and was still uncontrolled. Fed by drought-parched pine forest and grassland, the fire eventually destroyed 280 homes and forced the evacuation of 25,000 people in the town of Los Alamos. The question asked after the flames had been extinguished was how could a controlled burn, ordered by the National Park Service itself, end up nearly destroying a town?

A formal review of the disaster called for changes in the Park Service's prescribed burning policy. The changes included a more careful analysis and review of burn plans, better coordination and cooperation among federal agencies in developing burn plans, and use of a standard checklist before setting a prescribed fire. These and other new policies have been instituted or are under development. The 1995 U.S. Federal Fire Policy was also reviewed and updated. Specific changes include emphasizing the role of science in developing and implementing fire-management programs.

Prescribed burn policies in populated parts of Canada are similar to those in the United States and have been similarly updated because of damaging wildfires in British Columbia, Ontario, Quebec, and New Brunswick. The situation is slightly different in forested areas in northern Canada, where the population is small and is concentrated in widely spaced towns. Prescribed burns are generally not done in these areas because wildfires caused by lightning strikes are allowed to burn unless towns or highways are threatened or valuable forest resources are at risk. Natural fires in these areas can be very large. In 2004, more than 4500 km^2 of forest in Yukon Territory and eastern Alaska burned (Figure 10.14). Some of these fires were allowed to burn themselves out; others, how-

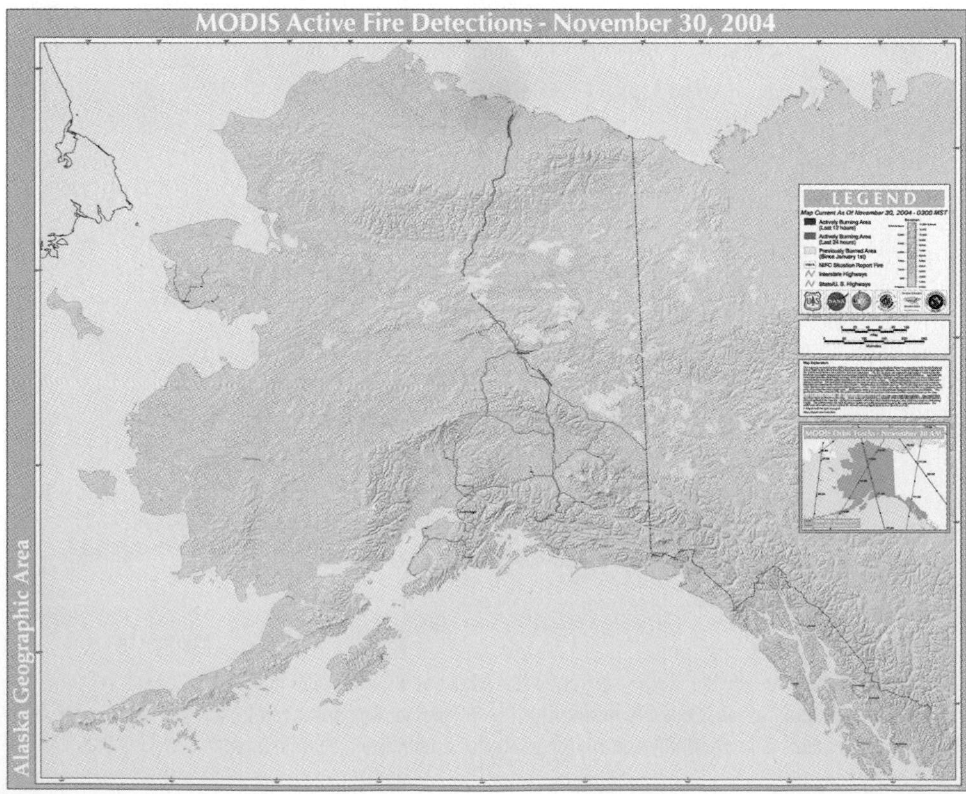

◀ **FIGURE 10.14 FIRES IN YUKON AND ALASKA** A map showing areas in Yukon Territory and Alaska that burned during the summer of 2004. Most of the wildfires occurred in wilderness areas and were allowed to burn. *(U.S. Department of Agriculture, Forest Service)*

ever, threatened small towns and mining operations and were vigorously fought.

In 2003, the U.S. Congress passed the Healthy Forests Restoration Act, a forest management plan with the stated objective of reducing large damaging wildfires by thinning trees on federal lands. The act reduces or limits the environmental review that is normally required for new logging projects. Those in support of the act state that the new management procedures will reduce the risk of catastrophic fires to towns in and around national forests, will save lives of forest residents and firefighters, and will protect wildlife, including threatened and endangered species. Those opposing the act counter that large-scale logging will occur far from communities at risk and will damage forests. They further argue that the best way to minimize risk from wildfires is by selectively removing vegetation around communities and homes and through education and planning.

10.6 Adjusting to the Wildfire Hazard

Perception of Wildfire Hazard

In general, people who live in seasonally hot and dry forested areas and scrublands do not fully appreciate the risk they face from wildfires.[27] Included in this group are hundreds of thousands of California residents. Wildfires occur every year in California, yet development continues on brush-covered hills. The demand for hillside property has raised property values in these areas, which means that the people whose property is most at risk from fire have paid a premium for the "privilege" of living there. Fire insurance and disaster assistance may worsen the situation—if people know their fire losses will be reimbursed by insurers or governments, they may conclude that there is no reason not to live where they choose, regardless of the risk. In the past century, hundreds of fires have burned scrublands and forests in California, and tens of thousands of homes and other structures have been destroyed. Yet, population and property values continue to increase in high-risk areas.

The result of this lack of understanding of wildfire risk was tragically illustrated in October 1991, when a wildfire destroyed about 3800 houses and apartments in the cities of Oakland and Berkeley (Figure 10.15). The fire killed 25 people and caused more than US$1.68 billion damage, making it one of the worst urban disasters in United States history.

The fire started on the evening of October 19, when flames escaped from a cooking fire in a camp of homeless people. Firefighters thought they had extinguished the fire and left the site around midnight. However, the next day was hot and windy, and embers left from the night before reignited the fire. Urbanization had reduced open land on the slopes above Berkeley and Oakland from 47 percent in 1939 to barely 20 percent in 1988. It also added fuel to the slopes, which previously were grass-covered with scattered oak and redwood trees. The additional fuel included numerous homes and non-native trees, mainly eucalyptus. When the fire reignited, it quickly became uncontrollable and firefighters could only evacuate residents. The fire moved through the urban landscape quickly; during the first hour it consumed a home every five seconds!

The Oakland wildfire was started by people, but other factors proved more important in making it a disaster: an ample fuel supply of buildings, brush, and trees, and hot, windy weather. Furthermore, from a fire-hazard perspective, land-use planning in the area was inadequate. Houses were not fire resistant, the density of buildings and the placement

◄ **FIGURE 10.15 KILLER WILDFIRE** A wildfire in the hills above Oakland, California, in 1991 devastated an entire neighbourhood, killing 25 people and destroying more than 2500 homes. *(Tom Benoit/Getty Images, Inc. Stone Allstock)*

of utilities were not regulated, and no rules required removal of excess vegetation from around buildings.[5]

Reducing Wildfire Risk

Wildfire risk can be reduced through education, codes and regulation, insurance, and evacuation.

Education Community awareness programs and presentations on fire safety in schools may help reduce the fire risk. Unfortunately, even with fire education programs, the risk may not seem "real" to many people who have never experienced a wildfire.

Codes and Regulations One way to reduce risk in fire-prone areas is to enact and enforce building codes that require structures be built with fire-resistant materials. For example, roofs of houses can be constructed with clay tiles instead of flammable cedar shingles or asphalt tiles. In seismically active areas, however, homes made with heavy clay tile roofs and masonry walls may not be safe during earthquakes. Making appropriate fire-resistant materials mandatory for new structures would significantly reduce the amount of damage caused by fires.

Fire Insurance Fire insurance allows people whose property has been destroyed by a fire to be reimbursed for part or all of their losses. However, as mentioned above, insurance may provide a false sense of security and prompt more people to live in fire-prone areas.

Evacuation Temporary evacuation of people from threatened areas is the most common response to wildfires. Evacuation ensures personal safety but does not protect homes and other fixed structures (see Survivor Story).

Reducing Fire Risk at Home

You can take actions to protect yourself from a fire (Table 10.2).[28,29] If you live or work in a forested area, you may want to acquire a book that describes how to prepare for a wildfire.[30]

TABLE 10.2 Reducing Your Fire Risk at Home

MAINTAIN HOME HEATING SYSTEMS

- Have your chimney and furnace regularly inspected and cleaned.
- Remove tree branches from above and around the chimney.

HAVE A FIRE SAFETY AND EVACUATION PLAN

- Install smoke alarms on every level of your home.
- Test them monthly and change the batteries at least once a year.
- Establish and practise fire evacuation plans.
- Mark your property with address signs that are clearly visible.
- Know which local emergency services are available and have those numbers posted.
- Maintain roads and driveways that are at least 3.7 m wide, with adequate turnaround space, so that emergency vehicles can access your home.

MAKE YOUR HOME FIRE RESISTANT

- Consider the use of fire-resistant roofing and building materials, such as stone, brick, concrete, and metal, when building or renovating a home.
- Keep roofs and eaves clear of leaves and other debris.
- Cover all exterior vents, attics, and eaves with metal mesh screens with openings no larger than 6 mm.
- Install multi-pane windows, tempered safety glass, or fireproof shutters to protect large windows from radiant heat.
- Use fire-resistant draperies.
- Keep tools for fire protection nearby: 30 m of garden hose, shovel, rake, ladder, and buckets.
- Make sure that water sources, such as hydrants and ponds, are accessible to the fire department.

LET THE LANDSCAPE AROUND YOUR HOME DEFEND YOU

- Trim grass on a regular basis up to 30 m around your home.
- Create defensible space by thinning trees and brush within 10 m of your home.
- Beyond 10 m, remove dead wood, woody debris, and low tree branches.
- Landscape your property with fire-resistant grasses and shrubs to prevent fire from spreading quickly.
- Stack firewood at least 10 m from your home and all secondary structures.
- Store flammable materials, liquids, and solvents in metal containers outside the home, at least 10 m from structures and wooden fences.

Source: Modified after Federal Emergency Management Agency. 1993. Wildfire: Are you prepared? FEMA Publication L-203. **www.usfa.fema.gov/downloads/pdf/publications/wildfire.pdf**. *Accessed November 2, 2006.*

SURVIVOR STORY

The Cedar Fire

Lisza Pontes knew that her home, near San Diego, California, was vulnerable to a wildfire. Thus she had made plans in case fire threatened her neighbourhood. But when the devastating Cedar fire reached the Pontes home in October 2003, none of her plans seemed to work.

"We had all these plans for what to do, and nothing happened that way," Pontes says. "We went through Plan B, Plan C, Plan D."

To begin with, Lisza and her husband did not awaken until the fire was close. None of the nine smoke alarms in the house activated because the house was well insulated against outside smoke.

Lisza's 24-year-old daughter was the first member of the family to awaken when she noticed the "odd orange glow" outside and the noise of the flames. "The sound is unbelievable," Pontes says. "It stays with me. It's surround sound, what I imagine a war zone is like." Outside, trees were exploding.

Strangely, Pontes does not remember either the heat or the smoke. "I'm asthmatic, and I don't remember coughing."

Once they had been awakened by their daughter, Pontes and her husband hastily prepared to evacuate. They rounded up their three dogs and wrapped themselves in wet towels.

Among her recollections of the fire, Pontes vividly recalls the wind that accompanied the blaze. "These fires create their own storm and their own wind," she says. Later she would learn that nearby gusts had been clocked at 130 km/h.

Pontes describes the air as having the "same strange, static feeling" that a friend of hers described feeling shortly before being struck by lightning. "The air was very electric," she remarks.

The Pontes got into their truck and began to flee, but it was knocked off the road when a neighbour's propane tank exploded. They had to retreat back up the hill, which was already burning, to reach their second vehicle. "It was really strange when we were running uphill, and the wind was whipping like crazy," she says. "At some point I remember wondering if my shoes would hold together." Pontes also recalls the odour of burning hair from the dog she carried in her arms.

They reached Lisza's old Mercedes and drove to the bottom of the driveway, which bordered a heavily wooded area. "That was an inferno," Pontes says. "That was when we first felt the heat."

They now were faced with the difficult decision of which way to go. "We had no idea where the fire had come from," she recalls. In the end, her husband decided to take the shortest road out.

The smoke had reduced visibility to almost zero, and they had to rely on occasional gusts of wind and familiar bumps in the road to pick their way out of the blaze. Pontes describes the light as a "Twilight-Zone orange. Not a normal light. We passed cars that were dead on the road. We were some of the last to get out of this area."

They were able to reach safety, but many others in the area did not. Twelve of their neighbours perished in the blaze. Of the 11 homes in their neighbourhood, only theirs survived (Figure 10.E). Their efforts to protect their home against such a disaster, including applying

◄ **FIGURE 10.E HOMES DESTROYED BY THE 2003 CEDAR FIRE** Many large homes in suburban areas of San Diego were burned in the Cedar fire, one of the worst wildfires in California's history. Fanned by Santa Ana winds, the fire claimed 14 lives, destroyed nearly 2300 homes, and burned an estimated 1100 km^2 of land. *(AP Wide World Photos)*

SURVIVOR STORY (Continued)

a fire-resistant coat of paint to the exterior of the house, paid off.

But their entire property, some 1.4 ha, was completely burned. And as Pontes notes, the damage was indiscriminate. "That's Mother Nature," she says. "She doesn't care."

—Chris Wilson

Summary

Wildfire is a high-temperature biochemical oxidation reaction that is rapid, self-sustaining, and releases heat, light, carbon dioxide, and other products. Wildfires in natural ecosystems maintain a rough balance between plant productivity and decomposition. The two main processes associated with wildfire are pre-ignition and combustion.

Two types of wildfires are distinguished by the part of the vegetation cover that burns. Surface fires burn in grasslands and along the forest floor. Fast-moving crown fires spread in the upper canopy of the forest.

Wildfire behaviour is influenced by fuel, weather, topography, and the fire itself. Predictions of fire behaviour require an understanding of ecosystem fire regimes.

Fire can increase runoff, erosion, flooding, and landslides. Natural service functions of fires include enriching soils with nutrients, initiating regeneration of plant communities, creating new habitat for animals, and reducing the risk of future large fires.

Fire management involves scientific research, data collection, education, and the use of prescribed burns. Large wildfires in hot, dry, windy weather are difficult to prevent and generally cannot be suppressed. Education, building restrictions, fire insurance, and evacuation are the main adjustments to wildfire hazard.

Key Terms

combustion (p. 295)
crown fire (p. 299)
extinction (p. 296)
fire regime (p. 307)
pre-ignition (p. 295)
prescribed burn (p. 308)
pyrolysis (p. 295)
surface fire (p. 298)
wildfire (p. 294)

Review Questions

1. How has the relationship between wildfires and people changed over time?
2. How are wildfires related to photosynthesis and plant decomposition?
3. What are the major gases and solid particles produced by a wildfire?
4. What are the three phases of a wildfire?
5. Explain how the two processes of the pre-ignition phase of a wildfire prepare plant material for combustion.
6. How often does ignition occur in a wildfire?
7. How do the processes of combustion differ from those of ignition?
8. What are the two types of combustion and how do they differ?
9. What are the three processes of heat transfer in a wildfire? Rank them in order of their importance.
10. What factors control the behaviour of a wildfire?
11. Describe the two types of fire.
12. How do wildfires affect erosion of the land?
13. What effects do wildfires have on the atmosphere?
14. Describe how climate change might change the frequency and intensity of wildfires.
15. How do wildfires affect vegetation, animals, and humans?
16. What are the natural service functions of wildfires?
17. What are the four main components of fire management?
18. What are the difficulties associated with prescribed burns?
19. Explain how people can adjust to the wildfire hazard.

Critical Thinking Questions

1. You live in an area where wildfires are possible. Make a list of actions you should take to protect your family and home.
2. The staff of a national park is reviewing its wildfire policy. They have called on you for advice. Their current policy is to suppress all fires as soon as they start and not to use controlled burns. They are considering switching to a policy of allowing natural fires to burn without human intervention. What would you suggest? List the pros and cons of each policy before making your decision.
3. Describe the features in and around your home that place it at risk in the event of a wildfire.

Selected Web Resources

Canadian Wildland Fire Information System
http://cwfis.cfs.nrcan.gc.ca/en/index_e.php From the Canadian Forest Service

Forest Fires in Canada
http://fire.cfs.nrcan.gc.ca/facts_e.php Forest fire facts and questions from Natural Resources Canada

http://nfdp.ccfm.org/compendium/fires/index_e.php Historic data on forest fires in Canada

British Columbia Ministry of Forests and Range
www.for.gov.bc.ca/protect/FAQ/index.htm Forest fire information from the Government of British Columbia

FEMA Backgrounder on Wildland Fire
www.fema.gov/hazard/wildfire/index.shtm Information on protecting yourself from wildland fire, from the U.S. Federal Emergency Management Agency

U.S. National Park Service
www.nps.gov/fire Fire information from the National Park Service

U.S. Geological Survey Wildland Fire Research and Information
www.usgs.gov/themes/Wildfire/fire.html Wildfire information from the U.S. Geological Survey

Effects of Fire on the Northern Great Plains
www.npwrc.usgs.gov/resource/habitat/fire/index.htm Publication of the U.S. Fish and Wildlife Service and the Cooperative Extension Service, South Dakota State University, placed online by the U.S. Geological Survey Northern Prairie Wildlife Research Center

USDA Forest Service Fire and Aviation Management
www.fs.fed.us/fire Information about the National Fire Plan, fire science, and fire management from the U.S. Forest Service

Monitoring of wildfires by satellite
http://activefiremaps.fs.fed.us MODIS active fire monitoring program, Canada and the United States

Biomass Burning and Global Change
http://asd-www.larc.nasa.gov/biomass_burn Wildfires and global change from NASA

CHAPTER 11

▶ **CHANGES IN ARCTIC ICE COVER** These two images show minimum Arctic sea ice cover in 1979 (top) and 2003 (bottom). Perennial sea ice decreased at a rate of 9 percent per decade over this period. The data used to produce these images were collected by the Special Sensor Microwave Imager as part of the Defense Meteorological Satellite Program. *(Images courtesy of Scientific Visualization Studio, GSFC/NASA)*

Learning Objectives

Climate has changed throughout geologic time, thus some change is normal. Evidence is mounting, however, that the current warming is unprecedented and is probably being caused by human-induced changes to Earth's atmosphere. Further warming may change the frequency or severity of some of the hazardous natural processes discussed in this book. A basic understanding of climate science is necessary to comprehend these changes. Your goals in reading this chapter should be to

- Understand the difference between climate and weather, and understand how their variability is related to natural hazards
- Know the basic concepts of atmospheric science, specifically the structure, composition, and dynamics of the atmosphere
- Understand how climate has changed during the recent geologic past and how human activity may be altering climate
- Know how global warming can affect the frequency or severity of natural hazards
- Know how people can slow global warming and adjust to the problems the warming causes

Climate Change

Arctic Threatened by Climate Change

Although people living in the mid-latitudes of North America argue about climate warming, Inuit and Dene in Arctic Canada are experiencing it. The Aboriginal peoples of northern Canada have witnessed a marked warming of climate, a decrease in Arctic sea-ice cover, increased permafrost thaw, and erosion of coastal villages. Satellite microwave sensors indicate that the area of summer sea ice in the Arctic Ocean has decreased by 9 percent per decade since the late 1970s. If this trend continues, the Arctic Ocean will be ice free in summer by the middle of the twenty-first century (Figure 11.1).

Researchers from the University of Colorado, University of Washington, NASA, and NOAA used satellite data to show that, since 2002, spring melting of sea ice north of Siberia and Alaska has occurred much earlier than it used to. In 2005 the melting trend spread through the entire Arctic. Only 5.3 million km^2 of sea ice were left in the Arctic in mid-September 2005, the smallest amount ever recorded.[1] At the same time, average air temperatures across most of the Arctic region were as much as 5.4°C warmer than average.

Even more ominous than the reduced area of sea ice is its thinning. Comparisons of data collected between 1993 and 1997 with similar data acquired between 1958 and 1976 indicate a mean reduction of sea-ice thickness of 1.3 m, or nearly 40 percent (Figure 11.2).[2]

The researchers suggest that the melting may contribute to even higher Arctic temperatures in the future. White ice reflects more of the Sun's energy than does dark ocean water. With more of the ocean exposed, the seawater absorbs more heat and reduces the amount of solar energy reflected back into space.

The reduction in Arctic ice cover is harming some northern animals. Polar bears, for example, use sea ice to hunt for marine mammals, such as seal. The bears now have a shorter season during which they can access the ice and, consequently, are experiencing problems finding their most important food source. Biologists have suggested that recent declines in the size and health of polar bears are due, in part, to this problem.

Another important consequence of the thinning of Arctic sea ice is that a "Northwest Passage" will open between Baffin Bay and the Chukchi and Bering seas. A commercial shipping passage through the Arctic Ocean, sought by Sir John Franklin during his fateful voyage on the H.M.S. *Erebus* in 1845, could become a reality before the middle of

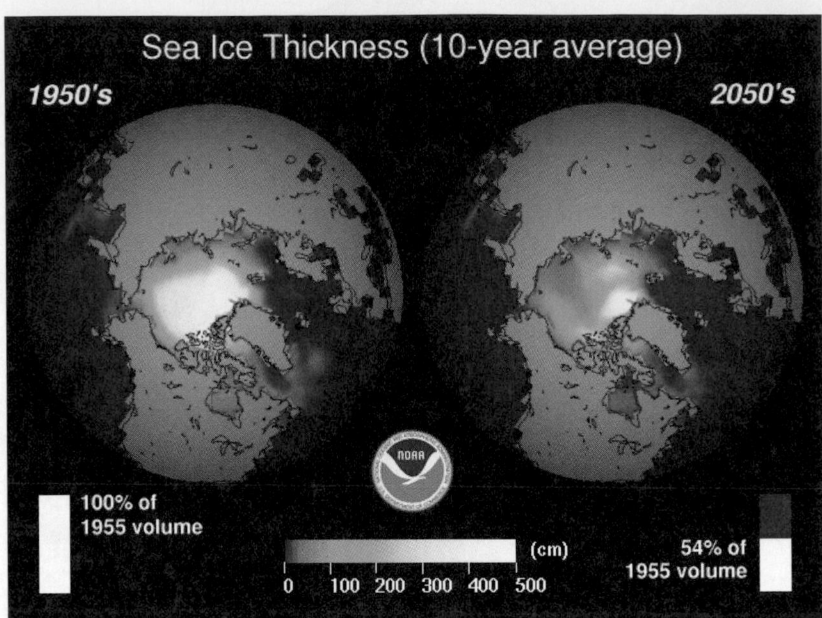

◄ **FIGURE 11.1 ARCTIC SEA ICE THINS** The projected change in the Arctic sea-ice thickness (10-year average) over 100 years, from 1950 to 2050. The volume of sea ice in the middle of this century may be only half what it was 100 years earlier. *(NOAA)*

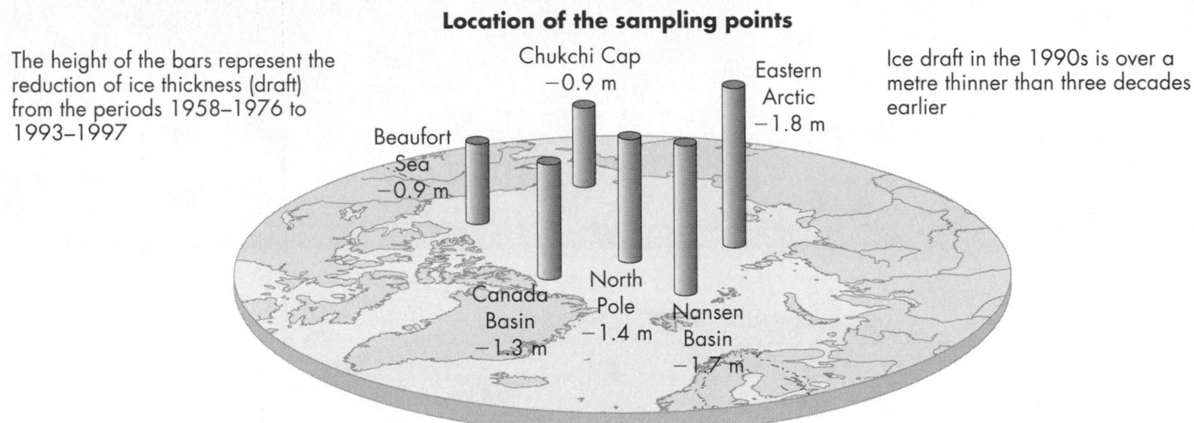

Thinning of the Arctic sea-ice cover

East ⟷ West

Metres

4
3
2
1
0

Chukchi Cap −0.9 m
Beaufort Sea −0.9 m
Canada Basin −1.3 m
North Pole −1.4 m
Nansen Basin −1.7 m
Eastern Arctic −1.8 m

■ Thickness of the ice during the period 1958–1978
■ Thickness of the ice during the period 1993–1997

East ⟷ West

Metres

0
1
2
3

Ice
Ice
−1.3 m
volume down
by 40%

All regions together

Thickness of the ice for the period 1958–1976

Thickness of the ice for the period 1993–1997

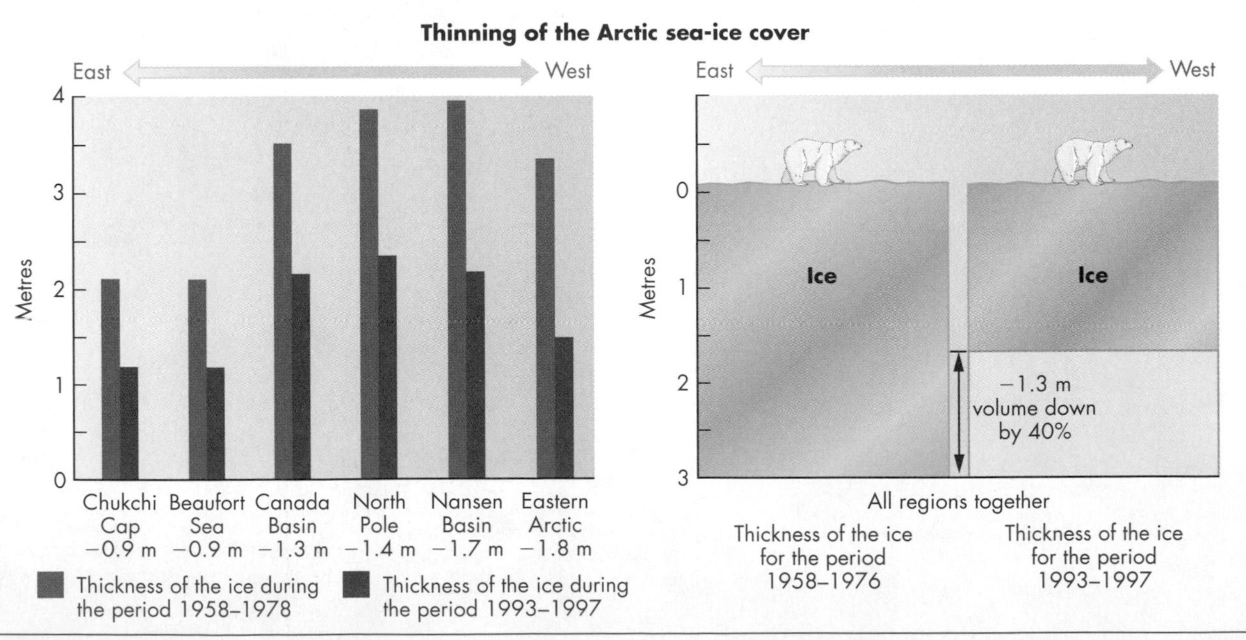

▲ **FIGURE 11.2 THINNING ARCTIC ICE PACK** A comparison of sea-ice draft data acquired on submarine cruises in 1958–1976 and 1993–1997. Sea-ice draft is the thickness of the submerged part of the ice. The data show that sea ice thinned more than 1 m, representing a 40 percent loss in ice volume. *(http://maps.grida.no/go/graphic/thinning_of_the_arctic_sea_ice; Rothrock et al., Thinning of the Arctic sea-ice cover, University of Washington, Seattle, 1999)*

this century. The economic advantages over the Panama Canal of a northern shipping route are considerable, but commercial shipping through the high Arctic raises environmental and sovereignty issues that Canada has not yet addressed.

While the Arctic sea ice has been thinning and retreating, the Greenland Ice Sheet has also been showing signs of trouble. The ice sheet has an average thickness of about 2 km, covers about 80 percent of Greenland, and is the second-largest ice body in the world, after the Antarctic Ice Sheet. Some scientists believe that global warming may push the ice sheet over a threshold, leading to the disappearance of the ice sheet in less than a few hundred years.

The Greenland Ice Sheet has experienced record melting in recent years and is likely to contribute substantially to sea-level rise and possibly to changes in ocean circulation in the future. The area of the ice sheet that experiences some melting increased by about 16 percent between 1979, when measurements were first made, and 2002. The most recent research, which uses data from 1996 to 2005, shows that the Greenland Ice Sheet is thinning faster.[3] In 1996 the ice sheet was losing about 96 km^3 of ice per year. In 2005, the loss increased to about 239 km^3 per year because of rapid thinning near the ice-sheet margins.[4] If the entire 2.85 million km^3 of ice were to melt, global sea level would rise by 6.5 m,[5] inundating coastal cities and removing several small island nations from the face of Earth.

11.1 Climate and Weather

Many people form opinions about global warming based on day-to-day or week-to-week changes in the weather. They do not appreciate the important distinction between climate and weather. **Climate** refers to the characteristic atmospheric conditions of a region over years or decades. **Weather** is the atmospheric conditions of a region for much shorter periods, typically days or weeks. For example, we associate the coast of British Columbia with mild temperatures, high humidity, and lots of rain during fall and winter. Thus, when travelling to Vancouver or Victoria in February, we would probably bring an umbrella. It is possible, however, that we would enjoy bright, sunny, dry weather during a weeklong stay in Vancouver or Seattle in winter, because weather can vary greatly on a daily basis.

If you were asked to characterize the climate of a region, you might do so in terms of its average temperature and precipitation. However, climate is more than averages. Two locales may have the same average annual temperature but very different climates. Halifax, Nova Scotia, and Kelowna, British Columbia, have nearly the same average temperature of 7°C–8°C, but the annual temperature range in Halifax is much less than in Kelowna, and Halifax receives much more precipitation than Kelowna. Although the two cities have the same average annual temperature, they clearly have different climates.

Climate Zones

Climate can be classified in many different ways. The simplest classification is by latitude—arctic, subarctic, mid-latitudinal, subtropical, and tropical. This classification, however, relies mainly on average temperature and does not take into account other factors that affect climate, such as precipitation and proximity to oceans and large lakes. The Koeppen climate system (Figure 11.3), developed by Vladimir Koeppen in the early twentieth century, uses the distribution of natural vegetation to define zones of similar temperature and precipitation. The system includes five major types of terrestrial climate (A, B, C, D, and E), four of which have subdivisions (Table 11.1).

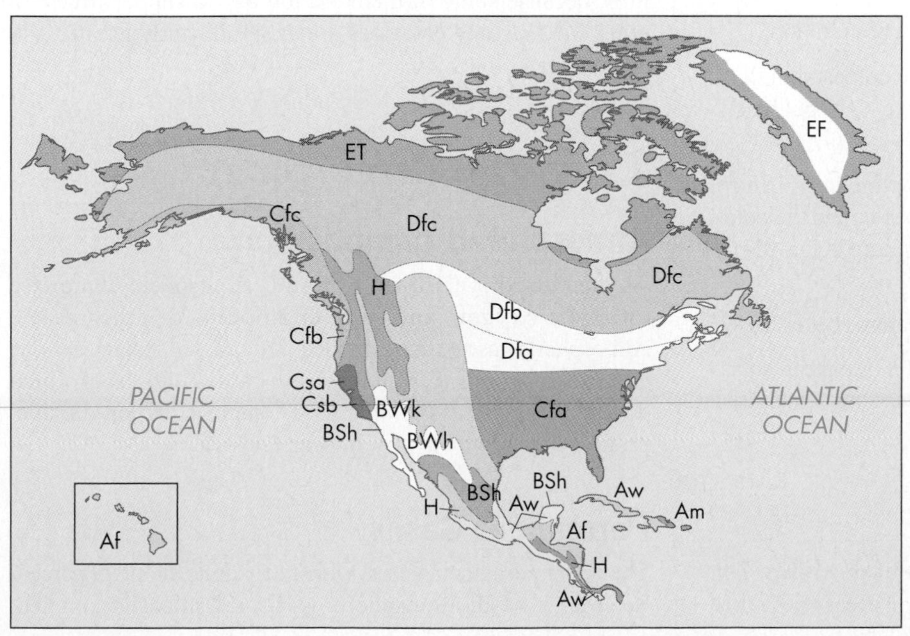

◀ **FIGURE 11.3 KOEPPEN CLIMATE MAP OF NORTH AMERICA** Climate zones in North America are based on the distribution of natural vegetation and associated temperature and precipitation. Major climate types: A = tropical, B = dry, C = mild mid-latitude, D = severe mid-latitude, and E = polar. Most of the major climate types are followed by a lowercase letter, specifying a subtype. See Table 11.1 for definitions and characteristics of the subtypes.

TABLE 11.1 Koeppen Climate System

Type	Subtype	Letter Code	Characteristics
A: Tropical	Tropical wet	Af	No dry season
	Tropical monsoonal	Am	Short dry season
	Tropical wet and dry	Aw	Winter dry season
B: Dry	Subtropical desert	BWh	Low-latitude arid
	Subtropical steppe	BSh	Low-latitude semi-arid
	Mid-latitude desert	BWk	Mid-latitude arid
	Mid-latitude steppe	BSk	Mid-latitude semi-arid
C: Mild	Mediterranean	Csa	Dry, hot summer
	Mid-latitude	Csb	Dry, warm summer
	Humid subtropical	Cfa	Hot summer, no dry season
		Cwa	Hot summer, brief winter dry season
	Marine west coast	Cfb	Mild throughout year, no dry season, warm summer
		Cfc	Mild throughout year, no dry season, cool summer
D: Severe	Humid continental	Dfa	Severe winter, no dry season, hot summer
	Mid-latitude	Dfb	Severe winter, no dry season, warm summer
		Dwa	Severe winter, winter dry season, hot summer
		Dwb	Severe winter, winter dry season, warm summer
	Subarctic	Dfc	Severe winter, no dry season, cool summer
		Dfd	Extremely severe winter, no dry season, cool summer
		Dwc	Severe winter, winter dry season, cool summer
		Dwd	Extremely severe winter, winter dry season, cool summer
E: Polar	Tundra	ET	No true summer
	Polar ice cap	EF	Perennial ice
H: Highland	Highland	H	Highland

Koeppen's major climate zones have the following characteristics:[6]

- A: Tropical—Average annual temperature is greater than 18°C. Most of this zone is located between the equator and Tropics of Cancer and Capricorn.
- B: Dry (desert)—Evaporation exceeds precipitation.
- C: Mild mid-latitude (subtropical)—The coldest month of the year has an average temperature above –3°C but below 18°C. Summers can be hot.
- D: Severe mid-latitude (humid, mid-continental)—Snow covers the ground occasionally during winter and the coldest month of the year has a mean temperature below –3°C. Summers are typically mild.
- E: Polar—All months have mean temperatures below 10°C.
- H: Highland (alpine)—Found in mountain or plateau areas. Precipitation and temperature differ over short distances.

The Koeppen System and Natural Processes

Climate has a major effect on many natural processes. For example, landslides may be more common in areas with rainy climates than with dry ones, and forest fires are most common in areas that are at least seasonally dry. The Koeppen classification system provides a map of Earth's climates, as well as information about the relation between climate and vegetation. Not all dry areas, for example, are prone to wildfires, because some of them are too dry to support trees; in other words, some dry areas are at significantly greater risk of fires than others are.

11.2 The Atmosphere

Atmospheric Composition

As mentioned in Chapter 8, Earth's atmosphere comprises nitrogen, oxygen, and smaller amounts of other gases. Atmospheric gases can be divided into two groups: *permanent gases*, notably nitrogen and oxygen, concentrations of which do not change; and *variable gases*, such as carbon dioxide, proportions of which vary in time and space.

Permanent Gases

The major permanent gases, which constitute about 99 percent by volume of all atmospheric gases, are nitrogen, oxygen, and argon (Table 11.2). Nitrogen generally occurs as molecules of two nitrogen atoms (N_2) and composes about 78 percent of the volume of all permanent gases. Although abundant, elemental nitrogen is relatively unimportant in atmospheric dynamics. It plays an important role in climate, however, when it combines with other gases, notably oxygen.

The second-largest component of Earth's atmosphere is oxygen, which forms 21 percent of atmospheric gases by volume. Like nitrogen, oxygen molecules consist mainly of two atoms (O_2). Oxygen gas is, of course, required by all animals, including humans. Like N_2, diatomic oxygen is relatively unimportant in atmospheric dynamics. However, as discussed below, some oxygen compounds have important effects on Earth's climate.

Argon makes up most of the remaining 1 percent of the permanent gases. The atmosphere also contains small amounts of neon, helium, krypton, xenon, and hydrogen. With the exception of hydrogen, these permanent gases are not chemically reactive and have little or no effect on climate.

Variable Gases

The variable gases (Table 11.2) account for only a small percentage of the total mass of the atmosphere, but some of them have important roles in atmospheric dynamics. The variable gases include carbon dioxide, water vapour, ozone, methane, and nitrogen oxides.

Carbon Dioxide Carbon dioxide (CO_2) currently makes up about 0.0381 percent of the atmosphere. Its concentration is so low that it is generally expressed in parts per million (ppm) rather than as a percentage. The concentration of carbon dioxide in the atmosphere is 0.000381, or 381 atoms per every million atoms of gas in the atmosphere, and is written as 381 ppm.

Carbon dioxide is released into the atmosphere naturally through volcanic activity, plant and animal respiration, wildfires, and decay of organic material. It is removed from the atmosphere through photosynthesis by green plants. Carbon dioxide also enters the atmosphere by the burning of fossil fuels by people. Since the industrial revolution, the amount of carbon dioxide added to the atmosphere from human, or **anthropogenic**, sources has risen. Currently, the total amount of CO_2 released into the atmosphere exceeds the amount removed by natural processes; thus, the concentration of this gas in the atmosphere is increasing.[5]

TABLE 11.2 Gases in the Atmosphere

Permanent Gases	Variable Gases
Nitrogen	Water vapour
Oxygen	Carbon dioxide
Argon	Ozone
Neon	Methane
Helium	Aerosols
Krypton	Nitrous oxides
Xenon	
Hydrogen	

Water Vapour As mentioned in Chapter 8, water vapour is produced by the evaporation of water at Earth's surface. It condenses to form clouds and eventually returns to the surface as precipitation as part of the hydrologic cycle (Chapter 1).

Ozone *Ozone* (O_3) is triatomic oxygen. It forms when an atom of oxygen (O) collides with and bonds to an oxygen molecule (O_2). Most ozone is found in the **stratosphere**, the layer of the atmosphere above the **troposphere**. It partially shields Earth from ultraviolet (UV) radiation from the Sun. Without the protective "ozone shield," plants and animals would be exposed to deadly levels of radiation. Chemical pollutants, primarily chlorofluorocarbons (CFCs) used in refrigerants and as propellants in spray cans, have partially depleted ozone in the stratosphere. **Ozone depletion** has increased the amount of UV radiation reaching Earth's surface, especially at high latitudes during spring months.[7] Reduced ozone in the stratosphere may increase the incidence of skin cancer and cataracts, and it may lower crop yields. Ozone depletion, however, is neither the cause nor the result of global warming.

Smaller concentrations of ozone are also found in the troposphere near Earth's surface, where it is produced by chemical reactions during the formation of smog. Unlike ozone in the stratosphere, which protects us, ozone in the troposphere irritates lungs and eyes and aggravates respiratory problems. Ground-level ozone develops from automobile emissions and the burning of coal or oil at large power plants.

Methane Another important variable gas is methane (CH_4), which is a major component of natural gas. Methane forms naturally, by bacterial decay, in moist places that lack oxygen, such as marshes, swamps, and the intestinal tracts of termites, cows, and sheep. Anthropogenic sources of methane include coalmines, oil wells, leaking natural gas pipelines, rice paddies, landfills, and livestock. The current concentration of methane in the atmosphere is about 1.7 ppm; it has increased to this level during the past few decades.[8] Methane is important in our discussion of climate because it is a powerful **greenhouse gas** that contributes to atmospheric warming.

Nitrogen Oxides Nitrogen oxide gases, sometimes referred to as nitrous oxides or NO_x because they include both nitrogen oxide and nitrogen dioxide, are variable gases present in the troposphere and the stratosphere. Natural sources of these gases include microbiological processes in soils and oceans, forest fires, and lightning strikes. Anthropogenic sources include automobiles, power plants, and jet aircraft.

Aerosols **Aerosols** are microscopic liquid and solid particles in the atmosphere. They are associated with volcanic eruptions and pollution and are important in cloud formation. Aerosols are the nuclei around which water droplets condense to form clouds.

Atmospheric Circulation

Much of the circulation in the atmosphere occurs in the lowest layer, the troposphere, and heat radiating from Earth's surface is trapped within it. Warm moist air rises in equatorial areas and moves north and south toward the poles (Figure 11.4a). As it rises, this air cools and loses moisture as rain. The cooler and drier air then descends between 15° and 30° latitude (Figure 11.4b).[9] The descending air produces semi-permanent cells of high pressure in these locations but little rainfall.[10] Atmospheric circulation cells also create regions of high pressure and low precipitation near the north and south poles. Land areas at these high latitudes are referred to as *polar deserts* (Figure 11.4a). Wind is produced by the movement of air from areas of high pressure to areas of low pressure.

11.3 Climate Change

Climate change has become an important and extensively studied subject in many fields of science. Understanding climate change requires knowledge of atmospheric dynamics and complex linkages among the atmosphere, lithosphere, hydrosphere, and biosphere.

Earth's climate has fluctuated greatly during the past 2 million years, alternating between periods of continental

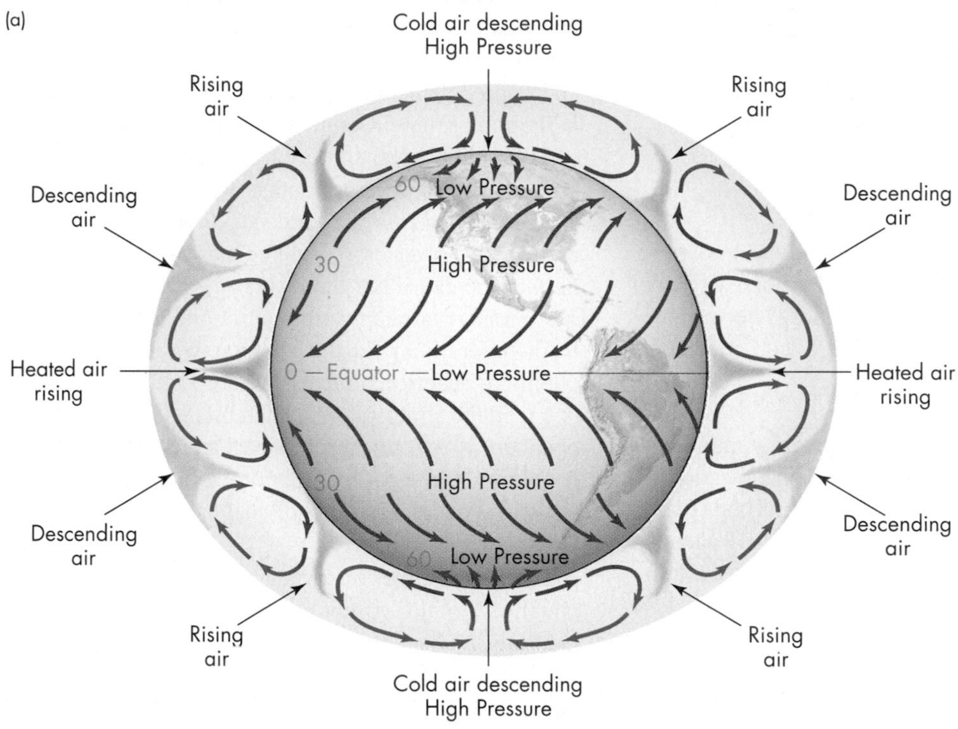

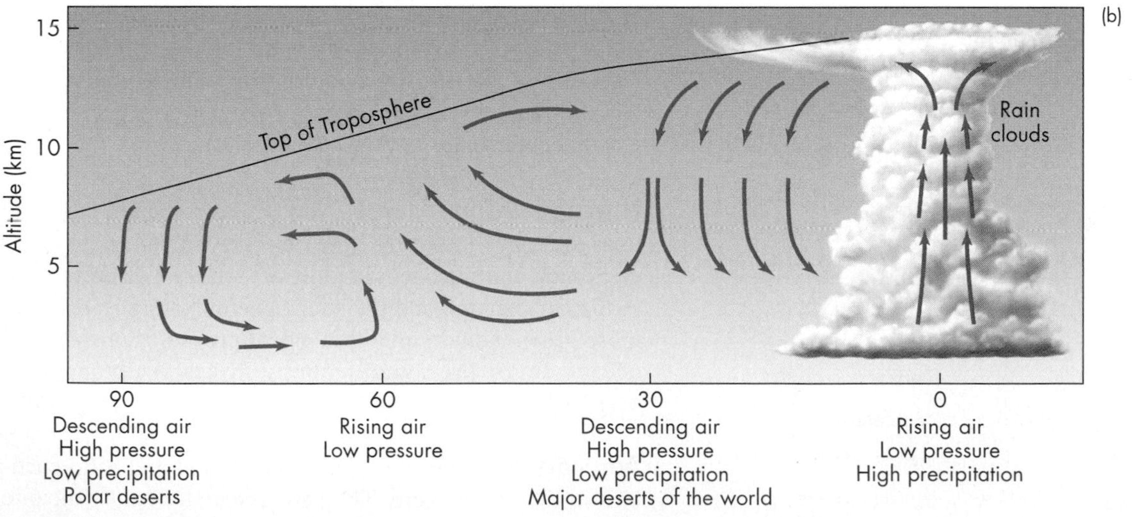

▲ **FIGURE 11.4 ATMOSPHERIC CIRCULATION** (a) The general circulation of the lower atmosphere showing zones of rising and descending air masses and corresponding areas of low and high air pressure. (b) An idealized diagram showing atmospheric circulation along a transect from the equator to a pole.

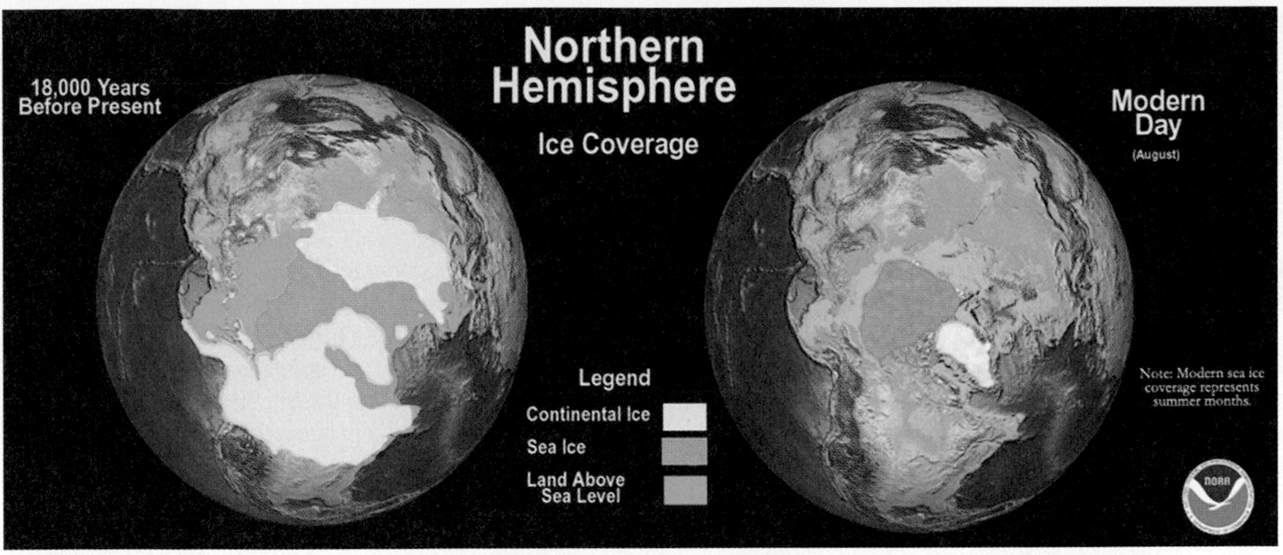

▲ **FIGURE 11.5 ICE SHEETS** The maximum extent of glaciers about 20,000 years ago during the late Pleistocene. Ice sheets covered most of Canada and northern Europe and part of Eurasia. *(Image courtesy of National Oceanic and Atmospheric Administration Paleoclimatology Program)*

glaciation, referred to as *glacial intervals,* and times of warmer climate with much less ice cover, referred to as *interglacial intervals*.[11] Today we live in an interglacial interval, with persistent warm conditions not experienced since the last interglaciation 125,000 years ago. However, many independent types of data show that the average temperature at the surface of Earth is increasing and could soon exceed the highest temperatures of the current and past interglaciations. Scientists refer to this phenomenon as *global warming*. Most scientists believe that the atmosphere is warming because fossil fuel consumption, land clearing, and other human activities are increasing the concentrations of carbon dioxide and other greenhouse gases.

Glaciations

Several glacial episodes have occurred during the past billion years.[11] Each of the glacial episodes spanned millions to tens of millions of years and was characterized by repeated *advances* and *retreats*, or growth and melting back of ice sheets. The initial cooling of the most recent of these periods began several tens of millions of years ago during the *Cenozoic Era* and culminated with the great glacial advances of the **Pleistocene Epoch**, which spans most of the past 2 million years. During Pleistocene glaciations, glacier ice covered as much as 30 percent of the land area of Earth, including nearly all of Canada, the northernmost conterminous United States, and much of Europe (Figure 11.5). The present sites of Toronto, Vancouver, and Montreal were covered by up to 2 km of ice at the peak of the last glaciation, only 16,000 to 20,000 years ago. The volume of fresh water stored in glaciers was so large at that time that global sea level was more than 100 m lower than today.[12]

We live in an interglacial interval called the **Holocene Epoch**, which began about 11,000 years ago. Only 10 percent of Earth's land area is presently covered by glacier ice, mainly in Antarctica and Greenland (Table 11.3). Glaciers also exist in Iceland and Arctic Canada and in the high mountains of Asia, North and South America, Europe, and New Zealand.

Causes of Glaciation The cause of glaciation, and thus climate change, has long been debated. No single factor, however, can explain glaciation. Rather, it is the result of several factors operating together.[11]

The positions of the continents significantly affect ocean and atmospheric circulation and determine how much land area lies in the mid-latitudes where continental glaciers form. When the continents are favourably situated for glaciation, small, regular changes in the amount of solar radiation reaching Earth's surface determine the advance and retreat of

TABLE 11.3 Glacier Ice on Earth

	Area (km^2)	Percentage	Volume (km^3)	Percentage
Antarctica	12,600,000	84	31,000,000	91
Greenland	1,800,000	12	2,800,000	8
Other*	540,000	4	120,000	< 1

*Ice caps and valley glaciers in Iceland, Europe, Asia, North America, South America, and New Zealand

continental ice sheets. Milutin Milankovitch, a Serbian geophysicist, proposed in the 1920s that cyclic variations in the shape of Earth's orbit around the Sun (eccentricity) and in the tilt (obliquity) and wobble (precession of the equinoxes) of Earth's axis of rotation lead to differences in the amount and distribution of radiation reaching the planet's surface (Figure 11.6). Let us consider each of the three **Milankovitch cycles** in turn.

The shape of Earth's orbit varies from being nearly circular to mildly elliptical on a cycle of about 100,000 years. The *eccentricity* of the orbit is a measure of its departure from circularity (Figure 11.6). Small seasonal differences in the amount of radiation reaching the planet's surface result from changes in eccentricity.

Earth's rotational axis wobbles, causing a slow 2.4° change in its tilt, or *obliquity*, with respect to the orbital plane (Figure 11.6b). These obliquity variations are cyclic, with a period of approximately 40,000 years. When the obliquity increases, the amplitude of the seasonal cycle of solar radiation reaching the surface increases. Summers in both hemispheres receive more radiation, and winters receive less radiation. At times of low obliquity, the opposite is true—both hemispheres receive relatively less radiation in summer and more radiation in winter. Cooler summers are thought to be favourable for the growth of glaciers because less of the previous winter's ice and snow melts.

The third orbital cycle identified by Milankovitch is the *precession of the equinoxes*, the change in the direction of Earth's axis of rotation relative to the Sun at the time of *perihelion* and *aphelion* (Figure 11.6c). Perihelion and aphelion are, respectively, the points in the orbit of Earth that are nearest and farthest from the Sun. Earth goes through one complete precession cycle in about 20,000 years. The axis of rotation moves like a top around a line perpendicular to the orbital plane because of forces exerted by the Sun and the Moon on the solid Earth. When Earth's rotational axis is aligned so that it points toward the Sun during perihelion, one polar hemisphere will have a greater difference between

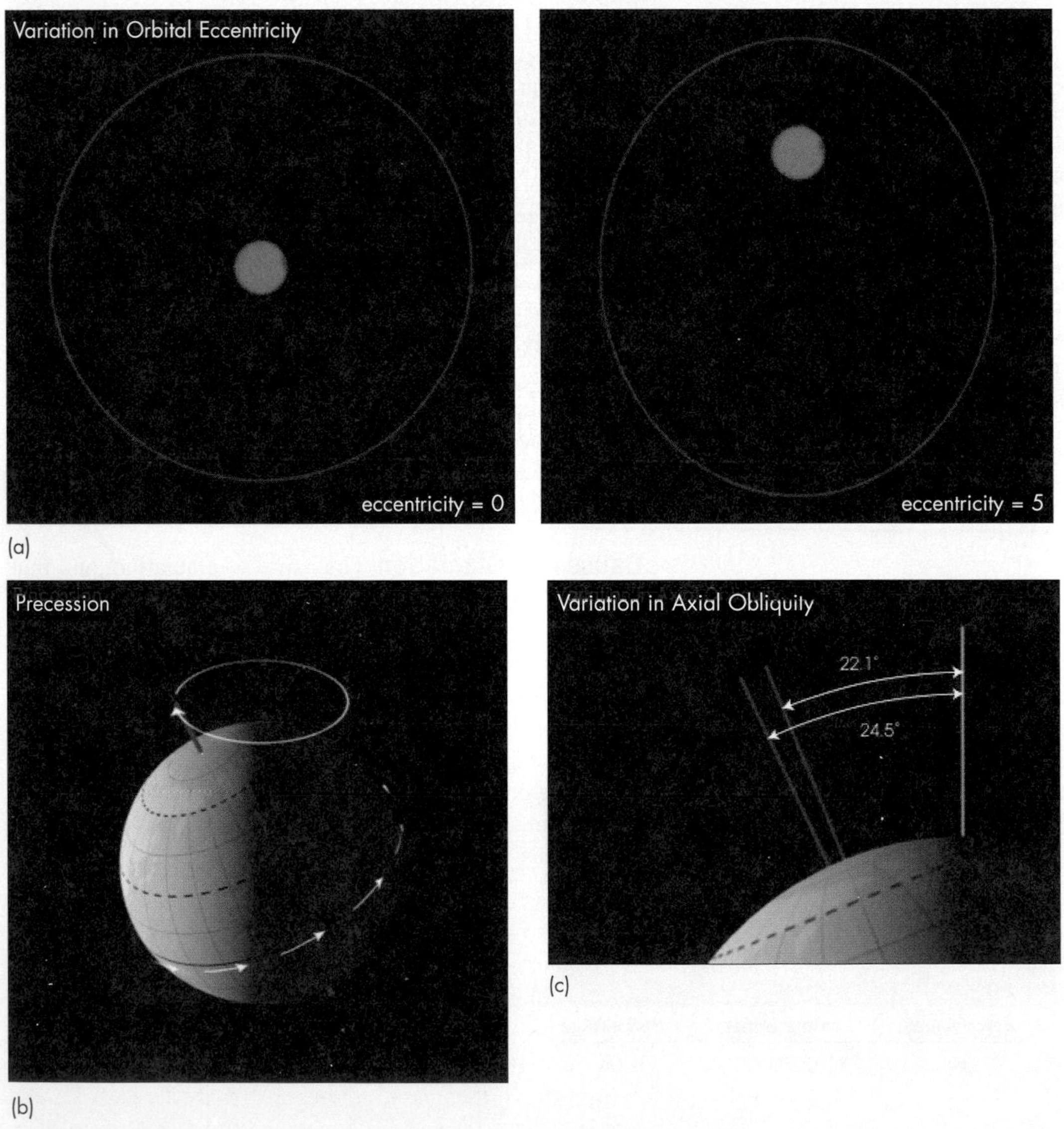

▲ **FIGURE 11.6 MILANKOVITCH CYCLES** Variations in (a) the eccentricity of Earth's orbit and the (b) wobble and (c) obliquity of its axis of rotation lead to differences in the amount and distribution of radiation reaching the planet's surface. *(NASA)*

the seasons than the other will. The hemisphere that is in summer at perihelion will receive much of the corresponding increase in solar radiation, but that same hemisphere will have a colder winter at aphelion. The other hemisphere will have a relatively warmer winter and cooler summer. When Earth's axis is aligned such that aphelion and perihelion occur during spring and autumn, the Northern and Southern hemispheres will have similar contrasts in seasons.

The three Milankovitch cycles can be combined to determine net changes in radiation that any point on Earth receives through time. These changes correlate well with major advances and retreats of continental ice sheets (Figure 11.7). However, correlation is not proof of causation. Milankovitch cycles cause only small changes in seasonality and the amount of solar radiation reaching Earth. They should be considered the metronome of climate, modulating fluctuations of ice sheets on timescales of thousands of years once other factors favour global glaciation. Neither the position of the continents nor Earth's orbital cycles can explain observed fluctuations on timescales of decades to centuries. The causes of these shorter-term variations, which are most relevant to the climate change during the remainder of this century, are discussed later in this chapter.

The Greenhouse Effect

The surface temperature of Earth is determined mainly by three factors: (1) the amount of sunlight the planet receives, (2) the amount of sunlight that is reflected from Earth's surface and therefore not absorbed, and (3) the degree to which the atmosphere retains heat radiated from Earth (Figure 11.8).[13] Most solar radiation that reaches Earth is in the ultraviolet (UV) range and thus has a relatively short wavelength. Approximately two-thirds of this radiation passes through Earth's atmosphere and reaches the surface of the planet, where most of it is absorbed and warms both the atmosphere and the surface. Some of this energy, however, is radiated back into the atmosphere from Earth's surface as infrared radiation. Some of the reradiated infrared radiation goes back into outer space and some is absorbed in the atmosphere by water vapour (H_2O), carbon dioxide (CO_2), methane (CH_4), nitrogen oxides (NO_x), and several other gases. The troposphere is much warmer than it would be if all of Earth's infrared radiation escaped into space. This effect is analogous to the trapping of heat by a greenhouse and is therefore referred to as the **greenhouse effect** (Figure 11.8).

Without the greenhouse effect, Earth's surface would be at least 33°C cooler than it is, all surface water would be frozen, and little, if any, life would exist.[14] Most of natural greenhouse warming is due to absorption of infrared radiation by water vapour and small particles of liquid water in the atmosphere. However, some of the warming is due to absorption of infrared radiation by carbon dioxide, methane, and nitrogen oxide gases, which are commonly termed greenhouse gases. In recent years the atmospheric concentration of these greenhouse gases has increased through human activities (Table 11.4).

Carbon dioxide accounts for 60 percent of the anthropogenic greenhouse effect (Table 11.4) and consequently is the most studied of the greenhouse gases. Cores of glacier ice up to several hundred thousand years old have been recovered from the Antarctic and Greenland ice sheets. The cores contain atmospheric air bubbles trapped at the time the ice formed. Measurements of gas concentrations in these bubbles indicate that atmospheric concentrations of CO_2 have ranged from a little less than 200 ppm to about 300 ppm over the past 160,000 years.[15] The highest levels of CO_2 date to the last major interglacial interval about 125,000 years ago and to ice that is forming today (Figure 11.9a and 11.9b).

The concentration of CO_2 in our atmosphere was approximately 280 ppm at the beginning of the Industrial Revolution. During the past two centuries, deforestation and the burning of fossil fuels, such as gasoline and coal, have markedly increased the concentration of CO_2 in the atmosphere (Figure 11.9b and 11.9c).Today the concentration is 381 ppm and is expected to reach at least 450 ppm by the year 2050, 1.5 times its preindustrial level.[14]

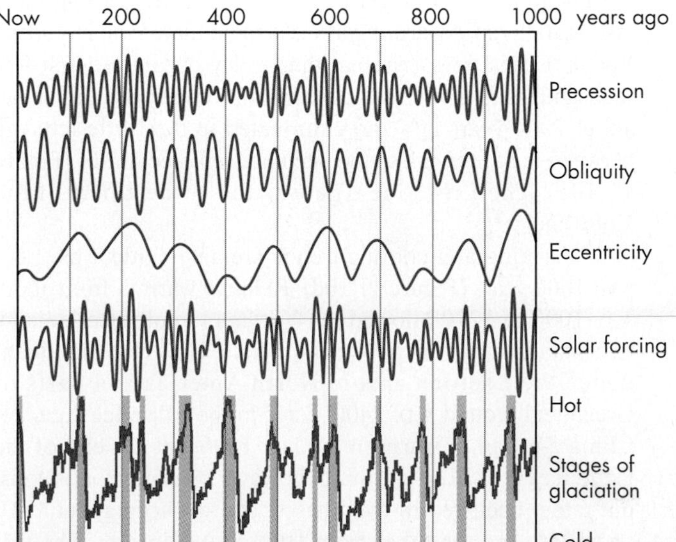

◀ **FIGURE 11.7 RELATION BETWEEN MILANKOVITCH CYCLES AND GLACIATION** Several quasi-periodic cycles occur as Earth spins and orbits the Sun. The curves have a large number of sinusoidal components, but a few components are dominant. Milutin Milankovitch studied changes in eccentricity, obliquity, and precession (top three curves), which collectively change the amount and location of solar radiation reaching Earth (*solar forcing*, fourth curve). Changes in the Northern Hemisphere are important because of the large amount of land there; land reacts to such changes more quickly than the oceans do. The lowest curve is an independent record of global ice extent, which is a proxy for Earth temperature. It is similar to the curve of solar forcing on timescales of tens of thousands of years. *(Wikipedia)*

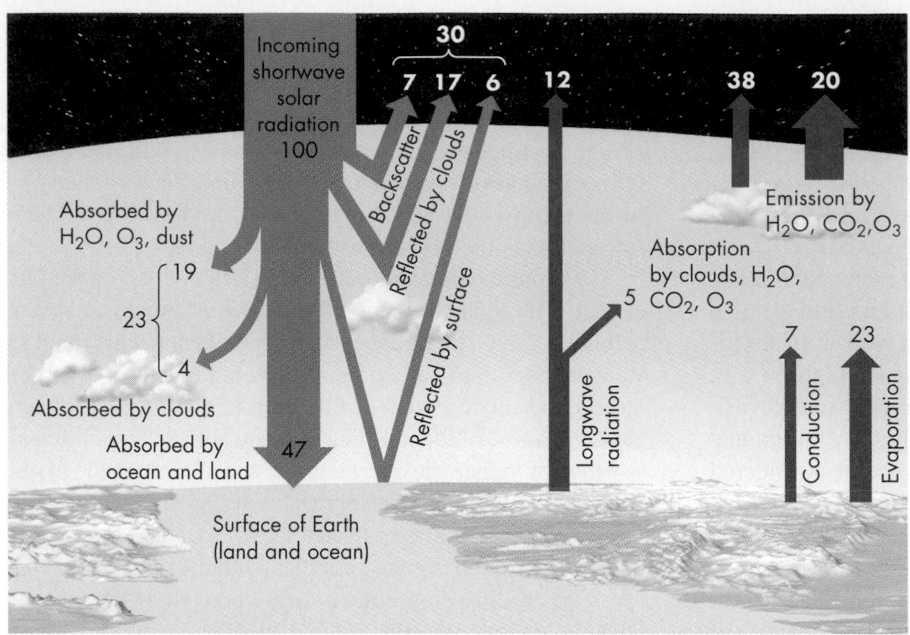

▲ **FIGURE 11.8 THE GREENHOUSE EFFECT** An idealized diagram showing Earth's energy balance. Approximately 47 percent of the incoming short-wave solar radiation (visible light, ultraviolet light, and some infrared radiation) is absorbed by Earth. Some of this energy is radiated back into the atmosphere as long-wave infrared (heat) radiation. A portion of the long-wave radiation is absorbed by water vapour, water, carbon dioxide, methane, and other gases in the atmosphere. These "greenhouse" gases reradiate some of the infrared energy and warm the atmosphere. Global warming has been attributed to increases in the concentrations of carbon dioxide and methane because of human activities. *(Modified after Trujillo, A. P., and H. V. Thurman, 2005. Essentials of oceanography, 8th ed. Upper Saddle River, NJ: Pearson Prentice Hall; and Lutgens, F. K. and E. J. Tarbuck. 2004. The atmosphere: An introduction to meteorology, 9th ed. Upper Saddle River, NJ: Pearson Prentice Hall)*

Global Temperature Change

Climate has changed on several timescales during the Pleistocene and Holocene epochs (Figure 11.10). On the longest timescale (Figure 11.10a), climate has fluctuated on cycles of about 100,000 years over the past 800,000 years. Low temperatures have coincided with major continental glaciations and high temperatures with interglacial intervals. The last major interglacial interval, which was a little warmer than today, is known as the Eemian interglaciation (Figure 11.10b). Global sea level about 125,000 years ago, during the Eemian interglaciation, was several metres higher than today. Climate fluctuated markedly and rapidly between about 15,000 and 11,000 years ago near the close of the last glaciation. A severe cold period, referred to as the *Younger Dryas*, dates to about 12,800 to 11,500 years ago (Figure 11.10c). The beginning of the Younger Dryas was extremely fast; the change from the relative warmth of the previous warm interval to the severe cold conditions of the Younger Dryas in northern Europe apparently occurred in a few decades or less. The termination of the Younger Dryas about 11,500 years ago was also abrupt; rapid warming at that time initiated the Holocene Epoch. Climate was warmer than today during the first few thousand years of the Holocene. Slow, stepped cooling began about 7000 years ago and culminated in the Little Ice Age between the thirteenth to the late nineteenth centuries (Figure 11.10c). The Little Ice Age was the coldest part of the Holocene.

TABLE 11.4 Rate of Increase and Relative Contribution of Several Gases to the Anthropogenic Greenhouse Effect

	Rate of Increase (% per year)	Relative Contribution (%)
CO_2	0.5	60
CH_4	< 1	15
N_2O	0.2	5
O_3*	0.5	8
CFC-11	4	4
CFC-12	4	8

*In the troposphere

Source: Data from Rodhe, H. 1990. A comparison of the contribution of various gases to the greenhouse effect. Science 248:1218, table 2. Copyright 1990 by the AAAS.

Warming and cooling trends are also evident over the past 1000 years (Figure 11.10d). Relative warmth from about A.D. 1000 to 1270 allowed the Vikings to colonize Iceland, Greenland, and northern North America. However, they abandoned their settlements in North America and parts of Greenland around A.D. 1400, early in the Little Ice Age.[16,17] Climate began to warm in the late 1800s, at the end of the Little Ice Age.[18] The warming, however, was not continuous, but rather occurred in two phases, one between about 1910 and 1940, and the other from 1980 to the present. The two

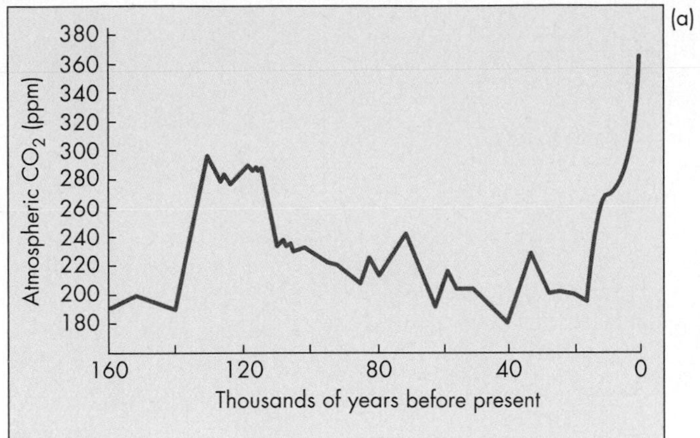

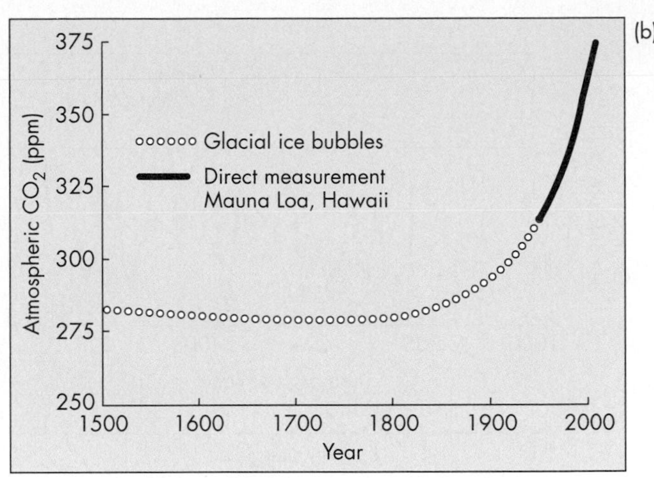

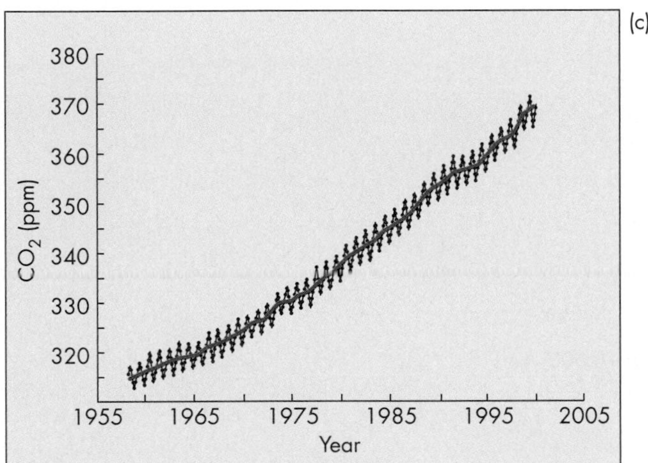

◀ **FIGURE 11.9 CARBON DIOXIDE IN THE ATMOSPHERE** (a) The concentrations of carbon dioxide in the atmosphere over the past 160,000 years, based on data from Antarctic ice cores. *(Data from Schneider, S. H. 1989. The changing climate. Scientific American 261.74)* (b) The average concentrations of atmospheric carbon dioxide from A.D. 1500 to 2000, based on measurements of air bubbles in glacier ice and on direct measurements of air at Mauna Loa on the island of Hawaii. *(Data in part from Post, W. M. et al. 1990. American Scientist 78[4]:210–226)* (c) Concentrations of carbon dioxide at Mauna Loa over the past 50 years. *(Source data from Scripps Institute of Oceanography, NOAA, and C. D. Keeling,* www.mlo.noaa.gov, *accessed January 1, 2004)*

warming intervals were separated by a period when climate cooled slightly and many glaciers around the world advanced (Figure 11.10e). The total increase in global mean temperature since the late nineteenth century is about 0.8°C. About half of the increase has been in the past 25 years, and the past two decades have been the warmest since global temperatures have been monitored.[5,19]

The average temperature in Canada has increased 0.8°C since 1900, but the increase has not been the same throughout the country (Figure 11.11). The Arctic has warmed much more than the southern part of the country; a small area of eastern Canada has even cooled over this period.

In August 2000, open water was found at the North Pole, and for a short time in 2006 an open channel extended across the Arctic Ocean to the pole. Norwegian researchers have predicted that the Arctic Ocean will be ice free during the summer within 50 years. An American study found that the Greenland Ice Sheet is losing ice and Antarctic ice shelves are *calving* more rapidly than normal.[20]

Mountainous areas also show the effects of recent warming. Ohio State University scientists recently reported that at least one-third of the glacier covering Mount Kilimanjaro, the highest peak in Africa, melted in the last 12 years. They predict that many mountain glaciers and ice caps in Africa and South America will disappear in the next 15 years.[21] It is likely that all remaining glaciers in Glacier National Park, Montana, will disappear within 30 years. Glaciers in western Canada (Figure 11.12), the Andes, Alps, and Himalayas have also been retreating at an alarming rate (Figure 11.13).

Why Does Climate Change?

What are the causes of climate change on timescales of years to centuries? As mentioned previously, Milankovitch cycles explain climate cycles on timescales of thousands of years to hundreds of thousands of years, but they cannot explain the changes of the past century. Other processes must be involved.

Our climate system appears to be capable of changing quickly from one state to another in as little as a few years. Part of what drives the climate system and allows it to change so rapidly is a global-scale circulation of ocean waters known as the **ocean conveyor belt**.

The ocean conveyor belt carries warm surface waters northward along the east side of the North Atlantic Ocean (Figure 11.14). The warm water cools and becomes more saline as it approaches Greenland. The cold salty water is denser than the surrounding water and thus sinks to the bottom, where it flows southward along the seafloor around Africa. The flow in the conveyor belt is huge, equal to about 100 times the mean discharge of the Amazon River. The heat that it releases is sufficient to keep northern Europe 5°C to 10°C warmer than it would be if the conveyor belt were not operating.

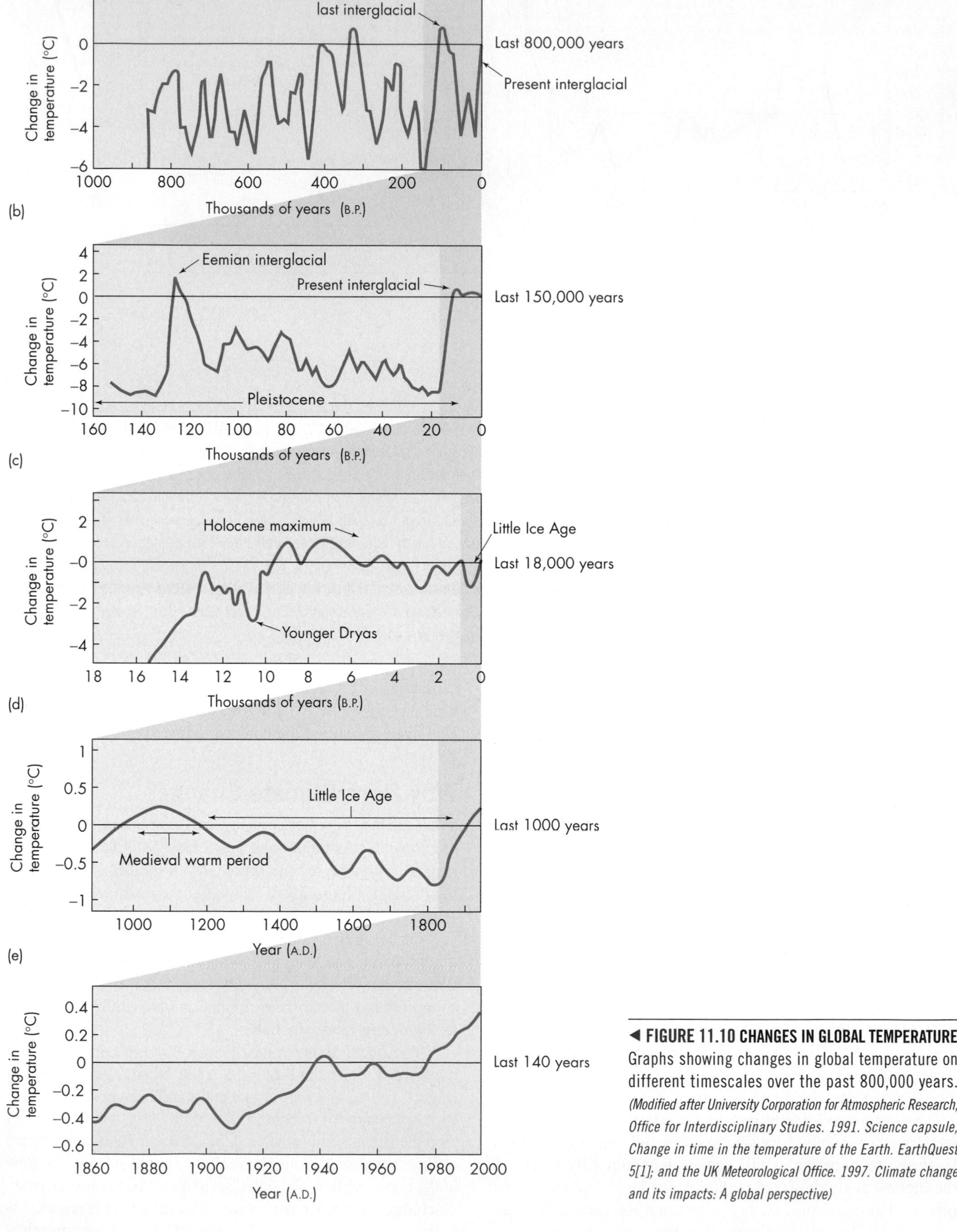

◄ **FIGURE 11.10 CHANGES IN GLOBAL TEMPERATURE** Graphs showing changes in global temperature on different timescales over the past 800,000 years. *(Modified after University Corporation for Atmospheric Research, Office for Interdisciplinary Studies. 1991. Science capsule, Change in time in the temperature of the Earth. EarthQuest 5[1]; and the UK Meteorological Office. 1997. Climate change and its impacts: A global perspective)*

(a) Annual temperature trends, 1901–2000

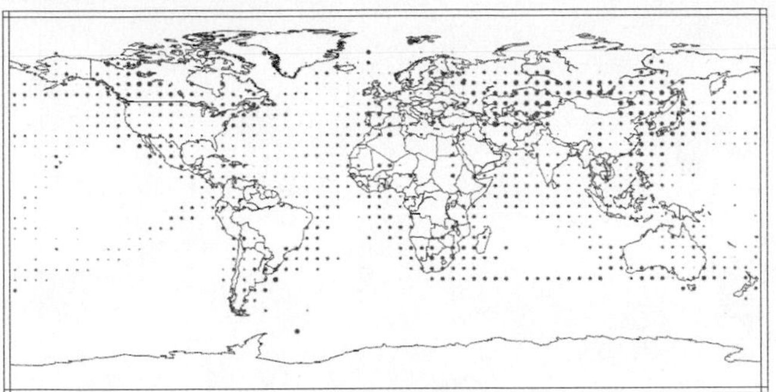

(b) Annual temperature trends, 1910–1945

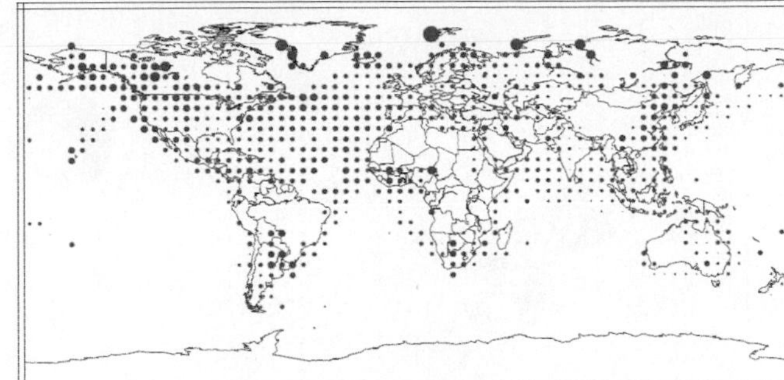

(c) Annual temperature trends, 1946–1975

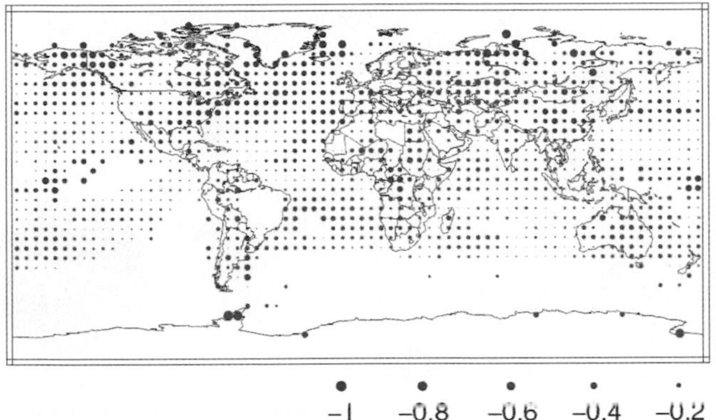

(d) Annual temperature trends, 1976–2000

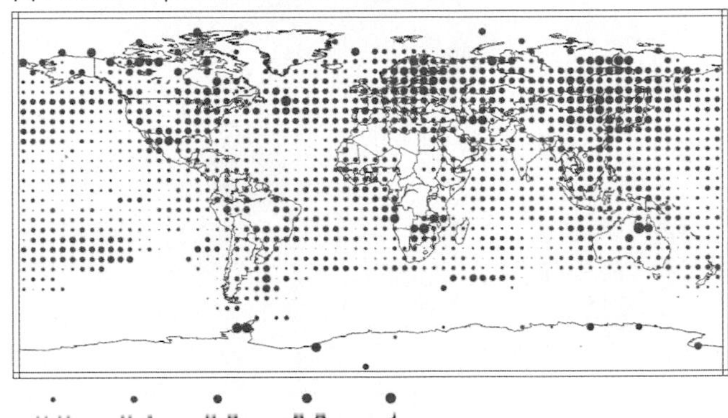

−1 −0.8 −0.6 −0.4 −0.2 0 0.2 0.4 0.6 0.8 1

▲ **FIGURE 11.11 CLIMATE CHANGE IN CANADA** Global annual surface temperature trends (°C/decade) for the periods (a) 1901–2000, (b) 1910–1945, (c) 1946–1975, and (d) 1976–2000. The red, blue, and green circles indicate areas that, respectively, warmed, cooled, or had little or no change. The size of each circle is proportional to the magnitude of the change. Average warming in Canada in the twentieth century was 0.8°C, but the warming was not uniform in either time or space. It was greatest in the last quarter of the century and in the Arctic. *(Intergovernmental Panel on Climate Change. 2001. Climate change 2001: The scientific basis. Cambridge, UK: Cambridge University Press)*

◀ **FIGURE 11.12 DISAPPEARING GLACIER** Icemaker Glacier, in the southern Coast Mountains of British Columbia, is about half the size it was in the late nineteenth century. Like most other glaciers in western North America, Icemaker Glacier has thinned and retreated because of twentieth-century climate warming. *(John J. Clague)*

N

0 2000 4000 Kilometres

−1.4 −1.2 −1 −0.8 −0.6 −0.4 −0.2 0 +0.2 +0.4 +0.6 +0.8 +1 +1.2 +1.4

Effective glacier thinning (m/yr)

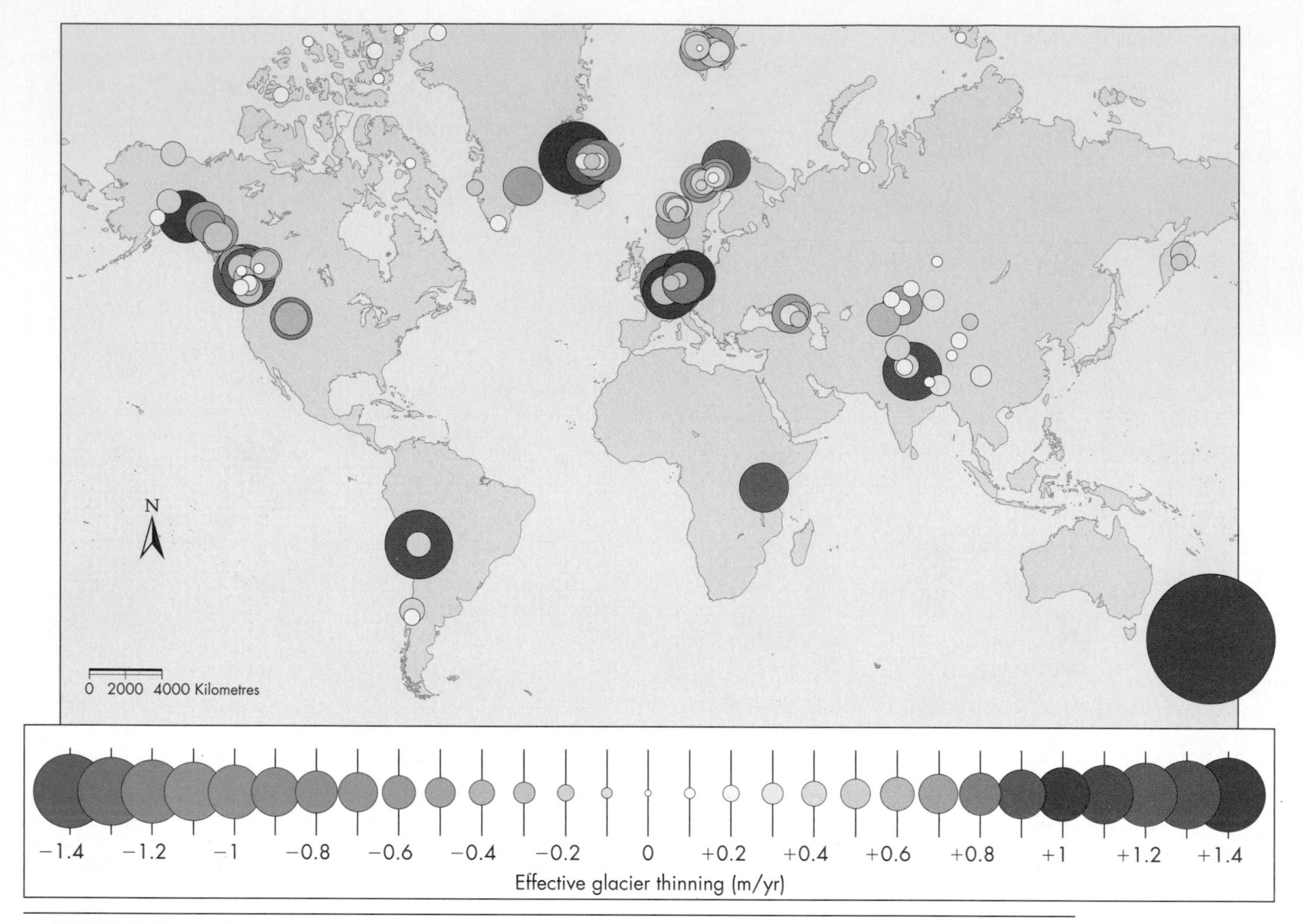

▲ **FIGURE 11.13 THINNING OF MOUNTAIN GLACIERS SINCE 1970** This map shows the average annual rate of thinning of 173 mountain glaciers between 1970 and 2004. Larger changes are plotted as larger circles and toward the back. Eighty-three percent of the surveyed glaciers thinned. *(Dyurgerov, M. B., and M. F. Meier. 2005. Glaciers and the changing Earth system: A 2004 snapshot. Institute of Arctic and Alpine Research Occasional Paper 58)*

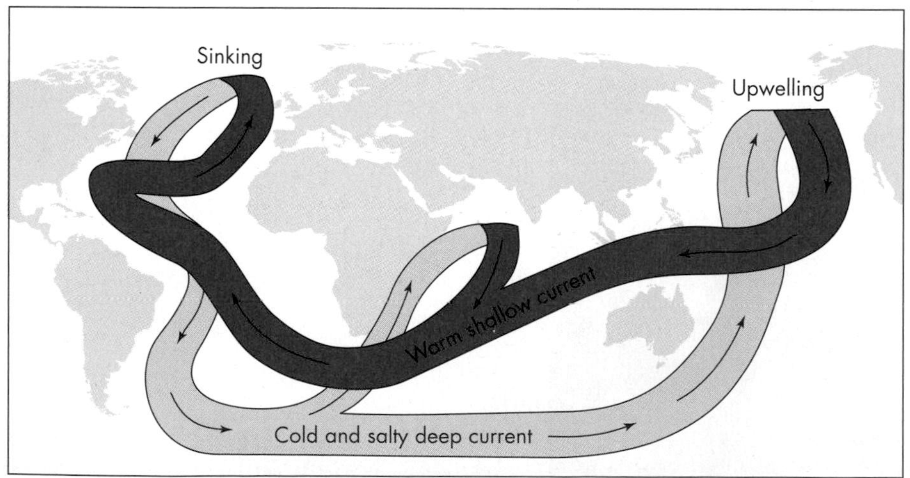

▲ **FIGURE 11.14 OCEAN CONVEYOR BELT** An idealized diagram of the oceanic conveyor belt current. The actual system is complex, but, in general, warm Atlantic surface water (red) is transported northward to near Greenland where it cools from contact with cold Arctic air. As the water becomes denser, it sinks to the bottom and flows south and then east to the Pacific Ocean, where upwelling occurs. The total flow rate is about 20 million m^3 per second, and the heat released to the atmosphere from the warm water keeps northern Europe 5°C to 10°C warmer than it would be without the conveyor belt. *(Modified after Broecker, W. 1997. Will our ride into the greenhouse future be a smooth one? Geology Today 7[5]:1–7)*

A report in 2001 from the Intergovernmental Panel on Climate Change concluded that, although uncertainties exist, (1) people have a discernible influence on global climate, (2) warming is now occurring, and (3) the mean surface temperature of Earth will likely increase from 1.4°C to 5.8°C during the twenty-first century.[5] People are producing large amounts of greenhouse gases that trap heat in the atmosphere, and the evidence is strong that increases in these gases are linked to an increase in the mean global temperature of Earth. A strong correlation can be shown between the concentration of atmospheric CO_2 and global temperature over at least the past 160,000 years (Figure 11.15). When CO_2 concentrations have been high, air temperatures have also been high; conversely, low concentrations of CO_2 correlate with periods of low global temperatures. However, to better understand global warming, we need to consider other important factors, sometimes called **forcing** factors, that influence climate. They include solar radiation, volcanic eruptions, and human input.

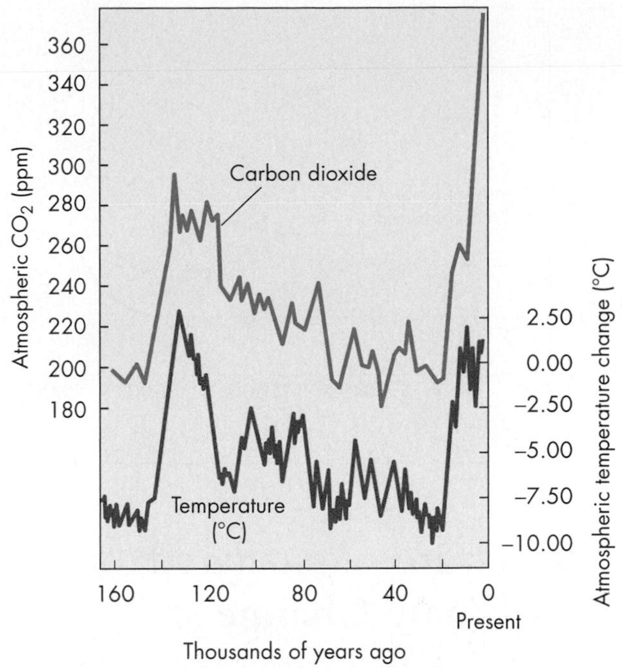

▲ **FIGURE 11.15 CARBON DIOXIDE AND TEMPERATURE** The changes in temperature and the concentration of atmospheric carbon dioxide over the past 160,000 years. The two variables are highly correlated, although scientists argue about what is cause and what is effect. *(Adapted from Schneider, S. H. 1989. The changing climate. Scientific American 261:74 © September, Scientific American, Inc. All rights reserved)*

Solar Forcing Variations in solar output should be evaluated as a cause of climate change because the Sun is the source of most of the surface heat on Earth. Scientists have found a way to estimate changes in solar output over the past 10,000 years or more. The method is based on the fact that carbon-14 in tree rings is a proxy of solar output. Cosmic rays originating from fusion reactions in the Sun pass through Earth's atmosphere and produce radioactive atoms of carbon-14 there. The larger the output of solar energy, the greater the abundance of atmospheric carbon-14 and, consequently, the higher the concentrations of the radioisotope in all living things, including trees. By measuring the concentration of carbon-14 in tree rings of known age, scientists can determine changes in solar output back through time. The record reveals that the Medieval Warm Period (A.D. 1000–1270) was a time of above-average solar radiation. Solar output was at a minimum during the major glacier advances of the Little Ice Age. It appears, therefore, that variability of energy output from the Sun can partially explain climatic variability during the past 1000 years. However, the effect is small—the inferred difference between solar output during the Medieval Warm Period and the Little Ice Age is only about 0.25 percent.[18]

Volcanic Forcing Explosive volcanic eruptions introduce large amounts of aerosols into the atmosphere. Aerosol particles reflect sunlight and can cool the atmosphere. Forcing by this mechanism is believed to have contributed to Little Ice Age cooling and climatic variability.[18]

Volcanic eruptions introduce some uncertainty into predictions of future climate conditions. The eruption of Mount Tambora, Indonesia, in 1815 was probably the largest explosive volcanic eruption of the past 10,000 years. Explosions, ash flows, and the tsunami from the eruption killed an estimated 90,000 people. About 50 km^3 of ash and volcanic gases were carried high into the atmosphere. The eruption caused months of cool weather, and Europe and North America suffered crop failures and famine during 1816, the "year without a summer." This event highlights the important linkages among geologic processes, the atmosphere, and people.[22] The linkage was also demonstrated following the 1991 eruption of Mount Pinatubo in the Philippines. Tremendous explosions sent volcanic ash up to 30 km into the stratosphere. The aerosol cloud of ash and sulphur dioxide gas remained in the atmosphere for several years and slightly cooled global climate during 1991 and 1992. Calculations suggest that the Mount Pinatubo aerosols offset the warming effects of additional greenhouse gases during 1991 and 1992. However, by 1994, most aerosols from the eruption had disappeared and atmospheric temperatures returned to previous higher levels.[23]

Human Forcing A recent study examined climate forcing over the past 1000 years, allowing us to place late twentieth-century warming within a longer-term context.[18] The study used a mathematical model to remove the climatic effects of variations in solar output and volcanic activity and to thus isolate the effect of human forcing. The study found that present warming greatly exceeds natural variability and is consistent with the warming predicted from greenhouse gas forcing (Figure 11.16). The potential effects and adjustments to this warming are described below.

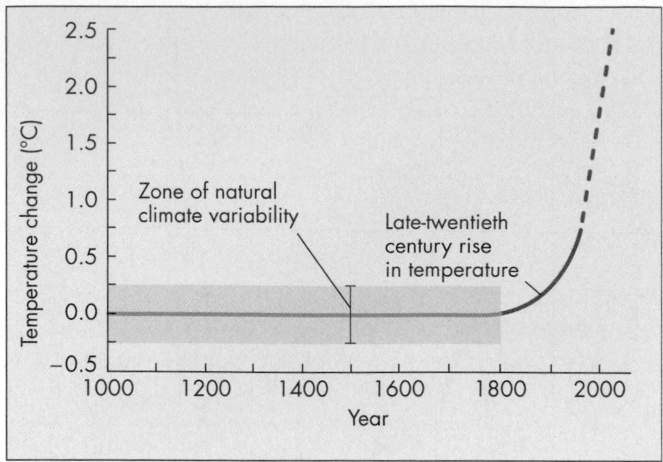

◄ **FIGURE 11.16 TEMPERATURE RISE IN THE TWENTIETH CENTURY** This graph is based on a computer model that removed the effects of solar and volcanic forcing to determine the impact of increases in greenhouse gases resulting from human activities. It suggests that the rise in global temperature in the twentieth century has been caused by human forcing. *(Modified after Crowley, T. J. 2000. Causes of climate change over the past 1000 years. Science 289:270–277)*

11.4 Hazards Associated with Climate Change

Surface processes and climate are intimately linked, and, as the name global warming suggests, all regions of the planet are subject to hazards associated with climate change (Figure 11.17). We know where tornadoes, hurricanes, blizzards, and wildfires occur in today's climate regime. If climate changes, these sites may shift, forcing people to cope with new problems. In addition, climate change will alter the location of agricultural zones, melt glaciers and thus contribute to sea-level rise, thaw permafrost, and stress plant and animal species by altering their habitat. Temperature increases may also accelerate desertification of arid lands and increase the frequency of severe droughts and wildfires.

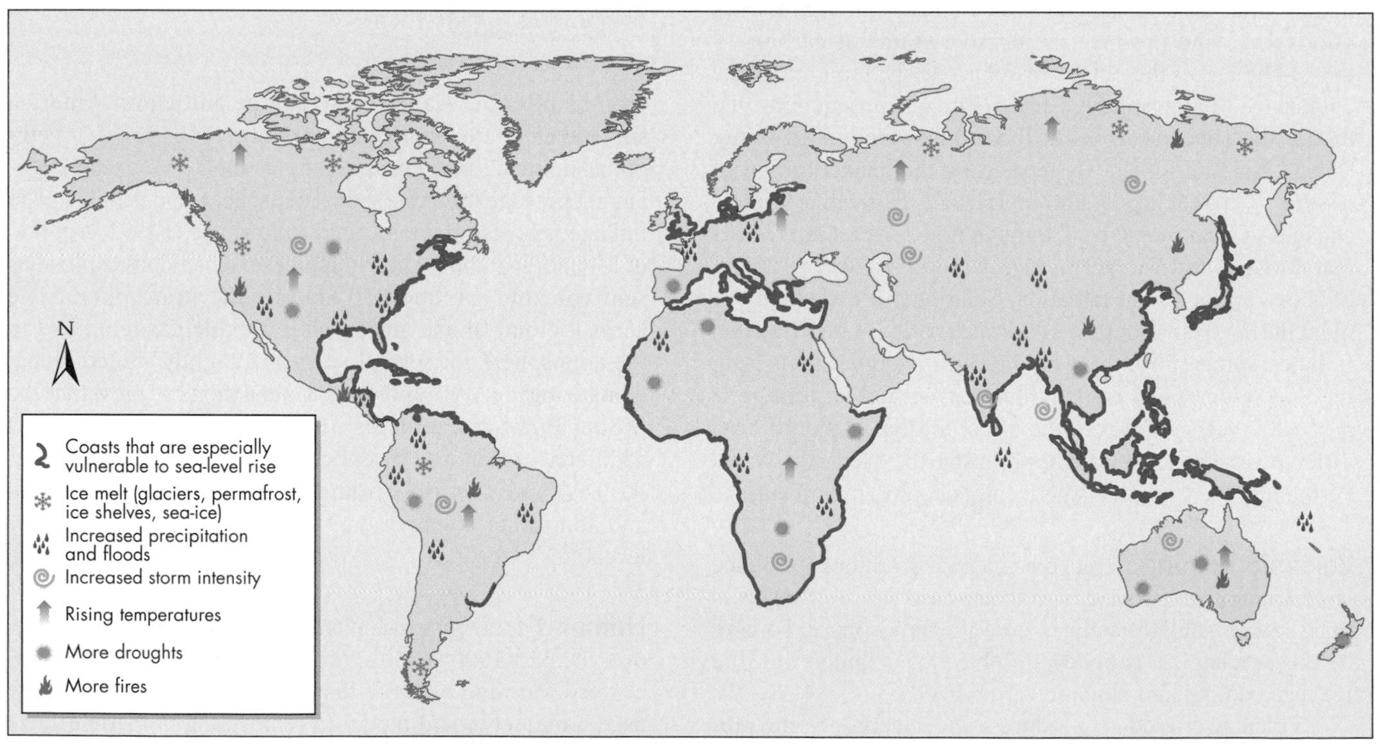

▲ **FIGURE 11.17 PROJECTED IMPACTS OF CLIMATE CHANGE** A global overview of climate change impacts in the twenty-first century. The effects include sea-level rise, more flooding, melting of glaciers and sea ice, permafrost degradation, more intense storms, rising temperatures, more droughts, and more wildfires. *(Modified from Abramowitz, J. 2001. Unnatural disasters. Worldwatch Paper 158, Washington, DC: Worldwatch Institute, based on data from Watson, R. T. et al. 1998. The regional impacts of climate change: An assessment of vulnerability. Special Report of IPCC Working Group II. Cambridge, U.K.; Cambridge University Press; McCarthy, J. J. et al., eds., Climate change 2001: Impacts, adaptation, and vulnerability: Contribution of Working Group II to the Third Assessment of the Intergovernmental Panel on Climate Change. Cambridge, U.K.: Cambridge University Press; and Revenga, C. et al. 1998. Watersheds of the world. Washington, DC: World Resources Institute and Worldwatch Institute)*

Climate Patterns

Global warming may significantly change rainfall patterns, soil moisture, and other climate factors that are important to agriculture. Some marginal agricultural areas in Canada and Eastern Europe may become more productive, whereas lands to the south will become more arid. However, such shifts do not necessarily mean that prime agricultural zones will also move north. Maximum production of grains and other foods depends just as much on soil conditions as on climate, and suitable soils will not be present in all areas that experience a more favourable climate for agriculture. The uncertainty around effects of climate change on agriculture is a major concern. Increasing global production of grain is crucial for feeding the growing human population.

Global warming may also increase the frequency or intensity of violent storms, an issue just as important as which areas become wetter, drier, warmer, or cooler. Warmer oceans could feed more energy into hurricanes and typhoons. More or larger hurricanes would increase the risk of living in low-lying coastal areas of Mexico and the United States that are experiencing rapid population growth.

A natural phenomenon called ENSO (El Niño/Southern Oscillation), or more commonly **El Niño**, dramatically illustrates how a change in ocean circulation can affect the frequency and intensity of storms, landslides, drought, and fires (see Case Study 11.1). El Niño is an oceanic and an atmospheric phenomenon related to unusually high surface temperatures in the eastern equatorial Pacific Ocean. It is accompanied by drought and high-intensity rainstorms in different places on

11.1 CASE STUDY

El Niño

El Niño is an oceanic and atmospheric phenomenon characterized by high surface temperatures in the eastern equatorial Pacific; drought in parts of southeast Asia, Australia, Africa, and South America; and wet weather and flooding in parts of the western and southern United States. An El Niño event probably begins with a slight reduction in the trade winds, after which warm water in the western equatorial Pacific Ocean begins to flow eastward (Figure 11.A). The eastward flow further reduces the strength of the trade winds, causing

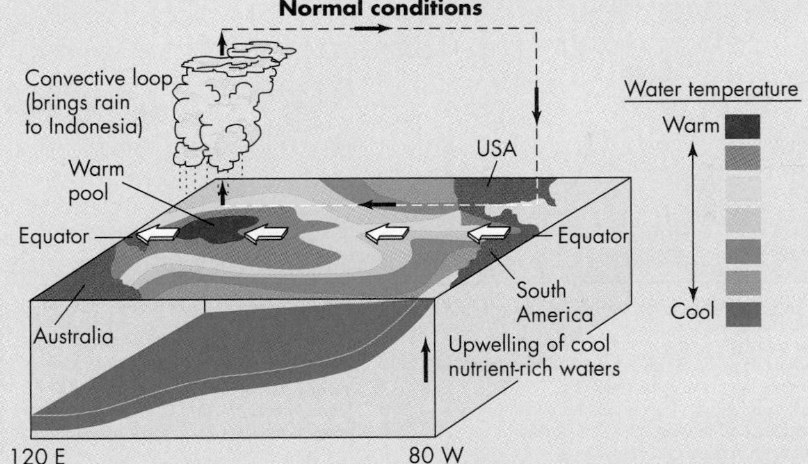

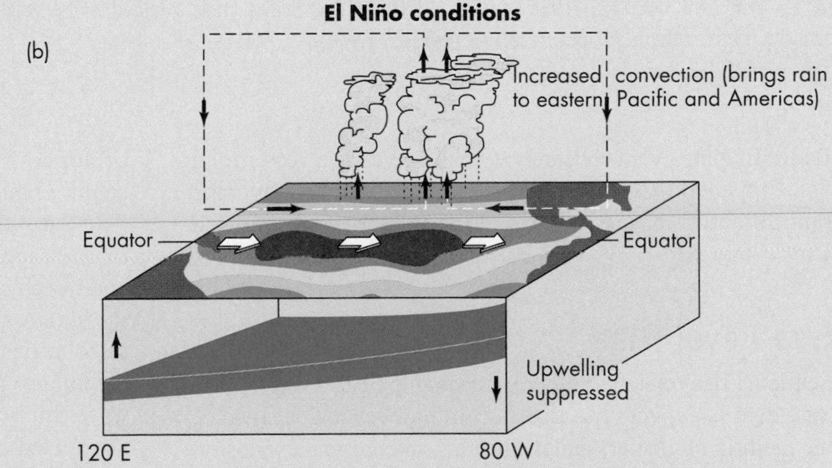

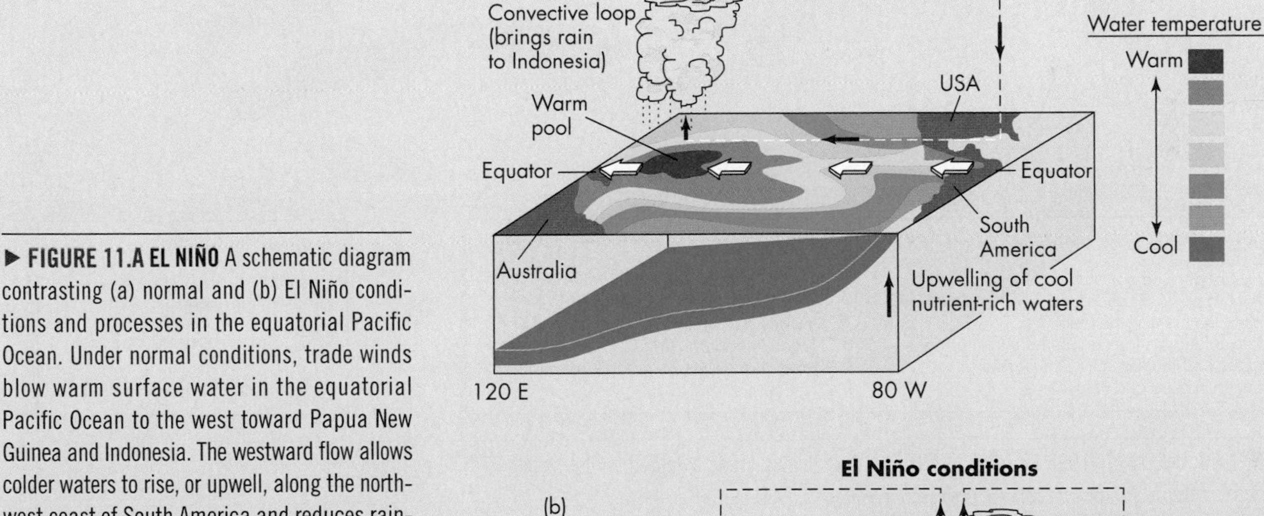

▶ FIGURE 11.A EL NIÑO A schematic diagram contrasting (a) normal and (b) El Niño conditions and processes in the equatorial Pacific Ocean. Under normal conditions, trade winds blow warm surface water in the equatorial Pacific Ocean to the west toward Papua New Guinea and Indonesia. The westward flow allows colder waters to rise, or upwell, along the northwest coast of South America and reduces rainfall in that area. During an El Niño event, winds blow the warm water east toward South America, upwelling of colder water is suppressed, and rainfall increases in parts of the Americas. *(Modified after National Oceanic and Atmospheric Administration/PMEL/TAO. 2002. NOAA El Niño page.* www.elnino.noaa.gov. *Accessed January 9, 2005)*

11.1 CASE STUDY *(Continued)*

more warm water to move eastward, until surface waters across the entire equatorial Pacific from Asia to the west coast of South America are warmer than normal.[24]

During El Niño years, extra amounts of water vapour are added to the atmosphere by evaporation of warm tropical waters. The increase in water vapour and changes in the trade winds increase rainfall in Peru, Ecuador, and the southern United States, cause more frequent and severe hurricanes along the Pacific coast of Mexico, and produce severe drought in Indonesia, Papua New Guinea, Australia, and Brazil.

A strong El Niño event in 1997 and 1998 contributed to hurricanes, floods, landslides, drought, and fires that caused widespread damage to crops, roads, buildings, and other structures (Figure 11.B). Australia, Papua New Guinea, Indonesia, the Americas, and Africa were particularly hard hit. Researchers disagree over the amount of damage the 1997–1998 El Niño caused, but all agree it was significant.[25,26]

The opposite of an El Niño event is a *La Niña*, during which eastern Pacific waters are cool and the southern United States experiences drought rather than floods. The alternation of El Niño and La Niña conditions is a natural phenomenon that was only recently recognized.[27] We don't understand the cause of these events, but scientists have voiced concern that global warming may increase their frequency and strength.

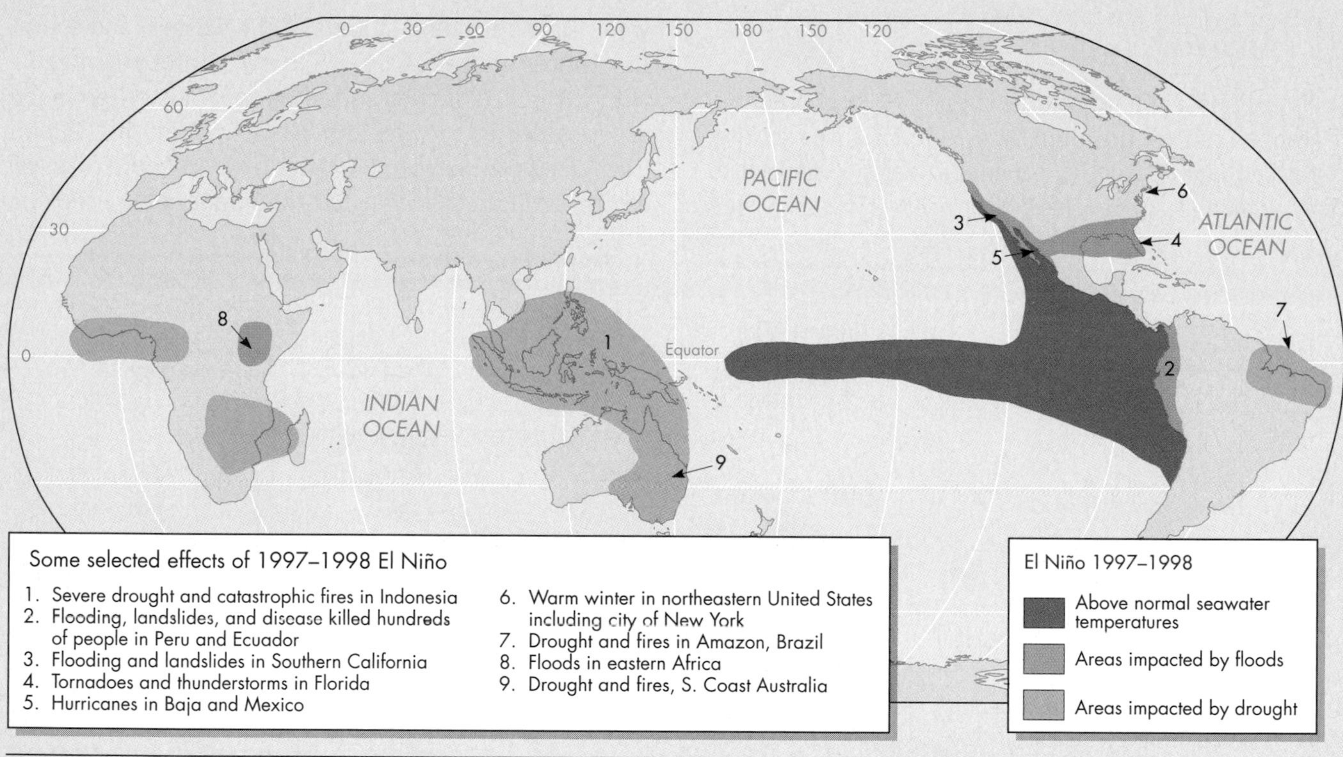

▲ **FIGURE 11.B THE 1997–1998 EL NIÑO EVENT** The map shows areas affected by the strong El Niño event in 1997 and 1998, and the event's effects. *(Data from National Oceanic and Atmospheric Administration, 1998)*

Earth. El Niño events occur every 5 to 10 years; a very strong one happened in 1997–1998 and resulted in above-average rainfall and flooding in parts of the western and southern United States.

Sea-Level Rise

Sea-level rise related to global warming is a serious problem. Sea level is expected to rise in coming decades because of the melting of glaciers and the heating and thermal expansion of upper ocean waters. Estimates of sea-level rise in this century range widely, from a few dozen centimetres to more than 2 m.[5] Even a 40 cm rise would have huge environmental and economic impacts—it would increase coastal erosion and threaten low-lying areas with flooding (see Professional Profile). A global sea-level rise of 1 m would be catastrophic to countries in the South Pacific and Indian Oceans, where the highest points are only a few metres above sea level (see Case Study 11.2). No coastal country, however, would be unaffected because sea-level rise threatens infrastructure at the present shoreline. Significant and extraordinarily expensive alterations would be needed to protect investments in these areas. Countries would have to choose between making very substantial investments in controlling coastal erosion and flooding or allowing beaches and estuaries to migrate landward over wide areas.[28]

PROFESSIONAL PROFILE

Rick Lohr, President of ICC

You would not expect the task of moving a 4400 t lighthouse to be "mostly nuts and bolts and hydraulics." But this is how Rick Lohr, president of the International Chimney Corporation (ICC), describes the task of moving the Cape Hatteras Lighthouse—the tallest brick lighthouse in the world—when erosion threatened to destroy the historic structure (Figure 11.C).

ICC was contracted to move the lighthouse to a safe location away from the shoreline in 1998. The company immediately developed a plan to ensure that the project would go smoothly. Among other things, it closely examined the 900 m path to the lighthouse's new home for weak spots that might cause the structure to collapse during the move.

"Sand compresses well, better than a lot of soils," Lohr says. "What you're concerned about is, are there any sinkholes?" To find out, ICC conducted what is known as "proof rolling," which involves moving a similar amount of weight along the route. The test did not require an extraordinary amount of weight; the total surface area of the structure at ground level, including the hydraulic jacks and rollers that ICC installed, was about 450 m^2, making the average pressure at any point on the route about 9 t/m^2.

The company made the move with a Unified Jack System, invented in the 1950s by Pete Freisen, an ICC employee. For this project, the system consisted of 120 jacks, which allowed the base of the lighthouse to remain flat during the move, no matter what the pressure. After cutting the lighthouse from its foundation, the 120 jacks were placed under the structure in a triangle comprising three groups of 40 jacks. The practice, which spread the load over three "centres of effort," is standard for all large moves, Lohr notes. "We move in three zones, no matter what the structure looks like." ICC used the same method for moving an entire terminal at Newark International Airport in 2000.

The theory behind this strategy, Lohr says, is that one of the three points of the triangular array of jacks can sink without stressing the structure itself. He compares the ICC support system to a tricycle: if a tricycle gets a flat tire, it tips in the direction of the flat, but the structure is not stressed. In contrast, if one of the four wheels of a wagon gets a flat, the base of the structure suffers stress near the flat wheel. "If you hit a soft spot, you just tip a little," and the jacks can be readjusted.

Such companies as ICC now use computers to calculate loads and the centre of gravity of structures, but the science of moving large objects has not changed since the early twentieth century. "Strangely enough," Lohr says, "everything is pretty basic."

—Chris Wilson

(a)

(b)

▲ **FIGURE 11.C MOVING A LIGHTHOUSE** The historic Cape Hatteras Lighthouse was moved in the summer of 1999 to prevent it from being destroyed by coastal erosion. (a) The lighthouse before it was moved, only about 100 m from the shore. *(Don Smetzer/Getty Images Inc.-Stone Allstock)* (b) The lighthouse being moved; it should be safe at its new location for at least the next 50 years. *(Reuters/Stringer/Getty Images Inc.-Hulton Archive Photos)*

11.2 CASE STUDY

Maldive Islands Threatened

The Maldives, a nation of 300,000 people and nearly 1200 small coral islands in the Indian Ocean, cannot afford to see ocean levels rise.

The islands are tropical paradises famous for their beaches of white sand, pristine coral gardens, and crystalline lagoons, but they are close to sea level—the average elevation of the Maldives is less than 1 m above sea level. If sea level continues to rise, much of this nation could face a watery burial.

Sea-level rise is already creating problems. The islands are vulnerable to tsunami and storms, and rising sea level will only make these problems worse.

The long-time president of the Maldives, Maumoon Abdul Gayoom, has for nearly two decades been a vocal advocate for an international reduction of emissions of carbon dioxide and other gases that contribute to global warming, particularly among major industrial nations, such as the United States. The nation even has a permanent mission to the United Nations in New York to argue its case.

After the capital city, Malé, suffered major damage from storm waves in the late 1980s, the Japanese government provided funding for a massive seawall to protect the island (Figure 11.D). The seawall is 3 m high and cost millions of dollars to construct. It protects Malé from storms but not from sea-level rise. If the sea rises significantly in the next decades—even a rise of 1 m would spell disaster for much of the archipelago—the only option for most of the nation's residents would be evacuation.

Although experts do not entirely agree on the threat that climate change poses to this island nation, Gayoom and others continue to pressure the United Nations to address the problem now, before the Maldives become a modern-day Atlantis.

—Chris Wilson

▲ **FIGURE 11.D AERIAL VIEW OF MALÉ IN THE MALDIVE ISLANDS** A seawall surrounds most of Malé, capital of the Maldives. The seawall was constructed to protect the island from waves up to 2 m high at a cost of about $4000/m^2$. Seawalls have been built on only a few of the 1192 islands that make up this country. Approximately 80 percent of the land area of the Maldives is less than 1 m above mean sea level. *(Peter Essick/Aurora & Quanta Productions Inc.)*

Thawing of Permafrost

Climate modellers suggest that the greatest warming during the remainder of this century will be at high latitudes, where the ground is frozen. Thawing of permafrost presents problems for people living in the Arctic and for many northern animals and plants. It also poses an additional problem: very large amounts of carbon are stored in frozen peat deposits in northern Canada and Siberia. With large-scale thawing of permafrost, some of these organic sediments will decay and release carbon dioxide into the atmosphere, thus producing additional climate warming. This scenario is an example of a positive feedback, a "runaway" situation in which the output of a process amplifies or increases the process itself.

Changes in the Biosphere

Global warming may already be causing changes that threaten ecological systems and people. The changes include shifts in the range and *habitats* of plants and animals. Examples of observed changes in range are the migration of mosquitoes carrying such diseases as malaria and dengue fever to higher elevations in Africa, South America, Central America, and Mexico; the recent appearance of West Nile virus in Canada; the northward movement of some butterfly species in Europe and birds in the United Kingdom; the invasion of alpine meadows in western North America by coniferous trees; and a shift in the distribution of alpine plants in Austria to higher elevations. Earlier melting of sea ice in the Arctic is stressing some seabirds, walruses, and polar bears; and the warming of shallow water in the Florida Keys, Bermuda, Australia's Great Barrier Reef, and many other tropical oceans is killing corals.[29]

Warming of several degrees Celsius will result in major changes in the natural vegetation zones defined by Vladimir Koeppen. For example, boreal forest (Dfc in Figure 11.3) will probably expand northward at the expense of polar tundra (ET). Similarly, grasslands and deserts may in the future extend north of their present limits. Many of the changes in vegetation assemblages may be facilitated by wildfires that remove plants no longer adapted to the area in which they occur. Other plants, rather than shifting latitudinally, will become more restricted, perhaps as isolated small populations.

Desertification and Drought

A change that is affecting many people is **desertification**. Desertification refers to *human-induced* degradation of productive land, leading ultimately to a more desert-like state.[30] Climate change may exacerbate the problem in areas that are already becoming warmer and drier.

Desertification is preceded and accompanied by loss of vegetation and degradation of soil, primarily through erosion.[10] Vegetation loss and soil erosion degrade the human environment by reducing food production, thereby contributing to malnutrition and famine.[10] The changes may be so severe that land loses its productiveness and may not recover for decades or centuries. This situation contrasts with drought, which is normally a short-term, reversible problem.[30]

Global warming may increase the length and severity of **drought** in some areas of the world. Drought is a normal part of our planet's climate system, and most regions experience unusually warm and dry weather leading to drought conditions. However, these conditions are more common and more severe in semi-arid and arid areas than in humid ones (Case Study 11.3). As climate changes, areas that become drier and warmer will have more droughts, which will put pressure on regional food and water supplies. Some areas with no significant history of drought may have to cope with it in the future. People living in these areas may be ill-equipped to deal with the problem.

11.3 CASE STUDY

Palliser Triangle

Nearly half of Canada's agricultural production comes from the Palliser Triangle, a semi-arid grassland area in southern Alberta and Saskatchewan, extending south from Red Deer to the U.S. border (Figure 11.E). The area was named after Captain John Palliser who surveyed it in 1857–1860 and declared it "forever comparatively useless for agriculture" because of the low precipitation and poor soil. In the 1870s, John Macoun, a government botanist, argued that the land would be good for growing wheat. He promoted it to immigrant farmers who began to farm in the triangle near the end of the nineteenth century.

The homesteaders struggled from the beginning. Drought intensified in 1929 and, together with poor agricultural practices, turned the area into a dust bowl in the 1930s, helping plunge Canada into the Great Depression. Farmers watched helplessly as their livelihoods blew away in clouds of fertile topsoil (Figure 11.F). The drought lasted from 1929 until 1937 and devastated 7.3 million ha, one-quarter of Canada's arable land, causing almost 14,000 farms to be abandoned.

The Prairie Farm Rehabilitation Administration of 1935 provided financial and technical support to the Prairie agricultural community. The agency instituted farm dugouts for watering livestock, strip farming to prevent soil drifting, the seeding of abandoned land for community pastures, and tree planting to protect the soil from wind erosion. Eventually, the new farming techniques and a series of wet years helped reestablish the Palliser Triangle as an important agricultural region, but

11.3 CASE STUDY (*Continued*)

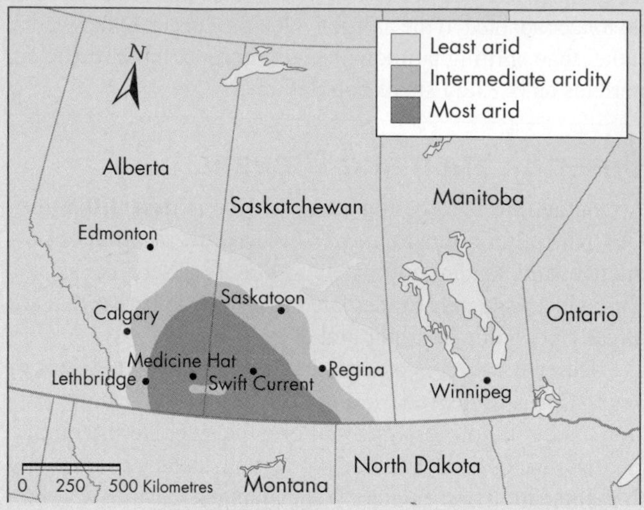

▲ **FIGURE 11.E PALLISER TRIANGLE** The extent of the Palliser Triangle in western Canada. This drought-prone area covers parts of Alberta, Saskatchewan, and Manitoba and is notable for its lack of trees and its dry climate.

farming has always been precarious and farmers repeatedly require government help to deal with drought conditions. During the drought of 1988, when mean annual temperature in the triangle was 2°C–4°C above the 30-year mean and precipitation was half the 1950–1980 average, wheat production fell by 29 percent, contributing to a $1.5 billion drop in farm receipts in Saskatchewan alone.[31]

Future sustainable agriculture in the driest parts of the region is threatened by global climate change, which is expected to result in more frequent drought. Global circulation model simulations indicate that global warming resulting from increased greenhouse gas concentrations in the atmosphere is likely to bring warmer, drier conditions to the northern Great Plains.[32] It is possible that drought will become more frequent than it has been since the area was first settled by Canadians more than 100 years ago.[33]

Canadian researchers have gathered large amounts of evidence that allow them to reconstruct climate in the Palliser Triangle thousands of years ago. Saline lakes in the region contain sediments that span the past 7000 years and contain microfossils and other proxy indicators of past climate. Analysis of these indicators makes it clear that the brief historical record does not capture the full range of climate variability that the region experiences. Within the past 2000 years, there have been periods, perhaps decades or more in length, that were significantly more arid than at any time in the past 100 years.[34] During these hyperarid periods, the water table was several metres lower than today and most lakes in the region were dry. Similarly, periods of sand dune activity in the nineteenth century imply more arid conditions than exist in the region today.[35] The data highlight the vulnerability of water resources on the Canadian Prairies and raise questions about the sustainability of agriculture during droughts that are likely later this century.

▲ **FIGURE 11.F THE CANADIAN DUST BOWL** The Palliser Triangle was struck by drought in the 1920s, which contributed to hardships among homesteaders during the Great Depression. *(Provincial Archives of Alberta, A.3742)*

Wildfires

The relation between climate change and wildfire is complex, and the two phenomena interact on a variety of levels. Scientists have predicted that global warming will lead to an increase in drought, El Niño events, and wildfires. Scientists in Spain studied a strip of Mediterranean coastline between 1968 and 1994, comparing the number and size of forest fires with the temperature and aridity of the area. They found that as the coastal area warmed and became more arid, the number of fires and the size of the area burned increased.[36] Another group of scientists used historical weather data and four different *global circulation models* (GCMs) to evaluate forest-fire hazard in Canada and Russia under a warmer climate. The study suggested that forest fires will be more frequent and severe and that the number of years between two successive fires will decrease.[37]

More frequent and more severe wildfires will have ecological impacts. Large wildfires may facilitate or accelerate replacement of ecosystems that are poorly adapted to a warmer climate with ones that can tolerate more warmth and drier conditions. For example, as climate warms, grassland and shrubland ecosystems may expand at the expense of coniferous forests in the forest-grassland transition zone in Canada and the United States.

11.5 Minimizing the Effects of Global Warming

A report released by the World Wide Fund for Nature in the fall of 2000 concluded that climate change is already increasing the frequency and intensity of natural disasters and that the trend is likely to continue. It predicts that most of the world will suffer an increase in violent rainstorms, droughts, tropical cyclones, and other climatic disruptions.[38]

If we accept the scientific consensus that Earth is becoming warmer,[5,39] we must work to minimize the detrimental effects of the warming. The problem is complex and global in scale, and it will be solved only if world leaders cooperate. International agreements must be made and honoured, and new technologies and mitigation techniques must be developed and implemented. Individuals will also have to change their attitudes toward fossil fuels and conservation. Only if citizens of our global community work together will we be able to reduce the inevitable warming and the problems it creates.

International Agreements

International agreements are required to reduce emissions of greenhouse gases. Negotiations have continued since the Earth Summit in Rio de Janeiro in 1992, when world leaders pledged to combat global warming. A United Nations Framework Convention on Climate Change held in Kyoto, Japan, in 1997 produced an international agreement, known as the *Kyoto Protocol*, to reduce emissions of greenhouse gases, especially carbon dioxide. The agreement established targets for nations to reach in reducing their emissions of these gases. The United States originally agreed to reductions, but in 2001 refused to be a signatory to the agreement, much to the disappointment of other nations. It also appears that Canada will not meet its Kyoto target.

Most anthropogenic CO_2 is produced by the burning of fossil fuels, therefore energy planning that relies more on alternative energy sources, such as wind, solar, or geothermal power, will lead to lower CO_2 emissions into the atmosphere. A greater use of nuclear energy would also reduce the requirement for carbon-based fuels,[40] but problems with nuclear power plant safety and, especially, waste disposal have led to much resistance in many countries to adopting this alternative source of energy. Curbing greenhouse gas emissions is expensive and may be difficult or impossible for developing nations without the help of the United States, Canada, Japan, and Europe.

An international summit in The Hague in 2000 focused on alternative methods of reducing greenhouse gas emissions to reach the emission targets in the Kyoto Protocol. The alternative methods include (1) clean development mechanisms by which firms and governments invest in projects or technologies that improve the "carbon balance" of developing nations, such as through reforestation to help absorb carbon dioxide; (2) joint implementation, which allows emission credits to be shared by developing states and rich countries that help the developing states achieve their goals either by investment or technology transfers; and (3) emission trading, where countries that easily meet their emissions targets can sell credits to countries that fail to meet theirs. Unfortunately, The Hague conference ended without an agreement, largely because of opposition to a proposal to allow countries to earn credits against their emissions quotas for the carbon dioxide absorbed by their farmlands and forests. This proposal was supported by Canada, the United States, and Japan, but it was strongly opposed by the European Union and most environmental groups.

We are dependent on carbon-based fuels, in part because their production and consumption are a major part of the world economy. The global economy cannot function at present without coal, natural gas, and oil. However, two possible scenarios for global warming and sea-level rise during the next 100 years demonstrate the importance of reducing our dependency on fossil fuels by transforming our global economy into one based on other energy sources (Figure 11.18). Both scenarios assume economic growth, with population peaking in the middle of the twenty-first century and declining thereafter. In the first scenario, more efficient energy technologies are introduced, but the energy system remains fossil-fuel intensive. Under this scenario, the average temperature on Earth will rise by about 4.5°C and sea level might rise 0.5 m. In the second scenario, the economic system has changed, reducing material consumption and introducing clean resource-efficient technologies. In this scenario, the average temperature will rise by about 2°C and sea level will rise less than 0.3 m.

All indications suggest that humanity is following the first scenario, with potentially grave consequences. Consumption

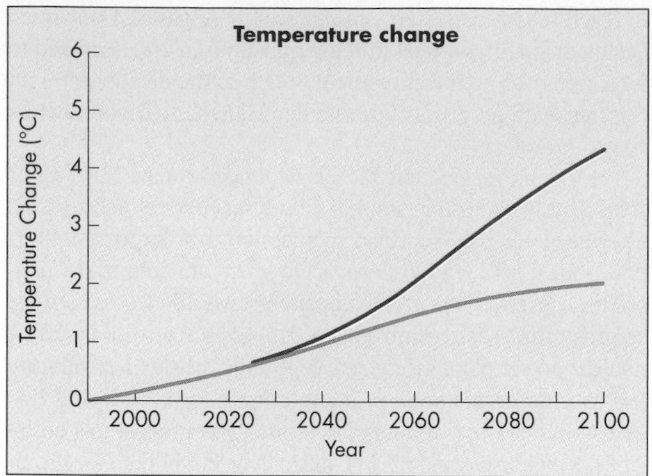

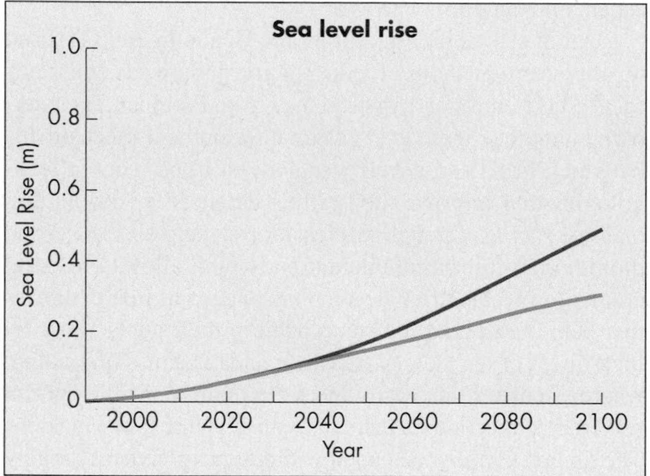

▲ **FIGURE 11.18 PROJECTED INCREASES IN TEMPERATURE AND SEA LEVEL** Graphs showing projected changes in (a) temperature and (b) sea level to the year 2100 under two scenarios. Scenario 1 (red line): rapid economic growth; energy systems based on extensive use of fossil fuels; new and more efficient technologies introduced; sometimes called the "business as usual" scenario. Scenario 2 (green line): rapid changes toward a service and information economy; reductions in material use; introduction of clean and resource-efficient technology. *(Modified from Intergovernmental Panel on Climate Change. 2001. Summary for policymakers. A report of Working Group I of the Intergovernmental Panel on Climate Change. Cambridge, U.K.: Cambridge University Press.* www.ipcc.ch/pub/spm22-01.pdf. *Accessed January 4, 2004)*

of fossil fuels continues to rise, largely because of increasing consumption in Canada, the United States, India, China, and other countries. Efforts to bring alternative sources of energy into widespread use have been resisted by some governments and companies. The global population continues to rise and, barring some catastrophe, probably will reach 10 billion by the middle of the twenty-first century.

Carbon Dioxide "Sinks"

As mentioned previously, plants use carbon dioxide during photosynthesis, releasing oxygen in the process. Therefore, large areas of forested land are considered "sinks" for CO_2. In this context, a **sink** is a biogeochemical storage reservoir. A notable example is a forest or wetland that sequesters atmospheric CO_2. Increasing the extent of forested land will reduce the amount of CO_2 in the atmosphere and thus may help reduce global warming.

Scientists and engineers are exploring innovative ideas of carbon sequestration, including pumping large quantities of CO_2 underground into abandoned oil reservoirs[41] and stimulating phytoplankton growth by fertilizing the oceans with iron.[42] Phytoplankton are floating microscopic organisms that remove CO_2 from the atmosphere by photosynthesis. Although preliminary results are promising, some scientists warn that ocean fertilization could release more greenhouse gases to the atmosphere than it removes.[43]

Adaptation

Scientists argue that some global warming is inevitable, that even with altered human behaviour, climate will continue to warm. This inevitability should not be used as an excuse for doing nothing, because the amount of warming will depend on how rapidly we make the transition from a carbon-based economy to one based on other sources of energy, such as hydrogen, wind, and solar power. It does, however, require that governments and people adapt to the changes in climate that are coming. **Adaptation** requires an understanding of the consequences of a warmer atmosphere, including the possibility of more and stronger hurricanes, sea-level rise, increased drought and more wildfires, and shifts in plant and animal communities.

Fossil Fuels and the Future Threat of Global Warming

From an environmental point of view and, perhaps, also political and social ones, global warming is best dealt with by reducing our dependency on fossil fuels and switching to clean energy alternatives. However, as the stalemate at The Hague climate conference indicates, this idea is difficult to accept because the global economy is based on carbon-based fuels. Major economic repercussions will accompany the shift away from the use of coal, gas, and oil as energy sources. However, a major shift from fossil fuel energy to alternative sources that produce less CO_2 will not happen overnight. Rather, it will require a transition period, perhaps decades. Yet, evidence from glacier ice cores indicates that significant climate change can occur abruptly, possibly within a decade.[44] If natural or human-induced warming were to occur quickly, people would find it difficult to adjust and the consequences would be serious. Human civilization was born and has developed to its present highly industrialized and integrated state in about 8000 years. That period has been one of relatively stable, warm climate that is unusual in the history of Earth. It is difficult to imagine the human suffering that might result late in this century from a quick change to harsher conditions at a time when there are several billion more people on Earth to feed.

Summary

An understanding of climate is essential for the study of natural hazards because the two are intimately linked. Climate is the characteristic atmospheric conditions within an area over a period of years to decades. Weather refers to atmospheric conditions over a much shorter timescale, typically days or weeks. The surface of Earth is divided into different climate zones, each of which is defined by its average precipitation and temperature and natural vegetation.

The atmosphere is the gaseous envelope that surrounds Earth and keeps it warm enough to support life. It comprises mainly nitrogen and oxygen, with smaller amounts of water vapour, argon, carbon dioxide, and other trace elements and compounds. Nitrogen, oxygen, and argon are permanent gases; their atmospheric concentrations do not vary over time. Carbon dioxide, water vapour, ozone, methane, and aerosols are variable gases. Their concentrations vary over time and they play an important role in the climate system.

Earth's climate has changed through geologic time. Several major glacial episodes have punctuated the past billion years of the planet's history. During each glacial episode, large ice sheets formed and decayed many times. Glacier advances were separated by warmer interglaciations, such as the one we are experiencing today. During peak glacial conditions, about 30 percent of Earth's land area was covered by glacier ice; present-day ice cover is only one-third this amount. Glaciation has many causes that operate on different timescales. On the longest timescale, tens of millions of years, glaciation is controlled by the position of the continents relative to the equator and the poles. On timescales of thousands to hundreds of thousands of years, variations in Earth's orbital pattern control the amount of solar energy reaching specific points on the planet. Changes in oceanic and atmospheric circulation, volcanic activity, and energy output from the Sun affect climate on the shortest timescales, that is, years to hundreds of years.

The most recent major glacial episode began early in the Cenozoic and intensified about 2.5 million years ago. Since then, Earth's mean annual temperature has fluctuated markedly. At present, Earth's temperature is rising because of a combination of natural and anthropogenic causes.

Trapping of heat by Earth's atmosphere is referred to as the greenhouse effect, and gases that contribute to this effect are called greenhouse gases. Carbon dioxide is an important greenhouse gas that has increased markedly in the atmosphere since the Industrial Revolution. The rise in global temperature since the end of the Little Ice Age in the late nineteenth century, and especially since 1980, appears to have been at least partly caused by large anthropogenic inputs of carbon dioxide and methane into the atmosphere.

Climate and natural hazards are intimately linked. Shifts in climate zones because of global warming may change the areas that are vulnerable to hurricanes, tornadoes, blizzards, drought, and wildfires. Global warming will also alter agricultural and weather patterns, accelerate the current rise in sea level, force plants and animals to migrate, and alter ecosystems. It may also lead to desertification of arid lands, drought, and an increase in frequency and intensity of wildfires.

Substantial scientific evidence demonstrates that climate is currently warming and that the warming is caused in part or largely by human activities. Governments must work together to slow global warming by decreasing our dependence on fossil fuels. Weaning ourselves from hydrocarbons requires adoption of a range of strategies, including conservation, large-scale development of alternative, non-carbon based sources of energy, and carbon sequestration.

Key Terms

adaptation (p. 338)
aerosol (p. 319)
anthropogenic (p. 319)
climate (p. 317)
desertification (p. 335)
drought (p. 335)
El Niño (p. 331)
forcing (p. 329)
greenhouse effect (p. 323)
greenhouse gas (p. 319)
Holocene Epoch (p. 321)
Milankovitch cycle (p. 322)
ocean conveyor belt (p. 325)
ozone depletion (p. 319)
Pleistocene Epoch (p. 321)
sink (p. 338)
stratosphere (p. 319)
troposphere (p. 319)
weather (p. 317)

Review Questions

1. What is the difference between climate and weather?
2. What is Koeppen's climate classification? On what is it based?
3. How does ozone differ from oxygen? Where is ozone found? Why is it important to humans?
4. What is methane? Why is it important to climate? What are the anthropogenic sources of methane?
5. What is an aerosol? How do aerosols influence climate?
6. Explain or draw the general global pattern of atmospheric circulation.
7. What is an interglacial interval?
8. What are the causes of continental glaciation?
9. Explain the greenhouse effect. Describe the types of radiation that are involved and the anthropogenic gases that contribute to greenhouse warming.
10. How do variations in Earth's orbit affect climate?
11. Explain solar, volcanic, and human forcing.
12. What natural hazards are associated with global warming?
13. What are the causes of sea-level rise?
14. How will global warming affect the biosphere?
15. What is desertification? How does it differ from drought?
16. Which parts of Earth are currently experiencing the greatest amounts of warming?

17. What will be the effects of sea-level rise?
18. What is the Kyoto Protocol?
19. What two sinks are being considered for removing carbon dioxide from the atmosphere?
20. Explain El Niño and its effects.

Critical Thinking Questions

1. In this chapter we discussed the possible effects of continued global warming. What do you think will be the effects of global warming in the area where you live? Would you expect any change in risk from natural hazards because of climate warming? Think about the ways global warming might change the lives and lifestyles of people living in your area. Have you seen any evidence of recent global warming?
2. Assessing the cause and rates of change is important in many disciplines. Have a discussion with your parents or someone of their age and write down the major changes that have occurred in their lifetimes as well as in your lifetime. Characterize these changes as gradual, abrupt, surprising, or chaotic, or use other similar descriptive words of your choice. Were the changes local, regional, or global? Analyze the changes and consider which ones were important to you personally.
3. How do you think global warming will affect you in the future? You can find information that will help you answer this question on the Environment Canada website (**www.ec.gc.ca/climate**) and on websites of provincial, territorial, state, natural resource, environmental protection, public health, or emergency preparedness agencies. What adjustments will you have to make? What can you do to mitigate the effects of the warming?
4. Some people, for cultural, political, religious, or other reasons, do not accept the conclusion that global warming is happening and that it is primarily caused by people. What do you see as the basis for their opinions or beliefs? How do you think they might be convinced otherwise? If you share their opinions or beliefs, indicate why you do and what it would take to convince you that climate is warming due to human activities.

Selected Web Resources

Intergovernmental Panel on Climate Change (IPCC)
www.ipcc.ch The largest organization addressing climate change; jointly established by the World Meteorological Organization and the United Nations Environmental Programme in 1988

Climate Change
http://climatechange.unep.net Information on climate change from the United Nations Environment Programme

Climate Change in Canada
www.ec.gc.ca/climate Information on air, weather, and climate change from Environment Canada

http://adaptation.nrcan.gc.ca A series of seven posters depicting regional impacts of climate change in Canada

www.davidsuzuki.org/Climate_Change Information on climate change in Canada from the David Suzuki Foundation

http://www.pembina.org/climate-change/index.php Information on climate change in Canada from the Pembina Institute

Canadian Institute for Climate Studies
www.cics.uvic.ca/climate/change/cimpact.htm Report on implications for Canada of climate change

A Paleo Perspective on Global Warming
www.ngdc.noaa.gov/paleo/globalwarming/paleostory.html From the National Oceanic and Atmospheric Administration

Global Warming
http://epa.gov/climatechange/index.html Comprehensive information about global warming from the U.S. Environmental Protection Agency

Global Change Master Directory
http://gcmd.gsfc.nasa.gov Data and services about global change from the National Aeronautics and Space Administration

Pew Center on Global Climate Change
www.pewclimate.org Social, political, commercial, and scientific aspects of global climate change from a nonprofit and nonpartisan organization

U.S. Climate Change Science Program
www.climatescience.gov United States government site integrating federal research on global change and climate change

HAZARD CITY: ASSIGNMENTS IN APPLIED GEOLOGY

Snowpack Monitoring

The Issue

Snow accumulates during winter as a "snowpack." A frozen reservoir of sorts, the snowpack stores water until temperatures rise and the snow melts. Scientists monitor snowpacks for several reasons. For example, runoff from the snowpack recharges reservoirs that provide municipal and agricultural water and electricity. The rate at which the snowpack melts in spring and summer is also important; rapid melting may result in flooding. As climate warms, snowpack monitoring will take on added importance because of the need to maximize water availability while reducing the snowmelt flood risk.

Your Task

Hazard City has been dealing with two surface water problems: (1) spring flooding caused by rapid melting of the Lava Mountain snowpack and (2) water supply shortages during late summer and fall. You have been asked to prepare a plan to more efficiently use Johnson Reservoir to control flooding while maximizing water storage for the city's water needs and for hydroelectric power generation. You face the following constraints: (1) the level of Johnson Reservoir is low at the beginning of the spring snowmelt season; thus, almost the entire capacity of the reservoir can be used to store runoff; and (2) at the end of the spring snowmelt season, the water level of Johnson Reservoir should be as high as safely possible in order to maximize the amount of water in storage for the long dry summer.

The task seems straightforward, but there is one complication: The volume of water produced by snowmelt in the spring greatly exceeds the capacity of Johnson Reservoir. If the reservoir is filled too early in the spring, it will not be able to contain all the snowmelt runoff, and large volumes of water will have to be released from the reservoir, causing flooding. The best solution is to allow the initial runoff to pass through the reservoir and then, when there is just enough snow left on Lava Mountain to top up the reservoir, capture all remaining runoff. To do this successfully, you need a way to estimate the amount of water locked up in the Lava Mountain snowpack at any given time. Your job is to learn about snowpack monitoring, review the data that have been collected on Lava Mountain, and determine the general pattern of snowpack accumulation and melting.

Average Completion Time

1 hour

CHAPTER 12

▶ SIBERIAN IMPACT
An artist's conception of a 25 m to 50 m asteroid approaching Earth just before exploding 7 km above Siberia with a force equal to 10 Mt (megatons) of TNT. The blast flattened and burned forest but left no crater.
(© Joe Tucciarone)

Learning Objectives

Our planet has been bombarded by objects from space since its birth 4.6 billion years ago. The impacts of the largest of these objects have been linked to mass extinctions of species, including the dinosaurs 65 million years ago. We continue to face a risk of impacts from asteroids, comets, and meteoroids. Your goals in reading this chapter should be to

- Know the differences among asteroids, meteoroids, and comets
- Understand aerial bursts and extra-terrestrial impacts
- Understand the possible causes of mass extinction
- Know the evidence for the hypothesis that an extraterrestrial impact produced a mass extinction at the end of the Cretaceous Period
- Know the likely physical, chemical, and biological consequences of impact from a large asteroid or comet
- Understand the risk of extraterrestrial impacts and aerial bursts

Impacts and Extinctions

The Tunguska Event

Shortly before 7:00 A.M. on June 30, 1908, hundreds of people in Siberia reported seeing a blue-white fireball with a glowing tail descend from the sky. The fireball exploded above the Tunguska River valley in a sparsely populated, heavily forested area. It was later determined that the explosion had the force of 10 Mt (megatons) of TNT, equivalent to 10 hydrogen bombs. Few of the witnesses were close to the explosion, but its sound was heard hundreds of kilometres away and the air blast was recorded at meteorological stations throughout Europe. The blast flattened and burned more than 2000 km^2 of forest over an area more than twice the size of New York City (Figure 12.1).

A herdsman witnessed the devastation on the ground. His hut was completely flattened by the blast and its roof was blown away. Other witnesses a few dozen kilometres from the explosion reported being blown into the air and losing consciousness. They awoke to find a transformed landscape of smoke and burning toppled trees.

Russia was in the midst of political upheaval at the time of the event, and consequently there was no immediate investigation. In 1924, however, geologists working in the region interviewed surviving witnesses and determined that the blast from the explosion was heard over an area of at least 1 million km^2, equivalent in size to the province of British Columbia. Scientists returned to the area in 1927, expecting to find the impact crater of an asteroid. When they found no crater, they concluded that the devastation had been caused by an aerial explosion of a stony asteroid, probably at an altitude of about 7 km.[1,2] The size of the asteroid responsible for the explosion was later estimated to be 25 m to 50 m in diameter.

It was fortunate that the Tunguska event occurred in a sparsely populated region. If the asteroid had exploded over London, Paris, or Tokyo, millions of people would have died. Tunguska-type events are thought to occur, on average, about once every 1000 years.[3]

12.1 Earth's Place in Space

Preston Cloud, a famous geologist, wrote in 1978: "Born from the wreckage of stars, compressed to a solid state by the force of its own gravity, mobilized by heat of gravity and radioactivity, clothed in its filmy garments of air and

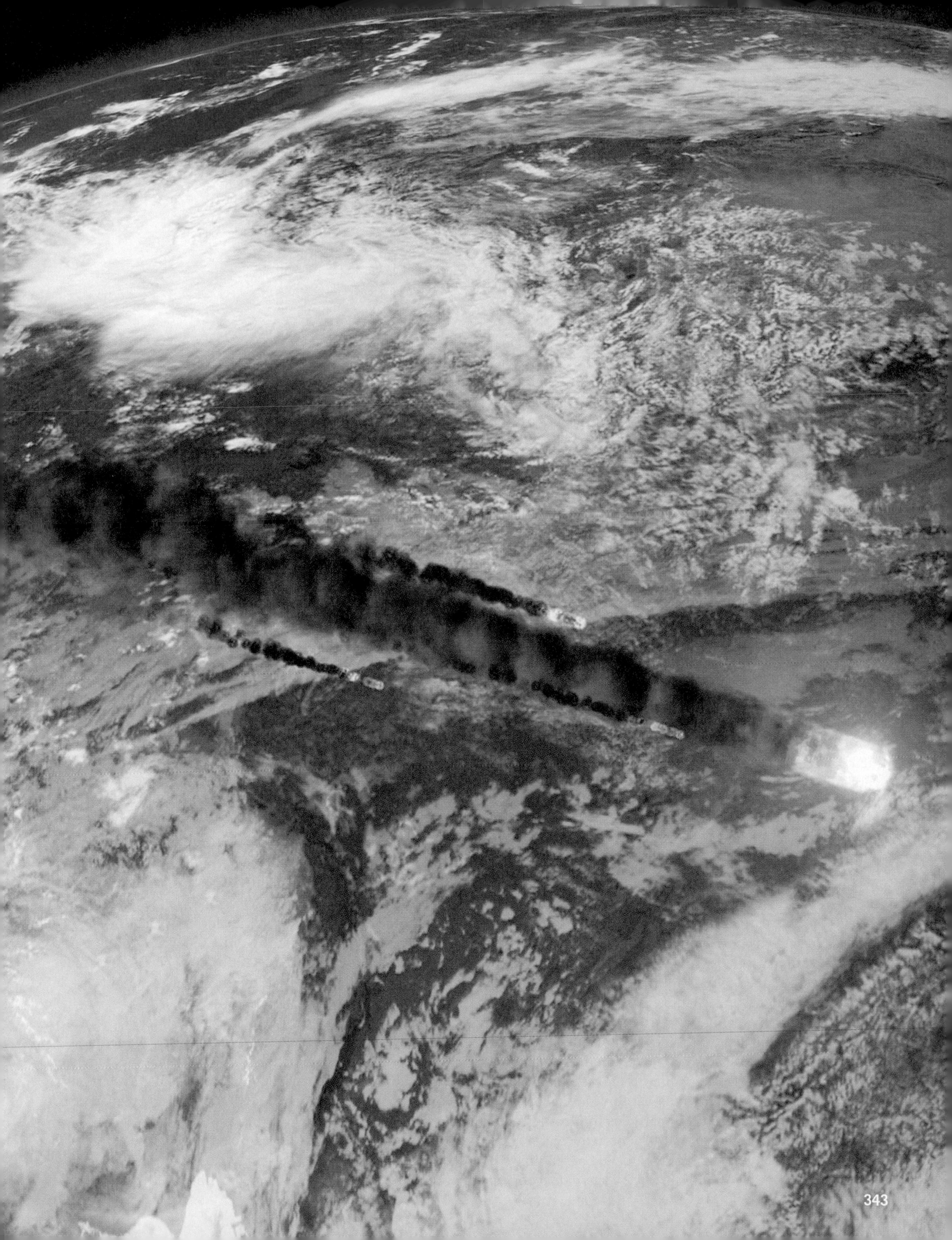

◀ **FIGURE 12.1 TUNGUSKA VALLEY, SIBERIA, 1908** An aerial burst downed trees over an area of about 2000 km^2. *(Sovfoto/Eastfoto)*

water by the hot breath of volcanoes, shaped and mineralized by 4.6 billion years of crustal evolution, warmed and peopled by the Sun, this resilient but finite globe is all our species has to sustain it forever."[4]

Some 14 billion years ago, long before the birth of Earth, the universe was created in an unimaginably large explosion, known as the "Big Bang." This explosion produced the atomic particles that later formed galaxies, stars, and planets (Figure 12.2). The first stars probably date to about 1 billion years after the Big Bang, and stars continue to form today.

A star's life span depends on its mass—large stars have higher internal pressure and burn up more quickly than small stars do. Stars with a mass equal to that of our Sun last around 10 billion years, whereas stars with masses 100 times that of our Sun have a life span of only about 100,000 years. The Sun is now a middle-aged star, about halfway through its life.

Stars die in a particularly spectacular way, releasing huge amounts of energy as *supernovas*. A supernova may have triggered gravitational collapse of a large molecular cloud from which our Sun formed 5 billion years ago. The Sun grew by accretion of matter from a flattened, pancake-like, rotating disk of hydrogen and helium dust called the *solar nebula*. It condensed under gravitational forces at the centre of the solar nebula. Other particles became trapped in orbits around the newly formed Sun as rings, similar to the rings around the planet Saturn today. The gravitational forces of the largest, densest particles attracted other particles in the rings until they condensed to form the planets that orbit the Sun (Figure 12.3). All planets in our solar system, including Earth, were bombarded early during their history by extraterrestrial objects ranging in size from dust particles to objects many kilometres in diameter. The bombardment occurred about 4.6 billion years ago[4,5] and is the part of the history that Cloud refers to when he states that Earth was "born from the wreckage of stars." Bombardment by asteroids and comets contributed to the growth of our planet. It did not cease 4.6 billion years ago but has continued to the present, although now at a slow rate.

Asteroids, Meteoroids, and Comets

Trillions of particles remain in our solar system. Astronomers group them according to their size and composition (Table 12.1). The particles range in size from interplanetary dust a fraction of a millimetre in diameter to **asteroids** up to 1000 km across.[6] Asteroids consist of rock, metallic material, or mixtures of the two. Most asteroids are located in an *asteroid belt* between Mars and Jupiter (Figure 12.3) and would pose no threat if they remained there. Unfortunately, asteroids move around and collide with one another; some asteroids are in orbits that intersect Earth's orbit.

Smaller particles, ranging from dust to objects a few metres across, are termed **meteoroids** (Table 12.1). A **meteor** is a meteoroid that has entered Earth's atmosphere. As a meteor moves through the atmosphere, it becomes hot and gives off light. Spectacular *meteor showers* occur when large numbers of meteors streak across the night sky.

Comets are distinguished from meteoroids and asteroids by their glowing tail of gas and dust (Figure 12.4). Comets range from a few metres to several hundred kilometres in

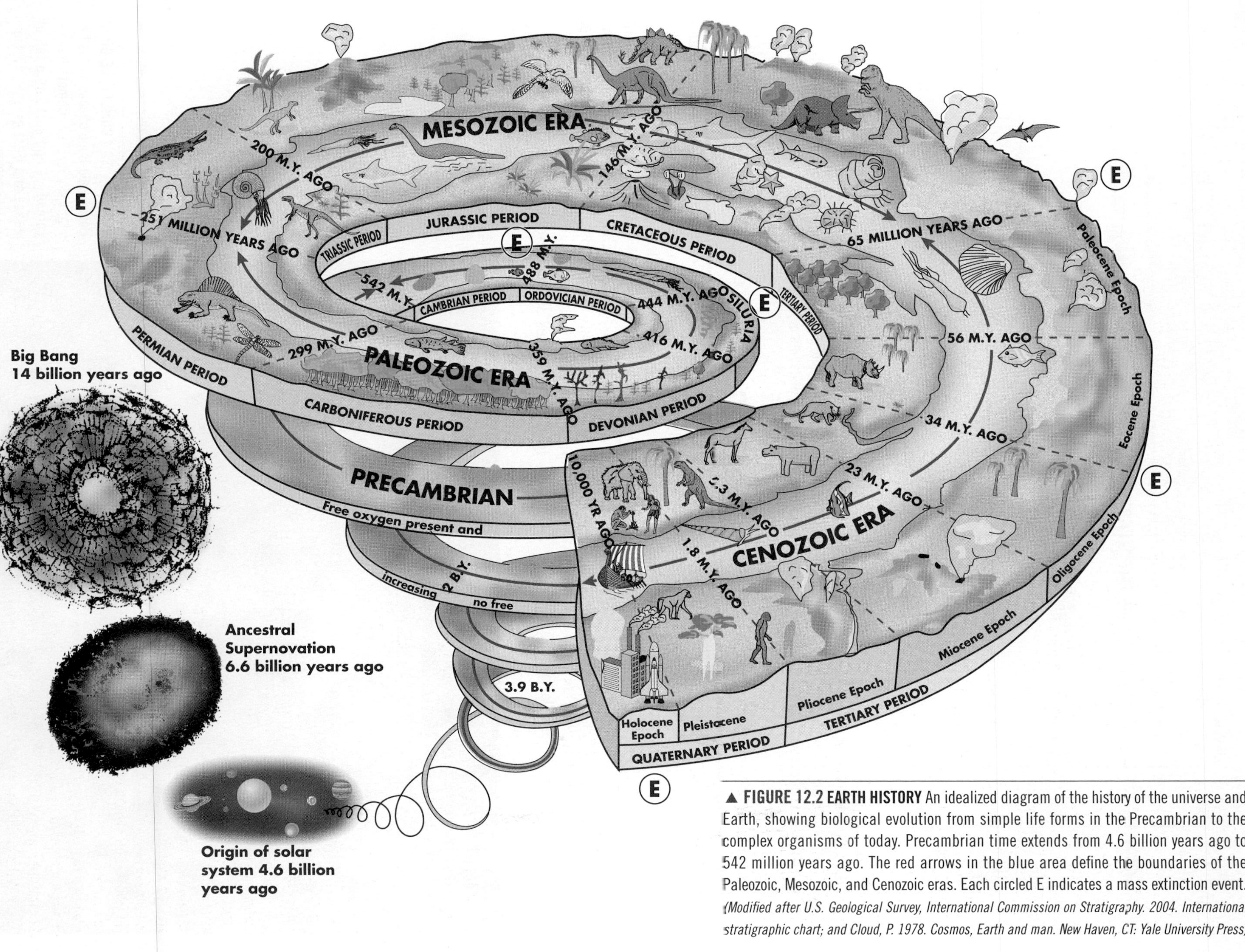

▲ **FIGURE 12.2 EARTH HISTORY** An idealized diagram of the history of the universe and Earth, showing biological evolution from simple life forms in the Precambrian to the complex organisms of today. Precambrian time extends from 4.6 billion years ago to 542 million years ago. The red arrows in the blue area define the boundaries of the Paleozoic, Mesozoic, and Cenozoic eras. Each circled E indicates a mass extinction event. *(Modified after U.S. Geological Survey, International Commission on Stratigraphy. 2004. International stratigraphic chart; and Cloud, P. 1978. Cosmos, Earth and man. New Haven, CT: Yale University Press)*

Neptune
Uranus
Saturn
Jupiter
Mars
Earth
Venus
Mercury
Pluto
Sun
Asteroid belt
Kuiper belt

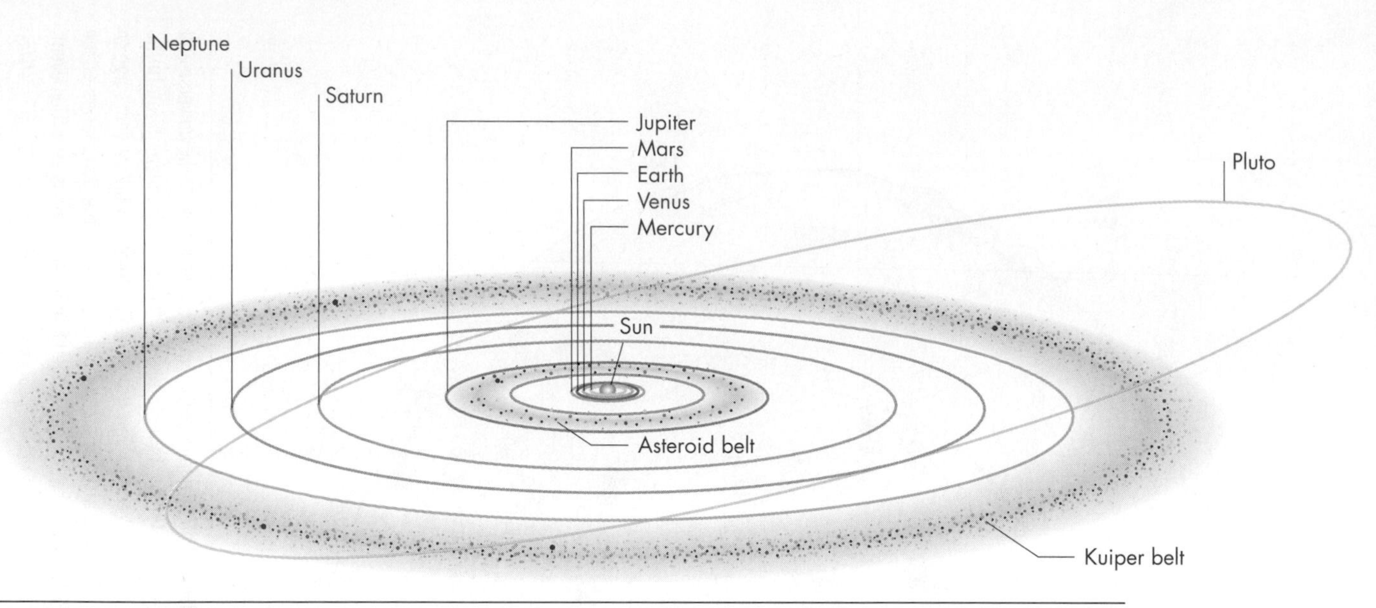

▲ **FIGURE 12.3 SOLAR SYSTEM** A diagram of our planetary system showing the asteroid and Kuiper belts. Orbits of the planets and belts are not to scale. (Note: In 2006, the International Astronomical Union reclassified Pluto as a "dwarf planet." It differs from the eight planets of our solar system in that it has "not cleared the neighbourhood around its orbit.")

diameter and are made of frozen water, solid carbon dioxide (dry ice), rock fragments, and dust. As a comet warms in Earth's atmosphere, its ices transform into a mixture of gases, producing a characteristic tail. Astronomers believe that comets formed outside the solar system and were thrown into an area beyond the dwarf planet Pluto called the **Oort Cloud.** The Oort Cloud is 50,000 AU (1.2×10^{14} km) from the Sun (1 AU, or astronomical unit, equals 240 million km, which is the distance from Earth to the Sun).[2] Comets also occur in the **Kuiper Belt** in the outer solar system.

12.2 Aerial Bursts and Impacts

Some asteroids and meteoroids contain carbonaceous material; others are made of iron and nickel; and still others consist of silicate minerals, such as olivine and pyroxene, which are common in igneous rocks (Table 12.1).[7] Asteroids and meteoroids consisting of silicate minerals are referred to as *stony*. They are also said to be *differentiated,* meaning that they have experienced igneous and, in some cases, metamorphic processes during their histories.

◄ **FIGURE 12.4 COMET HALE-BOPP** Comet Hale-Bopp streaks across the night sky in 1997. Comets have a core of ice and dust and a tail of gases and dust grains. *(© Aaron Horowitz/CORBIS)*

TABLE 12.1 Meteorites and Related Objects

Type	Diameter	Composition	Description
Asteroid	10 m–1000 km	Metallic or rocky	Metallic; some stony types are strong and hard, and may hit Earth. Weak, friable types likely will explode in the atmosphere at altitudes of several kilometres to hundreds of kilometres. Most asteroids originate in a belt between Mars and Jupiter.
Comet	A few metres to a few hundred kilometres	Frozen water, or carbon dioxide, or both with admixed small rock fragments and dust; like a dirty snowball	Weak and porous; comets generally explode in the atmosphere at altitudes of several kilometres to hundreds of kilometres. Most comets originate in the Kuiper Belt in the outer solar system and in the Oort Cloud, which is far outside the solar system, 50,000 AU[1] from the Sun. The tail of a comet is produced as ices melt and gases and dust particles are shed from the object.
Meteoroid	Dust to 10 metres	Stony, metallic, or carbonaceous (carbon-bearing)	Most originate from collisions of asteroids or comets. They may be strong or weak.
Meteor	Dust to centimetres	Stony, metallic, carbonaceous, or icy	Most meteors are destroyed in Earth's atmosphere. Light is produced by frictional heating.
Meteorite	Dust to asteroid size	Stony or metallic	Meteorites are meteors that hit Earth's surface. The most abundant type of stony meteorite is termed chondrite.[2]

[1] 1 AU is the distance from Earth to the Sun, about 240 million km.
[2] Chondrites contain chondrules, which are small (less than 1 mm) spheroidal glassy or crystalline inclusions.

Source: Data from Rubin, A. F. 2002. Disturbing the solar system. Princeton, NJ: Princeton University Press.

Asteroids, comets, and meteoroids travel at velocities of 12 km/s to 72 km/s (43,000 km/h to 259,000 km/h) when they enter Earth's atmosphere.[1] They produce bright light as they heat up during their descent. A meteoroid will either explode in an **aerial burst** at an altitude of less than 50 km or collide with Earth as a **meteorite** (Figure 12.5; see Survivor Story).

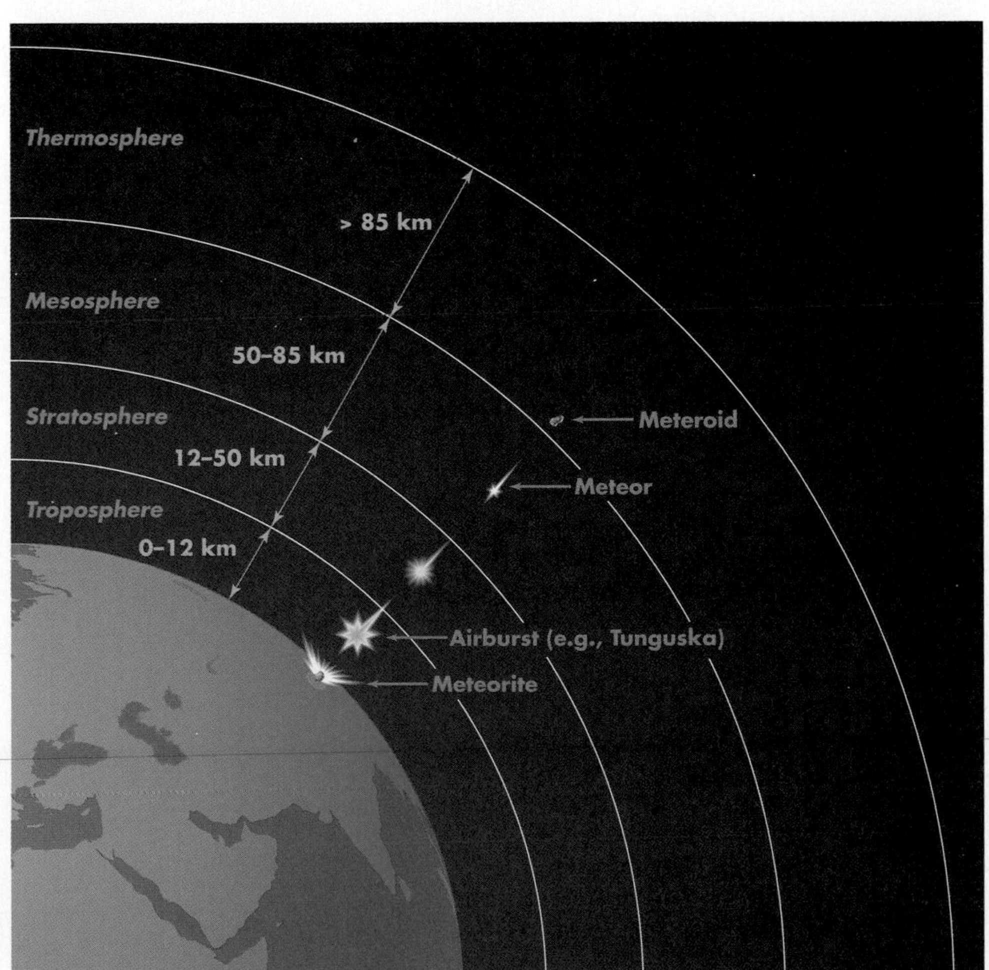

◀ **FIGURE 12.5 THE FATE OF A METEOROID IN EARTH'S ATMOSPHERE** An idealized diagram showing what happens to a meteoroid when it enters Earth's atmosphere. Meteors are small dust- to sand-sized meteoroids that emit light in the mesosphere and stratosphere. A large meteoroid may break apart in an aerial burst or crash into Earth. *(Modified after R. Baldini)*

SURVIVOR STORY

Meteorites in Illinois

When a meteorite shower lit up the sky on March 27, 2003, Pauline Zeilenga assumed the worst. Her first thought was that it was nuclear war.

She was in her living room with her husband, Chris, in their home in Park Forest, Illinois, when, shortly after midnight, the night sky lit up. "It wasn't like lightning," she says. "It was pitch black outside, and then the night literally turned to day. I said, 'What the heck was that?'"

About a minute later came "the loudest thunder you've ever heard," she adds. "But it kept going and going and going. And at a certain point, we realized it wasn't thunder, but an explosion."

It occurred to her that perhaps the Sears Tower had been hit, which was reasonable given that the United States and its allies had shortly before begun an extended bombing campaign in Iraq.

Then, when the thunder finally subsided, the couple heard a sound like that of hail as small objects struck the exterior of their house. Chris went outside and quickly identified the culprit behind the disturbance: meteorites peppering the Park Forest region. But Pauline wasn't convinced: "I was telling my husband, find out what it was."

The area teemed with scientists and meteorite enthusiasts in the days after the event. Larger meteorites, including the ones that punched holes in the roofs of houses in the region, are worth thousands of dollars (Figure 12.A).

Overall, Zeilenga concludes, the experience was one of a kind, once the shock had subsided. "It was the coolest," she says.

—Chris Wilson

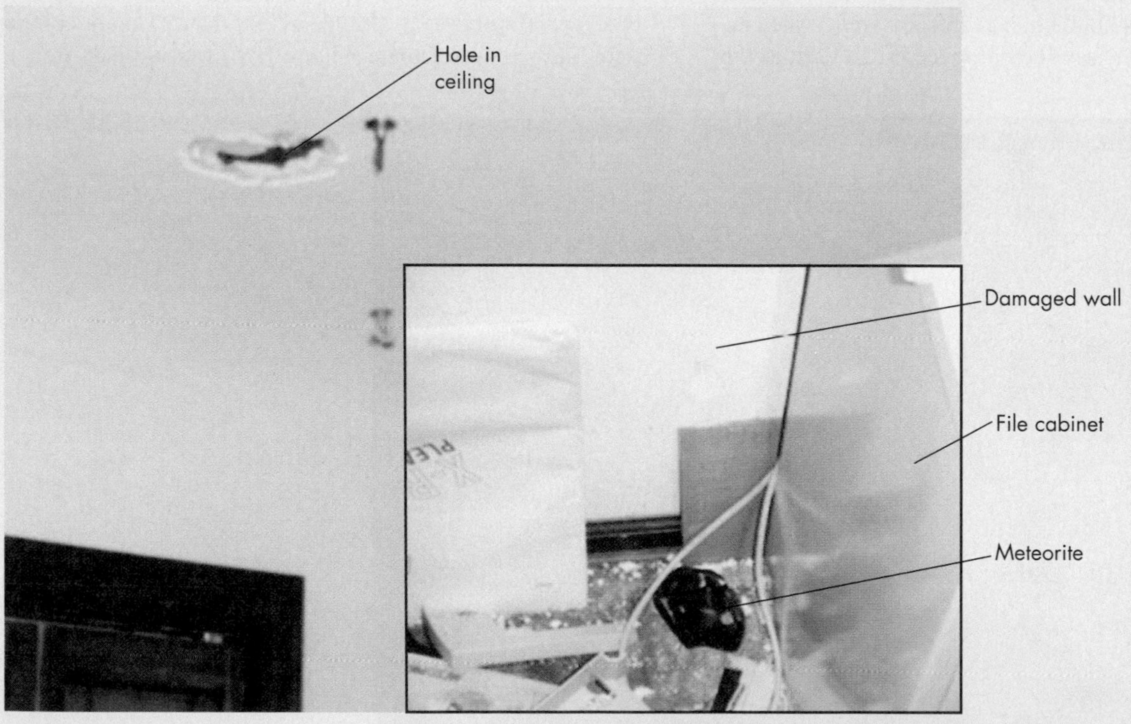

▲ **FIGURE 12.A PARK FOREST METEORITES** A meteorite produced this hole in the house of Ivan and Colby Navarro in a suburb of Chicago on March 27, 2003. The meteorite lies on the floor in the inset picture. Colby was working at a computer when the meteorite crashed through the roof, struck the printer, banged off the wall, and came to rest next to the filing cabinet. No one was injured by any of the meteorites, but roofs, windows, walls, and cars were damaged. Park Forest is the most populated area to be hit by a meteorite shower in modern times. *(© Ivan and Colby Navarro)*

Large numbers of meteorites have been collected from around the world, particularly from Antarctica, and more than 170 meteorite craters have been identified on Earth's surface. The Tunguska event mentioned at the beginning of this chapter was an aerial burst.

Impact Craters

The most direct and obvious evidence of the collision of extraterrestrial objects with Earth is the **impact craters** they produce (Figure 12.6).[6,7] The 50,000-year-old Barringer Crater, also known as Meteor Crater, in Arizona is an extremely well preserved, bowl-shaped depression with a pronounced upraised rim (Figure 12.7a). The crater is 1.2 km in diameter and up to 180 m deep. The hummocky terrain surrounding the crater and rising above the surrounding flat Arizona desert is underlain by a layer of debris, referred to as an **ejecta blanket**. This debris layer comprises fragments of rock that were blown out of the crater on impact. The crater we see today is not nearly as deep as the initial impact crater because large amounts of fragmented rock fell back into the crater shortly after impact, forming a type of rock termed *breccia* (Figure 12.7b). Rocks below the crater floor were fractured, shocked, and locally melted by the impact and the extreme temperatures it generated.

The origin of Barringer Crater was debated in the late nineteenth century after its existence first became widely known. Ironically, G. K. Gilbert, the famous geologist who postulated that craters on the Moon were formed by impacts, did not believe that Barringer Crater was formed in the same way. Careful field study later established that the crater was produced by the impact of a small asteroid, probably about 25 m to 100 m in diameter.[8]

Impact craters are easily distinguished from craters produced by other processes, notably volcanic activity. Impacts involve very high velocities and extreme pressures and temperatures that are not achieved with other geologic processes. Most of the energy of an impact is kinetic energy, or the energy of movement. This energy is transferred to Earth's surface through a shock wave that propagates into the uppermost part of the crust. The shock wave compresses, heats, melts, and excavates crustal rocks, producing a characteristic crater.[7,8] The shock wave can metamorphose rocks in the impact area, and melted material may mix with fragments of the impacting object itself. Most of the metamorphism involves high-pressure modification of minerals, such as quartz. Such high-pressure metamorphism is produced only by meteorite impacts and thus is helpful in confirming an impact origin for a crater.

Impact craters can be grouped into two types: simple and complex. Simple craters are typically small—a few kilometres in diameter—and do not have an uplifted centre. Barringer Crater is a typical small impact crater (Figure 12.7). Complex impact craters form in the same way as simple craters do, but are much larger (Figures 12.8 and 12.9). They can grow to more than 100 km across within seconds to several minutes of the impact. The crater rim collapses and the centre of the crater floor rises following the impact. Most impact craters

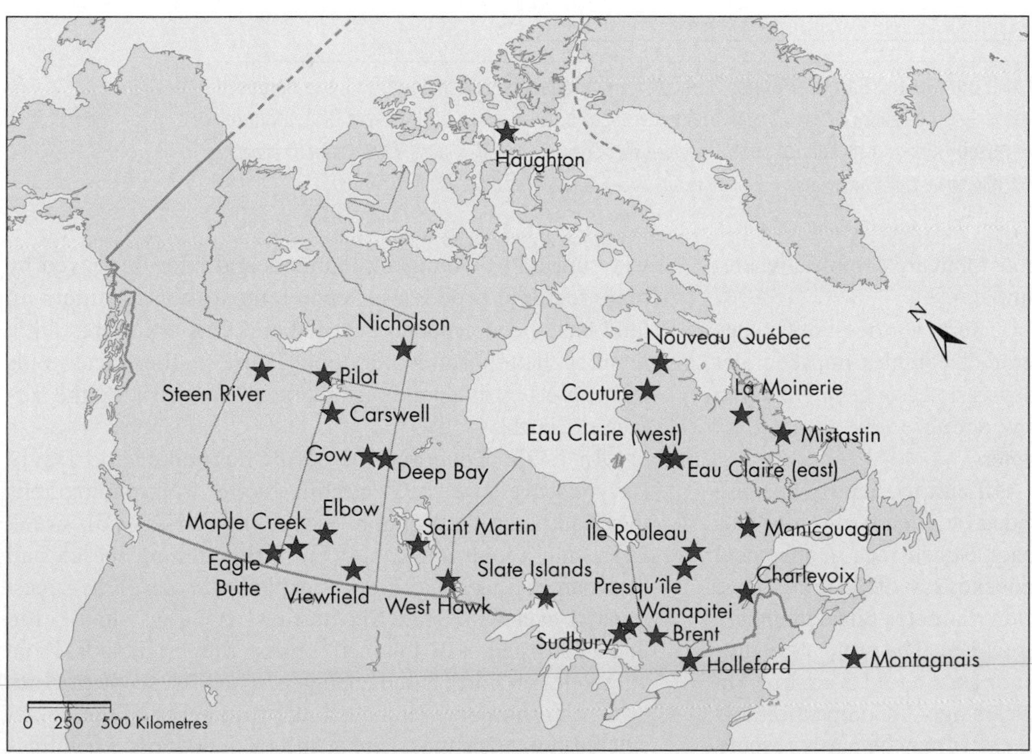

▲ **FIGURE 12.6 IMPACT CRATERS IN CANADA** A map showing locations of known large impact craters in Canada. All these craters are tens of millions to hundreds of millions of years old and thus have been extensively modified by erosion since they formed. Most of the craters are located on the Canadian Shield, an ancient part of Earth's crust. *(Modified from Grieve, R. A. F. 2001. Impact cratering on Earth. In A synthesis of geological hazards in Canada, ed. G. R. Brooks, pp. 207–224. Ottawa, ON: Geological Survey of Canada)*

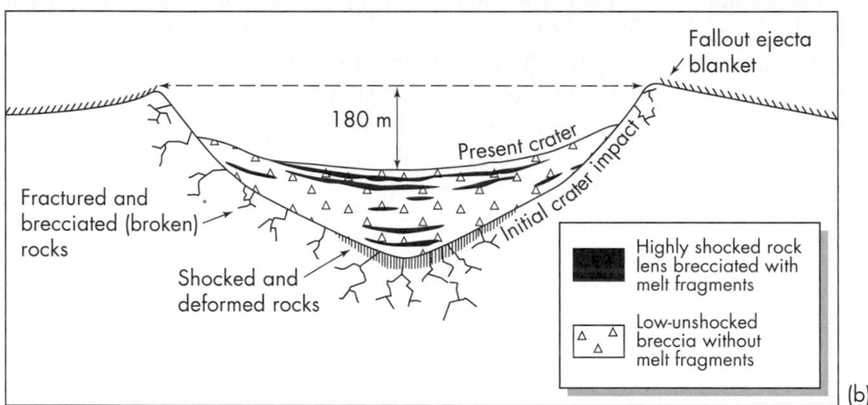

▲ **FIGURE 12.7 IMPACT CRATER IN ARIZONA** (a) The Barringer Crater is about 1.2 km wide and 180 m deep, and was produced by an asteroid impact about 50,000 years ago. *(© Charles O'Rear/CORBIS)* (b) A generalized cross-section of Barringer Crater. Simple impact craters like this typically have raised rims and no central peak. *(Modified after Grieve, R. and M. Cintala. 1999. Planetary impacts. In Encyclopedia of the solar system, eds. P. R. Weissman, L. McFadden, and T. V. Johnson, pp. 845–876. San Diego, CA: Academic Press)*

on Earth that are larger than about 6 km are complex, whereas smaller craters tend to be simple.

The Manicouagan impact structure, northeast of Quebec City, is a good example of an eroded, complex impact crater (Figure 12.9). A ring-shaped depression has been eroded in the impact breccia and is now occupied by a lake. The crater is about 100 km in diameter.[6,9]

Old impact craters can be difficult to identify because they have been extensively eroded or filled with sediments that are younger than the impact. Subsurface geophysical imaging and drilling in Chesapeake Bay off Virginia have revealed a crater about 85 km in diameter buried beneath about 1 km of sediment (Figure 12.8). The crater was produced by the impact of a comet or an asteroid 3 km to 5 km in diameter about 35 million years ago.[10] Compaction and faulting of sediments filling the crater may be partly responsible for the location of Chesapeake Bay.

Impact craters are much more common on the Moon than on Earth, for three reasons. First, most impact sites on Earth are in oceans where craters were not produced or were buried by younger sediments and later destroyed by plate tectonic processes. Second, most impact craters on land have been eroded or buried and thus are more subtle features than those on the Moon. Third, smaller meteoroids and comets burn up and disintegrate before striking the surface of Earth.

In 1993, Gene and Carolyn Shoemaker and David Levy discovered a comet circling Jupiter from photographs they had taken through a telescope in southern California. Less than a year and a half later, this comet, which had been named Shoemaker-Levy 9, exploded in one of the largest impacts ever witnessed. Shoemaker-Levy 9 was unusual in that it consisted of 21 fragments, many with bright tails. From telescopes on Earth and the Hubble Space Telescope in Earth orbit, astronomers watched as the fragments of the comet entered Jupiter's atmosphere at speeds of 60 km/s. Each fragment exploded, releasing 10,000 Mt to 100,000 Mt of energy, depending on its size. More energy was released during this event than could be produced by the simultaneous detonation of all nuclear weapons on Earth. Hot compressed gases

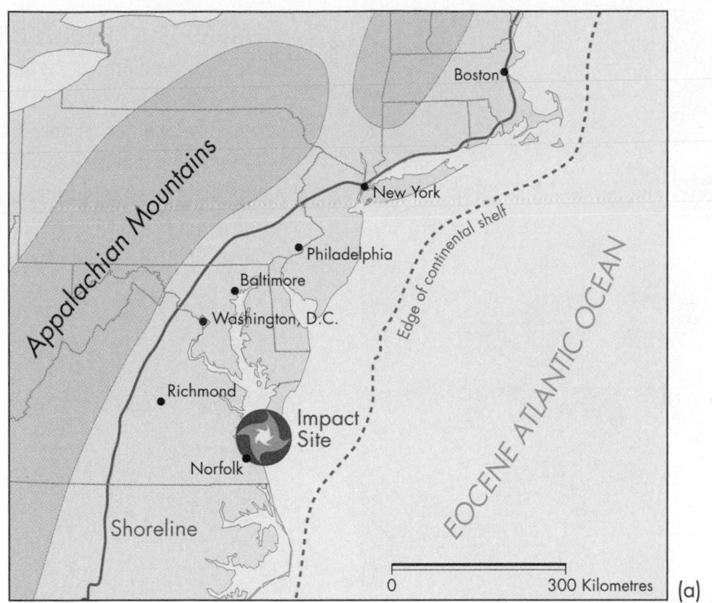

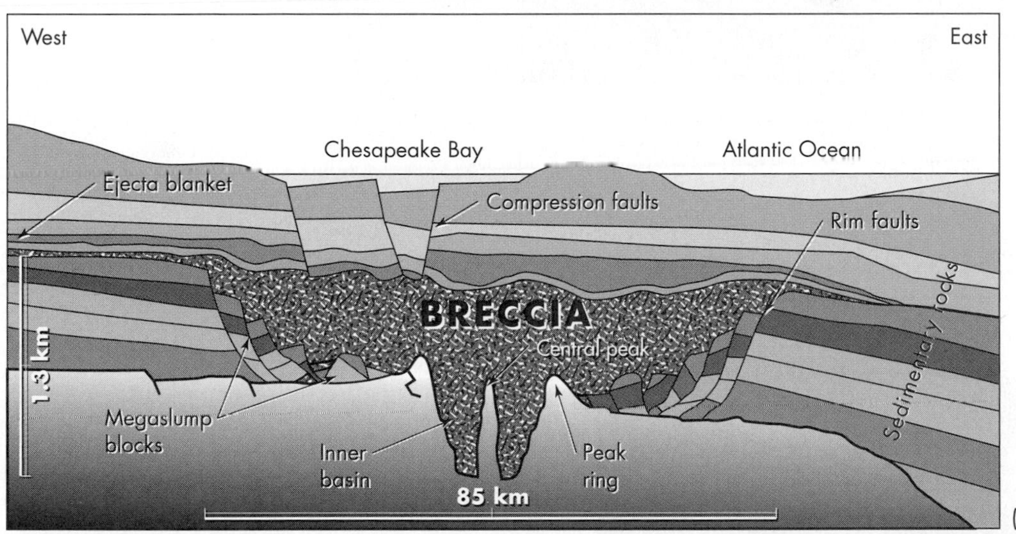

▲ **FIGURE 12.8 CHESAPEAKE BAY IMPACT CRATER** (a) A map showing the impact crater at the mouth of Chesapeake Bay. The crater formed about 35 million years ago when the shoreline of the Atlantic Ocean was located between the Appalachian Mountains and the U.S. cities labelled on the map (solid blue line). The dashed blue line is the seaward edge of the continental shelf 35 million years ago. (b) A cross-section of the Chesapeake Bay crater; note the 13X vertical exaggeration of the cross-section. The crater is approximately 85 km wide and 1.3 km deep. Cemented angular rock fragments (breccia) cover most of the crater floor. This buried crater was discovered by U.S. Geological Survey personnel during a groundwater investigation. *(Williams, S., P. Barnes, and E. J. Prager. 2000. U.S. Geological Survey Circular 1199).*

expanded violently upward from the lower part of Jupiter's atmosphere at velocities of up to 10 km/s. Gas plumes from the larger impacts rose more than 3000 km above Jupiter's surface. Large rings developed in Jupiter's atmosphere around the impact sites (Figure 12.10); the diameter of the rings exceeded the diameter of Earth! It was a remarkable show for astronomers and a sobering event, considering that a similar impact might one day occur on Earth.[2]

The idea that asteroids and comets might cause catastrophes on Earth, and even mass extinction of life, was strongly resisted by scientists until very recently (see Case Study 12.1). Several bizarre ideas were suggested to explain the Tunguska event in 1908, described at the beginning of this chapter, such as nuclear explosions and the explosion of an alien spaceship! This resistance is understandable, given that it wasn't until 1947 that Barringer Crater (Meteor Crater) in Arizona was finally accepted as a probable impact feature. Until that time, it was commonly referred to as a *cryptovolcanic* structure, meaning that a "hidden" volcanic event had produced it. Eventually, Barringer Crater was shown to be the result of an asteroid impact, probably with aerial bursts. After the impact of Shoemaker-Levy 9 on Jupiter, the idea that a comet or an asteroid could strike Earth was nearly universally accepted.

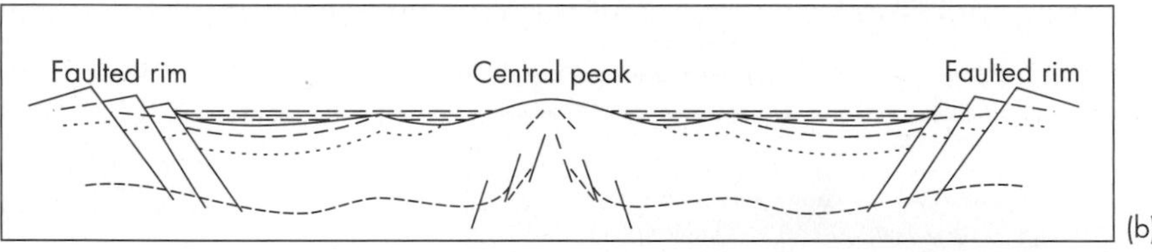

◄ **FIGURE 12.9 COMPLEX IMPACT CRATER IN QUEBEC** (a) Satellite image and (b) cross-section of the Manicouagan impact structure northeast of Quebec City. The ring-shaped lake is about 70 km in diameter. The Manicouagan structure, like many complex craters, has a faulted rim and a central elevated area produced by crustal rebound and faulting immediately after the impact. *(NASA Headquarters)*

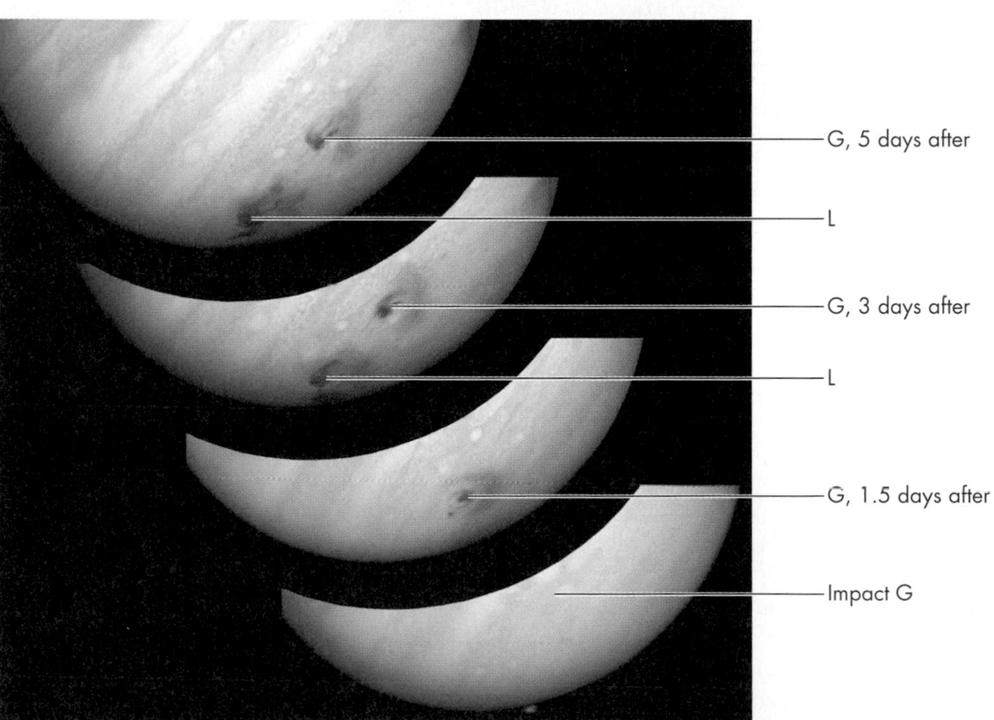

▲ **FIGURE 12.10 COMET HITS JUPITER** Spectacular impact of the comet Shoemaker-Levy 9 on Jupiter in 1994. The comet consisted of 21 fragments referred to as a "string of pearls." One fragment after another entered Jupiter's atmosphere and exploded. The four images shown here span a five-day period, from lower right to upper left. The reddish brown dots and rings mark the impact sites of fragments G and L. The diameter of the rings exceeds the diameter of Earth. *(R. Evans, J. Trauger, H. Hammel, and the HST Comet Science Team/NASA)*

12.1 CASE STUDY

Uniformitarianism, Gradualism, and Catastrophe

The idea that Earth could be hit by large objects from outer space was not widely accepted until the twentieth century, in spite of eyewitness accounts of meteorite impacts around the world. The first well-documented account may be a lethal meteorite that landed in Israel in the year 1420 B.C.[1] In the fifteenth century, Galileo invented the telescope and showed that the planets, including Earth, revolve around the Sun. The religious establishment of the day, however, did not accept this theory, and it dismissed the idea that extraterrestrial objects could strike Earth; in fact, Galileo was jailed for his beliefs.

In 1654, Irish Archbishop Ussher proclaimed that Earth was created in the year 4004 B.C. This belief was the dogma of the time and, given the power of the Church, was not to be disputed. However, people studying the formation of mountains and large river valleys could not understand how these features could form in only 6000 years. In 1785, the Scottish doctor James Hutton wrote an influential book that introduced the concept of gradualism, or uniformitarianism. According to this concept, Earth features and rocks have been produced by the same natural processes as those operating today. The *principle of uniformitarianism* has since been paraphrased as "the present is the key to the past." Hutton also argued that Earth must be much older than 6000 years to allow the gradual processes of erosion, deposition, and uplift to form mountain ranges and other features on Earth's surface.

In 1830, Charles Lyell wrote another important and influential book on geology, popularizing the role of gradual processes and casting aside the dogma of a very young Earth. He proclaimed that Earth had a long history that could be understood by studying present-day processes and the rock record. When Ussher's young Earth was the accepted belief, scientists were forced to conclude that most of the processes that formed our planet were catastrophic in nature. This perspective could explain Biblical events, such as Noah's Flood, but not much else. Once scientists recognized that Earth is old, they reconstructed its history from processes that could be carefully observed, such as uplift and erosion. Charles Darwin was strongly influenced by Charles Lyell's book, and he applied the ideas of an ancient Earth and uniformitarianism to his concept of biological evolution. The concept of gradualism became widely accepted in the twentieth century, culminating in the 1960s with the discovery that lithospheric plates move with respect to one another. The theory of *plate tectonics* explains the origin and position of continents through the slow processes of seafloor spreading, faulting, subduction, and uplift.

However, even as plate tectonics came into ascendancy, many scientists argued that catastrophic events have also played a role in shaping Earth. Some scientists pointed to large craters on Earth's surface that they believed were the result of asteroid impacts. Others argued that infrequent, relatively rapid extinctions over the last several hundred million years were difficult to explain by using gradualism. The extinctions involved the disappearance of a large percentage (commonly half or more) of the species of plants and animals existing at the time. Four mass extinctions occurred in the distant geologic past; another is occurring today as a result of human activity (Figure 12.2). A mass extinction 65 million years ago marks the Cretaceous-Tertiary boundary and probably was caused by the impact of an asteroid approximately 10 km in diameter beneath what is now Yucatan Peninsula in Mexico.

Scientific acceptance of the importance of catastrophic events in shaping Earth's history has led to a new concept, *punctuated uniformitarianism*. According to this concept, uniformitarianism explains the long geologic evolution of the lithosphere, but catastrophic events are responsible for mass extinctions and thus have played an important role in the evolution of life.

12.3 Mass Extinctions

A **mass extinction** can be defined as the sudden loss of large numbers of species of plants and animals.[11] Mass extinctions coincide with boundaries of geologic periods or epochs because the geologic timescale was originally organized on the basis of the appearance and disappearance of groups of fossil organisms. Many hypotheses have been suggested to explain mass extinctions, including rapid climate change, movements of Earth's lithospheric plates, and volcanic eruptions that injected huge amounts of ash into the atmosphere.

Geologists have documented five major mass extinctions during the past 550 million years. The earliest mass extinction, which occurred about 446 million years ago at the end of the Ordovician Period, involved the loss of about 100 families of animals. It coincided with continental glaciation in the Southern Hemisphere and may include two extinctions, one when climate cooled and a second when climate warmed following the glacial interval.[12] The next mass extinction occurred near the end of the Permian Period, about 250 million years ago, when 80 percent to 85 percent of all species on Earth died out.[12] An impact crater dating to about this time has recently been identified beneath the Antarctic Ice Sheet. Some scientists, however, argue that this mass extinction may not have been caused by a single event but rather spanned a period of about 7 million years. They suggest that global cooling, followed by rapid global warming, may have been responsible for the Permian mass extinction. Numerous large volcanic eruptions added huge amounts of ash and gases to the atmosphere, possibly contributing to the cooling. The boundary between the Cretaceous and Tertiary periods, the so-called *K-T boundary*, is marked by another mass extinction. This event was sudden—abundant evidence suggests that it was caused by the impact of a large asteroid.[13] Another mass extinction occurred near the end of the Eocene Epoch, about 34 million years ago. Limited evidence suggests that an asteroid or comet may have hit Earth at that time, but most scientists link this extinction to cooling and glaciation that began about 40 million years ago. Tectonic plate movements allowed a cold ocean current to begin to flow around Antarctica at this time. The current chilled Antarctica, allowing an ice sheet to develop there. Finally, a mass extinction began near the end of the Pleistocene Epoch and has accelerated during the past two centuries. Hunting of land animals by humans may have initiated this extinction, but the main causes in recent times have been the rapid increase in human population, deforestation, agriculture, overfishing, and pollution.[11]

Of the five extinctions, the K-T extinction is the one most closely linked to an extraterrestrial impact. The case for an impact-related mass extinction 65 million years ago is strong. The large dinosaurs, which had been at the top of the food chain for 100 million years or more, suddenly became extinct at this time.[13,14] Their demise allowed small mammals to diversify and evolve into the approximately 4000 species, including humans, that are alive today. Marine life also diversified and evolved.

K-T Boundary Mass Extinction

One of the great geologic detective stories of the past 50 years is the investigation of the K-T mass extinction. We now have evidence that, 65 million years ago, a comet or an asteroid smashed into Earth along the north shore of what is now Yucatan Peninsula. That event profoundly changed life and thus evolution. Dinosaurs disappeared, along with most species of plants and animals in the oceans and on land. Approximately 70 percent of all genera and their associated species died off. Some reptiles, including turtles, alligators, and crocodiles, and some birds, plants, and smaller mammals survived. We don't yet know why some species survived and others became extinct. We do know, however, that the demise of the dinosaurs on land and swimming reptiles in the oceans set the stage for the evolution of mammals, which ultimately led to the appearance of primates and the genus *Homo*. What would life be like today if the K-T extinction had not happened? It is likely that humans never would have evolved!

Because the K-T extinction was so important for human evolution, we will look more closely at how scientists came to the conclusion that it was caused by the impact of a large comet or asteroid. The story is full of intrigue, suspense, rivalries, and cooperation, which is typical of many great scientific discoveries. Walter Alvarez, a professor at the University of California, asked the question that started it all: What is the nature of the boundary between rocks of the Cretaceous and Tertiary periods?*

Alvarez studies rocks to decipher the history of Earth. In the 1970s, he developed an interest in rocks that span the Cretaceous-Tertiary boundary. With some colleagues, he went to Italy to study a very thin layer of clay that marks the K-T boundary there (Figure 12.11). The extinction of many species coincided with the clay layer—fossils found in rocks below the clay were absent in the rocks above it. The scientists asked the question, how rapidly did these species disappear? Put another way, how much time did the clay layer span? Was it a few years, a few thousand years, or millions of years? The approach they took was to measure the amount of *iridium* in the clay. Iridium is a platinum-group metal found in very small concentrations in meteorites. The global rate of accumulation of meteoritic dust and thus iridium on Earth is constant. Meteoric dust and iridium slowly accumulate on the deep ocean floor. Clay eroded from the continents and the remains of microscopic organisms slowly rain out on the ocean floor, diluting the iridium. The higher the rate of sedimentation, the more diluted the iridium becomes. Slow sedimentation allows time for more meteorite dust to accumulate, giving higher concentrations of iridium in deep ocean sediments.

What Walter Alvarez and his colleagues found was entirely unexpected. They had expected to measure about 0.1 ppb (parts per billion) of iridium in the clay layer, a value consistent with slow accumulation through time. The concentration of iridium would be even less with rapid sedimentation. Instead, they found concentrations of about 9 ppb, 100 times more than they had expected. Although 9 ppb is a very small concentration, it is much larger than can be explained through slow deposition over time. This discovery led them to a new hypothesis: the iridium might be derived from a single asteroid impact. The team's iridium discovery and their hypothesis of an extraterrestrial cause for the mass extinction at the K-T boundary were published in a journal in 1980.[15] They also reported in the same paper elevated concentrations of iridium in deep-sea sediments at the K-T boundary in Denmark and New Zealand.

The discovery of the iridium anomaly at several places around the world added credence to the impact hypothesis, but the researchers had no impact crater and their hypothesis was criticized. The Alvarez paper, however, prompted other scientists to search for a 65-million-year-old crater. Could the crater even be found? The asteroid may have produced only

*Walter Alvarez wrote a book titled *T. rex and the Crater of Doom*, which was published in 1997.[14] Interested readers should read this book for the complete story summarized briefly here.

◄ **FIGURE 12.11 EVIDENCE FOR AN EXTRATERRESTRIAL IMPACT** The Cretaceous-Tertiary (K-T) boundary in Italy is delineated by a thin clay layer located below the left knee of the scientist on the left side of the photograph. The layer has an anomalously high concentration of the metal iridium. This metal occurs in high concentrations in extraterrestrial objects, such as meteorites. Its presence here is consistent with an asteroid impact 65 million years ago, at the end of the Cretaceous Period. *(Courtesy of Walter Alvarez)*

a giant aerial burst, or it may have struck in the deep ocean and produced only a small crater. Or the crater may have gradually filled with sediment and thus become obscure.

As it turned out, the K-T crater was found; it is covered by Tertiary sediments but was discovered in 1991 by geologists studying the structural geology of Yucatan Peninsula.[16] They found a nearly circular, buried impact crater approximately 180 km in diameter. The boundary between nonfractured, younger rocks filling the crater and fractured rocks beneath and outside of the crater is clear. About half of the crater lies beneath the seafloor of the Gulf of Mexico; the other half underlies Tertiary sedimentary rocks on Yucatan Peninsula (Figure 12.12). A semicircular pattern of sinkholes, known to the Mayan people as *cenotes,* delineates the edge of the impact crater on land. The cenotes are 50 m to 500 m in diameter and presumably formed by slow chemical weathering of fractured limestone at the edge of the crater. The crater was originally 30 km to 40 km deep, but post-impact slumping of the crater walls filled much of the structure and sedimentation over the past 65 million years completely buried it. Samples of glassy melt rock were recovered below a massive layer interpreted to be impact breccia. The force of the impact excavated the crater, fractured the rock outside it, and produced the breccia. The glassy melt rock indicates that sufficient heat

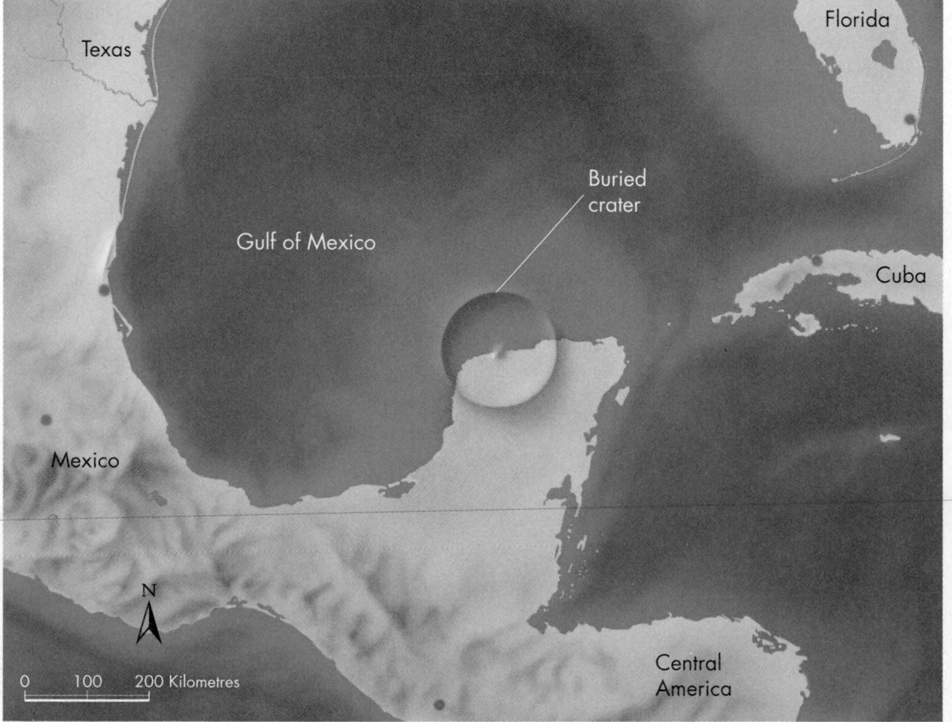

◄ **FIGURE 12.12 LARGE IMPACT CRATER IN MEXICO** A map showing the location of the Chicxulub impact crater on the north shore of Yucatan Peninsula. The crater underlies Tertiary sedimentary rocks on the peninsula and the adjacent seafloor of the Gulf of Mexico. It was produced by an asteroid impact 65 million years ago at the end of the Cretaceous Period. *(© D. Van Ravenswaay/Photo Researchers, Inc.)*

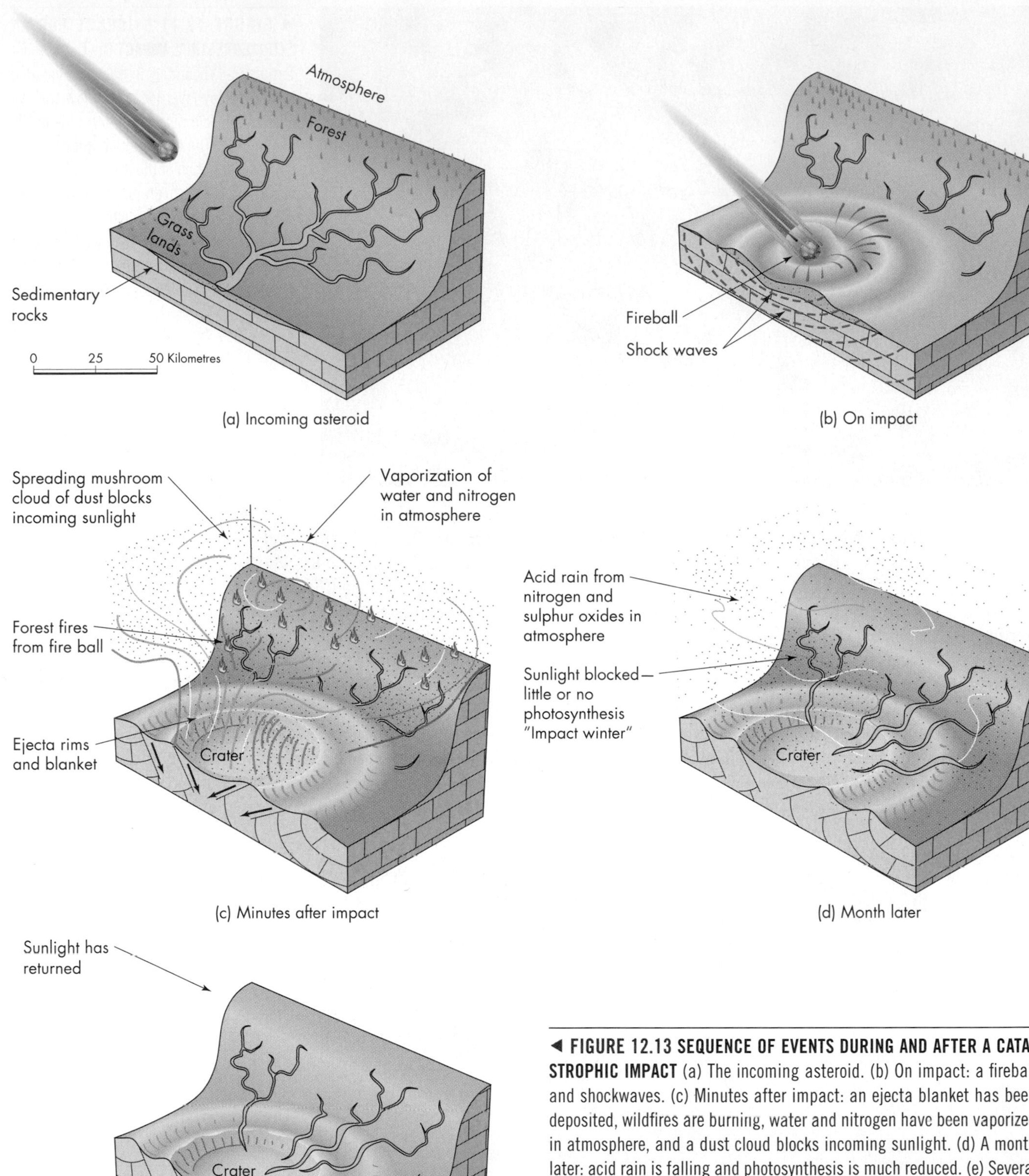

◀ **FIGURE 12.13 SEQUENCE OF EVENTS DURING AND AFTER A CATASTROPHIC IMPACT** (a) The incoming asteroid. (b) On impact: a fireball and shockwaves. (c) Minutes after impact: an ejecta blanket has been deposited, wildfires are burning, water and nitrogen have been vaporized in atmosphere, and a dust cloud blocks incoming sunlight. (d) A month later: acid rain is falling and photosynthesis is much reduced. (e) Several months later: sunlight returns, dust and acid have washed out of the atmosphere, and erosion and deposition are modifying the crater.

was generated by the impact to melt rocks below the crater floor.[17] Another study of the crater found glass mixed with and overlain by the breccia, as well as evidence of shock metamorphism, which is commonly associated with impact structures.[18] The results of the studies of the Yucatan Peninsula crater, which was named the Chicxulub crater, have been published and accepted. Most scientists now believe that the asteroid or comet that struck the area 65 million years ago did, in fact, cause the K-T mass extinction.

Once the site of the crater had been identified, scientists naturally asked how such an event could cause a global mass extinction.[14] The asteroid that struck Yucatan Peninsula 65 million years ago was huge, perhaps larger than Mount Everest is high. It entered Earth's atmosphere at a speed of about 30 km/s, which is 150 times faster than a jet airliner travels. The amount of energy released during its encounter with Earth is estimated to have been about 100 million Mt, roughly 10,000 times the energy of the entire nuclear arsenal of the world.

Walter Alvarez and numerous other scientists have proposed a likely sequence of events for the impact and its aftermath (Figure 12.13). At an altitude of 10 km and moving at 30 km/s, the asteroid would have taken less than half a second to reach Earth's surface (Figure 12.14). It blasted a hole in the crust nearly 200 km across and 40 km deep. Within about two seconds, shock waves crushed the rocks in the crater and partially melted them. A huge ejecta blanket was emplaced around the crater, and a cloud of pulverized rock and gases rose in a gigantic fireball, which formed a mushroom cloud. The explosion ejected material far beyond Earth's surface, and the fireball ignited fires far from the impact site. Vaporization of sulphur-bearing limestone at the impact site produced sulphuric acid in the atmosphere. Nitric acid was added through oxidation of nitrogen in the atmosphere. Thus, following the impact, acid rain probably fell for a long time. Dust in the atmosphere encircled Earth, and for months little or no sunlight reached the lower atmosphere. Plants on the land and in the ocean stopped growing because of the lack of sunlight. Acid rain was toxic to many organisms, particularly terrestrial and shallow marine plants and animals. As a result, the food chain was greatly disrupted or stopped functioning altogether because the base of the chain had been greatly damaged. Part of the impact occurred in the ocean and generated a tsunami with waves up to 1 km high. These waves raced across the Gulf of Mexico and inundated parts of North America.[14] Geologists have found tsunami deposits in southern Texas that appear to date to time of the asteroid impact.

In summary, an asteroid struck Earth 65 million years ago, causing a global killoff that we refer to as a mass extinction. The event eliminated the dinosaurs, which had flourished on Earth for more than 160 million years. The extinction, however, was not restricted to dinosaurs—many other species of terrestrial and marine animals and plants died at the same time. Should a similar event occur again, the loss of life would be immense. It might mean the extinction of humans and most large mammals and birds. These extinctions would trigger another period of rapid evolution.

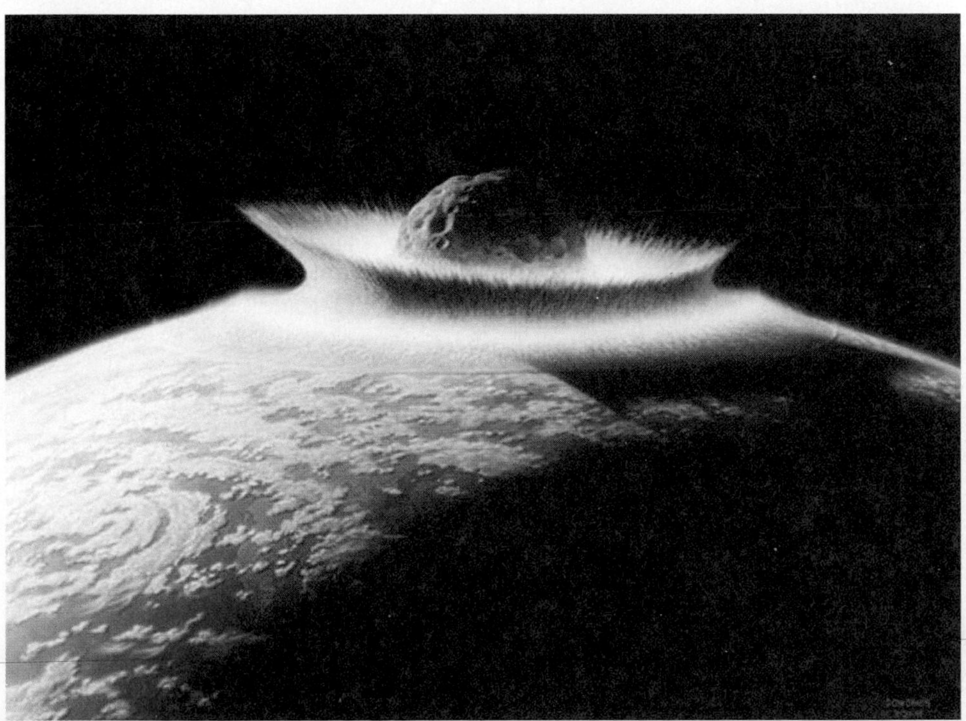

▲ **FIGURE 12.14 ASTEROID STRIKES EARTH** An artist's concept of the catastrophic impact of an asteroid with Earth 65 million years ago at the end of the Cretaceous Period. This event is thought to be responsible for a mass extinction of about 70 percent of the plant and animal genera on Earth, including the dinosaurs. *(Artist Don Davis/NASA)*

12.4 Impact Hazards and Risk

Risk Related to Impacts

The risk of an event is related to both its probability and its consequences. The consequences of an aerial burst or direct impact from an extraterrestrial object several kilometres in diameter would be catastrophic. Such an impact might occur at sea, but its effects would be felt worldwide with a high potential for mass extinction. Impact events of this magnitude on Earth probably have return periods of 1 million to a few million years (Figure 12.15). Smaller impacts are much more frequent and would still wreak havoc over a large area, causing great damage and loss of life. An object a few dozen metres in diameter would cause a regional catastrophe if it exploded in the atmosphere or struck land near a populated area. The size of the devastated area might be several thousand square kilometres. Even a small impact could kill millions of people if it occurred over or in a large city. Scientists term these smaller impacts "Tunguska-type" events.

Recent research suggests that aerial bursts from asteroids 50 m to 100 m in diameter occur, on average, once every 1000 years or less (Figure 12.15). By using the Tunguska event as an example of what such a blast could do, scientists have estimated that an urban area is likely to be destroyed about once every 30,000 years by an aerial burst or impact of a small asteroid. This conclusion is based on the distribution of 300 small asteroids known to have exploded in the atmosphere. Extrapolation of the data allows estimates to be made of the impacts of larger, even more damaging events.[3]

Predictions of the likelihood and type of future impacts have large statistical uncertainty. Deaths caused by an impact during a typical millennium could be as low as zero to as high as several hundred thousand. A truly catastrophic event could kill millions of people; averaging this number over thousands of years produces a relatively high average annual death toll.

Overall, the risk from extraterrestrial impacts is surprisingly high (Figure 12.16). The probability that you will be killed by a catastrophic impact is approximately 0.01 percent to 0.1 percent. In comparison, the probability that you will be killed in a car accident is approximately 0.008 percent and by drowning about 0.001 percent. Thus, the risk of dying from the impact or aerial burst of a large comet or asteroid is greater than other risks we normally face in life. However, we emphasize again that this risk is spread out over thousands of years. Although the average death toll in any one year may appear high, it is just that, an *average*. Remember that such events are rare. Certainly there is a risk, but the interval between large impacts is so long that we shouldn't lose any sleep worrying about a global catastrophe caused by an extraterrestrial object.

Managing the Impact Hazard

Scientists and policymakers have only recently become aware of the risk that we face from asteroids and comets. Are we helpless, or is there something we can do to minimize this risk? We are not helpless. First, we can identify objects in our solar system that could threaten Earth (see Case Study 12.2). A program to identify and categorize comets and asteroids that cross Earth's path is already in progress and could be

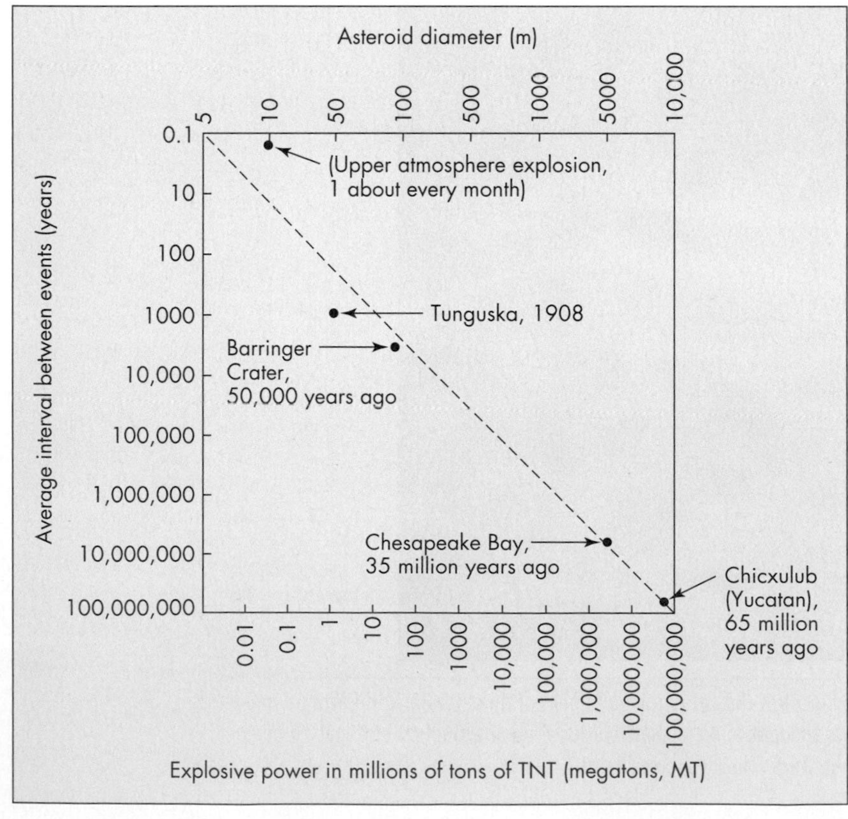

◄ **FIGURE 12.15 IMPACT FREQUENCY AND ENERGY** The relations among the size of asteroids or comets striking Earth, their frequency, and the energy released. *(Weissman, P. R., L. McFadden, and T. V. Johnson, eds. 1999. Encyclopedia of the Solar System. San Diego, CA: Academic Press; and Brown, P., R. E. Spalding, D. O. ReVelle, E. Tagliaferri, and S. P. Worden. 2002. The flux of near-Earth objects colliding with the Earth. Nature 420:294–296)*

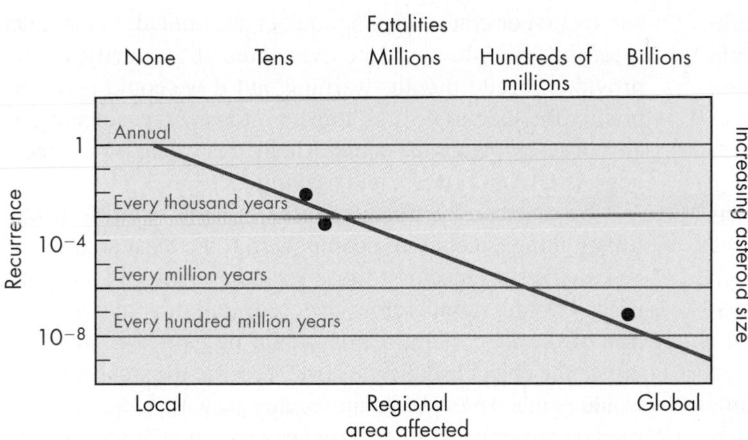

◄ **FIGURE 12.16 ASTEROID RISK** Graph showing fatalities and areas affected by asteroid impacts with different recurrence intervals. Small impacts that occur annually are of little risk. An impact with an average recurrence interval of 100 million years would kill billions of people.

12.2 CASE STUDY

Near-Earth Objects

Near-Earth objects (NEOs) reside and orbit between Earth and the Sun or have more elliptical orbits that, on occasion, bring them close to Earth. NEOs include meteoroids, asteroids, and comets, but only the larger objects, ranging in size from a few tens of metres to a few kilometres, pose a significant hazard (Figure 12.B). An aerial burst or impact by a NEO of a few dozen metres might cause a regional disaster. The impact of a NEO several kilometres in diameter would cause a global catastrophe.

As mentioned earlier, most asteroids originate in the asteroid belt located between Mars and Jupiter (Figure 12.3). As long as an asteroid remains in this belt, it does not become a NEO and poses no hazard to Earth. An asteroid's orbital path, however, may be disturbed by a collision or a near miss with another object. The path then may become more elliptical, bringing the object into the space between Earth and the Sun. The object may even regularly cross the orbital path of Earth. The current estimate of the number of asteroids with near-Earth orbits and diameters larger than 100 m is 135,000; of these, about 1500 are larger than 1 km, and 20 are larger than 5 km.[9]

Comets, another type of NEO, are generally a few kilometres in diameter and consist of dirty ice with a covering of rock particles and dust. Most comets originate far out in the solar system in the Oort Cloud. They are best known for the beautiful light they create in the night sky from dust and gases released from the ice as it is heated by solar radiation. The released gas and dust form a spherical cloud around the comet. A tail of gas and dust is "blown" out from the cloud and away from the Sun by the force of solar radiation, sometimes called the solar wind. If Earth passes through a comet's tail, dust and gas particles burn up in the atmosphere, producing a meteor shower.

▲ **FIGURE 12.B ASTEROID 243 IDA** Numerous craters on the surface of asteroid 243 Ida show that collisions between objects in the asteroid belt are common. Ida is approximately 52 km long and orbits the Sun once every five years at a distance of 441 million km. The photograph was taken by the NASA *Galileo* spacecraft in 1993. *(Jet Propulsion Laboratory/NASA Headquarters)*

The most famous of the comets that come close to Earth is Comet Halley. A spacecraft mission was conducted in 1986 to observe and study it. Sensors on the spacecraft found that the comet is a fluffy, porous body with very little strength. The nucleus of the comet consists of only about 20 percent ice; the remainder is empty space—a network of cracks and voids between loosely cemented materials.[1] Comet Halley crosses the space around Earth once every 76 years, giving every generation a chance to view it.

NEOs apparently have a relatively short life span, but meteoroids and asteroids are continuously ejected from the asteroid belt into near-Earth positions. Likewise, the orbits of some comets in the outer solar system may be perturbed by planets or other objects and become NEOs.

expanded to include objects in more size classes. The additional size classes would include objects less than 50 m in diameter, those 50 m to several hundred metres in diameter, and those several kilometres across. A program known as *Spacewatch,* which was begun in 1981, is producing an inventory of near-Earth objects (NEOs). Based on this inventory, scientists now think there are about 135,000 near-Earth asteroids up to 100 m in diameter. Another program known as the *Near-Earth Asteroid Tracking Project (NEAT)* was started in 1996 and is supported by the National Aeronautical and Space Administration (NASA). Its objective is to study the size, distribution, and movement of NEOs, with a focus on objects about 1 km in diameter. Both observation programs use cameras and telescopes to identify and monitor fast-moving objects.[9] Research to identify NEOs is likely to intensify in the future, with more and more objects catalogued and monitored. However, a complete evaluation will take a long time because many potentially dangerous objects have orbits that do not bring them close to Earth for decades. The good news is that most of the objects identified as potentially hazardous to Earth will not collide with our planet for at least several thousand years. Therefore, we have time to learn about them and develop appropriate technologies to reduce the risk.[1]

By one estimate, there are about 20 million asteroids in near-Earth orbits.[1] More than half are structurally weak, and if they entered Earth's atmosphere, they would probably explode at altitudes of about 30 km. These high-altitude explosions are spectacular but do not pose a significant hazard at the surface. The remaining objects are strong chondritic asteroids (Table 12.1). These relatively slow-moving objects could penetrate the atmosphere and explode at low altitudes or strike Earth's surface. Identifying all these objects will be extremely difficult, because there are nearly 10 million of them. Also, objects only a few dozen metres across are difficult to identify and track.[1] We are able, however, to identify and track objects of a few hundred metres in diameter.

Once a large NEO is known to be on a collision course with our planet, options to avoid or minimize the effects of an aerial burst or crater-forming impact are limited. For smaller asteroids, people could be evacuated if authorities were provided several months warning and if we could precisely predict the location of the impact. However, evacuating an area of several thousand square kilometres would be a tremendous, if not impossible, undertaking.[1]

No place on the planet is safe if a large asteroid strikes. Living things, including people, within the blast area would be killed instantaneously; those farther away would likely die in the ensuing months from the cold, acid rain, and destruction of the food chain. Little would be gained if we intercepted the object and blew it apart, because the smaller pieces would rain down on Earth and might cause more damage than a single larger body. And, in any case, we do not yet have the technology to destroy an incoming asteroid. A better approach would be to try to divert the path of the asteroid so that it misses Earth.

Let's assume we know that a 400 m asteroid will strike Earth in 100 years. The asteroid probably has been crossing Earth's orbit for millions of years and would miss, rather than strike, Earth if we could slightly alter its orbit years before the impact. This scenario is possible because we are able to identify a very large asteroid at least 100 years before impact and we could develop the technology to change the orbit of a threatening asteroid. Nuclear explosions in the vicinity of the asteroid would alter its path without breaking it up. The cost of the program required to develop such a capability would be huge, perhaps hundreds of billions of dollars. However, the expenditure will seem small when we are faced with the reality of a large asteroid on a collision course with Earth!

In summary, we continue to catalogue extraterrestrial objects that intersect Earth's orbit, and we are beginning to think about options to minimize the risk they pose (see Professional Profile). Because we have the ability to detect a large asteroid long before it reaches Earth, we may be able to intercept it and nudge it into a different orbit so that it misses our planet.

PROFESSIONAL PROFILE

Michael J. S. Belton, Astronomer

Is Earth headed for another Deep Impact? According to Dr. Michael J. S. Belton, even the smallest asteroid capable of penetrating Earth's atmosphere has the destructive energy of 1000 Hiroshima bombs or two simultaneous eruptions of Mount St. Helens. What's more, there's a 20 percent chance that such an asteroid will strike Earth in your lifetime.

Belton, a retired astronomer with the National Optical Astronomy Observatories, a consortium of 31 U.S. institutions and three international affiliates, now directs his own company, Belton Space Exploration Initiatives, LLC. The company is currently evaluating the technology required to avert an asteroid next time one comes our way (Figure 12.C).

▲ **FIGURE 12.C MICHAEL J. S. BELTON** Dr. Belton is deputy principal investigator of NASA's Deep Impact Project, established to look deep inside a comet. To accomplish its goal, NASA launched a satellite on January 12, 2005, to rendezvous with Comet Temep 1. When it reaches the comet, the satellite will shoot a blunt "impactor" into the comet's heart at a velocity 10 times that of a rifle bullet. The impactor has been designed to create a crater somewhere between the size of a house and a football stadium. The satellite will take pictures of the impactor's collision and the comet's interior as seen in the crater walls. *(Courtesy of Dr. Michael J. S. Belton/National Optical Astronomy Observatories)*

But before we start sending rockets equipped with nuclear detonators to intercept asteroids, as in the movies *Deep Impact* and *Armageddon,* we need a lot more information about these bodies.

In February 2004, a conference organized by the American Institute of Aeronautics and Astronautics (AIAA) brought together top experts on asteroid and comet impacts to discuss what steps need to be taken to eventually protect Earth from such a disaster. "Basically, the answer is a lot needs to be done," says Belton, who attended the conference. "We're going to have to learn a lot more."

Data are required on the interior and basic structure of asteroids, Belton notes. The surface material and physical characteristics are vital to any discussion of how an asteroid could be deflected or destroyed.

To fill the knowledge gaps, some scientists are proposing missions to asteroids to gather information. But such missions require large amounts of money. "Right now, there's serious discussion in the community about this, but there's not much discussion in the Administration, in the Congress," Belton says. In a presentation at the AIAA conference, he concluded that an adequate program to successfully avert a catastrophe is at least 20 years away.

In the meantime, several organizations are working to catalogue every NEO larger than 1 km in diameter. A NASA project called the Spaceguard Survey, which began in 1998, aims to identify 90 percent of all large NEOs by 2008.

A summary report of the AIAA conference recommended that the Spaceguard Survey be extended to NEOs as small as 100 m. When this project is completed, scientists may have a great deal more warning about asteroids with Earth's name on them.

—Chris Wilson

Summary

Near-Earth objects include asteroids, meteoroids, and comets. Some of these objects enter Earth's atmosphere and strike its surface. Small objects burn up in the atmosphere and are visible as meteors at night. Large objects, ranging from a few metres to hundreds of kilometres across, may explode in the atmosphere in an aerial burst or hit the surface of Earth. An impact by an asteroid as small as 5 km in diameter could cause a global catastrophe, including mass extinction of life. The largest and best-documented impact of such an object occurred 65 million years ago at the end of the Cretaceous Period—an asteroid about 10 km in diameter struck Earth, causing the extinction of 70 percent of plant and animal genera, including all of the dinosaurs.

The risk associated with an aerial burst or the direct impact of an extraterrestrial object is the product of its probability and the consequences should it occur. Relatively small events like the 1908 Tunguska aerial burst occur somewhere on Earth, on average, every 1000 years. A Tunguska-like event would cause catastrophic damage if it happened over an urban area. Asteroids large enough to produce a catastrophe on a hemispheric scale probably strike Earth every few million years. Such programs as Spacewatch and NEAT (Near-Earth Asteroid Tracking Project) will identify asteroids larger than a few hundred metres in diameter long before they reach Earth. With adequate warning, it may be possible to intercept and divert an approaching asteroid by using nuclear explosions. There are about 10 million smaller, potential Tunguska-type objects that could produce catastrophic damage to cities and towns. Identifying all these objects will be extremely difficult.

Key Terms

aerial burst (p. 347)
asteroid (p. 344)
comet (p. 344)
ejecta blanket (p. 349)
impact crater (p. 349)
Kuiper Belt (p. 346)
mass extinction (p. 353)
meteor (p. 344)
meteorite (p. 347)
meteoroid (p. 344)
Oort Cloud (p. 346)

Review Questions

1. Where is Tunguska? What happened there? Why is it important to our discussion of natural hazards?
2. What are the differences among an asteroid, a meteor, a comet, a meteoroid, and a meteorite?
3. What are meteorites and comets made of?
4. Where do comets and asteroids originate?
5. What are the characteristics of impact craters? How can these features be distinguished from other types of craters?
6. How do simple and complex impact craters differ?
7. Why does Earth have fewer impact craters than the Moon does?
8. Explain the significance of Comet Shoemaker-Levy 9.
9. What is the significance of Barringer Crater?
10. What hypotheses have been proposed to explain mass extinctions?
11. When did the greatest mass extinction in Earth history occur?
12. What is the K-T boundary? Why is it significant in the study of natural hazards?
13. Is the risk of dying from an asteroid impact greater or less than the risk of dying in an automobile accident?
14. What can be done to avert an extraterrestrial impact?

Critical Thinking Questions

1. What would be the likely effects of a Tunguska-type aerial burst over central North America? If the event could be predicted 100 years in advance, what could be done to minimize damage and loss of life, assuming the object's orbit could not be changed? Outline a plan to minimize death and destruction.
2. How would the effects of an asteroid impact differ depending on whether it struck the ocean or land? Consider what would happen physically and chemically to the water and how the impact craters might differ.
3. Compare the velocities of an asteroid or a comet, light waves, and sound waves. Why do they differ?

Selected Web Resources

Asteroid and Comet Impact Hazards
http://impact.arc.nasa.gov Information on impacts from NASA

Doomsday Asteroid
www.pbs.org/wgbh/nova/spacewatch NOVA Online feature on asteroids and comets

Disasteroids!
www.astro.uvic.ca/media/press/1.htm A *Canadian Geographic* article on asteroid research by Canadian astronomers and geologists

Spacewatch
http://spacewatch.lpl.arizona.edu From the Spacewatch program

Canadian Space Agency
www.space.gc.ca/asc/eng/default.asp Information on the Canadian Space Agency

Near-Earth Objects
http://cfa-www.harvard.edu/cfa/ps/NEO/TheNEOPage.html A collection of web links dealing with Near Earth objects

Near-Earth Object Tracking
http://neat.jpl.nasa.gov NASA effort to track asteroids and comets crossing Earth's orbit

www.casca.ca/ecass/issues/winter2000/features/neo/neo.htm Description of the near-Earth object tracing system by D. D. Balam of the University of Victoria

Asteroids
http://seds.lpl.arizona.edu/nineplanets/nineplanets/asteroids.html Information on asteroids from the University of Arizona's Lunar and Planetary Laboratory

The Barringer Crater
www.barringercrater.com From the Barringer Crater Company

Finding Impact Craters with Landsat
http://craters.gsfc.nasa.gov A classroom exercise that uses satellite images to find impact craters

The Chesapeake Bay Bolide Impact: A New View of Coastal Plain Evolution
http://marine.usgs.gov/fact-sheets/fs49-98 USGS Fact Sheet 049–98 on the Chesapeake Bay impact crater

The K-T Boundary
www.nmnh.si.edu/paleo/blast/k_t_boundary.htm From the Smithsonian Institution

APPENDIX A

Minerals

Characteristic Properties of Minerals

A *mineral* is a naturally occurring, homogeneous, inorganic, solid substance with a definite chemical composition and characteristic crystalline structure, colour, and hardness. Minerals can be identified from their physical properties. Crystal structure and chemical composition are the basis for mineral classification.

Some minerals have aesthetic or utilitarian value. For example, copper was valued by early people for its lustre and malleability and was used for jewellery and tools. Gemstones, such as rubies and sapphires, have always been valued for their beauty. Historically, one of the most valued minerals has been halite (NaCl), or common table salt, because all animals, including people, need it to live. Halite has been mined for thousands of years. Some clay minerals are valued because they can be moulded into pottery and decorative statues. Today, a wide variety of minerals are used in ceramics, electronics, metallurgy, agriculture, water treatment, and jewellery.

Identifying Minerals

Mineral identification requires observation and testing for particular properties, including hardness, specific gravity, fracture, cleavage, crystal form, colour, and lustre.

Hardness

Most physical properties of minerals reflect characteristics of their internal atomic structure, that is, the size, spacing, and strength of the bonding of the atoms within the mineral. Absolute hardness is difficult to measure, but in 1822 Austrian mineralogist Friedrich Mohs devised an ingenious 10-point scale of *relative hardness* (H) that is still widely used. The softest mineral on Mohs Scale is talc ($H = 1$); the hardest mineral is diamond ($H = 10$) (Table A.1). A change in absolute hardness from one Mohs number to the next is not the same, but any mineral or substance will scratch a mineral with a lower hardness. You can use common objects, such as a fingernail ($H = 2.2$), a copper penny (a Canadian penny minted before 1997; $H = 3.2$), and a glass plate ($H = 5.5$) to determine the hardness of common minerals.

You can determine whether a mineral is harder or softer than 5.5 by trying to scratch a glass plate with a fresh, unweathered surface of the mineral specimen. You must be certain that the mineral actually scratches the glass and does not just leave a line of powder on the surface of the plate. If you find that the mineral is softer than glass, then check to see whether it is harder than a copper penny. By this process, you can bracket the relative hardness (e.g., > 3.2 and < 5.5) of the unknown mineral.

Specific Gravity

Minerals have different specific gravities. *Specific gravity* is the density of a mineral or other material relative to the specific gravity of water, which is 1. The specific gravities of minerals range from about 2.2 for halite to 19.3 for gold. Most

Table A.1 Mohs Hardness Scale

	Relative Hardness[1]	Mineral	Comment	Hardness of Common Materials
Softest	1	Talc	Softest mineral, used to make powder	Graphite, "lead" in pencils (1–2)
	2	Gypsum	Used to make wall board	Fingernail (2.2)
	3	Calcite	Mineral forming marble and limestone	Copper penny[2] (3.2)
	4	Fluorite	Mined for fluorine, used in glass and enamel	
	5	Apatite	Tooth enamel	Steel knife blade, window glass (5.5–6)
	6	Orthoclase	Common rock-forming mineral	
	7	Quartz	The gemstone amethyst is purple quartz	Hard steel file (6.5)
	8	Topaz	Clear variety is a gemstone	
	9	Corundum	The gemstone ruby is red corundum; sapphire is the blue variety	
Hardest	10	Diamond	Hardest mineral, gemstones are brilliant	

[1] Note: The scale is relative; unit increases in hardness do not represent an equal increase in true hardness.
[2] A Canadian penny minted before 1997 or a U.S. penny minted before 1982.

minerals, however, have specific gravities between 2.5 and 4.5. To roughly estimate the specific gravity of an unknown mineral, take a small sample and heft it. This simple exercise allows you to reliably assign a low, medium, or high value of specific gravity to the specimen.

Cleavage

Many minerals break in a distinctive way (Table A.2). Those that break along smooth planar surfaces are said to have *cleavage*. Cleavage develops because the forces that bind atoms in a crystalline structure are rarely equal in all directions. A sure sign of cleavage is the presence of series of small, parallel, reflective steps on the broken face of a mineral. The atomic bonds perpendicular to these steps are the weakest bonds within the mineral. One way to recognize cleavage is to rotate the mineral specimen in your hands with light from the Sun or a lamp directed over your shoulders. The small, parallel cleavage steps will reflect light all at once.

Two aspects of cleavage are important in mineral identification: the number of cleavage surfaces and the angle between the surfaces. Minerals may have one, two, three, four, or six cleavage surfaces, or "planes" (Figure A.1). It may be difficult to estimate cleavage angles by eye, but it is generally sufficient to determine whether the angle is close to 90° or not. Care is required, however, because a cleavage plane can be confused with a crystal face that developed as the mineral grew. Unlike cleavage planes, crystal faces generally are not repetitive, nor do they form steps.

Crystal Form

Crystal form is the geometric shape that minerals acquire when they crystallize. It is a useful property for identifying some minerals but, unfortunately, most mineral specimens do not show crystal form. The pointed and elongate, hexagonal crystal form of quartz is diagnostic, as is the cube shape of pyrite.

Fracture

The broken surfaces of a mineral that are not cleavage planes are termed *fracture*. Most fracture is uneven or irregular, but there are two noteworthy exceptions: *conchoidal fracture* and *fibrous fracture*. Conchoidal fracture surfaces are uniformly curved and at least partially smooth. Surfaces reflect light continuously as the mineral specimen is slowly rotated. Broken glass exhibits conchoidal fracture.

Colour

The *colour* of a mineral can be misleading because some minerals have several different colours and different minerals can have the same colour. For example, normally clear quartz may be white, pink, purple, red, brown, yellow, green, or black, depending on the impurities that are present; and halite and quartz can have the same colour.

A better way of using colour to identify some minerals is to powder part of a specimen on an unglazed porcelain plate. The resulting *streak* is especially useful for identifying metallic minerals. For example, a hand specimen of the mineral hematite (Fe_2O_3) may be dull black or shiny silver, but its streak is always red. Streak tests can only be done with minerals that are softer than the porcelain streak plate, which has a hardness of about 6.5.

Lustre

Lustre refers to the way light is reflected from a mineral. Most minerals have either a metallic or a nonmetallic lustre. Minerals with metallic lustre appear silver, brass, or shiny black in reflected light and are opaque, even on thin edges. Words used to describe nonmetallic lustres include glassy,

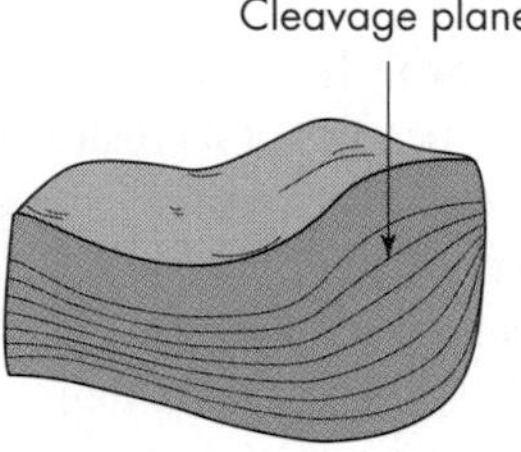

(a) One direction of cleavage. Mineral examples: muscovite and biotite micas

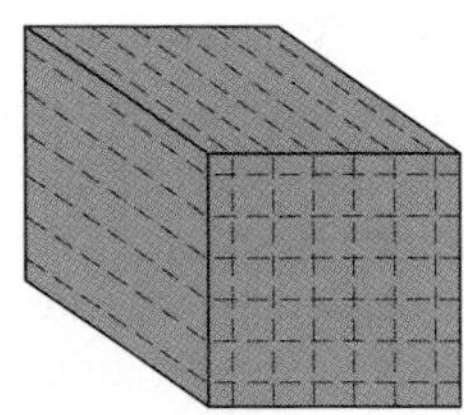

(b) Two directions of cleavage at right angles or nearly right angles. Mineral examples: feldspars, pyroxene

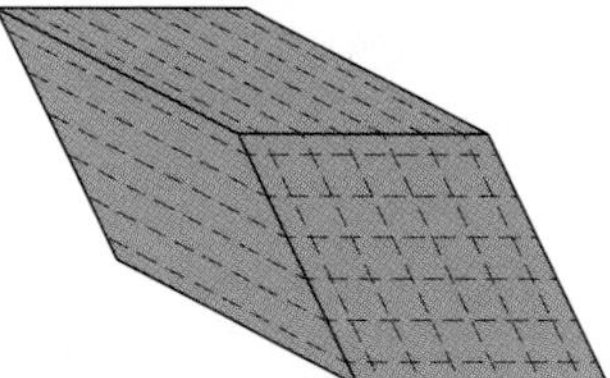

(c) Two directions of cleavage not at right angles. Mineral example: amphibole

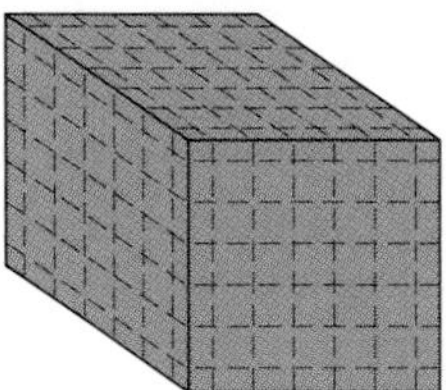

(d) Three directions of cleavage at right angles. Mineral examples: halite, galena

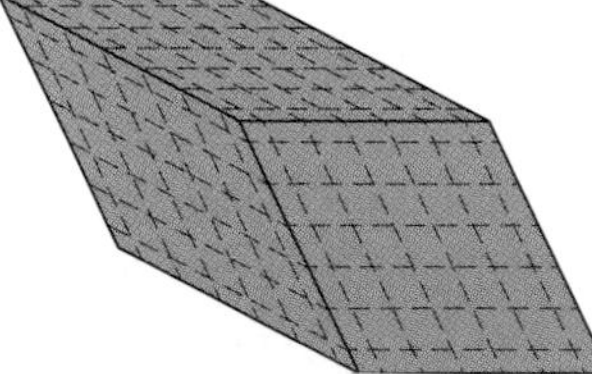

(e) Three directions of cleavage not at right angles. Mineral example: calcite

▲ **FIGURE A.1 COMMON TYPES OF CLEAVAGE** (a) Mica has one cleavage plane and breaks into sheets. (b) Feldspar and pyroxene have two cleavage planes at nearly right angles. (c) Amphibole has two cleavage planes that are not at right angles. (d) Halite and galena have three cleavage planes at right angles; crystals break into cubes. (e) Calcite has three cleavage planes, but they do not meet at right angles; crystals break into rhombohedral fragments. The cleavage planes of all minerals except mica are shown by dashed lines; the cleavage of mica is indicated by solid lines.

TABLE A.2 Properties and Significance of Selected Common Minerals

Mineral Class	Mineral	Chemical Formula	Colour	Hardness	Other Characteristics	Comment
Silicates	Plagioclase feldspar	$(Na, Ca)Al(Si,Al)Si_2O_8$	Commonly white or grey, but may be other colours	6	Two cleavages at approximately 90°; may have fine striations on one of the cleavage surfaces	One of the most common of the rock-forming minerals; a group of feldspars with sodium and calcium end members; important industrial minerals
	Alkali feldspar	$(Na, K)AlSi_3O_8$	Grey, white, pink, or salmon colour	6	Two cleavages at 90°; translucent to opaque with glassy lustre	One of the most common of the rock-forming minerals; used in porcelain and some industrial processes
	Quartz	SiO_2	Colourless, white, grey, pink, purple, and several other colours, depending on impurities	7	Crystals have six sides; conchoidal fracture; coarse crystalline varieties have glassy lustre, whereas micro-crystalline varieties have dull to waxy lustre	Common rock-forming mineral; resistant to most chemical weathering; basic constituent of glasses and fluxes; used as an abrasive; coloured varieties, such as amethyst and agate, are gemstones
	Pyroxene	$(Ca, Mg, Fe)_2Si_2O_6$	Green to black	5–6	Crystals are short and stout; two cleavages at about 90°	Important group of rock-forming minerals; particularly common in igneous rocks; weathers easily
	Amphibole	$(Na, Ca)_2(Mg,Al, Fe)_5Si_8O_{22}(OH)_2$	Green to black	5–6	Two cleavage surfaces intersect at an angle of 120°; has better developed cleavage and a higher lustre than pyroxene	Important group of rock-forming minerals, particularly in igneous and metamorphic rocks; intermediate susceptibility to weathering
	Olivine	$(Mg, Fe)_2SiO_4$	Generally green, but also yellow	6.5–7	Conchoidal fracture; commonly occurs in aggregates of small glassy grains	Important rock-forming mineral in some igneous and metamorphic rocks; weathers easily
	Clay	Hydrous aluminum silicates containing Ca, Na, Fe, Mg, and K	Generally white, but may be coloured because of impurities	1–2	Generally found as soft, earthy masses composed of microscopic grains; may have an earthy odour when moist; specific mineral species are difficult to identify in hand specimens	Clay minerals have many uses; some clay-rich soils are subject to damaging shrink-swell behaviour
	Chlorite	Hydrous Mg, Fe, Al silicate	Green to dark green	2–2.5	Layered or scaly masses with one cleavage; thin sheets are flexible and nonelastic; vitreous to pearly lustre	Important group of minerals in metamorphic rocks
	Talc	$Mg_3Si_4O_{10}(OH)_2$	Pale green, white, or grey	1	Layered or compact masses with one cleavage; thin sheets flexible and nonelastic; soapy feel with pearly to greasy lustre	Used in ceramics, paint, roofing paper, and cosmetics, and as ornamental stone
	Biotite (black mica)	$K(Mg, Fe)_3AlSi_3O_{10}(OH)_2$	Black, dark brown, or dark green	2.5–3	One cleavage; breaks into thin sheets	Important mineral in igneous and metamorphic rocks
	Muscovite (white mica)	$KAl_2(AlSi_3O_{10})(OH)_2$	White, light yellow, brown, pink, or green; colourless in thin sheets	2–3	One cleavage; breaks into thin sheets	Important mineral in igneous and metamorphic rocks; used in industrial roofing materials, paint, and rubber

TABLE A.2 *(Continued)*

Carbonates	Calcite	$CaCO_3$	Colourless, white; a range of colours result from impurities	3	Effervesces strongly in dilute hydrochloric acid; may break into rhombohedral fragments due to two cleavages at 78°; transparent variety displays double refraction (a single dot on a piece of paper appears as two dots when viewed through the mineral)	Main constituent of limestone and marble; associated with karst and sink-holes; weathers rapidly; used in some industrial processes, including the production of asphalts, fertilizers, insecticides, cement, and plastics
	Dolomite	Ca, $Mg(CO_3)_2$	Generally white, but may be light brown or pink	3.5–4	Slowly effervesces in dilute hydrochloric acid when powdered; two cleavages at 78°; may be transparent to translucent and have a vitreous to pearly lustre	Common mineral in dolostone and dolomitic limestone
	Malachite	$Cu_2CO_3(OH)_2$	Emerald green or dark green	3.5–4	Effervesces slightly in dilute hydrochloric acid, turning the acid solution green; commonly has swirling lighter and darker green bands	Valued as a decorative stone; used in jewellery; source of copper
Oxides[1]	Hematite	Fe_2O_3	Reddish brown, red, or dark grey	5.5–6.5	Streak is dark red	Found in small amounts in many igneous rocks, particularly basalt
	Magnetite	Fe_3O_4	Black	6	Magnetic	The most important ore of iron
	Goethite	FeO(OH)	Yellow, yellow-brown, or black	1–5.5	Occurs as earthy masses or crusts; streak is yellow-brown	Forms by chemical weathering of iron minerals; occurs as "rust"; formerly called limonite, which is now known to be a relatively rare mineral
Sulphides	Pyrite	FeS_2	Pale brassy yellow or brown	6–6.5	Commonly occurs as well formed cubic crystals with striations on crystal faces	Has been used in the production of sulphuric acid; source of sulphur in coal; contributes to the formation of acid-rich waters
	Chalcopyrite	$CuFeS_2$	Dark brassy to golden yellow; tarnishes to iridescent red, purple, or dark blue	3.5–4	Disintegrates easily; greenish-black streak; lacks cleavage	An important ore of copper; may be associated with gold and silver ores
	Galena	PbS	Silver grey	2.5	Grey to black streak; high specific gravity; metallic lustre	Primary ore of lead
Sulphates	Gypsum	$CaSO_4$ $2H_2O$	Generally colourless or white, but may occur in a variety of colours because of impurities	2	Transparent to opaque; one cleavage; may form fibrous crystals, but commonly is an earthy mass	Used as a construction material, in fertilizer, and as a flux for pottery
	Anhydrite	$CaSO_4$	White, grey, or colourless	3–3.5	Commonly massive fine aggregates; translucent to transparent; colourless streak	Used in the production of sulphuric acid, as a filler in paper, and as ornamental stone

[1] This class includes hydroxides.

TABLE A.2 (Continued)

Halides	Fluorite	CaF_2	A variety of colours; most commonly purple, yellow, white, or green	4	Occurs as crystals or massive aggregates; four cleavages	Used as a flux in the metal industry and in the production of hydrofluoric acid
	Halite	NaCl	Generally colourless or white, but may occur in a variety of colours because of impurities	2.5	Salty taste; cubic form; three cleavages	Common table salt; rock salt is used for snow and ice removal
Native elements	Gold	Au	Golden yellow	2.5–3	Crystals are rare; high specific gravity; ductile and malleable	Used as a monetary standard, in jewellery, dentistry, and the manufacture of computer chips and other electronic devices
	Diamond	C	Generally colourless, but also occurs in shades of yellow, brown, blue, pink, green, and orange	10	Brilliant lustre	A precious jewel; also used as an industrial abrasive
	Graphite	C	Black to grey	1–2	Occurs as foliated masses; black streak; greasy feel	Used in lubricants, dyes, and in pencils as "lead"
	Native sulphur	S	Yellow if pure; impure varieties are brown or black	1.5–2.5	Sulphurous smell similar to discharged fireworks or gunpowder	Byproduct of oil refining; used to manufacture sulphuric acid

Source: Modified from Davidson, J. P., W. E. Reed, and P. M. Davis. 1997. Exploring Earth. Upper Saddle River, NJ: Prentice Hall; and Birchfield, B. C., R. J. Foster, E. A. Keller, W. N. Melhom, D. G. Brookins, L. W. Mintt, and H. V. Thurman. 1982. Physical geology. Columbus, OH: Charles E. Merrill.

pearly, greasy, earthy, and resinous. Light will also pass through thin edges of a nonmetallic mineral.

Some minerals have more than one lustre. For example, some specimens of graphite have metallic lustre and others have nonmetallic lustres.

Steps in Identifying a Mineral

1. Decide whether the mineral has a metallic or a nonmetallic lustre and refer to Table A.3. If the mineral is metallic, determine the colour of its streak.
2. Determine the relative hardness of the mineral by first testing to see whether it will scratch glass or whether it can be scratched by a knife (Table A.1). Be aware that it may be difficult to determine hardness if the mineral's hardness is close to that of glass (about 5.5) or a pocketknife (about 5.1). In such cases, the mineral may lie within either the harder-than-glass or softer-than-glass parts of Table A.3.
3. Decide whether the mineral has cleavage. If cleavage is present, determine the number of cleavage planes and whether the angle between the planes is close to 90°. If cleavage is not present, determine the type of fracture.
4. Once you have provisionally identified the mineral, test for other physical or chemical properties (e.g., taste, reaction with dilute hydrochloric acid) listed for that mineral in Tables A.2 and A.3 to confirm your identification.

Identification of minerals in the field or in the laboratory, using simple tests and perhaps a hand lens to determine cleavage and other properties, is an exercise in pattern recognition. You will become more proficient at mineral identification after you have looked at many minerals and have learned how particular minerals differ. Sometimes, geologists require more information about mineral specimens or are unable to conclusively identify them in the field. In such cases, they use sophisticated analytical laboratory equipment to determine the chemical composition and internal structure of the specimens.

TABLE A.3 Key to Mineral Identification

To use this table, (1) decide whether the lustre of the mineral is nonmetallic or metallic—if nonmetallic, decide whether the mineral is light-coloured or dark-coloured; (2) use a glass plate to determine whether the mineral is harder or softer than glass; (3) look for evidence of cleavage; and (4) use the other properties shown here and in Table A.2 for final identification.

LIGHT-COLOURED NONMETALLIC LUSTRE			
Harder than glass			
	Shows cleavage	White, pink, or salmon-coloured; two cleavage planes at nearly right angles; hardness 6	Orthoclase (Alkali feldspar)
		White, grey, or greenish grey; two cleavage planes at nearly right angles; hardness 6; striations on one cleavage plane	Plagioclase
	No cleavage	Commonly white or clear, but can be any colour; glassy lustre; transparent to translucent; hexagonal crystals; hardness 7; conchoidal fracture	Quartz
		Green or yellowish green; glassy lustre; granular masses and crystals in rocks; hardness 6.5–7 (may be much less in granular masses)	Olivine
Softer than glass			
	Shows cleavage	Colourless or white; salty taste; three cleavages forming cubic fragments; hardness 2.5	Halite
		White, yellow, or colourless; three cleavages forming rhombohedral fragments; hardness 3; effervesces with dilute hydrochloric acid	Calcite
		Pink, colourless, white, or brown; rhombohedral cleavage; hardness 3.5–4; effervesces with dilute hydrochloric acid only if powdered	Dolomite
		White or transparent; one cleavage; hardness 2	Gypsum
		Pale green or white; soapy feel; one cleavage; hardness 1	Talc
		Colourless, light yellow, brown, or green; transparent in thin elastic sheets; one cleavage; hardness 2–3	Muscovite
		Colourless, yellow, pink, or light blue; four cleavages not at 90°; hardness 4	Fluorite
	No cleavage	Pale green or white; soapy feel; one cleavage; hardness 1	Talc
		White or transparent; hardness 2	Gypsum
		Yellow; resinous lustre; smells like fireworks; hardness 1.5–2.5	Sulphur
DARK-COLOURED NONMETALLIC LUSTRE			
Harder than glass			
	Shows cleavage	Black or dark green; two cleavage planes at nearly 90°; hardness 5–6	Pyroxene
		Black or dark green; two cleavage planes at about 120°; hardness 5–6	Amphibole
	No cleavage	Green; glassy lustre; granular masses and crystals in rocks; hardness 6.5–7 (may be much less in granular masses)	Olivine
		Can be any colour; glassy lustre; transparent to translucent; hexagonal crystals; hardness 7; conchoidal fracture	Quartz
		Steel grey or black; reddish-brown streak; earthy appearance; hardness 5.5–6.5	Hematite
Softer than glass			
	Shows cleavage	Black, greenish black, brown; one cleavage; hardness 2.5–3	Biotite
		Purple, green, or pink; four cleavages not at 90°; hardness 4	Fluorite
		Green; one cleavage; layered or scaly masses; hardness 2–2.5	Chlorite
	No cleavage	Black; smudges fingers; hardness 1–2; one cleavage, apparent only in large crystals	Graphite
		Dull to bright red; reddish-brown streak; earthy appearance; hardness 1–6.5	Hematite
		Yellowish brown, dark brown, to almost black; yellow-brown streak; earthy; hardness 1–5.5 (generally soft)	Goethite
METALLIC LUSTRE		Black; strongly magnetic; hardness 6	Magnetite
		Black; smudges fingers; hardness 1–2; one cleavage, apparent only in large crystals	Graphite
		Light brass yellow; black streak; cubic crystals, commonly with striations; hardness 6–6.5	Pyrite
		Dark brass yellow; may be tarnished; black streak; hardness 3.5–4; massive	Chalcopyrite
		Shiny grey; black streak; very heavy; cubic cleavage; hardness 2.5	Galena

Sources: Modified after Birchfield, B. C., R. J. Foster, E. A. Keller, W. N. Melhom, D. G. Brookins, L. W. Mintt, and H. V. Thurman. 1982. Physical geology. Columbus, OH: Charles E. Merrill; and Hamblin, W. K. and J. D. Howard. 2005. Exercises in physical geology, 12th ed. Upper Saddle River, NJ: Pearson Prentice Hall.

Rocks

Geologists define a *rock* as an aggregate of one or more minerals. The term is sometimes used in different ways by geological and civil engineers. Engineers consider *rock* to be Earth material that cannot be removed without blasting; its loose counterpart is *soil*—material that can be excavated with earth-moving equipment, such as a shovel or a bulldozer. An engineer might thus consider loosely compacted, poorly cemented sandstone to be a soil and dense clay a rock.

In traditional geologic studies, the term *soil* is restricted to surficial Earth material that has developed by in-situ weathering. Other loose material is termed *sediment*. These differences in terminology are more than academic; they can affect communication among engineers, scientists, architects, and planners.

Identifying Rocks

Rocks are made of minerals and, commonly, other substances, such as rock fragments, natural glass, and fossils. A few rocks consist of only one mineral, but most contain several minerals. As in the case of minerals, rock identification is primarily done by recognizing patterns. The first task is to decide whether the rock is igneous, sedimentary, or metamorphic, which may not be as easy as you might think. It is particularly difficult to identify rocks that are fine-grained, consisting of mineral grains that are not visible with the naked eye. Even if a rock is not fine-grained, it is advisable to examine it with a magnifying glass or hand lens.

Some general rules of thumb will assist you in identifying rocks:

1. If the sample comprises broken fragments of other rocks or minerals, it is sedimentary. The fragments may have rounded edges, a characteristic found only in sedimentary rocks.
2. If the rock has flat or elongate minerals oriented in the same direction or if it has parallel bands of different interlocking minerals, it is most likely metamorphic.
3. If the rock contains interlocking crystals of quartz and feldspar that are visible with the naked eye or can be seen easily with a hand lens, it is igneous.
4. If the rock is fine-grained but contains some larger crystals of feldspar or other minerals, it is probably an igneous rock that cooled at or just below Earth's surface.
5. If the rock is relatively soft and effervesces when dilute hydrochloric acid is applied, it is limestone or some other carbonate sedimentary rock, or it is marble, a metamorphic rock.
6. If the rock is grungy, soft, highly weathered, or altered, as many are in nature, you will have some difficulty identifying it!

Physical Properties of Rocks

Physical properties of rocks include colour, specific gravity, relative hardness, porosity, permeability, texture, and strength.

Colour The colour of a rock depends on the minerals present and how much weathering the rock has experienced. Most unweathered rocks at Earth's surface are brown, grey, or black. Chemical and biological weathering can produce iron oxides that change the colour of many rocks to yellow or orange.

Specific Gravity and Relative Hardness *Specific gravity* is the weight of the rock relative to the weight of water. Some rocks, such as pumice, are lighter than water and thus will float. Rocks with abundant iron- and magnesium-bearing minerals have much higher specific gravities.

There is no scale of relative hardness for rocks similar to the Mohs Scale for minerals. Soft rocks can be broken by hand, whereas a mallet or sledgehammer is required to break apart hard rocks.

Porosity and Permeability *Porosity* is the percentage of a rock's volume that is void space between grains and open fractures. *Permeability* is a measure of the ability of a rock to transmit a fluid, such as oil or water. Sedimentary rocks may have up to about 35 percent porosity. Many coarse-grained sedimentary rocks have high permeability, whereas fine-grained sedimentary rocks, such as shale, can be nearly impermeable. Nonfractured igneous rocks have very low porosity and low permeability, but permeability increases when these rocks become fractured. Fracturing is also required to give metamorphic rocks significant permeability.

Texture The *texture* of a rock refers to the size, shape, and arrangement of its crystals or grains. Crystal or grain size can be measured or described qualitatively. A rock with crystals or grains that are visible with the naked eye or with a magnifying hand lens is coarse-grained; one with crystals or grains that can only be seen clearly with a microscope is fine-grained.

Sorting is a measure of the range of grain sizes in a sedimentary rock. A sandstone consisting entirely of grains of similar size is described as *well sorted* (Figure B.1a, B.1c), whereas one comprising grains of a wide range of sizes is *poorly sorted* (Figure B.1b). Grain shape can differ from spherical to platy, and grains can also have rounded or sharp, angular edges. Likewise, the arrangement of crystals or grains can differ. Crystals can be interlocking, such as in granite

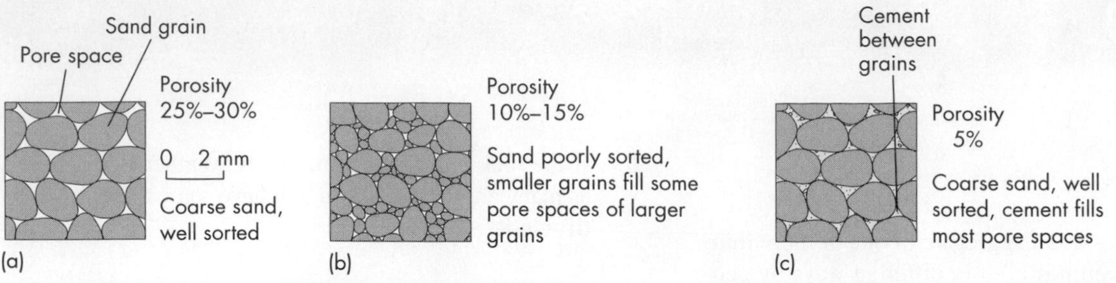

▲ **FIGURE B.1 SORTING AND CEMENTATION AFFECT POROSITY** (a) A well-sorted sand with 25 percent to 30 percent porosity. (b) A poorly sorted sand with 10 percent to 15 percent porosity. (c) A cemented, well-sorted sand with 5 percent porosity; common cements are calcium carbonate and silica.

or marble, or they can be aligned, such as mica grains in schist. Small grains may occupy spaces between large grains, such as in a poorly sorted sandstone (Figure B.1.b). Most of the larger grains in a very poorly sorted sedimentary rock are supported by finer, matrix grains (matrix-supported sedimentary rock); or they may be supported by one another, with the finer grains confined to the spaces between the larger grains (clast-supported sedimentary rock).

Some volcanic rocks have *vesicular texture*, characterized by numerous small cavities formed by gas expansion during cooling. Other volcanic rocks have *porphyritic texture*, with well formed large crystals floating in a fine-grained groundmass of smaller, commonly microscopic crystals.

The texture of a rock influences its porosity. Rocks that are poorly sorted or cemented generally have lower porosity than those that are well sorted and have little or no cement. Porosity in sandstone can range from about 5 percent to 30 percent depending on how much silt, clay, or cement is present in the pore space (Figure B.1).

Strength The *strength* of a rock is generally determined in the laboratory by subjecting a sample to compressive and shear forces. The sample will fracture or break when the forces exerted on it exceed the strength of the rock. Compressive strength is expressed as a force per unit area, such as newtons per square metre (N/m^2). Typical compressive strengths for common rock types are shown in Table B.1.

TABLE B.1 Strength of Common Rock Types

	Rock Type	Compressive Strength (10^6 N/m^2)	Comments
Igneous	Granite	100 to 280	Finer-grained granites with few fractures have the highest strengths
	Basalt	50 to greater than 280	Fractures or cavities weaken the rock
Metamorphic	Marble	100 to 125	Solution openings or fractures weaken the rock
	Gneiss	160 to 190	Strong rock
	Quartzite	150 to 600	Very strong rock
Sedimentary	Shale	Less than 2 to 215	May be a very weak rock
	Limestone	50 to 60	Clay layers, solution openings, or fractures weaken the rock
	Sandstone	40 to 110	Strength differs depending on the degree of fracturing, grain composition, and amount and type of mineral cement

Source: Data primarily from Bolz, R. E., and G. L. Tuve, eds. 1973. Handbook of tables for applied engineering science. Cleveland, OH: CRC Press.

Maps and Related Topics

Topographic Maps

A *topographic map* is a two-dimensional representation of the shape and elevation of the land surface. Elevations are shown by *contour lines,* which are lines of equal elevation above sea level. The vertical distance between successive contour lines is the *contour interval*. Common contour intervals used on topographic maps are 5 m, 10 m, 20 m, 40 m, 80 m, or 100 m. The contour interval selected for a particular map depends on the area's relief and the scale of the map. A small contour interval may be used if the difference in elevation between the highest and lowest points on a map (the relief) is small; in contrast, a larger contour interval will be used if the relief is large so that the user can resolve individual contour lines on steep slopes.

The *scale* of a topographic map, or any map, can be shown in several ways. First, it may be expressed as a ratio, such as 1 to 50,000 (1:50,000), which means that 1 cm on the map equals 50,000 cm (500 m) on the ground. Second, the map may have one or more graphic or bar scales that are subdivided in metres, kilometres, feet, or miles. Bar scales are generally placed at the bottom left or right of the map. Third, the scale of some maps is expressed in terms of specific units of length on the map, such as 1 cm equals 1 km. This means that 1 cm on the map is equivalent to 1 km on the ground. An alternative way of stating this equivalence is that the scale is 1 to 100,000. The most common scale for Natural Resources Canada topographic maps is 1:50,000; for U.S. Geological Survey maps, it is 1:24,000. Maps are produced in both countries, however, at a range scales to meet different needs. Small-scale topographic maps, for example 1:250,000, 1:500,000, and 1:1,000,000 maps, show more area than 1:25,000 or 1:50,000 large-scale maps.

Topographic maps also depict "cultural" features, including roads, buildings, railway and power lines, wharves, and tunnels. Lakes, the sea, streams, and rivers are shown in blue, and vegetation commonly is indicated in green. Symbols and patterns used for Canadian topographic maps are shown in Figure C.1; similar symbols are used for U.S. topographic maps.

Reading Topographic Maps

Reading or interpreting topographic maps is as much an art as it is a science. You become proficient at recognizing Earth landforms from the shapes of their contours after you have examined many topographic maps. It takes some time to acquire this skill, but some general rules will speed the process:

- Valleys containing streams have contours shaped like Vs, in which the apex of each V points in the upstream direction. This principle is sometimes termed the *rule of Vs.* A stream continues to higher elevations at least as far as contours form a V pattern. The Vs will end near the drainage divide, that is, the high point between two drainage basins.
- Where contour lines are close together, the slope or inclination of the land is relatively steep; where they are far apart, the slope is relatively low and the land is flatter. Most natural slopes become steeper upward; thus, contour lines are spaced relatively far apart near the bottom of the slope and become closer farther upslope. This change in contour spacing can be relatively abrupt on some slopes, delineating what are termed "breaks in slope." The foot of a mountain and the intersection of a valley wall with a floodplain are examples of breaks in slope.
- Contours near the crests of hills or mountains close on themselves. Closed contours are oval or round in the case of a conical peak and relatively long and narrow for a ridge. The elevation of the top of a mountain or hill is higher than the value of the last closed contour; it may be estimated by adding half the contour interval to the elevation of the highest closed contour line. For example, if the highest contour delineating a peak is 3000 m and the contour interval is 50 m, the approximate elevation of the top of the peak is 3025 m.
- Most topographic depressions are also shown with closed contours. Each closed contour has small hachure or tic marks that point toward the centre of the depression.
- Some topography is *hummocky,* that is, undulatory or uneven. Hummocky topography is commonly produced by mass wasting or glacial processes. It may appear on topographic maps as a series of hills and depressions with closed contour lines. However, the features will only appear on the map if their relief is greater than the contour interval.

In summary, after studying and working with different topographic maps, you will begin to see the pattern of contours as an actual landscape consisting of hills, valleys, and other features.

Locating Yourself on a Map

Working with a map requires knowing where you are in the landscape. One way to locate yourself on a map is to identify two or three distinctive features that you can see, such as a mountain peak, road intersection, or a prominent bend in a road or river that are also shown on the map. You can then use a compass to determine your location. With the compass, you take bearings to each of the prominent features you have identified outdoors and then draw lines on the map parallel to these bearings and extending from each of the identified features. Your location is where the lines intersect.

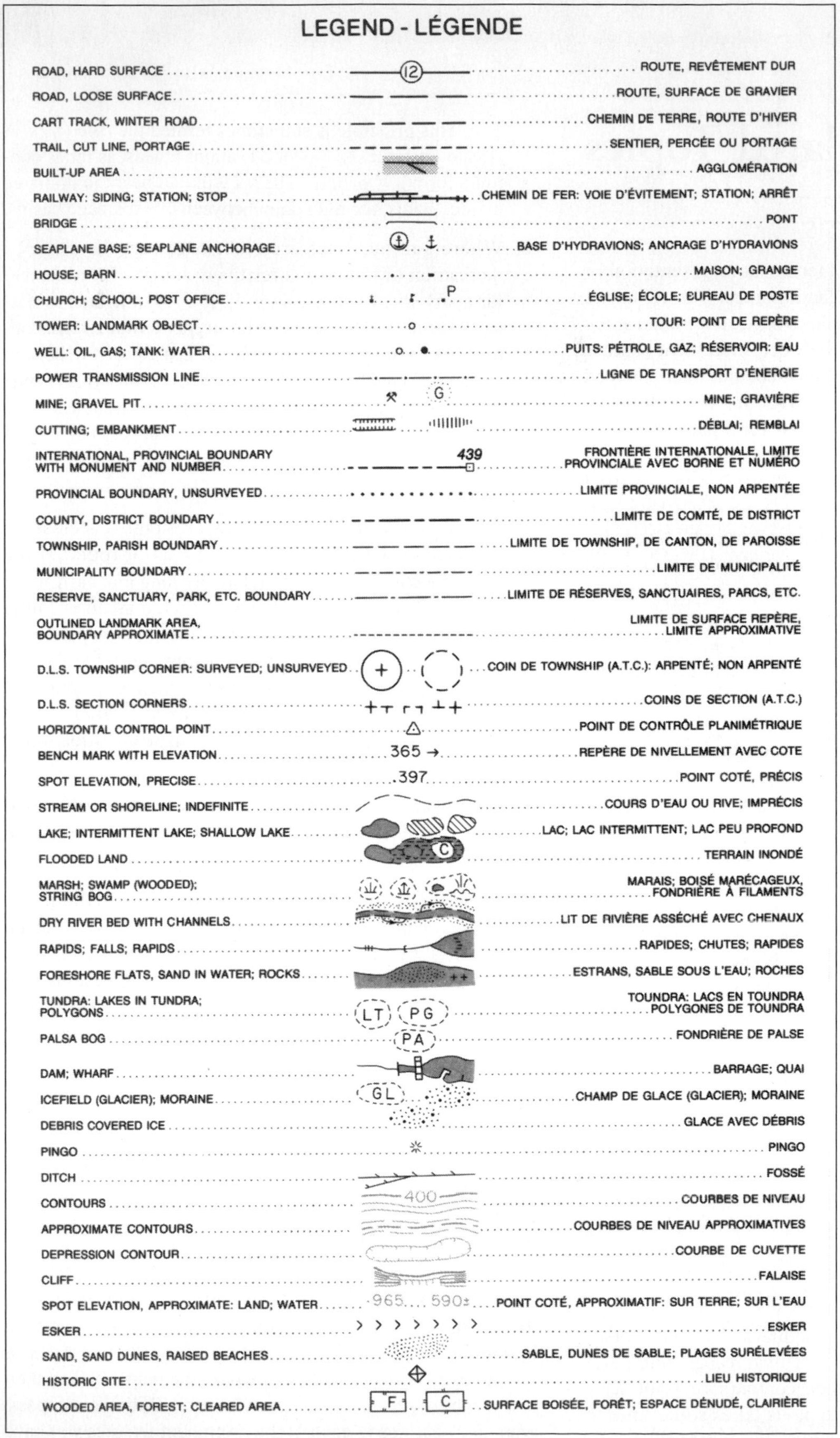

LEGEND - LÉGENDE

ROAD, HARD SURFACE	(12)	ROUTE, REVÊTEMENT DUR
ROAD, LOOSE SURFACE		ROUTE, SURFACE DE GRAVIER
CART TRACK, WINTER ROAD		CHEMIN DE TERRE, ROUTE D'HIVER
TRAIL, CUT LINE, PORTAGE		SENTIER, PERCÉE OU PORTAGE
BUILT-UP AREA		AGGLOMÉRATION
RAILWAY: SIDING; STATION; STOP		CHEMIN DE FER: VOIE D'ÉVITEMENT; STATION; ARRÊT
BRIDGE		PONT
SEAPLANE BASE; SEAPLANE ANCHORAGE		BASE D'HYDRAVIONS; ANCRAGE D'HYDRAVIONS
HOUSE; BARN		MAISON; GRANGE
CHURCH; SCHOOL; POST OFFICE	P	ÉGLISE; ÉCOLE; BUREAU DE POSTE
TOWER: LANDMARK OBJECT		TOUR: POINT DE REPÈRE
WELL: OIL, GAS; TANK: WATER		PUITS: PÉTROLE, GAZ; RÉSERVOIR: EAU
POWER TRANSMISSION LINE		LIGNE DE TRANSPORT D'ÉNERGIE
MINE; GRAVEL PIT	G	MINE; GRAVIÈRE
CUTTING; EMBANKMENT		DÉBLAI; REMBLAI
INTERNATIONAL, PROVINCIAL BOUNDARY WITH MONUMENT AND NUMBER	439	FRONTIÈRE INTERNATIONALE, LIMITE PROVINCIALE AVEC BORNE ET NUMÉRO
PROVINCIAL BOUNDARY, UNSURVEYED		LIMITE PROVINCIALE, NON ARPENTÉE
COUNTY, DISTRICT BOUNDARY		LIMITE DE COMTÉ, DE DISTRICT
TOWNSHIP, PARISH BOUNDARY		LIMITE DE TOWNSHIP, DE CANTON, DE PAROISSE
MUNICIPALITY BOUNDARY		LIMITE DE MUNICIPALITÉ
RESERVE, SANCTUARY, PARK, ETC. BOUNDARY		LIMITE DE RÉSERVES, SANCTUAIRES, PARCS, ETC.
OUTLINED LANDMARK AREA, BOUNDARY APPROXIMATE		LIMITE DE SURFACE REPÈRE, LIMITE APPROXIMATIVE
D.L.S. TOWNSHIP CORNER: SURVEYED; UNSURVEYED		COIN DE TOWNSHIP (A.T.C.): ARPENTÉ; NON ARPENTÉ
D.L.S. SECTION CORNERS		COINS DE SECTION (A.T.C.)
HORIZONTAL CONTROL POINT		POINT DE CONTRÔLE PLANIMÉTRIQUE
BENCH MARK WITH ELEVATION	365 →	REPÈRE DE NIVELLEMENT AVEC COTE
SPOT ELEVATION, PRECISE	.397	POINT COTÉ, PRÉCIS
STREAM OR SHORELINE; INDEFINITE		COURS D'EAU OU RIVE; IMPRÉCIS
LAKE; INTERMITTENT LAKE; SHALLOW LAKE		LAC; LAC INTERMITTENT; LAC PEU PROFOND
FLOODED LAND	C	TERRAIN INONDÉ
MARSH; SWAMP (WOODED); STRING BOG		MARAIS; BOISÉ MARÉCAGEUX, FONDRIÈRE À FILAMENTS
DRY RIVER BED WITH CHANNELS		LIT DE RIVIÈRE ASSÉCHÉ AVEC CHENAUX
RAPIDS; FALLS; RAPIDS		RAPIDES; CHUTES; RAPIDES
FORESHORE FLATS, SAND IN WATER; ROCKS		ESTRANS, SABLE SOUS L'EAU; ROCHES
TUNDRA: LAKES IN TUNDRA; POLYGONS	LT PG	TOUNDRA: LACS EN TOUNDRA POLYGONES DE TOUNDRA
PALSA BOG	PA	FONDRIÈRE DE PALSE
DAM; WHARF		BARRAGE; QUAI
ICEFIELD (GLACIER); MORAINE	GL	CHAMP DE GLACE (GLACIER); MORAINE
DEBRIS COVERED ICE		GLACE AVEC DÉBRIS
PINGO		PINGO
DITCH		FOSSÉ
CONTOURS	400	COURBES DE NIVEAU
APPROXIMATE CONTOURS		COURBES DE NIVEAU APPROXIMATIVES
DEPRESSION CONTOUR		COURBE DE CUVETTE
CLIFF		FALAISE
SPOT ELEVATION, APPROXIMATE: LAND; WATER	·965 ... 590±	POINT COTÉ, APPROXIMATIF: SUR TERRE; SUR L'EAU
ESKER	› › › › › ›	ESKER
SAND, SAND DUNES, RAISED BEACHES		SABLE, DUNES DE SABLE; PLAGES SURÉLEVÉES
HISTORIC SITE		LIEU HISTORIQUE
WOODED AREA, FOREST; CLEARED AREA	F C	SURFACE BOISÉE, FORÊT; ESPACE DÉNUDÉ, CLAIRIÈRE

▲ **FIGURE C.1 TOPOGRAPHIC MAP SYMBOLS** This chart shows some of the common symbols that Natural Resources Canada uses on its topographic maps. They are printed on the reverse side of the map. *(© 2007. Produced under licence from Her Majesty the Queen in Right of Canada, with permission of Natural Resources Canada)*

Today, we commonly use orbiting *Global Positioning System (GPS)* satellites to precisely locate ourselves and work with maps. Handheld GPS satellite receivers are now inexpensive and readily available, and they can provide horizontal positions on the ground with an accuracy of about 5 m to 10 m. They receive signals from at least four satellites and calculate the distance from each satellite to the operator's position on the ground. Extremely accurate clocks determine the time the signal takes to travel from the satellite to the ground. The signal travels at a known speed (about 300 million m/s; the speed of light), thus the travel time is proportional to the distance between the satellite and the receiver. With signals from at least four satellites, the computer in the GPS receiver calculates a position on Earth's surface. Positional accuracy can be further improved by using a method known as *differential GPS*. This method requires, in addition to a mobile, handheld GPS unit, a reference receiver at a known location (Figure C.2). Another way to increase positional accuracy is to average many measurements taken at the same location over a period of 10 minutes or more.

A GPS receiver can be linked directly to *geographic information system (GIS)* computer software so that positions can be plotted directly on a map and viewed on a computer display in the receiver, your vehicle, or a laptop computer. GPS and GIS technology have revolutionized the way geologists and other scientists map in the field. A note about the expression *"in the field"* is appropriate here. This expression means "outdoors," not the "field of geology." For example, a geologist leaving to study landslides triggered by heavy rains in Newfoundland and Labrador would say to her colleagues, "I am going into the field."

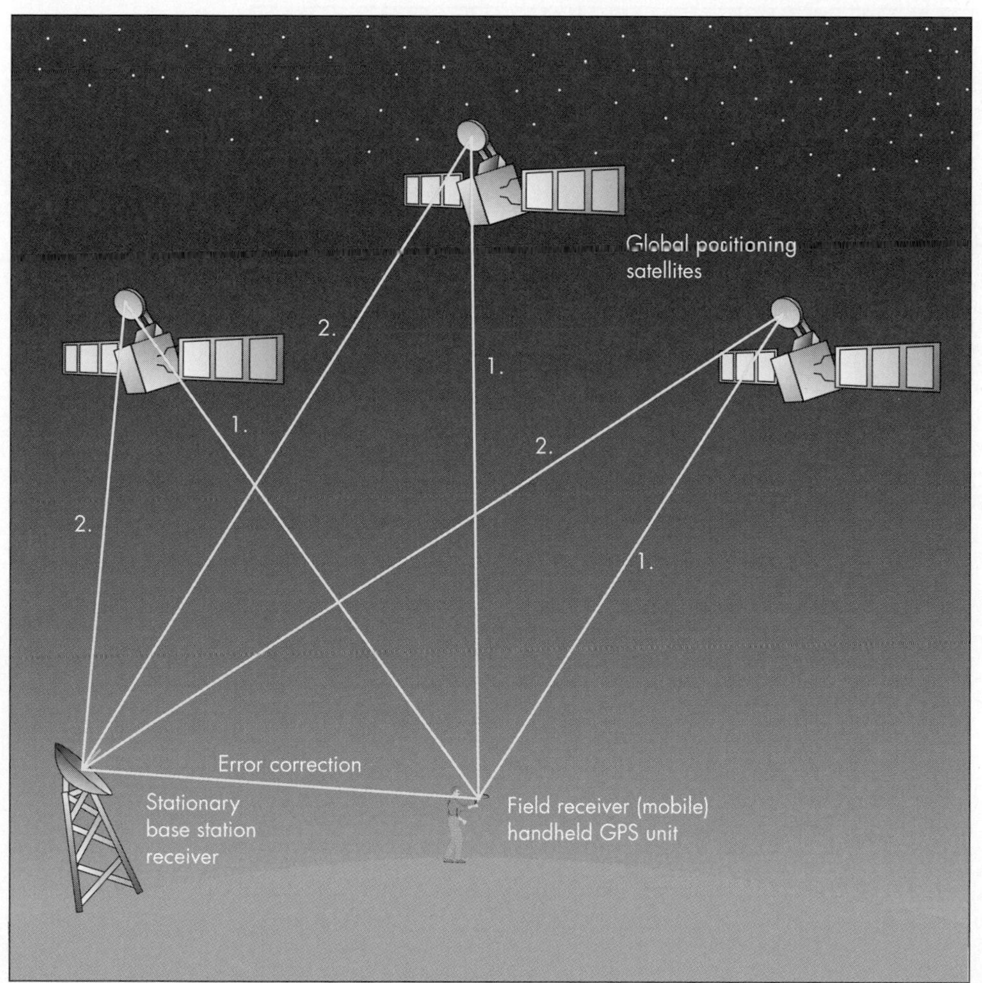

▲ **FIGURE C.2 USING THE GLOBAL POSITIONING SYSTEM** The U.S. Air Force Global Positioning System (GPS) consists of 24 operational satellites orbiting approximately 22,200 km above Earth. Each satellite transmits its own distinct signal, shown by the yellow lines numbered 1. The signals are recognized by receivers on the ground. Using extremely accurate timekeeping, the receiver calculates the distance to each satellite by determining the travel time of its signal. A receiver must process signals from at least four satellites to calculate a three-dimensional position on Earth's surface. Handheld GPS receivers can achieve a positional accuracy of 5 m to 10 m. Increased accuracy can be obtained with the differential GPS method by using a stationary base station. A stationary receiver calculates a position for the base station using the same satellites (yellow lines labelled 2) at the same time as the mobile receiver. The base station then compares the calculated position with its true position to establish a correction factor that can be used by the mobile GPS receiver to improve its positional accuracy. The accuracy of the differential GPS method is typically 2 m to 6 m.

An Example from a Coastal Landscape

In this example, we will look at topographic and cultural features in a coastal landscape (Figure C.3). If we were flying in a plane along this coastline, we would see a landscape consisting of two hills with an intervening valley (Figure C.3a). The coast along the hill to the right is a sea cliff, and in the centre is a sand spit formed by longshore drift. A hook at the

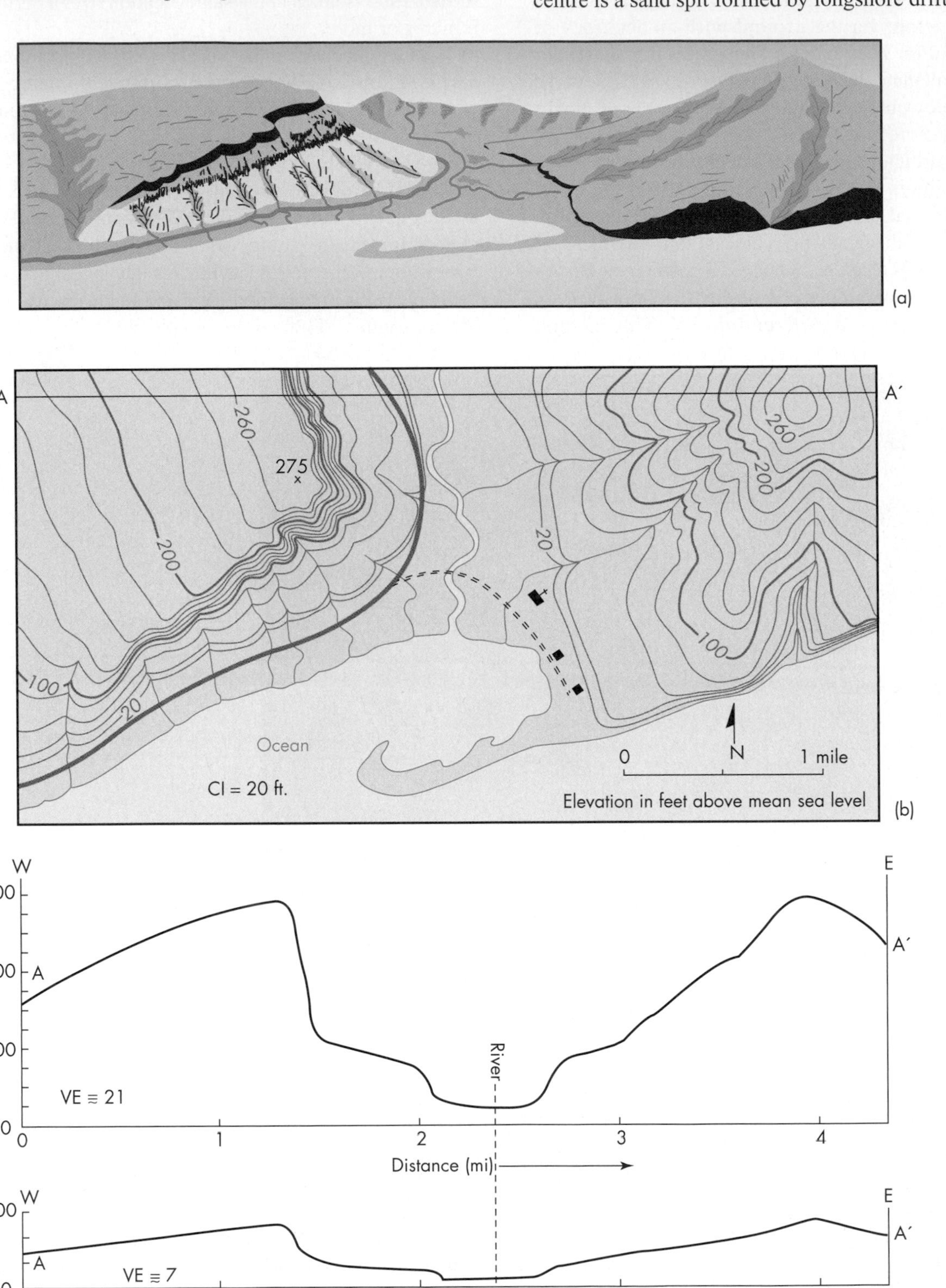

▲ **FIGURE C.3 TOPOGRAPHY OF A COASTAL LANDSCAPE** (a) An oblique view of the coastline shown on the map in part (b) of the figure. (b) Topographic map with a contour interval of about 20 ft. (6 m). (c) Topographic profiles along line A-A′ of the topographic map, drawn with vertical exaggerations (VE) of 21 and 7 times. Vertical exaggeration is the ratio of the vertical and horizontal scales of the topographic profile. In the real world, of course, the vertical and horizontal scales are the same; that is, there is no vertical exaggeration. As an experiment, try to make a topographic profile along line A-A′ with no vertical exaggeration. What do you conclude? *(From U.S. Geological Survey)*

end of the spit indicates that the direction of sand transport along the beach is from the right to the left.

The topographic map for the area has a contour interval of approximately 20 ft. (6 m) (Figure C.3b). The map indicates that the elevation of the highest hill on the east (right) side of the map is approximately 290 ft. (88.5 m) above sea level. This estimated elevation is halfway between 280 ft. (86 m), which is the highest contour on the hill, and 300 ft. (91 m), which would be the next contour if the hill were higher. Three streams flow from the hill, two into the ocean and one into a river. Notice that, along all three streams, the topographic contours V in the upstream direction toward the top of the hill.

Other information that may be "read" from the topographic map includes the following:

- The landform on the west (left) side of the map is a hill with a maximum elevation of 275 ft. (84 m). It has a gentle slope to the west and a steep slope to the east toward the river valley and southeast toward the ocean. The east and southeast slopes are particularly steep near the top of the hill where the contours are close together.
- The river at the centre of the map is flowing into a bay protected by the hooked sand spit. The relatively flat land next to the river is a floodplain, which is delineated by two 20 ft. (6 m) contour lines. A road extends south along the west side of the river and southwest along the coastline. A second, unimproved road crosses the river, providing access to a church and two other buildings.
- The east and southeast slopes of the 275 ft. (84 m) hill are drained by eight small streams, all but one of which flow southward into the ocean. These streams flow in relatively steep gullies eroded into the hillslope. The stream directly south of the 275 ft. (84 m) elevation mark is cutting headward into the steep hillside.

We continue our study of this area by constructing an east-west *topographic profile* along line A-A′ shown on the map. To construct this profile, we must first decide how much to exaggerate the vertical scale (Figure C.3c). Figure C.3c shows two topographic profiles, one with a *vertical exaggeration* (VE) of 21 and a second with a vertical exaggeration of 7. In the first profile 1 ft. (0.3 m) on the horizontal scale corresponds to 21 ft. (6.5 m) on the vertical scale. The vertical exaggeration of the lower profile is three times less than that of the upper profile.

Geologic Maps

Geologists are interested in the spatial distribution of different types of Earth materials. They make *geologic maps* to show the surface distribution of rocks and sediments in different areas. This task requires not only fieldwork but also interpretations that are consistent with the Earth history of the mapped area. Like any scientific endeavour, new observations become a test of the geologist's interpretations.

The first step in preparing a geologic map is to obtain a good topographic base map and aerial photographs of the area to be mapped. A geologist then goes into the field and makes observations of Earth materials in outcrops, or surface exposures. The geologist ultimately groups distinctive rock or sediment types into units called *formations.* Each formation must be "mappable," that is it must be thick and extensive enough to be depicted at the scale of the map. Each formation is separated from adjacent formations by boundaries known as *contacts,* which appear on the map as thin lines between polygons with different colours or patterns. The boundaries may be depositional, erosional (an unconformity), intrusive (for example, a granite intruding a sandstone), or tectonic (a fault).

The geologist also takes measurements of the three-dimensional orientation of the fabric of sedimentary and metamorphic rocks. These measurements, referred to as strike and dip, are generally made with a compass and a clinometer, which is a device for measuring angles in a vertical plane. Each strike and dip measurement is shown on the map by a T-shaped strike and dip symbol (Figures C.4 and C.5). *Strike* is the direction of the line formed by the intersection of a layer of the Earth material and a horizontal plane (Figure C.4). The *dip* direction is perpendicular to the strike, and the dip angle is the maximum angle between the layering and a horizontal plane.

Figure C.5a shows a simple, idealized geologic map of an area of approximately 1350 km^2. The map shows three formations, one consisting of sandstone, another of conglomerate, and a third of shale. The strike and dip symbols indicate the presence of an arch-like, underground geologic structure known as an anticline. The nature of this structure becomes apparent in a geologic cross-section and topographic profile constructed along the line E-E′ (Figure C.5b). Geologic maps

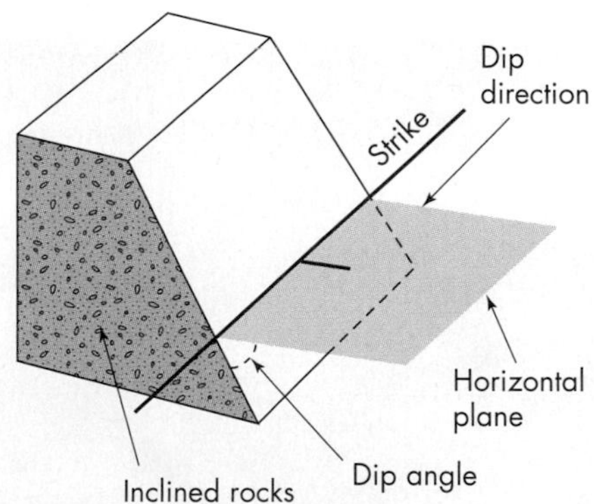

▲ **FIGURE C.4 STRIKE AND DIP** An idealized block diagram showing the strike and dip of beds of inclined sedimentary rocks. Strike is the bearing of the line formed by the intersection of the bedding plane and a horizontal plane (the long direction of a T-shaped symbol in this diagram). The dip direction is perpendicular (90°) to the strike (short direction of the T-shaped symbol). The dip angle is the angle between the bedding plane and a horizontal plane, measured in the dip direction. Together, the strike direction and the direction and amount of dip define the orientation of a plane in three-dimensional space.

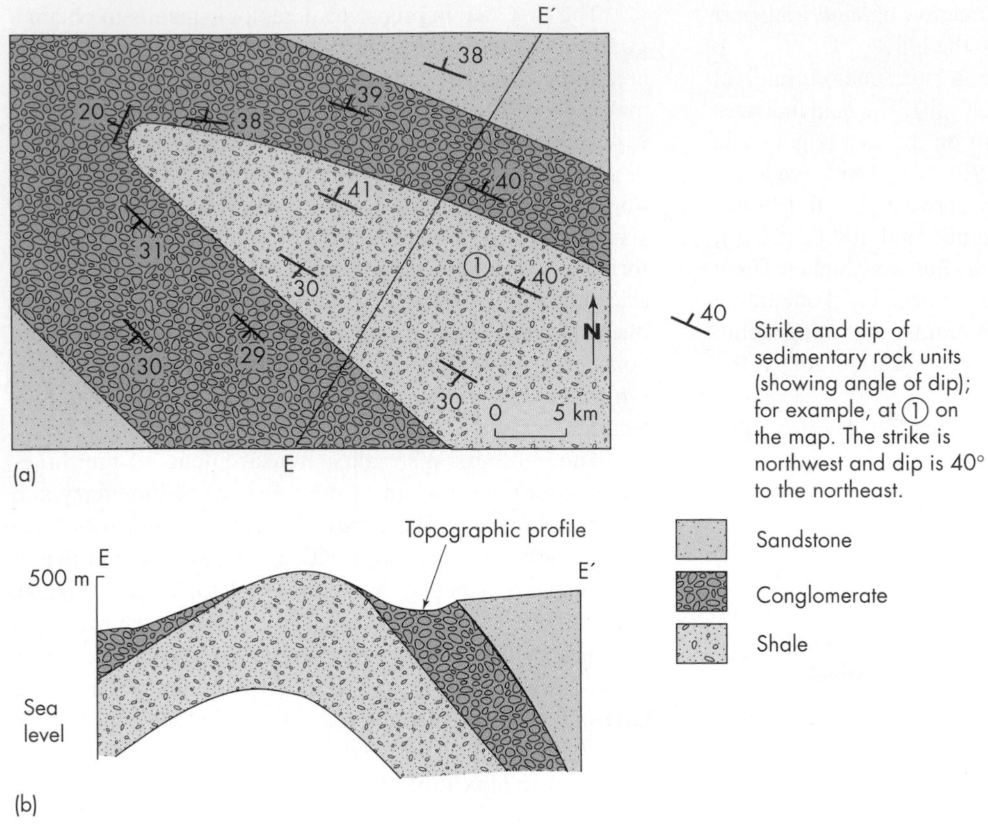

▲ **FIGURE C.5 GEOLOGIC MAP** (a) A simple, idealized geologic map showing three formations, each consisting of a different type of sedimentary rock. (b) Geologic cross-section and topographic profile along line E-E′. The cross-section shows that the three formations depicted on the geologic map have been warped into an arch-like geologic structure called an anticline.

at a variety of scales, from 1:250,000 to 1:24,000, are available from provincial, territorial, state, and federal geological surveys, including the Geological Survey of Canada and the U.S. Geological Survey.

Digital Elevation Models

Topographic data for most regions on Earth are available on computer disk. The datasets consist of gridded elevation

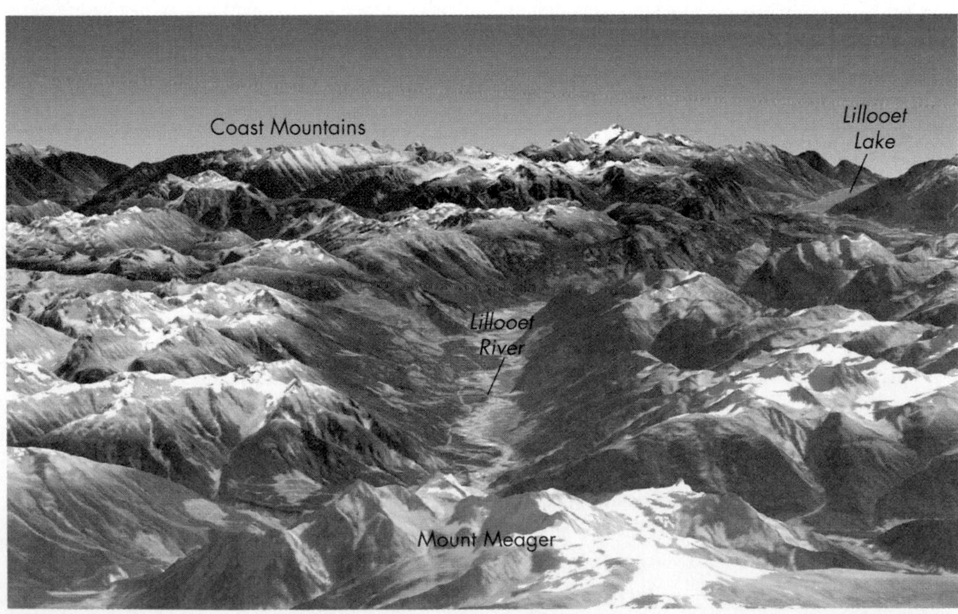

▲ **FIGURE C.6 DIGITAL ELEVATION MODEL** This digital elevation model (DEM) of the Lillooet River valley in southwest British Columbia is an oblique view to the southeast with considerable vertical exaggeration. *(Natural Resources Canada)*

values. The grid spacing, or distance between elevation values, can range from a few metres to 100 m or more. Computer programs are used to synthesize and display the data; colour shading is commonly added to enhance the topography. The resulting simulated representations of Earth's surface are known as *digital elevation models* (DEMs). The models can be rotated to view the electronic land surface from any angle, and the vertical dimension can also be exaggerated so that minor topographic features are visible. A DEM of the Lillooet River Valley north of Vancouver, British Columbia (Figure C.6) reveals the mountainous character of the region. DEMs are now an important research tool used not only for geologic mapping, but also for a wide variety of environmental purposes. To give you a better appreciation of the power of DEMs, we recommend that you explore the website Google Earth (http://earth.google.com).

Summary

Topographic maps and profiles, and geologic maps and cross-sections are essential for evaluating geology and Earth processes. Also important are digital elevation models, which are constructed from topographic data. A variety of special-purpose and derivative maps are useful for natural hazard studies. Examples include maps of recent landslides, floodplain and coastal flood hazard maps, and maps that show the engineering properties of surface rocks and sediments.

How Geologists Determine Geologic Time

To understand Earth history, we must determine ages of Earth events, materials, and landforms. The science of *geochronology* involves the use of a variety of *relative* and *absolute dating* techniques to reconstruct Earth history. Relative dating orders events chronologically using fossil evidence and fundamental geologic principles and laws. The oldest of these laws is the "law of superposition," proposed by Nicholas Steno in 1668 and applied by geologists for more than 300 years. The law of superposition states that in any succession of sediment or sedimentary rock that has not been deformed, the oldest layer is at the bottom, and layers become successively younger upward. Although relative ages can be determined based on superposition and on other laws and principles, relative dating cannot establish rates of geologic processes or the numeric ages of rocks.

An understanding of hazards and risk requires knowledge of rates of geologic processes and times of past geologic events, such as volcanic eruptions, earthquakes, tsunami, floods, and landslides. A chronology of these events is essential for estimating when they might recur.

Geologic, or "deep," time is very different from time as people normally perceive it. Geologic time and "normal" time are based on the same units of measure, years, but they differ vastly in duration and in the instruments used to measure duration. Normal time is measured in hours, days, seasons, years, or decades, and the standard instrument used to measure it is a clock. In contrast, geologic time is measured in thousands to billions of years. To measure time on these scales, geologists use naturally occurring *isotopes* of uranium (U), potassium (K), carbon (C), and other elements to date the materials in which they are found.

An isotope is a variety of an element with the same number of protons in its nucleus as all other forms of the same element, but with a different number of neutrons. The atomic mass of an element or isotope is the sum of its protons and neutrons. The element carbon, for example, has three isotopes, with atomic masses of 12, 13, and 14. All three carbon isotopes have 6 protons, but carbon-12 has 6 neutrons, carbon-13 has 7, and carbon-14 has 8.

Isotopes also differ in their stability. Carbon-12 and carbon-13 are stable isotopes and do not split apart under normal conditions. Most isotopes, however, are unstable and spontaneously and gradually decay into other isotopes. Unstable isotopes are commonly called *radioactive isotopes* because radiation is released when they decay. It is impossible to predict when an individual atom of an unstable isotope will decay, but the average decay time can be determined for a very large number of atoms. Each radioactive isotope has a constant rate of decay that is unaffected by physical forces.

A rock can be dated if a measurable quantity of a radioactive isotope is incorporated into one of its minerals when it forms and if the rock remains an isotopically closed system. The radioactive isotope functions as a clock that is running at a known rate. The radioactive isotope is called the *parent*, and the *stable isotope* that forms from the decay of the parent is termed the *daughter product*. Radioactive isotopes, particularly those of very heavy elements, decay through a series of steps, ending with production of a stable, nonradioactive isotope. For example, uranium-238 decays to stable lead-206 by means of 14 nuclear transformations.

An important characteristic of a radioactive isotope such as U-238 is its *half-life,* which is the time required for one-half of a specific amount of the isotope to decay. Every radioactive isotope has a unique and characteristic half-life (Table D.1). Over time, the amount of parent radioactive isotope in a substance exponentially decreases and the amount of the stable daughter isotope proportionally increases (Figure D.1). The actual amount of the radioactive isotope that was initially present in the material to be dated need not be known; rather, a numeric age can be obtained solely from the relative proportions of the parent and daughter isotopes, as long as the isotope's half-life is known.

In most cases, two important conditions must be met to obtain an accurate age. First, no new atoms of the parent isotope can have been added to the substance since it formed. This condition is met for many minerals in igneous rocks because the radioactive isotope is incorporated into the atomic structure of the mineral when it crystallizes from magma. Second, all atoms of the daughter isotope produced by radioactive decay must remain trapped in the substance. Minerals that crystallize in magmas generally do not "leak" daughter products of radioactive decay because, again, the atoms are strongly bonded in the crystal structure. Any such leakage would give an age that is too young. Some radioactive isotopes, including U-238, U-235, and K-40, have long half-lives (Table D.1) and can be used to date rocks millions to billions of years old. For example, a crystal of the mineral

TABLE D.1 Half-lives of Radioactive Isotopes Commonly Used in Absolute Dating

Parent Radioactive Isotope	Daughter Stable Isotope	Half-life
Uranium-238	Lead-206	4.5 billion yr
Uranium-235	Lead-207	700 million yr
Potassium-40	Argon-40	1.3 billion yr
Carbon-14	Nitrogen-14	5730 yr

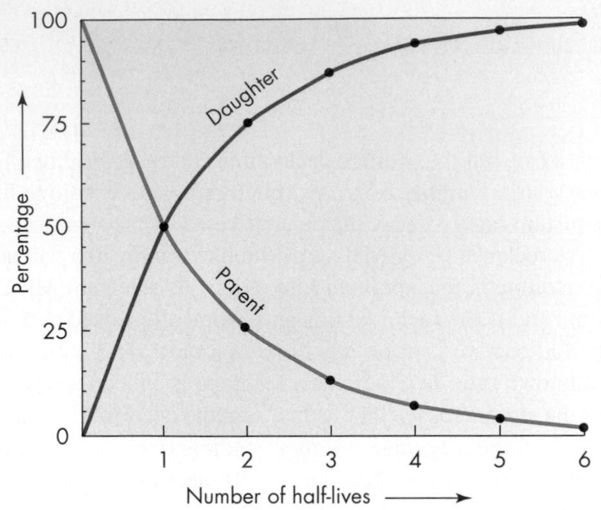

▲ **FIGURE D.1 RELATIVE PROPORTION OF PARENT AND DAUGHTER ISOTOPES OVER TIME** The amount of a parent radioactive isotope decreases by 50 percent of its remaining amount during each successive half-life. The increase in the daughter product mirrors the decrease in the parent.

zircon recovered from sandstone in western Australia was dated to 4.4 billion years before the present using the U-238 and U-235 decay systems. Absolute dating methods have been successfully used to assign ages to the divisions of the geologic time table and important Earth events such as episodes of mountain building, ice ages, and the appearance and disappearance of plant and animal species.

Anthropologists and archaeologists are particularly interested in the last 3 million years of Earth history, which is the time during which the human genus *Homo* evolved. Scientists who conduct research on natural hazards are commonly interested in only the past few hundred to few hundred thousand years. Several methods can be used to date this most recent period of Earth history. The radioactive isotope uranium-234, which decays to thorium-230, has been used to date a variety of materials, including corals, that are up to several hundred thousand years old.

A widely used method to date events younger than about 40,000 years is the *carbon-14* method (Figure D.2). Radiocarbon (C-14) occurs in small quantities in all living organisms and undergoes radioactive decay to stable nitrogen-14. The half-life of C-14 is 5730 years. C-14 is only incorporated into plant and animal tissue while the organism is alive. When it dies, the C-14 begins to decay to nitrogen-14 without any replenishment of new C-14. Common materials dated with the carbon-14 method are wood, bone, charcoal, and shell. With a half life of only 5730 years, the amount of C-14 left in a sample that is 40,000 years old is so small that it cannot be discriminated from background values.

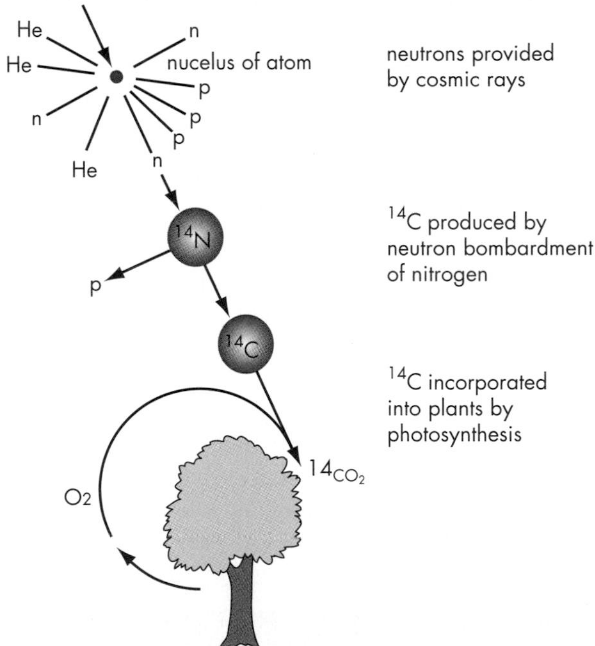

▲ **FIGURE D.2 RADIOCARBON DATING** Radiocarbon dating is a laboratory technique used to determine the age of carbon-bearing, fossil plant and animal material. The theoretical basis for the technique is shown in this schematic diagram. Cosmic rays strike nuclei in the upper atmosphere, producing neutrons. The neutrons, in turn, bombard nitrogen, the most abundant gas in the atmosphere. This bombardment produces the radioactive isotope carbon-14, which immediately combines with oxygen to form carbon dioxide. Carbon dioxide is incorporated directly into plants through the process of photosynthesis and indirectly into animals that eat them. Carbon-14 forms at a nearly constant rate in the atmosphere and occurs in known concentrations in living organisms. When a plant or animal dies, however, its radiogenic C-14 is no longer replenished and starts to decrease through beta decay. By measuring the concentration of the isotope in a fossil and knowing the decay rate of C-14, a measurement of the time elapsed since death of the organism can be made. *(From HyperPhysics by Rod Nave)*

Consequently, the use of this technique is limited to geologically young events. As with all absolute dating techniques, the carbon-14 method is based on assumptions, some of which are now known to be incorrect. For example, Willard Libby, who invented the carbon-14 method, assumed that the relation between real time and "radiocarbon time" is constant; in other words, one radiocarbon year equals one calendar year. Later, researchers demonstrated that the radiocarbon timescale is not linear, and they produced graphs that allow us to adjust, or "calibrate," radiocarbon ages.

The field of geochronology is expanding rapidly. Old techniques are being improved, and new ones are being developed. For example, it is now possible to estimate the amount of time that a landform has been exposed at Earth's surface by a variety of methods, collectively known as *exposure dating*. The basic idea is that some isotopes, including beryllium-10, aluminum-26, and chlorine-36, are produced when cosmic rays interact with Earth's atmosphere; they accumulate in measurable quantities in surface materials such as soil, alluvium, and exposed rock surfaces. Amounts of the isotopes that have accumulated in rock exposed to the atmosphere are related to the time of exposure of the surface.

Another technique, known as *lichenometry,* uses the slow growth of *lichens* on rock surfaces to determine the time that the rock has been exposed. Lichens are symbiotic organisms comprising photosynthetic algae and fungi. Some species grow in circular patches (thalli) at rates that are known or can be independently determined. Measurements of the size of lichen thalli provide estimates of the age of exposure of the rocks on which they are found. Lichenometry has been widely used to date moraines built during glacier advances and has also been successfully used in California and New Zealand to date rockfalls generated by large earthquakes. The method is generally restricted to events that are less than 1000 years old.

Some landforms can be dated by *dendrochronology,* which is the study of annual growth rings of trees. The width of the rings of trees in some environments, for example, arid areas or areas near treeline, vary from year to year depending on moisture availability and temperature. The distinctive sequence of wider and thinner rings in such trees is similar to bar codes on merchandise at a store. A regional master chronology extending back hundreds of years or more can be constructed using overlapping ring series from living and dead trees. Armed with this master chronology, a dendrochronologist can date a series of ring from a piece of fossil wood of unknown age. Dendrochronology has been extensively used to date prehistoric habitation sites, glacier fluctuations, landslides, and earthquakes and also to reconstruct past climate conditions with annual resolution.

Very accurate dating can also be done with *varves*. A varve is a layer of sediment deposited in one year in a lake or ocean. Sequences of varves can span thousands of years. Varves have been used in Scandinavia to date events at the end of the Pleistocene age.

The most accurate absolute ages are provided by the historical record, but these records are only a few hundred years long in many parts of the world, including Canada and the United States. Given the brevity of recorded history in much of the world, we must resort to numeric dating methods to establish the absolute chronologies that are crucial for understanding rates of geologic processes and the risk posed by hazardous natural processes.

GLOSSARY*

*Some words or terms in the Glossary have more than one meaning. The definitions that follow pertain to the usage in this book.

Aa A basaltic lava flow with a broken, blocky surface texture.

Absolute dating The determination of the geologic age of a fossil, sediment, rock, or geologic feature. Many absolute dating methods are based on the decay of radioactive isotopes and their daughter products.

Acceptable risk The level of risk that an individual or community will tolerate before taking action to reduce its exposure to the hazardous process that is responsible for the risk.

Active fault A fault capable of rupturing during an earthquake. A common criterion for labelling a fault as active is that it has moved in the past 10,000 years or several mappable displacements have occurred in the past 35,000 years. See *Inactive* and *Potentially active faults.*

Active layer The surface layer of sediment or rock in an area of permafrost that thaws during summer and is frozen at other times of the year. The active layer overlies material that is continuously frozen. See *Permafrost* and *Permafrost table.*

Adaptation The collective adjustments that governments and individuals will have to make to deal with the changing climate of the twenty-first century.

Adit An opening driven horizontally into the side of a mountain or hill to provide access to a mineral deposit.

Advance An interval, commonly spanning years or decades, during which a glacier thickens and becomes longer. See *Retreat.*

Aerial burst The explosion of a meteoroid in the atmosphere, generally at an altitude of 12 km to 50 km.

Aerosol A suspension of microscopic liquid and solid particles, such as mineral dust and soot, in the atmosphere.

Aftershock One of the many earthquakes that occur a few minutes to about a year after a larger earthquake and in the same general area. See *Foreshock* and *Mainshock.*

Albedo The fraction of solar radiation reflected from Earth back into space. Albedo is a measure of the reflectivity of the surface; ice, for example, has a high albedo, whereas water has a much lower one.

Alluvial fan A fan-shaped body of coarse sediment deposited by a stream where it emerges from a mountain valley onto flatter terrain. Fans may be composed of stream deposits, debris-flow deposits, or a combination of the two.

Alluvium The unconsolidated sediment deposited by a stream.

Anastomosing river A river characterized by a small number of relatively stable channels separated by islands.

Andesite A grey to reddish-brown volcanic rock consisting mainly of plagioclase and feldspar, with little or no quartz.

Anthropogenic Produced or caused by humans.

Apex In geomorphology, the head of a delta or alluvial fan.

Aphelion The point in a planet's orbit where it is farthest from the Sun. At present, Earth's aphelion occurs about July 1, when the planet is 4.8 million km farther from the Sun than at perihelion. The seasons in which aphelion and perihelion occur vary cyclically with a period of 21,000 years. See *Perihelion.*

Aquifer A water-bearing body of rock or sediment capable of providing useful amounts of groundwater to wells and springs.

Artificial bypass The human action that moves sand or other sediment around an obstruction. An example is dredging and pumping sand from the updrift to downdrift sides of a jetty or harbour mouth.

Artificial control A human action or engineered structure that reduces or eliminates adverse effects of a hazardous surface process.

Ash eruption An explosive volcanic eruption during which large amounts of fragmented, fine rock and glass are blown high into the atmosphere from the vent of a volcano.

Ash fall The deposition of a layer of fine airborne rock and glass that have been erupted from a volcano.

Ash flow See *Pyroclastic flow*

Asteroid A rocky or metallic body in outer space ranging from 10 m to 1000 km in diameter.

Asteroid belt The region between the orbits of Mars and Jupiter that contains most large asteroids in our solar system.

Asthenosphere The upper zone of Earth's mantle, located directly below the lithosphere; a hot, viscous, solid layer on which tectonic plates move.

Atmosphere A layer of gases surrounding a planet, such as Earth.

Atmospheric pressure The force per unit area exerted by the gases that surround a planet. Also called *barometric pressure* because it is commonly measured with a barometer.

Atmospheric stability A condition of equilibrium in which a rising or sinking parcel of air returns to its original position. The atmosphere is stable when surface air and air aloft have similar temperatures.

Attenuation The decrease in the intensity of a seismic wave away from the earthquake source.

Avalanche The rapid downslope movement of snow under the influence of gravity. Also called *snow avalanche.*

Avalanche cord A red cord attached to a skier, snowshoer, or snowmobiler that allows a rescuer to locate the person in the event of a snow avalanche.

Avalanche forecast An assessment of the likelihood and size of snow avalanches under existing or future conditions.

Avalanche shed A structure, generally made of concrete, that carries avalanching snow over a road or rail line.

Avalanche transceiver The portable devices carried by skiers, snowshoers, and snowmobilers that emit and receive a radio signal. In receive mode, avalanche transceivers can locate a buried avalanche victim at distances up to 80 m in 5 to 15 minutes. Also called *Beacons* or *Beepers.*

Avulse A sudden shift in the channel of a stream or river.

Bankfull discharge A water discharge that completely fills a stream channel. Most stream channels are formed and maintained by bankfull discharge.

Barometric pressure See *Atmospheric pressure.*

Barrier bar A long, narrow body of sand or gravel that extends parallel to the shoreline. See *Barrier island.*

Barrier island A long, narrow, and low body of sand that is separated from the mainland by a bay or lagoon.

Basalt Volcanic rock consisting of calcium-rich feldspar and other silicate minerals rich in iron and magnesium. Basalt has a relatively low silica content and forms shield volcanoes.

Base level The theoretical lowest elevation to which a river may erode at a particular time.

Beach An accumulation of sand, gravel, or both along the shore of a lake or ocean. Beaches are produced by wave and current action.

Beach drift The movement of sand grains along the shore by wave run-up and backwash. See *Littoral transport.*

Beach face The sloping part of a shoreline affected by run-up and backwash of waves. See *Berm* and *Swash zone.*

Beach nourishment The artificial addition of sand to a shoreline to create or enhance a beach.

Beacon See *Avalanche beacon.*

Bedload The sediment particles pushed or rolled along a river channel by the flowing water. See *Dissolved load, Suspended load,* and *Total load.*

Beeper See *Avalanche beacon.*

Bentonite The clay formed by the weathering of volcanic rock. It can absorb large amounts of water and expands to many times its dry volume.

Berm The relatively flat or landward-sloping part of a beach, located just landward of the swash zone, and formed of wave-deposited sediment; the part of the beach where most people sunbathe. See *Beach face* and *Swash zone.*

Biogeochemical cycle The cycling of chemical elements or compounds through the atmosphere, hydrosphere, biosphere, and lithosphere.

Blind fault In tectonics, a fault whose rupture plane does not extend to Earth's surface.

Blizzard A severe winter storm during which large amounts of falling or blowing snow create low visibility for an extended period. The definition of *blizzard* differs slightly in Canada and the United States: in Canada winds must exceed 40 km/h with visibility less than 1 km for at least 4 hours; in the United States winds must exceed 56 km/h with visibilities of less than 0.4 km for at least 3 hours.

Block An angular rock fragment more than 64 mm across, ejected from a volcano during an eruption.
Bluff A high, steep bank or cliff along a lakeshore or river valley.
Body wave A seismic wave that travels outward from the focus of an earthquake through the interior of Earth. See *Surface wave*.
Bomb A smooth-surfaced block of volcanic rock more than 64 mm across that is ejected in a semi-molten state from a volcano during an eruption. A bomb acquires a streamlined shape as it cools while falling to the ground.
Braided A river channel pattern characterized by numerous intertwining unstable channels separated by islands of sand and gravel. See *Braided river*.
Braided river A river with numerous intertwining channels separated by islands; see *Braided*.
Breaker zone That part of the beach and nearshore environment where waves build up, become unstable, and collapse toward the shore.
Breaking wave A wave that curls over, crashes, and rushes ashore in a turbulent state.
Breakup The disintegration and downstream dispersion of an ice layer that forms on a river during winter. Breakup generally occurs in the spring.
Breakwater A wall protecting a beach or harbour from waves; it may be attached to the beach or located offshore.
Breccia A rock composed of angular fragments; breccia may have a sedimentary, volcanic, tectonic, or impact origin.
Caldera A large crater produced by a violent volcanic eruption or the collapse of the summit area of a volcano after an eruption.
Calving A separation of large blocks of ice from the toe of a glacier flowing into a lake or the sea; the calved blocks are icebergs.
Carbon-14 An unstable isotope of carbon with a half-life of 5740 years. Radioactive decay of carbon-14 is the foundation for the radiocarbon dating method, which is used to date fossil plant and animal material up to about 40,000 years old.
Carrying capacity The maximum number of individuals of a species that can be supported by a particular environment without a population decline.
Cascadia subduction zone The elongate zone within Earth's lithosphere, located off the west coast of North America from northern California to central Vancouver Island, where the oceanic Juan de Fuca plate slowly moves eastward beneath North America.
Catastrophe An event that causes damage to people and property on such a scale that recovery is long and complex. Natural processes that produce catastrophes include floods, hurricanes, earthquakes, tsunami, volcanic eruptions, and large wildfires.
Catchment See *Drainage basin*.
Cave A natural subterranean cavity produced by slow solution of limestone or marble. Many caves consist of a series of chambers that are large enough for a person to enter.
Cave system See *Cave*.
Cenote A steep-walled collapse sinkhole that extends below the water table on Yucatan Peninsula, Mexico.
Channel pattern The areal pattern of a flowing stream. Channel patterns include straight, meandering, anastomosing, and braided.
Channel restoration The process by which a stream channel is returned to a more natural state.
Channelization The modification of a storm channel to permit more efficient conveyance of water and sediment. Channelization involves straightening, widening, and, in some instances, deepening and lining the channel.
Chute A straight, steep gully formed and maintained by avalanches, rock falls, or debris flows.
Cinder cone A conical volcano consisting of pyroclastic deposits. Also called a *scoria cone*.
Clearcutting The forestry practice of harvesting all trees from a tract of land.
Cleavage Preferential, parallel fracture planes in a mineral that correspond to weak planes in the mineral's atomic lattice.
Climate The characteristic weather of a place or region over many years or decades. See *Weather*.
Coastal erosion The loss of rock or sediment from a shoreline because of wave action, landslides, wind abrasion, and runoff.
Collapse sinkhole The depression in sediment or rock caused by the collapse of the roof of a cave.
Colluvium The broken rock or sediment deposited by mass movement processes, including creep and landslides.
Colour In mineralogy, the name associated with the visual spectrum of light reflected from a mineral or its powder.
Combustion The phase of a wildfire following ignition; it includes flaming, in which fine fuel and volatile gases are rapidly oxidized at high temperatures, and glowing or smouldering, which take place later at lower temperatures. See *Extinction* and *Pre-ignition*.
Comet An object that orbits the Sun and is composed of a sponge-like rocky core surrounded by ice and covered by carbon-rich dust; a tail of gas and dust glows as a comet approaches the Sun. Comets range from a few metres to a few hundred kilometres in diameter.
Community Internet Intensity Map An online map depicting the intensity of an earthquake. The map is based on e-mail reports of the severity of shaking and structural damage in many different places.
Composite volcano The steep-sided volcanic cone produced by alternating layers of pyroclastic debris and lava flows. Also known as a *stratovolcano*.
Compression test The application of a vertical force with the back of a shovel blade on a column of undisturbed snow to evaluate the strength of the snowpack. Any weak layers will fracture along the exposed vertical face of the snow column.
Compressional wave See *P wave*.
Compressive strength The greatest compressive stress that a material can bear without failing.
Conchoidal fracture The breakage of a rock or mineral along smooth but irregular surface.
Conduction The transfer of heat through a substance by molecular interactions. See *Convection* and *Radiation*.
Constructive interference The process by which two or more waves combine to form a larger wave, as for example on a lake or the sea.
Contact The boundary between two geologic units, generally shown as a line on a geologic map.
Continental shelf The shallow seafloor fringing a continent; it extends from the coastline to depths of 150 m to 200 m.
Continuous surface fire An intense wildfire that moves swiftly through brushlands, releasing large amounts of heat. See *Intermittent surface fire*.
Contour On a topographic map, a line along which all points are the same elevation above sea level. See *Contour interval* and *Contour line*.
Contour interval The vertical distance, in metres or feet, between successive contours on a topographic map. See *Contour*.
Contour line A line on a topographic map that delineates points of the same elevation. See *Contour* and *Contour interval*.
Controlled burn See *Prescribed burn*.
Convection The transfer of heat by movement of particles. For example, hot water rises to the surface in a pot of boiling water and displaces cooler water, which sinks. Heat may be transferred vertically by convection within storm clouds, and convection is the main way that heat is transferred in a wildfire. See *Conduction* and *Radiation*.
Convection cell A circulation loop in which warmer fluid rises and cooler, denser fluid sinks. Convection cells operate on a large scale in Earth's atmosphere and mantle.
Convergence The movement of two or more objects toward one another.
Convergent plate boundary A boundary between two converging tectonic plates. The most common type of convergent plate boundary is a subduction zone where one plate descends below another. Another type of convergent plate boundary is a collision zone where a plate crumples and elevates the leading edge of another plate (e.g., the boundary between the Indo-Australia and Eurasia plates in the Himalayas).
Cordilleran ice sheet The large body of glacier ice that covered most of western Canada and adjacent areas of the United States at times during the Pleistocene Epoch. See *Laurentide ice sheet*.
Coriolis effect The apparent deflection of a moving object because of Earth's rotation. The deflection is to the right in the Northern Hemisphere and to the left in the Southern Hemisphere.
Crater A bowl-shaped depression at the top of a volcano that has formed by an explosion or collapse of the summit area.
Creep The slow downslope movement of soil, sediment, and highly fractured rock because of the force of gravity.
Critical facility An important building or other structure that must be located and built to survive an earthquake or other natural disaster.
Cross-loaded A slab of potentially unstable snow deposited by wind blowing parallel to a ridge crest. Cross-loaded slabs can fail to produce snow avalanches. See *Top-loaded*.
Crown fire The flaming combustion of the upper canopy of a forest during a wildfire. Crown fires are commonly driven by high winds and are aided by steep slopes. See *Surface fire*.
Crust The outermost layer of Earth, composed of continental rocks rich in silicon and aluminum, and oceanic rocks rich in silicon and magnesium.

The crust ranges in thickness from 8 km beneath the oceans to more than 60 km beneath the continents.

Cryptovolcanic A geologic feature that appears to be disrupted by volcanic activity but lacks associated volcanic rocks.

Crystal form The characteristic geometric shape of a mineral imparted by its internal atomic structure.

Crystallization The process by which molecules precipitate from solution to form a mineral.

Cumulonimbus A cumulus cloud that grows vertically until it extends into the lower stratosphere. Cumulonimbus clouds may have anvil-shaped tops. See *Cumulus* and *Cumulus stage.*

Cumulus Any cloud that develops vertically. Cumulus clouds generally have flat bases and cauliflower-like tops. See *Cumulonimbus* and *Cumulus stage.*

Cumulus stage The first phase of thunderstorm development, characterized by the growth of domes and towers that transform a cumulus cloud into a cumulonimbus cloud. See *Dissipative stage* and *Mature stage.*

Curie point The temperature above which a magnetic mineral will lose its magnetism.

Cutbank A steep slope eroded on the outside of a bend in a stream channel.

Dacite A grey to pale brown volcanic rock with a silica content of 63 percent to 68 percent that consists of plagioclase, quartz, biotite, hornblende, and pyroxene.

Daughter product An isotope produced by radioactive decay of a parent isotope. See *Parent isotope* and *Radioactive isotope.*

Debris flow The rapid downslope movement of water-saturated sediment ranging in size from clay to boulders. Debris flows are triggered by heavy rain, rapid melting of snow and ice, or the sudden draining of a pond or lake.

Delta A flat, triangular, or fan-shaped landform built by a stream where it enters a lake or the ocean. See *Delta plain.*

Delta plain The nearly flat surface of a delta. The delta plain is cut by distributary channels and may support extensive marshes, swamps, and other wetlands. See *Delta.*

Dendrochronology The study of tree rings to date past events or to infer past climate.

Deposition The accumulation of sediment on land and in lakes and the sea; deposition occurs by mechanical processes, chemical precipitation, or the build-up of dead plant matter.

Desert An arid or semi-arid region that receives less than 250 mm of precipitation per year.

Desertification The conversion of land from a biologically productive state to one that resembles a desert.

Desiccation crack An open crack in mud produced by drying.

Differential GPS A method of positioning that provides more accurate locations than conventional GPS. Locations determined with a mobile GPS receiver are corrected using data provided by a fixed receiver at a reference station. See *Global Positioning System (GPS).*

Differentiated In the context of meteoroids and asteroids, rock that has been affected by igneous or metamorphic processes.

Digital elevation model (DEM) A three-dimensional, computer-generated model of the land surface.

Dip-slip fault See *Normal fault.*

Direct effect A change directly induced by an event. Direct effects of a disaster or catastrophe include death and injury, and property damage. Also known as *primary effect*. See *Indirect effect.*

Directivity In the context of an earthquake, increased intensity of shaking in the direction of the fault rupture.

Disappearing stream A surface stream or river that enters a cave and flows underground.

Disaster A brief event that causes great damage or loss of life in a limited geographic area.

Disaster preparedness The actions of individuals, families, communities, states, provinces, or nations to minimize losses from a natural disaster before it occurs. See *Preparedness.*

Discharge The volume of water flowing past a point in a stream channel over a specific period, typically a second. Discharge is commonly measured in cubic metres per second (m^3/s).

Dissipative stage The final phase of a thunderstorm, when the supply of moist air is blocked by downdrafts in the lower levels of the cloud; precipitation decreases, and the storm begins to diminish. See *Cumulus stage* and *Mature stage.*

Dissolved load The part of a stream's load that is carried in solution. See *Bedload, Suspended load*, and *Total load.*

Distributary channel A stream channel that branches from the main channel on a delta or alluvial fan.

Divergence The movement of two or more objects away from one another.

Divergent plate boundary A boundary between two tectonic plates that are moving away from one another, where new crust is created. Divergent plate boundaries include mid-ocean ridges and some continental rift zones.

Doppler effect A change in wave frequency that occurs when the distance between a sound source and a receptor increases or decreases. For example, the pitch of an ambulance siren is higher when the ambulance approaches than it is when it moves away.

Doppler radar An instrument that emits electromagnetic waves to detect the velocity of precipitation that is falling toward or away from the receiver. Doppler radar is used to detect rotation of air within a thunderstorm that may lead to tornadoes. See *Doppler effect.*

Downburst A localized area of strong winds in a downdraft beneath a severe thunderstorm.

Downdrift The direction toward which a current of water, such as a longshore current, is flowing. See *Updrift.*

Downstream flood A flood in the lower part of a drainage basin because of high discharges of many tributary streams. See *Upstream flood.*

Drainage basin An area that contributes surface water to a stream. Also known as *catchment* and *watershed.*

Driving force A force that increases the downward-directed stress on a slope. See *Resisting force.*

Drought An extended period of unusually low precipitation that produces a shortage of water for people, other animals, and plants.

Dryline An air mass boundary similar to a front, but the juxtaposed air masses differ in moisture content rather than temperature.

Dust storm A storm that transports large amounts of airborne silt and clay; visibility at eye level drops to less than 1 km for hours or days.

Dynamic equilibrium A state of balance between the work that a river does and the sediment load it receives. A stream in dynamic equilibrium maintains the gradient and cross-sectional shape it needs to move its sediment load.

Earth fissure A large, deep crack in loose sediment that forms when the water table falls and the sediment dries out.

Earth's energy balance The balance between incoming solar radiant energy and radiant energy leaving the planet.

Earthquake The sudden movement of rock on opposite sides of a fault; an earthquake releases strain that has accumulated within the rocks.

Earthquake cycle A hypothesis that explains successive earthquakes on a fault by a drop in elastic strain after an earthquake and the gradual accumulation of strain leading to the next quake.

Eccentricity A measure of the departure of Earth's orbit from circularity.

Ejecta blanket The layer of breccia surrounding an impact crater, typically forming an irregular area of low mounds and shallow depressions.

El Niño A combined meteorological and oceanographic event in the equatorial Pacific Ocean during which trade winds weaken or even reverse, surface waters become anomalously warm, and the westward-moving equatorial ocean current weakens or reverses. These changes affect weather in southeast Asia, Australia, New Zealand, and the Americas. See *La Niña.*

Elastic rebound The slow or rapid recovery of a strained body following the removal of a load.

Elastic strain The deformation that is reversed when stress is removed.

Electrical resistivity A measure of a material's ability to conduct an electrical current.

Electromagnetic energy The energy carried in waves by oscillations in electric and magnetic fields.

Electromagnetic spectrum The collection of electromagnetic waves of different wavelengths and frequencies.

Electromagnetic wave A wave that transfers energy in electric and magnetic fields.

E-line An imaginary line inland from the coast that marks the expected position of the shoreline after a particular number of years. See *E-zone.*

Epicentre The point on Earth's surface directly above the source, or focus, of an earthquake.

Evacuation The movement of people away from the site of a probable destructive natural event.

Expansive soil A type of clayey soil that, upon wetting and drying, expands and contracts, damaging foundations of buildings and other structures.

Exponential growth A type of compound growth characterized by a percentage increase in numbers or amount with each passing unit of time.

Exposure dating A variety of techniques used to determine the time that a boulder or bedrock surface has been exposed to cosmic rays at Earth's surface. The ratio of stable and unstable isotopes of certain elements present in minerals forming the surface layer of the rock is measured with a mass spectrometer. This ratio is proportional to the time the object has been exposed to cosmic rays.

Extinction The final phase of a wildfire, when all combustion, including smouldering, ceases because of insufficient heat, fuel, or oxygen. Also, the disappearance of a plant or animal species. See *Combustion* and *Pre-ignition*.

Extreme cold Cold weather capable of causing injury or death. Extreme cold is associated with temperatures considerably below normal and moderate to strong winds. What constitutes extreme cold may differ across a country. Near-freezing temperatures are considered to be extreme cold in regions unaccustomed to cold winter weather.

Eye wall The portion of a hurricane bordering the eye; it is the region with the highest winds and heaviest rainfall.

E-zone The area between the shore and an E-line that is expected to be lost because of erosion within a specified period. See *E-line*.

Factor of safety The ratio of resisting to driving forces on a slope. A slope with a factor of safety less than 1 may fail.

Fair weather waterspout A rapidly rotating cylindrical or funnel-shaped cloud over an ocean or lake. A waterspout differs from most tornadoes in that it builds upward from the water surface to the overlying cloud, typically has lower wind velocities, and is not associated with a thunderstorm.

Fall A type of landslide in which rock or sediment bounds and rolls down a steep slope.

Fault A fracture along which adjacent rocks have moved relative to one another.

Fault creep The slow, continuous movement of rock or sediment along a fracture. Also called *tectonic creep*.

Fault scarp A linear escarpment at Earth's surface formed by movement along a fault during an earthquake.

Faulting The differential displacement of rocks on opposite sides of a fault. See *Fault*.

Fetch The distance that wind blows over a body of water. Fetch influences the height of windblown waves.

Fibrous fracture A type of mineral fracture characterized by breakage along elongated fine fibres. Some types of asbestos and gypsum have fibrous fracture.

Fiord A glacially overdeepened valley, usually narrow and steep-sided, extending below sea level and filled with sea water. Also spelled *fjord*.

Fire break A strip of land that is cleared of trees and woody fuel to stop or control the spread of fire.

Fire management The control of wildfires to minimize loss of human life and property damage; accomplished through scientific research, public education, remote sensing of vegetation to determine fire potential, and prescribed burns.

Fire regime The potential for wildfire inferred from fuel types, terrain, and past fire behaviour.

Fissure In the context of volcanoes, a large fracture or crack in the upper crust that becomes a volcanic vent when lava or pyroclastic material erupts.

Flash flood The overbank flow resulting from a rapid increase in stream discharge; commonly occurs in upstream parts of drainage basins and in small tributaries downstream.

Flashy discharge The stream flow characterized by a rapid increase in discharge following precipitation.

Flood basalt An areally extensive series of basaltic lava flows. Also known as *plateau basalt*.

Flood discharge The volume of water conveyed by a stream per unit time when a river is in flood and likely to damage property. See *Flood stage*.

Flood fringe The higher part of a floodplain where floodwaters are relatively shallow and slow. Some new development may be permitted on the flood fringe provided that it is adequately flood-proofed. See *Floodplain*.

Flood stage The level of a stream at which water escapes the channel and threatens property. See *Flood discharge*.

Flooding The high water that inundates low-lying areas adjacent to a stream, lake, or the sea; includes stream overbank flows that deposit sediment on a floodplain and storm surges that raise water levels along a coast.

Floodplain The flat land adjacent to a stream produced by overbank flow and lateral channel migration.

Floodplain regulation The government restrictions on land use in areas subject to flooding by streams.

Flow A type of landslide in which material moves downslope in a viscous fluid state; includes debris flows and mudflows.

Flowstone A general term for an accumulation of calcium carbonate precipitated from water in a cave.

Flux The rate at which a substance moves from one part of a natural system to another.

Focus The point on a fault within Earth where rocks first rupture during an earthquake; seismic energy radiates out from this point. Also known as *hypocentre*. See *Epicentre*.

Footwall The rock directly below an inclined fault. See *Hanging wall*.

Force An influence that exerts a stress on a body or that accelerates the body.

Forcing A factor that may cause climate to change, for example solar radiation, aerosols, and greenhouse gases.

Forecast The public announcement that a flood, earthquake, volcanic eruption, or other event is likely to occur during a specified period, commonly with a statement of probability.

Foreshock A small to moderate earthquake that occurs before and in the same general area as the main earthquake. See *Aftershock* and *Mainshock*.

Formation A distinctive, mappable body of rock or sediment; commonly given a geographic name (e.g., Rundle Formation) and formally defined in a scientific publication.

Fractionation Progressive changes in the chemistry of a slowly cooling magma because of sequential crystallization of different minerals.

Fracture An uneven or curving surface along which a mineral or rock breaks. Types of fractures include irregular, splintery, fibrous, or conchoidal.

Free face A near-vertical cliff of exposed rock.

Frequency The number of electromagnetic waves that pass a point in a second; commonly expressed in cycles per second or hertz (Hz). Frequency is the inverse of the wave period.

Front The boundary between two air masses that differ in temperature and, commonly, moisture content. See *Occluded front* and *Stationary front*.

Frostbite An injury to body tissues caused by exposure to extreme cold.

F-scale A series of values from F0 to F5 that describes the intensity of a tornado. The scale was developed by T. Theodore Fugita in 1971. Also called the *Fujita scale*.

Fujita scale See *F-scale*.

Funnel cloud A narrow, rotating column of air extending downward from a thunderstorm. A funnel cloud becomes a tornado if it reaches the ground.

Gabion A metal wire basket filled with rocks. Gabions are placed along stream banks to prevent erosion and on slopes to reduce the amount of sediment or rock falling onto roads, rail lines, and other structures.

Geochronology The science of dating rocks, sediments, fossils, and landforms, and of determining the sequence of events in Earth's history.

Geographic information system (GIS) A three-dimensional, computer-generated model used to store, manipulate, retrieve, and display spatial data and to make maps using these data.

Geologic cycle The four associated sequences of Earth processes: the hydrologic, rock, tectonic, and geochemical cycles.

Geologic map A two-dimensional representation of surface Earth within a defined geographic area.

Geyser A spring that ejects hot water and steam at regular or irregular intervals. The most famous geyser is Old Faithful in Yellowstone National Park.

Glacial interval A period in Earth history when climate was cooler, and glaciers and sea ice were more extensive, than today.

Global circulation model (GCM) A computer program or programs that use mathematical equations to predict atmospheric and ocean circulation and climate in the future.

Global Positioning System (GPS) A system of linked satellites and ground receivers that allows accurate location of points on Earth's surface. GPS can be used to detect changes in the land surface related to volcanic activity, earthquakes, and landslides. See *Differential GPS*.

Global warming The hypothesis that consumption of fossil fuels and land clearing, which produce carbon dioxide and other greenhouse gases, are increasing the mean temperature of Earth's lower atmosphere.

Gradient The average slope of a stream channel, that is, the ratio of the vertical drop of the stream over the horizontal distance of the drop; commonly expressed as a dimensionless number (m/m).

Great earthquake An earthquake of moment magnitude 8 or larger.

Greenhouse effect Trapping of heat in the lower atmosphere by water vapour, carbon dioxide, methane, chlorofluorocarbons (CFCs), and other gases.

Greenhouse gas Water vapour, carbon dioxide, methane, nitrogen oxides, chlorofluorocarbons, and other gases that absorb infrared radiation and warm the lower atmosphere.

Groin A long, narrow rock, concrete, or other structure generally constructed perpendicular to the coast to protect the shoreline from erosion. Groins trap sediment in the zone of littoral drift.

Groin field A group of adjacent groins along a coast. See *Groin*.

Ground acceleration The rate at which the velocity of seismic waves increases per unit time. Ground acceleration is commonly expressed as a fraction or percentage of gravitational acceleration, which is 980 cm/s^2. Maximum ground acceleration is an important measure of the amount of structural damage the earthquake causes.

Ground penetrating radar (GPR) An electronic instrument that uses electromagnetic waves to image Earth's shallow subsurface. GPR is used to locate subsurface strata, caves, the water table, and buried pipes and tanks.

Groundwater mining The extraction of groundwater at an unsustainable rate that is faster than the water is replenished.

Gust front The leading edge of strong and variable surface winds produced by downdraft during a thunderstorm.

Habitat An environment in which adapted plants and animals thrive.

Hailstone A rounded or irregular piece of ice that has increased in size while moving up and down within the clouds of a thunderstorm.

Half-life The amount of time over which one-half of the atoms of a particular radioactive isotope decay. See *Isotope*.

Hanging wall The rock directly above an inclined fault. See *Footwall*.

Hardness The resistance of a mineral to scratching. See *Relative hardness*.

Hazard See *Natural hazard*.

Headland A peninsula on an irregularly shaped coastline that is more resistant to erosion than the surrounding shoreline.

Headwaters The tributaries of a stream or river near its source.

Heat energy The energy produced by random molecular motion. Heat energy may be transferred by conduction, convection, or radiation.

Heat index See *Humidex index*.

Hoar The crystals of ice formed from snow by sublimation of water vapour.

Hoar frost The hoar that forms at the snowpack surface.

Holocene Epoch The interval of Earth history between 10,000 years ago and the present. The Holocene Epoch is commonly referred to as *Postglacial* time. See *Pleistocene Epoch*.

Hot spot A hypothesized, nearly stationary source of heat within the mantle that is the source of volcanic activity at specific, fixed points on Earth's surface.

Hot spring A natural discharge of groundwater at a temperature higher than that of the human body. See *Thermal spring*.

Humidex index A numerical value that describes a person's perception of air temperature by taking into account relative humidity. Also called a *Heat index*.

Humidity Amount of water vapour in the air.

Hummocky The irregular ground characterized by numerous mounds and depressions.

100-year flood The largest flood likely to occur along a stream within any 100-year period; the 100-year flood has a 1 percent probability of occurring in any given year.

Hurricane A tropical cyclone with sustained winds of at least 118 km/h (119 km/h in the United States). Hurricanes are called typhoons in the western North Pacific Ocean and South China Sea, tropical cyclones in the South Pacific and southern Indian Ocean, and cyclonic storms in the northern Indian Ocean. See *Tropical cyclone, Tropical depression, Tropical disturbance*, and *Tropical storm*.

Hurricane warning An alert issued for an area where hurricane conditions are expected within 24 hours. In Canada, this alert applies to areas that are likely to experience high waves and coastal flooding, but not necessarily hurricane-strength winds. See *Hurricane*.

Hurricane watch An alert for an area that may experience hurricane conditions in the near future. In the United States, the alert is restricted to a 36-hour period. See *Hurricane*.

Hydrograph A graph showing the discharge of a stream over time.

Hydrologic cycle A cyclic circulation of water between the oceans and atmosphere by means of evaporation, precipitation, surface runoff, and groundwater flow.

Hydrophobic layer A layer within soil that has accumulated water-repellent organic chemicals. Hydrophobic layers commonly develop in drier climates after very hot fires.

Hypocentre See *Focus*.

Hypothesis A tentative explanation for an observation, a phenomenon, or a scientific problem that can be tested by further investigation.

Ice storm A period of freezing rain during which thick layers of ice accumulate on cold surfaces.

Igneous rock The rock formed by crystallization of magma. Extrusive igneous rock crystallizes on or very near Earth's surface; intrusive igneous rock crystallizes at depth.

Impact crater The bowl-shaped depression produced by the impact of an asteroid.

Impervious cover A surface covered with concrete, asphalt, roofs, or other structures that impedes infiltration of water into the ground. The percentage of the land with impervious cover increases as urbanization proceeds.

Inactive fault A fault that has not moved in the past 2 million years. See *Active* and *Potentially active faults*.

Indirect effect A secondary effect of an event. Indirect effects of a disaster or catastrophe include emotional distress, lost production and wages, donation of money, goods, and services, and payment of taxes to finance recovery. Also called a *secondary effect*. See *Direct effect*.

Injection well A drilled hole into which water, carbon dioxide, or hazardous waste is pumped.

Instrumental intensity The measurements of earthquake ground motion made with a seismograph. The data are used to produce maps showing perceived ground shaking and potential structural damage.

Insurance The guarantee of monetary compensation for a specified loss in return for payment of a premium.

Intensity A measure of the severity of shaking and damage caused by an earthquake at a specific place. The Modified Mercalli Scale provides a numerical estimate of an earthquake's effects on people and structures. See *Instrumental intensity, Magnitude*, and *Modified Mercalli Intensity Scale*.

Interglacial interval A period in Earth history when climate was relatively warm and the extent of glacier and sea ice on the planet was similar to that of today.

Intermittent surface fire A wildfire that burns grass, shrubs, dead and downed tree limbs, leaf litter, and other debris and that moves relatively slowly with glowing or smouldering combustion and periodic flaming. See *Continuous surface fire*.

Interplate earthquake An earthquake on a fault that bounds two lithosphere plates.

Intraplate earthquake An earthquake on a fault in the interior of a continent, far from a plate boundary.

Ion An electrically charged atom or molecule produced by the loss or gain of electrons.

Iridium A platinum-group metal that is more abundant in meteorites than in Earth's crust. High concentrations of the element in a clay layer separating Cretaceous and early Tertiary rocks have been attributed to an asteroid impact.

Isostatic depression The lowering of a part of Earth's surface because of an imposed load such as glacier ice.

Isotope A form of a chemical element distinguished by its number of neutrons; may be stable or unstable. See *Radioactive* and *stable isotopes*.

Jack-strawed The tilting of trees because of downslope movement of rock or sediment in which they are rooted. Jack-strawed trees are a good indicator of recent or active landsliding.

Jetty A long, narrow rock, concrete, or other structure generally constructed perpendicular to the shore at the mouth of a river or an inlet to a lagoon, estuary, or bay. Jetties are commonly constructed in pairs and are designed to stabilize a channel, control sediment deposition, or deflect large waves.

Jökulhlaup An outburst flood from a glacier-dammed lake.

Joule The basic unit of energy in the metric system (symbol J); equivalent to the work done by a force of 1 N (newton) acting over a distance of 1 m.

Karst An area of carbonate rock characterized by features produced by dissolution of calcite and dolomite, notably fissures, sinkholes, and caves. Surface drainage in karst areas is poor, and streams may flow underground.

Karst plain A generally flat land surface containing numerous sinkholes developed in limestone or marble. See *Karst*.

Karst topography A landscape characterized by sinkholes, caverns, and subterranean drainage. See *Karst*.

Kinetic energy The energy associated with the motion of an object. See *Potential energy*.

K-T boundary The boundary between the Cretaceous and Tertiary periods, dating to approximately 65 million years ago.

Kuiper Belt A ring-like zone of abundant comets in the outer solar system. See *Oort Cloud*.

Kyoto Protocol The international agreement to reduce emissions of greenhouse gases in an effort to manage global warming. It is now legally binding in at least 128 countries, including Russia and most European nations. The United States is not a signatory.

La Niña A combined meteorological and oceanographic event during which surface ocean waters in the eastern tropical Pacific Ocean become anomalously cool. A La Niña event commonly begins during the summer and lasts one to three years. It is the counterpart to the El Niño "warm event," and, to a considerable degree, its development is the mirror image of El Niño, although La Niña events tend to be more irregular in their behavior and duration. See *El Niño*.

Lag time The length of time between the peak rainfall during a storm and the ensuing maximum discharge of a stream. Urbanization generally decreases the lag time.

Lahar A debris flow or mudflow on the slope of a volcano. Some scientists restrict the term to warm or hot debris flows triggered by eruptions, whereas other scientists apply it to any volcanic debris flow, whether it is eruptive or not.

Landslide The failure and downward and outward movement of a body of rock or sediment under the influence of gravity.

Landslide hazard map A two-dimensional representation of the land surface showing landslides and potentially unstable areas that may experience landslides in the future. See *Landslide risk map*.

Landslide risk map A two-dimensional representation of the land surface of an area showing different levels of risk that people face from landslides; see *Landslide hazard map*.

Land-use planning The development of a plan for future development of an area. The plan may recommend zoning restrictions and infrastructure that is appropriate for the community and its natural environment. Land-use planning is based on analysis of existing human activities and environmental conditions, including natural hazards.

Lapilli The gravel-size pyroclastic debris ranging in size from 2 mm to 64 mm.

Latent heat The energy created by random molecular motion; it is absorbed or released when a substance undergoes a phase change, for example during evaporation or condensation.

Latent heat of vaporization The energy absorbed by water molecules when they evaporate. See *Latent heat*.

Lateral blast A volcanic eruption characterized by an explosion directed away from the volcano more or less parallel to the ground surface; may occur when the side of a volcano collapses, as happened at Mount St. Helens in May 1980.

Laurentide ice sheet The large body of glacier ice that covered most of Canada and adjacent areas of the United States at times during the Pleistocene Epoch. At its maximum, the Laurentide ice sheet extended from the Rocky Mountains on the west to Atlantic Canada on the east. See *Cordilleran ice sheet*.

Lava The molten rock (magma) that flows from a volcano.

Lava flow The molten rock (magma) that flows downslope from a volcanic vent, cools, and solidifies.

Lava tube A natural conduit or tunnel through which lava has flowed. A lava tube is a type of cave.

Levee A linear mound or embankment bordering a stream. Levees include natural features consisting of fine sediment deposited by overbank flood flows and artificial embankments constructed by humans to protect adjacent land from flooding.

Lichen A group of fungi that grow symbiotically with algae. Lichens commonly have crustlike or branching forms.

Lichenometry A dating method that uses the maximum size of certain species of lichens to establish the age of relatively young landforms, including moraines and landslide deposits. See *Lichen*.

Lightning A natural, high-voltage electrical discharge between a cloud and the ground, between two clouds, or within a cloud. The discharge takes a few tenths of a second and emits a flash of light that is followed by thunder.

Linkage A physical or causal relationship between two objects or phenomena.

Liquefaction The transformation of water-saturated granular material from a solid state to a liquid state. Liquefaction commonly occurs during strong earthquakes.

Lithification The hardening of loose sediment into sedimentary rock by cementation and compaction.

Lithosphere The outermost layer of Earth, approximately 100 km thick, comprising the crust and the upper mantle. The lithosphere comprises tectonic plates that move slowly with respect to one another.

Littoral transport The movement of nearshore sediment parallel to the coast because of the return flow of water from waves. See *Longshore currents* and *Beach drift*.

Longitudinal profile With respect to streams, a graph showing the decrease in elevation of a streambed between its head and its mouth.

Longshore bar A submerged, elongate ridge of sand roughly parallel to the shore. Longitudinal bars are produced by wave action. See *Longshore trough*.

Longshore current A water flow parallel to the shore. Longshore currents develop in the surf zone where waves strike the coast at an angle. They are responsible for longshore drift. See *Littoral transport* and *Beach drift*.

Longshore drift The sand transported parallel to the shore by a longshore current. See *Longshore current* and *Beach drift*.

Longshore trough A submerged, elongate depression parallel to the shore and bordered by a longshore bar.

Love wave An earthquake-generated wave that travels along the surface and is characterized by a transverse, snake-like form.

Lustre The appearance of a mineral in reflected light. Lustre may be metallic or nonmetallic.

Maar A flat-bottomed, roughly circular volcanic crater produced by a single explosive eruption and commonly filled with water.

Magma The molten rock formed deep within Earth's crust or in upper mantle.

Magnitude The amount of energy released during an earthquake (symbol **M**); see *Intensity*.

Magnitude-frequency concept The concept that the size (intensity and extent) of an event is inversely proportional to its probability.

Mainshock The largest earthquake in a series of associated earthquakes. See *Aftershock* and *Foreshock*.

Major earthquake An earthquake of moment magnitude of 7.0 to 7.9.

Mass extinction The sudden disappearance of large numbers of plant and animal species.

Mass wasting A comprehensive term for any type of downslope movement of rock or sediment.

Material amplification An increase in the intensity of earthquake ground shaking because of the type and thickness of geologic material through which the seismic waves pass. Also called *seismic amplification*.

Mature stage The second phase of a thunderstorm, when downdrafts move from the base of a cumulonimbus cloud and produce heavy precipitation. Tornadoes touch down during this phase of the storm. See *Cumulus stage and Dissipative stage*.

Meander An arcuate bend in the channel of a stream with a snake-like form. Sediment is deposited on a point bar on the inside of the meander bend and is eroded from a cutbank on the outside of the bend. See *Meandering*.

Meander cutoff A crescent- or horseshoe-shaped stream channel that was abandoned when the stream established a shorter, more direct course across the narrow neck of a meander. The abandoned channel may be filled with water. See *Oxbow lake*.

Meander scroll A series of point bars formed by deposition of sediment on the inner bank of a meander. Migration of the meander loop produces a corrugated topography comprising sequentially deposited bars.

Meandering A single, sinuous channel that migrates back and forth across its floodplain over time. See *Meander*.

Meandering river A river with a single, sinuous channel that migrates back and forth across its floodplain over time. See *Meander*.

Mesocyclone An area 3 km to 10 km in diameter on the flank of a supercell storm characterized by rotating clouds.

Mesoscale convective complex A large, circular, and long-lived group of thunderstorms that interact with one another.

Mesosphere The zone about 50 km to 80 km above Earth's surface where temperature decreases with altitude. The mesosphere is directly above the stratosphere. See *Stratosphere* and *Troposphere*.

Metamorphic rock The rock produced at depth in Earth's crust from preexisting sedimentary, igneous, or metamorphic rocks through the action of heat, pressure, and chemically active fluids. Foliated metamorphic rocks consist of aligned mineral grains or bands of alternating light and dark minerals; nonfoliated metamorphic rocks have neither of these characteristics.

Meteor An extraterrestrial particle up to several centimetres in size that is consumed by frictional heat as it passes through Earth's atmosphere. Light emitted from the burning meteor forms a shooting star. See *Meteorite* and *Meteoroid*.

Meteor shower A large number of meteoroids that generate light as they pass through Earth's atmosphere. Meteor showers commonly occur when Earth passes through the tail of a comet. See *Meteor, Meteorite,* and *Meteoroid.*

Meteorite An extraterrestrial particle of dust to asteroid size that hits Earth's surface. See *Meteor* and *Meteoroid.*

Meteoroid An extraterrestrial particle in space that is smaller than 10 m in diameter and larger than dust size; it may form from the breakup of an asteroid. See *Meteor* and *Meteorite.*

Microearthquake An earthquake of moment magnitude less than 3. Also called a *very minor earthquake.*

Microzonation The detailed delineation of areas that are subject to different types and degrees of earthquake hazards. Microzonation is used in earthquake mitigation and land-use planning.

Mid-ocean ridge A long, relatively narrow mountain range on the ocean floor where new crust is formed by seafloor spreading. Mid-oceanic ridges are commonly found in the central parts of oceans; an example is the Mid-Atlantic Ridge.

Milankovitch cycles The cyclic variations in Earth's orbital path that produce changes in the amount of solar radiation reaching Earth's surface through time. The orbital cycles have periodicities of approximately 20,000, 40,000, and 100,000 years. See *Eccentricity, Obliquity,* and *Precession of the equinoxes.*

Mineral A naturally occurring, inorganic crystalline substance with an ordered atomic structure and a specific chemical composition.

Mitigation Any actions taken to offset the harmful effects of a hazardous natural event. Mitigation includes avoidance, construction to reduce the impact of the event, purchase of insurance, and education.

Modified Mercalli Intensity Scale An earthquake intensity scale with 12 categories of ground shaking and structural damage.

Moment magnitude A numerical measure of the amount of energy released by an earthquake. It is based on the seismic moment, which is defined as the product of the average amount of slip on the fault, the rupture area, and the shear modulus of the ruptured rocks. In simple terms, *shear modulus* is the measure of how hard a rock mass must be pushed to shear it. See *Magnitude.*

Mound A pile of rocks, gravel, or debris heaped in the run-out zone of an avalanche track to slow and break up avalanches. They commonly are built in groups.

Natural hazard A natural process that poses a potential threat to people and property.

Natural service function As used in this book, a benefit that arises from a natural event that may damage people or the environment.

Near-Earth Asteroid Tracking Project (NEAT) A NASA-supported program, begun in 1996, to study the size distribution and orbital paths of near-Earth objects and to identify all near-Earth asteroids larger than about 1 km.

Near-Earth object (NEO) The asteroids that orbit between Earth and the Sun or that occasionally enter the solar system and pass close to Earth.

Newton The force necessary to accelerate a 1 kg mass 1 m/s each second that it is in motion (symbol N).

Nor'easter A severe storm that tracks along the Atlantic coast of Canada and the United States and is immediately preceded by continuously blowing northeasterly winds. Nor'easters commonly produce hurricane-strength winds, intense precipitation, and large waves along the coast.

Normal fault A fault along which the hanging wall has moved down relative to the footwall. Also called a *dip-slip fault.* See *Reverse, Strike-slip,* and *Thrust faults.*

Nuée ardente See *Pyroclastic flow.*

Obliquity A change in the tilt of Earth's axis of rotation with respect to its plane of orbit.

Occluded front A composite front formed when a cold front overtakes a warm front, forcing the warm air mass aloft. See *Front* and *Stationary front.*

Ocean conveyor belt The large-scale circulation pattern in the Atlantic, Indian, and southwest Pacific oceans, driven by differences in water temperature and density; also called thermohaline current. Northward-flowing warm water maintains the moderate climate of northern Europe; if this flow were to slow, stop, or shift, glacial conditions might return to portions of the Northern Hemisphere.

Oort Cloud A zone of comets outside the solar system. See *Kuiper Belt.*

Organic sediment The *in situ* accumulation of partially decayed plant material, mainly peat. Organic sediment is common in swamps, marshes, bogs, and fens.

Organizational stage The initial phase of a tornado, when a funnel cloud forms from rotating winds within a severe thunderstorm. See *Rope stage* and *Shrinking stage.*

Outflow boundary A line separating an air mass cooled by a thunderstorm and the surrounding air. It behaves like a cold front and is characterized by a shift in wind and drop in temperature. In large thunderstorms, the outflow boundary may persist for more than 24 hours and cause instability that leads to new storms.

Overbank flow The floodwater that escapes the channel of a stream or river and spreads onto the surrounding floodplain.

Overwash The inundation of beaches, dunes, and, in some cases, an entire barrier island by a storm surge. Overwash commonly transports sand from the beach and dunes inland. See *Washover channel.*

Oxbow lake A crescent-shaped lake occupying an abandoned meander of a river or stream. See *Meander cutoff.*

Ozone A pungent, reactive form of oxygen that is most abundant in the stratosphere where it protects Earth from high levels of ultraviolet radiation. Ozone is a pollutant in the lower atmosphere.

Ozone depletion The loss of stratospheric ozone because of releases of chlorofluorocarbons (CFCs) and other gases into the atmosphere.

P wave A seismic wave that travels from the hypocentre of an earthquake by compressing and extending rock and fluids along its path. P waves are the fastest of all earthquake waves. Also called a *Primary* or *Compressional wave.*

Pahoehoe A basaltic lava flow with a ropy surface texture; also called *ropy lava.*

Paleoseismicity The occurrence of earthquakes in the geologic past.

Paleoseismologist A scientist who documents prehistoric earthquakes and deformation by studying young sediments, rocks, and landforms.

Parcel A poorly defined body of air several hundred cubic metres in volume that acts independently of surrounding air.

Parent isotope A radioactive isotope that decays into one or more daughter isotopes. Most absolute age dating is done by measuring the ratio of parent and daughter isotopes in rocks. See *Daughter product* and *Radioactive isotope.*

Peat A sediment consisting mostly of fresh or decomposed plant remains, such as woody material, mosses, roots, and leaves. Peat is water-saturated in its natural state.

Perihelion The point in a planet's orbit where it is nearest the Sun. At present, Earth's perihelion occurs about January 1, when the planet is 4.8 million km nearer the Sun than at aphelion. The seasons in which aphelion and perihelion occur vary cyclically with a period of 21,000 years. See *Aphelion.*

Permafrost Rock or sediment that is colder than 0°C continuously for at least two years and contains disseminated or segregated ice. Permafrost underlies about 20 percent of Earth's land area, including about half of Canada, and is commonly dozens to hundreds of metres thick.

Permafrost table The upper surface of permanently frozen ground, directly below the active layer. See *Permafrost* and *Active layer.*

Permanent gas An atmospheric gas, such as nitrogen or oxygen, that cannot be compressed by pressure alone and is present in generally constant amounts. See *Variable gas.*

Permeability A measure of the ability of rock or sediment to transmit fluids such as water or oil.

Pillow A bulbous mass of basalt produced by extrusion of molten rock from the front of a cooling lava flow into a lake or the sea. Some lava flows consist largely of pillows and pillow fragments. See *Pillow breccia.*

Pillow breccia Basalt consisting of fragments of pillows. See *Pillow.*

Piping The slow subsurface removal of silt and fine sand from a sedimentary deposit by groundwater. Piping may produce subsurface cavities, tunnels, and sinkholes.

Plate tectonics A theory that explains the global distribution of earthquakes, active volcanoes, mountains, and other geologic features by the movement of large fragments of the Earth's crust on less rigid mantle rocks.

Plateau basalt See *Flood basalt.*

Pleistocene Epoch The period of Earth history from 1.8 million years ago to 10,000 years ago, characterized by recurrent widespread continental glaciation. The Pleistocene is one of two epochs of the Quaternary Period and is commonly referred to as the *Ice Age.* See *Holocene Epoch.*

Plunging breaker A type of breaking wave in which the crest falls into the trough as the wave approaches the shoreline. Plunging breakers are associated with relatively steep beaches. See *Rolling breaker.*

Point bar An accumulation of sand or gravel along the inside of a meander bend of a stream.

Point-release avalanche A type of snow avalanche in which a small mass of failed snow grows in size as it travels downslope, leaving a track with the shape of an inverted V.

Polar desert An arid, cold, high-latitude area that receives less than 250 mm of precipitation per year.

Pool A common erosional bedform in meandering and straight stream channels; characterized by slow-moving, deep water during low flow stages.

Pore water The water occupying pore space in sediment or sedimentary rock.

Porosity The percentage of void or pore space in sediment or sedimentary rock.

Porphyritic texture A texture of volcanic and shallow intrusive igneous rocks characterized by large crystals of feldspar or other minerals in a groundmass of fine interlocking crystalline material.

Postglacial time See *Holocene Epoch*.

Potential energy The energy contained in an object by virtue of its position above a reference level. See *Kinetic energy*.

Potentially active fault A fault capable of producing an earthquake. See *Active* and *Inactive faults*.

Power The rate at which work is done.

Precession of the equinoxes A change in the direction of Earth's axis of rotation relative to the Sun at the time of aphelion and perihelion. See *Aphelion* and *Perihelion*.

Precursor A physical, chemical, or biological phenomenon that immediately precedes an earthquake, volcanic eruption, landslide, or other hazardous event.

Preheating A process operating during the pre-ignition phase of a wildfire, in which fuel loses water and other volatile chemical compounds. See *Pre-ignition*.

Pre-ignition The initial phase of a wildfire, during which fuel is brought to a temperature and water content allowing ignition; involves pre-heating and pyrolysis. See *Preheating, Combustion,* and *Extinction*.

Preparedness A state of readiness achieved by an individual in order to minimize damage and injury from a natural disaster, war, or pandemic. See *Disaster preparedness*.

Prescribed burn A fire purposely set and contained within a designated area to reduce the amount of fuel available for a wildfire. Also called a *controlled burn*.

Primary effect See *Direct effect*.

Primary wave See *P wave*.

Principle of uniformitarianism The scientific law stating that the geologic processes occurring today operated in the past and can therefore be used to explain past geologic events.

Punctuated uniformitarianism The concept that rare, catastrophic events have caused major changes to Earth's surface and biota.

Pyroclastic deposit The accumulation of volcanic debris blown from a volcano during an explosive eruption; the debris ranges from ash particles to blocks and bombs.

Pyroclastic flow A rapid flow of incandescent ash, blocks, and gas that have been explosively erupted from a volcano. Pyroclastic flows result from the collapse of an eruption column or lava dome. Also called *ash flow* or *nueé ardente*.

Pyroclastic rock Rock composed of volcanic glass, mineral crystals, and lithic fragments ejected during an explosive volcanic eruption.

Pyroclastic surge A hot, gaseous, turbulent flow of pyroclastic material that travels at high velocities down the flank of a volcano. Pyroclastic surges are less dense than pyroclastic flows.

Pyrolysis A group of chemical processes, operating at high temperatures, that split large fuel molecules into smaller ones; the products of these processes are volatile gases, mineral ash, tars, and carbonaceous char.

Quick clay The clayey sediment that may liquefy when disturbed, as during an earthquake.

Radiation The transfer of energy by electromagnetic waves or by moving subatomic particles. Radiation is the main mechanism by which heat is transferred from the Sun to Earth, from Earth's surface to its atmosphere, and, to a lesser extent, from a wildfire to the atmosphere. See *Conduction* and *Convection*.

Radioactive isotope An unstable element that decays into another isotope of the same element or into a different element. Radioactive isotopes emit ionizing radiation such as gamma rays and subatomic alpha and beta particles. See *Daughter product* and *Parent isotope*.

Rayleigh wave A seismic wave that travels at Earth's surface with a retrograde elliptical motion.

Reactive response The action or response of a person or government to an accident, natural disaster, or catastrophe.

Recurrence interval The time between successive floods, earthquakes, or other disastrous events. Recurrence intervals are commonly expressed as average values (in years), based on a series of events.

Refraction The bending of surface waves as they enter shallow water. Waves move forward at a faster velocity in deep water than in shallow water.

Relative dating The placement of geologic materials, events, landforms, and fossils in a chronological sequence without determining their ages.

Relative hardness The ease with which a mineral can be scratched. Relative hardness is ranked using the Mohs Hardness Scale, in which diamond is assigned a value of 10 and talc a value of 1. Other minerals have intermediate values. See *Hardness*.

Relative humidity The ratio of the amount of water vapour in air to a hypothetical amount that would saturate the air at a given temperature and pressure; commonly expressed as a percentage.

Relief The difference in elevation between a high point, such as a mountain top, and an adjacent lower one, for example a valley floor.

Residence time The length of time that an element, compound, or other substance spends at one place or within a specific part of a natural system.

Resisting force A force that impedes the downslope movement of rock or sediment. See *Driving force*.

Resonance An increase in the amplitude of seismic waves when their frequency matches the natural vibrational frequency of an object.

Resurgent caldera The uplift of the central part of a giant volcanic crater that formed earlier during an explosion or collapse of the volcano's summit. See *Caldera*.

Retreat The interval of time during which a glacier thins and retreats. See *Advance*.

Retrofitting The renovation of engineered structures to withstand ground shaking and other, secondary effects of an earthquake.

Return period See *Recurrence interval*.

Return stroke The downward flow of electrons during a cloud-to-ground lightning discharge. This discharge produces the bright light of a lightning flash. See *Lightning* and *Step-leader*.

Reverse fault A fault along which the hanging wall has moved upward relative to the footwall. See *Dip-slip, Normal, Strike-slip,* and *Thrust faults*.

Rhyolite A fine-grained, light-coloured, silica-rich volcanic rock consisting of feldspar, quartz, and ferromagnesian minerals.

Richter scale The range of earthquake magnitude values determined from trace deflections on a standard seismograph at a distance of 100 km from the epicentre. The Richter scale is logarithmic—an increase in magnitude of one, for example from 3 to 4, corresponds to a ten-fold increase in peak ground motion amplitude and a 30-fold increase in the total energy released by the earthquake. See *Magnitude*.

Ridge An elongated area of high atmospheric pressure.

Riffle A shallow section of stream channel where, at low flow, water moves rapidly over a gravel bed.

Rift A long, narrow trough bounded by normal faults. Rifts are produced when crustal rocks are pulled apart.

Ring of Fire A popular name given to the chain of active volcanoes bordering much of the Pacific Ocean.

Rip current The seaward flow of water in a narrow zone from the beach to beyond the breaker zone.

Riprap Large broken stones placed to protect a riverbank or shoreline from erosion.

Risk The product of the probability of a hazardous event and the expected damage if the event does occur.

Risk analysis The evaluation of the probability that a hazardous event will occur and its possible consequences, including death, injury, and property damage. See *Risk*.

River A large natural stream. See *Stream*.

Rock A solid, natural aggregate of one or more minerals, natural glass, or fossils.

Rock avalanche The downward and outward movement of fragmenting rock at high velocities. Rock avalanches may run out long distances on relatively gentle slopes.

Rock cycle A group of interrelated processes that produce igneous, metamorphic, and sedimentary rocks.

Rogue wave An abnormally large ocean wave produced by constructive interference of smaller waves.

Rope stage The final decaying phase of a tornado, during which upward-spiralling air in the funnel comes into contact with downdrafts from the thunderstorm. See *Organizational stage* and *Shrinking stage*.

Rotational A type of landslide in which material moves downward and outward on a well-defined, upward-curving slip surface.

Rule of Vs The principle that a contour line has a V-shape where it crosses a stream valley and that the apex of the V points upstream.

Runoff The water that flows over the land surface; includes overland flow on slopes and channelized stream flow.

Run-out zone The lower part of an avalanche path where snow is deposited. See *Start zone* and *Track*.

Runup The upward rush of a wave on a shore; also, the distance that a tsunami surges inland from the shoreline.

Rural-urban interface The area where forest, scrubland, or grassland borders developed, populated areas.

Rutschblock test A field test of snowpack stability in which a skier jumps on an excavated column of undisturbed snow. A score is applied based on the loading required to release a block from the upper part of the column.

S wave A seismic wave that travels in a snake-like fashion through solid material from the hypocentre of an earthquake. Also called a *secondary* or *shear wave*.

Sackung A German term for deep-seated rock creep; involves complex internal deformation of a failing rock mass along multiple shear planes. Surface features associated with sackung include ridge-top depressions, uphill-facing scarps, and bulging of the lower part of the slope.

Sand storm A storm with high winds that transport sand particles to heights of up to 2 m above the ground. Most sand storms occur in arid areas.

Scale The relation between map distance and the corresponding real distance on Earth's surface. Scale is expressed as a ratio, such as 1:50,000, or by a segmented bar placed on the map.

Scientific method The principles and processes of discovery and demonstration that are characteristic of scientific investigation. The scientific method involves observation of phenomena, the formulation of a hypothesis, experimentation to demonstrate the truth or falseness of the hypothesis, and a conclusion that validates or modifies the hypothesis.

Scoria cone See *Cinder cone*.

Sea cliff A steep coastal bluff produced by wave erosion, landsliding, and, in some cases, groundwater seepage.

Seamount An underwater mountain that rises from the ocean floor and has a peaked or flat-topped summit below the sea surface.

Seawall The engineered structures built along the shoreline to retard erosion and protect buildings from damage by waves and currents.

Secondary effect See *Indirect effect*.

Secondary succession The sequential changes in vegetation over time following a disturbance such as a wildfire.

Secondary wave See *S wave*.

Sector collapse A sudden collapse of the flank of a volcano, generally just before or during a volcanic eruption.

Sediment The fragments of inorganic or organic detritus transported and deposited by wind, water, gravity, or glacier ice.

Seismic amplification See *Material amplification*.

Seismic gap The segment of an active fault that could produce a large earthquake, but has not done so recently.

Seismic source The part of a fault that ruptures to produce an earthquake.

Seismic wave A wave produced by sudden displacement of rocks along a fault; Seismic waves move through or along the surface of Earth.

Seismogram A written or electronic record of an earthquake made by a seismograph. See *Seismograph*.

Seismograph An instrument that records earthquakes. See *Seismogram*.

Sensible heat The energy produced by random molecular motion. Sensible heat can be physically sensed and measured, such as with a thermometer.

ShakeMap A computer-generated map of the shaking that people feel in different areas during an earthquake, produced in near real time.

Shear strength The internal resistance of a body of rock or sediment to shear and failure.

Shear wave See *S wave*.

Shield volcano A gently sloping, broad, convex volcano consisting of basalt lava flows; the largest type of volcano. See *Stratovolcano*.

Shovel test A simple field test of snowpack stability, in which the upper part of a column of undisturbed snow is pulled with a shovel.

Shrinking stage The late phase of a tornado, when the funnel thins and begins to tilt as its supply of warm moist air decreases. See *Rope stage* and *Shrinking stage*.

Silent earthquake See *Slow earthquake*.

Silicosis A respiratory disease caused by inhalation of crystalline silica dust.

Sink A temporary or permanent repository for a chemical element or compound, such as carbon dioxide.

Sinkhole A surface depression formed by solution of underlying limestone or by collapse of a cave.

Slab avalanche A type of avalanche in which large cohesive blocks of snow move rapidly downslope.

Sliding The downslope movement of a block of rock or sediment along a planar or curved slip plane. The block may remain nearly intact or it may break up into fragments.

Slip rate The long-term, average rate of displacement along a fault, generally expressed in millimetres or centimetres per year.

Slope An inclination of the land surface, expressed in degrees or percent.

Slope stability map A depiction of the land surface showing its susceptibility to landslides.

Slow earthquake A seismic event involving movement along a fault over a period of days to months. Also called a *Silent earthquake*.

Sluff A snow slide that is generally too small to bury a person.

Slump A type of landslide characterized by sliding along an upward-curved slip surface. See *Slumping*.

Slump block A mass of rock or sediment that has moved downward and outward along a curved slip surface. See *Slump* and *Slumping*.

Slumping The downslope movement of a block of rock or sediment along a curved slip surface. See *Slump*.

Smectite A group of clay minerals that can adsorb large amounts of water; a common constituent of shrink-swell clay.

Snow avalanche See *Avalanche*.

Soil Surface rock or sediment that has been altered by mechanical, chemical, and biological processes and is a medium for plant growth. Engineers define *soil* as unconsolidated sediment that can be excavated or removed without blasting.

Soil slip The failure and rapid downslope movement of a thin layer of weathered rock or sediment. The slip surface is located in or at the base of weathered slope deposits lying on unweathered material.

Solar nebula A pancake-like, rotating disk of hydrogen and helium dust. The Sun formed by accretion of hydrogen and helium within a solar nebula about five billion years ago.

Sorting The size range of particles forming a sediment or sedimentary rock. Poorly sorted sediment consists of particles of a wide range of size; well-sorted sediment comprises particles of similar size.

Spacewatch A program started in 1981 to identify near-Earth asteroids and comets.

Specific gravity The density of a mineral or rock relative to the density of water.

Spilling breaker A breaking wave that tumbles forward as it moves shoreward. Spilling breakers are associated with gently sloping beaches. See *Plunging breaker*.

Spit A long, narrow ridge of sand or gravel that extends parallel to the shore from a point of land on a coast.

Splitting wedge A masonry or concrete wedge-shaped structure designed to deflect avalanching snow away from a building.

Spot fire A small fire ignited by wind-blown, burning embers ahead of the flaming front of a wildfire.

Spring A continuous discharge of groundwater where the water table intersects the ground surface.

Squall line A line of thunderstorms accompanied by high winds and heavy rain. A squall line commonly forms in advance of a cold front.

Stable isotope An isotope that does not decay naturally into another isotope of the same element or into a different element. See *Radioactive isotope*.

Stage The level of water in a stream channel. Flood stage is the level at which the stream overflows its channel and spills onto its floodplain.

Stalactite A cylindrical or conical deposit of calcium carbonate that extends downward from the roof of a cave or an overhang. Stalactites form where carbonate-rich waters drip from the cave roof. See *Flowstone* and *Stalagmite*.

Stalagmite A cylindrical or conical deposit of calcium carbonate on the floor of a cave. Stalagmites form where carbonate-rich waters drip from the roof to the floor of a cave. See *Flowstone* and *Stalactite*.

Start zone The highest part of an avalanche path, where the snowpack fails. See *Run-out zone* and *Track*.

Stationary front A transition zone between two different air masses that are not moving. See *Front*.

Step-leader A channel of ionized air that approaches the ground in a series of nearly invisible bursts; this channel becomes the path for the luminous return stroke of a cloud-to-ground lightning strike. See *Return stroke*.

Stony meteorite Meteorites consisting of silicate minerals (75 percent to 90 percent) and metallic alloys of nickel and iron (10 percent to 25 percent).

Stony meteorites are a diverse group, ranging from samples of matter that date to the beginning of the solar system to differentiated rocks derived from primitive planetary bodies. See *Differentiated*.

Storm surge Wind-driven waves that flood low-lying coastal areas. Storm surges accompany hurricanes, nor'easters, and other severe storms.

Strain A change in the shape or size of a body because of application of a stress.

Stratosphere The zone in Earth's atmosphere above the troposphere, where temperature is either constant or increases with altitude. The stratosphere contains significant quantities of ozone, which protects life from ultraviolet radiation. See *Mesosphere* and *Troposphere*.

Stratovolcano A steep-sided, explosive volcano formed of pyroclastic deposits and lava flows. Also called a *composite volcano*. See *Shield volcano*.

Streak The colour of a mineral in its powdered form. A streak may be produced by rubbing a mineral specimen on an unglazed ceramic plate.

Stream A ribbon-like body of water flowing in a channel; includes brooks, creeks, and rivers. See *River*.

Strength The ability of rock or sediment to resist deformation. Strength results from cohesive and frictional forces in the material.

Strike and dip Two measurements that geologists make to define the three-dimensional orientation of planar features, including bedding, foliation, and faults.

Strike-slip fault A fault that displaces rocks laterally, with little or no vertical component of movement. See *Dip-slip, Normal, Reverse,* and *Thrust faults*.

Strong earthquake An earthquake of moment magnitude 6.0 to 6.9.

Subaqueous landslide A landslide that occurs on the floor of a lake or the sea.

Subduction The process by which one tectonic plate descends beneath another and eventually melts in the mantle.

Subduction earthquake An earthquake resulting from sudden slip along the fault that separates two lithospheric plates at a subduction zone. The largest earthquakes on Earth are subduction earthquakes. See *Subduction* and *Subduction zone*.

Subduction zone An elongate zone, typically hundreds to more than one thousand kilometres long, where two crustal plates converge, one moving slowly under the other. See *Subduction*.

Subsidence The lowering of Earth's surface because of sediment compaction, an earthquake, or other natural processes.

Suction vortices The small, intense, rotating wind cells that are responsible for much of the damage done by a tornado.

Supercell An unusually long-lived thunderstorm with a rotating updraft on the storm's flank.

Supercell storm See *Supercell*.

Supernova An explosion of a star, accompanied by an extremely bright emission of vast amounts of energy.

Surf zone The nearshore area between the zone of breaking waves and the swash zone.

Surface fire A wildfire that burns primarily along the ground, consuming fuels such as grasses, shrubs, dead and downed limbs, and leaf litter. See *Continuous surface fire, Intermittent surface fire,* and *Crown fire*.

Surface wave A seismic wave that travels along the ground surface. Surface waves are generally strongest close to the epicentre, where they may cause much structural damage. See *Body wave*.

Suspended load The sediment particles transported in suspension within a river or stream. See *Bedload, Dissolved load,* and *Total load*.

Swash zone An area along the shoreline where waves run up and recede.

Swell The sets of storm-produced waves with more-or-less uniform heights and lengths. Wave sets travel long distances with relatively little loss of energy.

Talus The fragments of rock that have fallen from a cliff or steep slope and accumulated at its base. Talus may form aprons and cones of blocky rubble.

Tectonic Pertaining to the structure or deformation of Earth's crust.

Tectonic creep See *Fault creep*.

Tectonic cycle The cyclic production and destruction of lithosphere through slow movement of tectonic plates; part of the geologic cycle.

Tectonic plate A very large, fault-bounded block of crust and upper mantle that slowly moves on top of the asthenosphere. Tectonic plates form at mid-oceanic ridges and are destroyed at subduction zones. Also called a *lithospheric plate*.

Tensile strength The greatest extensional stress that a material can bear without failing.

Tephra A general term for fragmented volcanic material blown out of a volcano; includes ash, lapilli, blocks, and bombs.

Texture The size, shape, and arrangement of mineral and lithic particles in rock. Also, the size distribution of mineral and rock particles in sediment.

Thaw flow slide A shallow, commonly fast-moving landslide resulting from failure of the active layer in an area of permafrost.

Thermal spring A flow of heated groundwater onto land or into a river, lake, or ocean; includes warm springs and hot springs. See *Hot spring*.

Thermokarst An irregular terrain formed by melt of permafrost.

Thermosphere The outermost zone of Earth's atmosphere (above 80 km in altitude), characterized by little gas and an upward increase in temperature.

Thrust fault A low-angle reverse fault along which older rocks are displaced over younger rocks. See *Dip-slip, Normal, Reverse,* and *Strike-slip* faults.

Tidal bore A high landward-flowing wave caused by the collision of tidal currents in an estuary.

Tombolo A long, narrow ridge of sand or gravel that forms part of the shoreline of a lake or the sea. The ends of a tombolo are attached to rocky headlands.

Top-loaded A slab of potentially unstable snow deposited leeward of the crest of a slope or the top of a mountain by wind. See *Cross-loaded*.

Topographic map A two-dimensional representation of Earth's surface that uses contour lines to depict elevation.

Topographic profile A continuous profile of the elevation of the land along a line drawn on a topographic map.

Topple The pivoting of a rock mass about a point.

Tornadic waterspout A rapidly rotating column of air extending downward from a thunderstorm to an ocean, lake, or other water body.

Tornado A violently rotating, funnel-shaped column of air extending downward from a severe thunderstorm to the ground.

Total load The sum of the dissolved, suspended, and bed load that a stream or river carries.

Tower karst A landscape of steep-sided hills rising above a plain or above sinkholes that have formed by dissolution of limestone. See *Karst*.

Track The middle part of a snow avalanche path, where the avalanche accelerates and achieves its highest velocity. See *Run-out* and *Start zones*.

Transform boundary See *Transform fault*.

Transform fault A strike-slip fault that connects segments of mid-ocean ridges and forms the boundary between two plates; the San Andreas fault in California is an example. Also called a *transform boundary*.

Translational The downslope movement of rock or sediment along a well-defined, planar surface.

Triangulation The act of locating an epicentre using distances from three seismographs.

Tributary A stream that flows into a larger stream.

Troglobite An organism, such as a blind salamander, that spends its entire life in a cave.

Tropical cyclone A large thunderstorm complex rotating around an area of low pressure over warm water in the tropics or subtropics; includes tropical depressions, tropical storms, hurricanes, typhoons, severe tropical cyclones, and cyclonic storms. See *Hurricane, Tropical depression,* and *Tropical storm*.

Tropical depression A low-pressure centre in the tropics with winds less than 63 km/h, which is the threshold for a tropical storm. See *Hurricane, Tropical cyclone, Tropical disturbance,* and *Tropical storm*.

Tropical disturbance An area of disorganized but common thunderstorms associated with a low-pressure trough; the formative stage of a tropical depression, tropical storm, or hurricane. See *Hurricane, Tropical cyclone, Tropical depression,* and *Tropical storm*.

Tropical storm An organized system of thunderstorms centred on an area of low pressure. A tropical storm derives its energy from warm ocean waters and has sustained winds of between 63 km/h and 119 km/h. It is stronger than a tropical depression but weaker than a hurricane. See *Hurricane, Tropical cyclone, Tropical depression,* and *Tropical disturbance*.

Tropopause The boundary between the troposphere and the stratosphere.

Troposphere The lowermost layer of the atmosphere, characterized by a decrease in temperature with altitude. See *Stratosphere* and *Mesosphere*.

Trough An elongate area of low atmospheric pressure.

Tsunami The waves generated by a sudden upward or downward movement of a large area of the seafloor or by an asteroid impact. Causes of tsunami include subduction earthquakes, collapse of the flank of a volcano, large landslides, and asteroid impacts.

Tuya A flat-topped, steep-sided, extinct volcano that erupted into a lake beneath a former ice cap or ice sheet.

Updrift The direction from which a current of water, such as a longshore current, is flowing; see *Downdrift*.

Uplift An increase in the elevation of an area because of tectonic or volcanic processes.

Upstream flood A flood in the upper part of a drainage basin, typically produced by intense rainfall over a relatively small area. See *Downstream flood*.

Vadose zone The layer of porous material between the ground surface and the water table, with a moisture content less than saturation and a pressure less than atmospheric.

Valley fever A potentially fatal respiratory illness caused by fungal spores present in desert soils.

Variable gas A gas such as carbon dioxide or water vapour that is present in the atmosphere in variable amounts and cannot be compressed with pressure alone. See *Permanent gas*.

Varve A bed or lamina of sediment deposited in a single year. A varve commonly comprises a silt layer deposited in summer and an overlying clay layer deposited in winter.

Vein A tabular body of rock that fills a fracture or fissure in an older rock. Veins form by precipitation of minerals from subsurface fluids.

Vertical exaggeration (VE) The ratio of the vertical scale of a diagram or model to the horizontal scale. Vertical exaggeration is used in many geologic cross-sections to clearly show relationships.

Very minor earthquake See *Microearthquake*.

Vesicular texture A texture characterized by abundant irregular cavities that give some volcanic rocks (mainly basalt) a frothy appearance. The cavities, or vesicles, form when gas escapes from magma as it cools and crystallizes.

Viscosity A material's resistance to flow. Viscosity results from the internal friction of a material's molecules. Substances with a high viscosity do not flow readily; those with a low viscosity are more fluid.

Vog A volcanic fog or smog consisting of sulphur dioxide, other volcanic gases, sulphuric acid, and dust. On Hawaii, vog is an acrid blue haze produced by gases emitted from Kilauea volcano.

Volcanic crisis A circumstance in which a volcanic eruption, or the prospect of a volcanic eruption, presents a danger to a large number of people.

Volcanic dome A volcano formed from viscous magma with a high silica content; eruptive activity is generally explosive.

Volcanic vent A circular or elongate opening in the ground, through which lava and pyroclastic debris are erupted.

Vortex A spinning column of air.

Wall cloud A localized, persistent wall of condensed water vapour at the base of a severe thunderstorm. Wall clouds may rotate and are commonly associated with tornadoes.

Warning An announcement that a hazardous event, such as a hurricane or tornado, could happen in the near future.

Washover channel An erosional channel extending across a beach or through a coastal dune. Washover channels form during storm surges. See *Overwash*.

Watch An alert issued by a meteorological agency that weather conditions are favourable for severe weather such as tornadoes, a hurricane, a severe thunderstorm, or a blizzard.

Watershed See *Drainage basin*.

Watt The basic unit of power (symbol W), equal to 1 J/s.

Wave height The vertical distance between the crest and adjacent trough of a wave.

Wave normal The direction perpendicular to the crest of a wave.

Wave period The time that successive crests of a wave take to pass a reference point; the inverse of the frequency of the wave. See *Frequency*.

Wave train A set of waves that constitutes a tsunami. See *Tsunami*.

Wavelength The horizontal distance between successive crests or troughs of a wave; applied to seismic, electromagnetic, water, and other waveforms. See *Wave period*.

Weather The atmospheric conditions, including air temperature, humidity, and wind speed, that characterize a particular place. See *Climate*.

Weathering The changes in the mineralogy, chemistry, and texture of rocks at or near Earth's surface because of physical, chemical, and biological activity.

Wildfire An uncontrolled fire in a forest, scrubland, or grassland.

Wind chill The additional cooling effect that wind has on humans in cold weather. Wind chill indexes quantify how humans lose heat in moving cold air.

Wind slab A thick, poorly bonded layer of snow deposited on a slope by wind. Wind slabs are the source of many snow avalanches.

Work The application of a force to overcome resistance or to produce molecular change.

Younger Dryas A period of cold climate in the North Atlantic region that began abruptly about 12,600 years ago and ended about 11,400 years ago. Younger Dryas cooling was triggered by a change in ocean thermohaline circulation in the North Atlantic, probably caused by the draining of one or more ice-dammed lakes in North America.

REFERENCES

CHAPTER 1

1. **Lay, T., Kanamori, H., Ammon, C., Nettles, M., Ward, S., Aster, R., Beck, S., Bilek, S., Brudzinski, M., Butler, R., DeShon, H., Ekström, G., Satake, K.,** and **Sipkin, S.** 2005. The great Sumatra-Andaman earthquake of 26 December 2004. *Science* 308:1127–33.
2. **UN Office of the Special Envoy for Tsunami Recovery.** 2004. http://www.tsunamispecialenvoy.org/country/humantoll.asp. Accessed 10/29/06.
3. **Natural Resources Canada.** 2004. *The atlas of Canada: Natural hazards.* http://atlas.gc.ca/site/english/maps/environment/naturalhazards. Accessed 1/29/05.
4. **Public Safety and Emergency Preparedness of Canada.** 2001. *Natural hazards of Canada.* http://www.ocipep.gc.ca/info_pro/Posters/naturalhazards/index_e.asp. Accessed 1/29/05.
5. **Advisory Committee on the International Decade for Natural Hazard Reduction.** 1989. *Reducing disaster's toll.* National Research Council. Washington, DC: National Academy Press.
6. **Wikipedia.** 2006. *Hurricane Katrina.* http://en.wikipedia.org/wiki/Hurricane Katrina. Accessed 11/29/06.
7. **White, G. F.,** and **Haas, J. E.** 1975. *Assessment of research on natural hazards.* Cambridge, MA: MIT Press.
8. **Le Pichon, X.** 1968. Sea-floor spreading and continental drift. *Journal of Geophysical Research* 73:3661–97.
9. **Dewey, J. F.** 1972. Plate tectonics. *Scientific American* 22:56–68.
10. **Fowler, C. M. R.** 1990. *The solid Earth.* Cambridge, UK: Cambridge University Press.
11. **Cox, A.,** and **Hart, R. B.** 1986. *Plate tectonics.* Boston: Blackwell Scientific Publications.
12. **Crowe, B. W.** 1986. Volcanic hazard assessment for disposal of high-level radioactive waste. In *Active tectonics,* ed. Geophysics Study Committee, pp. 247–60. National Research Council. Washington, DC: National Academy Press.
13. **Jones, R. A.** 1986. New lessons from quake in Mexico. *Los Angeles Times,* September 26.
14. **Campillo, M., Gariel, J. C., Aki, K.,** and **Sanchez-Sesma, F. J.** 1989. Destructive strong ground motion in Mexico city: Source, path, and site effects during the great 1985 Michoacan earthquake. *Bulletin of the Seismological Society of America* 79:1718–35.
15. **Reilinger, R., Toksoz, N., McClusky, S.,** and **Barka, A.** 2000. 1999 Iszmit, Turkey earthquake was no surprise. *GSA Today* 10(1):1–6.
16. **Brown, L. R., Flavin, C.,** and **Postel, S.** 1991. *Saving the planet.* New York: W.W. Norton & Co.
17. **Population Reference Bureau.** 2000. *World population data sheet.* Washington, DC.
18. **Smil, V.** 1999. How many billions to go? *Nature* 401:429.
19. **Abramovitz, J. N.,** and **Dunn, S.** 1998. *Record year for weather-related disasters.* Vital Signs Brief 98-5. Washington, DC: World Watch Institute.
20. **Kates, R. W.,** and **Pijawka, D.** 1977. From rubble to monument: The pace of reconstruction. In *Disaster and reconstruction,* eds. J. E. Haas, R. W. Kates, and M. J. Bowden, pp. 1–23. Cambridge, MA: MIT Press.
21. **Costa, J. E.,** and **Baker, V. R.** 1981. *Surficial geology: Building with the Earth.* New York: John Wiley & Sons.

CHAPTER 2

1. **Bent, A.,** and **Evans, S. G.** 2004. The **M** 7.6 El Salvador earthquake of 13 January 2001 and implications for seismic hazard in El Salvador. In *Natural hazards in El Salvador,* eds. W. I. Rose, J. J. Bommer, D. Lopez, M. J. Carr, and J. J. Major, pp. 397–404. Geological Society of America Special Paper 375.
2. **Bilham, R.,** and **Srivastav, S. K.,** eds. 2003. The Bhuj earthquake, Gujarat, India, 2001. *Proceedings, Indian Academy of Sciences: Earth and Planetary Sciences* 112:313–484.
3. **Clague, J. J.** 2001. *The Nisqually earthquake: A wakeup call from south of the border. Innovation* [Association of Professional Engineers and Geoscientists of the Province of British Columbia] 5(5):14–17.
4. **Radbruch, D. H.,** and **Bonilla, M. G.** 1966. *Tectonic creep in the Hayward fault zone, California.* U.S. Geological Survey Circular 525.
5. **Steinbrugge, K. V.,** and **Zacher, E. G.** 1960. Creep on the San Andreas fault. In *Focus on environmental geology,* ed. R. W. Tank, pp. 132–37. New York: Oxford University Press.
6. **Cervelli, P.** 2004. The threat of silent earthquakes. *Scientific American.* 290:86–91.
7. **Rogers, G.,** and **Dragert H.** 2003. Episodic tremor and slip on the Cascadia subduction zone: The chatter of silent slip. *Science* 300:1942–43.
8. **Bolt, B. A.** 2004. *Earthquakes,* 5th ed. San Francisco: W.H. Freeman.
9. **Hough, S. E., Friberg, P. A., Busby, R., Field, E. F., Jacob, K. H.,** and **Borcherdt, R. D.** 1989. Did mud cause freeway collapse? *EOS, Transactions, American Geophysical Union* 70(47):1497, 1504.
10. **Yeats, R. S.** 2001. *Living with earthquakes in California: A survivor's guide.* Corvallis, OR: Oregon State University Press.
11. **Jones, R. A.** 1986. New lessons from quake in Mexico. *Los Angeles Times,* September 26.
12. **Hanks, T. C.** 1985. *The National Earthquake Hazards Reduction Program: Scientific status.* U.S. Geological Survey Bulletin 1659.
13. **Camby, T. Y.** 1990. California earthquake: Prelude to the big one. *National Geographic* 177(5):76–105.
14. **Advisory Committee on the International Decade for Natural Hazard Reduction.** 1989. *Reducing disaster's toll.* National Research Council. Washington, DC: National Academy Press.
15. **Hough, S.** 2002. *Earthshaking science: What we know (and don't know) about earthquakes.* Princeton, NJ: Princeton University Press.
16. **Atwater, B. F., Musumi-Rokkaku, S., Satake, K., Tsuji, Y., Ueda, K.,** and **Yamaguchi, D. K.** 2005. *The orphan tsunami of 1700: Japanese clues to a parent earthquake in North America.* U.S. Geological Survey Professional Paper 1707.

17. **Clague, J. J.** 1997. Evidence for large earthquakes at the Cascadia subduction zone. *Reviews of Geophysics* 35:439–60.

18. **Satake, K., Shimazaki, K., Tsuji, Y.,** and **Ueda, K.** 1996. Time and size of a giant earthquake in Cascadia inferred from Japanese tsunami records of January 1700. *Nature* 378:246–49.

19. **Sieh, K.,** and **LeVay, S.** 1998. *The Earth in turmoil: Earthquakes, volcanoes and their impact on humankind*. New York: W.H. Freeman.

20. **Hamilton, R. M.** 1980. Quakes along the Mississippi. *Natural History* 89:70–75.

21. **Mueller, K., Champion, J., Guccione, E. M.,** and **Kelson, K.** 1999. Fault slip rates in the modern New Madrid Seismic Zone. *Science* 286:1135–38.

22. **Adams, J. J.,** and **Basham, P. W.** 1989. The seismicity and seismotectonics of Canada east of the Cordillera. *Geoscience Canada* 16:3–16.

23. **Office of Emergency Preparedness.** 1972. *Disaster preparedness*, 11:1, 3. Washington, DC.

24. **Federal Emergency Management Agency.** 2004. *Disaster facts*. http://www.fema.gov/library/df1.shtm. Accessed 1/18/04.

25. **Youd, T. L., Nichols, D. R., Helley, E. J.,** and **Lajoie, K. R.** 1975. Liquefaction potential. In *Studies for seismic zonation of the San Francisco Bay region*, ed. R. D. Borcherdt, pp. 68–74. U.S. Geological Survey Professional Paper 941A.

26. **Atwater, B. F., Nelson, A. R., Clague, J. J., Carver, G. A., Yamaguchi, D. K., Bobrowsky, P. T., Bourgeois, J., Darienzo, M. E., Grant, W. C., Hemphill-Haley, E., Kelsey, H. M., Jacoby, G. C., Nishenko, S. P., Palmer, S. P., Peterson, C. D.,** and **Reinhart, M. A.** 1995. Summary of coastal geologic evidence for past great earthquakes at the Cascadia subduction zone. *Earthquake Spectra* 11:1–18.

27. **Plafker, G.** 1965. Tectonic deformation associated with the 1964 Alaska earthquake. *Science* 148:1675–87.

28. **Bucknam, R. C., Hemphill-Haley, E.,** and **Leopold, E. B.** 1992. Abrupt uplift within the past 1700 years at southern Puget Sound, Washington. *Science* 158:1611–14.

29. **Plafker, G.,** and **Ericksen, G. E.** 1978. Nevados Huascarán avalanches, Peru. In *Rockslides and avalanches: 1, Natural phenomena,* ed. B. Voight, pp. 277–314. New York: Elsevier.

30. **U.S. Geological Survey.** 1996. *USGS response to an urban earthquake, Northridge '94.* U.S. Geological Survey Open-File Report 96–263.

31. **Pakiser, L. C., Eaton, J. P., Healy, J. H.,** and **Raleigh, C. B.** 1969. Earthquake prediction and control. *Science* 166:1467–74.

32. **Yeats, R. S., Sieh, K.,** and **Allen, C. R.** 1997. *The geology of earthquakes*. New York: Oxford University Press.

33. **Evans, D. M.** 1966. Man-made earthquakes in Denver. *Geotimes* 10:11–18.

34. **Reed, C.** 2002. Triggering quakes with waste. *Geotimes* 47(3):7.

35. **Frohlich, C.,** and **Davis, S. D.** 2002. *Texas earthquakes*. Austin, TX: University of Texas Press.

36. **Page, R. A., Boore, D. M., Bucknam, R. C.,** and **Thatcher, W. R.** 1992. *Goals, opportunities, and priorities for the USGS Earthquake Hazards Reduction Program*. U.S. Geological Survey Circular 1079.

37. **California Geological Survey.** Alquist-Priolo earthquake fault zones. http://www.consrv.ca.gov/CGS/rghm/ap/index.htm. Accessed 10/30/06.

38. **Committee on the Science of Earthquakes.** 2003. *Living on an active Earth: Perspectives on earthquake science*. National Research Council. Washington, DC: National Academies Press.

39. **Scholz, C.** 1997. Whatever happened to earthquake prediction? *Geotimes* 42(3):16–19.

40. **Press, F.** 1975. Earthquake prediction. *Scientific American* 232:14–23.

41. **Scholz, C. H.** 1990. *The mechanics of earthquakes and faulting.* New York: Cambridge University Press.

42. **Rikitakr, T.** 1983. *Earthquake forecasting and warning*. London: D. Reidel.

43. **Silver, P. G.,** and **Wakita, H.** 1996. A search for earthquake precursors. *Science* 273:77–78.

44. **Allen, C. R.** 1983. Earthquake prediction. *Geology* 11:682.

45. **Hait, M. H.** 1978. Holocene faulting, Lost River Range, Idaho. *Geological Society of America Abstracts with Programs* 10(5):217.

46. **Gori, P. L.** 1993. The social dynamics of a false earthquake prediction and the response by the public sector. *Bulletin of the Seismological Society of America* 83:963–80.

47. **Yeats, R. S.** 1998. *Living with earthquakes in the Pacific Northwest.* Corvallis, OR: Oregon State University Press.

48. **Hickman, S. H.,** and **Langbein, J.** 2002. *The Parkfield Experiment: Capturing what happens in an earthquake.* U.S. Geological Survey Fact Sheet FS 0049–02.

49. **Holden, R., Lee, R.,** and **Reichle, M.** 1989. *Technical and economic feasibility of an earthquake warning system in California*. California Division of Mines and Geology Special Publication 101.

50. **Munich Reinsurance Company of Canada.** 1992. *Earthquake: Economic impact study.* Toronto, ON: Munich Reinsurance Company of Canada.

51. **Coburn, A.,** and **Spence, R.** 2002. *Earthquake protection,* 2nd ed. Chichester, UK: John Wiley & Sons.

52. **Castell, G.** 2002. *Earthquake! Preparing for the big one: British Columbia*. Vancouver, BC: Pacific Rim Earthquake Preparedness Program.

53. **Morgan, L.** 1993. *Earthquake survival manual.* Kenmore, WA: Epicenter Press.

CHAPTER 3

1. **Wright, T. L.,** and **Pierson, T. C.** 1992. *Living with volcanoes*. U.S. Geological Survey Circular 1073.

2. **Pendick, D.** 1994. Under the volcano. *Earth* 3(3):34–39.

3. **Decker, R.,** and **Decker, B.** 1998. *Volcanoes,* 3rd ed. New York: W. H. Freeman.

4. **Hickson, C. J.,** and **Edwards, B. R.** 2001. Volcanoes and volcanic hazards. In *A Synthesis of geological hazards in Canada*, ed. G. R. Brooks, pp. 145–81. Geological Survey of Canada Bulletin 548.

5. **Hickson, C.** 2005. *Mt. St. Helens: Surviving the stone wind.* Vancouver, BC: Tricouni Press.

6. **Fisher, R. V., Heiken, G.,** and **Hulen, J. B.** 1997. *Volcanoes.* Princeton, NJ: Princeton University Press.

7. **Mathews, W. H.** 1956. "Tuyas," flat-topped volcanoes in northern British Columbia. *American Journal of Science*, 245:560–70.

8. **Francis, P.** 1983. Giant volcanic calderas. *Scientific American* 248(6):60–70.

9. **Schmincke, H.** 2004. *Volcanism*. New York: Springer-Verlag.

10. **Clague, D. A.**, and **Dalrymple, G. B.** 1987. The Hawaiian-Emperor volcanic chain: Part I, Geologic evolution. In *Volcanism in Hawaii*, eds. R. W. Decker, T. L. Wright, and P. H. Stauffer, pp. 5–73. U.S. Geological Paper 1350.

11. **Westgate, J. A.**, and **Naeser, N. D.** 1995. Tephrochronology and fission-track dating. In *Dating methods for Quaternary deposits*, eds. N. W. Rutter and N. R. Catto, pp. 15–28. St. John's, NL: Geological Association of Canada.

12. **Rogers, G. C.**, and **Souther, J.G.** 1983. Hotspots trace plate movements. *Geoscience* 12(2):10–13.

13. **Scott, K. M., Hildreth, W.**, and **Gardner, C. A.** 2000. *Mount Baker; Living with an active volcano*. U.S. Geological Survey Fact Sheet FS 0059–00.

14. **IAVCEE Subcommittee on Decade Volcanoes.** 1994. Research at decade volcanoes aimed at disaster prevention. *EOS, Transactions, American Geophysical Union* 75(30):340, 350.

15. **Office of Emergency Preparedness.** 1972. *Disaster preparedness.* 1, 3.

16. **Crandell, D. R.**, and **Waldron, H. H.** 1969. Volcanic hazards in the Cascade Range. In *Geologic hazards and public problems,* conference proceedings, eds. R. Olsen and M. Wallace, pp. 5–18. Office of Emergency Preparedness Region 7.

17. **Brown, A. S.** 1969. Aiyansh lava flow, British Columbia. *Canadian Journal of Earth Sciences* 6:1460–68.

18. **Simkin, T., Siebert, L.**, and **Blong, R.** 2001. Volcano fatalities—Lesson from the historical record. *Science* 291:255.

19. **Fisher, R. V., Smith, A. L.**, and **Roobol, M. J.** 1980. Destruction of St. Pierre, Martinique, by ash-cloud surges, May 8 and 20, 1902. *Geology* 8:472–76.

20. **Neal, C. A., Casadevall, T. J., Miller, T. P., Hendley II, J. W.**, and **Stauffer, P. H.** 1998. *Volcanic ash—Danger to aircraft in the North Pacific*. U.S. Geological Survey Fact Sheet 030–97.

21. **Holloway, M.** 2000. The killing lakes. *Scientific American* 286(3):90–99.

22. **Thorarinsson, S.**, and **Sigvaldason, G. E.** 1973. The Hekla eruption of 1970. *Bulletin Volcanologique* 36:269–88.

23. **Scarth, A.** 1999. *Vulcan's fury: Man against the volcano*. New Haven: Yale University Press.

24. **U.S. Geological Survey.** 1997. *Volcanic air pollution*. U.S. Geological Survey Fact Sheet 169–97.

25. **Crandell, D. R.**, and **Mullineaux, D. R.** 1969. *Volcanic hazards at Mount Rainier, Washington*. U.S. Geological Survey Bulletin 1283.

26. **Baxter, P. J.** 2005. *Human impacts of volcanoes*. New York: Cambridge University Press.

27. **Hammond, P. E.** 1980. Mt. St. Helens blasts 400 meters off its peak. *Geotimes* 25(8):14–15.

28. **Gardner, C.** 2005. Monitoring a restless volcano: The 2004 eruption of Mount St. Helens. *Geotimes* 50(3):24–29.

29. **Pendick, D.** 1995. Return to Mount St. Helens. *Earth* 4(2):24–33.

30. **Watts, A. B.**, and **Masson, D. G.** 1995. A giant landslide on the north flank of Tenerife, Canary Islands. *Journal of Geophysical Research* 100:24487–98.

31. **American Geophysical Union.** 1991. Pinatubo cloud measured. *EOS, Transactions, American Geophysical Union* 72(29):305–06.

32. **Francis, P.** 1976. *Volcanoes*. New York: Pelican Books.

33. **Richter, D. H., Eaton, J. P., Murata, K. J., Ault, W. U.**, and **Krivoy, H. L.** 1970. *Chronological narrative of the 1959–60 eruption of Kilauea Volcano, Hawaii*. U.S. Geological Survey Professional Paper 537E.

34. **Tilling, R. I.** 2000. Volcano notes. *Geotimes* 45(5):19.

35. **Murton, B. J.**, and **Shimabukuro, S.** 1974. Human response to volcanic hazard in Puna District, Hawaii. In *Natural hazards,* ed. G. F. White, pp. 151–59. New York: Oxford University Press.

36. **Mason, A. C.**, and **Foster, H. L.** 1953. Diversion of lava flows at Oshima, Japan. *American Journal of Science* 251:249–58.

37. **Williams, R. S., Jr.**, and **Moore, J. G.** 1973. Iceland chills a lava flow. *Geotimes* 18(8):14–18.

CHAPTER 4

1. **Ehley, P. L.** 1986. The Portuguese Bend landslide: Its mechanics and a plan for its stabilization. In *Landslides and landslide mitigation in southern California*, ed. P. L. Ehley, pp. 181–90, Guidebook for fieldtrip, Cordilleran Section of the Geological Society of America meeting, Los Angeles, CA.

2. **Varnes, D. J.** 1978. Slope movement types and processes. In *Landslides; Analysis and control*, eds. R. L. Schuster and R. J. Krizek, pp. 1–33. National Research Council, Transportation Research Board Special Report 176.

3. **Pestrong, R.** 1974. *Slope stability*. American Geological Institute. New York: McGraw-Hill.

4. **Weichert, D., Horner, R. B.**, and **Evans, S. G.** 1994. Seismic signatures of landslides; The 1990 Brenda Mine collapse and the 1965 Hope rockslides. *Bulletin of the Seismological Society of America* 84:1523–32.

5. **Clague, J. J., Mundro, A.**, and **Murty, T.** 2003. Tsunami hazard and risk in Canada. *Natural Hazards* 28:433–61.

6. **Nilsen, T. H., Taylor, F. A.**, and **Dean, R. M.** 1976. *Natural conditions that control landsliding in the San Francisco Bay Region*. U.S. Geological Survey Bulletin 1424.

7. **Burroughs, E. R., Jr.**, and **Thomas, B. R.** 1977. *Declining root strength in Douglas fir after felling as a factor in slope stability*. USDA Forest Service Research Paper INT-190.

8. **Terzaghi, K.** 1950. *Mechanism of landslides*. In *Application of geology to engineering practice,* ed. S. Paige, pp. 83–123. Geological Society of America Berkey Volume.

9. **McCulloch, D. S.**, and **Bonilla, M. G.** 1970. *Effects of the earthquake of March 27, 1964, on the Alaska Railroad.* U.S. Geological Survey Professional Paper 545–D.

10. **Leggett, R. F.** 1973. *Cities and geology*. New York: McGraw-Hill.

11. **Peckover, F. L.**, and **Kerr, J. W. G.** 1977. Treatment and maintenance of rock slopes on transportation routes. *Canadian Geotechnical Journal* 4:487–507.

12. **Lewkowicz, A. G.**, and **Harris, C.** 2005. Frequency and magnitude of active-layer detachment failures in discontinuous and continuous permafrost, northern Canada. *Permafrost and Periglacial Processes* 16:115–30.

13. **Schuster, R. L.** 1996. Socioeconomic significance of landslides. In *Landslides: Investigation and mitigation,* eds. A. K. Turner and R. L. Schuster, pp. 12–35. Transportation Research Board Special Report 247, National Research Council. Washington, DC: National Academy Press.

14. **Flemming, R. W.,** and **Taylor, F. A.** 1980. *Estimating the cost of landslide damage in the United States.* U.S. Geological Survey Circular 832.

15. **Clague, J. J., Brooks, G. R., Evans, S. G.,** and **VanDine, D. F.** 2000. Quaternary and engineering geology of the Fraser and Thompson River valleys, southwestern British Columbia. In *Guidebook for geological field trips in southwestern British Columbia and northern Washington,* eds. G. J. Woodsworth, L. E. Jackson, Jr., J. L. Nelson, and B. C. Ward, pp. 49–86. Vancouver, BC: Geological Association of Canada, Cordilleran Section.

16. **Kiersch, G. A.** 1965. Vaiont reservoir disaster. *Geotimes* 9(9):9–12.

17. **University of California,** and **SNEP Science Team and Special Consultants.** 1996. Sierra Nevada ecosystems. In *Sierra Nevada Ecosystem Project, Final report to Congress, Vol. 1.* Berkeley, CA. **http://ceres.ca.gov/snep/pubs/v1.html.** Accessed 10/10/04.

18. **Swanson, F. J.,** and **Dryness, C. T.** 1975. Impact of clear-cutting and road construction on soil erosion by landslides in the Western Cascade Range, Oregon. *Geology* 7:393–96.

19. **Jones, F. O.** 1973. *Landslides of Rio de Janeiro and the Sierra das Araras Escarpment, Brazil.* U.S. Geological Survey Professional Paper 697.

20. **Leighton, F. B.** 1966. Landslides and urban development. In *Engineering geology in southern California,* eds. R. Lung and R. Proctor, pp. 149–97, special publication, Los Angeles Section, Association of Engineering Geologists.

21. **Eisbacher, G. H.,** and **Clague, J. J.** 1981. Urban landslides in the vicinity of Vancouver, British Columbia, with special reference to the December 1979 rainstorm. *Canadian Geotechnical Journal* 18:205–16.

22. **Jones, D. K. C.** 1992. Landslide hazard assessment in the context of development. In *Geohazards,* eds. G. J. McCall, D. J. Laming, and S. C. Scott, pp. 117–41. New York: Chapman & Hall.

23. **Briggs, R. P., Pomeroy, J. S.,** and **Davies, W. E.** 1975. *Landsliding in Allegheny County, Pennsylvania.* U.S. Geological Survey Circular 728.

24. **Slosson, J. E., Yoakum, D. E.,** and **Shuiran, G.** 1986. Thistle, Utah, landslide: Could it have been prevented? In *Proceedings of the 22nd Symposium on Engineering Geology and Soils Engineering,* ed. S. H. Wood, pp. 281–303. Boise, ID: 22nd Symposium on Engineering Geology and Soils Engineering.

25. **Spiker, E. C.,** and **Gori, P. L.** 2003. *National landslides mitigation strategy—A framework for loss reduction.* U.S. Geological Survey Circular 1244.

26. **Piteau, D. R.,** and **Peckover, F. L.** 1978. Engineering of rock slopes. In *Landslides,* eds. R. Schuster and R. J. Krizek, pp. 192–228. Transportation Research Board Special Report 176, National Research Council. Washington, DC: National Academy Press.

27. **U.S. Geological Survey and Pierce County, Washington Department of Emergency Management.** 1999. *Mount Rainier Volcano Lahar Warning System Pilot Project.* **http://volcanoes.usgs.gov/About/Highlights/RainierPilot/Pilot highight.html.** Accessed 10/16/04.

CHAPTER 5

1. **Jamieson, B.** 2001. Snow avalanches. In *A synthesis of geological hazards in Canada,* ed. G. R. Brooks, pp. 81–100. Geological Survey of Canada Bulletin 548.

2. **Perla, R. I.** 1980. Avalanche release, motion and impact. In *Dynamics of snow and ice masses,* ed. S. C. Colbeck, pp. 397–462. New York: Academic Press.

3. **Armstrong, B. R.,** and **Williams, K.** 1992. *The avalanche handbook.* Golden, CO: Fulcrum Publishing.

4. **Schaerer, P. A.** 1981. Avalanches. In *Handbook of snow: Principles, processes, management and use,* eds. D. M. Gray and D. H Male, pp. 475–516. Pergamon Press.

5. **Colbeck, S. C.** 1991. The layered character of snow covers. *Reviews of Geophysics* 29:81–96.

6. **McClung, D. M.,** and **Schaerer, P. A.** 1993. *The avalanche handbook.* Seattle, WA: The Mountaineers.

7. **Abromeit, D., Deveraux, A. M.,** and **Overby, B.** 2004. *Avalanche basics.* U.S. Forest Service, National Avalanche Center. **http://www.fsavalanche.org.** Accessed 10/17/04.

8. **Daffern, T.** 1993. *Avalanche safety for skiers and climbers,* 2nd ed. Calgary, AB: Rocky Mountain Books.

9. **Jamieson, B.** 1997. *Backcountry avalanche awareness,* 6th ed. Revelstoke, BC: Canadian Avalanche Association.

10. **Woods, J.** 1962. *Snow war: An illustrated history of Rogers Pass, Glacier National Park,* 3rd ed. Toronto, ON: Canadian Parks and Wilderness Society.

11. **Morrall, J. F.,** and **Abdelwahab, W. M.** 1992. Estimating traffic delays and the economic cost of recurrent road closures on rural highways. *Logistics and Transportation Review* 29:159–77.

12. **LaChapelle, E. R.** 1980. The fundamental processes in conventional avalanche forecasting. *Journal of Glaciology* 26:75–84.

13. **Mears, A. J.** 1992. *Snow-avalanche hazard analysis for land-use planning and engineering.* Colorado Geological Survey Bulletin 49.

14. **Schweizer, J.,** and **Föhn, P. M. B.** 1996. Avalanche forecasting—and expert system approach. *Journal of Glaciology* 42:318–32.

15. **Fredston, J.,** and **Fesler, D.** 1994. *Snow sense: A guide to evaluating snow avalanche hazard.* Anchorage, AK: Alaska Mountain Safety Center.

16. **Falk, M., Brugger, H.,** and **Adler-Kastner, L.** 1994. Avalanche survival chances. *Nature,* 368:21.

17. **Tremper, B.** 2001. *Staying alive in avalanche terrain.* Seattle, WA: The Mountaineers.

CHAPTER 6

1. **Gamma Remote Sensing.** 2000. *Land Subsidence in Venezia.* **http://www.gamma-rs.ch/ findit.php?search_term=Land\Subsidence&content= venezia.** Accessed 11/14/04.

2. **Galloway, D., Jones, D. R.,** and **Ingebritsen, S. E.** 1999. Introduction. In *Land subsidence in the United States,* eds. D. Galloway, D. R. Jones, and S. E. Ingebritsen, pp. 111–20. U.S. Geological Survey Circular 1182.

3. **Bloom, A. L.** 1991. *Geomorphology: A systematic analysis of late Cenozoic landforms.* Englewood Cliffs, NJ: Prentice Hall.

4. **Nelson, F. E., Anisimov, O. A.,** and **Shiklomanov, N. I.** 2001. Subsidence risk from thawing permafrost. *Nature* 410:669–890.

5. **Goldman, E.** 2002. Even in the high Arctic nothing is permanent. *Science* 297:1493–94.

6. **Hodek, R. J., Johnson, A. M.,** and **Sandri, D. B.** 1984. Soil cavities formed by piping, In *Sinkholes; their geology, engineering and environmental impact*, ed. B. F. Beck, pp. 249–54. Rotterdam: A.A. Balkema.

7. **Cockfield, W. E.,** and **Buckham, A. E.** 1946. Sink-hole erosion in the white silts at Kamloops, British Columbia. *Transactions of the Royal Society of Canada* 40:1–10.

8. **Penvenne, L.** 1996. The disappearing delta. *Earth* 5(4):16–17.

9. **Fischetti, M.** 2001. Drowning New Orleans. *Scientific American* 287(10):76–85.

10. **Ingebritsen, S. E., McVoy, C., Glaz, B.,** and **Park, W.** 1999. Florida Everglades: Subsidence threatens agriculture and complicates ecosystem restoration. In *Land subsidence in the United States,* eds. D. Galloway, D. R. Jones, and S. E. Ingebritsen, pp. 95–106. U.S. Geological Survey Circular 1182.

11. **Wilding, L. P.,** and **Tessier, D.** 1988. Genesis of Vertisols. Shrink-swell phenomena. In *Vertisols: Their distribution, properties, classification and management,* eds. L. P. Wilding and R. Puentes, pp. 55–81. College Station, TX: Texas A&M University Soil Management Support Services Technical Monograph No. 18.

12. **Mathewson, C. C., Castleberry, II, J. P.,** and **Lytton, R. L.** 1975. Analysis and modeling of the performance of home foundations on expansive soils in central Texas. *Bulletin of the Association of Engineering Geologists* 17(4):275–302.

13. **Clague, J. J.** 1997. Evidence for large earthquakes at the Cascadia subduction zone. *Reviews of Geophysics* 35:439–60.

14. **Schmidt, W.** 2001. Sinkholes in Florida. *Geotimes* 46(1):18.

15. **Liquori, A., Maple, J. A.,** and **Heuer, C. E.** 1983. The design and construction of the Alyeska Pipeline. *International Conference on Permafrost, Proceedings* 3(2):151–57.

16. **Comiso, J. C.,** and **Parkinson, C. L.** 2004. Satellite-observed changes in the Arctic. *Physics Today* 57(8):38–44.

17. **Waltham, T.** 2005. The flooding of New Orleans. *Geology Today* 21:225–31.

18. **Hart, S. S.** 1974. Potentially swelling soil and rock in the Front Range Urban Corridor. *Environmental Geology* 7. Denver: Colorado Geological Survey.

19. **Harris, R. C.** 2004. Giant desiccation cracks in Arizona. *Arizona Geology* 34(2):1–4.

20. **Troving, K. A.,** and **Belson, C. S.** 2001. *Top ten list of endangered karst ecosystems.* Karst Waters Institute, **http://www.karstwaters.org/TopTen3/topten3.htm.** Accessed 11/14/04.

21. **Poland, J. F.,** and **Davis, G. H.** 1969. Land subsidence due to withdrawal of fluids. In *Reviews in engineering geology,* eds. D. J. Varnes and G. Kiersch, pp. 187–269. Boulder, CO: Geological Society of America.

22. **Bull, W. B.** 1974. *Geologic factors affecting compaction of deposits in a land subsidence area.* Geological Society of America Bulletin 84:3783–802.

23. **Kenny, R.** 1992. Fissures. *Earth* 1(3):34–41.

24. **Craig, J. R., Vaughan, D. J.,** and **Skinner, B. J.** 1996. *Resources of the Earth,* 2nd ed. Upper Saddle River, NJ: Prentice Hall.

25. **Rahn, P. H.** 1996. *Engineering geology,* 2nd ed. Upper Saddle River, NJ: Prentice Hall.

26. **Kappel, W. M., Yager, R. M.,** and **Miller, T. S.** 1999. The Retsof Salt Mine collapse. In *Land subsidence in the United States,* eds. D. Galloway, D. R. Jones, and S. E. Ingebritsen, pp. 111–20. U.S. Geological Survey Circular 1182.

27. **Péwé, T. L.** 1982. *Geologic hazards of the Fairbanks area, Alaska.* Alaska Division of Geological and Geophysical Surveys Special Report 15.

28. **Noe, D. C., Jochim, C. L.,** and **Rogers, W. P.** 1999. *A guide to swelling soils for Colorado homebuyers and homeowners.* Colorado Geological Survey Special Publication 43.

29. **Coplin, K. S.,** and **Galloway, D.** 1999. Houston-Galveston, Texas: Managing coastal subsidence. In *Land subsidence in the United States,* eds. D. Galloway, D. R. Jones, and S. E. Ingebritsen, pp. 35–48. U.S. Geological Survey Circular 1182.

30. **Galloway, D., Jones, D. R.,** and **Ingebritsen, S. E.** 1999. Mining ground water. In *Land subsidence in the United States,* eds. D. Galloway, D. R. Jones, and S. E. Ingebritsen, pp. 7–13. U.S. Geological Survey Circular 1182.

CHAPTER 7

1. **Andrews, J.** 1993. *Flooding—Canada water book.* Ottawa, ON: Environment Canada.

2. **Brooks, G. R., St. George, S., Lewis, C. F. M., Medioli, B. E., Nielsen, E., Simpson, S.,** and **Thorleifson, L. H.** 2003. *Geoscientific insights into Red River flood hazards in Manitoba.* Geological Survey of Canada Open-File Report 4473.

3. **Committee on Alluvial Fan Flooding.** 1996. *Alluvial fan flooding.* National Research Council. Washington, DC: National Academy Press.

4. **Edelen, G. W., Jr.** 1981. Hazards from floods. In *Facing geological and hydrologic hazards, earth-science considerations,* ed. W. W. Hays, pp. 39–52. U.S. Geological Survey Professional Paper 1240–B.

5. **Keller, E. A.,** and **Capelli, M. H.** 1992. Ventura River flood of February, 1992: A lesson ignored? *Water Resources Bulletin* 28(5):813–31.

6. **Keller, E. A.,** and **Florsheim, J. L.** 1993. Velocity reversal hypothesis: A model approach. *Earth Surface Processes and Landforms* 18:733–48.

7. **Clague, J. J.,** and **Evans, S. G.** 1994. *Formation and failure of natural dams in the Canadian Cordillera.* Geological Survey of Canada Bulletin 464.

8. **Beyer, J. L.** 1974. Global response to natural hazards: Floods. In *Natural hazards,* ed. G. F. White, pp. 265–74. New York: Oxford University Press.

9. **Linsley, R. K., Jr., Kohler, M. A.,** and **Paulhus, J. L.** 1958. *Hydrology for engineers.* New York: McGraw-Hill.

10. **Leopold, L. B.** 1968. *Hydrology for urban land planning.* U.S. Geological Survey Circular 554.

11. **Brooks, G. R., Evans, S. G.,** and **Clague, J. J.** 2001. Floods. In *A synthesis of geological hazards in Canada,* ed. G. R. Brooks, pp. 101–43. Geological Survey of Canada Bulletin 548.

12. **Seaburn, G. E.** 1969. *Effects of urban development on direct runoff to East Meadow Brook, Nassau County, Long Island, New York.* U.S. Geological Survey Professional Paper 627B.

13. **Brooks, G. R.** 2005. *Geomorphic effects and impacts from severe July 1996 flooding in the Saguenay area, Quebec.* Natural Resources Canada. **http://gsc.nrcan.gc.ca/floods/saguenay1996/index_e.php.** Accessed 11/05/06.

14. **McCain, J. F., Hoxit, L. R., Maddox, R. A., Chappell, C. F.,** and **Caracena, F.** 1979. Meteorology and hydrology in Big Thompson River and Cache la Poudre River Basins. In *Storm and flood*

of July 31–August 1, 1976, in the Big Thompson River and Cache la Poudre River Basins, Larimer and Weld Counties, Colorado. U.S. Geological Survey Professional Paper 1115A.

15. **Shroba, R. R., Schmidt, P. W., Crosby, E. J.,** and **Hansen, W. R.** 1979. Geologic and geomorphic effects in the Big Thompson Canyon area, Larimer County. In *Storm and flood of July 31–August 1, 1976, in the Big Thompson River and Cache la Poudre River Basins, Larimer and Weld Counties, Colorado.* U.S. Geological Survey Professional Paper 1115B.
16. **Bradley, W. C.,** and **Mears, A. I.** 1980. Calculations of flows needed to transport coarse fraction of Boulder Creek alluvium at Boulder, Colorado. *Geological Society of America Bulletin,* Part II, 91:1057–90.
17. **Wikipedia.** *Yellow River.* **http://en.wikipedia.org/wiki/Huang_He.** Accessed 11/05/06.
18. **Agricultural Research Service.** 1969. *Water intake by soils*. Miscellaneous Publication No. 925. U.S. Department of Agriculture.
19. **Strahler, A. N.,** and **Strahler, A. H.** 1973. *Environmental geoscience*. Santa Barbara, CA: Hamilton Publishing.
20. **Lliboutry, L., Arnao, B. M., Pautre, A.,** and **Schneider, B.** 1977. Glaciological problems set by the control of dangerous lakes in Cordillera Blanca, Peru. *Journal of Glaciology* 18:239–54.
21. **Mason, K.** 1929. Indus floods and Shyok glaciers. *Himalayan Journal* 1:10–20.
22. **Office of Emergency Preparedness.** 1972. *Disaster preparedness*, 1, 3. Washington, DC.
23. **Dolan, R., Howard, A.,** and **Gallenson, A.** 1974. Man's impact on the Colorado River and the Grand Canyon. *American Scientist* 62:392–401.
24. **Lavender, D.** 1984. Great news from the Grand Canyon. *Arizona Highways Magazine,* January:33–38.
25. **Hecht, J.** 1996. Grand Canyon flood a roaring success. *New Scientist* 151:8.
26. **Lucchitta, I.,** and **Leopold, L. B.** 1999. Floods and sandbars in the Grand Canyon. *Geology Today* 9:1–7.
27. **Mackin, J. H.** 1948. Concept of the graded river. *Geological Society of America Bulletin* 59:463–512.
28. **Clague, J.,** and **Turner, B.** 2003. *Vancouver, city on the edge: Living with a dynamic geological landscape.* Vancouver, BC: Tricouni Press.
29. **Pinter, N., Thomas, R.,** and **Wollsinski, J. H.** 2001. Assessing flood hazard on dynamic rivers. *EOS, Transactions, American Geophysical Union* 82:333–39.
30. **Pinter, N.** 2005. One step forward, two steps back on U. S. floodplains. *Science* 308:207–08.
31. **Mount, J. F.** 1997. *California rivers and streams*. Berkeley, CA: University of California Press.
32. **Rahn, P. H.** 1984. Flood-plain management program in Rapid City, South Dakota. *Geological Society of America Bulletin* 95:838–43.
33. **Baker, V. R.** 1984. Questions raised by the Tucson flood of 1983. In *Proceedings of the 1984 meetings of the American Water Resources Association and the Hydrology Section of the Arizona–Nevada Academy of Science,* pp. 211–19.
34. **Baker, V. R.** 1994. Geologic understanding and the changing environment. *Transactions of the Gulf Coast Association of Geological Societies* 44:1–8.
35. **U.S. Congress.** 1973. *Stream channelization: What federally financed draglines and bulldozers do to our nation's streams.* House Report No. 93–530. Washington, DC: U.S. Government Printing Office.
36. **Wikipedia.** *Red River Floodway.* **http://en.wikipedia.org/wiki/Red_River_Floodway.** Accessed 11/05/06.
37. **Rosgen, D.** 1996. *Applied river morphology*. Lakewood, CO: Wildland Hydrology.
38. **Pilkey, O. H.,** and **Dixon, K. L.** 1996. *The Corps and the shore*. Washington, DC: Island Press.
39. **Baker, V. R.** 1976. Hydrogeomorphic methods for the regional evaluation of flood hazards. *Environmental Geology* 1:261–81.
40. **Bue, C. D.** 1967. *Flood information for floodplain planning*. U.S. Geological Survey Circular 539.
41. **Smith, K.,** and **Ward, R.** 1998. *Floods*. New York: John Wiley and Sons.
42. **Canada Department of Environment.** 2003. *Canada Flood Reduction Program*. **http://www2.ec.gc.ca/water/en/manage/flood/e_fdrp.htm**. Accessed 11/05/06.

CHAPTER 8

1. **Grazulis, T. P.** 2001. *The tornado: Nature's ultimate windstorm*. Norman: University of Oklahoma Press.
2. **Aguado, E.,** and **Burt, J. E.** 2002. *Understanding weather and climate,* 2nd ed. Upper Saddle River, NJ: Prentice Hall.
3. **Wilson, J. W.,** and **Changnon, S. A., Jr.** 1971. *Illinois tornadoes*. Urbana, IL: Illinois State Water Survey Circular 103.
4. **Smith, J.,** ed. 2001. *The facts on file dictionary of weather and climate*. New York: Checkmark Books.
5. **Christopherson, R. W.** 2003. *Geosystems: An introduction to physical geography,* 5th ed. Upper Saddle River, NJ: Prentice Hall.
6. **American Meteorological Society.** 2002. *Updated recommendations for lightning safety—2002.* **http://www.ametsoc.org/POLICY/Lightning_Safety_Article.pdf**. Accessed 12/18/04.
7. **National Weather Service.** 2004. *Lightning—The underrated killer.* **http://www.lightningsafety.noaa.gov/overview.htm.** Accessed 12/18/04.
8. **Environment Canada.** 2002. *Lightning activity.* **http://weatheroffice.ec.gc.ca/lightning/index_e.html**. Accessed 12/18/04.
9. **National Weather Service.** 2004. *Lightning safety outdoors.* **http://www.lightningsafety.noaa.gov/outdoors.htm**. Accessed 12/18/04.
10. **Burt, Christopher C.** 2004. *Extreme weather: A guide and record book*. New York: W.W. Norton.
11. **Wikipedia.** *Edmonton tornado*. **http://en.wikipedia.org/wiki/Edmonton**. Accessed 11/07/06.
12. **National Oceanic and Atmospheric Administration National Weather Service Key West Forecast Office.** 2003. *Waterspouts*. **http://www.srh.noaa.gov/eyw/HTML/spoutweb.htm**. Accessed 12/4/04.
13. **Environment Canada.** 2004. *Tornadoes.* **http://www.pnr-rpn.ec.gc.ca/air/summersevere/ae00s02.en.html**. Accessed 12/4/04.
14. **Environment Canada.** 2002. *Blizzards.* **http://www.pnr-rpn.ec.gc.ca/air/wintersevere/blizzards.en.html**. Accessed 12/19/04.
15. **National Weather Service.** 2001. *Winter storms: The deceptive killers.* **http://www.nws.noaa.gov/om/winterstorm/winterstorms.pdf**. Accessed 12/19/04.
16. **Environment Canada.** 2004. *Blizzards and winter weather hazards.* **http://www.**

msc-smc.ec.gc.ca/cd/brochures/blizzard_e.cfm. Accessed 12/15/04.

17. **The National Snow and Ice Data Center.** 2004. *The blizzards of 1996.* Boulder, CO: University of Colorado. http://nsidc.org/snow/blizzard/plains.html. Accessed 12/15/04.

18. **Government of Quebec.** 1999. *Facing the unforeseeable; lessons from the ice storm of '98.* Montreal, QC: Publications du Québec, Montreal.

19. **Subcommittee on Disaster Reduction.** 2003. *Reducing disaster vulnerability through science and technology: An interim report of the Subcommittee on Disaster Reduction.* Washington, DC: Committee on the Environment and Natural Resources, National Science and Technology Council, Executive Office of the President of the United States.

20. **Whitton, J.** 1980. *Disasters.* New York: Pelican Books.

21. **Houghton, J.** 2004. *Global warming: The complete briefing*, 3rd ed. Cambridge, UK: Cambridge University Press.

22. **Goldenberg, S., Landsea, C., Mestas-Nunez, A. M.,** and **Gray, W. M.** 2001. The recent increase in hurricane activity: Causes and implications. *Science* 293:474–79.

23. **National Oceanic and Atmospheric Administration National Weather Service Storm Prediction Center.** 2002. *Storm Prediction Center.* http://www.spc.noaa.gov/misc/aboutus.html. Accessed 12/4/04.

24. **Godschalk, D. R., Brower, D. J.,** and **Beatly, T.** 1989. *Catastrophic coastal storms: Hazard mitigation and development management.* Durham, NC: Duke University Press.

25. **Federal Emergency Management Agency.** 2004. *Safe rooms and community shelters.* http://www.fema.gov/mit/saferoom. Accessed 12/17/04.

26. **Albey, M.** 1998. *The ice storm: An historic record in photographs of January, 1998.* Toronto: McClelland & Stewart.

CHAPTER 9

1. **Minkel, J. R.** 2004. Surf's up—Way up. *Scientific American* 291(4):38.

2. **Davis, R. E.,** and **Dolan, R.** 1993. Nor'easters. *American Scientist* 81:428–39.

3. **Bartsch-Winkler, S. R.,** and **Winkler, D. K.** 1988. Catalogue of worldwide tidal bore occurrences and characteristics. *U.S. Geological Survey Circular* C 1022.

4. **Komar, P. D.** 1998. *Beach processes and sedimentation*, 2nd ed. Upper Saddle River, NJ: Prentice Hall.

5. **Johnson, J. W.** 1956. Dynamics of nearshore sediment movement. *Bulletin of the American Association of Petroleum Geologists* 40:2211–32.

6. **Fitzpatrick, P. J.** 1999. *Natural disasters: Hurricanes; A reference handbook.* Santa Barbara, CA: ABC-CLIO.

7. **U.S. Geological Survey.** 2005. *Magnitude 9.0 Sumatra-Andaman Island earthquake SAIE.* Earthquake hazards program EHP. http://earthquake.usgs.gov. Accessed 1/13/05.

8. **Owen, J.** 2005. Tsunami family saved by schoolgirl's geography lesson. *National Geographic News.* http://news.nationalgeographic.com/news/2005/01/0118_050118_tsunami_geography_lesson.html. Accessed 2/3/05.

9. **Chapman, C.** 2005. The Asian tsunami in Sri Lanka: A personal experience. *EOS, Transactions, American Geophysical Union* 86(2):13–14.

10. **Watson, P.** 2005. Swept into the world: Ancient knowledge saved endangered tribes from the tsunami, but the aid that poured in from outside could imperil their future. *Los Angeles Times.* http://www.latimes.com/news/nationworld/world/la-fg-tribes3feb03,0,2790810.story?coll=la-home-headlines. Accessed 2/3/05.

11. **Misra, N.** 2005. Nat Geo TV shows help tsunami islander save 1,500. *National Geographic News.* http://news.nationalgeographic.com/news/2005/01/0107_050107_tsunami_natgeo.html. Accessed 2/3/05.

12. **Schiermier, Q.** 2005. Tsunamis: A long-term threat. *Nature* 433:4.

13. **Dudley, W. C.,** and **Lee, M.** 1998. *Tsunami!,* 2nd ed. Honolulu, HI: University of Hawaii Press.

14. **Hokkaido Tsunami Survey Group.** 1993. Tsunami devastates Japanese coastal region. *EOS, Transactions of the American Geophysical Union* 74(37):417–32.

15. **Winchester, S.** 2003. *Krakatoa: The day the world exploded: August 27, 1883.* New York: Harper Perennial.

16. **McSaveney, M. J., Goff, J. R., Darby, D. J., Goldsmith, P., Barnett, A., Elliott, S.,** and **Nongkas, M.** 2000. The 17 July 1998 tsunami, Papua New Guinea; Evidence and initial interpretation. *Marine Geology* 170:81–92.

17. **Heezen, B. C.,** and **Ewing, E. M.** 1952. Turbidity currents and submarine slumps, and the 1929 Grand Banks [Newfoundland] earthquake. *American Journal of Science* 250:849–873.

18. **Fine, I. V., Rabinovich, A. B., Bornhold, B. D., Thomson, R. E.,** and **Kulikov, E. A.** 2005. The Grand Banks landslide-generated tsunami of November 18, 1929: Preliminary analysis and numerical modeling. *Marine Geology* 215:45–57.

19. **Miller, D. J.** 1960. Giant waves in Lituya Bay, Alaska. *U.S. Geological Survey Professional Paper* P 0354-C:51–86.

20. **McMurtry, G. M., Fryer, G. J., Tappin, D. R., Wilkinson, I. P., Williams, M., Fietzke, J., Garbe-Schoenberg, D.,** and **Watts, P.** 2004. Megatsunami deposits on Kohala Volcano, Hawaii, from flank collapse of Mauna Loa. *Geology* 32:741–44.

21. **Ward, S. N.,** and **Day, S.** 2001. Cumbre Vieja Volcano: Potential collapse and tsunami at La Palma, Canary Islands. *Geophysical Research Letters* 28:3397–400.

22. **National Oceanic and Atmospheric Administration (NOAA).** 1998. *Population at risk from natural hazards* by Sandy Ward and Catherine Main. NOAA's State of the Coast Report. Silver Spring, MD: NOAA. http://oceanservice.noaa.gov/websites/retiredsites/sotc_pdf/PAR.PDF. Accessed 1/3/05.

23. **Clague, J. J.,** and **Bornhold, B. D.** 1980. Morphology and littoral processes of the Pacific coast of Canada. In *The coastline of Canada, littoral processes and shore morphology*, ed. S. B. McCann. Geological Survey of Canada Paper 80-10:339–80.

24. **Larsen, J. I.** 1973. *Geology for planning in Lake County, Illinois.* Illinois State Geological Survey Circular 481.

25. **Buckler, W. R.,** and **Winters, H. A.** 1983. Lake Michigan bluff recession. *Annals of the Association of American Geographers* 73(1):89–110.

26. **Shaw, J., Taylor, R. B., Forbes, D. L., Solomon, S.,** and **Ruz, M.-H.** 1998. *Sensitivity of the coasts of Canada to sea-level rise.* Geological Survey of Canada Bulletin 505.

27. **U.S. Department of Commerce** and **U.S. Department of Interior.** 2005. *Fact sheet: Tsunami detection and warnings.* http://www.publicaffairs.noaa.gov/grounders/pdf/tsunami-factsheet2005.pdf. Accessed 2/4/05.

28. **Clague, J. J., Munro, A.**, and **Murty, T.** 2003. Tsunami hazard and risk in Canada. *Natural Hazards* 28:43–461.

29. **Atwater, B. F., Musumi-Rokkatku, S., Satake, K., Tsuji, Y, Ueda, K.**, and **Yamaguichi, D. K.** 2005. *The orphan tsunami of 1700: Japanese clues to a parent earthquake in North America.* U.S. Geological Survey Professional Paper P 1707.

30. **Smith, K.** 2001. *Environmental hazards: Assessing risk and reducing disaster*. New York: Routledge.

31. **El-Ashry, M. T.** 1971. Causes of recent increased erosion along United States shorelines. *Geological Society of America Bulletin* 82:2033–38.

32. **Forbes, D. L., Taylor, R. B.**, and **Shaw, J.** 1989. Shorelines and rising sea levels in eastern Canada. *Episodes* 12:23–28.

33. **Norris, R. M.** 1977. Erosion of sea cliffs. In *Geologic hazards in San Diego*, eds. P. L. Abbott and J. K. Victoris. San Diego, CA: San Diego Society of Natural History.

34. **Flanagan, R.** 1993. Beaches on the brink. *Earth* 2(6):24–33.

35. **Burt, C. C.** 2004. *Extreme weather: A guide and record book*. New York: W.W. Norton.

36. **Centers for Disease Control.** 2004. *Fact sheet: Health effects of tsunamis*. Centers for Disease Control and Prevention, Department of Health and Human Services. Atlanta, GA. **http://www.bt.cdc.gov/disasters/tsunamis/healtheff.asp**. Accessed 2/4/05.

37. **U.S. Department of Commerce.** 1978. *State of Maryland coastal management program and final environmental impact statement*. Washington, DC: U.S. Department of Commerce.

38. **Leatherman, S. P.** 1984. Shoreline evolution of North Assateague Island, Maryland. *Shore and Beach,* July:3–10.

39. **Wilkinson, B. H.**, and **McGowen, J. H.** 1977. Geologic approaches to the determination of long-term coastal recession rates, Matagorda Peninsula, Texas. *Environmental Geology* 1:359–65.

40. **Clague, J. J.** 1989. Sea levels on Canada's Pacific coast: Past and future trends. *Episodes* 12(1):29–33.

41. **Committee on Coastal Erosion Zone Management.** 1990. *Managing coastal erosion*. National Research Council. Washington, DC: National Academy Press.

42. **Carter, R. W. G.**, and **Oxford, J. D.** 1982. When hurricanes sweep Miami Beach. *Geographical Magazine* 54(8):442–48.

43. **Pilkey, O. H.**, and **Dixon, K. L.** 1996. *The Corps and the shore*. Washington, DC: Island Press.

44. **Environment Canada.** 2004. *Canadian Hurricane Centre*. Meteorological Service of Canada. **http://www.ns.ec.gc.ca/weather/hurricane/index_e.html**. Accessed 1/1/05.

45. **National Weather Service.** 2003. *National Hurricane Center*. **http://www.nhc.noaa.gov/aboutnhc.shtml**. Accessed 1/3/05.

46. **National Hurricane Center.** 2004. *Hurricane basics*. **http://www.nhc.noaa.gov/HAW2/english/basics.shtml**. Accessed 1/3/05.

47. **Lutgens, F. K.**, and **Tarbuck, E. J.** 2004. *The atmosphere*. Upper Saddle River, NJ: Prentice Hall.

48. **U.S. Air Force 53rd Weather Reconnaissance Squadron.** 2004. *Tropical cyclone mission*. Biloxi, MS: U.S. Air Force Reserve 403rd Wing. **http://www.hurricanehunters.com/cyclone.htm**. Accessed 1/1/05.

49. **Federal Emergency Management Agency.** 2004. *What should I do? Before hurricane season starts*. **http://www.fema.gov/hazards/hurricanes/whatshouldido.shtm# before**. Accessed 1/3/05.

50. **Clague, J., Yorath, C., Franklin, R.**, and **Turner, B.** 2006. *At risk: Earthquakes and tsunamis on the west coast*. Vancouver, BC: Tricouni Press.

51. **Rowntree, R. A.** 1974. Coastal erosion: The meaning of a natural hazard in the cultural and ecological context. In *Natural hazards: Local, national, global*, ed. G. F. White, pp. 70–79. New York: Oxford University Press.

CHAPTER 10

1. **Wikipedia.** *2003 Okanagan Mountain Park fire*. **http://en.wikipedia.org/wiki/2003_Okanagan_Mountain_Park_Fire**. Accessed 11/11/06.

2. **Ruddiman, W. F.** 2001. *Earth's climate; Past and future*. New York: W.H. Freeman.

3. **Ruddiman, W. F.** 2005. *Plows, plagues, and petroleum: How humans took control of climate*. Princeton, NJ: Princeton University Press.

4. **Rossotti, H.** 1993. *Fire*. Oxford, UK: Oxford University Press.

5. **Pyne, S. J., Andrews, P. L.**, and **Laven, R. D.** 1996. *Introduction to wildland fire,* 2nd ed. New York: John Wiley & Sons, Inc.

6. **Integrated Forest Fire Management Project.** 1998. *IFFM/ GTZ Interim Report about the fire situation in Kalimantan Timur and the on-going activities*. **http://www.iffm.org/iffm/firesit.htm**. Accessed 3/25/05.

7. **Schindler, L.** 1998. *Fire management in Indonesia—quo vadis?* International Cross Sectoral Forum on Forest Fire Management in South East Asia. **http://www.iffm.org/itto.html**. Accessed 1/27/05.

8. **Schweithelm, J.** 1998. *The fire this time: An overview of Indonesia's forest fires in 1997/1998*. Washington, DC: World Wide Fund for Nature.

9. **Ward, D.** 2001. Combustion chemistry and smoke. In *Forest fires: Behavior and ecological effects,* eds. E. A. Johnson and K. Miyanishi, pp. 57–77. San Diego, CA: Academic Press.

10. **Minnich, R. A.** 2002. Personal written correspondence.

11. **Arno, S. F.**, and **Allison-Bunnell, S.** 2002. *Flames in our forests*. Washington, DC: Island Press.

12. **Florida Division of Forestry.** 2001. *Fire and forest protection*. **http://www.fl-dof.com/fire2001**. Accessed 1/25/02.

13. **Atlas of Canada.** 2006. *Forest fires*. **http://atlas.nrcan.gc.ca/site/english/maps/environment/forestfires/1**. Accessed 11/11/06.

14. **Chandler, C., Cheney, P., Thomas, P., Trabaud, L.**, and **Williams, D.** 1983. *Fire in forestry: Vol. I—Forest fire behavior and effects*. New York: John Wiley & Sons.

15. **DeBano, L. F.** 1981. *Water repellent soils: A state-of-the-art*. U.S. Forest Service General Technical Report INT-79.

16. **U.S. Geological Survey.** 2000. *USGS wildland fire research*. **http://www.usgs.gov/themes/Wildfire/wildland_fire.pdf**. Accessed 1/27/05.

17. **Canadian Forestry Service.** 2006. *Forest fire in Canada*. **http://fire.cfs.nrcan.gc.ca/facts_e.php**. Accessed 11/11/06.

18. **Westerling, A. L., Cayan, D.R., Brown, T. J., Hall, B. L.**, and **Riddle, L. G.** 2004. Climate, Santa Ana winds and autumn wildfires in southern California. *EOS, Transactions, American Geophysical Union* 85(31):294, 296.

19. **Tolmé, P.** 2004. Will global warming cause more wildfires? *National Wildlife* 42(5):14–16.

20. **Fried, J. S., Torn, M. S.,** and **Mills, E.** 2004. The impact of climate change on wildfire severity: A regional forecast for northern California. *Climatic Change* 64:169–91.

21. **Canadian Forestry Service.** 2005. *Mountain pine beetle.* **http://www.pfc.forestry.ca/entomology/mpb/index_e.html.** Accessed 6/15/06.

22. **British Columbia Forest Service.** 2001. *Mountain pine beetles in British Columbia.* **http://www.for.gov.bc.ca/hfp/mountain_pine_beetle.** Accessed 6/15/06.

23. **British Columbia Ministry of Forests and Range.** No date. *Large wildfires.* **http://www.for.gov.bc.ca/protect/reports/LargeFires.htm.** Accessed 11/11/06.

24. **Canadian Council of Forest Ministers.** 2006. *Forest fires—Introduction.* **http://nfdp.ccfm.org/compendium/fires/index_e.php.** Accessed 11/11/06.

25. **Minnich, R. A.** 1983. Fire mosaics in southern California and northern Baja California. *Science* 219:1287–94.

26. **Minnich, R. A. Garbour, M. G., Burk, J. H.,** and **Sosa-Ramiriz,** J. 2000. California mixed-conifer forests under unchanged fire regimes in Sierra San Pedro Martir, Baja California, Mexico. *Journal of Biogeography* 27:105–29.

27. **U.S. Forest Service.** 1996. *Federal wildland fire policy: Wildland/urban interface protection.* **http://www.fs.fed.us/land/wdfire7c.htm.** Accessed 1/27/05.

28. **Federal Emergency Management Agency.** 2004. *Fact Sheet: Wildland Fires.* **http://www.fema.gov/hazards/fires/wildlanf.shtm.** Accessed 1/27/05.

29. **Partners in Protection.** 2005. *Partners in Protection: Working together for safer communities in the wildland urban interface.* **http://www.partnersinprotection.ab.ca.** Accessed 6/15/06.

30. **Arrowood, J. C.** 2003. *Living with wildfires: Prevention, preparation, and recovery.* Denver, CO: Bradford Publishing Company.

CHAPTER 11

1. **NASA Goddard Space Flight Centre.** 2005. *Arctic sea ice continues to decline: Arctic temperatures continue to rise in 2005.* **http://www.nasa.gov/centers/goddard/news/topstory/2005/arcticice_decline.html.** Accessed 6/14/06.

2. **Yu, Y., Maykut, G. A.,** and **Rothrock, D. A.** 2004. Changes in the thickness distribution of Arctic sea ice between 1958–1970 and 1993–1997. *Journal of Geophysical Research* 109(C8):13.

3. **Rignot, E.,** and **Kanagaratnam, P.** 2006. Changes in the velocity structure of the Greenland ice sheet. *Science* 311:986–90.

4. **BBC News.** 2006. *Greenland melt speeding up.* **http://news.bbc.co.uk/2/hi/science/nature/4783199.stm.** Accessed 11/11/06.

5. **Intergovernmental Panel on Climate Change.** 2001. *Climate change 2001: The scientific basis. Contribution of Working Group I to the third assessment report of the Intergovernmental Panel on Climate Change.* Cambridge, UK: Cambridge University Press.

6. **Aguado, E.,** and **Burt, J. E.** 1999. *Understanding weather and climate.* Upper Saddle River, NJ: Prentice Hall.

7. **Hill, M. K.** 2004. *Understanding environmental pollution: A primer.* Cambridge, UK: Cambridge University Press.

8. **Environmental Protection Agency.** 2004. *Methane: Science.* **http://www.epa.gov/methane/scientific.html.** Accessed 1/20/05.

9. **Goudie, A.** 1984. *The nature of the environment,* 3rd ed. Oxford, UK: Blackwell Scientific.

10. **Grainger, A.** 1990. *The threatening desert.* London, UK: Earthscan Publications, Ltd.

11. **Bennett, M. R.,** and **Glasser, N. F.** 1996. *Glacial geology: Ice sheets and landforms.* Chichester, UK: John Wiley and Sons.

12. **Dawson, A. G.** 1992. *Ice Age Earth: Late Quaternary geology and climate.* New York: Routledge.

13. **Moss, M. E.,** and **Lins, H. F.** 1989. *Water resources in the twenty-first century.* U.S. Geological Survey Circular 1030.

14. **Titus, J. G.,** and **Seidel, S. R.** 1986. In *Effects of changes in the stratospheric ozone and global climate. Vol. 1,* ed. by J. G. Titus, pp. 3–19. Washington, DC: U.S. Environmental Protection Agency.

15. **NASA.** 1990. *EOS: A mission to planet Earth.* Washington, DC: NASA.

16. **Lamb, H. H.** 1977. *Climate: Present, past and future. Vol. 2, Climatic History and the Future.* New York: Barnes & Noble Books.

17. **Marsh, W. M.,** and **Dozier, J.** 1981. *Landscape.* Reading, MA: Addison-Wesley.

18. **Crowley, T. J.** 2000. Causes of climate change over the past 1000 years. *Science* 289:270–77.

19. **Karl, T. R.** 1995. Trends in U.S. climate during the twentieth century. *Consequences* 1(1):3–12.

20. **Brown, L. R.** 2000. *Climate change has world skating on thin ice.* World Watch Issue Alert. Washington, DC: Worldwatch Institute. **http://www.worldwatch.org/chairman/issue/000829.html.** Accessed 11/29/00.

21. **Ohio State University.** 2001. Ice caps in Africa, tropical South America likely to disappear within 15 years. *Research News.* **http://www.acs.ohio-state.edu/units/research/archive/glacgone.htm.** Accessed 11/29/01.

22. **Evans, R.** 2002. Blast from the past. *Smithsonian.* 33(4):52–57.

23. **McCormick, P. P., Thomason, L. W.,** and **Trepte, C. R.** 1995. Atmospheric effects of the Mt. Pinatubo eruption. *Nature* 373:39–436.

24. **University Corporation for Atmospheric Research.** 1994. *El Niño and climate prediction.* Washington, DC: NOAA Office of Global Programs.

25. **Dennis, R. E.** 1984. A revised assessment of worldwide economic impacts:1982–1984 El Niño/Southern Oscillation Event. *EOS, Transactions, American Geophysical Union* 65(45):910.

26. **Canby, T. Y.** 1984. El Niño's ill winds. *National Geographic* 165:144–81.

27. **Philander, S. G.** 1998. Who Is El Niño? *EOS, Transactions, American Geophysical Union* 79(13):170.

28. **Titus, J. G., Leatherman, S. P., Everts, C. H., Moffatt and Nichol Engineers, Kriebel, D. L.,** and **Dean, R. G.** 1985. Potential impacts of sea level rise on the beach at Ocean City, Maryland. Washington, DC: U.S. Environmental Protection Agency.

29. **Holmes, N.** 2000. Has anyone checked the weather (map)? *The Amicus Journal* 21(4):50–51.

30. **Mainguet, M.** 1994. *Desertification,* 2nd ed. Berlin, Germany: Springer-Verlag.

31. **Wheaton, E. E.,** and **Arthur, L. M.** 1989. Executive summary. In *Environmental and economic impacts*

of the 1988 drought: With emphasis on Saskatchewan and Manitoba, eds. E. E. Wheaton and L. M. Arthur, pp. iii–xxiv. Saskatchewan Research Council Publication No. 3-2330-4-E-89.

32. **Karl, T. R., Heim, R. R., Jr.,** and **Qualye, R. G.** 1991. The greenhouse effect in central North America: If not now, when? *Science* 251:1058–61.

33. **Lemmen, D. S., Vance, R. E., Wolfe, S. A.,** and **Last, W. M.** 1997. Impacts of future climate change on the southern Canadian prairies: A paleoenvironmental perspective. *Geoscience Canada* 24:121–33.

34. **Vance, R. E., Mathewes, R. W.,** and **Clague, J. J.** 1992. A 70-year record of lake-level change on the northern Great Plains: A high resolution proxy of past climate. *Geology* 20:879–82.

35. **Wolfe, S. A.,** and **Lemmen, D. S.** 1999. Monitoring of dune activity in the Great Sand Hills region, Saskatchewan. In *Holocene climate and environmental change in the Palliser Triangle: A geoscientific context for evaluation of the impacts of climate change on the southern Canadian prairies*, eds. D. S. Lemmen and R. E. Vance, pp. 19–210. Geological Survey of Canada Bulletin 534.

36. **Pinol, J., Terradas, J.,** and **Lloret, F.** 1998. Climate warming, wildfire hazard, and wildfire occurrence in coastal eastern Spain. *Climatic Change* 38:345–57.

37. **Stocks, B. J., Fosberg, M. A., Lynham, T. J., Mearns, L., Wotton, B. M., Yang, Q., Jin, J.-Z., Lawrence, K., Hartley, G. R., Mason, J. A.,** and **McKenney, D. W.** 1998. Climate change and forest fire potential in Russian and Canadian boreal forests. *Climate Change* 38:1–13.

38. **World Wide Fund for Nature.** 2000. *Climate change and extreme weather events*. **http://panda.org/resources/publications/climate/xweather/index.html.** Accessed 11/29/00.

39. **Oreskes, N.** 2004. The scientific consensus on climate change. *Science* 306:1686.

40. **Nameroff, T.** 1997. The climate change debate is heating up. *GSA Today* 7(12):11–13.

41. **White, D. J., Burrowes, G., Davis, T., Hajnal, Z., Hirsche, K., Hutcheon, I., Majer, E., Rostron, B.,** and **Whittaker, S.** 2004. Greenhouse gas sequestration in abandoned oil reservoirs: The International Energy Agency Weyburn pilot project. *GSA Today* 14(7):4–10.

42. **Watson, A. J., Bakker, D. C. E., Ridgwell, A. J., Boyd, P. W.,** and **Law, C. S.** 2000. Effect of iron supply on Southern Ocean CO_2 uptake, and implications for glacial atmospheric *Nature* 407:730–33.

43. **Chisholm, S. W.** 2000. Oceanography: Stirring times in Southern Ocean. *Nature* 407:685–87.

44. **Alley, R. B.** 2004. Abrupt climate change. *Scientific American* 291(5):62–69.

CHAPTER 12

1. **Lewis, J. S.** 1996. *Rain of iron and ice*. Redding, MA: Addison-Wesley Publishing Co., Inc.

2. **Rubin, A. F.** 2002. *Disturbing the solar system*. Princeton, NJ: Princeton University Press.

3. **Brown, P., Spalding, R. E., ReVelle, D. O., Tagliaferri, E.,** and **Worden, S. P.** 2002. The flux of small near-Earth objects colliding with the Earth. *Nature* 420:294–96.

4. **Cloud, P.** 1978. *Cosmos, Earth and Man*. New Haven, CN: Yale University Press.

5. **Davidson, J. P., Reed, W. E.,** and **Davis, P. M.** 1997. *Exploring Earth*. Upper Saddle River, NJ: Prentice Hall.

6. **Grieve, R. A. F.** 2001. Impact cratering on Earth. In *A synthesis of geological hazards in Canada,* ed. G.R. Brooks, pp. 207–24. Geological Survey of Canada Bulletin 548.

7. **Gehrels, T.**, ed. 1995. *Hazards due to comets and asteroids*. Tucson, AZ: University of Arizona Press.

8. **Grieve, R.,** and **Cintala, M.** 1999. Planetary impacts. In *Encyclopedia of the solar system,* San Diego, CA: Academic Press.

9. **Weissman, P. R., McFadden, L.,** and **Johnson, T. V.,** eds. 1999. *Encyclopedia of the solar system.* San Diego, CA: Academic Press.

10. **Williams, S. J., Barnes, P.,** and **Prager, E. J.** 2000. *U.S. Geological Survey coastal and marine geology research—Recent highlights and achievements.* U.S. Geological Survey Circular 1199.

11. **Dott, R. H. Jr.,** and **Prothero, D. R.** 1994. *Evolution of the Earth,* 5th ed. New York: McGraw-Hill.

12. **Stanley, S. M.** 2005. *Earth system history*. New York: W. H. Freeman.

13. **Hildebrand, A. R.** 1993. The Cretaceous/Tertiary boundary impact (or the dinosaurs didn't have a chance). *Journal of the Royal Astronomical Society of Canada* 87:7–118.

14. **Alvarez, W.** 1997. *T. rex and the crater of doom*. New York: Vintage Books, Random House, Inc.

15. **Alvarez, L. W., Alvarez, W., Asaro, F.,** and **Michel, H. V.** 1980. Extraterrestrial cause for Cretaceous-Tertiary extinction. *Science* 208:1095–108.

16. **Pope, K. O., Ocampo, A. C.,** and **Duller, C. E.** 1991. Mexican site for the K/T impact crater? *Nature* 351:105.

17. **Swisher, C. C. III, Grajales-Nishimura, J. N., Montanari, A., Margolis, S. V., Claeys, P., Alvarez, W., Ranne, P., Cedillo-Pardo, E., Maurrasse, F. J-N. R., Curtis, G. H., Smit, J.,** and **McWilliams, M. O.** 1992. Coeval $^{40}Ar/^{39}Ar$ ages of 65.0 million years ago from Chicxulub crater melt rocks and Cretaceous-Tertiary boundary tektites. *Science* 257:954–58.

18. **Hildebrand, A. R., Penfield, G. T., Kring, D. A., Pilkington, N., Camargo, Z. A., Jacobsen, S. B.,** and **Boynton, W. V.** 1991. Chicxulub crater: A possible Cretaceous/Tertiary boundary impact crater on the Yucatan peninsula, Mexico. *Geology* 19:867–71.

INDEX

F

G

H

M

"AS IS" LICENSE AGREEMENT AND LIMITED WARRANTY

READ THIS LICENSE CAREFULLY BEFORE OPENING THIS PACKAGE. BY OPENING THIS PACKAGE, YOU ARE AGREEING TO THE TERMS AND CONDITIONS OF THIS LICENSE. IF YOU DO NOT AGREE, DO NOT OPEN THE PACKAGE. PROMPTLY RETURN THE UNOPENED PACKAGE AND ALL ACCOMPANYING ITEMS TO THE PLACE YOU OBTAINED THEM. ***THESE TERMS APPLY TO ALL LICENSED SOFTWARE ON THE DISK EXCEPT THAT THE TERMS FOR USE OF ANY SHAREWARE OR FREEWARE ON THE DISKETTES ARE AS SET FORTH IN THE ELECTRONIC LICENSE LOCATED ON THE DISK:***

1. GRANT OF LICENSE and OWNERSHIP: The enclosed computer programs <<and any data>> ("Software") are licensed, not sold, to you by Pearson Canada Inc. ("We" or the "Company") in consideration of your adoption of the accompanying Company textbooks and/or other materials, and your agreement to these terms. You own only the disk(s) but we and/or our licensors own the Software itself. This license allows instructors and students enrolled in the course using the Company textbook that accompanies this Software (the "Course") to use and display the enclosed copy of the Software for academic use only, so long as you comply with the terms of this Agreement. You may make one copy for back up only. We reserve any rights not granted to you.

2. USE RESTRICTIONS: You may not sell or license copies of the Software or the Documentation to others. You may not transfer, distribute or make available the Software or the Documentation, except to instructors and students in your school who are users of the adopted Company textbook that accompanies this Software in connection with the course for which the textbook was adopted. You may not reverse engineer, disassemble, decompile, modify, adapt, translate or create derivative works based on the Software or the Documentation. You may be held legally responsible for any copying or copyright infringement which is caused by your failure to abide by the terms of these restrictions.

3. TERMINATION: This license is effective until terminated. This license will terminate automatically without notice from the Company if you fail to comply with any provisions or limitations of this license. Upon termination, you shall destroy the Documentation and all copies of the Software. All provisions of this Agreement as to limitation and disclaimer of warranties, limitation of liability, remedies or damages, and our ownership rights shall survive termination.

4. DISCLAIMER OF WARRANTY: THE COMPANY AND ITS LICENSORS MAKE NO WARRANTIES ABOUT THE SOFTWARE, WHICH IS PROVIDED "AS-IS." IF THE DISK IS DEFECTIVE IN MATERIALS OR WORKMANSHIP, YOUR ONLY REMEDY IS TO RETURN IT TO THE COMPANY WITHIN 30 DAYS FOR REPLACEMENT UNLESS THE COMPANY DETERMINES IN GOOD FAITH THAT THE DISK HAS BEEN MISUSED OR IMPROPERLY INSTALLED, REPAIRED, ALTERED OR DAMAGED. THE COMPANY DISCLAIMS ALL WARRANTIES, EXPRESS OR IMPLIED, INCLUDING WITHOUT LIMITATION, THE IMPLIED WARRANTIES OF MERCHANTABILITY AND FITNESS FOR A PARTICULAR PURPOSE. THE COMPANY DOES NOT WARRANT, GUARANTEE OR MAKE ANY REPRESENTATION REGARDING THE ACCURACY, RELIABILITY, CURRENTNESS, USE, OR RESULTS OF USE, OF THE SOFTWARE.

5. LIMITATION OF REMEDIES AND DAMAGES: IN NO EVENT, SHALL THE COMPANY OR ITS EMPLOYEES, AGENTS, LICENSORS OR CONTRACTORS BE LIABLE FOR ANY INCIDENTAL, INDIRECT, SPECIAL OR CONSEQUENTIAL DAMAGES ARISING OUT OF OR IN CONNECTION WITH THIS LICENSE OR THE SOFTWARE, INCLUDING, WITHOUT LIMITATION, LOSS OF USE, LOSS OF DATA, LOSS OF INCOME OR PROFIT, OR OTHER LOSSES SUSTAINED AS A RESULT OF INJURY TO ANY PERSON, OR LOSS OF OR DAMAGE TO PROPERTY, OR CLAIMS OF THIRD PARTIES, EVEN IF THE COMPANY OR AN AUTHORIZED REPRESENTATIVE OF THE COMPANY HAS BEEN ADVISED OF THE POSSIBILITY OF SUCH DAMAGES. SOME JURISDICTIONS DO NOT ALLOW THE LIMITATION OF DAMAGES IN CERTAIN CIRCUMSTANCES, SO THE ABOVE LIMITATIONS MAY NOT ALWAYS APPLY.

6. GENERAL: THIS AGREEMENT SHALL BE CONSTRUED AND INTERPRETED ACCORDING TO THE LAWS OF THE PROVINCE OF ONTARIO. This Agreement is the complete and exclusive statement of the agreement between you and the Company and supersedes all proposals, prior agreements, oral or written, and any other communications between you and the company or any of its representatives relating to the subject matter.

Should you have any questions concerning this agreement or if you wish to contact the Company for any reason, please contact in writing: Permissions, Pearson Canada Inc., 26 Prince Andrew Place, Toronto, Ontario, M3C 2T8.

OPERATING INSTRUCTIONS

Insert the CD-ROM and Hazard City will start automatically. Once the program starts, click on the "walkthrough" button for a narrated introduction to the Assignments in Applied Geology. The program may also be started through your file manager by navigating to the CD-ROM drive and clicking on "START.html." The ReadMe file contains additional, valuable technical and operating information.

For technical support, call the Prentice Hall media support line at 800-677-6337, Monday to Friday, 8 am to 8 pm EST, and Sunday, 5 pm to 12 am EST. Or visit our media support website at **http://247prenhall.com**, where email support is available 24/7.

SYSTEM REQUIREMENTS

PC:

- Windows NT/2000/XP
- Pentium III 450 processor
- In addition to the minimum RAM required by the operating system you are running, this CD requires 64 MB of RAM
- 800 x 600 or 1024 x 768 pixel screen resolution
- Color monitor running "Thousands of Colors"
- Audio-capable system is recommended
- CD-ROM drive
- Speakers
- Internet Explorer 5.5 or 6.0 or Netscape Communicator 7.0 or Firefox
- Flash 6 or 7 browser plug-in installed
- Internet connection for associated websites

Macintosh:

- OS X
- G3
- In addition to the minimum RAM required by the operating system you are running, this CD requires 64 MB of RAM
- 800 x 600 or 1024 x 768 pixel screen resolution
- Color monitor running "Thousands of Colors" or higher
- Audio-capable system is recommended
- CD-ROM drive
- Speakers
- Internet Explorer 5.2 or Netscape Communicator 7.0 or Safari or Firefox
- Flash 6 or 7 browser plug-in installed
- Internet connection for associated websites